PRENTICE HALL
MATHEMATICS
COURSE 1

Pearson Prentice Hall™ is a trademark of Pearson Education, Inc.
Pearson® is a registered trademark of Pearson plc.
Prentice Hall® is a registered trademark of Pearson Education, Inc.
Instant Check System™ is a trademark of Pearson Education, Inc.
Success Tracker™ is a trademark of Pearson Education, Inc.

SAT® is a registered trademark of the College Board, which was not involved in the production of and does not endorse this product.

ISBN 0-13-203169-8
1 2 3 4 5 6 7 8 9 10   10 09 08 07 06

Pennsylvania Mathematics Teacher Handbook

Table of Contents

These pages provide a brief overview of where each Eligible Content of Pennsylvania Assessment Anchors for Grade 6 is introduced, developed, and mastered in this book.

These pages identify the lessons in this book that address selected Eligible Content from the Pennsylvania Grade 6 Assessment Anchors and Eligible Content. Also shown is the progression made in the Eligible Content from prior years to this year, and then in later years. Math Background with focus on selected Eligible Content is provided for great teaching moments!

These pages list each Prentice Hall Course 1 lesson along with all of the Mathematics Assessment Anchors and Eligible Content that are addressed by the lesson. Pacing suggestions for two different teaching schedules— regular and block—are offered for each lesson. Special references to the Pennsylvania Workouts and Pennsylvania Progress Monitoring Assessments are listed within each chapter.

These pages have been developed specifically for students in Pennsylvania and are contained in the front of the student edition for this course. The Student Guide to the Pennsylvania Assessment Anchors and Eligible Content summarizes the standards that students will be exploring this year, and the Workouts for Pennsylvania Assessment Anchors and Eligible Content Mastery allow students to master the concepts addressed in those standards.

Scope and Sequence for the Pennsylvania Assessment Anchors

The following chart provides an overview of where within Prentice Hall Course 1 Mathematics the Eligible Content of the Pennsylvania Assessment Anchors is introduced, developed, and mastered.

M6.A NUMBERS AND OPERATIONS

Assessment Anchor M6.A.1 Demonstrate an understanding of numbers, ways of representing numbers, relationships among numbers, and number systems.

		Introduce	Develop	Master
M6.A.1.1	Express numbers in equivalent forms.			
M6.A.1.1.1	Represent common percents as fractions and/or decimals (e.g., $25\% = \frac{1}{4} = .25$) – common percents are 1%, 10%, 25%, 50%, 75%, 100%.	7-6	7-6	7-6
M6.A.1.1.2	Convert between fractions and decimals and/or differentiate between a terminating decimal and a repeating decimal.	4-9	4-9	4-9
M6.A.1.1.3	Represent a number in exponential form.	4-2	4-2	4-2
M6.A.1.1.4	Represent a mixed number as an improper fraction.	4-6	6-2, 6-4	6-2, 6-4
M6.A.1.2	Compare quantities and/or magnitudes of numbers.			
M6.A.1.2.1	Compare and/or order whole numbers, mixed numbers, fractions, and/or decimals (do not mix fractions and decimals – decimals through thousandths).	1-1, 4-6, 4-8	1-1, 4-6, 4-8	1-1, 4-6, 4-8
M6.A.1.3	Apply number theory concepts (i.e. factors, multiples).			
M6.A.1.3.1	Find the Greatest Common Factor (GCF) of two numbers (through 50) and/or use the GCF to simplify fractions.	4-4, 4-5	6-1, 6-2	6-3, 6-4
M6.A.1.3.2	Find the Least Common Multiple (LCM) of two numbers (through 50) and/or use the LCM to find the common denominator of two fractions.	4-7, 4-8	5-3, 5-4	5-5
M6.A.1.3.3	Use divisibility rules for 2, 3, 5, and/or 10 to draw conclusions and/or solve problems.	4-1	4-1	4-1

introduced   developed   mastered

KEY

Introduce	Develop	Master

M6.A NUMBERS AND OPERATIONS (cont.)

M6.A.1.4	Use or develop models to represent percents.			
M6.A.1.4.1	Model percents (through 100%) using drawings, graphs, and/or sets (e.g., circle graph, base ten blocks, etc)	7-6a	7-6a	7-6a

Assessment Anchor M6.A.2 Understand the meanings of operations, use operations, and understand how they relate to each other.

M6.A.2.1	Select and/or use operations to simplify or solve problems.			
M6.A.2.1.1	Complete equations by using the following properties: associative, commutative, distributive, and identity.	1-3, 3-8	1-3, 3-8	1-3, 3-8

Assessment Anchor M6.A.3 Compute accurately and fluently and make reasonable estimates.

M6.A.3.1	Apply estimation strategies to a variety of problems.			
M6.A.3.1.1	Use estimation to solve problems involving whole numbers and decimals (up to 2 digit divisors and 4 operations).	1-2	1-7	1-8
M6.A.3.2	Solve problems with and without the use of a calculator.			
M6.A.3.2.1	Solve problems involving operations (+, −, ×, ÷) with whole numbers, decimals, (through thousandths) and fractions (avoid complicated LCDs)—straight computation or word problems.	1-2, 1-3, 1-4, 1-7, 1-8. 1-9	5-2, 5-3, 5-4, 5-5, 5-6	6-1, 6-2, 6-3, 6-4, 6-5

M6.B MEASUREMENT

Assessment Anchor M6.B.1 Demonstrate an understanding of measurable attributes of objects and figures, and the units, systems, and processes of measurement.

M6.B.1.1	Compare and/or determine elapsed time.			
M6.B.1.1.1	Determine and/or compare elapsed time to the minute (time may cross AM to PM or more than one day).	5-7	5-7	5-7

Assessment Anchor M6.B.2 Apply appropriate techniques, tools, and formulas to determine measurements.

M6.B.2.1	Choose or use appropriate tools and/or units to determine measurements within the same system.			
M6.B.2.1.1	Use or read a ruler to measure to the nearest $\frac{1}{16}$ inch or millimeter.	4-6b	9-5a	9-5a
M6.B.2.1.2	Choose the more precise measurement of a given object (e.g., smaller measurements are more precise).	9-1	9-1	9-1
M6.B.2.1.3	Measure angles using a protractor up to 180°—protractor must be drawn—one side of the angle to be measured should line up with the straight edge of the protractor.	8-2	8-2	8-2
M6.B.2.2	Solve problems involving length, perimeter, area, and/or volume of geometric figures.			
M6.B.2.2.1	Find the perimeter of any polygon (may include regular polygons where only the measure of one side is given—same units throughout).	9-3	9-3	9-3
M6.B.2.3	Identify, label, and/or list properties of angles or triangles.			
M6.B.2.3.1	Define, label, and/or identify right, straight, acute, and obtuse angles.	8-2	8-2	8-2

M6.C GEOMETRY

Assessment Anchor M6.C.1 Analyze characteristics and properties of two- and three- dimensional geometric shapes and demonstrate understanding of geometric relationships.

M6.C.1.1	Define and/or use basic properties of triangles, quadrilaterals, pentagons, hexagons, heptagons, octagons, nonagons, decagons, and circles.			
M6.C.1.1.1	Identify, classify, and/or compare polygons (up to ten sides.)	8-5	8-5	8-5
M6.C.1.1.2	Identify and/or describe properties of all types of triangles (scalene, equilateral, isosceles, right, acute, obtuse).	8-4	8-4	8-4
M6.C.1.1.3	Identify and/or determine the measure of the diameter and/or radius of a circle (when one or the other is given).	9-5	9-5	9-5
M6.C.1.1.4	Identify and/or use the total number of degrees in a triangle, quadrilateral, and/or circle.	8-4a, 8-4	8-5a	8-5
M6.C.1.2	Represent and/or use concepts and relationships of lines and line segments.			
M6.C.1.2.1	Identify, describe, and/or label parallel, perpendicular, or intersecting lines.	8-1	8-1	8-1
M6.C.1.2.2	Identify, draw, and/or label points, planes, lines, line segments, rays, angles, and vertices.	8-1, 8-2	8-1, 8-2	8-1, 8-2

Assessment Anchor M6.C.3 Locate points or describe relationships using the coordinate plane.

M6.C.3.1	Identify, plot, or match points given an ordered pair.			
M6.C.3.1.1	Plot, locate, or identify points in Quadrant I and/or on the x and y axes with intervals of 1, 2, 5, or 10 units—up to a 200 by 200 grid. Points may be in-between lines.	11-8	11-8	11-8

M6.D ALGEBRAIC CONCEPTS

Assessment Anchor M6.D.1 Demonstrate an understanding of patterns, relations and functions.

M6.D.1.1	Create or extend patterns.			
M6.D.1.1.1	Create, extend, or find a missing element in a pattern displayed in a table, chart, or graph (pattern must show at least 3 repetitions—may use up to 2 operations with whole numbers).	3-1	3-1	3-1
M6.D.1.2	Analyze patterns.			
M6.D.1.2.1	Determine a rule based on a pattern or illustrate a pattern based on a given rule (displayed on a table, chart, or graph; pattern must show at least 3 repetitions).	3-1	3-1	3-1

Assessment Anchor M6.D.2 Represent and/or analyze mathematical situations and structures using algebraic symbols, words, tables, and graphs.

M6.D.2.1.	Select and/or use appropriate strategies to solve number sentences.			
M6.D.2.1.1	Identify the inverse operation needed to solve a one-step equation.	3-5	3-6, 3-7	5-6, 6-5
M6.D.2.1.2	Solve a one-step equation (i.e., using the inverse operation—whole numbers only).	3-5	3-6, 3-7	5-6, 6-5
M6.D.2.2	Create and/or interpret expressions or equations that model problem situations.			
M6.D.2.2.1	Match an equation or expression involving one variable, to a verbal math situation (one operation only).	3-2, 3-3	3-2, 3-3	3-2, 3-3

M6.E DATA ANALYSIS AND PROBABILITY

Assessment Anchor M6.E.1 Formulate questions that can be addressed with data and/or collect, organize, display, and analyze data.

M6.E.1.1	Interpret data shown in frequency tables, histograms, circle, bar or double bar graphs, line or double line graphs, or line plots.			
M6.E.1.1.1	Analyze data and/or answer questions pertaining to data represented in frequency tables, circle graphs, double bar graphs, double line graphs or line plots (for circle graphs, no computation with percents).	2-3	p. 79	7-8
M6.E.1.1.2	Choose the appropriate representation for a specific set of data (choices should be the same type of graph).	2-4	2-4	2-4
M6.E.1.1.3	Display data in frequency tables, circle graphs, double bar graphs, double line graphs, or line plots using a title, appropriate scale, labels, and a key when needed. Circle graphs for open-ended items must show a center point and tic marks.	2-3	p. 79	7-8

Assessment Anchor M6.E.2 Select and use appropriate statistical methods to analyze data.

M6.E.2.1	Describe data sets using mean, median, mode, and/or range.			
M6.E.2.1.1	Determine/calculate the mean, median, mode, and/or range of displayed data (data can be displayed in a table or line plot—use whole numbers only up to 2 digits).	2-1, 2-2	2-3, 2-4	2-3, 2-4

Assessment Anchor M6.E.3 Understand and apply basic concepts of probability.

M6.E.3.1	Determine all possible combinations, outcomes, and/or calculate the probability of a simple event.			
M6.E.3.1.1	Define and/or find the probability of a simple event (express as a fraction in lowest terms).	10-2	10-2	10-2
M6.E.3.1.2	Determine/show all possible combinations involving no more than 20 total arrangements (e.g., tree diagram, table, grid).	10-1	p. 481	10-2

Pennsylvania Assessment Anchors and Eligible Content Correlation and Professional Development

Use these pages to acquaint yourself with selected Pennsylvania Assessment Anchors and Eligible Content with respect to where previous standards have brought the students and where this year's standards will lead their studies going forward.

Correlation

M6.A Numbers and Operations

Eligible Content	Prentice Hall Course 1 Mathematics Lessons
M6.A.1.1.1. Represent common percents as fractions and/or decimals (e.g., 25% $= \frac{1}{4} = .25$)—common percents are 1%, 10%, 25%, 50%, 75%, 100%.	7-6
M6.A.1.2.1. Compare and/or order whole numbers, mixed numbers, fractions and/or decimals (do not mix fractions and decimals—decimals through thousandths).	1-1, 1-6, 4-8
M6.A.2.1.1. Complete equations by using the following properties: associative, commutative, distributive and identity.	1-3, 3-8
M6.A.3.1.1. Use estimation to solve problems involving whole numbers and decimals (up to 2-digit divisors and 4 operations).	1-2, 1-7, 1-8

Professional Development

Math Background

Numbers often have to be changed from one form to another in order for students to make comparisons or perform computations. To change a decimal to a fraction, write the fraction as you would say the decimal. Then simplify. For example, the word form of the decimal 0.4 is four tenths.

$$0.4 = \frac{4}{10} = \frac{2}{5}$$

To change a fraction to a decimal, divide the numerator by the denominator.

$$\frac{5}{8} = 5 \div 8 = 0.625$$

To change a percent to a fraction, write the percent as a fraction with a denominator of 100 and then simplify.

$$5\% = \frac{5}{100} = \frac{1}{20}$$

To change a percent to a decimal, drop the percent sign and divide by 100.

$$62\% = 62 \div 100 = 0.62$$

Math Progression

Prior Years
Students developed number sense by identifying and naming decimals and fractions. They learned ways to recognize equal values, such as by changing a common fraction to its decimal equivalent.

This Year
Students' understanding of numbers will expand to include percents and ratios. They will continue to work with different types of numbers as they learn new methods for comparing values and expressing equivalent values.

Going Forward
Students will continue to explore the relationships among fractions, decimals, and percents. They will also focus on representing large numbers by using scientific notation.

Correlation

M6.B Measurement

Eligible Content	Prentice Hall Course 1 Mathematics Lessons
M6.B.1.1.1. Determine and/or compare elapsed time to the minute (time may cross A.M. to P.M. or more than one day).	5-7
M6.B.2.1.1. Use or read a ruler to measure to the nearest $\frac{1}{16}$ inch or millimeter.	4-6b, 9-5a
M6.B.2.2.1. Find the perimeter of any polygon (may include regular polygons where only the measure of one side is given—same units throughout).	9-3

Professional Development

Math Background

Many students may already be familiar with the concepts of perimeter and area. The *perimeter* of a polygon is the distance around the polygon. Perimeter is measured in linear units, such as feet or meters. The *area* of a two-dimensional figure is a measure of the amount of space it encloses. Area is measured in square units, such as square feet or square meters.

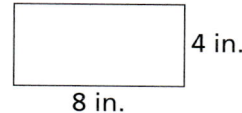

Perimeter = 8 + 4 + 8 + 4 = 24 inches
Area = $\ell \times w$ = 8 × 4 = 32 square inches

Math Progression

Prior Years

Students focused on choosing appropriate measurement units and on making basic unit conversions, such as 1 foot = 12 inches. They measured angles using protractors and solved problems involving elapsed time.

This Year

Students will determine the perimeters and areas of simple polygons and estimate these measures for more complex figures. They will also solve measurement problems involving rates.

Going Forward

Students will continue to use models and formulas to find measures, including the area of composite shapes and the circumference and area of circles. They will also learn to convert between units of area.

Correlation

M6.C Geometry

Eligible Content	Prentice Hall Course 1 Mathematics Lessons
M6.C.1.1.2. Identify and/or describe properties of all types of triangles (scalene, equilateral, isosceles, right, acute, obtuse).	8-4
M6.C.1.2.1. Identify, describe, and/or label parallel, perpendicular, or intersecting lines.	8-1
M6.C.1.2.2. Identify, draw, and/or label points, planes, lines, line segments, rays, angles, and vertices.	8-1, 8-2

Professional Development

Math Background

Geometric figures are classified by their properties. For example, triangles can be classified by their angle measures. An *acute* triangle has three angles that measure less than 90°. A *right* triangle has one angle that measures exactly 90°, and an *obtuse* triangle has one angle that measures greater than 90°.

A *prism* is a three-dimensional figure with two bases that are polygons. The bases are parallel and congruent. All other faces of a prism are rectangles. A *pyramid* is a three-dimensional figure with one base that is a polygon. All other faces of a pyramid are triangles. Both pyramids and prisms are named for the shape of their bases.

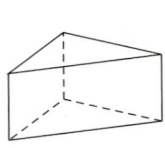
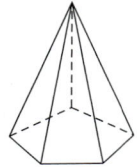

Triangular Prism   Pentagonal Pyramid

Math Progression

Prior Years

Students focused on identifying and describing basic two-dimensional figures. They explored slides, flips, and turns of geometric figures and graphed points in the first quadrant of the coordinate plane.

This Year

Students will describe pairs of lines based on their relative positions and classify angles, triangles, and solid figures based on their geometric properties. They will also solve basic coordinate geometry problems.

Going Forward

Students will determine the effects of a change in scale on the perimeter and area of geometric figures. They will graph ordered pairs and transform geometric figures in all four quadrants of the coordinate plane.

Correlation

M6.D Algebraic Concepts

Eligible Content	Prentice Hall Course 1 Mathematics Lessons
M6.D.1.2.1. Determine a rule based on a pattern or illustrate a pattern based on a given rule (displayed on a table, chart or graph; pattern must show at least 3 repetitions).	3-1
M6.D.2.1.2. Solve a one-step equation (i.e., using the inverse operation— whole numbers only).	3-5, 3-6, 3-7, 5-6, 6-5
M6.D.2.2.1. Match an equation or expression involving one variable, to a verbal math situation (one operation only).	3-2, 3-3

Professional Development

Math Background

A table of values can illustrate the relationship between two variables. Students can write rules in the form of verbal descriptions or algebraic equations to describe such patterns.

For example, the table below shows the relationship between the number and cost of lemons.

Number of Lemons (*n*)	Cost in Dollars (*c*)
2	0.25
4	0.50
6	0.75
8	1.00

By looking for a pattern in this table, students can determine that dividing each number in the first column by 8 gives the corresponding number in the second column. Algebraically, this relationship can be expressed by the equation $c = n \div 8$.

Any rule used to describe a pattern in a table must be applicable for all values in the table. For example, the rule $c = n - 1.75$ does not describe the pattern shown above because this equation is true only for the first pair of values.

Math Progression

Prior Years
Students focused on using reasoning skills to extend and complete patterns found in numerical and pictorial sequences.

This Year
Students will analyze more complex patterns involving numbers and geometric figures. They will write rules to describe these patterns, and they will explore simple functions by using tables of values.

Going Forward
Students' understanding of patterns will broaden to include sequences of fractions and integers. They will also describe patterns and functions by using algebraic expressions and equations.

Correlation

M6.E Data Analysis and Probability

Eligible Content	Prentice Hall Course 1 Mathematics Lessons
M6.E.1.1.1. Analyze data and/or answer questions pertaining to data represented in frequency tables, circle graphs, double bar graphs, double line graphs, or line plots (for circle graphs, no computation with percents).	2-5a, 2-3, 7-8
M6.E.2.1.1. Determine/calculate the mean, median, mode, and/or range of displayed data (data can be displayed in a table or line plot—use whole numbers only up to 2 digits).	2-1, 2-2, 2-3, 2-4
M6.E.3.1.1. Define and/or find the probability of a simple event (express as a fraction in lowest terms).	10-2

Professional Development

Math Background

A *tree diagram* is a visual way to model a complete list of possible outcomes for an event. The tree diagram below shows the possible outcomes of tossing two coins.

First Toss	Second Toss	Outcome
H	H	HH
	T	HT
T	H	TH
	T	TT

The probability of an event is the ratio of the number of favorable outcomes to the total number of possible outcomes. The probability of getting two heads when two coins are tossed is $\frac{1}{4}$ because there is 1 favorable outcome (HH) and 4 possible outcomes (HH, HT, TH, and TT).

Math Progression

Prior Years

Students focused on representing and interpreting data in tables, bar graphs, and line graphs. They also explored basic concepts related to probability. For example, they wrote fractions to express the likelihood of simple events.

This Year

Students will analyze data using measures of central tendency as well as more complex graphical displays. They will model the possible outcomes of a given situation and determine which outcomes have an equal chance of occurring.

Going Forward

Students will continue to interpret displays of data, with emphasis on circle graphs and 3-circle Venn diagrams. They will apply the fundamental counting principle and distinguish between theoretical and experimental probability.

Course 1 Pennsylvania Leveled Pacing Chart

This Pennsylvania Leveled Pacing Chart is provided as a guide to help you customize your course and to provide for differentiated instruction. This chart covers the content of the book and helps students cover Eligible Content they need for success on the Pennsylvania System of School Assessment (PSSA).

The suggested number of days for each chapter is based on a traditional 45-minute class period and on a 90-minute block period. The total of 160 days of instruction leaves time for assessments, projects, assemblies, or other special days.

Differentiated Instruction

✔ Content to prepare for the PSSA test
✔ Reviews the previous year
✔ Content to cover after the PSSA test or for Enrichment

	Assessment Anchors and Eligible Content	Core	Advanced
Chapter 1 Whole Numbers and Decimals	**Traditional 15 days Block 8 days**		
1-1 Understanding Whole Numbers	M6.A.1.2.1	✔	✔
1-2 Estimating With Whole Numbers	M6.A.2.1.1, M6.A.3.2.1	✔	✔
1-3 Properties of Numbers	M6.A.3.1.1, M6.A.3.2.1	✔	✔
1-4 Order of Operations	M6.A.3.2.1	✔	✔
1-5a Activity Lab, Hands On: Exploring Decimal Models		✔	
1-5 Understanding Decimals		✔	
1-6 Comparing and Ordering Decimals	M6.A.1.2.1	✔	✔
1-7a Activity Lab, Hands On: Using Models	M6.A.3.2.1	✔	✔
1-7 Adding and Subtracting Decimals	M6.A.3.1.1, M6.A.3.2.1	✔	✔
• Vocabulary Builder: High-Use Academic Words		✔	
1-8a Activity Lab, Hands On: Modeling Decimal Multiplication	M6.A.3.2.1	✔	✔
1-8 Multiplying Decimals	M6.A.3.1.1, M6.A.3.2.1	✔	✔
1-8b Activity Lab, Technology: Multiplying and Dividing Decimals by 10, 100, and 1,000	M6.A.3.2.1	✔	✔
1-9 Dividing Decimals	M6.A.3.2.1	✔	✔
• Guided Problem Solving: Choosing the Right Operation	M6.A.2.1.1	✔	✔
1-9b Activity Lab, Data Analysis: Using Decimals	M6.A.3.2.1	✔	✔
Problem Solving Application: Applying Decimals	M6.A.3.2.1	✔	✔
Pennsylvania Workout, p. PA5	M6.A.1.2.1, M6.A.3.1.1, M6.A.3.2.1	✔	✔
Chapter 2 Data and Graphs	**Traditional 13 days Block 7 days**		
2-1a Activity Lab, Hands On: Exploring the Mean	M6.E.2.1.1	✔	✔
2-1 Finding the Mean	M6.E.2.1.1	✔	✔
• Vocabulary Builder: High-Use Academic Words		✔	
2-2 Median and Mode	M6.E.2.1.1	✔	✔
2-3 Frequency Tables and Line Plots	M6.E.1.1.1, M6.E.1.1.3, M6.E.2.1.1	✔	✔
2-4 Bar Graphs and Line Graphs	M6.E.1.1.2, M6.E.2.1.1	✔	✔
• Extension: Double Bar and Line Graphs	M6.E.1.1.1, M6.E.1.1.3	✔	✔
2-4b Activity Lab, Technology: Making Bar Graphs	M6.E.1.1.1, M6.E.1.1.3	✔	✔
2-5 Using Spreadsheets to Organize Data			✔
2-5b Activity Lab, Technology: Spreadsheets and Graphs	M6.E.1.1.2, M6.E.1.1.3	✔	✔
2-6 Stem-and-Leaf Plots	Prepares for M7.E.1.1.1		✔
• Guided Problem Solving: Solving Multiple-Step Problems	M6.A.3.1.1	✔	✔
2-7 Misleading Graphs and Statistics	Prepares for M8.E.1.1.1		✔
• Extension: Random Samples and Surveys	Prepares for M8.E.1.1.1		✔
Problem Solving Application: Applying Data Analysis	M6.A.1.2.1	✔	✔
Pennsylvania Workout, p. PA6	M6.E.1.1.1, M6.E.2.1.1	✔	✔
Pennsylvania Benchmark Test 1 in PA PMA, pp. 7–12			
Chapter 3 Patterns and Variables	**Traditional 15 days Block 8 days**		
3-1 Describing a Pattern	M6.D.1.1.1, M6.D.1.2.1	✔	✔
3-2a Activity Lab, Hands On: Patterns and Expressions	M6.D.1.1.1	✔	✔
3-2 Variables and Expressions	M6.D.2.2.1	✔	✔
3-3a Activity Lab: Modeling Expressions	M6.D.2.2.1	✔	✔
3-3 Writing Algebraic Expressions	M6.D.2.2.1	✔	✔
3-3b Activity Lab: Arithmetic Sequences	M6.D.1.2.1	✔	✔
3-4 Using Number Sense to Solve One-Step Equations	M6.D.2.1.1, M6.D.2.1.2	✔	✔
• Vocabulary Builder: High-Use Academic Words		✔	

Assessment Anchors and Eligible Content	Core	Advanced

	Assessment Anchors and Eligible Content	Core	Advanced
3-5a Activity Lab, Hands On: Modeling Equations	M6.D.2.1.1, M6.D.2.1.2	✔	✔
3-5 Solving Addition Equations	M6.D.2.1.1, M6.D.2.1.2	✔	✔
3-6 Solving Subtraction Equations	M6.D.2.1.1, M6.D.2.1.2	✔	✔
3-7a Activity Lab, Hands On: Modeling Division Equations	M6.D.2.1.1, M6.D.2.1.2	✔	✔
3-7 Solving Multiplication and Division Equations	M6.D.2.1.1, M6.D.2.1.2	✔	✔
• Guided Problem Solving: Writing Equations to Solve Problems	M6.D.2.1.1, M6.D.2.1.2	✔	✔
3-8 The Distributive Property	M6.A.2.1.1	✔	✔
3-8b Activity Lab, Algebra Thinking: Understanding Properties	M6.A.2.1.1	✔	✔
Problem Solving Application: Applying Patterns	M6.B.1.1.1	✔	✔
Pennsylvania Workout, p. PA7	M6.A.2.1.1, M6.D.1.1.1, M6.D.2.1.2, M6.D.2.2.1	✔	✔
Chapter 4 Number Theory and Fractions	**Traditional 15 days Block 8 days**		
4-1 Divisibility and Mental Math	M6.A.1.3.3	✔	✔
4-2 Exponents	M6.A.1.1.3	✔	✔
4-3 Prime Numbers and Prime Factorization	Prepares for M7.A.2.1.1		✔
4-4 Greatest Common Factor	M6.A.1.3.1	✔	✔
4-5a Activity Lab, Hands On: Modeling Fractions			✔
4-5 Equivalent Fractions	M6.A.1.3.1	✔	✔
4-5b Activity Lab, Technology: Simplifying Fractions	M6.A.1.3.1	✔	✔
4-6a Activity Lab, Hands On: Exploring Improper Fractions	M6.A.1.1.4	✔	✔
4-6 Mixed Numbers and Improper Fractions	M6.A.1.1.4	✔	✔
• Vocabulary Builder: Making Word Lists		✔	
4-6b Activity Lab, Hands On: Fractions and Measurement	M6.B.2.1.1	✔	✔
4-7 Least Common Multiple	M6.A.1.3.2	✔	✔
4-8 Comparing and Ordering Fractions	M6.A.1.2.1, M6.A.1.3.2	✔	✔
• Guided Problem Solving: Practice Solving Problems	M6.A.1.2.1	✔	✔
4-9 Fractions and Decimals	M6.A.1.1.2	✔	✔
4-9b Activity Lab, Data Collection: Conducting a Survey	M6.A.1.2.1, M6.E.2.1.1	✔	✔
Problem Solving Application: Applying Fractions	M6.A.1.1.2, M6.A.1.2.1	✔	✔
Pennsylvania Workout, p. PA8	M6.A.1.1.2, M6.A.1.1.3, M6.A.1.1.4, M6.A.1.2.1, M6.A.1.3.1, M6.A.1.3.2, M6.A.1.3.3	✔	✔
Pennsylvania Benchmark Test 2 in PA PMA, pp. 13–18			
Chapter 5 Adding and Subtracting Fractions	**Traditional 13 days Block 7 days**		
5-1 Estimating Sums and Differences	M6.A.3.1.1, M6.A.3.2.1	✔	✔
5-2a Activity Lab, Hands On: Modeling Fraction Operations	M6.A.3.2.1	✔	✔
5-2 Fractions With Like Denominators	M6.A.3.2.1	✔	✔
5-3a Activity Lab, Modeling Unlike Denominators	M6.A.3.2.1	✔	✔
5-3 Fractions With Unlike Denominators	M6.A.3.2.1, M6.A.1.3.2	✔	✔
5-4a Activity Lab, Hands On: Using Mixed Numbers	M6.A.1.1.4, M6.A.3.1.1, M6.A.3.2.1	✔	✔
5-4 Adding Mixed Numbers	M6.A.3.2.1, M6.A.1.3.2	✔	✔
5-5 Subtracting Mixed Numbers	M6.A.3.2.1, M6.A.1.3.2	✔	✔
5-5b Activity Lab, Technology: Using a Fraction Calculator	M6.A.1.1.4, M6.A.3.2.1	✔	✔
5-6a Activity Lab, Data Analysis: Using Pictographs	M6.A.3.2.1	✔	✔
5-6 Equations With Fractions	M6.A.3.2.1	✔	✔
• Guided Problem Solving: Practice Solving Problems	M6.A.3.2.1, M6.D.2.1.1, M6.D.2.1.2	✔	✔
5-7 Measuring Elapsed Time	M6.B.1.1.1	✔	✔
Problem Solving Application: Applying Mixed Numbers	M6.A.1.2.1, M6.A.3.1.1, M6.A.3.2.1	✔	✔
Pennsylvania Workout, p. PA9	M6.A.3.2.1, M6.B.1.1.1, M6.D.2.1.1, M6.D.2.1.2	✔	✔
Chapter 6 Multiplying and Dividing Fractions	**Traditional 13 days Block 7 days**		
6-1a Activity Lab, Hands On: Modeling Fraction Multiplication	M6.A.3.2.1	✔	✔
6-1 Multiplying Fractions	M6.A.3.2.1, M6.A.1.3.1	✔	✔
6-1b Activity Lab, Algebra Thinking: Understanding Equality	M6.A.3.1.1, M6.A.3.2.1, M6.D.2.1.2	✔	✔
6-2 Multiplying Mixed Numbers	M6.A.1.1.4, M6.A.3.2.1, M6.A.1.3.1	✔	✔
6-3a Activity Lab, Hands On: Fraction Division	M6.A.3.2.1	✔	✔
6-3 Dividing Fractions	M6.A.3.2.1, M6.A.1.3.1	✔	✔
6-4 Dividing Mixed Numbers	M6.A.3.2.1	✔	✔
6-4b Activity Lab, Technology: Using a Calculator for Fractions	M6.A.3.2.1	✔	✔
6-5 Solving Fraction Equations by Multiplying	M6.A.3.2.1, M6.D.2.1.1, M6.D.2.1.2	✔	✔
• Guided Problem Solving: Practice Solving Problems	M6.A.3.2.1	✔	✔
6-6 The Customary System	M6.B.2.1.3	✔	✔

	Assessment Anchors and Eligible Content	Core	Advanced
6-7 Changing Units in the Customary System	Prepares for M7.B.1.1.1		✔
6-7b Activity Lab, Hands On: Measuring Objects	M6.B.2.1.1	✔	✔
Problem Solving Application: Applying Mixed Numbers	M6.A.3.2.1	✔	✔
Pennsylvania Workout, p. PA10	M6.A.1.1.4, M6.A.3.2.1, M6.D.2.1.2	✔	✔
Pennsylvania Benchmark Test 3 in PA PMA, pp. 19–24			
Chapter 7 Ratios, Proportions, and Percents	**Traditional 15 days Block 7 days**		
7-1 Ratios	M6.A.1.3.1, M6.A.3.2.1	✔	✔
• Vocabulary Builder: High-Use Academic Words		✔	
7-1b Activity Lab, Hands On: Modeling Ratios	Prepares for M7.A.2.2.1		✔
7-2 Unit Rates	Prepares for M7.A.2.2.4		✔
7-3 Understanding Proportions	M6.A.1.2.1, M6.A.3.2.1	✔	✔
7-4 Solving Proportions	Prepares for M7.A.2.2.2, M7.A.2.2.5		✔
7-4b Activity Lab, Hands On: Predicting Results	Prepares for M7.A.2.2.2		✔
7-5 Scale Drawings	Prepares for M7.B.2.3.1, M7.B.2.3.2		✔
7-6a Activity Lab, Hands On: Modeling Percents	M6.A.1.4.1	✔	✔
7-6 Percents, Fractions, and Decimals	M6.A.1.1.1	✔	✔
7-7 Finding the Percent of a Number	Prepares for M7.A.2.2.4, M8.A.2.2.1		✔
7-8a Activity Lab, Hands On: Exploring Circle Graphs	M6.E.1.1.1	✔	✔
7-8 Circle Graphs	M6.E.1.1.1, M6.E.1.1.3	✔	✔
• Guided Problem Solving: Practice Solving Problems	Prepares for M7.A.2.2.1		✔
7-8b Activity Lab, Technology: Reporting Survey Results	Prepares for M8.E.1.1.1		✔
7-9 Estimating With Percents	Prepares for M8.A.3.2.1		✔
• Extension: Percents Under 1% or Over 100%			✔
Problem Solving Application: Applying Proportions	M6.A.3.1.1, M6.B.2.1.1	✔	✔
Pennsylvania Workout, p. PA11	M6.A.1.1.1, M6.A.1.1.4, M6.A.2.1.2, M6.A.3.2.1, M6.D.2.1.1, M6.E.1.1.1, M6.E.1.1.3	✔	✔
Chapter 8 Tools of Geometry	**Traditional 14 days Block 7 days**		
8-1 Points, Lines, Segments, and Rays	M6.C.1.2.1, M6.C.1.2.2	✔	✔
8-2a Activity Lab, Hands On: Using Angle Benchmarks	M6.B.2.1.3	✔	✔
8-2 Angles	M6.B.2.3.1, M6.B.2.1.3, M6.C.1.2.2	✔	✔
• Extension: Basic Constructions	Prepares for M8.C.1.1.2		✔
8-3 Special Pairs of Angles	Prepares for M8.C.1.1.2		✔
8-3b Activity Lab, Hands On: Exploring Parallel Lines	M6.C.1.2.1	✔	✔
8-4a Activity Lab, Technology: Investigating Angles in a Triangle	M6.C.1.1.4	✔	✔
8-4 Classifying Triangles	M6.C.1.1.2, M6.C.1.1.4	✔	✔
• Vocabulary Builder: High-Use Academic Words		✔	
8-5a Activity Lab, Hands On: Angles in a Quadrilateral	M6.C.1.1.4	✔	✔
8-5 Exploring and Classifying Polygons	M6.C.1.1.1, M6.C.1.1.4	✔	✔
8-6 Congruent and Similar Figures	Prepares for M7.C.1.2.1, M7.C.1.2.2		✔
• Guided Problem Solving: Practice Solving Problems	Prepares for M7.C.1.2.1		✔
8-7 Line Symmetry			✔
8-8 Transformations			✔
8-8b Activity Lab, Hands On: Tessellations			✔
Problem Solving Application: Applying Geometry	M6.C.1.1.1, M6.B.2.1.1	✔	✔
Pennsylvania Workout, p. PA12	M6.B.2.1.3, M6.B.2.3.1, M6.C.1.1.1, M6.C.1.1.2, M6.C.1.2.2	✔	✔
Pennsylvania Benchmark Test 4 in PA PMA, pp. 25–30			
Chapter 9 Geometry and Measurement	**Traditional 1days Block 8 days**		
9-1 Metric Units of Length, Mass, and Capacity	M6.B.2.1.2	✔	✔
9-1b Activity Lab: Converting Metric Units	Prepares for M7.B.1.1.1		✔
9-2 Converting Units in the Metric System	Prepares for M7.B.1.1.1		✔
• Vocabulary Builder: Using Concept Maps		✔	
9-3 Perimeters and Areas of Rectangles	M6.B.2.2.1	✔	✔
9-4a Activity Lab, Hands On: Comparing Areas	Prepares for M7.B.2.1.3		✔
9-4 Areas of Parallelograms and Triangles	Prepares for M7.B.2.1.3		✔
9-5a Activity Lab, Data Collection: Exploring Circles	M6.C.1.1.3	✔	✔
9-5 Circles and Circumference	M6.C.1.1.3	✔	✔
• Guided Problem Solving: Practice Solving Problems			✔
9-6 Area of a Circle	Prepares for M7.B.2.1.2		✔

	Assessment Anchors and Eligible Content	Core	Advanced
9-7a Activity Lab, Hands On: Three-Dimensional Views	Prepares for M7.C.1.1		✔
9-7 Three-Dimensional Figures and Spatial Reasoning	Prepares for M7.C.1.1		✔
9-8 Surface Areas of Prisms	Prepares for M8.C.1.1.1		✔
9-9a Activity Lab, Hands On: Exploring Volume	Prepares for M8.B.2.3.2		✔
9-9 Volumes of Rectangular Prisms	Prepares for M8.B.2.3.2		✔
9-10a Activity Lab, Hands On: Exploring Cylinders	Prepares for M8.B.2.3.3		✔
9-10 Surface Areas and Volumes of Cylinders	Prepares for M8.B.2.3.3		✔
Problem Solving Application: Applying Measurement	M6.B.2.2.11, M6.C.1.1.1	✔	✔
Pennsylvania Workout, p. PA13	M6.B.2.2.1, M6.C.1.1.1, M6.C.1.1.3	✔	✔
Chapter 10 Exploring Probability	**Traditional 9 days Block 4 days**		
10-1 Tree Diagrams and the Counting Principle	M6.E.3.1.2	✔	✔
• Extension: Permutations	M6.E.3.1.2	✔	✔
10-2 Probability	M6.E.3.1.1	✔	✔
10-3 Experimental Probability	M6.E.3.1.1	✔	✔
10-3b Activity Lab, Data Collection: Experimental and Theoretical Probabilities	M6.E.3.1.1	✔	✔
• Vocabulary Builder: High-Use Academic Words		✔	
10-4 Making Predictions From Data	Prepares for M8.E.4.1.2		✔
10-4b Activity Lab, Technology: Simulations			✔
10-5 Independent Events	M6.E.3.1.1	✔	✔
• Extension: Dependent Events	M6.E.3.1.1	✔	✔
• Guided Problem Solving: Practice Solving Problems	M6.E.3.1.1, M6.E.3.1.2	✔	✔
Problem Solving Application: Applying Probability	M6.E.3.1.1	✔	✔
Pennsylvania Workout, p. PA14	M6.A.1.3.1, M6.A.3.1.1, M6.A.3.2.1, M6.D.1.1.1, M6.D.1.2.1, M6.E.3.1.1	✔	✔
Chapter 11 Integers	**Traditional 14 days Block 7 days**		
11-1 Exploring Integers	Prepares for M7.A.1.2.3		✔
11-2 Comparing and Ordering Integers	M6.A.1.2.1	✔	✔
11-3a Activity Lab, Hands On: Modeling Addition of Integers	M6.A.3.2.1	✔	✔
11-3 Adding Integers	M6.A.3.2.1	✔	✔
11-4a Activity Lab, Hands On: Modeling Subtraction of Integers	M6.A.3.2.1	✔	✔
11-4 Subtracting Integers	M6.A.3.2.1	✔	✔
11-5 Multiplying Integers	M6.A.3.2.1	✔	✔
• Guided Problem Solving: Practice Solving Problems	M6.B.1.1.1, M6.D.2.1.2, M6.E.1.1.1	✔	✔
11-6 Dividing Integers	M6.A.3.2.1	✔	✔
11-7 Solving Equations with Integers	M6.D.2.1.1, M6.D.2.1.2	✔	✔
11-7b Activity Lab, Algebra Thinking: Thinking About Solutions	M6.D.2.1.2	✔	✔
11-8a Activity Lab, Technology: Graphing Points	M6.C.3.1.1	✔	✔
11-8 Graphing in the Coordinate Plane	M6.C.3.1.1	✔	✔
• Extension: Reflections in the Coordinate Plane			✔
11-9 Applications of Integers	M6.A.1.2.1, M6.A.3.2.1, M6.E.1.1.1, M6.E.1.1.3	✔	✔
11-10 Graphing Functions	M6.D.1.1.1, M6.C.3.1.1	✔	✔
Problem Solving Application: Applying Integers	M6.A.1.2.1, M6.A.3.2.1	✔	✔
Pennsylvania Workout, p. PA15	M6.A.1.1.2, M6.A.1.1.4, M6.A.1.3.1, M6.A.3.1.1, M6.A.3.2.1, M6.C.3.1.1, M6.D.2.1.1, M6.D.2.1.2	✔	✔
Chapter 12 Equations and Inequalities	**Traditional 8 days Block 4 days**		
12-1 Solving Two-Step Equations	Prepares for M8.D.2.1.1		✔
12-1b Activity Lab, Algebra Thinking: Using Equation Language	Prepares for M8.D.2.1.1		✔
12-2 Inequalities	Prepares for M7.D.2.2.1		✔
12-3 Solving One-Step Inequalities	Prepares for M8.D.2.1.1		✔
12-3b Activity Lab: Data Analysis: Applying Inequalities	Prepares for M8.D.2.1.1		✔
12-4a Activity Lab, Hands On: Exploring Squares	Prepares for M8.A.1.1.2		✔
12-4 Exploring Square Roots and Rational Numbers	Prepares for M8.A.1.1.2		✔
12-5 Introducing the Pythagorean Theorem	Prepares for M8.C.1.2.		✔
• Guided Problem Solving: Practice Solving Problems	Prepares for M8.C.1.2.1		✔
Problem Solving Application: Applying Equations	Prepares for M8.D.2.1.1		✔
Pennsylvania Workout, p. PA16	M6.A.1.1.3, M6.A.1.3.1, M6.A.3.1.1, M6.A.3.2.1, M6.D.1.1.1, M6.D.1.2.1, M6.D.2.1.1, M6.D.2.1.2	✔	✔
Pennsylvania Benchmark Test 5 in PA PMA, pp. 31–38			

Pennsylvania Assessment Anchors and Eligible Content

The Pennsylvania Department of Education has worked hard to create the Assessment Anchors. The Anchors are designed to help you create and develop the tools you will need to be successful in school, the workplace, and your daily life. The Eligible Content within those Anchors helps you to identify specific skills.

M6.A. Numbers and Operations

There are three anchors in this reporting category (M6.A.1 to M6.A.3). The Eligible Content within them identifies 12 skills for you to master (M6.A.1.1.1 to M6.A.3.2.1).

What It Means To You

As you work to master this anchor, you will develop your number sense. You will learn how to compare and order numbers; for instance, you will understand that $\frac{1}{2} > \frac{1}{3}$. In addition, you will become familiar with how to convert between different forms of numbers, such decimals and fractions. You will also gain the ability to find the Greatest Common Factor (GCF) and the Least Common Multiple (LCM) of two numbers and to use models to represent percents. In addition, you will use the order of operations to solve problems, and you will also learn to estimate. For instance, you will be able to determine that $1\frac{1}{2}$ is a reasonable estimate for the sum shown to the right.

$$\frac{37}{40} + \frac{7}{12}$$

M6.B Measurement

There are two anchors in this reporting category (M6.B.1 and M6.B.2). The Eligible Content within them identifies 6 skills for you to master (M6.B.1.1.1 to M6.B.2.3.1).

M6.C Geometry

There are three anchors in this reporting category (M6.C.1 to M6.C.3). The Eligible Content within them identifies 7 skills for you to master (M6.C.1.1.1 to M6.C.3.1.1).

What It Means To You

As you work to master this standard, you will learn to reason geometrically. For instance, you will learn how to classify and compare different types of polygons, such as the isosceles triangle to the right. You will also become familiar with how to find the measures of missing angles in triangles, quadrilaterals, and circles. In addition, you will be able to identify parallel and perpendicular lines and describe the relationship that exists between them. You will also plot points in all four quadrants of the coordinate plane.

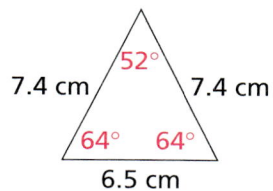

M6.D Algebraic Concepts

There are three anchors in this reporting category (M6.D.1 to M6.D.3). The Eligible Content within them identifies 5 skills for you to master (M6.D.1.1.1 to M6.D.2.2.1).

What It Means To You

Mastering these skills will help you think algebraically. For instance, you will learn to create and extend patterns and sequences, such as the one to the right, and you will also learn to write rules to represent those patterns. In addition, you will learn to solve one-step equations and how to represent certain phrases and sentences with algebraic expressions and equations.

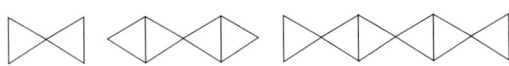

M6.E Data Analysis and Probability

There are three anchors in this reporting category (M6.E.1 and M6.E.3). The Eligible Content within them identifies 6 skills for you to master (M6.E.1.1.1 to M6.E.3.1.2).

What It Means To You

These skills are designed to develop your ability to analyze data. You will learn how to choose the most appropriate type of graph to represent a particular set of data. In particular, you will study frequency tables, circle graphs, double-bar graphs, and double-line graphs. You will also learn how to calculate the mean, median, mode, and range of a data set and how to find the probability of a simple event. For example, the spinner at the right contains six colored sections, but only one of them is green. So the probability that the spinner lands on green is $\frac{1}{6}$.

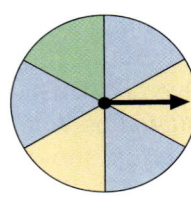

Workout for Pennsylvania Assessment Anchors and Eligible Content Mastery

Ready to go after Chapter 1

? For help, go to the lesson in green.

1. A group of 6 adults and 25 students went to a play. Tickets for adults cost $7, and tickets for students cost $4. What was the total cost of the group's tickets?
   (Lesson 1-4)

   A $142
   B $178
   C $185
   D $199

2. Which expression is **not** equivalent to the others?
   (Lesson 1-4)

   A $13 \cdot (20 + 2)$
   B $13 \cdot 20 + 13 \cdot 2$
   C $22 \cdot (10 + 3)$
   D $(10 + 13) \cdot (10 + 2)$

3. Which list shows the numbers given below in order from **least** to **greatest**?
   (Lesson 1-6)

   0.09   0.099   0.01   0.1

   A 0.099, 0.01, 0.1, 0.09
   B 0.01, 0.09, 0.099, 0.1
   C 0.09, 0.01, 0.099, 0.1
   D 0.01, 0.1, 0.09, 0.099

4. Fresh cod is on sale for $4.95 per pound. You buy four pieces, which have a total weight of 5.2 pounds. What is the total cost of the cod?
   (Lesson 1-8)

   A $24.85
   B $24.95
   C $25.63
   D $25.74

5. Which of the labeled points on the number line below represents a number between 3.14 and 3.26?
   (Lesson 1-6)

   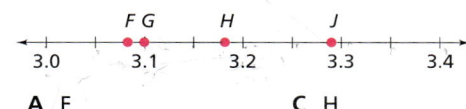

   A F   C H
   B G   D J

6. Felipe had $15.00. He bought a bike lock for $8.95 and a water bottle for $3.27. How much money does Felipe have left?
   (Lesson 1-7)

   A $2.78   C $6.05
   B $3.22   D $9.32

7. Amma is solving the problem 0.162×0.12. She knows that the product has the digits 1944, but she does not know where to place the decimal point. Which of these shows the product with the decimal point in the correct place?
   (Lesson 1-8)

   A 0.01944   C 1.944
   B 0.1944   D 19.44

8. **Open-Ended** Leo hiked 5.4 miles in Delaware Canal State Park in 3 hours.
   A. If he hiked the same distance each hour, how many miles did he hike in the first hour?
   B. Show or explain your work. Label your answer with the correct units.
   (Lesson 1-9)

Assessment Anchors and Eligible Content
M6.A.1.2.1, M6.A.3.1.1, M6.A.3.2.1

Pennsylvania Workouts

Correlation to Pennsylvania Assessment Anchors and Eligible Content

Item	Assessment Anchors and Eligible Content
1	M6.A.3.2.1
2	M6.A.3.2.1
3	M6.A.1.2.1
4	M6.A.3.1.1
5	M6.A.1.2.1
6	M6.A.3.2.1
7	M6.A.3.1.1
8	M6.A.3.2.1

Answers

1. A
2. D
3. B
4. D
5. C
6. A
7. A
8. A. 1.8 miles;
   B. $\dfrac{x}{5.4} = \dfrac{1}{3}$
   $3x = 5.4$
   $x = 1.8$

Prescribing Intervention

Item	Intervention	Item	Intervention
1	Lesson 1-4, Example 2	5	Lesson 1-6, Example 1
2	Lesson 1-4, Example 1	6	Lesson 1-7, Examples 1, 3
3	Lesson 1-6, Example 3	7	Lesson 1-8, Example 3
4	Lesson 1-8, Example 3	8	Lesson 1-9, Example 1

Correlation to Pennsylvania Assessment Anchors and Eligible Content

Item	Assessment Anchors and Eligible Content
1	M6.E.2.1.1
2	M6.E.1.1.1
3	M6.E.2.1.1
4	M6.E.1.1.1
5	M6.E.2.1.1

Answers

1. **C**

2. **D**

3. **A**

4. **C**

5. **A.** The range is $68.

   B. 164 − 96 = 68

Workout for Pennsylvania Assessment Anchors and Eligible Content Mastery

Ready to go after Chapter 2

❓ **For help, go to the lesson in green.**

1. Alyssa's scores on her math quizzes are listed below.

98, 78, 85, 98, 78, 98, 88

What is the **mean** of Alyssa's scores? **(Lesson 2-1)**

A 87   C 89
B 88   D 98

2. The frequency table shows the number of trees in the front yards of houses on one block.

TREES IN FRONT YARDS

Number of Trees	Frequency
0	1
1	3
2	5
3	0
4	1
5	1

How many of the houses on this block have at least 2 trees in their front yards? **(Lesson 2-3)**

A 2   C 5
B 4   D 7

3. A camping store sells six different tents. The prices of the tents are listed below.

$50, $75, $225, $120, $120, $90

What is the **median** of the prices? **(Lesson 2-2)**

A $105   C $120
B $113   D $158

4. The bar graph shows the number of people who watched four different television programs.

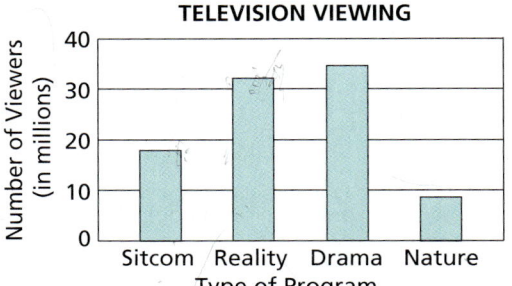

TELEVISION VIEWING

About how many more people watched the reality program than watched the sitcom? **(Lesson 2-4)**

A 6 million
B 10 million
C 14 million
D 18 million

5. Open-Ended The table shows the Norwoods' heating bills last winter.

HEATING BILLS

Month	Amount
December	$125
January	$164
February	$108
March	$96

A. What was the **range** of the Norwoods' heating bills of the months shown in the table?

B. Show or explain how you determined your answer. **(Lesson 2-3)**

 Assessment Anchors and Eligible Content
M6.E.1.1.1, M6.E.2.1.1

Prescribing Intervention

Item	Intervention	Item	Intervention
1	Lesson 2-1, Example 2	4	Lesson 2-4, Example 1
2	Lesson 2-3, Example 1	5	Lesson 2-2, Example 3
3	Lesson 2-2, Example 1		

Workout for Pennsylvania Assessment Anchors and Eligible Content Mastery

Ready to go after Chapter 3

? For help, go to the lesson in green.

1. What is the next number in the following sequence?
(Lesson 3-1)

6.2, 5.5, 4.8, 4.1,

- A 3.4
- B 3.5
- C 3.7
- D 3.8

2. What is the value of the expression $3x + 5$ when $x = 3$?
(Lesson 3-2)

- A 11
- B 14
- C 24
- D 38

3. The table below shows the relationship between the number of bagels a customer buys at a bakery and the cost of the bagels.

BAGEL COSTS

Number Bought	Total Cost
1	$0.80
2	$1.60
4	$3.20
6	$4.80

Which expression can be used to find the cost of b bagels?
(Lesson 3-3)

- A $0.80b$
- B $0.80 + b$
- C $4.80b + 6$
- D $4.80 + 6b$

4. What value of n makes the following equation true?
(Lesson 3-7)

$$6n = 84$$

- A 14
- B 16
- C 484
- D 504

5. Which expression is equivalent to $(6 \times 10) + (6 \times 7)$?
(Lesson 3-8)

- A $6 \times (10 + 7)$
- B $6 + (10 \times 7)$
- C $(6 + 6) \times (10 + 7)$
- D $(6 \times 6) + (10 + 7)$

6. Open-Ended Nicholas had several quarts of paint. He used 3.75 quarts to paint a fence. Afterward, he had 2.25 quarts of paint left. The equation $q - 3.75 = 2.25$ can be used to find q, the number of quarts of paint Nicholas had before he started painting.

- A. How many quarts of paint did Nicholas have?
- B. Show or explain how you determined your answer.
(Lesson 3-6)

Pennsylvania Workouts

Correlation to Pennsylvania Assessment Anchors and Eligible Content

Item	Assessment Anchors and Eligible Content
1	M6.D.1.1.1
2	M6.D.2.1.2
3	M6.D.1.2.1, M6.D.2.2.1
4	M6.D.2.1.1, M6.D.2.1.2
5	M6.A.2.1.1
6	M6.D.2.1.2

Answers

1. A

2. B

3. A

4. A

5. A

6. A. 6 quarts

   B. $q - 3.75 = 2.25$

   $q - 3.75 + 3.75 = 2.25 + 3.75$

   $q = 6$

Prescribing Intervention

Item	Intervention	Item	Intervention
1	Lesson 3-1, Example 2	4	Lesson 3-7, Example 1
2	Lesson 3-2, Example 2	5	Lesson 3-8, Example 1
3	Lesson 3-3, Example 3	6	Lesson 3-6, Example 1

Correlation to Pennsylvania Assessment Anchors and Eligible Content

Item	Assessment Anchors and Eligible Content
1	M6.A.1.1.2
2	M6.A.1.1.3
3	M6.A.1.3.3
4	M6.A.1.2.1
5	M6.A.1.1.4
6	M6.A.1.3.2
7	M6.A.1.3.1

Answers

1. C

2. B

3. A

4. A

5. D

6. B

7. A. $\frac{14}{25}$ of Tony's cards are National League cards.

   B. $\frac{56}{100} = \frac{14}{25}$

Workout for Pennsylvania Assessment Anchors and Eligible Content Mastery

Ready to go after Chapter 4

> ? **For help, go to the lesson in green.**

1. Oren needs to buy $\frac{3}{8}$ pound of sliced turkey. How is this weight written as a decimal?
   (Lesson 4-9)

   A 0.26 pound
   B 0.38 pound
   C 0.375 pound
   D 0.425 pound

2. Which expression has a value of 13?
   (Lesson 4-2)

   A $(3 + 2)^2$
   B $3^2 + 2^2$
   C $3 + (2)^2$
   D $3^3 + 2^2$

3. Which of these numbers is divisible by 3?
   (Lesson 4-1)

   A 48
   B 53
   C 61
   D 74

4. Paul needs to buy a replacement windowpane. The windowpane must be at least $\frac{1}{4}$ inch thick. The table lists available thicknesses of glass. How many of these glass sizes are at least $\frac{1}{4}$ inch thick?
   (Lesson 4-8)

Glass Thickness (in inches)	$\frac{1}{8}$	$\frac{3}{16}$	$\frac{5}{16}$	$\frac{7}{32}$

   A 1
   B 2
   C 3
   D 4

5. In March, Tara ran 23 quarter-mile laps, or $\frac{23}{4}$ miles. How is this distance written as a mixed number?
   (Lesson 4-6)

   A $2\frac{3}{4}$ miles   C $4\frac{2}{3}$ miles
   B $3\frac{1}{2}$ miles   D $5\frac{3}{4}$ miles

6. A computer checks for viruses every 12 days and backs up files every 16 days. If the computer checked for viruses and backed up files today, how many days will it be before the computer again performs both of these tasks on the same day?
   (Lesson 4-7)

   A 36 days
   B 48 days
   C 64 days
   D 72 days

7. **Open-Ended** Tony collects baseball cards. He has sorted his cards into the categories shown below.

   BASEBALL CARDS

League	Number of Cards
National League	56
American League	42
Assorted minor leagues	2

   A. In simplest form, what fraction of Tony's cards consists of National League cards?
   B. Show or explain all your work.
   (Lesson 4-5)

> **PA** **Assessment Anchors and Eligible Content**
> M6.A.1.1.2, M6.A.1.1.3, M6.A.1.1.4, M6.A.1.2.1, M6.A.1.3.1, M6.A.1.3.2, M6.A.1.3.3

Prescribing Intervention

Item	Intervention	Item	Intervention
1	Lesson 4-9, Example 2	5	Lesson 4-6, Example 3
2	Lesson 4-2, Example 3	6	Lesson 4-7,
3	Lesson 4-1, Example 2		More Than One Way
4	Lesson 4-8, Example 1	7	Lesson 4-5, Example 3

Workout for Pennsylvania Assessment Anchors and Eligible Content Mastery

Ready to go after Chapter 5

For help, go to the lesson in green.

1. When standing on the ground, Kim can reach to a height of $6\frac{1}{12}$ feet. If she stands on a stool that is $1\frac{1}{2}$ feet tall, what is the height of the highest shelf Kim can reach without jumping?
(Lesson 5-4)

A $7\frac{1}{6}$ feet

C $7\frac{5}{6}$ feet

B $7\frac{7}{12}$ feet

D $7\frac{11}{12}$ feet

2. A cook used $\frac{3}{4}$ cup of milk to make hot chocolate and $\frac{2}{4}$ cup of milk to make oatmeal. How many cups of milk did the cook use in all?
(Lesson 5-2)

A $\frac{5}{8}$ cup

B $1\frac{1}{4}$ cups

C $1\frac{3}{8}$ cups

D $2\frac{3}{4}$ cups

3. The library is $\frac{7}{10}$ mile from city hall and $\frac{3}{5}$ mile from the middle school. How much further from the library is city hall than the middle school?
(Lesson 5-3)

A $\frac{1}{10}$ mile

B $\frac{1}{5}$ mile

C $\frac{3}{10}$ mile

D $\frac{4}{5}$ mile

4. For a picnic, Elise mixes $3\frac{1}{4}$ cups of orange juice, $1\frac{1}{2}$ cups of cranberry juice, and $\frac{3}{8}$ cup of carrot juice. How much juice does she have?
(Lesson 5-4)

A 4 cups

C 5 cups

B $4\frac{5}{8}$ cups

D $5\frac{1}{8}$ cups

5. Sharon lives $2\frac{2}{5}$ miles from the pool and has already walked $1\frac{7}{10}$ miles. How much further does Sharon have to walk?
(Lesson 5-5)

A $\frac{3}{5}$ mile

C $\frac{7}{10}$ mile

B $\frac{3}{10}$ mile

D $1\frac{3}{10}$ miles

6. What is the solution to $x - \frac{2}{5} = \frac{2}{3}$?
(Lesson 5-6)

A $x = \frac{4}{15}$

C $x = 1\frac{1}{15}$

B $x = \frac{1}{2}$

D $x = 1\frac{1}{2}$

7. Toya's mother picks her up from school at 3:42 P.M. They arrive home at 4:17 P.M. How long did it take to make the trip home?
(Lesson 5-7)

A 25 minutes

C 55 minutes

B 35 minutes

D 75 minutes

8. **Open-Ended** Mr. Saguchi buys $\frac{1}{2}$ gallon of white paint. He uses $\frac{2}{5}$ gallon of paint.

A. Write and solve an equation to find n, the number of gallons of paint left.

B. Which inverse operation is used?
(Lesson 5-6)

Assessment Anchors and Eligible Content
M6.A.3.2.1, M6.B.1.1.1, M6.D.2.1.1, M6.D.2.1.2

Pennsylvania Workouts

Correlation to Pennsylvania Assessment Anchors and Eligible Content

Item	Assessment Anchors and Eligible Content
1	M6.A.3.2.1
2	M6.A.3.2.1
3	M6.A.3.2.1
4	M6.A.3.2.1
5	M6.A.3.2.1
6	M6.A.3.2.1, M6.D.2.1.2
7	M6.B.1.1.1
8	M6.A.3.2.1, M6.D.2.1.1, M6.D.2.1.2

Answers

1. B

2. B

3. A

4. D

5. C

6. C

7. B

8. A. $n + \frac{2}{5} = \frac{1}{2}$
   $n = \frac{1}{10}$ gallon

   B. Subtraction is used as an inverse operation.

Prescribing Intervention

Item	Intervention	Item	Intervention
1	Lesson 5-4, Example 1	5	Lesson 5-5, Example 1
2	Lesson 5-2, Example 2	6	Lesson 5-6, Example 2
3	Lesson 5-3, Example 3	7	Lesson 5-7, Example 3
4	Lesson 5-4, Example 2	8	Lesson 5-6, Example 3

Correlation to Pennsylvania Assessment Anchors and Eligible Content

Item	Assessment Anchors and Eligible Content
1	M6.A.3.2.1
2	M6.A.1.1.4, M6.A.3.2.1
3	M6.A.3.2.1
4	M6.A.1.1.4, M6.A.3.2.1
5	M6.D.2.1.2
6	M6.A.3.2.1
7	M6.A.3.2.1

Answers

1. B

2. D

3. D

4. B

5. B

6. A

7. A. $\frac{2}{25}$ pound

   B. No. Answers may vary.

   Sample answer: Compare the two fractions by rewriting them with common denominators: $\frac{2}{25} = \frac{16}{200}$ and $\frac{1}{8} = \frac{25}{200}$. Since $\frac{16}{200}$ is less than $\frac{25}{200}$, the turkey sandwiches do not contain enough meat.

Workout for Pennsylvania Assessment Anchors and Eligible Content Mastery

Ready to go after Chapter 6

? For help, go to the lesson in green.

1. What is the product of $\frac{3}{4}$ and $\frac{8}{9}$?
   (Lesson 6-1)

   A $\frac{1}{3}$ C $\frac{11}{13}$

   B $\frac{2}{3}$ D $\frac{11}{36}$

2. A carpenter has $2\frac{1}{2}$ boxes of nails. A full box of nails weighs $4\frac{1}{4}$ pounds. What is the total weight of the carpenter's nails?
   (Lesson 6-2)

   A $8\frac{1}{8}$ pounds

   B $8\frac{3}{4}$ pounds

   C $10\frac{1}{4}$ pounds

   D $10\frac{5}{8}$ pounds

3. What is 4 divided by $\frac{5}{6}$?
   (Lesson 6-3)

   A $\frac{5}{24}$

   B $\frac{3}{10}$

   C $3\frac{1}{3}$

   D $4\frac{4}{5}$

4. What is the value of the expression
   $$4\frac{2}{3} \div 3\frac{1}{2}?$$
   (Lesson 6-4)

   A $\frac{3}{4}$

   B $1\frac{1}{3}$

   C $1\frac{3}{5}$

   D $2\frac{2}{3}$

5. Bananas cost $0.44 per pound. Raul needs $\frac{7}{8}$ pounds of bananas to make one batch of banana bread. What is the **greatest** number of batches Raul can make from $1.54 worth of bananas?
   (Lesson 6-5)

   A 3
   B 4
   C 5
   D 6

6. Which of the following expressions is equivalent to
   $$\frac{\frac{5}{9}}{\frac{2}{5}}$$
   (Lesson 6-3)

   A $\frac{5}{9} \times \frac{5}{2}$ C $\frac{9}{5} \times \frac{5}{2}$

   B $\frac{5}{9} \times \frac{2}{5}$ D $\frac{9}{5} \times \frac{2}{5}$

7. **Open-Ended** A worker at a sandwich shop uses $\frac{4}{5}$ pounds of sliced turkey to make 10 sandwiches.

   A. If the turkey is divided evenly among the 10 sandwiches, how many pounds of turkey does each sandwich contain?

   B. Each sandwich sold in the shop should have at least $\frac{1}{8}$ pound of meat. Do the 10 turkey sandwiches meet this requirement? Show or explain all your work.
   (Lesson 6-3)

 Assessment Anchors and Eligible Content M6.A.1.1.4, M6.A.3.2.1, M6.D.2.1.2

Prescribing Intervention

Item	Intervention	Item	Intervention
1	Lesson 6-1, Example 1	5	Lesson 6-5, Example 3
2	Lesson 6-2, Example 2	6	Lesson 6-3, Example 2
3	Lesson 6-3, Example 3	7	Lesson 6-3, Example 3
4	Lesson 6-4, Example 3		

Workout for Pennsylvania Assessment Anchors and Eligible Content Mastery

Ready to go after Chapter 7

? For help, go to the lesson in green.

1. Which is equivalent to 0.08?
(Lesson 7-6)

   A 0.08%
   B 0.8%
   C 8%
   D 80%

2. Wendy surveyed 75 students about their favorite movies. The table shows her results.

   SURVEY RESULTS

Favorite Movie	Frequency
Comedy	42
Action	26
Drama	7

   Wendy plans to make a circle graph of her data. What percent of the circle should represent students whose favorite movies are comedies?
   (Lesson 7-8)

   A 32%
   B 42%
   C 56%
   D 78%

3. At a pizza restaurant, $\frac{2}{5}$ of the pizzas sold are cheese pizzas. What percent of the pizzas sold are cheese pizzas?
(Lesson 7-6)

   A 2.5%
   B 20%
   C 25%
   D 40%

4. The Castillos have 2 gallons of orange juice in their refrigerator. They drink $\frac{2}{3}$ of the orange juice. How many gallons of orange juice did they drink?
(Lesson 6-1)

   A $\frac{1}{3}$ gallons   C $1\frac{1}{3}$ gallons
   B $\frac{2}{3}$ gallons   D $1\frac{2}{3}$ gallons

5. Saul made a bookshelf that is 24 inches wide. What is the **greatest** number of books he can place side by side on the shelf if each book is $1\frac{3}{4}$ inches thick?
(Lesson 6-4)

   A 13   C 15
   B 14   D 16

6. What value of x makes the following equation true?
(Lesson 6-5)

   $$\frac{2}{5}x = 9$$

   A $\frac{2}{45}$ C $\frac{18}{5}$
   B $\frac{5}{18}$ D $\frac{45}{2}$

7. **Open-Ended** A chef needs $1\frac{1}{3}$ cups of rice to make one batch of gumbo. How many cups of rice will the chef need to make 7 batches of gumbo? Write your answer as a mixed number. Show or explain your work.
(Lesson 6-2)

Pennsylvania Workouts

Pennsylvania Student Handbook **PA11**

Correlation to Pennsylvania Assessment Anchors and Eligible Content

Item	Assessment Anchors and Eligible Content
1	M6.A.1.1.1
2	M6.E.1.1.1, M6.E.1.1.3
3	M6.A.1.1.1
4	M6.A.3.2.1
5	M6.A.1.1.4, M6.A.3.2.1
6	M6.A.2.1.2, M6.A.3.2.1, M6.D.2.1.1
7	M6.A.1.1.4, M6.A.3.2.1

Answers

1. C

2. C

3. D

4. C

5. A

6. D

7. $9\frac{1}{3}$ cups; $1\frac{1}{3} \times 7 =$
   $\frac{4}{3} \times \frac{7}{1} =$
   $\frac{28}{3} = 9\frac{1}{3}$

Prescribing Intervention

Item	Intervention	Item	Intervention
1	Lesson 7-6, Example 3	5	Lesson 6-4, Example 3
2	Lesson 7-8, Example 2	6	Lesson 6-5, Example 2
3	Lesson 7-6, Example 4	7	Lesson 6-2, Example 3
4	Lesson 6-1, Example 2		

Correlation to Pennsylvania Assessment Anchors and Eligible Content

Item	Assessment Anchors and Eligible Content
1	M6.B.2.1.3
2	M6.C.1.1.2
3	M6.C.1.1.1
4	M6.B.2.3.1, M6.B.2.1.3, M6.C.1.2.2
5	M6.C.1.1.1, M6.C.1.1.2

Answers

1. C

2. D

3. A

4. B

5. isosceles acute; Answers may vary. Sample answer: The triangle is isosceles because two of its sides have the same length. The triangle is acute because each of its angles measures less than 90°.

Workout for Pennsylvania Assessment Anchors and Eligible Content Mastery

Ready to go after Chapter 8

? For help, go to the lesson in green.

1. Use your protractor to help you solve this problem. What is the measure of the angle shown below?
(Lesson 8-2)

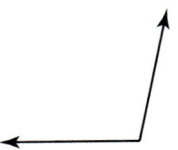

- **A** 78°
- **B** 82°
- **C** 102°
- **D** 118°

2. The diagram shows three stars in a constellation.

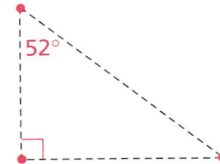

The stars form the vertices of what kind of triangle?
(Lesson 8-4)

- **A** acute
- **B** equilateral
- **C** obtuse
- **D** right

3. What do rectangles have in common with rhombuses?
(Lesson 8-5)

- **A** Both have 2 pairs of parallel sides.
- **B** Both have 4 congruent sides.
- **C** Both are types of squares.
- **D** Both are types of trapezoids.

4. The map shows the walking paths in a town park.

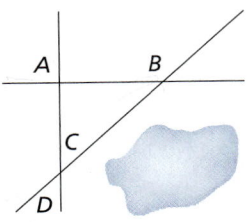

Which of the angles labeled on the map is obtuse?
(Lesson 8-2)

- **A** A
- **B** B
- **C** C
- **D** D

5. **Open-Ended** Classify the triangle shown below by its sides and by its angles. Explain how you determined your answer.
(Lesson 8-4)

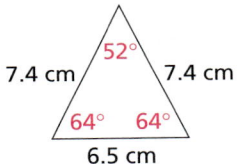

 Assessment Anchors and Eligible Content
M6.B.2.1.3, M6.B.2.3.1 M6.C.1.1.1, M6.C.1.1.2, M6.C.1.2.2

Prescribing Intervention

Item	Intervention	Item	Intervention
1	Lesson 8-2, Example 2	4	Lesson 8-2, Example 2
2	Lesson 8-4, Example 1	5	Lesson 8-4, Examples 1, 3
3	Lesson 8-5, Example 3		

Workout for Pennsylvania Assessment Anchors and Eligible Content Mastery

Ready to go after Chapter 9

? For help, go to the lesson in green.

1. The circular lid of a garbage can has a diameter of 0.5 meters. To the nearest tenth of a meter, what is the circumference of the lid?
   (Lesson 9-5)

   $C = 2\pi r$

   A 0.9 meter   **C** 1.6 meters
   B 1.0 meter   **D** 3.1 meters

2. The length of a rectangular swimming pool is 4 meters longer than its width. If the length of the pool is 8 meters, what is the perimeter of the pool?
   (Lesson 9-3)

   $P = 2l + 2w$

   A 12 meters   **C** 24 meters
   B 16 meters   **D** 32 meters

3. Robert has a rectangular vegetable garden and a square flower garden.

   12 ft

   8 ft   9 ft

   Vegetable Garden   Flower Garden

   If Robert buys fencing to enclose each garden, how many more feet of fencing will he need for the vegetable garden than for the flower garden?
   (Lesson 9-3)

   A 2 ft
   B 4 ft
   C 11 ft
   D 15 ft

4. A poster has the dimensions shown in the diagram.

   24 in.

   18 in.

   Annual Flower Show

   What is the perimeter of the poster in feet?
   (Lesson 9-3)

   A 3.5 ft
   B 7 ft
   C 8 ft
   D 84 ft

5. What type of polygon is shown below?
   (Lesson 8-5)

   A quadrilateral
   B hexagon
   C octagon
   D decagon

6. **Open-Ended** A circular track has a radius of 55 meters. Eric ran 3 laps around the track. To the nearest meter, find the distance Eric ran. (Use 3.14 = π.) Label your answer with the correct units. Show your work.
   (Lesson 9-5)

PA   **Assessment Anchors and Eligible Content**
M6.B.2.2.1, M6.C.1.1.1, M6.C.1.1.3

Pennsylvania Workouts

Item	Assessment Anchors and Eligible Content
1	M6.C.1.1.3
2	M6.B.2.2.1
3	M6.B.2.2.1
4	M6.B.2.2.1
5	M6.C.1.1.1
6	M6.C.1.1.3

Answers

1. **C**

2. **C**

3. **B**

4. **B**

5. **C**

6 1,036 meters

   $C = \pi d$

   $C \approx 3.14 \times 110$

   $C \approx 345.4$

   $345.4 \times 3 \text{ laps} \approx 1,036.2$

Prescribing Intervention

Item	Intervention	Item	Intervention
1	Lesson 9-5, Example 3	4	Lesson 9-3, Example 1
2	Lesson 9-3, Example 1	5	Lesson 8-5, Example 1
3	Lesson 9-3, More Than One Way	6	Lesson 9-5, Example 3

Correlation to Pennsylvania Assessment Anchors and Eligible Content

Item	Assessment Anchors and Eligible Content
1	M6.E.3.1.1
2	M6.A.1.3.1
3	M6.E.3.1.1
4	M6.A.3.2.1
5	M6.A.3.1.1
6	M6.D.1.1.1, M6.D.1.2.1
7	M6.E.3.1.1

Answers

1. D

2. D

3. B

4. B

5. B

6. B

7. 40%; $\frac{6}{15} = .40 = 40\%$

Workout for Pennsylvania Assessment Anchors and Eligible Content Mastery

Ready to go after Chapter 10

❓ For help, go to the lesson in green.

1. Cody is playing a board game. Each turn, he rolls a number cube with faces numbered 1 to 6. If he rolls a number greater than 2 on his next turn, he will win the game. What is the probability that Cody will win the game on his next turn?
(Lesson 10-2)

A $\frac{1}{6}$ 　　 C $\frac{1}{3}$

B $\frac{1}{4}$ 　　 D $\frac{2}{3}$

2. In the 2001–2002 basketball season, the home team won 30 of their 82 games. In simplest form, what fraction of their games did they win?
(Lesson 4-5)

A $\frac{3}{14}$ 　　 C $\frac{1}{27}$

B $\frac{15}{16}$ 　　 D $\frac{15}{41}$

3. A sock drawer contains 6 black socks, 10 white socks, and 4 blue socks. If Yolanda takes a sock from the drawer at random, what is the probability that the sock will be black?
(Lesson 10-2)

A $\frac{3}{7}$ 　　 C $\frac{1}{6}$

B $\frac{3}{10}$ 　　 D $\frac{1}{20}$

4. What is the sum of $\frac{2}{7}$ and $\frac{6}{7}$?
(Lesson 5-2)

A $\frac{8}{14}$ 　　 C $\frac{12}{7}$

B $\frac{8}{7}$ 　　 D $\frac{12}{14}$

5. The table shows the number of hours Sophie spent babysitting last week.

BABYSITTING HOURS

Day	Hours Worked
Thursday	1.5
Friday	3.0
Saturday	4.5

How many hours did Sophie spend babysitting last week?
(Lesson 1-7)

A 8 hours 　　 C 9.5 hours

B 9 hours 　　 D 10 hours

6. The table shows the times at which the first three buses are scheduled to leave a bus stop.

Bus	Scheduled Departure Time
1	6:15 A.M.
2	6:40 A.M.
3	7:05 A.M.

If this pattern continues, at what time is the fourth bus scheduled to leave the bus stop?
(Lesson 3-1)

A 7:25 A.M. 　　 C 7:40 A.M.

B 7:30 A.M. 　　 D 7:45 A.M.

7. Open-Ended A box of bagels contains, 9 plain bagels, 4 blueberry bagels, and 2 raisin bagels. If one bagel is chosen at random from the box, what is the probability that it will be a blueberry or raisin bagel? Express your answer as a percent. Show all your work.
(Lesson 10-2)

 Assessment Anchors and Eligible Content
M6.A.1.3.1, M6.A.3.1.1, M6.A.3.2.1, M6.D.1.1.1, M6.D.1.2.1, M6.E.3.1.1

Prescribing Intervention

Item	Intervention	Item	Intervention
1	Lesson 10-2, Example 1	5	Lesson 1-7, Example 1
2	Lesson 4-5, Example 2	6	Lesson 3-1, Example 1
3	Lesson 10-2, Example 1	7	Lesson 10-2, Example 1
4	Lesson 5-2, Example 1		

Workout for Pennsylvania Assessment Anchors and Eligible Content Mastery

Correlation to Pennsylvania Assessment Anchors and Eligible Content

Item	Assessment Anchors and Eligible Content
1	M6.C.3.1.1
2	M6.A.1.1.2
3	M6.D.2.1.1, M6.D.2.1.2
4	M6.A.3.1.1
5	M6.C.3.1.1
6	M6.A.1.1.4, M6.A.1.3.1, M6.A.3.2.1

Ready to go after Chapter 11

? For help, go to the lesson in green.

1. Points F, G, and H on the coordinate plan below represent 3 vertices of a rectangle.

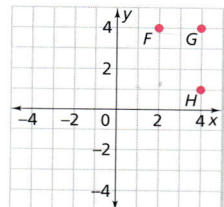

What are the coordinates of point J, the fourth vertex of the rectangle?
(Lesson 11-8)

A (1, 1)   C (2, 1)
B (1, 2)   D (2, 2)

2. Which list shows these numbers in order from **least** to **greatest**?
(Lesson 4-9)

$$0.67 \quad \frac{2}{3} \quad \frac{7}{12} \quad 0.6$$

A $0.6, \frac{7}{12}, 0.67, \frac{2}{3}$

B $\frac{7}{12}, 0.6, \frac{2}{3}, 0.67$

C $\frac{2}{3}, 0.6, 0.67, \frac{7}{12}$

D $\frac{7}{12}, \frac{2}{3}, 0.67, 0.6$

3. Six movie tickets cost a total of $45.00. The equation $6c = \$45.00$ can be used to find c, the cost of one movie ticket. What value of c makes the equation true?
(Lesson 3-7)

A $9.00
B $8.50
C $7.50
D $7.00

4. Cheddar cheese costs $3.32 per pound. Mr. Roldan bought two packages of cheese, one weighing 1.2 pounds and the other weighing 0.9 pound. To the nearest cent, what is the cost of the cheese Mr. Roldan bought?
(Lesson 1-8)

A $9.96   C $4.88
B $6.97   D $4.19

5. Which point represents the location of the ordered pair (2, 4)?
(Lesson 11-8)

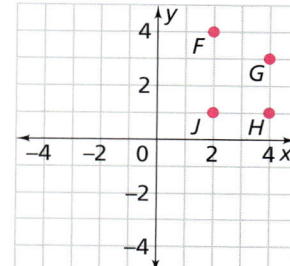

A Point F C Point H
B Point G D Point J

6. Open-Ended Toni is making outfits for the 32 members of the school drill team. Each outfit requires $2\frac{5}{8}$ yards of fabric. Toni has 80 yards of fabric.

A. How many more yards of fabric will she need to make outfits for the entire team?

B. Show all your work. Label your answer with the correct units.
(Lesson 6-2)

Answers

1. C

2. B

3. C

4. B

5. A

6. A. 4 yards

   B. $2\frac{5}{8} \times 32 = 84$

     $84 - 80 = 4$

Pennsylvania Workouts

Prescribing Intervention

Item	Intervention	Item	Intervention
1	Lesson 11-8, Example 1	4	Lesson 1-8, Example 2
2	Lesson 4-9, Example 3	5	Lesson 11-8, Example 2
3	Lesson 3-7, Example 2	6	Lesson 6-2, More Than One Way

Correlation to Pennsylvania Assessment Anchors and Eligible Content

Item	Assessment Anchors and Eligible Content
1	M6.D.1.1.1, M6.D.1.2.1
2	M6.A.3.2.1
3	M6.D.2.1.1, M6.D.2.1.2
4	M6.A.1.1.3
5	M6.A.3.1.1
6	M6.A.3.2.1
7	M6.A.3.2.1
8	M6.A.1.3.1

Answers

1. D

2. D

3. D

4. D

5. A

6. C

7. C

8. A. 8 teams

   B. Answers may vary. Sample answer: Find the GCF of 16 and 88. First write the prime factorization of each number. Then multiply the common factors.

Workout for Pennsylvania Assessment Anchors and Eligible Content Mastery

Ready to go after Chapter 12

? For help, go to the lesson in green.

1. Which rule can be used to find the number of triangles in each design of the following pattern?
   (Lesson 3-1)

   A Start with 1 triangle and add 1 triangle repeatedly.
   B Start with 1 triangle and add 2 triangles repeatedly.
   C Start with 2 triangles and add 1 triangles repeatedly.
   D Start with 2 triangles and add 2 triangles repeatedly.

2. What is the value of $\frac{8}{9} - \frac{2}{9}$?
   (Lesson 5-2)

   A $\frac{1}{4}$ C $\frac{5}{9}$

   B $\frac{1}{3}$ D $\frac{2}{3}$

3. What is the solution of the equation
   $$\frac{r}{4.8} = 6?$$
   (Lesson 3-7)

   A $r = 0.80$ C $r = 24.8$
   B $r = 1.25$ D $r = 28.8$

4. What is the value of 6^3?
   (Lesson 4-2)

   A 9
   B 18
   C 36
   D 216

5. A postal worker needs to mail 15 packages. Ten of the packages weigh 0.6 pound each, and the remaining packages weigh 0.9 pound each. What is the total weight of the packages?
   (Lesson 1-8)

   A 10.5 pounds
   B 15.0 pounds
   C 19.5 pounds
   D 22.5 pounds

6. The expression $\frac{5}{9} + \frac{1}{3}$ is equivalent to —
   (Lesson 5-3)

   A $\frac{1}{2}$ C $\frac{8}{9}$

   B $\frac{2}{3}$ D 1

7. Mr. Morales bought a pair of windshield wipers and 8.5 gallons of gasoline for a total of $36.24. The price of the windshield wipers was $13.12. What was the price of the gasoline per gallon?
   (Lesson 1-9)

   A $2.46
   B $2.58
   C $2.72
   D $2.83

8. **Open-Ended** Sixteen coaches and 88 baseball players will be split into teams. Each team will have the same number of coaches and the same number of players.

   A. At most, how many teams can there be?
   B. Explain the process you used to determine your answer. Show all your work.
   (Lesson 4-4)

 Assessment Anchors and Eligible Content
M6.A.1.1.3, M6.A.1.3.1, M6.A.3.1.1, M6.A.3.2.1, M6.D.1.1.1, M6.D.1.2.1, M6.D.2.1.1, M6.D.2.1.2

Prescribing Intervention

Item	Intervention	Item	Intervention
1	Lesson 3-1, Example 1	5	Lesson 1-8, Example 2
2	Lesson 5-2, Example 3	6	Lesson 5-3, Example 1
3	Lesson 3-7, Example 3	7	Lesson 1-9, Example 2
4	Lesson 4-2, Example 2	8	Lesson 4-4, Example 3

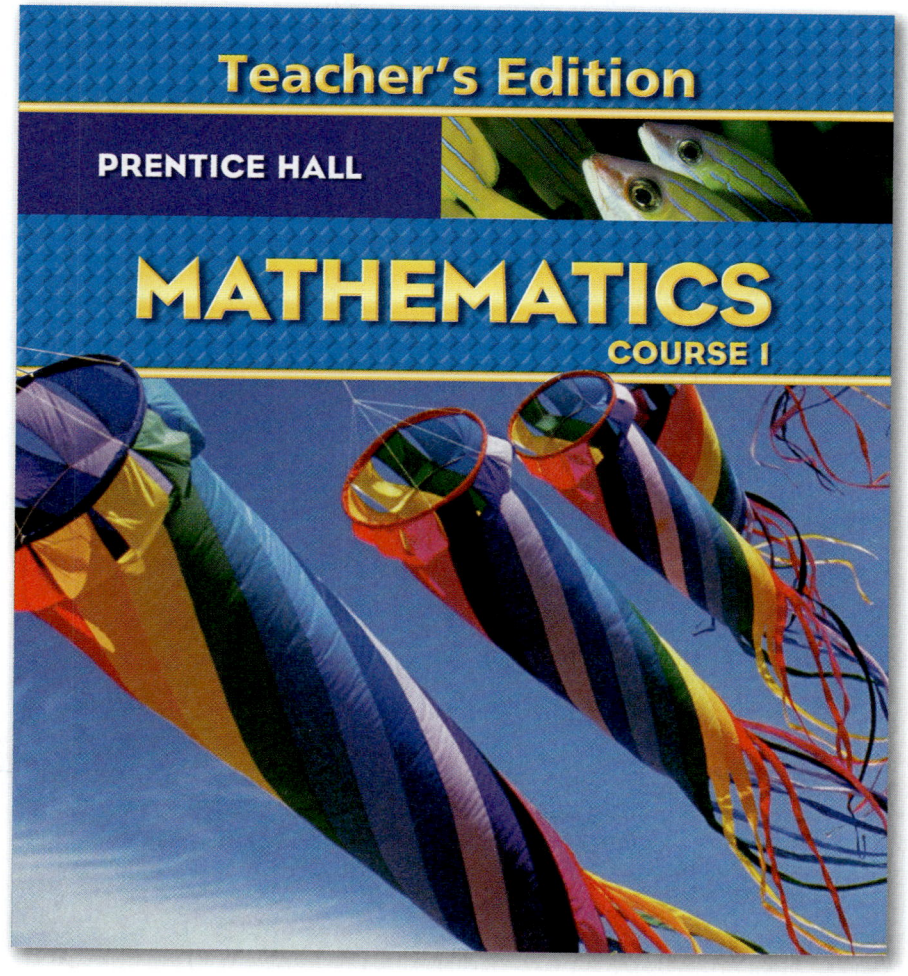

Teacher's Edition

PRENTICE HALL

MATHEMATICS
COURSE 1

Randall I. Charles

Mark Illingworth

Bonnie McNemar

Darwin Mills

Alma Ramirez

Andy Reeves

PEARSON

Prentice
Hall

Boston, Massachusetts
Upper Saddle River, New Jersey

Acknowledgments appear on pp. T698–T699, which constitute an extension of this copyright page.

Copyright ©2008 by Pearson Education, Inc., publishing as Pearson Prentice Hall, Boston, Massachusetts 02116.
All rights reserved. Printed in the United States of America. This publication is protected by copyright, and permission should be obtained from the publisher prior to any prohibited reproduction, storage in a retrieval system, or transmission in any form or by any means, electronic, mechanical, photocopying, recording, or likewise. For information regarding permission(s), write to: Rights and Permissions Department, One Lake Street, Upper Saddle River, New Jersey 07458.

Pearson Prentice Hall™ is a trademark of Pearson Education, Inc.
Pearson® is a registered trademark of Pearson plc.
Prentice Hall® is a registered trademark of Pearson Education, Inc.
Instant Check System™ is a trademark of Pearson Education, Inc.
Success Tracker™ is a trademark of Pearson Education, Inc.
PresentationExpress™ is a trademark of Pearson Education, Inc.
TeacherExpress™ is a trademark of Pearson Education, Inc.
StudentExpress™ is a trademark of Pearson Education, Inc.
LessonLab™ is a trademark of Pearson Education, Inc.

DK is a registered trademark of Dorling Kindersley Limited.
Exam*View*® and **Lesson*View*®** are registered trademarks of FSCreations, Inc.
Mind*Point*® Quiz Show is a registered trademark of FSCreations, Inc.

ISBN 0-13-133999-0
1 2 3 4 5 6 7 8 9 10   10 09 08 07 06

Prentice Hall Math Course 1
Teacher's Edition Contents

Mathematics Teacher Handbook

Student Edition With Teacher Notes

Series Author

Randall I. Charles, Ph.D., is Professor Emeritus in the Department of Mathematics and Computer Science at San Jose State University, San Jose, California. He began his career as a high school mathematics teacher, and he was a mathematics supervisor for five years. Dr. Charles has been a member of several NCTM committees and is the former Vice President of the National Council of Supervisors of Mathematics. Much of his writing and research has been in the area of problem solving. He has authored more than 75 mathematics textbooks for kindergarten through college. *Scott Foresman-Prentice Hall Mathematics Series Author Kindergarten through Algebra 2*

Program Authors

Mark Illingworth has taught in both elementary and high school math programs for more than twenty years. During this time, he received the Christa McAuliffe sabbatical to develop problem solving materials and projects for middle grades math students, and he was granted the Presidential Award for Excellence in Mathematics Teaching. Mr. Illingworth's specialty is in teaching mathematics through applications and problem solving. He has written two books on these subjects and has contributed to math and science textbooks at Prentice Hall.

Bonnie McNemar is a mathematics educator with more than 30 years' experience in Texas schools as a teacher, administrator, and consultant. She began her career as a middle school mathematics teacher and served as a supervisor at the district, county, and state levels. Ms. McNemar was the director of the Texas Mathematics Staff Development Program, now known as TEXTEAMS, for five years, and she was the first director of the Teachers Teaching with Technology (T³) Program. She remains active in both of these organizations as well as in several local, state, and national mathematics organizations, including NCTM.

Darwin Mills, an administrator for the public school system in Newport News, Virginia, has been involved in secondary level mathematics education for more than fourteen years. Mr. Mills has served as a high school teacher, a community college adjunct professor, a department chair, and a district level mathematics supervisor. He has received numerous teaching awards, including teacher of the year for 1999–2000, and an Excellence in Teaching award from the College of Wooster, Ohio, in 2002. He is a frequent presenter at workshops and conferences. He believes that all students can learn mathematics if given the proper instruction.

Alma Ramirez is co-director of the Mathematics Case Project at WestEd, a nonprofit educational institute in Oakland, California. A former bilingual elementary and middle school teacher, Ms. Ramirez has considerable expertise in mathematics teaching and learning, second language acquisition, and professional development. She has served as a consultant on a variety of projects and has extensive experience as an author for elementary and middle grades texts. In addition, her work has appeared in the 2004 NCTM Yearbook. Ms. Ramirez is a frequent presenter at professional meetings and conferences.

Andy Reeves, Ph.D., teaches at the University of South Florida in St. Petersburg. His career in education spans 30 years and includes seven years as a middle grades teacher. He subsequently served as Florida's K–12 mathematics supervisor, and more recently he supervised the publication of The Mathematics Teacher, Mathematics Teaching in the Middle School, and Teaching Children Mathematics for NCTM. Prior to entering education, he worked as an engineer for Douglas Aircraft.

Contributing Author

Denisse R. Thompson, Ph.D., is a Professor of Mathematics Education at the University of South Florida. She has particular interests in the connections between literature and mathematics and in the teaching and learning of mathematics in the middle grades. Dr. Thompson contributed to the Guided Problem Solving features.

Reviewers

Course 1 Reviewers

Donna Anderson
Math Supervisor, 7–12
West Hartford Public Schools
West Hartford, Connecticut

Nancy L. Borchers
West Clermont Local Schools
Cincinnati, Ohio

Kathleen Chandler
Walnut Creek Middle School
Erie, Pennsylvania

Jane E. Damaske
Lakeshore Public Schools
Stevensville, Michigan

Frank Greco
Parkway South Middle School
Manchester, Missouri

Rebecca L. Jones
Odyssey Middle School
Orlando, Florida

Marylee R. Liebowitz
H. C. Crittenden Middle School
Armonk, New York

Kathy Litz
K. O. Knudson Middle School
Las Vegas, Nevada

Don McGurrin
Wake County Public School System
Raleigh, North Carolina

Ron Mezzadri
K–12 Mathematics Supervisor
Fair Lawn School District
Fair Lawn, New Jersey

Sylvia O. Reeder-Tucker
Prince George's County Math
    Department
Upper Marlboro, Maryland

Julie A. White
Allison Traditional Magnet Middle
    School
Wichita, Kansas

Charles Yochim
Bronxville Middle School
Bronxville, New York

Course 2 Reviewers

Cami Craig
Prince William County Public Schools
Marsteller Middle School
Bristow, Virginia

Donald O. Cram
Lincoln Middle School
Rio Rancho, New Mexico

Pat A. Davidson
Jacksonville Junior High School
Jacksonville, Arkansas

Yvette Drew
DeKalb County School System
Open Campus High School
Atlanta, Georgia

Robert S. Fair
K–12 District Mathematics Coordinator
Cherry Creek School District
Greenwood Village, Colorado

Michael A. Landry
Glastonbury Public Schools
Glastonbury, Connecticut

Nancy Ochoa
Weeden Middle School
Florence, Alabama

Charlotte J. Phillips
Wichita USD 259
Wichita, Kansas

Mary Lynn Raith
Mathematics Curriculum Specialist
Pittsburgh Public Schools
Pittsburgh, Pennsylvania

Tammy Rush
Consultant, Middle School
    Mathematics
Hillsborough County Schools
Tampa, Florida

Judith R. Russ
Prince George's County Public Schools
Capitol Heights, Maryland

Tim Tate
Math/Science Supervisor
Lafayette Parish School System
Lafayette, Louisiana

Dondi J. Thompson
Alcott Middle School
Norman, Oklahoma

Candace Yamagata
Hyde Park Middle School
Las Vegas, Nevada

Course 3 Reviewers

Linda E. Addington
Andrew Lewis Middle School
Salem, Virginia

Jeanne Arnold
Mead Junior High School
Schaumburg, Illinois

Sheila S. Brookshire
A. C. Reynolds Middle School
Asheville, North Carolina

Jennifer Clark
Mayfield Middle School
Putnam City Public Schools
Oklahoma City, Oklahoma

Nicole Dial
Chase Middle School
Topeka, Kansas

Christine Ferrell
Lorin Andrews Middle School
Massillon, Ohio

Virginia G. Harrell
Education Consultant
Hillsborough County, Florida

Jonita P. Howard
Mathematics Curriculum Specialist
Lauderdale Lakes Middle School
Lauderdale Lakes, Florida

Patricia Lemons
Rio Rancho Middle School
Rio Rancho, New Mexico

Susan Noce
Robert Frost Junior High School
Schaumburg, Illinois

Carla A. Siler
South Bend Community School Corp.
South Bend, Indiana

Kathryn E. Smith-Lance
West Genesee Middle School
Camillus, New York

Kathleen D. Tuffy
South Middle School
Braintree, Massachusetts

Patricia R. Wilson
Central Middle School
Murfreesboro, Tennessee

Patricia Young
Northwood Middle School
Pulaski County Special School District
North Little Rock, Arkansas

Content Consultants

Ann Bell
Mathematics
Prentice Hall Consultant
Franklin, Tennessee

Blanche Brownley
Mathematics
Prentice Hall Consultant
Olney, Maryland

Joe Brumfield
Mathematics
Prentice Hall Consultant
Altadena, California

Linda Buckhalt
Mathematics
Prentice Hall Consultant
Derwood, Maryland

Andrea Gordon
Mathematics
Prentice Hall Consultant
Atlanta, Georgia

Eleanor Lopes
Mathematics
Prentice Hall Consultant
New Castle, Delaware

Sally Marsh
Mathematics
Prentice Hall Consultant
Baltimore, Maryland

Bob Pacyga
Mathematics
Prentice Hall Consultant
Darien, Illinois

Judy Porter
Mathematics
Prentice Hall Consultant
Fuquay Varina, North Carolina

Rose Primiani
Mathematics
Prentice Hall Consultant
Harbor City, New Jersey

Jayne Radu
Mathematics
Prentice Hall Consultant
Scottsdale, Arizona

Pam Revels
Mathematics
Prentice Hall Consultant
Sarasota, Florida

Barbara Rogers
Mathematics
Prentice Hall Consultant
Raleigh, North Carolina

Michael Seals
Mathematics
Prentice Hall Consultant
Edmond, Oklahoma

Margaret Thomas
Mathematics
Prentice Hall Consultant
Indianapolis, Indiana

Whole Numbers and Decimals

Assessment and Test Prep

CHAPTER 2

Data and Graphs

Table of Contents

CHAPTER 3

Patterns and Variables

Student Support

Vocabulary 🔊

Vocabulary Review, 108, 113, 118,
  124, 130, 134, 138, 144
New Vocabulary, 108, 113, 124,
  130, 134, 138, 144
Vocabulary Builder, 128
Vocabulary Tip, 124, 126
Exercises, 110, 115, 126, 132,
  140, 146

GO Online

Video Tutor Help, 131
Active Math, 109, 118
Homework Video Tutor, 111, 116,
  121, 127, 133, 136, 141, 146
Lesson Quiz, 111, 115, 121, 127,
  133, 135, 141, 147
Vocabulary Quiz, 150
Chapter Test, 152

GPS Guided Problem Solving

Exercises, 110, 115, 121, 127, 132,
  136, 140, 146
**Writing Equations to Solve
  Problems,** 142
DK Applications: Applying Patterns,
  154–155

Assessment and Test Prep

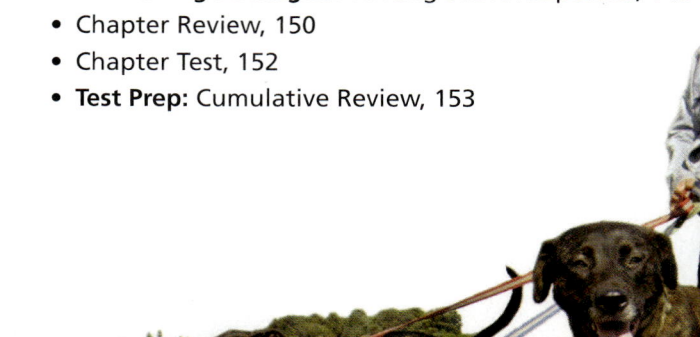

CHAPTER 4

Number Theory and Fractions

Student Support

Vocabulary 🔊

Vocabulary Review, 158, 162, 166, 171, 176, 182, 188, 192, 198
New Vocabulary, 158, 162, 166, 171, 176, 182, 188, 192, 198
Vocabulary Builder, 187
Vocabulary Tip, 162, 185, 198
Exercises, 160, 164, 168, 173, 178, 184, 190, 194

GO Online

Video Tutor Help, 159, 163
Active Math, 167, 193
Homework Video Tutor, 161, 165, 169, 174, 179, 185, 191, 195, 201
Lesson Quiz, 161, 165, 169, 173, 179, 185, 191, 195, 201
Vocabulary Quiz, 204
Chapter Test, 206

GPS Guided Problem Solving

Exercises, 160, 164, 168, 173, 178, 184, 190, 194, 200
Practice Solving Problems, 196
DK Applications: Applying Fractions, 208–209

Assessment and Test Prep

Table of Contents

Contents   **xi**

CHAPTER 5

Adding and Subtracting Fractions

CHAPTER 6

Multiplying and Dividing Fractions

Student Support

 **Vocabulary** 🔊

Vocabulary Review, 261, 266, 272, 276, 282, 288, 292
New Vocabulary, 272
Vocabulary Tip, 262, 290, 292
Exercises, 274

GO 🌐 **Online**

Video Tutor Help, 272, 277
Active Math, 266, 276
Homework Video Tutor, 263, 269, 275, 279, 285, 291, 295
Lesson Quiz, 263, 269, 275, 279, 285, 291, 295
Vocabulary Quiz, 298
Chapter Test, 300

GPS **Guided Problem Solving**

Exercises, 263, 269, 274, 278, 284, 290, 294
Practice Solving Problems, 286
DK Applications: Applying Mixed Numbers, 302–303

Assessment and Test Prep

Table of Contents

Contents   **xiii**

T13

CHAPTER 7

Ratios, Proportions, and Percents

Assessment and Test Prep

Student Support

Vocabulary 🔊

GO Online

GPS Guided Problem Solving

CHAPTER 8

Tools of Geometry

Student Support

Vocabulary 🔊

Vocabulary Review, 362, 367, 374, 380, 386, 392, 398, 402

New Vocabulary, 362, 367, 374, 380, 386, 392, 398, 402

Vocabulary Builder, 384

Vocabulary Tip, 362, 374, 403

Exercises, 364, 370, 376, 382, 389, 394, 399, 404

GO Online

Video Tutor Help, 368, 381

Active Math, 363, 387, 393

Homework Video Tutor, 365, 371, 377, 383, 390, 395, 401, 405

Lesson Quiz, 365, 371, 377, 383, 389, 395, 401, 405

Vocabulary Quiz, 408

Chapter Test, 410

Math at Work, 391

GPS Guided Problem Solving

Exercises, 364, 370, 376, 382, 389, 394, 400, 404

Practice Solving Problems, 396

DK Applications: Applying Geometry, 412–413

Assessment and Test Prep

Contents XV

CHAPTER 9

Geometry and Measurement

Student Support

Vocabulary 🔊

Vocabulary Review, 416, 421, 426, 432, 438, 444, 449, 453, 458, 462

New Vocabulary, 416, 426, 432, 438, 449, 453, 458

Vocabulary Builder, 425

Vocabulary Tip, 426, 438, 447, 449

Exercises, 418, 429, 434, 440, 451, 454, 459

GO Online

Active Math, 445

Homework Video Tutor, 419, 424, 430, 435, 441, 447, 452, 455, 460, 465

Lesson Quiz, 419, 423, 429, 435, 441, 447, 451, 455, 459, 465

Vocabulary Quiz, 468

Chapter Test, 470

Math at Work, 436

GPS Guided Problem Solving

Exercises, 418, 423, 429, 434, 441, 446, 452, 455, 460, 465

Practice Solving Problems, 442

DK Applications: Applying Measurement, 472–473

Assessment and Test Prep

Next 96 km

CHAPTER 10

Exploring Probability

CHAPTER 11

Integers

Student Support

Vocabulary ◄))

Vocabulary Review, 516, 520, 524, 530, 534, 540, 543, 548, 554, 558
New Vocabulary, 516, 548
Vocabulary Tip, 530, 548, 559
Exercises, 517, 550, 555, 561

GO Online

Video Tutor Help, 531, 535
Active Math, 521, 549, 559
Homework Video Tutor, 519, 522, 527, 532, 537, 542, 545, 551, 557, 561
Lesson Quiz, 519, 521, 527, 533, 537, 541, 545, 551, 557, 561
Vocabulary Quiz, 564
Chapter Test, 566
Math at Work, 552

GPS Guided Problem Solving

Exercises, 518, 522, 526, 532, 536, 542, 545, 550, 556, 561
Practice Solving Problems, 538
DK Applications: Applying Integers, 568–569

Assessment and Test Prep

xviii   Contents

CHAPTER 12

Equations and Inequalities

Student Support

 **Vocabulary**

Vocabulary Review, 572, 578, 582, 587, 591
New Vocabulary, 572, 578, 587, 591
Vocabulary Tip, 588
Exercises, 574, 580, 589, 593

GO Online

Video Tutor Help, 592
Active Math, 573, 587, 591
Homework Video Tutor, 575, 581, 584, 590, 593
Lesson Quiz, 575, 581, 583, 589, 598
Vocabulary Quiz, 598
Chapter Test, 600

GPS Guided Problem Solving

Exercises, 575, 580, 584, 589, 594
Practice Solving Problems, 595
DK Applications: Applying Equations, 604–605

Assessment and Test Prep

- **Test-Taking Strategies:** Estimating the Answer, 597
- Chapter Review, 598
- Chapter Test, 600
- **Test Prep:** Cumulative Review, 601

Table of Contents

ect Your Learning

ugh problem solving, activities, and the Web

ons: Real-World Applications

Throughout this book you will find links to the Prentice Hall Web site. Use the Web Codes provided with each link to gain direct access to online material. Here's how to **Go Online**:

1. Go to PHSchool.com
2. Enter the Web Code
3. Click Go!

Lesson Web Codes

Lesson Quiz Web Codes: There is an online quiz for every lesson. Access these quizzes with Web Codes aqa-0101 through aqa-1205 for Lesson 1-1 through Lesson 12-5. See page 19.

Homework Video Tutor Web Codes: For every lesson, there is additional support online to help students complete their homework. Access the Homework Video Tutors with Web Codes aqe-0101 through aqe-1205 for Lesson 1-1 through Lesson 12-5. See page 25.

Lesson Quizzes
Web Code format: aqa-0204
02 = Chapter 2   04 = Lesson 4

Homework Video Tutor
Web Code format: aqe-0605
06 = Chapter 6   05 = Lesson 5

Chapter Web Codes

Chapter	Vocabulary Quizzes	Chapter Tests	Chapter Projects
1	aqj-0151	aqa-0152	aqd-0161
2	aqj-0251	aqa-0252	aqd-0261
3	aqj-0351	aqa-0352	aqd-0361
4	aqj-0451	aqa-0452	aqd-0461
5	aqj-0551	aqa-0552	aqd-0561
6	aqj-0651	aqa-0652	aqd-0661
7	aqj-0751	aqa-0752	aqd-0761
8	aqj-0851	aqa-0852	aqd-0861
9	aqj-0951	aqa-0952	aqd-0961
10	aqj-1051	aqa-1052	aqd-1061
11	aqj-1151	aqa-1152	aqd-1161
12	aqj-1251	aqa-1252	aqd-1261
End-of-Course		aqa-1254	

Additional Web Codes

Video Tutor Help:
Use Web Code aqe-0775 to access engaging online instructional videos to help bring math concepts to life. See page 32.

Data Updates:
Use Web Code aqg-9041 to get up-to-date government data for use in examples and exercises. See page 35.

Math at Work:
For information about each Math at Work feature, use Web Code aqb-2031. See page 20.

Differentiate Instruction with Ease

Students develop and learn in different ways at different paces. Accessible content, presented in a variety of formats, acknowledges these unique differences while providing options for learning. The goal of *Prentice Hall Mathematics* is for all students to be successful and for you to have the tools you need to accomplish this. *Prentice Hall Mathematics* Grade 6 through Algebra 2 provides better solutions for meeting the needs of every student in the classroom by achieving two goals:

- Providing superior teacher support materials for planning how to effectively differentiate instruction
- Providing unique resources for the various populations of students.

Differentiated Instruction
Solutions for All Learners

Adapted Resources for Differentiating Instruction

In addition to the support provided in the Teacher's Editions, Prentice Hall has created resources developed uniquely for Below Level and Special Needs students.

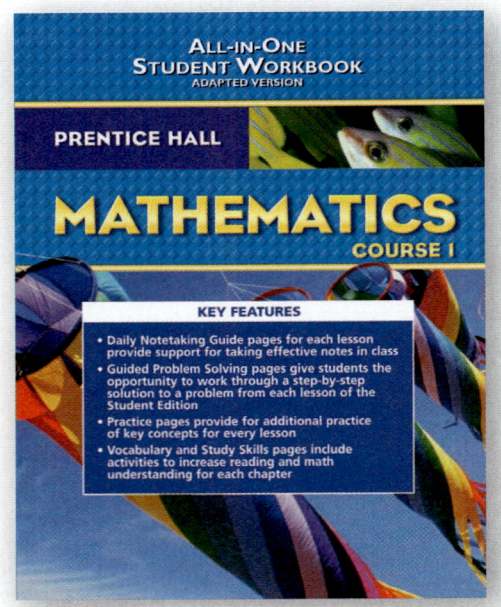

All-in-One Student Workbook Adapted Version

This resource includes adapted practice and adapted daily notetaking worksheets to support special needs students. By providing these critical resources ready for you to use, you can cover the same mathematical content with the students, but provide a more appropriate resource for them to take notes and practice the lesson's mathematics.

Differentiated Assessments

Prentice Hall Mathematics also recognizes the importance of not only differentiating instruction, but also differentiating the assessments used to monitor student progress and inform future instruction. To achieve this, three versions of each chapter test are provided: L2 for Below Level L3 for All Students and L4 for Advanced Learners.

ExamView 5.0 Assessment Suite

To provide the ultimate flexibility in creating assessments and practice worksheets for all students, the *Prentice Hall Mathematics ExamView* Test Banks contain adapted items written exclusively for your Special Needs and Below Level students.

Prentice Hall Mathematics Teacher's Editions offer comprehensive support in differentiating instruction.

L1 Special Needs
L2 Below Level
L3 All Students
L4 Advanced Learners
ELL English Language Learners

Prentice Hall Mathematics uses a consistent method for identifying resources for differentiating instruction. This consistency helps you to easily identify and choose the appropriate resources for your students.

Planning and Using Differentiated Resources

These chapter level support pages provide you an easy-to-read overview of the resources available and suggested ways in the instructional lesson to use the resources.

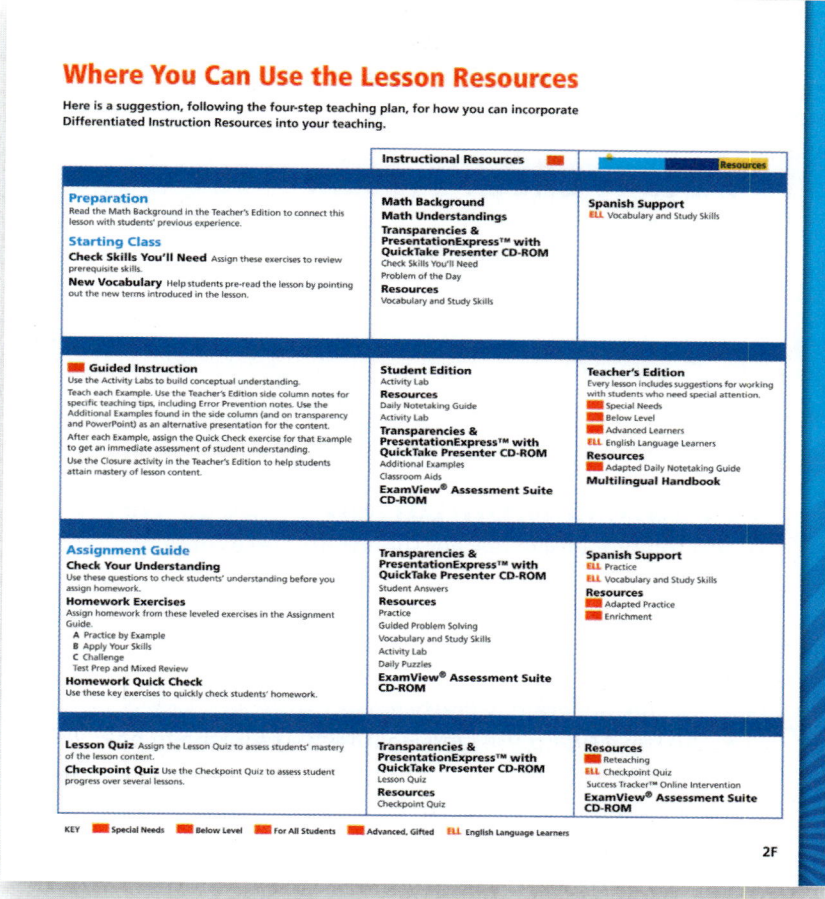

Where You Can Use the Lesson Resources

Here is a suggestion, following the four-step teaching plan, for how you can incorporate Differentiated Instruction Resources into your teaching.

	Instructional Resources	Resources
Preparation Read the Math Background in the Teacher's Edition to connect this lesson with students' previous experience. **Starting Class** **Check Skills You'll Need** Assign these exercises to review prerequisite skills. **New Vocabulary** Help students pre-read the lesson by pointing out the new terms introduced in the lesson.	Math Background Math Understandings Transparencies & PresentationExpress™ with QuickTake Presenter CD-ROM Check Skills You'll Need Problem of the Day **Resources** Vocabulary and Study Skills	Spanish Support **ELL** Vocabulary and Study Skills
Guided Instruction Use the Activity Labs to build conceptual understanding. Teach each Example. Use the Teacher's Edition side column notes for specific teaching tips, including Error Prevention notes. Use the Additional Examples found in the side column (and on transparency and PowerPoint) as an alternative presentation for the content. After each Example, assign the Quick Check exercise for that Example to get an immediate assessment of student understanding. Use the Closure activity in the Teacher's Edition to help students attain mastery of lesson content.	Student Edition Activity Lab **Resources** Daily Notetaking Guide Activity Lab Transparencies & PresentationExpress™ with QuickTake Presenter CD-ROM Additional Examples Classroom Aids ExamView® Assessment Suite CD-ROM	Teacher's Edition Every lesson includes suggestions for working with students who need special attention. **L1** Special Needs **L2** Below Level **L4** Advanced Learners **ELL** English Language Learners **Resources** **L1** Adapted Daily Notetaking Guide **Multilingual Handbook**
Assignment Guide **Check Your Understanding** Use these questions to check students' understanding before you assign homework. **Homework Exercises** Assign homework from these leveled exercises in the Assignment Guide. A Practice by Example B Apply Your Skills C Challenge Test Prep and Mixed Review **Homework Quick Check** Use these key exercises to quickly check students' homework.	Transparencies & PresentationExpress™ with QuickTake Presenter CD-ROM Student Answers **Resources** Practice Guided Problem Solving Vocabulary and Study Skills Activity Lab Daily Puzzles ExamView® Assessment Suite CD-ROM	Spanish Support **ELL** Practice **ELL** Vocabulary and Study Skills **Resources** **L2** Adapted Practice **L4** Enrichment
Lesson Quiz Assign the Lesson Quiz to assess students' mastery of the lesson content. **Checkpoint Quiz** Use the Checkpoint Quiz to assess student progress over several lessons.	Transparencies & PresentationExpress™ with QuickTake Presenter CD-ROM Lesson Quiz **Resources** Checkpoint Quiz	**Resources** **L1** Reteaching **ELL** Checkpoint Quiz Success Tracker™ Online Intervention ExamView® Assessment Suite CD-ROM

KEY ■ Special Needs ■ Below Level ■ For All Students ■ Advanced, Gifted **ELL** English Language Learners

2F

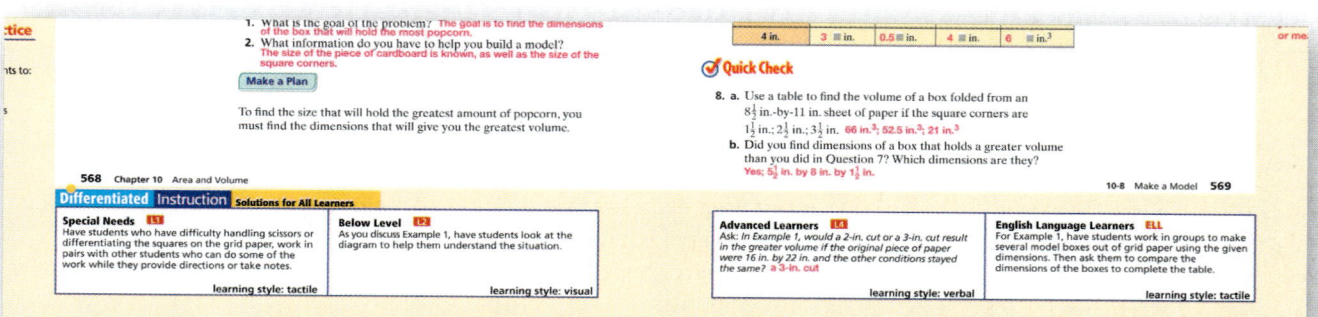

Differentiated Instruction teaching notes

These useful notes help you differentiate the lesson for all learners, including Special Needs, Below Level, Advanced, and English Language Learners.

Assessment to Inform Instruction

Assessment is integral to mathematics instruction. Student assessment should occur often and with a variety of different measures. *Prentice Hall Mathematics* provides an ongoing assessment strand that addresses assessment *for* learning and assessment *of* learning. The formative assessment features (before and during instruction) offer a variety of methods for teachers to assess student understanding and inform future instruction. The summative assessment features (after instruction) document student mastery of mathematical concepts and skills and further prepare students for success in today's tests.

Instant Check System™ for Ongoing Assessment

This unique feature of *Prentice Hall Mathematics* ensures that students make progress every day, in every lesson. It helps teachers assess necessary prerequisite skills and monitor student understanding. The Instant Check System™ assessments include:
- Check Your Readiness – Assesses prerequisite skills for each chapter
- Check Skills You'll Need – Assesses prerequisite skills for each lesson
- Quick Check – Assesses student understanding after every example in the book
- Check Your Understanding – Assesses understanding before the homework exercises
- Check Point – Assesses understanding after completing lessons

Progress Monitoring Assessments

This comprehensive teacher support resource contains all the program assessments needed to evaluate student understanding, monitor student progress, and inform future instruction. The following assessments are included:
- Screening Test
- Benchmark Tests
- Test-Taking Strategy Practice
- Quarter, Mid-Course, and Final Tests – regular and below level versions
- Comprehensive Report Forms
- Answers to all of the tests

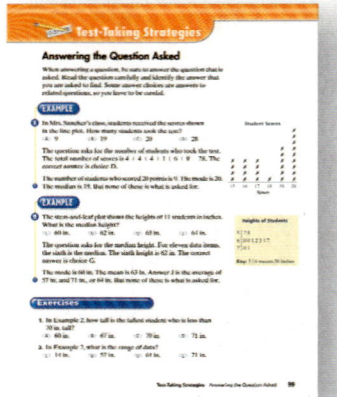

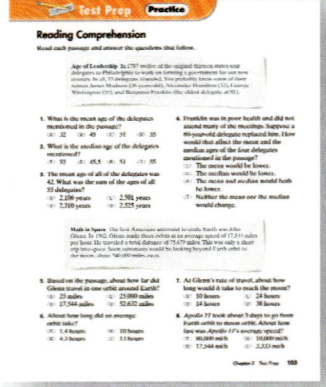

Preparation for High-Stakes Assessment

Prentice Hall Mathematics recognizes how critical it is for teachers to prepare every student for test success.
The following features help achieve this:
- Separate Test-Taking Strategy lessons focus on specific strategies necessary for test success.
- Test Prep exercises, focusing on all major question types, are included after every lesson.
- After every chapter, Test Prep review pages provide additional practice for students.

Help All Students Become Problem Solvers

One of the major goals of a mathematics program is to develop students' ability to solve problems in class, on assessments, in the context of real-world situations, and outside the classroom. *Prentice Hall Mathematics* helps support this goal by embedding problem-solving instruction in every lesson, providing targeted support for problem-solving strategies throughout the Student Edition, and including sufficient problems to help students practice and reinforce problem solving skills.

Guided Problem Solving Features

These features throughout the Student Edition provide scaffolded support in solving problems. The student walks through how to solve one representative problem, focusing on both the reasoning and the computation that must be done.

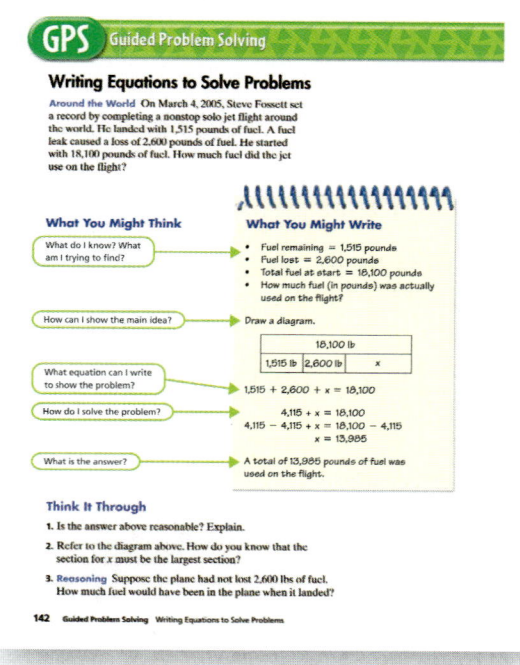

Activities and Activity Labs

Throughout the Student Edition are in-lesson activities and full feature Activity Labs. These provide students an opportunity to complete more in-depth problems and applications of the mathematical content they're learning.

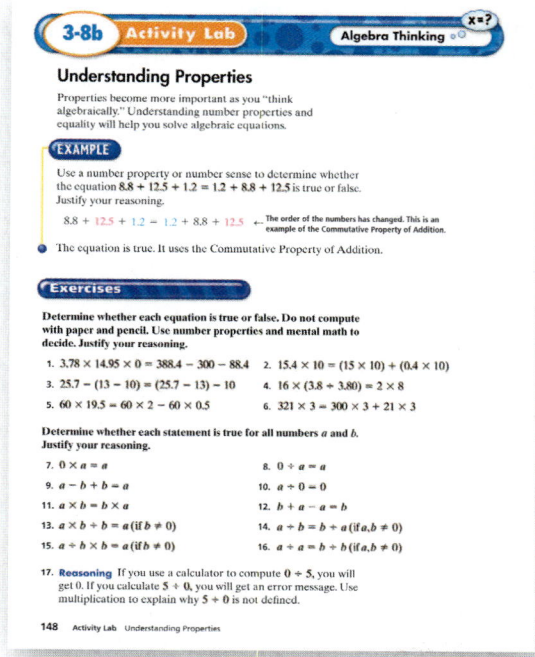

Problem Solving Practice

Every lesson in the Student Edition includes a comprehensive, leveled exercise set. This provides students the opportunity to solve a variety of problems and apply problem solving strategies on a daily basis. Furthermore, additional problems have been added to the end of each book in the Extra Skill and Word Problem Practice section.

Technology – not simply added, but added value

Take Learning to a New Level

StudentEXPRESS™ CD-ROM
A suite of learning tools to help students study, learn, and succeed in class. An interactive textbook with instructional videos, built-in activities, vocabulary support, and instant feedback assessments make this the most powerful student study tool available. Interactive Text also available online.

Homework Video Tutor and Online Active Math
Homework Video Tutors provide built-in homework help for every lesson. Narrated by real teachers, these engaging interactive tutorials cover the key concepts of each day's lesson. Additionally, Online Active Math interactivities provide an opportunity to explore math concepts.

Use Assessment Technology to Inform Instruction

ExamView® 5.0 Assessment Suite
The most powerful test generator available—with the most comprehensive test banks. Create and modify custom-made tests with ease. Access the Math Art Gallery to instantly add math images to your questions. Also-instantly translate any test into Spanish.

MindPoint® Quiz Show
This creative product allows teachers to involve the entire class in a fun, end-of-chapter review game.

Success Tracker™ Online
Personalized for each student with individual assessment, diagnosis, and remediation. Color-coded reports make it easy for teachers to monitor progress.

Superior Planning and Teaching Tools

TeacherEXPRESS™ CD-ROM— powered by LessonView® planning software
An Interactive Teacher's Edition, LessonView planning software, correlations to national and state standards, instructional tools, plus professional development to help teachers plan, teach, and assess.

PresentationEXPRESS™ CD-ROM with ExamView® QuickTake Presenter
This innovative component includes all the transparencies in interactive, PowerPoint format, making it easier for you to teach and to customize based on your teaching preferences. QuickTake assessments are embedded in every lesson, allowing teachers to quickly and easily monitor student progress.

Worksheets Online
All program worksheets are also conveniently posted online so you and your students can access them anywhere - one more way to make your planning and assignment management easier.

Professional Development
that meets your needs

In-Service On Demand

Now, you have the freedom to access your Prentice Hall in-service training online, anytime, anywhere, at PHSchool.com. This online tutorial library offers in-service training specifically for the Prentice Hall textbook and technology you're teaching with right now.

In-service designed around you!
In-Service On Demand is Prentice Hall's new Web site of in-service training tutorials for your Prentice Hall products. Now you can access the same training for using your Prentice Hall textbook and technology that you would learn in a traditional in-service—from the convenience of your computer!

In-Service for your Prentice Hall program!
The In-Service On Demand library features video-based tutorials to help you maximize the effectiveness of the Prentice Hall program you use. This extensive library is continually being updated with tutorials for Prentice Hall's newest products! Visit the site as often as you like!

In-Service is just a click away!
1. Go to PHSchool.com and click on In-Service On Demand.
2. Select mathematics and then select your *Prentice Hall Mathematics* book.
3. Watch the video-based tutorials and get the in-service training you need when and where it's convenient for you.
4. Download and print PDF tutorial guides on what you've just seen.

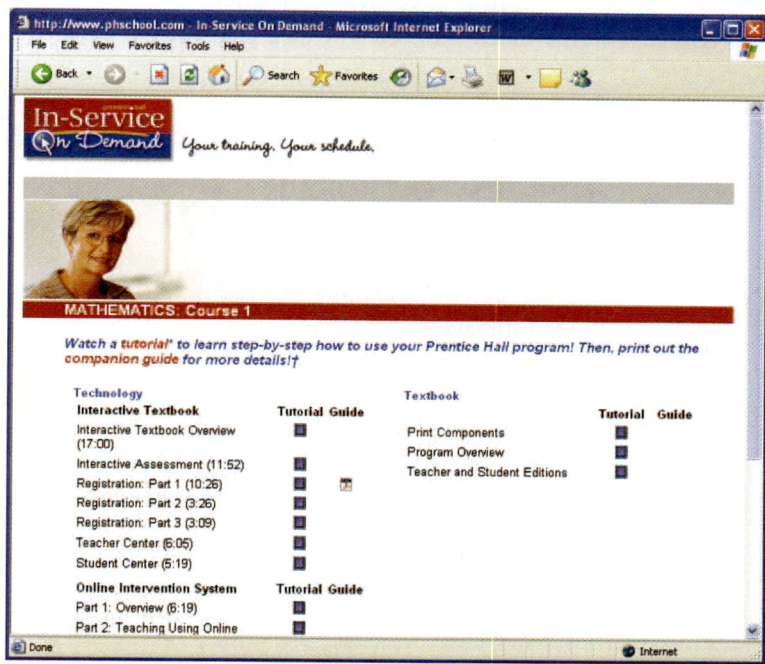

Day-to-Day Professional Development

Math Background in Teacher's Edition
Support instruction at the chapter and lesson level as every Chapter of Prentice Hall Mathematics begins with Math Background related to the content of the chapter in both middle school and high school.

Research-Based and Proven Effective

The stakes for mathematics educators are high. You are expected to raise student achievement. Prentice Hall Mathematics programs are backed by efficacy research to give you the confidence to meet this challenge.

In developing Prentice Hall programs, the use of research is a guiding, central construct. This research was conducted in three phases:

1 Exploratory Needs Assessment
(Quantitative and Qualitative)

Key research events include —
- Teacher interviews
- Classroom observations
- Mail surveys
- Reviews of educational research

2 Formative, Prototype Development and Field Testing
(Quantitative and Qualitative)

Key research events include —
- Field testing of prototypes
- Classroom observations
- Teacher reviews
- Supervisor reviews
- Educator advisory panels

3 Summative, Validation Research
(Experimental and Quasi-Experimental Study Designs & Qualitative Research)

Key research events include —
- Pre-publication learner verification research
- Post-publication efficacy studies
- Classroom observations
- Evaluation of in-market results on standardized tests
- Effect size studies

The facing page contains an example of the latest research carried out for Prentice Hall Middle School Mathematics.

2005 Research Results:
Prentice Hall
Middle School Mathematics

Independent research confirms Middle School students using Prentice Hall Mathematics achieve greater success in mathematics

Results of independent research indicate that students using Prentice Hall Mathematics Course 2 showed significant improvement, outperforming students using other mathematics programs. The randomized control trial, conducted by PRES Associates, Inc., a national educational evaluation firm with central offices in Jackson, WY, confirmed students using the Prentice Hall curricula showed greater improvement from pre- to post-tests than their counterparts using other programs as measured by two different standardized assessments. Improvement was evident on all mathematics objectives measured. Additionally, the program was especially effective with low-performing students.

The study is part of a multi-year research effort commissioned by the publisher and is one of many slated to evaluate the effectiveness of Prentice Hall's educational materials across disciplines and grade levels. Participants represented a mix of urban and urban-fringe districts with diverse socio-economic, ethnic, and academic backgrounds.

Among the key findings, PRES Associates reported:
- Student performance significantly improved from the beginning of the school year to its end as measured by the TerraNova Basic Multiple Assessment, chosen because it is aligned to national NCTM standards and has proven reliability and validity.
- Students using Prentice Hall Mathematics Course 2 improved to a greater extent in pre- to post-test scores than those using other programs.
- Assessment results suggest that Prentice Hall Mathematics Course 2 is particularly effective with low-performing students, as evidenced by the significant gains in low-performing student test scores.
- Prentice Hall Mathematics Course 2 students reported feeling significantly more comfortable with math than students using other programs. They also reported higher math aspirations (i.e., plans to take advanced math in high school).
- Teachers participating in the study reported that Prentice Hall Mathematics Course 2 provided significantly better assistance than other programs in the following areas (1) individualizing instruction, (2) reinforcing previously taught concepts, (3) providing test preparation, and (4) making connections to real-life.
- Teachers identified many aspects of the Prentice Hall program as effective, including the Guided Problem Solving workbook, Check Skills You'll Need exercises, and Check Understanding exercises.

The study was designed to fully meet the evidence criteria put forth by the What Works Clearinghouse, the Federal agency established in 2002 to provide the educators and the public with a trusted source of scientific evidence of what works in education. This study was designed so that accurate and appropriate inferences could be made regarding the effectiveness of the Prentice Hall Mathematics Course 2 program.

Visit PHSchool.com/MathResearch for the full report and additional research in support of Prentice Hall Mathematics programs.

Mathematics Strands

The following 10 strands are from the NCTM Principles and Standards. The Background and Progression sections highlight content students usually have mastered when they enter middle grades and the progression expected using *Prentice Hall Mathematics Courses 1, 2,* and *3.*

Number and Operations

- Understand numbers, ways of representing numbers, relationships among numbers, and number systems
- Understand meanings of operations and how they relate to one another
- Compute fluently and make reasonable estimates

Background and Progression Students usually enter middle grades with computational facility with whole numbers, and varying degrees of mastery of fractions and decimals.

In *Course 1*, students reach mastery of all decimal and fraction operations. They work with percents and develop estimation skills. Concepts of scale and ratio are introduced. (Chapters 1, 5, 6, and 7)

In *Course 2*, students reach mastery of integer operations, rates, and ratios. They work with percent applications and exponents. (Chapters 1, 2, 5, and 6)

In *Course 3*, students reach mastery of percent and proportion applications. They continue to work with exponents, including using square roots. (Chapters 2, 3, and 4)

Algebra

- Understand patterns, relations, and functions
- Represent and analyze mathematical situations and structures using algebraic symbols
- Use mathematical models to represent and understand quantitative relationships
- Analyze change in various contexts

Background and Progression Students usually enter middle grades having represented patterns through words, tables, and graphs. They also have some experience with symbolic representation of unknown quantities.

In *Course 1*, students use variables in equations and patterns. Models are introduced for percents, proportions, integers, and properties of equality. (Chapters 3, 7, and 11)

In *Course 2*, students continue to use models, tables, graphs, and symbolic notation to represent algebraic relationships. They solve equations and interpret the slope of a line. (Chapters 4, 9, and 10)

In *Course 3*, students solve equations and use equivalent forms for expressions containing parentheses, like terms, and exponents. They relate slope and y-intercept to graphs and linear relationships. (Chapters 1, 6, 11, and 12)

Geometry

- Analyze characteristics and properties of two- and three-dimensional geometric shapes and develop mathematical arguments about geometric relationships
- Specify locations and describe spatial relationships using coordinate geometry and other representational systems
- Apply transformations and use symmetry to analyze mathematical situations
- Use visualization, spatial reasoning, and geometric modeling to solve problems

Background and Progression Students entering middle grades have usually mastered names and characteristics of common polygons and simple solids.

In *Course 1*, students use grids, nets, and block diagrams to build concepts of area and volume. They explore symmetry and transformations. The coordinate plane is introduced. (Chapters 8 and 9)

In *Course 2*, students continue to use two-dimensional representations of three-dimensional figures. They study congruent and similar figures and transformations. (Chapters 5, 7, 8, and 10)

In *Course 3*, students draw inferences about lengths, areas, and volumes of similar two- and three-dimensional figures. They study both reflectional and rotational symmetry. (Chapters 3, 7, and 8)

Measurement

- Understand measurable attributes of objects and the units, systems, and processes of measurement
- Apply appropriate techniques, tools, and formulas to determine measurements

Background and Progression Students entering middle grades have usually worked with customary and metric units. They often know formulas for the perimeter and area of simple figures.

In *Course 1*, students choose units, convert units, and estimate measures within the customary and metric systems. They develop and use formulas related to polygons. They explore surface area and volume. (Chapters 6 and 9)

In *Course 2*, students develop and use formulas to find areas of irregular figures, and to find surface area and volume of prisms and cylinders. (Chapters 5 and 8)

In *Course 3*, students continue to convert units. They extend their understanding of formulas to include pyramids, cones, and spheres. (Chapters 4, 7, and 8)

Data Analysis and Probability

- Formulate questions that can be addressed with data and collect, organize, and display relevant data to answer them
- Select and use appropriate statistical methods to analyze data
- Understand and apply basic concepts of probability

Background and Progression Students in middle grades have experience with gathering, displaying, and analyzing data. They have used simple probabilities to express the likelihood of an event.

In *Course 1*, students master measures of central tendency, simple line graphs, bar graphs, and probabilities. They make line plots, circle graphs, and stem-and-leaf plots. (Chapters 2, 7, and 10)

In *Course 2*, students continue to study line plots, stem-and-leaf plots, and bar graphs. They analyze survey techniques for bias, and make scatter plots to analyze data. (Chapter 11)

In *Course 3*, students place and interpret trend lines on scatter plots. They also develop probability concepts for compound events. (Chapters 9 and 10)

Problem Solving

- Build new mathematical knowledge through problem solving
- Solve problems that arise in mathematics and in other contexts
- Apply and adapt a variety of appropriate strategies to solve problems
- Monitor and reflect on the process of mathematical problem solving

Background and Progression Throughout *Prentice Hall Mathematics*, students use a consistent framework for problem solving, which identifies four phases: Understand the Problem, Make a Plan, Carry Out the Plan, Check the Answer.

In each course, students learn specific strategies and apply them to a variety of problems. They practice and apply these strategies through guided problem solving. (Problem Solving Handbook)

Reasoning and Proof

- Recognize reasoning and proof as fundamental aspects of mathematics
- Make and investigate mathematical conjectures
- Develop and evaluate mathematical arguments and proofs
- Select and use various types of reasoning and methods of proof

Background and Progression At the elementary level, students use mathematical reasoning in the development of number sense and classification skills.

In *Prentice Hall Mathematics*, reasoning is an integral part of students' daily work. Every lesson contains a mix of Reasoning, Number Sense, and Error Analysis exercises. Students have the opportunity to explain their thinking using mathematical concepts and properties. Activities throughout the program provide students with opportunities to use inductive reasoning.

Communication

- Organize and consolidate their mathematical thinking through communication
- Communicate their mathematical thinking coherently and clearly to peers, teachers, and others
- Analyze and evaluate the mathematical thinking and strategies of others
- Use the language of mathematics to express mathematical ideas precisely

Background and Progression To effectively communicate mathematically, students need ample opportunity to express math in words, in symbols, through models, and orally.

Prentice Hall Mathematics integrates a vocabulary strand that includes short help tips related to vocabulary and symbols as well as full-page features.

Students also have opportunities to write about mathematics. Many exercises ask students to justify their work, explain a process, or draw a conclusion.

Connections

- Recognize and use connections among mathematical ideas
- Understand how mathematical ideas interconnect and build on one another to produce a coherent whole
- Recognize and apply mathematics in contexts outside of mathematics

Background and Progression By the upper elementary grades, most students are able to distinguish which one of several approaches might be best to solve a problem.

In *Prentice Hall Mathematics*, students use alternative methods in More Than One Way features (every chapter). These situations give a rich mix of numeric, algebraic, geometric, and experimental approaches to problems. Each lesson also includes real-world Examples and exercises that provide contexts in mathematics.

Representation

- Create and use representations to organize, record, and communicate mathematical ideas
- Select, apply, and translate among mathematical representations to solve problems
- Use representations to model and interpret physical, social, and mathematical phenomena

Background and Progression Students entering middle grades have experience using concrete and visual models to help develop number concepts.

In *Prentice Hall Mathematics*, visualization continues with consistent modeling of numbers, operations, and relationships.

Algebraic relationships are represented through tables, patterns, graphs, words, and notation. The use of variables is introduced gradually through the program.

By the end of *Course 3*, students have learned to identify the most appropriate vehicle for presenting data, which means choosing among various types of graphs.

Course 1 Leveled Pacing Chart

This Leveled Pacing Chart is provided as a guide to help you customize your course and to provide for differentiated instruction. The suggested number of days for each chapter is based on a traditional 45-minute class period and on a 90-minute block period. The total of 160 days of instruction leaves time for assessments, projects, assemblies, or other special days that vary from school to school.

Differentiated Instruction
Solutions for All Learners

	Below Level L2	On Level	Advanced L4
Chapter 1 Whole Numbers and Decimals Traditional 15 days Block 8 days			
1-1 Understanding Whole Numbers	✓	✓	
1-2 Estimating With Whole Numbers	✓	✓	✓
1-3 Properties of Numbers	✓	✓	✓
1-4 Order of Operations	✓	✓	
1-5a Activity Lab, Hands On: Exploring Decimal Models	✓	✓	
1-5 Understanding Decimals	✓	✓	✓
1-6 Comparing and Ordering Decimals	✓	✓	✓
1-7a Activity Lab, Hands On: Using Models	✓	✓	
1-7 Adding and Subtracting Decimals	✓	✓	✓
Vocabulary Builder: High-Use Academic Words	✓	✓	✓
1-8a Activity Lab, Hands On: Modeling Multiplication of Decimals	✓	✓	
1-8 Multiplying Decimals	✓	✓	✓
1-8b Activity Lab, Technology: Multiplying and Dividing Decimals by 10, 100, and 1,000	✓	✓	✓
1-9 Dividing Decimals	✓	✓	✓
1-9b Activity Lab, Data Analysis: Using Decimals	✓	✓	✓
Guided Problem Solving: Choosing the Right Operation	✓	✓	✓
Problem Solving Application: Applying Decimals	✓	✓	✓
Chapter 2 Data and Graphs Traditional 13 days Block 7 days			
2-1a Activity Lab, Hands On: Exploring the Mean	✓	✓	✓
2-1 Finding the Mean	✓	✓	✓
Vocabulary Builder: High-Use Academic Words	✓	✓	✓
2-2 Median and Mode	✓	✓	✓
2-3 Frequency Tables and Line Plots	✓	✓	✓
2-4 Bar Graphs and Line Graphs	✓	✓	✓
2-4b Activity Lab, Algebra Thinking: Making Bar Graphs	✓	✓	✓
Extension: Double Bar and Line Graphs			✓
2-5 Using Spreadsheets to Organize Data	✓	✓	✓
2-5b Activity Lab, Technology: Spreadsheets and Graphs	✓	✓	✓
2-6 Stem-and-Leaf Plots		✓	✓
Guided Problem Solving: Solving Multiple-Step Problems	✓	✓	✓
2-7 Misleading Graphs and Statistics	✓	✓	✓
Extension: Random Samples and Surveys			✓
Problem Solving Application: Data Analysis	✓	✓	✓
Chapter 3 Patterns and Variables Traditional 15 days Block 8 days			
3-1 Describing a Pattern	✓	✓	✓
3-2a Activity Lab, Hands On: Patterns and Expressions	✓	✓	
3-2 Variables and Expressions	✓	✓	✓
3-3a Activity Lab: Representing Real-World Situations	✓	✓	✓
3-3 Writing Algebraic Expressions	✓	✓	✓
3-3b Activity Lab: Arithmetic Sequences	✓	✓	✓
3-4 Using Number Sense to Solve One-Step Equations	✓	✓	✓
Vocabulary Builder: High-Use Academic Words	✓	✓	✓

	Below Level L2	On Level	Advanced L4
3-5a Activity Lab, Hands On: Modeling Equations	✓	✓	✓
3-5 Solving Addition Equations	✓	✓	✓
3-6 Solving Subtraction Equations	✓	✓	✓
3-7a Activity Lab, Hands On: Modeling Division Equations	✓	✓	✓
3-7 Solving Multiplication and Division Equations	✓	✓	✓
Guided Problem Solving: Writing Equations to Solve Problems	✓	✓	✓
3-8 The Distributive Property	✓	✓	✓
3-8b Activity Lab, Algebra Thinking: Understanding Properties	✓	✓	✓
Problem Solving Application: Applying Patterns	✓	✓	✓
Chapter 4 Number Theory and Fractions Traditional 15 days Block 8 days			
4-1 Divisibility and Mental Math	✓	✓	✓
4-2 Exponents	✓	✓	✓
4-3 Prime Numbers and Prime Factorization	✓	✓	✓
4-4 Greatest Common Factor	✓	✓	✓
4-5a Activity Lab, Modeling Fractions	✓	✓	
4-5 Equivalent Fractions	✓	✓	✓
4-5b Activity Lab, Technology: Simplifying Fractions	✓	✓	✓
4-6a Activity Lab, Hands On: Exploring Improper Fractions	✓	✓	
4-6 Mixed Numbers and Improper Fractions	✓	✓	✓
4-6b Activity Lab, Hands On: Fractions and Measurement	✓	✓	✓
Vocabulary Builder: Making Word Lists	✓	✓	✓
4-7 Least Common Multiple	✓	✓	✓
4-8 Comparing and Ordering Fractions	✓	✓	✓
Guided Problem Solving: Practice Solving Problems	✓	✓	✓
4-9 Fractions and Decimals	✓	✓	✓
4-9b Activity Lab, Data Analysis: Conducting a Survey	✓	✓	✓
Problem Solving Application: Applying Fractions	✓	✓	✓
Chapter 5 Adding and Subtracting Traditional 13 days Block 6 days			
5-1 Estimating Sums and Differences	✓	✓	✓
5-2a Activity Lab, Hands On: Modeling Fraction Operations	✓	✓	
5-2 Fractions With Like Denominators	✓	✓	✓
5-3a Activity Lab, Modeling Unlike Denominators	✓	✓	✓
5-3 Fractions With Unlike Denominators	✓	✓	✓
5-4a Activity Lab, Hands On: Using Mixed Numbers	✓	✓	✓
5-4 Adding Mixed Numbers	✓	✓	✓
5-5 Subtracting Mixed Numbers	✓	✓	✓
5-5b Activity Lab, Technology: Using a Fraction Calculator	✓	✓	✓
5-6a Activity Lab, Data Analysis: Using Pictographs	✓	✓	✓
5-6 Equations With Fractions	✓	✓	✓
Guided Problem Solving: Practice Solving Problems	✓	✓	✓
5-7 Measuring Elapsed Time	✓	✓	✓
Problem Solving Application: Applying Mixed Numbers	✓	✓	✓
Chapter 6 Multiplying and Dividing Fractions Traditional 13 days Block 6 days			
6-1a Activity Lab, Hands On: Modeling Fraction Multiplication	✓	✓	
6-1 Multiplying Fractions	✓	✓	✓
6-1b Activity Lab, Algebra Thinking: Understanding Equality	✓	✓	✓
6-2 Multiplying Mixed Numbers	✓	✓	✓
6-3a Activity Lab, Hands On: Fraction Division	✓	✓	
6-3 Dividing Fractions	✓	✓	✓
6-4 Dividing Mixed Numbers	✓	✓	✓
6-4b Activity Lab, Technology: Using a Calculator for Fractions	✓	✓	✓
6-5 Solving Fraction Equations by Multiplying	✓	✓	✓
Guided Problem Solving: Practice Solving Problems	✓	✓	✓
6-6 The Customary System	✓	✓	✓

Leveled Pacing Chart

	Below Level L2	On Level	Advanced L4
6-7 Changing Units in the Customary System	✓	✓	✓
6-7b Activity Lab, Hands On: Measuring Objects	✓	✓	
Problem Solving Application: Applying Mixed Numbers	✓	✓	✓

Chapter 7 Ratios, Proportions, and Percents — Traditional 15 days   Block 7 days

	Below Level L2	On Level	Advanced L4
7-1 Ratios	✓	✓	✓
7-1b Activity Lab, Hands On: Modeling Ratios	✓	✓	
Vocabulary Builder: High-Use Academic Vocabulary	✓	✓	✓
7-2 Unit Rates	✓	✓	✓
7-3 Understanding Proportions	✓	✓	✓
7-4 Solving Proportions	✓	✓	✓
7-4b Activity Lab, Hands On: Making Predictions	✓	✓	✓
7-5 Scale Drawings	✓	✓	✓
7-6a Activity Lab, Hands On: Modeling Percents	✓	✓	
7-6 Percents, Fractions, and Decimals	✓	✓	✓
7-7 Finding the Percent of a Number	✓	✓	✓
7-8a Activity Lab, Hands On: Exploring Circle Graphs	✓	✓	✓
7-8 Circle Graphs	✓	✓	✓
7-8b Activity Lab, Technology: Reporting Survey Results	✓	✓	✓
Guided Problem Solving: Practice Solving Problems	✓	✓	✓
7-9 Estimating With Percents	✓	✓	✓
Extension: Percents Under 1% or Over 100%			✓
Problem Solving Application: Applying Proportions	✓	✓	✓

Chapter 8 Tools of Geometry — Traditional 14 days   Block 7 days

	Below Level L2	On Level	Advanced L4
8-1 Points, Lines, Segments, and Rays	✓	✓	✓
8-2a Activity Lab, Hands On: Using Angle Benchmarks	✓	✓	✓
8-2 Angles	✓	✓	✓
Extension: Basic Constructions			✓
8-3 Special Pairs of Angles	✓	✓	✓
8-3b Activity Lab, Hands On: Exploring Parallel Lines	✓	✓	✓
8-4a Activity Lab, Technology: Investigating Angles in a Triangle		✓	✓
8-4 Classifying Triangles	✓	✓	✓
Vocabulary Builder: High-Use Academic Words	✓	✓	✓
8-5a Activity Lab, Hands On: Angles in a Quadrilateral	✓	✓	✓
8-5 Exploring and Classifying Polygons	✓	✓	✓
8-6 Congruent and Similar Figures	✓	✓	✓
Guided Problem Solving: Practice Solving Problems	✓	✓	✓
8-7 Line Symmetry		✓	✓
8-8 Transformations		✓	✓
8-8b Activity Lab, Hands On: Tessellations			
Problem Solving Application: Applying Geometry	✓	✓	✓

Chapter 9 Geometry and Measurement — Traditional 16 days   Block 8 days

	Below Level L2	On Level	Advanced L4
9-1 Metric Units of Length, Mass, and Capacity	✓	✓	✓
9-1b Activity Lab, Hands On: Metric Units	✓	✓	✓
9-2 Converting Units in the Metric System	✓	✓	✓
Vocabulary Builder: Using Concept Maps	✓	✓	✓
9-3 Perimeters and Areas of Rectangles	✓	✓	✓
9-4a Activity Lab, Hands On: Comparing Areas	✓	✓	✓
9-4 Areas of Parallelograms and Triangles	✓	✓	✓
9-5a Activity Lab, Data Collection: Exploring Circles	✓	✓	✓
9-5 Circles and Circumference	✓	✓	✓
Guided Problem Solving: Practice Solving Problems	✓	✓	✓
9-6 Area of a Circle	✓	✓	✓
9-7a Activity Lab, Hands On: Views of Three-Dimensional Objects		✓	✓

	Below Level **L2**	On Level	Advanced **L4**
9-7 Three-Dimensional Figures and Spatial Reasoning	✓	✓	✓
9-8 Surface Areas of Prisms	✓	✓	✓
9-9a Activity Lab, Hands On: Exploring Volume	✓	✓	✓
9-9 Volumes of Rectangular Prisms	✓	✓	✓
9-10a Activity Lab, Hands On: Exploring Cylinders	✓	✓	✓
9-10 Surface Areas and Volumes of Cylinders	✓	✓	✓
Problem Solving Application: Applying Measurement	✓	✓	✓

Chapter 10 Exploring Probability   Traditional 9 days   Block 4 days

	Below Level **L2**	On Level	Advanced **L4**
10-1 Tree Diagrams and the Counting Principle	✓	✓	✓
Extension: Permutations			✓
10-2 Probability	✓	✓	✓
10-3 Experimental Probability	✓	✓	✓
10-3b Activity Lab, Data Collection: Comparing Experimental and Theoretical	✓	✓	✓
Vocabulary Builder: High-Use Academic Words	✓	✓	✓
10-4 Making Predictions From Data	✓	✓	✓
10-4b Activity Lab, Technology: Simulations		✓	✓
10-5 Independent Events			✓
Extension: Dependent Events			✓
Guided Problem Solving: Practice Solving Problems	✓	✓	✓
Problem Solving Application: Applying Probability	✓	✓	✓

Chapter 11 Integers   Traditional 14 days   Block 7 days

	Below Level **L2**	On Level	Advanced **L4**
11-1 Exploring Integers	✓	✓	✓
11-2 Comparing and Ordering Integers	✓	✓	✓
11-3a Activity Lab, Hands On: Modeling Addition of Integers	✓	✓	
11-3 Adding Integers	✓	✓	
11-4a Activity Lab, Hands On: Modeling Subtraction of Integers	✓	✓	
11-4 Subtracting Integers	✓	✓	
11-5 Multiplying Integers	✓	✓	✓
Guided Problem Solving: Practice Solving Problems	✓	✓	✓
11-6 Dividing Integers	✓	✓	✓
11-7 Solving Equations with Integers	✓	✓	✓
11-7b Activity Lab, Algebra Thinking: Thinking About Solutions	✓	✓	✓
11-8a Activity Lab, Technology: Graphing Points	✓	✓	✓
11-8 Graphing in the Coordinate Plane	✓	✓	✓
Extension: Reflections in the Coordinate Plane			✓
11-9 Applications of Integers			✓
11-10 Graphing Functions	✓	✓	✓
Problem Solving Application: Applying Integers	✓	✓	✓

Chapter 12 Equations and Inequalities   Traditional 8 days   Block 4 days

	Below Level **L2**	On Level	Advanced **L4**
12-1 Solving Two-Step Equations		✓	✓
12-1b Activity Lab, Algebra Thinking: Using Equation Language	✓	✓	✓
12-2 Inequalities		✓	✓
12-3 Solving One-Step Inequalities		✓	✓
12-3b Activity Lab, Analyzing Data: Applying Inequalities	✓	✓	✓
12-4a Activity Lab, Hands On: Exploring Squares			✓
12-4 Exploring Square Roots and Rational Numbers			✓
12-5 Introducing the Pythagorean Theorem			✓
Guided Problem Solving: Practice Solving Problems	✓	✓	✓
Problem Solving Application: Applying Equations	✓	✓	✓

Leveled Pacing Chart

Using Your Book

for Success

Welcome to *Prentice Hall Course 1.*
There are many features built into the daily lessons of this text that will help you learn the important skills and concepts you will need to be successful in this course. Look through the following pages for some study tips that you will find useful as you complete each lesson.

Getting Ready to Learn

Check Your Readiness

Complete the *Check Your Readiness* exercises to see what topics you may need to review before you begin the chapter.

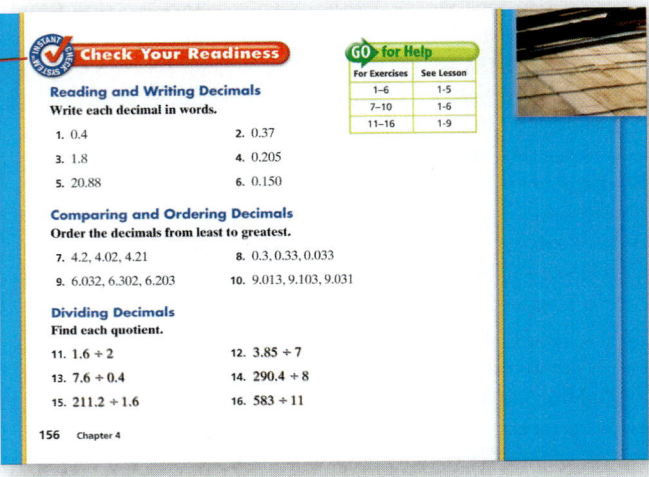

Check Skills You'll Need

Complete the *Check Skills You'll Need* exercises to make sure you have the skills needed to successfully learn the concepts in the lesson.

New Vocabulary

New Vocabulary is listed for each lesson, so you can pre-read the text. As each term is introduced, it is highlighted in yellow.

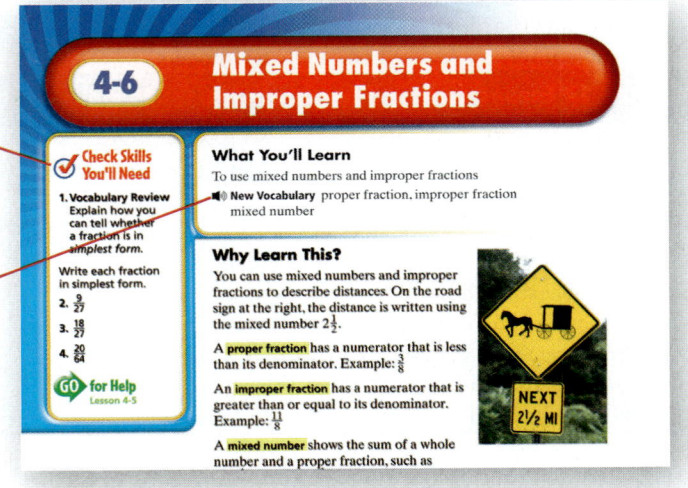

Built-In Help

Go for Help

Look for the green labels throughout your book that tell you where to "Go" for help. You'll see this built-in help in the lessons and in the homework exercises.

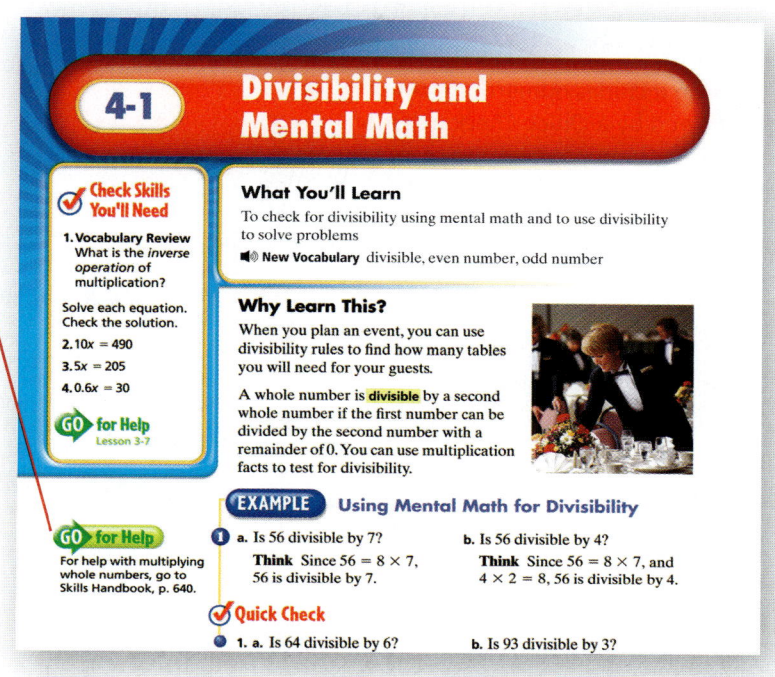

Video Tutor Help

Go online to see engaging videos to help you better understand important math concepts.

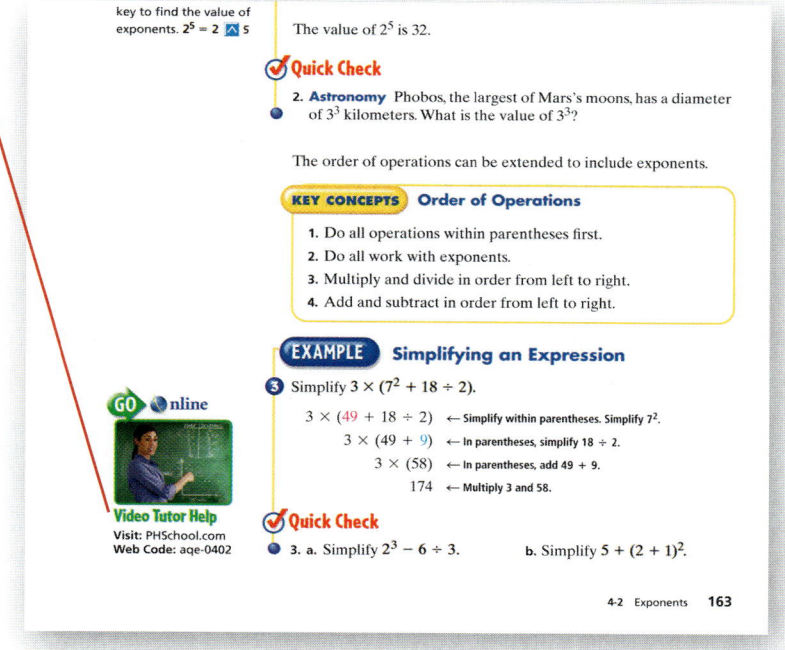

Understanding the Mathematics

Quick Check

Every lesson includes numerous examples, each followed by a *Quick Check* question that you can do on your own to see if you understand the skill being introduced. Check your progress with the answers at the back of the book.

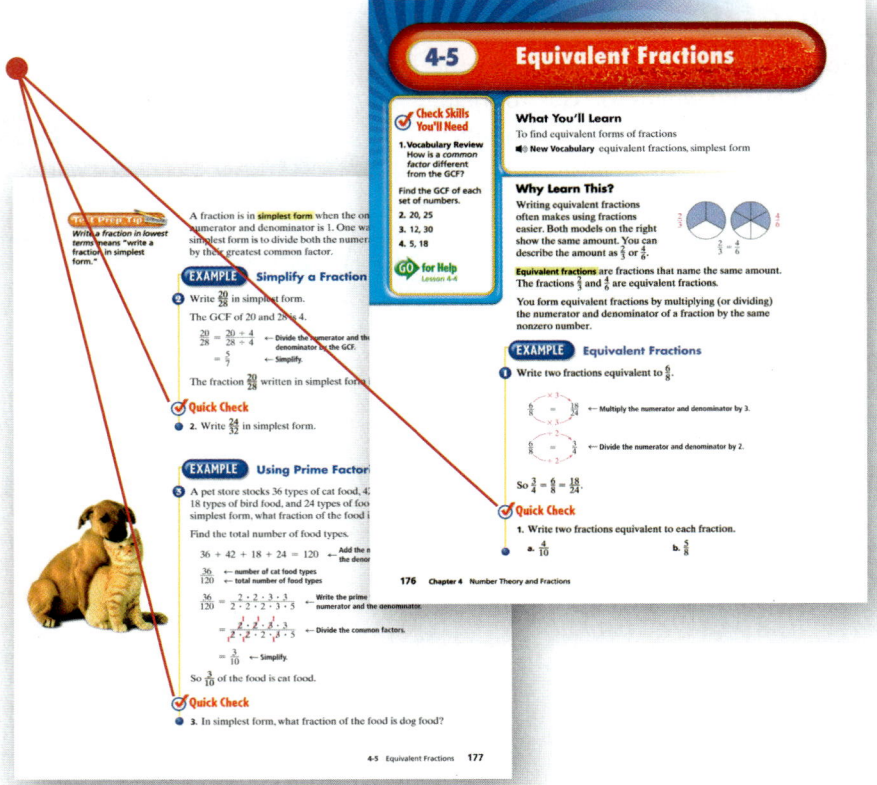

Understanding Key Concepts

Frequent *Key Concept* boxes summarize important definitions, formulas, and properties. Use these to review what you've learned.

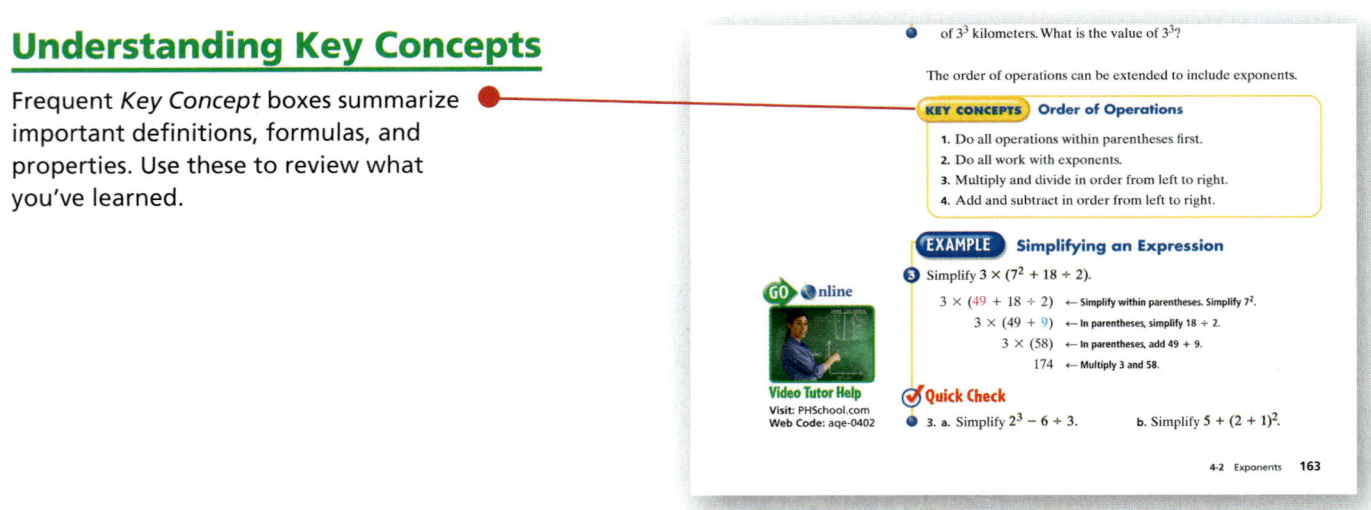

Online Active Math

Make math come alive with these online activities. Review and practice important math concepts with these engaging online tutorials.

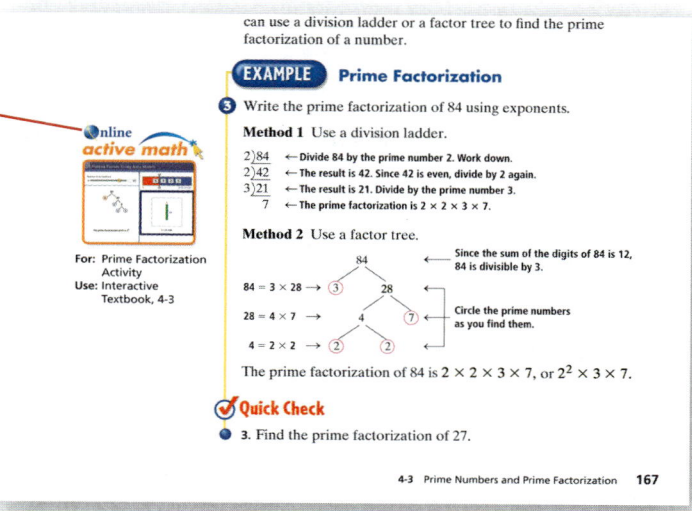

Vocabulary Support

Understanding mathematical vocabulary is an important part of studying mathematics. *Vocabulary Tips* and *Vocabulary Builders* throughout the book help focus on the language of math.

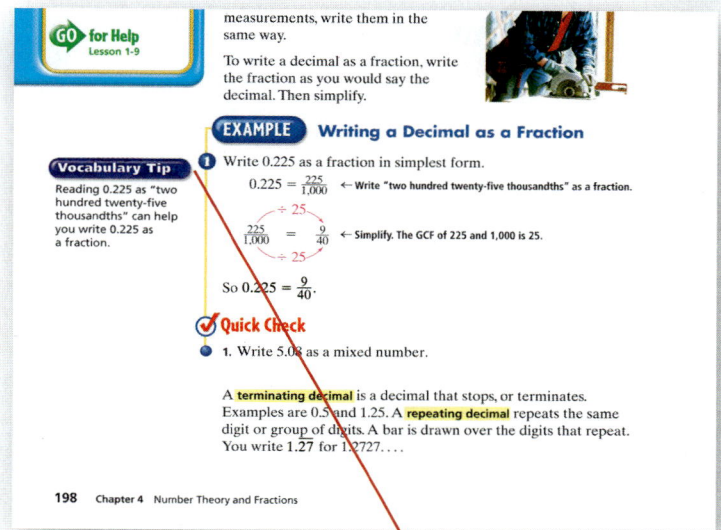

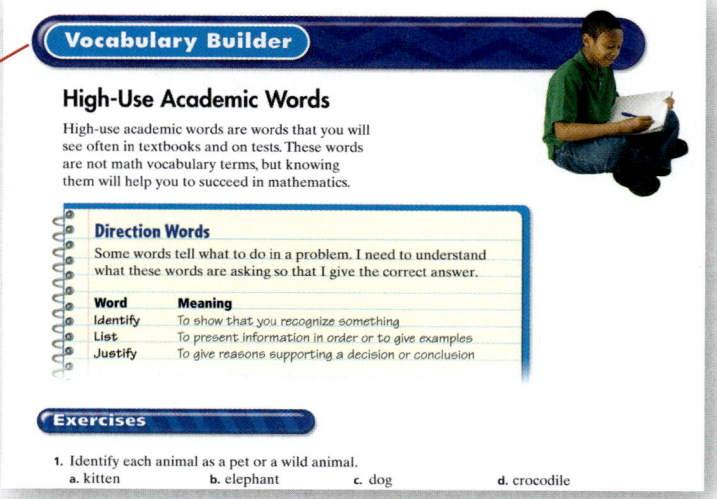

Understanding the Mathematics

Guided Problem Solving

These features throughout your Student Edition provide practice in problem solving. Solved from a student's point of view, this feature focuses on the thinking and reasoning that goes into solving a problem.

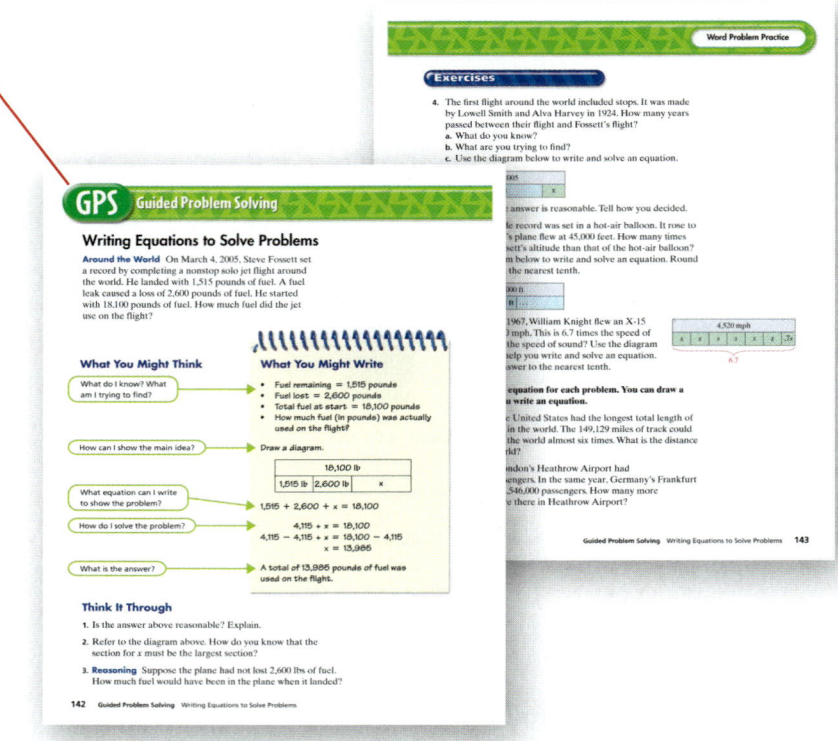

Activity Labs

Activity Labs throughout the book give you an opportunity to explore a concept. Apply the skills you've learned in these engaging activities.

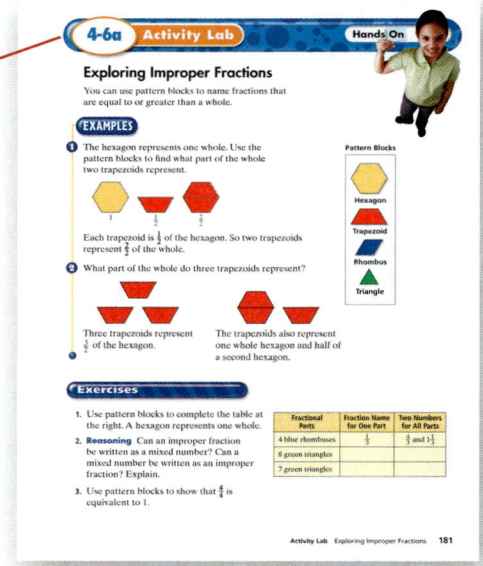

Practice What You've Learned

There are numerous exercises in each lesson that give you the practice you need to master the concepts in the lesson. The following exercises are included in each lesson.

Check Your Understanding

These exercises help you prepare for the Homework Exercises.

Practice by example

These exercises refer you back to the Examples in the lesson, in case you need help with completing these exercises.

Apply your skills

These exercises combine skills from earlier lessons to offer you richer skill exercises and multi-step application problems.

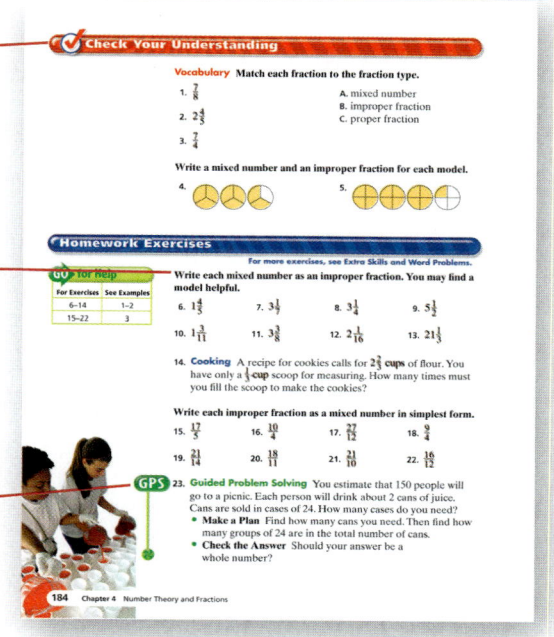

Homework Video Tutor

These interactive tutorials provide you with homework help for *every lesson*.

Challenge

This exercise gives you an opportunity to extend and stretch your thinking.

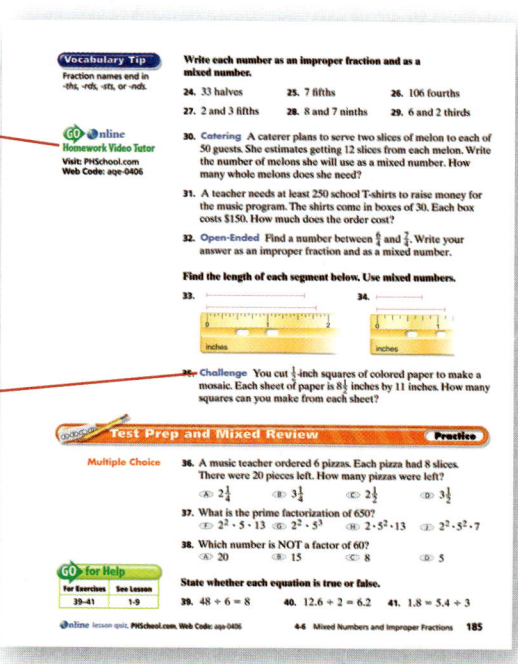

Beginning-of-Course Diagnostic Test

Intervention This Diagnostic Test covers pre-course skills that students need to succeed in this math program. For intervention, direct students to the following pages from the Skills Handbook in the back of their textbooks.

Exercises	Page
1, 2	634
3–4	635
6–10	636
11–16	637
17–23	638
24–30	640
31–36	639

1. Write the place value of the underlined digit in 5$\underline{2}$3,411,396.

2. Write the place value of the underlined digit in 402,659. ($\underline{2}$)

3. Round 742 to the tens place.

4. Round 4,078 to the hundreds place.

5. Round 116,830 to the thousands place.

Add.

6.   4,208
      + 6,967

7. 591 + 79

8.   7,223
      + 4,279

9. 3,208 + 564

10. four thousand sixty-two plus nine hundred eighteen

Subtract.

11.   57
      − 42

12. 79 − 31

13.   8,841
      − 3,194

14.   116,493
      − 90,287

15. 2,051 − 988

16. nine thousand minus five hundred thirty eight

Multiply.

17. 594 × 8

1. ten millions
2. thousands
3. 740
4. 4,100
5. 117,000

6. 11,175
7. 670
8. 11,502
9. 3,772

10. 4,980
11. 15
12. 48
13. 5,647

14. 26,206
15. 1,063
16. 8,462
17. 4,752

18. $1,174 \times 6$

19. six thousand eighty-one times seven

20. 54×917

21. 806×255

22. one thousand sixty-nine times forty-eight

23. one hundred thirty-three times four thousand, two hundred eighty-six

Divide.

24. $6\overline{)822}$

25. $964 \div 6$

26. one thousand, two hundred eighty-seven divided by nine

27. $6,432 \div 24$

28. $504 \div 24$

29. $1,756 \div 29$

30. $5\overline{)1,016}$

Multiply using mental math.

31. $4,729 \times 10$

32. $462 \times 10,000$

33. $706,215 \times 100$

Divide using mental math.

34. $120 \div 10$

35. $17,000 \div 1,000$

36. $8,203,000 \div 100$

18. 7,044
19. 42,567
20. 49,518
21. 205,530
22. 51,312

23. 570,038
24. 137
25. 160 R4
26. 143
27. 268

28. 21
29. 60 R16
30. 203 R1
31. 47,290
32. 4,620,000

33. 70,621,500
34. 12
35. 17
36. 82,030

Problem Solving Handbook

Using the Problem Solving Plan

Throughout this text, students will be encouraged to use the four-step problem-solving plan that is outlined in this lesson. This approach gives students a simple yet effective framework for organizing their work in the process of solving a problem. Rather than having students haphazardly approach the task of problem solving, this four-step plan gives them an organized procedure to follow for a wide range of problems.

Guided Instruction

Students should remember these key phrases: Understand the Problem; Make a Plan; Carry out the Plan; Check for Reasonableness.

Call attention to the list of problem-solving strategies in the text. Ask for an example of each.

Have students brainstorm strategies that they can use to solve real-world problems such as Make a Table. Write up their ideas on poster board and display them in the room for students' reference.

Error Prevention!

Students often focus on one condition of a problem and forget another. Stress the importance of checking that a proposed solution satisfies all the conditions of the problem.

USING THE Problem Solving Plan

One of the most important skills you can have is the ability to solve problems. An integral part of learning mathematics is how adept you become at unraveling problems and looking back to see how you found the solution. Maybe you don't realize it, but you solve problems every day—some problems are easy to solve, and others are challenging and require a good plan of action. In this Problem Solving Handbook, you will learn how to work though mathematical problems using a simple four-step plan:

THE 4-STEP PLAN

1. **Understand** **Understand the problem.**
   Read the problem. Ask yourself, "What information is given? What is missing? What am I being asked to find or to do?"

2. **Plan** **Make a plan to solve the problem.**
   Choose a strategy. As you use problem solving strategies throughout this book, you will decide which one is best for the problem you are trying to solve.

3. **Carry Out** **Carry out the plan.**
   Solve the problem using your plan. Organize your work.

4. **Check** **Check the answer to be sure it is reasonable.**
   Look back at your work and compare it against the information and question(s) in the problem. Ask yourself, "Is my answer reasonable? Did I check my work?"

Problem Solving Strategies

Creating a good plan to solve a problem means that you will need to choose a strategy. What is the best way to solve that challenging problem? Perhaps drawing a diagram or making a table will lead to a solution. A problem may seem to have too many steps. Maybe working a simpler problem is the key. There are a number of strategies to choose from. You will decide which strategy is most effective.

As you work through this book, you will encounter many opportunities to improve your problem solving and reasoning skills. Working through mathematical problems using this four-step process will help you to organize your thoughts, develop your reasoning skills, and explain how you arrived at a particular solution.

Putting this problem solving plan to use will allow you to work through mathematical problems with confidence. Getting in the habit of planning and strategizing for problem solving will result in success in future math courses and high scores on those really important tests!

Good Luck!

THE STRATEGIES

Here are some examples of problem solving strategies. Which one will work best for the problem you are trying to solve?

- **Draw a Picture**
- **Look for a Pattern**
- **Systematic Guess and Check**
- **Act It Out**
- **Make a Table**
- **Work a Simpler Problem**
- **Work Backward**
- **Write an Equation**

Draw a Picture

Drawing a picture often helps to clarify relationships among the given numbers and provides a concrete place for students to start.

Guided Instruction

Have volunteers read the text. Call attention to the problem-solving steps:
- Understand the Problem
- Make a Plan
- Carry Out the Plan
- Check the Answer

Example

Discuss the volleyball courts. Ask questions such as:
- *Do you think volleyball courts would be placed so close to each other? Why or why not?*
- *How much space would you leave between each?*

Draw a Picture

When to Use This Strategy Drawing a picture can help you visualize and understand a word problem.

Volleyball A volleyball tournament will be held on a soccer field that is 110 yards long and 80 yards wide. Each volleyball court is 25 yd long by 15 yd wide. How many courts will fit on the field?

Understand The field is 110 yd by 80 yd. Each volleyball court is 25 yd by 15 yd. You are asked to find how many courts will fit on the field.

Plan To help decide, first *draw a picture* of the field. Then show how many courts will fit on the field.

Carry Out Mark off 7 courts along the length of the field and 3 courts along the width of the field. Since $3 \times 7 = 21$, you can fit 21 courts in the field.

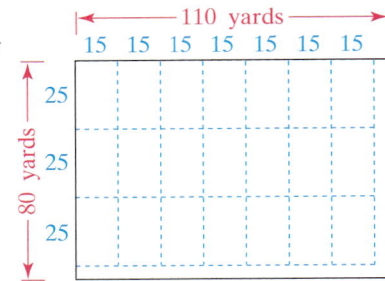

Check Check the answer by dividing the area of the field by the area of a court. Use the formula area = length × width.

$$\frac{\text{soccer field}}{\text{volleyball court}} \rightarrow \frac{110 \text{ yards} \times 80 \text{ yards}}{25 \text{ yards} \times 15 \text{ yards}} \rightarrow \frac{8{,}800 \text{ square yards}}{375 \text{ square yards}} \approx 23$$

So 21 courts is a reasonable answer.

● Practice

1. **Carpentry** A bookcase is made from wood that is 3 in. thick. The bookcase has four shelves, including the top. The space between shelves is 20 inches. Find the height of the bookcase.

2. **Lighting** Lights are placed every 2 feet along both sides of a 14-foot driveway. How many lights are needed?

3. **Gardening** A rectangular garden is 4 feet by 3 feet. A landscaper plants flowers 1 ft apart along the edges and corners. How many plants does the landscaper need?

1. **72 in.**
2. **16 lights**
3. **14 plants**

Look for a Pattern

When to Use This Strategy In problems where more objects are added, you can *look for a pattern* to solve the problem.

Seating A rectangular table seats two people on each end and three on each side. How many seats are available if you push the ends of five tables together?

Understand There are five rectangular tables. Each table seats two people on each end and three on a side.

Plan To find the number of seats when five tables are pushed together, start by finding the number of seats when there are fewer tables.

Carry Out Start with 1, 2, and 3 tables.

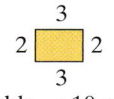

1 table → 10 seats

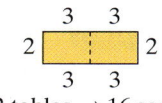

2 tables → 16 seats

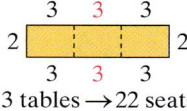

3 tables → 22 seats

Extend the pattern by adding six seats for each new table.

Number of Tables	1	2	3	4	5
Number of Seats	10	16	22	28	34

Check Five tables pushed together seat 5×6, or 30, people on the sides and 2 people on each end, or $30 + 2 + 2 = 34$.

Practice

1. **Savings** A high school student has started a new job. He plans to save $1 in the first week, $2 in the second week, $4 in the third week, and $8 in the fourth week. If this pattern of savings could continue, how much would he save in the tenth week?

2. A rectangular table seats four people on each side and three on each end. How many seats are available if the ends of seven tables are pushed together?

3. Your younger brother is pulling a sled up a hill. Each minute he moves forward 20 feet but also slides back 3 feet. How long will it take him to pull his sled 130 feet up the hill?

Look for a Pattern often "partners" with other problem-solving strategies. In this lesson, the partner is *Make a Table.*

Guided Instruction

Point out to students that they are also using the problem-solving strategy *Draw a Picture.* Have four student volunteers read the text aloud. Have each point out one problem-solving step.
- Understand the Problem
- Make a Plan
- Carry Out the Plan
- Check the Answer

Differentiated Instruction

Special Needs **L1**

Give students several blank 2-in.-by-3-in. cards. Have them label the 2-in. sides "2 seats" and the 3-in. sides "3 seats." Students use the cards to form the rectangle chains and calculate the number of available seats.

Problem Solving Handbook

1. $512

2. 62 seats

3. about 8 minutes

Systematic Guess and Check

The *Systematic Guess and Check* strategy involves trying, checking, and revising. Students make a reasonable estimate of the solution, check if the estimate satisfies the conditions of the problem, and revise the number if necessary. Students arrive at the correct solution by making increasingly more reasonable tries and revisions.

Guided Instruction

Ask students what is true about each of the first two columns in the table. **The number of tickets sold equals 120.** As students work through the problem have them identify each of the problem solving steps:
- Understand the Problem
- Make a Plan
- Carry Out the Plan
- Check the Answer

Error Prevention!

Students might focus on one condition of a problem and forget another. For instance, they might say there were 32 adult tickets (and 100 child tickets) because $32 \times \$10 + 100 \times \$8 = \$1,120$. While $1,120 is the correct total sales, the total number of tickets would be $32 + 100 = 132$, which is incorrect.

Systematic Guess and Check

When to Use This Strategy Sometimes problems have a limited number of possible answers. Sometimes the solution to a problem involves several related numbers. Using *systematic guess and check* can get you closer to the right answer.

Movie tickets cost $10 for adults and $8 for children. On Friday the total sales from 120 tickets was $1,120. How many adult tickets were sold?

Understand Adult tickets cost $10. Children's tickets cost $8. The theater collected $1,120 by selling 120 tickets. You need to find how many adult tickets were sold.

Plan To find how many adult tickets were sold, make an initial guess, check the results, and then revise your guess.

Carry Out Try 40 adult tickets and 80 children's tickets. Organize the data in a table. If the total is too low, increase the number of expensive, adult, tickets. If the total is too high, decrease the number of adult tickets.

Adult Tickets	Children's Tickets	Total Sales
$40 \times \$10 = \$400$	$80 \times \$8 = \$640$	$\$400 + \$640 = \$1,040$
$50 \times \$10 = \$500$	$70 \times \$8 = \$560$	$1,060
$90 \times \$10 = \$900$	$30 \times \$8 = \$240$	$1,140
$80 \times \$10 = \$800$	$40 \times \$8 = \$320$	$1,120

Check With 80 adult tickets and 40 children's tickets, the number of tickets sold is equal to 120, and the total sales are $1,120.

● Practice

1. **Business** A vendor sells salads and juices. A salad costs $3.00 and a juice costs $2.50. The vendor earned $216 by selling 80 items. How many juices were sold?

2. **Pet Care** A rectangular turtle cage is made with 40 feet of wire fence. The length is 6 feet greater than the width. What are the length and width of the turtle cage?

1. **48 juices**
2. **13 ft; 7 ft**

Act It Out

When to Use This Strategy Sometimes the best way to solve a problem is to imitate the actions described in the problem.

Ten students stand in a circle. Starting with the first student, the teacher begins counting as follows: "One, two, three, four, five, six, out!" When a student is called out, he or she has to leave the circle. The teacher then continues until only one student is left. Which student is it?

Understand The teacher is counting out every seventh student as she goes around in a circle. The students are numbered 1 to 10. You need to find the number of the last student left in.

Plan Using 10 pennies you can *act out* the steps and see who wins.

Carry Out Arrange the pennies in a circle. Start counting, pointing at the pennies one at a time. Every time you reach seven, remove the penny you point to. When you are done counting, you are left with the ninth penny. The ninth student is left.

Check If you complete the table, you get the same result.

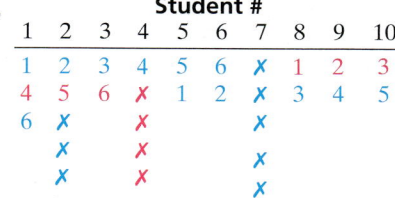

Student #									
1	2	3	4	5	6	7	8	9	10
1	2	3	4	5	6	✗	1	2	3
4	5	6	✗	1	2	✗	3	4	5
6	✗		✗		✗		✗		
	✗		✗		✗		✗		
	✗		✗		✗		✗		

⬤ Practice

1. If the teacher has 12 students and counts out every ninth student, which student will be left?

2. An uncle is giving some baseball cards away to five nieces and nephews. He decides the fairest way to do this is to give just one card to the first child, then two to the second, and so on. If everybody gets three turns, how many cards will each niece or nephew have?

3. Four robots stand in the corners of a four-by-four grid. All four robots are facing in the same direction. They move at the same time. If a robot sees another robot directly ahead, it takes one step forward, and if not, it stays in place but turns right. Where are the robots after three moves?

The *Act It Out* strategy emphasizes the Carry Out the Plan step. It is effective where a strategy, such as completing a table or solving a simpler problem, are difficult or don't work. In many cases, it has the added benefit of increased classroom participation.

Guided Instruction

Have a student volunteer read the problem aloud. Have other students point out the problem-solving steps:
- Understand the Problem
- Make a Plan
- Carry Out the Plan
- Check the Answer

Differentiated Instruction

Special Needs **L1**
In order to make the Carry Out the Plan step easier for students to see, label each of the pennies from 1 to 10 using a small piece of tape.

Problem Solving Handbook

1. **the second student**

2. **18; 21; 24; 27; 30**

3. **Answers may vary. Sample:**

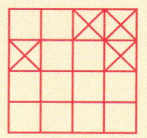

T51

Make a Table

Making a table helps students organize the information in a problem. Once the information is organized, students can observe patterns and find missing information.

Guided Instruction

Have students read the problem and identify the four problem-solving steps:
• Understand the Problem
• Make a Plan
• Carry Out the Plan
• Check the Answer

Teaching Tip
Remind students to simplify their answers when adding fractions or mixed numbers.

Visual Learners
Have students use a number line marked in $\frac{1}{4}$ miles to solve the problem.

Make a Table

When to Use This Strategy Organizing data in a table can help you see connections.

Exercise Tara wants to walk in a charity event. In her first week of training, she walks three miles each day. Each week after that, she adds $\frac{3}{4}$ mile to her daily distance. In which week of training does Tara walk six miles per day?

Understand During the first week, Tara walks three miles each day. Each week, she walks an additional $\frac{3}{4}$ mile. You need to find the week in which her daily walk is six miles.

Plan *Make a table* that shows weeks and distance. Add rows until the distance reaches six miles.

Carry Out Label the first column Week and the second column Distance. Fill in the values for each week. Tara walks 6 miles during her fifth week of training.

Check You can check by working backward. In five weeks there were 4 increases of $\frac{3}{4}$ mile. $\frac{3}{4} + \frac{3}{4} + \frac{3}{4} + \frac{3}{4} = 3$. So the total increase was 3 miles. The 3 miles plus the original 3 miles per day is 6 miles.

Week	Distance (miles/day)
1	3
2	$3 + \frac{3}{4} = 3\frac{3}{4}$
3	$3\frac{3}{4} + \frac{3}{4} = 4\frac{1}{2}$
4	$4\frac{1}{2} + \frac{3}{4} = 5\frac{1}{4}$
5	$5\frac{1}{4} + \frac{3}{4} = 6$

Practice

1. **Money** In how many ways can you make 25 cents using pennies, nickels, and dimes?

2. Find the smallest number that meets both of these conditions.
   • When you divide the number by 7, the remainder is 1.
   • When you divide the number by 9, the remainder is 7.

3. A certain farm has both chickens and goats. Each chicken has 2 legs. Each goat has 4 legs. There are 35 animals on the farm. All together the chickens and goats have 100 legs. How many chickens and how many goats does the farm have?

1. **12 ways**

2. **43**

3. **20 chickens, 15 goats**

Work a Simpler Problem

When to Use This Strategy Using simpler numbers can sometimes help you solve a difficult problem.

Floor Tiles You tile a rectangular floor $17\frac{1}{2}$ ft by $13\frac{3}{4}$ ft. You are using square tiles that are $1\frac{1}{4}$ ft on each side. How many tiles do you need?

Understand The rectangular floor is $17\frac{1}{2}$ feet long and $13\frac{3}{4}$ feet wide. Each tile is a square with sides $1\frac{1}{4}$ feet long. You must find how many tiles are needed to cover the floor.

Plan First, *work a simpler problem*. Then use the same approach to solve the harder problem. Multiply each number by 4 to remove the fractions. Replace $17\frac{1}{2}$ with $17\frac{1}{2} \times 4 = 70$. Replace $13\frac{3}{4}$ with $13\frac{3}{4} \times 4 = 55$, and $1\frac{1}{4}$ with $1\frac{1}{4} \times 4 = 5$.

Simpler Problem A rectangular floor is 70 feet by 55 feet. How many 5 ft-by-5 ft tiles do you need to cover the floor?

Carry Out For one row of tiles to cover the length of the room, you need $70 \div 5$, or 14, tiles. For enough rows to cover the width of the room, you need $55 \div 5$, or 11, rows. So you need 14×11, or 154, tiles.

Now solve the original problem. For one row of tiles, you need $17\frac{1}{2} \div 1\frac{1}{4}$, or 14, tiles. For enough rows to cover the width, you need $13\frac{3}{4} \div 1\frac{1}{4}$, or 11, rows. So you need 14×11, or 154, tiles.

(Diagram: a rectangle labeled $17\frac{1}{2}$ ft across the top and $13\frac{3}{4}$ ft down the left side, with a tile of $1\frac{1}{4}$ ft shown in the corner.)

Check Because all the lengths in the simpler problem are four times as long, the answers to both problems should be the same. They are, so the answer checks.

Practice

1. On a school day, José spends $5\frac{1}{4}$ hours in classes. Each class lasts $\frac{3}{4}$ hour. How many classes does José have?

2. Sewing A tailor has a section of material that is $28\frac{1}{2}$ feet long. He wants to cut it into pieces, each one $1\frac{1}{2}$ feet long. How many cuts will he have to make?

Work a Simpler Problem

Problems sometimes appear intimidating simply because they involve fractions, decimals, or greater whole numbers. In this lesson, students learn how to approach such problems by first considering numbers that are more manageable. With the "difficult" numbers temporarily set aside, students can focus their attention on making a plan for solving the problem.

Guided Instruction

Point out that using the strategy *Work a Simpler Problem* is useful when it is difficult to get started on a problem or the problem involves numbers that appear "difficult."

Elicit the problem-solving steps:
- Understand the Problem
- Make a Plan
- Carry Out the Plan
- Check the Answer

Tell students that they may need to use them for both the simpler problem and the original problem.

Problem Solving Handbook

1. **7 classes**

2. **18 cuts**

T53

Work Backward

Many problems give a set of initial conditions and the student is expected to arrive at a result. In other problems, the result is given and the student's task is to determine what the initial conditions must have been. Such problems can be solved by using inverse operations to reverse the steps that led to the result. This process is called the *Work Backward* strategy.

Guided Instruction

Have students identify the reverse steps. They might say, "The problem ends with $18 left, so I should start with $18. The problem says he spent $5 for admission, so I should *add* $5 on to get $23. Then the problem says he spent $14 in the souvenir shop, so I should *add* $14 to get $37."

Have students identify the problem-solving steps as they work the problem:
- Understand the Problem
- Make a Plan
- Carry Out the Plan
- Check the Answer

Differentiated Instruction

Tactile Learners
Have students act out the steps of the solution using play money.

Work Backward

When to Use This Strategy Some problems involve a series of steps that lead to a final result. If you are asked to find the initial amount, you can *work backward* from the final result by using inverse operations.

Zoo Luis went to the zoo for a school trip. He paid $5 for admission. He spent $14 at the souvenir shop. When he got home, he had $18 left. How much money did he start with?

Understand You know how much money Luis had when he got home. You know how much he spent. You want to know how much money he started with.

Plan To find the amount Luis started with, begin with the amount he had at the end. Then *work backward.* To undo each operation, use its inverse.

Carry Out To undo the amounts Luis spent, add.

$18   ← Luis had $18 left at the end.

$18 + $14 = $32   ← He spent $14 at the souvenir shop. Add.

$32 + $5 = $37   ← He spent $5 on admission. Add.

Luis started with $37.

Check Read the problem again. Start with $37. Subtract the amounts as Luis spends money in the problem. $37 − $5 = $32. $32 − $14 = $18. The answer checks.

● Practice

1. You divide a number by 2, add 7, and then multiply by 5. The result is 50. What is the number?

2. **Shopping** Brenda spent half her money at a store in a mall. At another store, she spent half her remaining money and $6 more. She had $2 left. How much did Brenda have when she arrived at the mall?

3. **Hobbies** Kai sold half his baseball cards to Ana, half of the remaining cards to Joe, and the last 10 to Chip. How many cards did Kai sell in all?

1. 6

2. $32

3. 40 cards

Write an Equation

When to Use This Strategy To *write an equation* is one way of organizing the information needed to solve a problem.

Discount A bicycle is on sale for $139.93. This is 30% off the regular price. What is the regular price of the bicycle?

Understand The sale price of the bicycle, $139.93, is 30% off the regular price. You need to find the regular price.

Plan Translate the words into an equation. You will pay $100\% - 30\% = 70\%$ of the regular price.

Carry Out The percent you pay times the regular price equals the sale price.

Words percent you pay times regular price equals sale price

Let r = the regular price.

Equation   70%   × r = $139.93

$$0.7r = 139.93 \quad \leftarrow \text{ Write 70\% as a decimal: 0.7.}$$
$$0.7r \div 0.7 = 139.93 \div 0.7 \quad \leftarrow \text{ Divide each side by 0.7 to find } r.$$
$$r = \$199.90 \quad \leftarrow \text{ Simplify.}$$

The regular price of the bicycle is $199.90.

Check The regular price is about $200. The sale price is about 70% of $200, or $140. This is close to the sale price.

● Practice

1. **Media** A magazine has 5,580,000 subscribers this year. This number is down 7% from last year. How many subscribers were there last year?

2. A "light" popcorn has 120 Calories per serving. This is 25% fewer Calories than a serving of regular popcorn. How many Calories does each serving of regular popcorn have?

3. The sign at the entrance of a store reads, "30% off all winter apparel! Discount given at the register." The price tag of a coat is missing. The register rings up a price before tax of $55.93. What is the regular price of the coat?

Real-world problems often require multiple solution steps. Writing an equation is often helpful. The most challenging step is finding a word relationship that can be translated into an equation with numbers, symbols, and a variable.

Guided Instruction

Walk students through the problem-solving steps:
- Understand the Problem
- Make a Plan
- Carry Out the Plan
- Check the Answer

as they apply to this problem. The Plan step is where students change words to an equation.

Alternative Method
Share an alternative way of writing an equation for this problem using 30% off as shown below.

$$r - 0.3r = 139.93$$
$$(1 - 0.3)r = 139.93$$
$$0.7r = 139.93$$
$$r = 139.90$$

Problem Solving Handbook

---

1. **6,000,000 subscribers**

2. **160 calories**

3. **$79.90**

1 Whole Numbers and Decimals

Chapter at a Glance

Lesson Titles, Objectives, and Features	Assessment	NCTM Standards	Local Standards
1-1 Understanding Whole Numbers • To write and compare whole numbers	Lesson Quiz	1, 5, 6, 7, 8, 9, 10	
1-2 Estimating With Whole Numbers • To estimate by rounding and by using compatible numbers	Lesson Quiz	1, 4, 6, 7, 8, 9, 10	
1-3 Properties of Numbers • To understand and use the properties of numbers	Lesson Quiz	1, 5, 6, 7, 8, 9, 10	
1-4 Order of Operations • To use the order of operations to simplify expressions and solve problems	Lesson Quiz Checkpoint Quiz 1	1, 5, 6, 7, 8, 9, 10	
1-5a Activity Lab, Hands On: Exploring Decimal Models **1-5 Understanding Decimals** • To read, write, and round decimals	Lesson Quiz	1, 4, 5, 6, 7, 8, 9, 10	
1-6 Comparing and Ordering Decimals • To compare and order decimals using models and place value	Lesson Quiz	1, 4, 5, 6, 7, 8, 9, 10	
1-7a Activity Lab, Hands On: Using Models **1-7 Adding and Subtracting Decimals** • To add and subtract decimals and to solve problems involving decimals **Vocabulary Builder:** High-Use Academic Words	Lesson Quiz	1, 4, 5, 6, 7, 8, 9, 10	
1-8a Activity Lab: Modeling Decimal Multiplication **1-8 Multiplying Decimals** • To multiply decimals and to solve problems by multiplying decimals **1-8b Activity Lab, Technology:** Multiplying and Dividing Decimals by 10, 100, and 1,000	Lesson Quiz Checkpoint Quiz 2	1, 4, 5, 6, 7, 8, 9, 10	
1-9 Dividing Decimals • To divide decimals and to solve problems by dividing decimals **1-9b Activity Lab, Data Analysis:** Using Decimals **Guided Problem Solving:** Choosing the Right Operation	Lesson Quiz	1, 4, 5, 6, 7, 8, 9, 10	
Problem Solving Application: Applying Decimals			

NCTM Standards 2000
1 Number and Operations   2 Algebra   3 Geometry   4 Measurement   5 Data Analysis and Probability
6 Problem Solving   7 Reasoning and Proof   8 Communication   9 Connections   10 Representation

Correlations to Standardized Tests

All content for these tests is contained in *Prentice Hall Math,* Course 1. This chart reflects coverage in this chapter only.

	1-1	1-2	1-3	1-4	1-5	1-6	1-7	1-8	1-9
Terra Nova CAT6 (Level 16)									
Number and Number Relations	✓	✓	✓	✓	✓	✓	✓	✓	✓
Computation and Numerical Estimation	✓	✓	✓	✓	✓	✓	✓	✓	✓
Operation Concepts		✓			✓	✓	✓	✓	✓
Measurement		✓	✓	✓	✓	✓	✓		
Geometry and Spatial Sense									
Data Analysis, Statistics, and Probability	✓	✓	✓	✓	✓	✓	✓		
Patterns, Functions, Algebra	✓	✓	✓	✓	✓	✓	✓	✓	✓
Problem Solving and Reasoning	✓	✓	✓	✓	✓	✓	✓	✓	✓
Communication	✓	✓	✓	✓	✓	✓	✓	✓	✓
Decimals, Fractions, Integers, Percent					✓	✓	✓	✓	✓
Order of Operations				✓	✓	✓	✓	✓	✓
Terra Nova CTBS (Level 16)									
Whole Numbers, Decimals, Fractions	✓	✓	✓		✓	✓	✓	✓	✓
Numeration, Number Theory	✓	✓	✓	✓	✓	✓	✓	✓	✓
Data Interpretation	✓	✓	✓	✓	✓	✓	✓		
Pre-algebra	✓	✓	✓	✓	✓	✓	✓	✓	✓
Measurement		✓	✓	✓	✓	✓	✓		✓
Geometry									
ITBS (Level 12)									
Number Properties and Operations	✓	✓	✓	✓	✓	✓	✓	✓	✓
Algebra	✓	✓	✓	✓	✓	✓	✓	✓	✓
Geometry									
Measurement		✓	✓	✓	✓	✓	✓		
Probability and Statistics					✓	✓	✓	✓	✓
Estimation	✓	✓	✓	✓	✓	✓	✓	✓	✓
SAT10 (Int 2 Level)									
Number Sense and Operations	✓	✓	✓	✓	✓	✓	✓	✓	✓
Patterns, Relationships, and Algebra	✓	✓	✓	✓	✓	✓	✓	✓	✓
Data, Statistics, and Probability	✓	✓	✓	✓	✓	✓	✓		
Geometry and Measurement		✓	✓	✓	✓	✓	✓		
NAEP									
Number Sense, Properties, and Operations	✓	✓	✓	✓	✓	✓	✓	✓	✓
Measurement									
Geometry and Spatial Sense									
Data Analysis, Statistics, and Probability									
Algebra and Functions									

CAT6 California Achievement Test, 6th Ed. **CTBS** Comprehensive Test of Basic Skills **ITBS** Iowa Test of Basic Skills, Form M
SAT10 Stanford Achievement Test, 10th Ed. **NAEP** National Assessment of Educational Progress 2005 Mathematics Objectives

Math Background

Skills Trace

BEFORE Chapter 1
Grade 5 presented operations with whole numbers and decimals.

DURING Chapter 1
Course 1 extends operations with decimals to estimating, comparing, and ordering.

AFTER Chapter 1
Throughout this course, students use decimal operations to solve real-world problems.

1-1 Understanding Whole Numbers

Math Understandings
- Our numeral system is a base-10 system that uses these ten digits: 0, 1, 2, 3, 4, 5, 6, 7, 8, 9.
- The position of a digit in a numeral determines its value.

In the numeral 254, the *place* of the digit 5 is the tens place. The *value* of the digit 5 is 5 tens, or 50. Use commas to separate the periods in a numeral, as shown in this chart.

Trillions Period			Billions Period			Millions Period			Thousands Period			Ones Period		
Hundreds	Tens	Ones	Hundreds	Tens	Ones	Hundreds	Tens	Ones	Hundreds	Tens	Ones	Hundreds	Tens	Ones
		2,	6	2	3,	6	8	4,	6	0	8,	0	0	0

Write a numeral in *standard form*, *expanded form*, or as words.

1-2 Estimating With Whole Numbers

Math Understandings
- Estimation is used when an exact answer is not needed.
- Most estimation techniques involve replacing numbers with ones that are close and easy to compute mentally.

To estimate the sum or difference of whole numbers, round to the same place. Look at the number to the right of the place you are rounding to. If it is a 5 or greater, round up. If it is less than 5, round down.

To estimate the product or quotient of two whole numbers, use compatible numbers and compute mentally. Basic facts and powers of ten help find compatible numbers.

1-3 Properties of Numbers

Math Understandings
- The properties of addition and multiplication often let you do mental computations more easily.
- The Commutative Property, the Associative Property, and the Identity Property apply to both addition and multiplication of whole numbers.

PROPERTIES OF ADDITION

Commutative Property
Changing the order of the addends does not change the sum.
$$2.5 + 3 = 3 + 2.5$$

Associative Property
Changing the grouping of the addends does not change the sum.
$$(2.5 + 3) + 4 = 2.5 + (3 + 4)$$

Identity Property
The sum of 0 and any number is that number.
$$2.5 + 0 = 0 + 2.5 = 2.5$$

PROPERTIES OF MULTIPLICATION

Commutative Property
Changing the order of the factors does not change the product.
$$7 \times 4 = 4 \times 7$$

Associative Property
Changing the grouping of the factors does not change the product.
$$(3 \times 5) \times 2 = 3 \times (5 \times 2)$$

Identity Property
The product of 1 and any number is that number.
$$9 \times 1 = 1 \times 9 = 9$$

1-4 Order of Operations

Math Understandings

- Mathematicians have agreed upon a sequence for performing arithmetic operations, called the order of operations, so that any mathematical expression will always have the same value.

An **expression** is a mathematical phrase containing numbers and operation symbols. A partial **order of operations** follows.

Order of Operations

1. Do all operations within parentheses first.
2. Multiply and divide in order from left to right.
3. Add and subtract in order from left to right.

1-5 Understanding Decimals

Math Understandings

- Digits to the left of the decimal point have whole number values; digits to the right have decimal values.
- Rounding decimals is similar to rounding whole numbers.

Extend the place-value chart to include values for decimals.

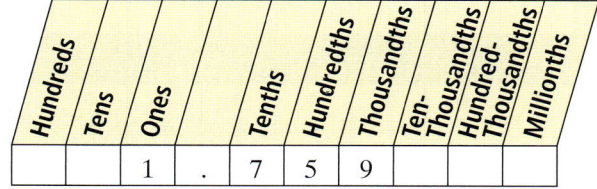

1-6 Comparing and Ordering Decimals

Math Understandings

- To compare two decimals, align the decimal points and annex zeros. Compare the digits starting with the greatest place value.
- After comparing pairs of decimals, you can order them.

To compare two decimals, write them so that each number has the same number of decimal places, and compare from left to right. To order decimals, compare pairs of numbers.

1-7 Adding and Subtracting Decimals

Math Understandings

- To find sums or differences of decimals, line up the decimal points, annex zeros, and rename as needed.
- To simplify an expression, replace it with the simplest name for its value.

Use rounding or front-end estimation to check the reasonableness of a sum or difference.

1-8 Multiplying Decimals
1-9 Dividing Decimals

Math Understandings

- To multiply decimals, multiply as with whole numbers. Then place the decimal.
- You can indicate multiplication in three ways.
- You can divide decimals by whole numbers and decimals.

To multiply decimals, add the number of decimal places in the factors to find the number of decimal places in the product. Dividing decimals is similar to dividing whole numbers. Place the decimal point in the quotient above the decimal point in the dividend.

Additional Professional Development Opportunities

Math Background Notes for Chapter 1: Every lesson has Math Background in the PLAN section.

Research Overview, Mathematics Strands
Additional support for these topics and more is in the front of the Teacher's Edition.

LessonLab
LessonLab, a Pearson Education company, offers comprehensive, facilitated professional development designed to help teachers to improve student achievement. To learn more, please visit lessonlab.com.

Chapter 1 Resources

Print Resources	1-1	1-2	1-3	1-4	1-5	1-6	1-7	1-8	1-9	For the Chapter
L3 Practice	•	•	•	•	•	•	•	•		
L1 Adapted Practice	•	•	•	•	•	•	•	•		
L3 Guided Problem Solving	•	•	•	•	•	•	•	•		
L2 Reteaching	•	•	•	•	•	•	•	•		
L4 Enrichment	•	•	•	•	•	•	•	•		
L3 Daily Notetaking Guide	•	•	•	•	•	•	•	•		
L1 Adapted Daily Notetaking Guide	•	•	•	•	•	•	•	•		
L3 Vocabulary and Study Skills Worksheets	•		•		•		•	•		•
L3 Daily Puzzles	•	•	•	•	•	•		•		
L3 Activity Labs	•	•	•	•	•	•		•		
L3 Checkpoint Quiz				•				•		
L3 Chapter Project										•
L2 Below Level Chapter Test										•
L3 Chapter Test										•
L4 Alternative Assessment										•
L3 Cumulative Review										•

Spanish Resources **ELL**	1-1	1-2	1-3	1-4	1-5	1-6	1-7	1-8	1-9	For the Chapter
L3 Practice	•	•	•	•		•	•	•	•	
L3 Vocabulary and Study Skills Worksheets	•		•		•		•	•		•
L3 Checkpoint Quiz				•			•			
L2 Below Level Chapter Test										•
L3 Chapter Test										•
L4 Alternative Assessment										•
L3 Cumulative Review										•

Transparencies	1-1	1-2	1-3	1-4	1-5	1-6	1-7	1-8	1-9	For the Chapter
Check Skills You'll Need	•	•	•	•	•	•	•	•		
Additional Examples	•	•	•	•	•	•	•	•		
Problem of the Day	•	•	•	•	•	•	•	•		
Classroom Aid				•		•	•			
Student Edition Answers	•	•	•	•	•	•	•	•	•	•
Lesson Quiz	•	•	•	•	•	•	•	•		
Test-Taking Strategies										•

Technology	1-1	1-2	1-3	1-4	1-5	1-6	1-7	1-8	1-9	For the Chapter
Interactive Textbook Online	•	•	•	•	•	•	•	•	•	•
StudentExpress™ CD-ROM	•	•	•	•	•	•	•	•	•	•
Success Tracker™ Online Intervention	•	•	•	•	•	•	•	•	•	•
TeacherExpress™ CD-ROM	•	•	•	•	•	•	•	•	•	•
PresentationExpress™ with QuickTake Presenter CD-ROM	•	•	•	•	•	•	•	•	•	•
ExamView® Assessment Suite CD-ROM	•	•	•	•	•	•	•	•	•	•
MindPoint® Quiz Show CD-ROM										•
Prentice Hall Web Site: PHSchool.com	•	•	•	•	•	•	•	•	•	•

Also available: **Prentice Hall Assessment System**
- Progress Monitoring Assessments
- Skills and Concepts Review
- Test Prep Workbook

Other Resources
Algebra Readiness Tests
All-in-One Student Workbook
All-in-One Student Workbook, Adapted Version
Multilingual Handbook

Solution Key
Math Notes Study Folder
Spanish Cumulative Assessment

Where You Can Use the Lesson Resources

Here is a suggestion, following the four-step teaching plan, for how you can incorporate Differentiated Instruction Resources into your teaching.

	Instructional Resources L3	**Differentiated Instruction Resources**
1. Plan		
Preparation Read the Math Background in the Teacher's Edition to connect this lesson with students' previous experience. **Starting Class** **Check Skills You'll Need** Assign these exercises to review prerequisite skills. **New Vocabulary** Help students pre-read the lesson by pointing out the new terms introduced in the lesson.	**Math Background** **Math Understandings** **Transparencies & PresentationExpress™ with QuickTake Presenter CD-ROM** Check Skills You'll Need Problem of the Day **Resources** Vocabulary and Study Skills	**Spanish Support** **ELL** Vocabulary and Study Skills
2. Teach		
L3 Guided Instruction Use the Activity Labs to build conceptual understanding. Teach each Example. Use the Teacher's Edition side column notes for specific teaching tips, including Error Prevention notes. Use the Additional Examples found in the side column (and on transparency and PowerPoint) as an alternative presentation for the content. After each Example, assign the Quick Check exercise for that Example to get an immediate assessment of student understanding. Use the Closure activity in the Teacher's Edition to help students attain mastery of lesson content.	**Student Edition** Activity Lab **Resources** Daily Notetaking Guide Activity Lab **Transparencies & PresentationExpress™ with QuickTake Presenter CD-ROM** Additional Examples Classroom Aids **ExamView® Assessment Suite CD-ROM**	**Teacher's Edition** Every lesson includes suggestions for working with students who need special attention. **L1** Special Needs **L2** Below Level **L4** Advanced Learners **ELL** English Language Learners **Resources** **L1** Adapted Daily Notetaking Guide **Multilingual Handbook**
3. Practice		

Assignment Guide
Check Your Understanding
Use these questions to check students' understanding before you assign homework.
Homework Exercises
Assign homework from these leveled exercises in the Assignment Guide.
  A Practice by Example
  B Apply Your Skills
  C Challenge
  Test Prep and Mixed Review
Homework Quick Check
Use these key exercises to quickly check students' homework.
	Transparencies & PresentationExpress™ with QuickTake Presenter CD-ROM
	Student Answers
	Resources
	Practice
	Guided Problem Solving
	Vocabulary and Study Skills
	Activity Lab
	Daily Puzzles
	ExamView® Assessment Suite CD-ROM
		Spanish Support
		ELL Practice
		ELL Vocabulary and Study Skills
		Resources
		L1 Adapted Practice
		L4 Enrichment

4. Assess & Reteach		
Lesson Quiz Assign the Lesson Quiz to assess students' mastery of the lesson content. **Checkpoint Quiz** Use the Checkpoint Quiz to assess student progress over several lessons.	**Transparencies & PresentationExpress™ with QuickTake Presenter CD-ROM** Lesson Quiz **Resources** Checkpoint Quiz	**Resources** **L2** Reteaching **ELL** Checkpoint Quiz Success Tracker™ Online Intervention **ExamView® Assessment Suite CD-ROM**

KEY **L1** Special Needs **L2** Below Level **L3** For All Students **L4** Advanced, Gifted **ELL** English Language Learners

Whole Numbers and Decimals

Check Your Readiness

Answers are in the back of the textbook.

For Intervention, direct students to:

Rounding to the Nearest Ten
Skills Handbook, p. 637

Adding and Subtracting Whole Numbers
Skills Handbook, p. 639

Multiplying Whole Numbers
Skills Handbook, p. 640

Dividing Whole Numbers
Skills Handbook, p. 642

What You've Learned

- In a previous course, you compared and ordered whole numbers.
- You used addition, subtraction, multiplication, and division to solve problems involving whole numbers.
- You used rounding to estimate reasonable results for problems involving whole numbers.

Check Your Readiness

GO for Help

For Exercises	See Skills Handbook
1–6	p. 637
7–12	p. 639
13–16	p. 640
17–20	p. 642

Rounding to the Nearest Ten
Round each number to the nearest ten.

1. 312 **310** **2.** 7,525 **7,530** **3.** 38 **40**

4. 55 **60** **5.** 699 **700** **6.** 1,989 **1,990**

Adding and Subtracting Whole Numbers
Add or subtract.

7. $59 + 116$ **175** **8.** $182 - 37$ **145** **9.** $8,745 + 5,447$ **14,192**

10. $4,823 - 1,796$ **3,027** **11.** $9,004 + 996$ **10,000** **12.** $2,049 - 657$ **1,392**

Multiplying Whole Numbers
Multiply.

13. 9×83 **747** **14.** 64×71 **4,544** **15.** 437×100 **43,700** **16.** 33×14 **462**

Dividing Whole Numbers
Divide.

17. $50 \div 10$ **5** **18.** $85 \div 5$ **17** **19.** $256 \div 8$ **32** **20.** $1,944 \div 27$ **72**

Chapter 1 Overview

In this chapter, students work with whole numbers and decimals. They extend their understanding of whole numbers, their properties, order of operations, and estimations. Then they compare, order, add, subtract, multiply, and divide decimals. They use patterns to multiply and divide decimals by powers of 10.

Activating Prior Knowledge

Students build on and extend their knowledge of whole numbers, their properties, and their operations to understand and compute with decimals. Ask questions such as:
- *Use the order of operations to simplify: $4 + 8 \times 2$.* **20**
- *What is the missing number in this sequence: 1, 10, 100, _____, 10,000, 100,000,...?* **1,000**

What You'll Learn Next

- In this chapter, you will learn how to compare and order decimals.
- You will use addition, subtraction, multiplication, and division to solve problems involving decimals.
- You will use rounding and compatible numbers to estimate reasonable results.
- You will use the order of operations to simplify numerical expressions.

🔊 Key Vocabulary

- associative properties (pp. 12–13)
- commutative properties (pp. 12–13)
- compatible numbers (p. 9)
- expanded form (p. 23)
- expression (p. 16)
- front-end estimation (p. 32)
- identity properties (pp. 12–13)
- order of operations (p. 16)
- standard form (p. 4)

 Problem Solving Application On pages 56 and 57, you will work an extended activity on order forms.

Chapter 1   3

3

Objective
To write and compare whole numbers

Examples
1 Estimating by Rounding
2 Estimating With Compatible Numbers
3 Application: Food Drive

Math Understandings: p. 2C

Math Background

The *expanded form* of a number is a sum of the values of each digit. For example, the *standard form* number 1,275 can be written in expanded form as
1,000 + 200 + 70 + 5. In words, the number 1,275 is read as "one thousand, two hundred seventy-five." All three forms of a number represent equivalent values.

More Math Background: p. 2C

Lesson Planning and Resources

See p. 2E for a list of the resources that support this lesson.

Bell Ringer Practice

✓ **Check Skills You'll Need**
Use student page, transparency, or PowerPoint. For intervention, direct students to:
Place Value of Whole Numbers
Skills Handbook, p. 636

✓ Check Skills You'll Need

1. **Vocabulary Review**
Give an example of a number that is a *whole number* and one that is not.

Write the value of the digit 2 in each number. **1–5. See back of book.**
2. 28   3. 8,672
4. 12,980   5. 246

GO for Help
Skills Handbook p. 636

GO for Help

For help with identifying place value, go to Skills Handbook p. 636.

1. **twenty-six billion, two hundred thirty-six million, eight hundred forty-eight thousand, eighty dollars**

What You'll Learn

To write and compare whole numbers

◀) **New Vocabulary** standard form

Why Learn This?

You can use the place and value of whole numbers to understand large numbers, such as the distance between stars.

The **standard form** of a number uses digits and place value. The *place* of the digit 5 in 254 is tens. The *value* of 5 is 5 tens, or 50.

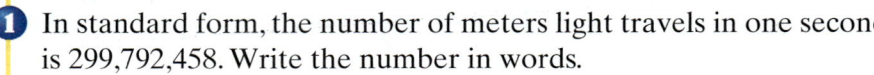

EXAMPLE   Writing Whole Numbers
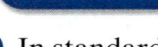

1 In standard form, the number of meters light travels in one second is 299,792,458. Write the number in words.

Use a place value chart to identify the place value of each digit.

Millions			Thousands			Ones		
Hundreds	Tens	Ones	Hundreds	Tens	Ones	Hundreds	Tens	Ones
2	9	9	7	9	2	4	5	8

299 millions   792 thousands   458 ones

299,792,458 written in words is two hundred ninety-nine million, seven hundred ninety-two thousand, four hundred fifty-eight.

✓ Quick Check

1. Write the value of $26,236,848,080 in words.

Differentiated Instruction   Solutions for All Learners

Special Needs L1
To help students remember how to position the less than and greater than signs, ask them to point the smaller side, or closed side, towards the lesser number. They can also note the open side faces the greater number.

learning style: visual

Below Level L2
Create a page of "empty" place-value charts similar to the one shown below Example 1. Guide students to accurately identify the starting place and not to skip zeros as they fill in the charts.

learning style: visual

You can use place value or a number line to compare whole numbers. The numbers from left to right on a number line are in order from least to greatest.

990 991 992 993 994 995 996 997 998 999 1,000 1,001 1,002

EXAMPLE **Comparing Whole Numbers**

2 Use < or > to complete: 995 ▓ 998.

Method 1 Use a number line.

On the number line above, 995 is to the left of 998. So 995 < 998.

Method 2 Use place value.

The first two digits are the same.

995
998

8 is greater than 5.

Since 8 is greater than 5 in the ones place, 995 < 998.

✓ Quick Check

2. Use < or > to complete: 129,631 ▓ 142,832. **<**

To order whole numbers, start with the greatest place value and compare the digits. Do this for each place value. Then write the numbers in order from least to greatest.

EXAMPLE **Ordering Whole Numbers**

3 Write in order from least to greatest: 12,875; 12,675; 12,695.

The first two digits are the same.

8 is greater than 6, so 12,875 is the greatest number.

12,**8**75
12,**6**75 ← Compare the tens digit in the remaining
12,**6**95   numbers. 9 is greater than 7, so 12,695 is the
                next greatest number.

The order from least to greatest is 12,675; 12,695; and 12,875.

✓ Quick Check

3. Write in order from least to greatest: 9,897; 9,987; 978.
   978; 9,897; 9,987

Activity Lab
Use before the lesson.

All in One Teaching Resources
Activity Lab 1-1: Greatest Number

Guided Instruction

Example 1
Ask: *What is the place of the digit 7 in 299,792,458?* The place of the digit 7 is hundred thousands.

Example 2
Ask: *How do you write 998 is greater than 995?* 998 > 995

Error Prevention!

Some students may have difficulty differentiating between the greater and less than symbols. Remind them that the larger side of the symbol opens toward the greater number.

PowerPoint
Additional Examples

1 Write 42,046,708,002 in words.
forty-two billion, forty-six million, seven hundred eight thousand, two

2 Use < or > to complete:
60,201 ▓ 60,102. >

3 Write in order from least to greatest: 12,374; 13,341; 12,472. 12,374; 12,472; 13,341

All in One Teaching Resources
• Daily Notetaking Guide 1-1 **L3**
• Adapted Notetaking 1-1 **L1**

Closure

• *What is the expanded form of a number?* the sum that shows the place value of each digit
• *How do you compare whole numbers?* Compare digits starting with the greater place value or use a number line.

Advanced Learners **L4**
In meters per second, the speed of light in Example 1 is 299,792,458 m/s. How might the number of yards compare to the number of meters if the speed of light were measured in yards instead of meters per second? **It would be greater; yards are shorter than meters.**

learning style: verbal

English Language Learners **ELL**
When students are asked to write numbers using words, it is helpful to have a chart with number words that they can use. Asking them to say the number aloud before writing it helps correct any errors before they write.

learning style: verbal

Vocabulary Tip

To compare numbers, use these symbols.

< is read as "is less than."
= is read as "is equal to."
> is read as "is greater than."

Assignment Guide

Check Your Understanding
Go over Exercises 1–7 in class before assigning the Homework Exercises.

Homework Exercises
A Practice by Example   8–24
B Apply Your Skills   25–28
C Challenge   29
Test Prep and
    Mixed Review   30–34

Homework Quick Check
To check students' understanding of key skills and concepts, go over Exercises 12, 23, 25, 26, and 27.

Differentiated Instruction **Resources**

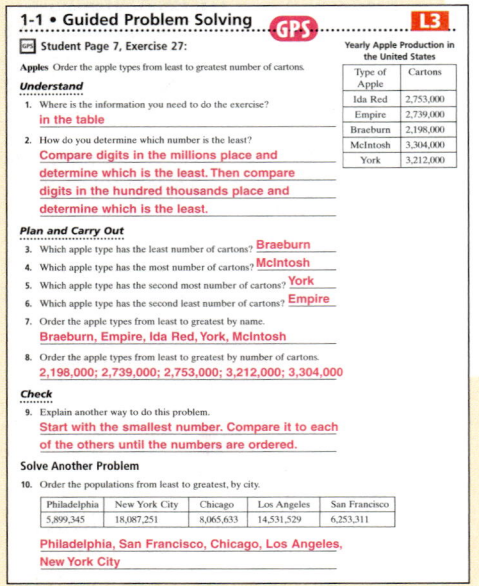

✓ Check Your Understanding

1. Vocabulary Write one thousand, two hundred seventy-three in standard form. **1,273**

2. Answers may vary. Sample: the 7 in the tens place of 471 > the 1 in the tens place of 417.

2. Writing in Math  Explain how you know that $471 < 417$ is false.

Write each number in words.

3. 362: three __?__ sixty-__?__
hundred; two

4. 1,400: one __?__, four __?__
thousand; hundred

Use < or > to complete each statement.

5. 322 ■ 332   **<**
6. 745 ■ 739   **>**
7. 1,187 ■ 1,278   **<**

Homework Exercises

For more exercises, see Extra Skills and Word Problems.

GO for Help

For Exercises	See Example
8–14	1
15–20	2
21–24	3

A **Write each number in words.** **8–13. See margin.**

8. 30,987
9. 145,675
10. 1,345,000
11. 7,347,200
12. 9,871,060,540
13. 63,380,509,710

14. History An estimate in A.D. 14 placed the population of the Roman empire at 4,937,000. Write the number in words.
four million, nine hundred thirty-seven thousand

Use < or > to complete each statement.

15. 366 ■ 36   **>**
16. 54,001 ■ 54,901   **<**
17. 8,801 ■ 810   **>**
18. 84,123 ■ 9,996   **>**
19. 29,286 ■ 29,826   **<**
20. 31,010 ■ 30,101   **>**

Write the numbers in order from least to greatest.

21. 910; 990; 901
901; 910; 990

22. 1,172; 1,472; 1,142; 1,572
1,142; 1,172; 1,472; 1,572

23. 17,444; 17,671; 17,414
17,414; 17,444; 17,671

24. 20,403; 23,404; 23,040
20,403; 23,040; 23,404

B GPS **25. Guided Problem Solving** The average distance between Earth and the sun is one hundred forty-nine million, four hundred seventy-six thousand kilometers. Write the distance in standard form.
• Use a place value chart. **149,476,000 kilometers**

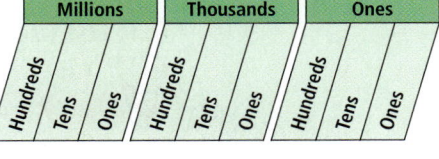

8. thirty thousand, nine hundred eighty-seven

9. one hundred forty-five thousand, six hundred seventy-five

10. one million, three hundred forty-five thousand

11. seven million, three hundred forty-seven thousand, two hundred

12. nine billion, eight hundred seventy-one million, sixty thousand, five hundred forty

13. sixty-three billion, three hundred eighty million, five hundred nine thousand, seven hundred ten

26. Social Studies The land area of Oklahoma is 68,667 square miles. Washington includes about 66,544 square miles and Missouri includes about 68,886 square miles. Order the three states from least to greatest number of square miles.
Washington, Oklahoma, Missouri

27. Order the apple types by number of
GPS cartons from least to greatest.
27–28. See margin.

28. Computers There are 4,256 kilobytes of memory available on a digital music player. Is there enough space for a file that uses 4,290 kilobytes? Explain.

C 29. Challenge The sum of the digits of a two-digit number is 12. The tens digit is three times the ones digit. What is the number? **93**

Yearly Apple Production in the United States

Type of Apple	Cartons
Ida Red	2,753,000
Empire	2,739,000
Braeburn	2,198,000
McIntosh	3,304,000
York	3,212,000

Source: U.S. Apple Association

Test Prep and Mixed Review
Practice

Multiple Choice

30. The six highest waterfalls in the world are listed below.

Waterfall	Country	Height (ft)
Angel	Venezuela	3,212
Mongefossen	Norway	2,540
Ostre Mandola Foss	Norway	2,152
Tugela	South Africa	2,800
Utigord	Norway	2,625
Yosemite	United States	2,425

Source: The Top 10 of Everything

Which statement is NOT supported by the data? **C**
Ⓐ The highest waterfall is Angel.
Ⓑ The lowest waterfall is in Norway.
Ⓒ The heights are in order from greatest to least.
Ⓓ Three of the world's highest waterfalls are in Norway.

31. An auditorium has 10 rows with 22 seats in each row. There are 160 people seated. How many seats are empty? **H**
Ⓕ 100 seats
Ⓖ 80 seats
Ⓗ 60 seats
Ⓙ 40 seats

Find each sum.

32. 375 + 15 **390**   **33.** 1,820 + 309 **2,129**   **34.** 2,617 + 1,904 **4,521**

GO for Help

For Exercises	See Skills Handbook
32–34	p. 638

27. Braeburn, Empire, Ida Red, York, McIntosh

28. No; the 4,290-kilobyte file is greater than the 4,256 kilobytes of memory.

Test Prep

Resources
For additional practice with a variety of test item formats:
• Test-Taking Strategies, p. 51
• Test Prep, p. 55
• Test-Taking Strategies with Transparencies

4. Assess & Reteach

PowerPoint
Lesson Quiz

1. Write three hundred four thousand in standard form.
304,000

2. Write in order from least to greatest: 6,947; 6,794; 9,644.
6,794; 6,947; 9,644

Alternative Assessment

Each student in a pair writes two whole numbers greater than 1,000. Partners exchange papers and write each other's numbers in expanded form and in words.

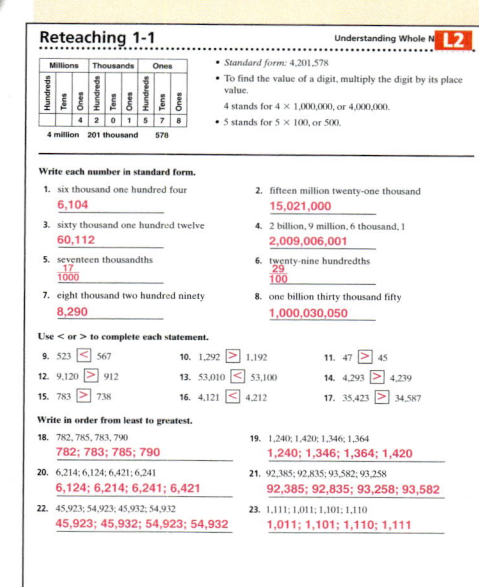

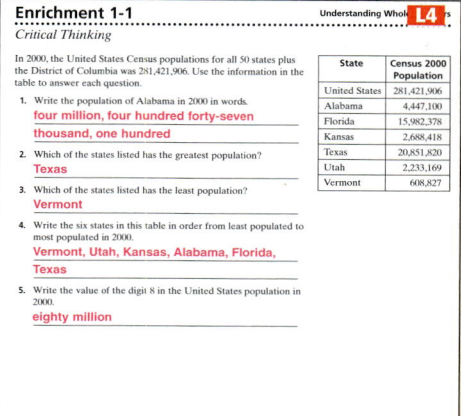

Objective
To estimate with whole numbers by rounding and by using compatible numbers

Examples
1 Estimating by Rounding
2 Estimating With Compatible Numbers
3 Application: Food Drive

Math Understandings: p. 2C

Math Background

Whole numbers are rounded to the nearest 10, 100, and 1,000. You can round whole numbers to estimate sums, differences, and products. Two common estimation strategies are *rounding* and *compatible numbers*. Rounding is helpful to add and subtract numbers. Compatible numbers are used to estimate products and quotients.

More Math Background: p. 2C

Lesson Planning and Resources

See p. 2E for a list of the resources that support this lesson.

Bell Ringer Practice

✓ **Check Skills You'll Need**
Use student page, transparency, or PowerPoint. For intervention, direct students to:
Rounding Whole Numbers
Skills Handbook, p. 637

✓ **Check Skills You'll Need**

1. **Vocabulary Review**
   The *place* of the digit 7 in 2,704 is __?__. **hundreds**

   Round each number to the nearest ten.

   2. 47 **50**   3. 62 **60**

   4. 136 **140**   5. 485 **490**

**for Help**
Skills Handbook
p. 637

Vocabulary Tip

When you *round* a number, you look for the nearest simpler number.

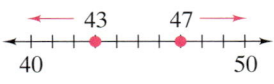

What You'll Learn

To estimate with whole numbers by rounding and by using compatible numbers

◀)) **New Vocabulary** compatible numbers

Why Learn This?

When you buy materials such as fabric or wood, you can use estimation to decide how much material you need.

To estimate, you select numbers that are close to the exact numbers, but are easier to use for computing. Rounding is one method you use in estimation.

Round to the nearest	**Ten**	**Hundred**

Look at the value to the → 47   12**3** ← Look at the value to the
right of the tens place.   ↓   ↓   right of the hundreds place.
7 ≥ 5, so round up.   50   100   2 < 5, so round down.

To estimate sums and differences, round each number to the same place before you add or subtract.

EXAMPLE   **Estimating by Rounding**

① Estimate $37 + 62 + 48$. First round each number to the nearest ten.

$$
\begin{array}{rll}
37 & 7 \geq 5, \text{ so round up.} \rightarrow & 40 \\
62 & 2 < 5, \text{ so round down.} \rightarrow & 60 \\
+\,48 & 8 \geq 5, \text{ so round up.} \rightarrow & +\,50 \\
\hline
& & 150
\end{array}
$$

So $37 + 62 + 48 \approx 150$.   ← The symbol ≈ means "is approximately equal to."

✓ **Quick Check**

1. Estimate. First round each number to the nearest ten.
   a. $97 + 22 + 48$ **about 170**   **b.** $94 - 32 - 41$ **about 20**

Differentiated Instruction   **Solutions for All Learners**

Special Needs **L1**
Make sure students understand they are rounding to the nearest ten in Example 1. Have them circle the number they are rounding, and underline the number they will use to determine whether to round up or down.

         learning style: visual

Below Level **L2**
Some students are confused by "unnecessary" digits. Have them circle the digit immediately to the right of the desired rounding place. Students can then cross out all other digits to the right of it.

         learning style: visual

Compatible numbers are numbers that are easy to compute mentally. They are particularly useful for estimating products and quotients.

$$38 \div 6$$
$$\downarrow \qquad \downarrow$$
$$36 \div 6 \quad \leftarrow$$ Since you can divide 36 by 6 mentally, 36 and 6 are compatible.

$$6 \times 78$$
$$\downarrow \qquad \downarrow$$
$$5 \times 80 \quad \leftarrow$$ 5 and 80 are compatible because 5 and 80 can be multiplied mentally.

Test Prep Tip

When you are asked to find "about how many," you are being asked to estimate.

EXAMPLE **Estimating With Compatible Numbers**

② Estimate $298 \div 16$ using compatible numbers.

$$298 \div 16$$
$$\downarrow \qquad \downarrow$$
$$300 \div 16 \quad \leftarrow$$ Change 298 to 300 because 300 is easier to use mentally.
$$\downarrow \qquad \downarrow$$
$$300 \div 15 = 20 \quad \leftarrow$$ Change 16 to 15 because 15 is compatible with 300.

So $298 \div 16 \approx 20$.

✓ **Quick Check**

2. Estimate using compatible numbers.
   a. 8×39 **about 320**
   b. $672 \div 52$ **about 14**

EXAMPLE **Application: Food Drive**

③ **Multiple Choice** Northern Middle School had a food drive. Each of the 22 homerooms collected about 290 cans of food. About how many cans were collected in all?

   Ⓐ 400 Ⓑ 600 Ⓒ 4,000 Ⓓ 6,000

$$
\begin{array}{r}
290 \\
\times\ 22 \\
\end{array}
\quad
\begin{array}{l}
\leftarrow \text{300 is easier to work with than 299.} \rightarrow \\
\leftarrow \text{20 is easier to multiply by than 22.} \rightarrow
\end{array}
\quad
\begin{array}{r}
300 \\
\times\ 20 \\
\hline
6{,}000
\end{array}
$$

So $290 \times 22 \approx 6{,}000$. The correct answer is choice D.

✓ **Quick Check**

3. You have 324 cards for a strategy game. To play the game, a person needs 12 cards. About how many different people can play using your set of cards? **about 30**

---

2. Teach

Activity Lab

Use before the lesson.

All in One Teaching Resources

Activity Lab 1-2: Visual Thinking

Guided Instruction

Before students estimate with compatible numbers, spend some time practicing how to identify compatible numbers. Emphasize the relationship between the numbers in basic division facts and in basic multiplication facts. Give students pairs of numbers. Ask:
• *Are 5 and 3 compatible numbers?* **no**
• *Are 6 and 2 compatible numbers?* **Yes; 6 is divisible by 2.**

PowerPoint

Additional Examples

① Estimate $97 - 21$ by rounding to the nearest ten. **80**

② Estimate $358 \div 9$ by using compatible numbers. **40**

③ Each of the 29 students in Mrs. Wong's class read about 512 pages of a novel. About how many pages did they read in all? **15,000**

All in One Teaching Resources

• Daily Notetaking Guide 1-2 **L3**
• Adapted Notetaking 1-2 **L1**

Closure

• *When is rounding appropriate to use?* **when you estimate the sum or difference of numbers**
• *When should you use compatible numbers to estimate?* **when you estimate products and quotients**

Advanced Learners **L4**
Challenge students to explain why rounding might be inaccurate when estimating products or quotients. Use Example 2 to demonstrate.

learning style: verbal

English Language Learners **ELL**
Have students work in pairs. One partner should focus on explaining how to estimate by rounding using examples. The other partner should explain estimation using compatible numbers.

learning style: verbal

Assignment Guide

Check Your Understanding
Go over Exercises 1–10 in class before assigning the Homework Exercises.

Homework Exercises
A	Practice by Example	11–28
B	Apply Your Skills	29–36
C	Challenge	37
	Test Prep and	
	Mixed Review	38–41

Homework Quick Check
To check students' understanding of key skills and concepts, go over Exercises 15, 21, 31, 32, and 36.

Differentiated Instruction Resources

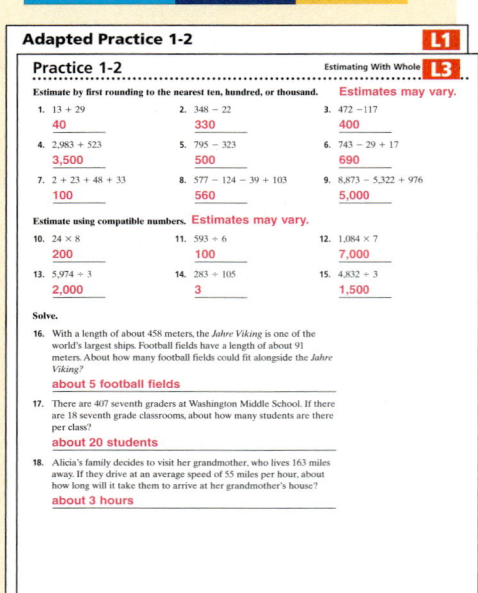

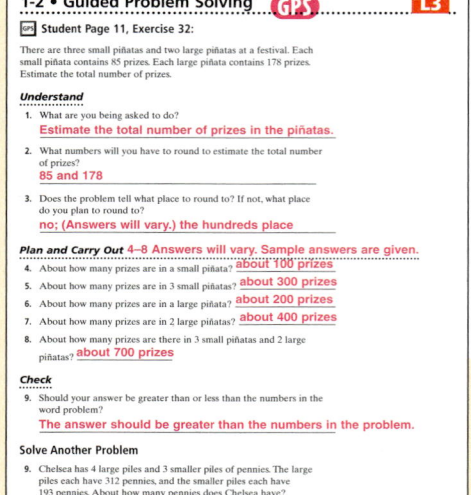

Check Your Understanding

1. **Vocabulary** In a division problem, are 60 and 6 compatible numbers? Explain. **Yes; 60 can be divided by 6 mentally.**

2. **Error Analysis** A classmate estimated that $29 + 42 + 37$ is about $20 + 40 + 40$, or 100. Explain your classmate's error.

   Answers may vary. Sample: 29 was rounded down to 20, but should have been rounded up to 30.

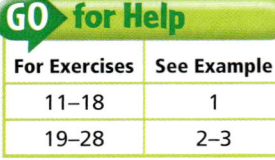

GO for Help

For help with rounding numbers, go to Skills Handbook, p. 637.

Estimate. Round the underlined number first.

3. $70 - \underline{29}$ **40**
4. $200 + \underline{812}$ **1,000**
5. $\underline{87} - 20$ **70**
6. $\underline{189} + 400$ **600**

Estimate using compatible numbers.

7. $103 \div 11 \approx 100 \div$ 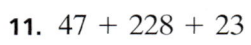 **10** (10)
8. $52 \times 18 \approx$ ■ $\times 20$ **1,000** (50)
9. $597 \div 31 \approx$ ■ $\div 30$ **20** (600)
10. $94 \times 13 \approx 90 \times$ ■ **900** (10)

Homework Exercises

For more exercises, see Extra Skills and Word Problems.

GO for Help

For Exercises	See Example
11–18	1
19–28	2–3

11. about 300
12. about 400
13. about 190
14. about 70
15. about 4,000
16. about 14,000

A **Estimate. Round each number first.** 11–16. See left.

11. $47 + 228 + 23$
12. $653 - 295$
13. $34 + 68 + 93$
14. $59 + 26 - 23$
15. $6,963 - 3,098$
16. $8,043 + 5,983$
17. $42 + 86 + 51 + 38$ **about 220**
18. $257 - 109 - 46 - 21$ **about 80**

Estimate using compatible numbers.

19. $2 \times 3,978$ **about 8,000**
20. $102 \div 25$ **about 4**
21. $611 \div 58$ **about 10**
22. 997×5 **about 5,000**
23. $1,089 \div 521$ **about 2**
24. $4,978 \div 983$ **about 5**
25. 48×41 **about 2,000**
26. $207 \div 51$ **about 4**
27. $69 \div 7$ **about 10**

28. **World History** The Chinese kwan note was used in the 1300s. It was about 93 centimeters long. The United States dollar bill is almost 16 centimeters long. About how many times longer was the kwan note? **about 6**

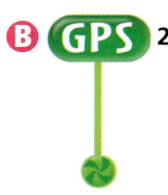

B **GPS** 29. **Guided Problem Solving** You need $78 to buy a new video game. You earn $9 one week and $22 the next week. About how much more do you need to earn to buy the game?
   • Do you need to find an exact answer? **about $50**
   • About how much have you already earned?

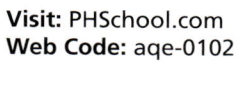
30. Travel You are going on a vacation 1,038 miles away. The first day you travel 284 miles. The second day you travel 326 miles. About how much farther do you have to go? **about 400 mi**

31. Savings Suppose you saved $443 in one year.
a. Estimate the average amount you saved each week. **about $9**
b. Reasoning Explain why you chose the method you used.
Compatible numbers make division easy to compute mentally.

32. There are three small piñatas and two large piñatas at a
GPS festival. Each small piñata contains 85 prizes. Each large piñata contains 178 prizes. Estimate the total number of prizes.
about 670 prizes

Choose a Method Use either rounding or compatible numbers to estimate each answer.

33. 429 + 889
about 1,300

34. 1,142 − 720
about 400

35. 551 ÷ 86
about 6

36. Writing in Math The cost of four copies of a book is $37. Estimate the cost of one book. Is your estimate higher or lower than the book's actual cost? Explain. **Answers may vary. Sample: $10; the estimate is higher because $37 was rounded up to $40.**

C 37. Challenge A ball has a mass of 238 grams. A box holds 9 balls. The total mass of the balls and the box is 2,437 grams. Estimate the mass of the box. **about 400 g**

Test Prep and Mixed Review
Practice

Multiple Choice

38. A family of five went to pick berries. They filled 11 containers. Each container held about 18 ounces of berries. About many ounces of berries did the family pick? **C**
Ⓐ 100
Ⓒ 200
Ⓑ 150
Ⓓ 300

39. A science teacher says that Jupiter's average distance from the sun is "seven hundred seventy-eight million, three hundred thousand kilometers." Susan is writing this distance in her notebook. Which number should she write? **H**
Ⓕ 78,030,000
Ⓖ 78,300,000
Ⓗ 778,300,000
Ⓙ 778,300,000,000

For Exercises	See Lesson
40–41	1-1

Write in order from least to greatest.

40. 287, 278, 275, 281
275, 278, 281, 287

41. 4,567; 4,678; 4,687; 4,541
4,541; 4,567; 4,678; 4,687

Test Prep

Resources
For additional practice with a variety of test item formats:
• Test-Taking Strategies, p. 51
• Test Prep, p. 55
• Test-Taking Strategies with Transparencies

4. Assess & Reteach

PowerPoint
Lesson Quiz

Estimate. Round each number first.

1. 263 + 107 + 621 **1,000**

2. 37 + 21 **60**

Estimate using compatible numbers.

3. 898 × 51 **45,000**

4. 211 × 29 **6,000**

5. Rob received 39 e-mails yesterday. If he receives the same number everyday, about how many e-mails will he receive in March? **1,200**

Alternative Assessment

Students write an addition or subtraction problem where they can use rounded numbers to estimate the answer. Then they write a multiplication or division problem where they can use compatible numbers to estimate the answer. Students swap with a partner and solve each other's problems.

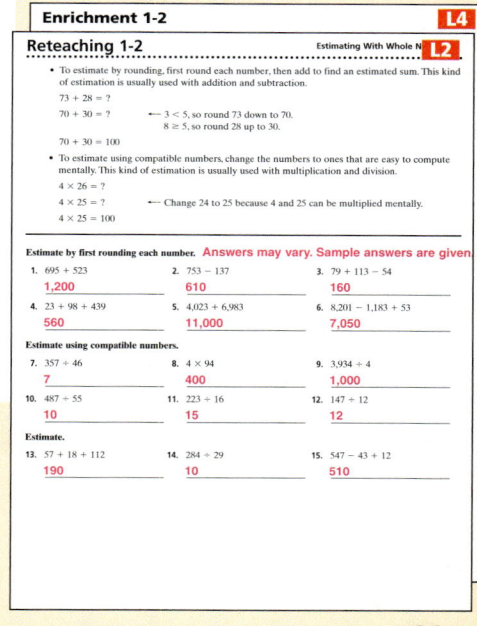

11

Objective
To understand and use the properties of numbers

Examples
1 Using the Properties of Addition
2 Using the Properties of Multiplication

Math Understandings: p. 2C

Math Background

This lesson introduces the properties of addition and multiplication. The Commutative and Associative Properties of addition and multiplication state the order or grouping of addends and factors make no difference to the result. The Identity Property states that a number added to or multiplied by the identity remains the same.

More Math Background: p. 2C

Lesson Planning and Resources

See p. 2E for a list of the resources that support this lesson.

Bell Ringer Practice

☑ **Check Skills You'll Need**
Use student page, transparency, or PowerPoint. For intervention, direct students to:
Multiplying Whole Numbers
Skills Handbook, p. 640

✓ Check Skills You'll Need

1. **Vocabulary Review**
   Multiplication of whole numbers can be described as repeated __?__.
   addition

   Find each product.

   2. 5×30 **150**

   3. 6×15 **90**

   4. 50×7 **350**

GO for Help
Skills Handbook p. 640

What You'll Learn

To understand and use the properties of numbers

◄)) **New Vocabulary** commutative properties, associative properties, identity properties

Why Learn This?

The properties of numbers can help you do mental math.

> **KEY CONCEPTS** **Properties of Numbers**
>
> **Commutative Property of Addition** Changing the order of addends does not change the sum.
> $$9 + 5 = 5 + 9$$
>
> **Associative Property of Addition** Changing the grouping of addends does not change the sum.
> $$(9 + 5) + 4 = 9 + (5 + 4)$$
>
> **Identity Property of Addition** The sum of 0 and any number is that number.
> $$0 + 9 = 9$$

You can simplify a mathematical phrase by replacing it with the simplest name for the value of the phrase. So to simplify $4 + 5$, you write 9 for its value.

EXAMPLE Using the Properties of Addition

1 **Field Trips** The table shows two groups of students who went on a field trip. Use mental math to find the total number of students.

Room	Number of Students
101	32
102	28

What you think

First I will think of 28 as $20 + 8$. Next, I will add $8 + 32$ to get 40. $40 + 20$ is 60. So $32 + 28 = 60$.

Differentiated Instruction Solutions for All Learners

Special Needs L1
Students may need to "prove" that $9 + 5 = 5 + 9$ by adding the 9 and 5 and the 5 and 9 using counters. Have them try several addition or multiplication problems with counters to prove the commutative properties.

learning style: tactile

Below Level L2
Be sure students understand that addition and multiplication have different identity elements. For addition it is 0, but for multiplication it is 1. Give several examples orally of each.

learning style: verbal

Why it works

$$32 + 28 = 32 + (20 + 8) \quad \leftarrow \text{Rewrite 28 as } 20 + 8.$$
$$= 32 + (8 + 20) \quad \leftarrow \text{Use the Commutative Property of Addition.}$$
$$= (32 + 8) + 20 \quad \leftarrow \text{Use the Associative Property of Addition.}$$
$$= 40 + 20 \quad \leftarrow \text{Add inside the parentheses first.}$$
$$= 60 \quad \leftarrow \text{Simplify.}$$

The total number of students is 60.

✓ Quick Check

1. **Mental Math** Find $36 + 25 + 34$. **95**

KEY CONCEPTS **Properties of Numbers**

Commutative Property of Multiplication Changing the order of factors does not change the product.
$$4 \times 6 = 6 \times 4$$

Associative Property of Multiplication Changing the grouping of factors does not change the product.
$$(4 \times 6) \times 2 = 4 \times (6 \times 2)$$

Identity Property of Multiplication The product of 1 and any number is that number.
$$4 \times 1 = 4$$

$4 \times 25 = 100$

EXAMPLE **Using the Properties of Multiplication**

2. **Mental Math** Find $4 \times 8 \times 25$.

What you think

First I will multiply 4 and 25. $4 \times 25 = 100$, and $8 \times 100 = 800$.

Why it works

$$4 \times 8 \times 25 = 4 \times 25 \times 8 \quad \leftarrow \text{Commutative Property of Multiplication}$$
$$= (4 \times 25) \times 8 \quad \leftarrow \text{Associative Property of Multiplication}$$
$$= 100 \times 8 \quad \leftarrow \text{Multiply inside the parentheses.}$$
$$= 800 \quad \leftarrow \text{Simplify.}$$

✓ Quick Check

2. **Mental Math** Find $20 \times (6 \times 5)$. **600**

1-3 Properties of Numbers **13**

Activity Lab

Use before the lesson.

All in One Teaching Resources
Activity Lab 1-3: Mental Math

Guided Instruction

Example 1
Ask: *Why can you rewrite 28 as 20 + 8?* **28 in expanded form is 2 tens 8 ones or 20 + 8.**

Example 2
Ask: *What do the parentheses in step 2 tell you?* **Multiply the 4 × 25 inside the parentheses first.**

Teaching Tip
Students may differentiate between Commutative and Associative Properties by thinking of *commuters* as going back and forth each day and *associates* as groups of friends or colleagues.

PowerPoint
Additional Examples

❶ Use mental math to find the total number of books in a carton that contains 43 math books, 15 history books, and 57 science books. **115 books**

❷ Use mental math to find $2 \times 17 \times 50$. **1,700**

All in One Teaching Resources
• Daily Notetaking Guide 1-3 **L3**
• Adapted Notetaking **L1**

Closure

• Have students give examples for the Commutative, Associative, and Identity Properties of Addition and Multiplication.
Sample answers:

$3 + 2 = 2 + 3$
$3 + (7 + 5) = (3 + 7) + 5$
$5 + 0 = 5$

$5 \times 4 = 4 \times 5$
$(2 \times 4) \times 3 = 2 \times (4 \times 3)$
$6 \times 1 = 6$

Advanced Learners **L4**
Challenge Advanced Learners to test the Distributive Property for sets of whole numbers.
$a \times (b + c) = ab + ac$

English Language Learners **ELL**
Have students make two cards to show related words and symbols. Write *sum*, *addends* and the addition symbol on one card. Write *factors*, *product*, and the multiplication symbol on the other.

learning style: visual

learning style: visual

Assignment Guide

Check Your Understanding
Go over Exercises 1–6 in class before assigning the Homework Exercises.

Homework Exercises
A Practice by Example   7–25
B Apply Your Skills   26–33
C Challenge   34
Test Prep and
    Mixed Review   35–39

Homework Quick Check
To check students' understanding of key skills and concepts, go over Exercises 14, 21, 29, 30, and 32.

Differentiated Instruction **Resources**

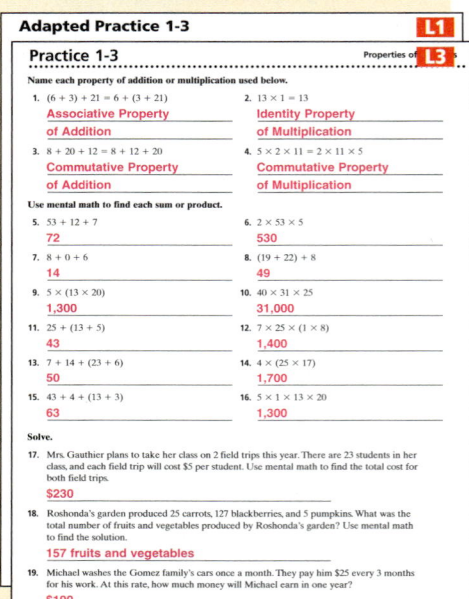

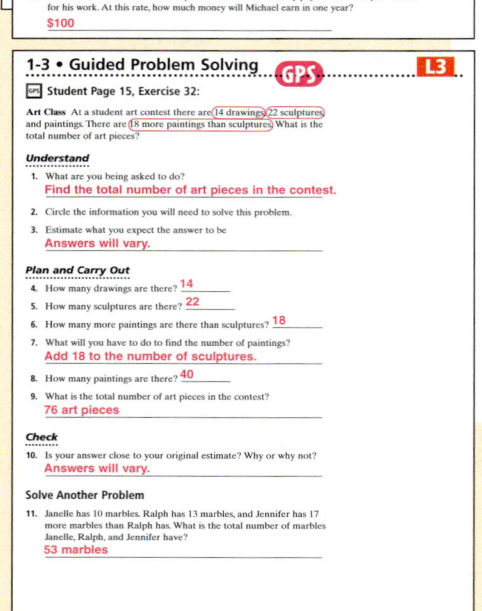

✓ Check Your Understanding

1. **Vocabulary** Name the property used in this statement:
   $25 + 27 + 15 = 25 + 15 + 27$. **Comm. Prop. of Add.**

2. Give a reason to justify each step.
   $(4 \times 9) \times 5 = (9 \times 4) \times 5$ __?__ **Comm. Prop. of Mult.**
   $= 9 \times (4 \times 5)$ __?__ **Assoc. Prop. of Mult.**
   $= 9 \times 20$ __?__ **Multiply inside the parentheses**
   $= 180$ __?__ **Simplify.**

3. **Writing in Math** Use mental math to find $(25 \times 9) \times 8$.
   Describe the steps you used. **1,800; Check students' work.**

Use mental math to find each sum or product.

4. $4 + 26$ **30**   5. $33 + 0 + 17$ **50**   6. $50 \times 7 \times 2$ **700**

Homework Exercises

For more exercises, see Extra Skills and Word Problems.

GO for Help

For Exercises	See Example
7–16	1
17–25	2

A Use mental math to find each sum.

7. $0 + 57 + 4$ **61**   8. $32 + 48$ **80**   9. $18 + 6 + 42$ **66**

10. $(8 + 17) + 13$ **38**   11. $81 + 23 + 19$ **123**   12. $(17 + 24) + 183$ **224**

13. $837 + 14 + 26$ **877**   14. $24 + 33 + 167$ **224**   15. $160 + 0 + 2,740$ **2,900**

16. A train started a trip pulling 9 cars. At the first stop, 17 cars were added to the train. At the second stop, 11 more cars were added. How many cars was the train pulling then? **37 cars**

Use mental math to find each product.

17. $5 \times 47 \times 2$ **470**   18. $70 \times 1 \times 4$ **280**   19. $25 \times 13 \times 4$ **1,300**

20. $20 \times (19 \times 50)$ **19,000**   21. $40 \times (33 \times 25)$ **33,000**   22. $5 \times 683 \times 20$ **68,300**

23. $65 \times (100 \times 2)$ **13,000**   24. $4 \times 20 \times 1,000$ **80,000**   25. $5 \times 8 \times 25$ **1,000**

B  26. **Guided Problem Solving** Four running clubs raised money in a 24-hour relay race. Club A ran 183 miles, Club B ran **590 mi** 144 miles, Club C ran 117 miles, and Club D ran 146 miles. What was the total number of miles that all four clubs ran?
   • Which pairs of numbers can you add using mental math?
   • What is the sum of each of those pairs?

34. **Answers may vary. Sample: Subtraction and division are not commutative.
   $8 - 4 \neq 4 - 8$ and $8 \div 4 \neq 4 \div 8$.
   Subtraction and division are not associative. $(8 - 4) - 2 \neq 8 - (4 - 2)$
   and $(8 \div 4) \div 2 \neq 8 \div (4 \div 2)$.**

Use <,=, or > to complete each statement.

27. $41 + 29$ **=** 70

28. $737 + 373$ **>** $4 \times 11 \times 25$

29. **Modeling** Draw a model to show the statement is true:
$8 + 6 + 2 = (8 + 2) + 6$. **Check students' work.**

30. Answers may vary. Sample: No; the Assoc. Prop. does not work when operations are combined.

30. **Error Analysis** Below is a friend's solution to a problem. Is your friend correct? Explain.

$$100 \times (5 + 9) = (100 \times 5) + 9 = 500 + 9 = 509$$

31. **Choose a Method** You plan to earn $15 per week for a charity. Will you use estimation, mental math, paper and pencil, or a calculator to determine how many weeks it will take you to earn $1,000? Explain why.
Answers may vary. Sample: calculator because it is faster

32. **Art Class** In a student art contest there are 14 drawings, 22 sculptures, and some paintings. There are 18 more paintings than sculptures. What is the total number of art pieces?
76 art pieces

33. The monthly rate for a 3-year subscription to an online music service is $10. What is the total cost for 3 years? **$360**

C 34. **Challenge** Is subtraction commutative? Is division? Is either operation associative? Explain using examples. **See margin.**

Test Prep and Mixed Review **Practice**

Multiple Choice

35. Gary is asked to find two whole numbers that have a sum of 9 and a product that is double the sum. He writes 7 and 2. Why is Gary's answer incorrect? **B**
   Ⓐ The sum of 7 and 2 is not 9.
   Ⓑ The product of 7 and 2 is not double the sum.
   Ⓒ The sum of 7 and 2 is 9.
   Ⓓ The product of 7 and 2 is double the sum.

36. Last night Martha spent 29 minutes on social studies homework, 13 minutes on English, and 22 minutes on science. About how much time did she spend on all three subjects? **H**
   Ⓕ 40 minutes   Ⓗ 1 hour
   Ⓖ 50 minutes   Ⓙ 1 hour and 10 minutes

GO for Help

For Exercises	See Lesson
37–39	1-1

Use < or > to complete each statement.

37. $98,410$ **>** $98,140$ 38. $78,296$ **>** $78,269$ 39. $40,000$ **<** $300,009$

4. Assess & Reteach

Lesson Quiz

Use mental math to find each sum.

1. $72 + 26 + 18$ **116**

2. $113 + 25 + 207$ **345**

Use mental math to find the product.

3. $5 \times 84 \times 20$ **8,400**

4. $40 \times 13 \times 25$ **13,000**

5. Name the property used in the statement.
$25 \times (4 \times 19) = (25 \times 4) \times 19$
Associative Property of Multiplication

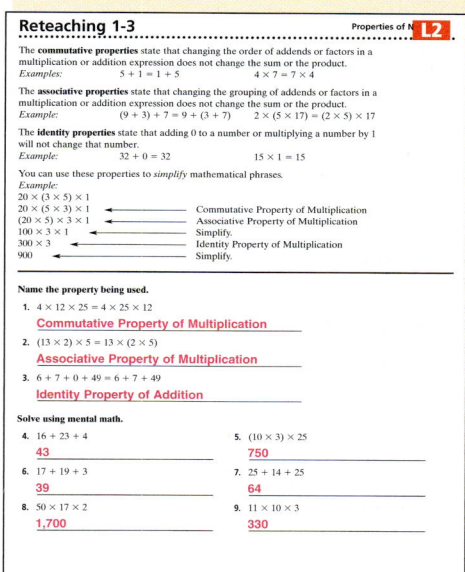

Alternative Assessment

Have students write and label an example of the commutative, associative, and identity properties for addition. Repeat for multiplication.

Test Prep

Resources

For additional practice with a variety of test item formats:
• Test-Taking Strategies, p. 51
• Test Prep, p. 55
• Test-Taking Strategies with Transparencies

15

Objective
To use the order of operations to simplify expressions and solve problems

Examples
1. Finding the Value of Expressions
2. Using Expressions to Solve Problems

Math Understandings: p. 2D

Math Background

The order of operations for expressions involving parentheses (grouping symbols) and the four basic operations are presented in this lesson. The order of operations is accepted worldwide. Without agreement, simple expressions such as $5 + 3 \cdot 2$ could have two different answers $(5 + 6 = 11$ or $8 \cdot 2 = 16)$. The order of operations ensures that everyone obtains the same result, which in this expression is 11.

More Math Background: p. 2D

Lesson Planning and Resources

See p. 2E for a list of the resources that support this lesson.

Bell Ringer Practice

✓ **Check Skills You'll Need**
Use student page, transparency, or PowerPoint. For intervention, direct students to:
Estimating With Whole Numbers
Lesson 1-2
Extra Skills and Word Problems Practice, Ch. 1

✓ **Check Skills You'll Need**

1. Vocabulary Review
Name the property that lets you write $35 + 5 = 5 + 35$.

Use mental math to find each sum.

2. $35 + 17 + 5$ **57**

3. $22 + 0 + 8$ **30**

4. $124 + (25 + 26)$ **175**

 **for Help**
Lesson 1-2

Check Skills You'll Need

1. Comm. Prop. of Add.

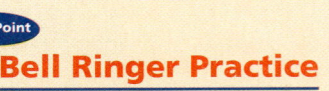

Players must put on soccer equipment— socks, shoes with cleats, and shin guards—in a certain order.

What You'll Learn

To use the order of operations to simplify expressions and solve problems

🔊 **New Vocabulary** order of operations, expression

Why Learn This?

A problem such as $18 + 11 \times 6$ requires you to do more than one operation. To find the correct answer, you need to know which operation to do first. Should you add first, or multiply?

Diane's Work (addition first)

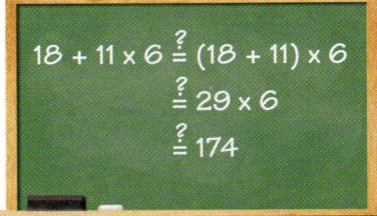

$$18 + 11 \times 6 \stackrel{?}{=} (18 + 11) \times 6$$
$$\stackrel{?}{=} 29 \times 6$$
$$\stackrel{?}{=} 174$$

Dana's Work (multiplication first)

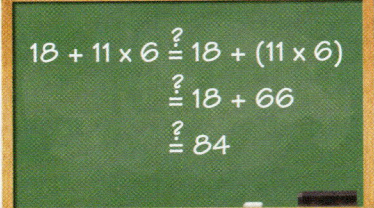

$$18 + 11 \times 6 \stackrel{?}{=} 18 + (11 \times 6)$$
$$\stackrel{?}{=} 18 + 66$$
$$\stackrel{?}{=} 84$$

Only one answer is correct. To make sure everyone gets the same value, you use the **order of operations.**

KEY CONCEPTS   **Order of Operations**

1. Do all operations within parentheses first.
2. Multiply and divide in order from left to right.
3. Add and subtract in order from left to right.

Based on the order of operations, you multiply before you add.

$$18 + 11 \times 6 = 18 + 66 = 84$$

So Dana's answer is correct.

An **expression** is a mathematical phrase that contains numbers and operation symbols. In the work above, $18 + 11 \times 6$ is an expression.

Differentiated **Instruction** **Solutions for All Learners**

Special Needs **L1**
Have students rewrite, in shorthand, the order of operations. For example, **1.** ( ); **2.** × or ÷; **3.** + or −. They can keep this list on hand as they work through the problems in this lesson.

learning style: visual

Below Level **L2**
Discuss with students the importance of parentheses in this set of exercises.

$(8 + 3) \cdot (4 - 2)$ **22** $(8 + 3) \cdot 4 - 2$ **42**

$8 + (3 \cdot 4) - 2$ **18** $8 + 3 \cdot (4 - 2)$ **14**

learning style: visual

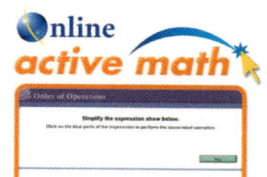

For: Order of Operations Activity
Use: Interactive Textbook, 1-4

EXAMPLE   Finding the Value of Expressions

1 Find the value of each expression.

a. $6 + 96 \div 3 = 6 + 32$ ← Divide 96 by 3.
$= 38$ ← Add.

b. $30 - (6 + 2) \times 3 = 30 - 8 \times 3$ ← Add 6 and 2 within the parentheses.
$= 30 - 24$ ← Multiply 8 and 3.
$= 6$ ← Subtract 24 from 30.

✓ Quick Check

1. Find the value of each expression.
a. $34 + 5 \times 2 - 17$ **27**   b. $(6 + 18) \div 3 \times 2$ **16**

EXAMPLE   Using Expressions to Solve Problems

2 **Multiple Choice** Suppose you buy the items shown on the store receipt. What is the total cost of the items, including the tax?

Ⓐ $160   Ⓒ $190
Ⓑ $170   Ⓓ $1,570

CRAWFORD'S

ITEMS ORDERED
JEANS   3@ $35.00 EACH
DISCOUNT   -$5.00
SHIRTS   4@ $15.00 EACH

TAX $10.00
TOTAL

You can write an expression to help you find the total cost.

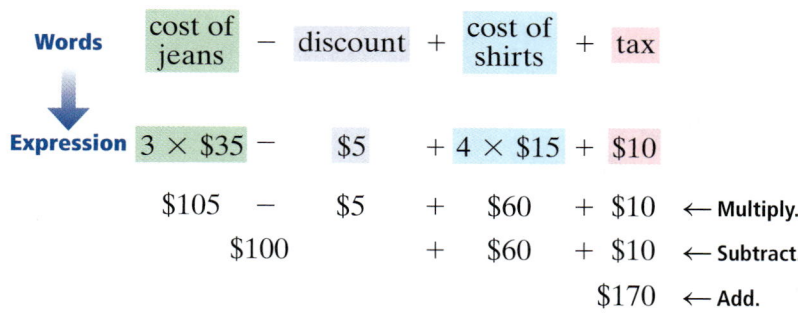

Words   cost of jeans   −   discount   +   cost of shirts   +   tax

Expression $3 \times \$35$ − $5   + $4 \times \$15$ + $10

$105   − $5   + $60   + $10   ← Multiply.
$100   + $60   + $10   ← Subtract.
                     $170   ← Add.

The total cost is $170. The correct answer is choice B.

✓ Quick Check

2. You are paid $7 per hour to rake leaves. Your brother is paid $5 per hour. You worked 4 hours and your brother worked 3 hours. How much did the two of you earn together? **$43**

1-4   Order of Operations   **17**

Test Prep Tip
You can model a problem using words that describe the quantities in the problem.

2. Teach

Activity Lab
Use before the lesson.

All in One Teaching Resources
Activity Lab 1-4: Order of Operations

Guided Instruction

Example 1
Ask: *What do the parentheses in an expression indicate?*
Operations in parentheses need to be done first.

Example 2
Ask: *Why do you subtract $5 before adding $10?* **Subtracting $5 comes before adding $10 when working left to right.**

Teaching Tip
You may want to share <u>M</u>y <u>D</u>ear <u>A</u>unt <u>S</u>ally with students so that they remember to <u>M</u>ultiply, <u>D</u>ivide, <u>A</u>dd, and <u>S</u>ubtract in that order.

PowerPoint
Additional Examples

1 Find the value of
$20 - 5 \times 8 \div 2$. **0**

2 Find the value of
$\$350 + 8 \times \$50 - 2 \times \$350$.
$50

All in One Teaching Resources
• Daily Notetaking Guide 1-4 **L3**
• Adapted Notetaking 1-4 **L1**

Closure

• *What is an expression?* **a mathematical phrase that contains numbers and operation symbols**
• *What is the order in which operations must be performed?* **Do all operations within parentheses; multiply and divide in order from left to right; add and subtract in order from left to right.**

Advanced Learners   L4
Have students use 3 numbers, 2 operation signs, and 1 set of parentheses to write as many expressions as possible and simplify them. **Sample: 12, 7, 2, +, −; 12 − (2 + 7) = 3, and so on**

learning style: visual

English Language Learners   ELL
In Example 2, make sure students understand what the *tax* (sales tax) means. Also, make sure they understand what a *discount* is, and why it is calculated before the tax is added.

learning style: verbal

3. Practice

Assignment Guide

Check Your Understanding
Go over Exercises 1–8 in class before assigning the Homework Exercises.

Homework Exercises
A Practice by Example   9–26
B Apply Your Skills   27–33
C Challenge   34
Test Prep and
   Mixed Review   35–40

Homework Quick Check
To check students' understanding of key skills and concepts, go over Exercises 15, 24, 28, 32, and 33.

Differentiated Instruction **Resources**

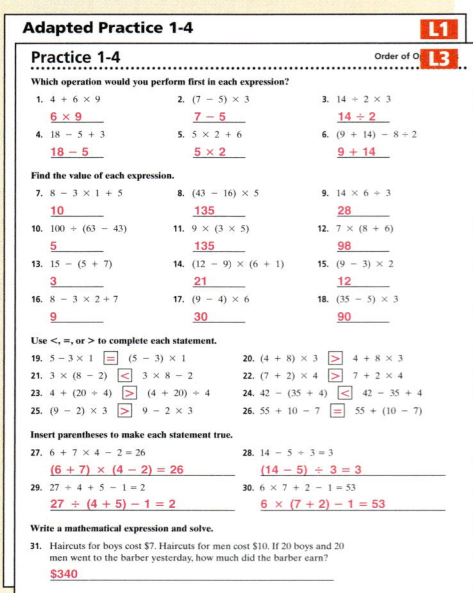

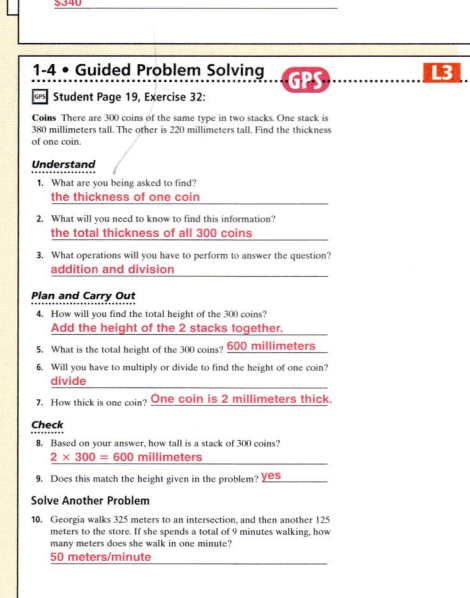

✓ Check Your Understanding

1. **Vocabulary** A mathematical phrase that contains numbers and operation symbols is a(n) __?__.   **expression**

2. **Error Analysis** A student says that the value of the expression $5 + 25 \div 5$ is 6. What error did the student make?
The student added before dividing.

Which operation should you do first?

3. $6 - 2 \times 2$ 4. $33 - (4 + 6)$ 5. $6 \times (2 - 5)$ 6. $7 + 4 \times 3$
multiplication   **addition**   **subtraction**   **multiplication**

Use <, =, or > to complete each statement.

7. $(1 + 2) \times 2 \; \boxed{>} \; 1 + 2 \times 2$ 8. $3 \times (4 - 2) \; \boxed{<} \; 3 \times 4 - 2$

Homework Exercises

For more exercises, see Extra Skills and Word Problems.

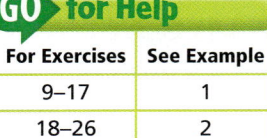 **GO for Help**

For Exercises	See Example
9–17	1
18–26	2

A **Find the value of each expression.**

9. $450 \div 45 + 5$ **15**   10. $29 - 4 \times 7$ **1**   11. $16 + 36 \div 12$ **19**

12. $14 - (7 + 5) \div 2$ **8**   13. $(13 + 21) \times 2$ **68**   14. $400 \div (44 - 24)$ **20**

15. $16 - (2 + 4) \times 2$ **4**   16. $26 + 5 - 4 \times 3$ **19**   17. $13 + 5 \times 12 - 4$ **69**

18. $4 \times \$40 - \$5$ **$155**   19. $\$50 + \$20 \div 2$ **$60**

20. $\$100 - 2 \times \$30$ **$40**   21. $\$35 \times 2 + \$42 \div 2$ **$91**

22. $3(\$28 + \$32) - \$10$ **$170**   23. $\$15 \times 10 + \$30 \times 2$ **$210**

24. $(\$45 \times 4 + \$125 \times 3) \div 5$ **$111**   25. $(\$75 \times 5) + (\$25 \times 6) - \$10$ **$515**

26. **Marbles** You buy 2 red rainbow marbles for 50¢ each, 3 bumblebee marbles for 90¢ each, and 2 tricolor marbles for 65¢ each. Find the total cost of the marbles. **500¢ or $5**

B **GPS** 27. **Guided Problem Solving** A group of 25 students and 3 adults goes to an art museum. Admission costs $6 per student and $9 per adult. There is a $15 discount for groups of 20 or more. Find the total cost for the trip. **$162**
   - **Make a Plan** Write an expression for the cost of both the students and the adults. Next, find the total cost of the trip.
   - **Carry Out the Plan** An expression for the total cost for students and adults is $25 \times \$\blacksquare + 3 \times \$\blacksquare - \blacksquare$.

33. **First subtract the numbers in parentheses. Then divide 8 by 4. Multiply that result by 6. Then add to the difference found in the parentheses.**

Careers Nutritionists help people plan their diets.

Reasoning Insert parentheses to make each statement true.

28. $11 - 7 \div 2 = 2$
$(11 - 7) \div 2 = 2$

29. $1 + 2 \times 15 - 4 = 33$
$(1 + 2) \times (15 - 4) = 33$

Nutrition Use the table to answer Exercises 30 and 31.

30. How many grams of protein are in 6 oz of chicken and 2 c of vegetables? **46 g**

31. How many grams of protein are in 9 oz of chicken, 2 c of vegetables, and 1 c of rice? **76 g**

Food	Serving Size	Protein
Chicken	3 oz	21 g
Vegetables	1 c	2 g
Rice	1 c	9 g

32. **Coins** There are 300 coins of the same type in two stacks. One stack is 380 millimeters tall. The other is 220 millimeters tall. Find the thickness of one coin. **2 mm**

33. **Writing in Math** Explain the steps you would use to find the value of the expression $8 \div 4 \times 6 + (7 - 5)$. **See margin.**

C **34.** **Challenge** Copy the statement: $14 \blacksquare 7 \blacksquare 2 \blacksquare 3 = 7$. Insert operations symbols to make the statement true.
$14 \div 7 + 2 + 3 = 7$

Test Prep and Mixed Review
Practice

Multiple Choice

35. A group of 11 boys and 9 girls goes to a movie. Admission costs $7 per person. Which expression does NOT show the total amount the group will pay? **B**
- Ⓐ $\$7 \times (11 + 9)$
- Ⓑ $\$7 \times 11 \times 9$
- Ⓒ $(\$7 \times 11) + (\$7 \times 9)$
- Ⓓ $\$7 \times 20$

36. There are 6 bike racks at a park. Each bike rack can hold 14 bikes. If there are 11 bikes, which method can be used to find the number of empty spaces in the bike racks? **J**
- Ⓕ Add 6 to the product of 11 and 14.
- Ⓖ Subtract 6 from the product of 11 and 14.
- Ⓗ Add 11 to the product of 6 and 14.
- Ⓙ Subtract 11 from the product of 6 and 14.

37. For which sum is 2,200 a reasonable estimate? **B**
- Ⓐ $422 + 1,085 + 897$
- Ⓑ $280 + 1,375 + 466$
- Ⓒ $605 + 786 + 1,022$
- Ⓓ $1,532 + 963 + 45$

Estimate using compatible numbers.

38. $57 \div 6$ **about 10** **39.** 14×4 **about 60** **40.** $627 \div 23$ **about 30**

Alternative Assessment

Have students bring to class various empty food containers that show nutritional information. They can use the information about protein, carbohydrates, vitamins, and so forth to create word problems similar to Exercises 30 and 31. Students can challenge classmates to solve their problems.

Test Prep

Resources
For additional practice with a variety of test item formats:
- Test-Taking Strategies, p. 51
- Test Prep, p. 55
- Test-Taking Strategies with Transparencies

PowerPoint
Lesson Quiz

Evaluate each expression.

1. $9 + 5 \times 6 - 7$ **32**

2. $(12 - 8) \times 10 \div 5$ **8**

3. $(4 \times 62) + (4 \times 85)$ **588**

4. $200 - (99 \div 3) \times 2$ **134**

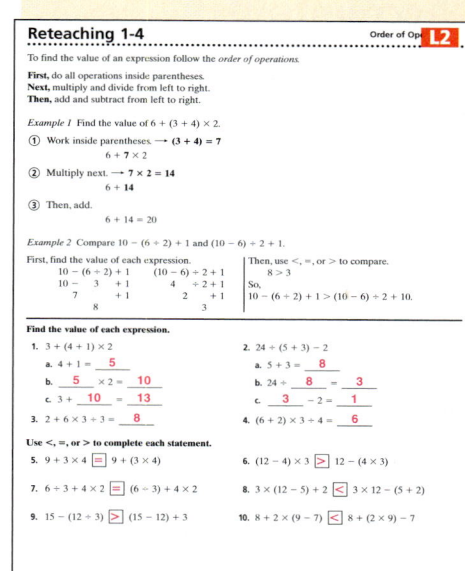

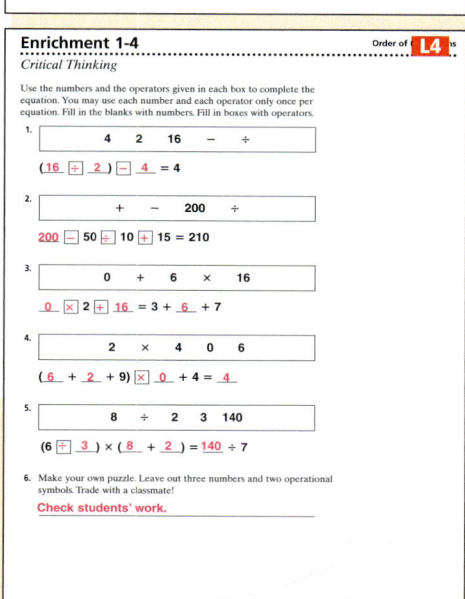

Accountant

Students should be aware of the importance of accountants to businesses large and small. Many accountants set up private practices. Others become financial officers in large corporations. Mathematics is a critical part of any accountant's education.

Guided Instruction

Show students examples of financial statements such as tax forms, profit and loss statements, and statements of operating expenses. Have students identify where mathematics is used. Ask students if any family members or friends are accountants or have jobs in financial services. Ask students to discuss the skills the person needs. Then, ask questions, such as:

- *How do you think an accountant spends his or her working day?*
- *What math skills would an accountant need?*
- *Why are accountants important to businesses large and small?*

Checkpoint Quiz 1 | **Lessons 1-1 through 1-4**

Use < or > to complete each statement.

1. 455 $>$ 45 **2.** 39,382 $<$ 39,832 **3.** 21,040 $>$ 20,401

Use rounding or compatible numbers to estimate each answer.

4. 553 − 385 **about 200** **5.** 5,964 + 3,088 **about 9,000** **6.** 1,085 ÷ 523 **about 2**

Use mental math to find each answer.

7. 19 + 7 + 31 **57** **8.** (6 + 18) + 14 **38** **9.** 25 × 10 × 4 **1,000**

Find the value of each expression.

10. 30 − 6 × 5 **0** **11.** (12 + 23) × 2 **70** **12.** $60 + $30 ÷ 3 **$70**

13. The peregrine falcon can fly about 280 feet in one second. About how far can it fly in 4 seconds? **about 1,200 feet**

14. Jupiter has many satellites. Leda is 6,893,000 miles from Jupiter. Himalia is 7,134,000 miles from Jupiter. Lysithea is about 7,283,000 miles from Jupiter. Elara is 7,293,000 miles from Jupiter. Order the distances from least to greatest. **6,893,000; 7,134,000; 7,283,000; 7,293,000**

 **WORK** **Accountant**

Accountants usually work in some area of finance. They must enjoy working with numbers and know how to budget money well.

They use mathematics to prepare and analyze financial reports, tax returns, and budgets. Accountants also help individuals and companies track financial history and plan for future growth.

Accountants' reports help people make good business decisions.

Go Online **PHSchool.com** **For:** Information on accounting **Web Code:** aqb-2031

20

Exploring Decimal Models

You can use grid models or base-ten pieces to represent decimals. For both types of models, the large square represents the whole.

Grid Models

Tenths model   Hundredths model

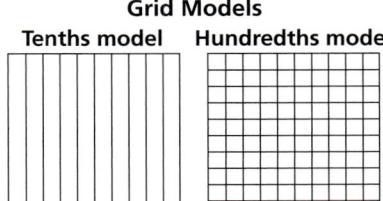

Base-Ten Pieces

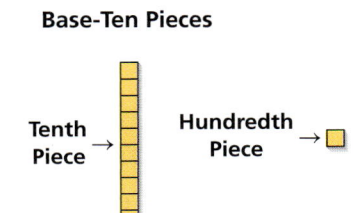

Tenth Piece →   Hundredth Piece →

EXAMPLE   Modeling Decimals

Write the decimal for the model below, in words and in numerals.

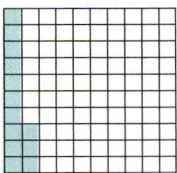

There are 100 squares. Thirteen squares are shaded.

Words   thirteen hundredths
↓
Numerals   0.13

Exercises

Write a decimal for each model.

1. 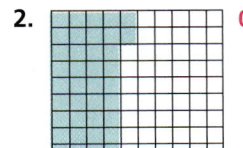   0.3

2. 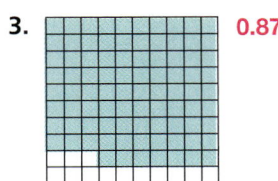   0.42

3.   0.87

Model each decimal using a grid model or base-ten pieces. 4–7. See back of book.

4. two tenths

5. forty hundredths

6. eighty-five hundredths

7. a. Draw models for five tenths and for fifty hundredths.
   b. **Number Sense** Show that the decimals are equal.

4.

5.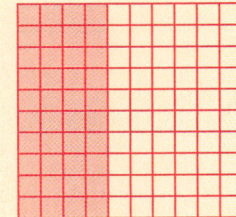

6.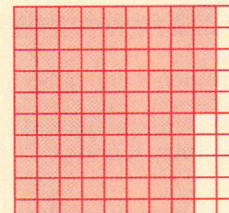

Activity Lab

Exploring Decimal Models

Students use grid models or base-ten pieces to represent or model decimals.

Guided Instruction

Example

Model the decimal. Have students model the decimal at their desks and write the decimal in words and with numerals. Guide them to see that 13 of 100 squares are shaded so the decimal is 0.13. Point out the convention of using a 0 before the decimal point for decimals less than 1.

Exercises

Have students work independently or in pairs on the Exercises. Suggest they use grids or base-ten pieces to help as they do Exercise 7.

Differentiated Instruction

Visual or Tactile Learners
Ask students if they prefer grid models or base-ten pieces. Explain that both show the same information. Have students explain their preferences for visual or tactile models.

Resources

- Activity Lab 1-5: Decimal Counting
- grid models
- base-ten pieces
- Classroom Aid 2, 9, 10
- Student Manipulatives Kit

Objective
To read, write, and round decimals

Examples
1 Writing a Decimal in Words
2 Standard Form and Expanded Form
3 Rounding Decimals

Math Understandings: p. 2D

Math Background

The number 341 is read as "three hundred forty-one." The decimal 3.41 is read as "three and forty-one hundredths." When writing decimals as word expressions, "and" is used to represent the decimal point in decimals greater than 1. So "and" is not used in whole numbers or decimals less than 1.

More Math Background: p. 2D

Lesson Planning and Resources

See p. 2E for a list of the resources that support this lesson.

Bell Ringer Practice

✓ **Check Skills You'll Need**
Use student page, transparency, or PowerPoint. For intervention, direct students to:
Understanding Whole Numbers
Lesson 1-1
Extra Skills and Word Problems Practice, Ch. 1

✓ Check Skills You'll Need

1. **Vocabulary Review**
Write one thousand, three hundred twenty-one in *standard form.* **1,321**

Write each whole number in words.

2. 28   3. 8,672

4. 612,980   5. 58,026

GO for Help
Lesson 1-1

Check Skills You'll Need

2. twenty-eight

3. eight thousand, six hundred seventy-two

4. six hundred twelve thousand, nine hundred eighty

5. fifty-eight thousand, twenty-six

1a. sixty-seven and three tenths

b. six and seven hundred thirty-four thousandths

c. sixty-seven hundredths

What You'll Learn

To read, write, and round decimals

🔊 **New Vocabulary** expanded form

Why Learn This?

Decimal numbers allow you to write very precise values. In sports, the difference between first place and second place sometimes depends on decimal places.

You can extend the place value chart to include values for decimal places. When you read a decimal that is greater than 1, read the decimal point as "and."

EXAMPLE Writing a Decimal in Words

1 **Fuel** The price of a gallon of gasoline is $2.459. Write 2.459 in words.

Begin by writing 2.459 in a place value chart.

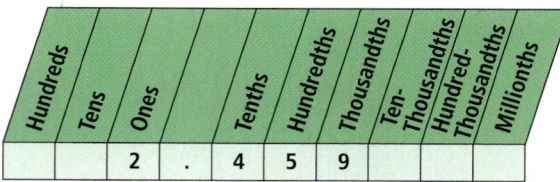

Hundreds	Tens	Ones		Tenths	Hundredths	Thousandths	Ten-Thousandths	Hundred-Thousandths	Millionths
		2	.	4	5	9			

2.459   ← **Three decimal places indicate thousandths.**

two and four hundred fifty-nine thousandths

✓ Quick Check

1. Write each decimal in words. **1a–c. See left.**
   a. 67.3   b. 6.734   c. 0.67

Differentiated Instruction Solutions for All Learners

Special Needs L1
For Example 3, it might help students to highlight the numbers they are rounding to, even if they are underlined. Remind them to look to the right of the highlighted number every time they round.

learning style: visual

Below Level L2
Have students write decimals in expanded form before writing them in words. For Example 1, students would first write 2.459 as 2 + 0.4 + 0.05 + 0.009.

learning style: visual

You can write decimals in both standard form and expanded form. **Expanded form** is a sum that shows the place and value of each digit of a number.

Standard Form		**Expanded Form**		
0.75	=	0.7	+	0.05
↑		↑		↑
seventy-five hundredths		seven tenths	+	five hundredths

 **EXAMPLE** **Standard Form and Expanded Form**

② **Sports** At a gymnastics meet, the best score on the pommel horse was nine and forty-two thousandths. Write the score in standard form and in expanded form.

9.   ← **Write the whole number part. Place the decimal point.**

9.■■■   ← **Thousandths is three places to the right of the decimal point.**

9.■42   ← **Place 42 to the far right.**

9.042   ← **Insert a zero for tenths.**

Standard form: 9.042   Expanded form: 9 + 0.04 + 0.002

✓ **Quick Check**

2. The winning car in a race won by fifteen hundredths of a second. Write the decimal in standard and expanded forms.
   0.15; 0.1 + 0.05

Rounding decimals is similar to rounding whole numbers.

The value to the right of 3 →	0.3**2**	0.3**6**	← The value to the right of 3
is < 5, so round **down** to	↓	↓	is ≥ 5. So round **up**.
nearest tenth.	0.3	0.4	

 **EXAMPLE** **Rounding Decimals**

③ Round 0.426 to the nearest hundredth.

0.42**6**   ← **Look at the digit to the right of the hundredths place.**
  ↑
  6 is ≥ 5, so round up.

So 0.426 rounded to the nearest hundredth is 0.43.

✓ **Quick Check**

3. Round each decimal to the underlined place.
   a. 2.3<u>4</u>28 **2.34**   b. 0.173<u>4</u>7 **0.1735**   c. 9.0<u>5</u>3 **9.1**

2. Teach

Activity Lab

Use before the lesson.
Student Edition Activity Lab, Hands On 1-5a, Exploring Decimal Models, p. 21

All in One Teaching Resources
Activity Lab 1-5: Decimal Counting

Guided Instruction

Example 1
Ask: *Why do you think the gasoline price is $2.459 rather than $2.50?* Sample: Purchasers see that the price is under $2.50 and it seems cheaper.

Example 3
Ask: *When rounding a decimal to a given place, at which place do you look first?* at the place to the right of the given place

PowerPoint
Additional Examples

① Write 1.0936 in words. one and nine hundred thirty-six ten-thousandths

② There are four thousand five hundred thirty-six ten-thousandths kilograms in one pound. Write this number in standard and expanded form.
0.4536;
0.4 + 0.05 + 0.003 + 0.0006

③ Round 0.539 to the nearest tenth. 0.5

All in One Teaching Resources
• Daily Notetaking Guide 1-5 **L3**
• Adapted Notetaking 1-5 **L1**

Closure

• *When writing a number in words, when do you use "and"?*
Use "and" for the decimal point with numbers greater than 1.

Advanced Learners **L4**	**English Language Learners** **ELL**
Have students create a chart with three headings—*expanded form, standard form,* and *words.* Have them use selected numbers from Exercises 1–33 to complete the chart.	Have students make a chart of number words that includes decimal numerals.
learning style: visual	learning style: visual

23

Assignment Guide

Check Your Understanding
Go over Exercises 1–10 in class before assigning the Homework Exercises.

Homework Exercises
A Practice by Example 11–33
B Apply Your Skills 34–44
C Challenge 45
Test Prep and
Mixed Review 46–50

Homework Quick Check
To check students' understanding of key skills and concepts, go over Exercises 19, 28, 36, 43, and 44.

Differentiated Instruction **Resources**

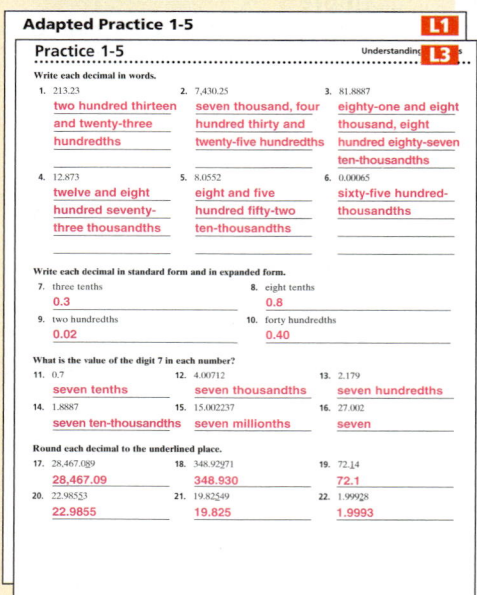

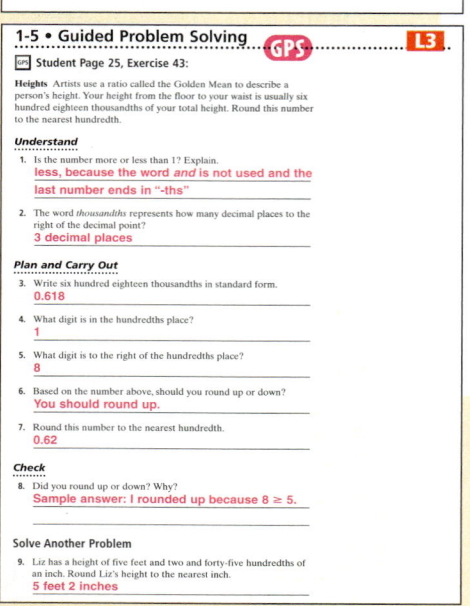

Check Your Understanding

1. **Number Sense** In the number 12.057, which digit has the greater value, the 5 or the 7? Explain. **5; it is in the hundredths place. 7 is in the thousandths place.**
2. **Open-Ended** Write a decimal with 4 decimal places in words and in standard form. Then round the decimal to the nearest hundredth. **Check students' work.**

Find the value of the digit 3 in each number.

3. 0.3 **3 tenths**   4. 0.237 **3 hundredths**   5. 7.553 **3 thousandths**   6. 8.2103 **3 ten-thousandths**

Write each decimal in expanded form.

7. 1.2 **1 + 0.2**   8. 8.4 **8 + 0.4**   9. 7.52 **7 + 0.5 + 0.02**   10. 0.239 **0.2 + 0.03 + 0.009**

Homework Exercises

For more exercises, see Extra Skills and Word Problems.

GO for Help

For Exercises	See Example
11–20	1
21–25	2
26–33	3

A Write each decimal in words. **11–20. See margin.**

11. 2.3   12. 6.02   13. 0.006   14. 2.061   15. 3.08

16. 0.40   17. 50.603   18. 1.28   19. 3.004   20. 0.23

Write each decimal in standard form and in expanded form.

21. forty and nine thousandths
40.009; 40 + 0.009
22. sixty-four hundredths
0.64; 0.6 + 0.04
23. seven hundred thousandths
0.700; 0.7
24. nine and twenty hundredths
9.20; 9 + 0.2

25. **Running** A marathon is twenty-six and two tenths miles long. Write the number in standard form and in expanded form. **26.2; 26 + 0.2**

Round each decimal to the underlined place.

26. 0.6<u>8</u>3 **0.68**   27. 2.<u>7</u>248 **2.7**   28. 3.41<u>4</u>69 **3.4147**   29. 10.9<u>5</u>6 **10.96**

30. 6.2<u>4</u>7 **6.25**   31. 0.<u>5</u>54 **0.6**   32. 4.0<u>6</u>25 **4.1**   33. 4.8<u>9</u>6 **4.90**

B 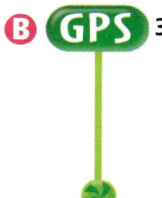 34. **Guided Problem Solving** The diameter of a white blood cell is twelve ten-thousandths of a centimeter. Round the diameter to the nearest thousandth of a centimeter. **0.001**
• What is twelve ten-thousandths in standard form?
• Is the digit to the right of the thousandths place *less than, greater than,* or *equal to* 5?

11. **two and three tenths**
12. **six and two hundredths**
13. **six thousandths**
14. **two and sixty-one thousandths**
15. **three and eight hundredths**
16. **forty hundredths**
17. **fifty and six hundred three thousandths**
18. **one and twenty-eight hundredths**
19. **three and four thousandths**
20. **twenty-three hundredths**
39. **4 ten-thousandths, or 0.0004**
40. **4 hundredths, or 0.04**
41. **4 thousandths, or 0.004**
42. **4 hundreds, or 400**

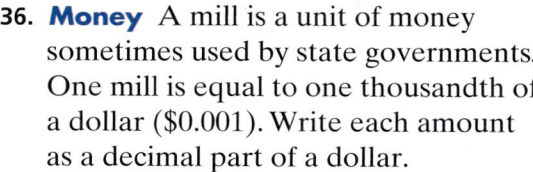
35. B: $0.9 million; $900,000

C: $1.6 million; $1,600,000

35. According to the bar graph, sales for Company A were 0.7 million dollars. As a whole number, this is written $700,000. Write the annual sales for each company as a decimal and as a whole number. **See left.**

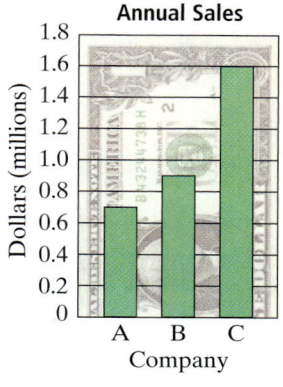

Annual Sales

36. **Money** A mill is a unit of money sometimes used by state governments. One mill is equal to one thousandth of a dollar ($0.001). Write each amount as a decimal part of a dollar.

a. 6 mills
$.006

b. 207 mills
$.207

c. 53 mills
$.053

Find the value of the digit 4 in each number. **39–42. See margin.**

37. 0.4
4 tenths, or 0.4

38. 42.3926
4 tens, or 40

39. 17.55643

40. 1.2468

41. 121.004

42. 425.209

43. **GPS** Artists use a ratio called the Golden Mean to describe a person's height. Your height from the floor to your waist is usually six hundred eighteen thousandths of your total height. Round this number to the nearest hundredth. **0.62**

44. **Writing in Math** Describe how the values of the digit 2 in the number 22.222 change as you move from right to left. **The value of each 2 is 10 times greater than the value of the 2 to its right.**

C 45. **Challenge** Extend the place value chart to write 0.0000001 in words. **one ten-millionth**

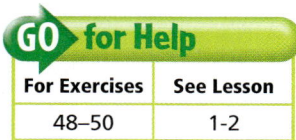

Test Prep and Mixed Review
Practice

Multiple Choice

46. At a sale, shirts were marked down $5 each. Lisa bought 3 shirts for $39. Find the price of each shirt before the sale. **C**

Ⓐ $7 Ⓑ $13 Ⓒ $18 Ⓓ $24

47. You and three friends bought a large pizza for $13.00. Each of you paid an equal share of the cost. Which method can be used to find the amount each person paid? **H**

Ⓕ Divide 13.00 by 3. Ⓗ Divide 13.00 by 4.
Ⓖ Multiply 13.00 by 4. Ⓙ Multiply 13.00 by 3.

Mental Math **Use mental math to find each sum or product.**

48. $(20 \times 3) \times 5$ **300** **49.** $70 + 0$ **70** **50.** $2 \times (42 \times 5)$ **420**

GO for Help

For Exercises	See Lesson
48–50	1-2

---

4. Assess & Reteach

PowerPoint
Lesson Quiz

1. Write 99.124 in expanded form.
90 + 9 + 0.1 + 0.02 + 0.004

2. Write fifty-five and thirty-four thousandths in standard form.
55.034

3. Write 500.04 in words. **five hundred and four hundredths**

Round each decimal to the underlined place.

4. 1.5<u>4</u>9 **1.55** **5.** 0.3<u>3</u>9 **0.3**

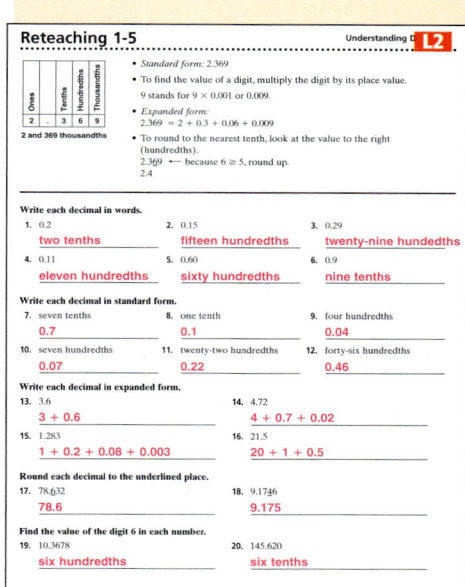

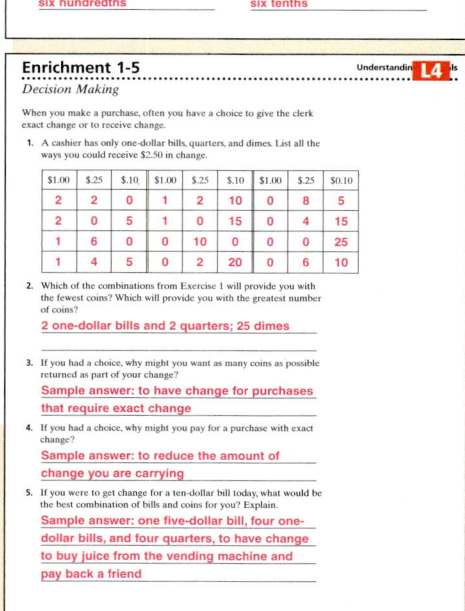

Alternative Assessment

Each student in a pair writes three decimals greater than one. Partners exchange papers and write each other's decimals in expanded form and in words. They then round each decimal to the nearest tenth.

Test Prep

Resources
For additional practice with a variety of test item formats:
• Test-Taking Strategies, p. 51
• Test Prep, p. 55
• Test-Taking Strategies with Transparencies

Objective
To compare and order decimals using models and place value

Examples
1   Using Models to Compare Decimals
2   Comparing Decimals
3   Ordering Decimals

Math Understandings: p. 2D

Math Background

The number 0.6, or 6 tenths, is equivalent to 0.60, or 60 hundredths. Place values are used to compare decimal numbers, in a similar way to how they are used to compare whole numbers. For example, 0.56 is less than 0.6 because 56 hundredths is less than 60 hundredths.

More Math Background: p. 2D

Lesson Planning and Resources

See p. 2E for a list of the resources that support this lesson.

Bell Ringer Practice

✓ Check Skills You'll Need
Use student page, transparency, or PowerPoint. For intervention, direct students to:
Understanding Whole Numbers
Lesson 1-1
Extra Skills and Word Problems Practice, Ch. 1

26

✓ Check Skills You'll Need

1. Vocabulary Review
Explain how to *order* numbers.

Use < or > to complete each statement.

2. 430 $\boxed{>}$ 340

3. 2,005 $\boxed{<}$ 2,050

GO for Help
Lesson 1-1

Check Skills You'll Need

1. **Answers may vary. Sample: Compare the digits, starting with the greatest place value.**

GO for Help

For help using a number line, go to Lesson 1-1, Example 2.

What You'll Learn

To compare and order decimals using models and place value

Why Learn This?

Many measurements are recorded using decimals. You can use decimals to compare measurements in many applications, including construction and science.

You can use grid models and number lines to compare decimals.

EXAMPLE   Using Models to Compare Decimals

❶ Use models to compare 0.4 and 0.36. Which number is greater?

Method 1 Use grid models.

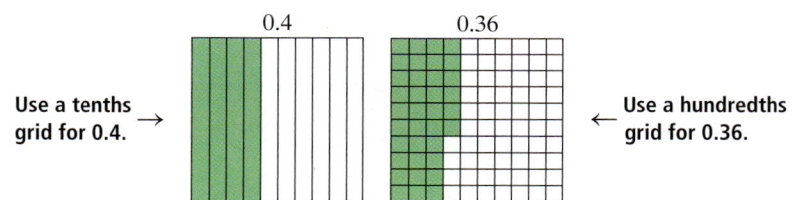

Use a tenths grid for 0.4. →   ← Use a hundredths grid for 0.36.

A greater area is shaded for 0.4 than for 0.36. So 0.4 is greater than 0.36.

Method 2 Use a number line.

← Make a number line showing hundredths.

Since 0.4 is to the right of 0.36, 0.4 is greater than 0.36.

✓ Quick Check

See back of book.

1. Use models to compare 0.59 and 0.6. Which number is greater?

26   Chapter 1   Whole Numbers and Decimals

Differentiated Instruction   Solutions for All Learners

Special Needs L1
Before the lesson, review how numbers on a number line are ordered. Remind students numbers increase from left to right and decrease from right to left on the number line. This will help students compare decimals using a number line model.

learning style: visual

Below Level L2
Have students compare decimals that can be represented by dollars and cents, such as $5.10 and $1.05.

learning style: visual

EXAMPLE **Comparing Decimals**

② Use <, =, or > to complete the statement 3.18 ▮ 3.8.

Step 1 Line up the decimal points of the numbers.

3.18
3.80 ← Write a **zero** at the end of 3.8 so each number has two decimal places.

Step 2 Compare the digits starting with the highest place value.

The ones digits are the same.　　The tenths digits are different. 1 is less than 8.

3.18
3.80

Since 1 tenth < 8 tenths, 3.18 < 3.8.

✓ **Quick Check**

2. Use <, =, or > to complete the statement 0.56 ▮ 0.543.
    >

You can also use a number line or place value to order decimals.

EXAMPLE **Ordering Decimals**

③ **Science** Order these bodies of water from least to most salty.

Salt per Liter in Major Bodies of Water

Body of Water	Arctic Ocean	Dead Sea	Caspian Sea	Black Sea
Salt per Liter	0.032 kg	0.28 kg	0.013 kg	0.018 kg

SOURCE: *Natural Wonders of the World*

Compare the digits starting with the highest place values.

2 is the greatest tenths digit, so 0.280 is the greatest decimal.

0.032　　0.032　← In the remaining numbers, 3 is the
0.280　　0.280　　greatest hundredths digit. So 0.032 is
0.013　　0.013　　the second-greatest decimal.
0.018　　0.018　← 8 is the greatest thousandths digit. So
　　　　　　　　　　0.018 is the third-greatest decimal.

The decimals from least to greatest are 0.013, 0.018, 0.032, and 0.28. The bodies of water from least to most salty are the Caspian Sea, the Black Sea, the Arctic Ocean, and the Dead Sea.

✓ **Quick Check**

3. Order 3.059, 3.64, and 3.46 from least to greatest. **3.059, 3.46, 3.64**

1-6 Comparing and Ordering Decimals   **27**

---

2. Teach

Activity Lab

All in One Teaching Resources

Activity Lab 1-6: Ordering Decimals

Guided Instruction

Example 1
Ask: *How much greater is 0.4 than 0.36?* **0.04**

Example 2
Ask: *What is another way to write the comparison 3.18 < 3.8?*
3.8 > 3.18

Example 3
Ask: *Why do you write a zero at the end of 0.28?* **so each number has the same number of decimal places**

Technology Tip
You can use a computer program to order decimals automatically by using the *sort* feature. The decimals can be arranged in ascending or descending order.

Science
Sodium is an element found in the common compound sodium chloride, NaCl, or salt. Federal laws require manufacturers to list elements and compounds found in foods.

PowerPoint
Additional Examples

❶ Draw models for 0.5 and 0.54. Which number is greater?

 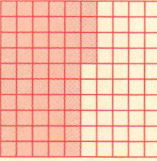

0.54 > 0.5

❷ Use <, =, or > to complete each statement.
 a. 0.1 ▮ 0.10 **=**
 b. 0.28 ▮ 0.82 **<**
 c. 0.6 ▮ 0.06 **>**

❸ Order 0.8, 0.084, 0.48, and 0.84 from least to greatest.
 0.084, 0.48, 0.8, 0.84

27

Closure

- Give three different methods for ordering decimals. **place value, a number line, and decimal models**
- Explain using place value to compare two decimals. **Sample: Annex zeros so that each number has the same number of decimal places. Then compare the decimal values as if they were whole numbers.**

● More Than One Way

Nutrition Use the table at the right. Order the foods by sodium content from least to greatest.

Food	Sodium
Half of a bagel	0.19 g
1 corn tortilla	0.04 g
3 pieces of Melba toast	0.12 g
5 crackers	0.195 g
1 slice of wheat bread	0.132 g

Elena's Method

I can use mental math to order the decimals.

$$0.19 \qquad 0.04 \qquad 0.12 \qquad 0.195 \qquad 0.132$$

First, I compare the tenths place in all the numbers. $0 < 1$, so 0.04 is the least number.

Next, I compare the hundredths place in the remaining numbers. $2 < 3 < 9$, so $0.12 < 0.13 < 0.19$.

Finally, I compare 0.19 and 0.195. Since $0.19 = 0.190$ and $0 < 5$, $0.19 < 0.195$.

The correct order is 0.04, 0.12, 0.132, 0.19, and 0.195. The foods from least to greatest sodium content are corn tortilla, Melba toast, wheat bread, bagel, and crackers.

Leon's Method

I can order the decimals by graphing them on a number line.

I see that all the numbers are between 0 and 0.2. I will make a number line marked in hundredths.

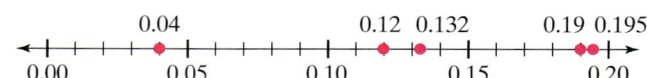

The decimals from least to greatest are 0.04, 0.12, 0.132, 0.19, and 0.195. The foods from least to greatest sodium content are corn tortilla, Melba toast, wheat bread, bagel, and crackers.

Choose a Method

Order the values 0.964, 0.26, 0.576, 0.059, 0.9, 0.96, and 0.264 from least to greatest. Describe your method and explain why you chose it.

0.059, 0.26, 0.264, 0.576, 0.9, 0.96, 0.964; check students' methods.

Check Your Understanding

1. **Reasoning** Explain how you can use place value to show that 1.679 > 1.697 is false. **See margin.**

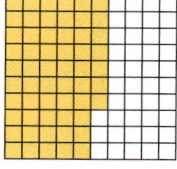

Two decimal models are shown at the left.

2. What decimal does each model represent? **0.57; 0.4**

3. Which decimal is greater? **0.57**

Select the value on the right that makes each statement true.

4. 2.37 > ■ 2.74, 2.32, 2.38
2.32

5. 0.57 < ■ 0.575, 0.502, 0.567
0.575

6. Order 1.2, 1.3, 0.9, and 0.8 from least to greatest.
0.8, 0.9, 1.2, 1.3

Homework Exercises

For more exercises, see Extra Skills and Word Problems.

GO for Help

For Exercises	See Example
7–9	1
10–15	2
16–21	3

A Use models to compare each pair of decimals. Which number is greater? **7–9. See back of book.**

7. 0.4 and 0.5
8. 0.35 and 0.53
9. 0.2 and 0.02

Use <, =, or > to complete each statement.

10. 0.3 **>** ■ 0.27
11. 5.7 **=** ■ 5.70
12. 0.601 **>** ■ 0.60

13. 0.4389 **<** ■ 0.45
14. 0.36 **<** ■ 0.365
15. 10.9 **>** ■ 10.02

Order each set of decimals from least to greatest.

16. 0.5, 0.7, 0.65
0.5, 0.65, 0.7

17. 17.1, 17.7, 13.7
13.7, 17.1, 17.7

18. 0.503, 0.53, 0.529
0.503, 0.529, 0.53

19. 9.2, 9.02, 9.209, 9.024
9.02, 9.024, 9.2, 9.209

20. 1.79, 1.991, 2.185, 1.979
1.79, 1.979, 1.991, 2.185

21. 5.5506, 5.5660, 5.561, 5.58
5.5506, 5.561, 5.5660, 5.58

B  22. **Guided Problem Solving** The United States won the women's Olympic 100-meter run in all the years listed. What is the fastest time listed?
- Is the fastest time the least or the greatest time? **10.54 s**
- What is the greatest place value in which the times differ?

Year	Time (seconds)
1984	10.97
1988	10.54
1992	10.82
1996	10.94
2000	10.75

SOURCE: *The World Almanac*

1. **Answers may vary. Sample: I would compare the values of numbers in similar places. In the hundredths place, 1.697 has 9 hundredths. 1.697 > 1.679**

---

3. Practice

Assignment Guide

Check Your Understanding
Go over Exercises 1–6 in class before assigning the Homework Exercises.

Homework Exercises

A	Practice by Example	7–21
B	Apply Your Skills	22–28
C	Challenge	29
	Test Prep and Mixed Review	30–33

Homework Quick Check
To check students' understanding of key skills and concepts, go over Exercises 9, 18, 23, 27, and 28.

Differentiated Instruction Resources

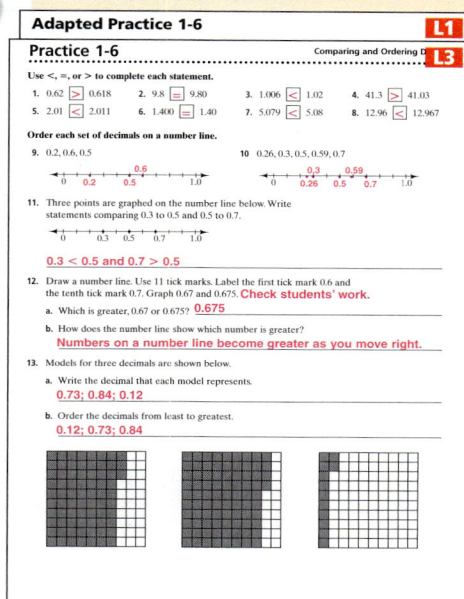

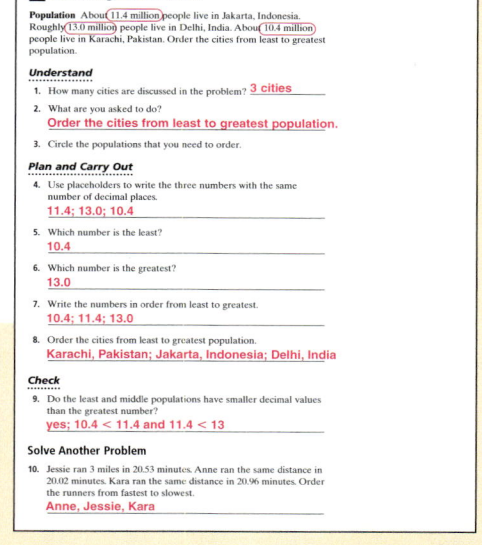

Lesson Quiz

1. Use a model to compare 0.29 and 0.3. Which number is greater? **0.3**

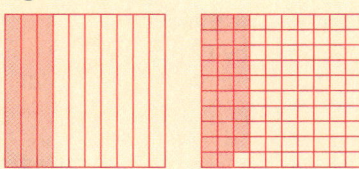

Use <, =, or > to complete each statement.

2. 0.499 ■ 0.501 **<**

3. 0.7 ■ 0.70 **=**

Order from least to greatest.

4. 0.54, 0.511, 0.5, 0.55 **0.5, 0.511, 0.54, 0.55**

5. 2.79, 2.7, 2.708, 2.77 **2.7, 2.708, 2.77, 2.79**

Teaching Tip
When comparing whole numbers and decimals, remind students to write the whole numbers using an equivalent form. So 13 would be written as 13.0 or 13.00.

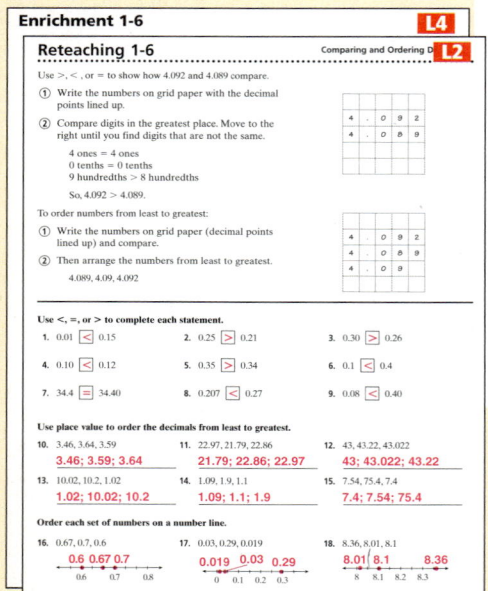

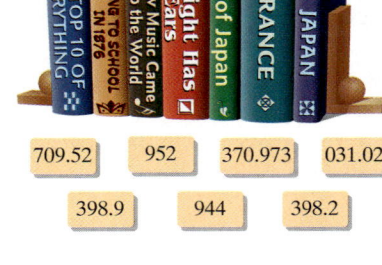

709.52   952   370.973   031.02

398.9   944   398.2

GO Online
Homework Video Tutor
Visit: PHSchool.com
Web Code: aqe-0106

23. **Choose a Method** The Dewey Decimal System assigns a number to every nonfiction book. The books at the left are in the correct order from left to right. Match each label to its book by ordering the labels from least to greatest. **031.02; 370.973; 398.2; 398.9; 709.52; 944; 952**

Select the values on the right that make each statement true.

24. $4.18 < \blacksquare < 4.25$ 4.25, 4.17, 4.27, 4.2025, 4.319, 4.198
    4.198, 4.2025

25. $0.57 < \blacksquare < 0.67$ 0.6595, 0.5025, 0.6095, 0.62, 0.567
    0.6595, 0.6095, 0.62

26. **Open-Ended** Write six numbers between 2.2 and 2.222. Order the numbers from least to greatest. **Answers may vary. Sample: 2.21, 2.211, 2.212, 2.213, 2.214, 2.215**

27. **Population** About 11.4 million people live in Jakarta, Indonesia. Roughly 13.0 million people live in Delhi, India. About 10.4 million people live in Karachi, Pakistan. Order the cities from least to greatest population. **Karachi, Jakarta, Delhi**

28. **Writing in Math** Alia ran the 100-yard dash in 11.88 seconds. Patty ran it in 11.9 seconds. Who ran faster? Explain. **Alia; 11.88 < 11.9**

29. **Challenge** Estimate the decimals represented by A, B, and C.

A ___ B ___ C
0.0 ___ 0.5 ___ 1.0
A: 0.25; B: 0.77; C: 1.05

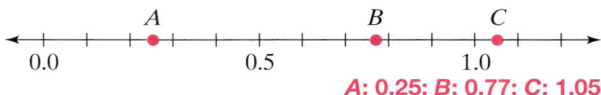

Test Prep and Mixed Review   **Practice**

Multiple Choice

30. Consuela measured the length of each finger on her hand. The table shows her data. Which list shows these measurements in order from least to greatest? **A**

    Ⓐ 4.5 cm, 6.5 cm, 6.7 cm, 7.1 cm
    Ⓑ 7.1 cm, 6.7 cm, 6.5 cm, 4.5 cm
    Ⓒ 7.1 cm, 6.5 cm, 6.7 cm, 4.5 cm
    Ⓓ 4.5 cm, 6.7 cm, 6.5 cm, 7.1 cm

Length of Each Finger	
Finger	**Length (cm)**
Index	6.5
Middle	7.1
Ring	6.7
Pinkie	4.5

31. Mrs. Xing drives at a constant speed of 60 miles per hour. How can you find how long it takes her to drive 420 miles? **H**
    Ⓕ Multiply 60 by 420.   Ⓗ Divide 420 by 60.
    Ⓖ Subtract 60 from 420.   Ⓙ Add 420 to 60.

GO for Help

For Exercises	See Lesson
32–33	1-3

Find the value of each expression.

32. $(\$15 \times 4) - (\$5 \times 9)$ **$15**   33. $15 + 4 \times 6 - 13$ **26**

Test Prep

Resources
For additional practice with a variety of test item formats:
• Test-Taking Strategies, p. 51
• Test Prep, p. 55
• Test-Taking Strategies with Transparencies

Using Models

You can use models to add or subtract two decimals.

EXAMPLE **Modeling Decimal Sums**

1 Use a model to find 0.4 + 0.03.

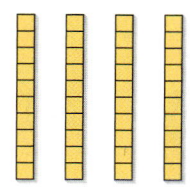 + 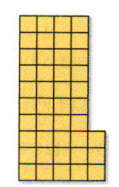 =

Start with four tenth pieces.   **Add three hundredth pieces.**   **Count the total number of hundredth pieces.**

● There are a total of 43 hundredths pieces, so 0.4 + 0.03 = 0.43.

EXAMPLE **Modeling Decimal Differences**

2 Use a model to find 1.4 − 0.6.

Use two tenths grids. Shade ten tenths in one grid and four tenths in the other grid.

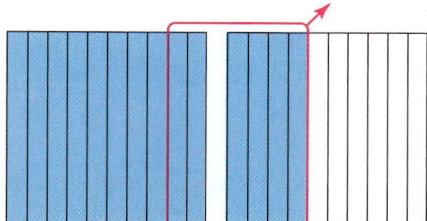

← Remove six tenths from fourteen tenths.

● There are eight tenths left, so 1.4 − 0.6 = 0.8.

Exercises

Use a model to find each sum or difference. 1–5. See back of book for model.

1. 0.1 + 0.8 **0.9**   **2.** 1.5 − 1.2 **0.3**   **3.** 0.06 + 0.55 **0.61**   **4.** 1.54 − 0.72 **0.82**

5. a. Use a model to find 0.41 + 0.59.
   b. Number Sense Explain why there are no hundredths in the answer.

Activity Lab

Using Models

Students use place-value pieces and grids to model finding decimal sums and differences.

Guided Instruction

Example 1

Model the addition on a hundredths grid on an overhead projector as students work along with you at their seats. You may wish to provide graph paper on which students can mark off 10 × 10 grids.

Example 2

Ask: *Look at the model for 1.4 − 0.6. How would you model the subtraction 1.4 − 0.65?* **Sample: Make two hundredths grids; Shade all 10 columns on one and 4 columns on the other to show 1.4; cross out or color in 6 columns and 5 small squares.**

Exercises

Have students work independently or in pairs on the Exercises. Suggest they use place-value pieces or grids to help them with any exercises for which they are having difficulty.

Differentiated Instruction

Tactile Learners
Students can model Example 2 using place-value pieces. Model the first decimal and remove the model of the second decimal.

Resources

- Activity Lab 1-7: Fraction Tiles
- place-value models
- grids
- Classroom Aid 2, 9, 10
- Student Manipulatives Kit

Objective
To add and subtract decimals and to solve problems involving decimals

Examples
1 Finding Decimal Sums
2 Using Front-End Estimation
3 Finding a Difference

Math Understandings: p. 2D

Math Background

The first step in adding and subtracting decimals is to line up the decimal points. Then the digits with the same place value are added or subtracted. When subtracting, you may need to annex zeros as placeholders and rename digits. For instance, $2.1 - 0.3$ involves renaming 2.1 as 1 and 11 tenths. $11 - 3$ results in 8 tenths, so $2.1 - 0.3$ is 1.8.

The lesson introduces front-end estimation and finding whether an answer is reasonable using estimation.

More Math Background: p. 2D

Lesson Planning and Resources

See p. 2E for a list of the resources that support this lesson.

Bell Ringer Practice

✓ **Check Skills You'll Need**
Use student page, transparency, or PowerPoint. For intervention, direct students to:
Estimating With Whole Numbers
Lesson 1-2
Extra Skills and Word Problems Practice, Ch. 1

✓ **Check Skills You'll Need**

1. **Vocabulary Review**
   __?__ is a method of estimation that compares a digit's value to 5.
   Rounding
   Round each number to the underlined place.

   2. <u>7</u>2   **70**   3. 1<u>0</u>8   **110**

   4. <u>1</u>49 **100**   5. 3,1<u>9</u>6
                                    3,200

GO for Help
Lesson 1-2

GO Online

Video Tutor Help
Visit: PHSchool.com
Web Code: aqe-0775

What You'll Learn

To add and subtract decimals and to solve problems involving decimals

🔊 **New Vocabulary** front-end estimation

Why Learn This?

To find the sum or difference of two amounts of money, you need to add or subtract decimals.

If you estimate before you add or subtract, you can tell whether your answer is reasonable. One way to estimate is to round.

EXAMPLE **Finding Decimal Sums**

1 Find $3.026 + 14.7 + 1.38$.

Step 1 Estimate. $3.026 + 14.7 + 1.38$
                        $\approx 3 \quad + 15 \quad + 1$, or 19

Step 2 Add.   ⌐——— Line up the decimal points.

$$
\begin{array}{r}
3.026 \\
14.700 \\
+ \ 1.380 \\
\hline
19.106
\end{array}
$$

← Write **zeros** so that all of the decimals have the same number of digits to the right of the decimal point.

Check for Reasonableness The sum 19.106 is reasonable, since it is close to 19.

✓ **Quick Check**

1. Find $0.84 + 2.0 + 3.32$. Estimate first.   **about 6; 6.16**

In **front-end estimation,** you estimate by first adding the "front-end digits." Then you estimate the sum of the remaining digits. You adjust the sum of the front-end digits as necessary.

Differentiated Instruction Solutions for All Learners

Special Needs L1
Doing two sets of calculations to estimate and add might become cumbersome for some students. Remind them that over time, they can do the estimation mentally and only write the actual addition with paper and pencil.

learning style: verbal

Below Level L2
Focus on the need to line up the decimal points by having students perform basic additions like the following:

$0.2 + 0.05$ **0.25** $0.25 + 3$ **3.25**
$0.01 + 0.3 + 6$ **6.31**

learning style: visual

Popcorn
Small $3.98
Medium $6.49
Large $9.08
Junior $3.47

EXAMPLE Using Front-End Estimation

2 **Food** Use front-end estimation to estimate the total cost of buying one of every size of popcorn shown at the left.

Step 1 Add the front-end digits. These are the dollar amounts.

$$
\begin{array}{r}
\$3.98 \\
\$6.49 \\
\$9.08 \\
+\ \$3.47 \\
\hline
\$21
\end{array}
$$

Step 2 Estimate the total cents. Then adjust the dollar amounts.

$$
\begin{array}{r}
\$3.98 \quad \rightarrow \quad \text{about \$1}\\
\$6.49 \quad \Big\} \\
\$9.08 \quad \quad \text{about \$1}\\
+\ \$3.47 \quad \Big\} \\
\hline
\$21 \quad \quad \quad \text{about \$2}
\end{array}
$$

The total cost is about $21 + $2, or $23.

✓ Quick Check

2. Use front-end estimation to estimate the total cost of one small popcorn and two large popcorns. **about $22**

EXAMPLE Finding a Difference

3 A basketball hoop is 46 cm across. A basketball is 24.28 cm across. What is the difference between these measurements?

Estimate $46 - 24.28 \approx 46 - 24$, or 22

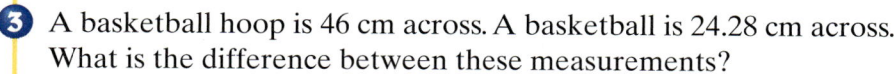

Write 46 with a decimal point and two zeros.	Rename 46 as 45 and 10 tenths.	Rename 10 tenths as 9 tenths and 10 hundredths.
$\begin{array}{r}46.00\\ -24.28\\ \hline\end{array}$	$\begin{array}{r}\overset{45\ \ 10}{46.00}\\ -24.28\\ \hline\end{array}$	$\begin{array}{r}\overset{\ \ \ 9}{\underset{}{45\ 10\ 10}}\\ 46.00\\ -24.28\\ \hline 21.72\end{array}$

The difference is 21.72 cm.

Check for Reasonableness 21.72 is close to 22, so the answer is reasonable.

✓ Quick Check

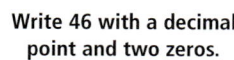

3. Use the graph at the right. How much greater is the women's record discus throw than the men's throw? **2.72 m**

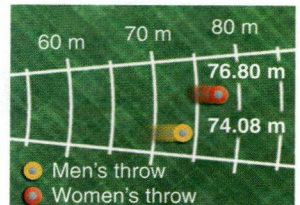

60 m   70 m   80 m
76.80 m
74.08 m
● Men's throw
● Women's throw

1-7 Adding and Subtracting Decimals   **33**

2. Teach

Activity Lab
Use before the lesson.
Student Edition Activity Lab, Hands On 1-7a, Using Models, p. 31

All in One Teaching Resources
Activity Lab 1-7: Fraction Tiles

Guided Instruction

Example 1
Ask: *Why does 14.7 round to 15?*
0.7 is greater than or equal to 0.5.

Example 3
Remind students that 46.00 is an equivalent form of the whole number 46. Sometimes it is necessary to write whole numbers as decimals when subtracting.

PowerPoint
Additional Examples

1 First estimate and then find the sum $6.8 + 4.65 + 2.125$.
estimate: 14; sum: 13.575

2 Use front-end estimation and adjust to estimate each sum.
 a. $25.1 + 33.2 + 71.0$ **130**
 b. $\$4.99 + \$2.95$ **$8**

3 Professional ice hockey rinks can be from 25.9 m to 30.0 m wide. What is the difference between these widths? **4.1 m**

All in One Teaching Resources
• Daily Notetaking Guide 1-7 **L3**
• Adapted Notetaking 1-7 **L1**

Closure

• *How do you add or subtract decimals?* **Sample: Align the decimal points; annex zeros as needed; then add or subtract as you do with whole numbers.**
• *How do you use front-end estimation to find sums?* **Add front-end digits. Then adjust.**

Advanced Learners **L4**
Have students find each sum.

$0.345 + 0.543$ **0.888**
$2.468 + 8.642$ **11.11**
$98.76 + 67.89$ **166.65**

learning style: visual

English Language Learners **ELL**
The idea of annexing zeros can easily be misunderstood. Students do not always understand that zeros can only be annexed to the right end of the decimal. Explain, using examples such as $4.5 = 4.50$ and $4.50 \neq 4.05$.

learning style: visual

Assignment Guide

Check Your Understanding
Go over Exercises 1–7 in class before assigning the Homework Exercises.

Homework Exercises
A Practice by Example   8–27
B Apply Your Skills   28–35
C Challenge   36
Test Prep and
  Mixed Review   37–44

Homework Quick Check
To check students' understanding of key skills and concepts, go over Exercises 11, 16, 29, 33, and 34.

Differentiated Instruction **Resources**

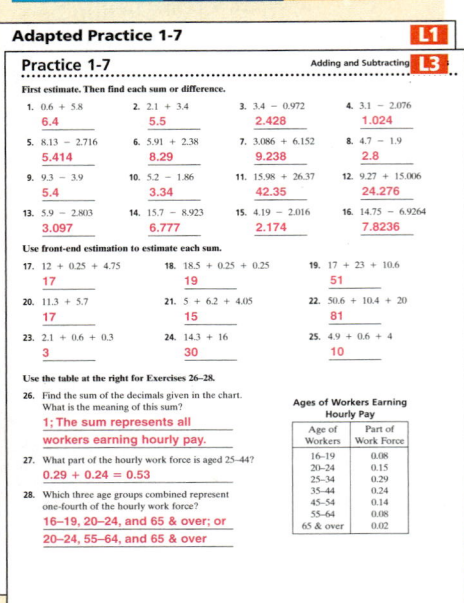

Check Your Understanding

1. **Error Analysis** Explain and correct the error in the work at the right. **The decimal points were not lined up before subtracting. 5.8 − 2 = 3.8**

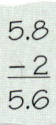

$$\begin{array}{r} 5.8 \\ -\ 2 \\ \hline 5.6 \end{array}$$

Find each sum or difference.

2. 6.37 + 2.45 **8.82**

$$\begin{array}{r} 6.3\,7 \\ +\ \blacksquare.\blacksquare\blacksquare \\ \hline \end{array}$$

3. 8.9 − 7.52 **1.38**

$$\begin{array}{r} \blacksquare.\blacksquare\blacksquare \\ -\ 7.5\,2 \\ \hline \end{array}$$

4. 7.3 + 4 **11.3**

$$\begin{array}{r} 7.3 \\ +\ \blacksquare.\blacksquare \\ \hline \end{array}$$

Use front-end estimation to estimate each sum.

5. $6.70 + $2.40 **$9**   6. $8.92 + $7.10 **$16**   7. $7.10 + $4 **$11**

Homework Exercises

For more exercises, see **Extra Skills and Word Problems.**

GO for Help

For Exercises	See Example
8–13	1
14–17	2
18–27	3

Ⓐ **First estimate. Then find each sum.**

8. 0.6 + 3.4 **about 4; 4**

9. 6.2 + 0.444 **about 6; 6.644**

10. 8.001 + 0.77 **about 9; 8.771**

11. 7 + 11.436 + 3.08 **about 21; 21.516**

12. 0.445 + 8.99 + 3 **about 12; 12.435**

13. 0.33 + 1.11 + 3.2 **about 4; 4.64**

Use front-end estimation to estimate each sum.

14. $4.89 + $3.97 **about $9**

15. $6.15 + $8.86 **about $15**

16. $14.65 + $27.29 + $63.85 **about $106**

17. $16.81 + $19.94 + $11.49 **about $48**

First estimate. Then find each difference.

18. 22.2 − 4.3 **about 18; 17.9**

19. 8.91 − 6.08 **about 3; 2.83**

20. 9.45 − 3.76 **about 5; 5.69**

21. 9.1 − 6.05 **about 3; 3.05**

22. 0.8 − 0.126 **about 1; 0.674**

23. 4 − 1.29 **about 3; 2.71**

24. 60 − 2.037 **about 58; 57.963**

25. 9 − 0.45 **about 9; 8.55**

26. 6.72 − 2.45 **about 5; 4.27**

27. A digital camera costs $174.99 online. At a local store, the same camera costs $222.98. What is the difference in prices? **$47.99**

Ⓑ **GPS** 28. **Guided Problem Solving** Jonah had $340.87 in his checking account. He deposited $52 and wrote a check for $38.72. Find his new balance. **$354.15**

• How did Jonah's balance change after he deposited $52?

• How did the balance change after he wrote the check?

Adapted Practice 1-7 L1

Practice 1-7   Adding and Subtracting L3

First estimate. Then find each sum or difference.

1. 0.6 + 5.8 **6.4**   2. 2.1 + 3.4 **5.5**   3. 3.4 − 0.972 **2.428**   4. 3.1 − 2.076 **1.024**

5. 8.13 − 2.716 **5.414**   6. 5.91 + 2.38 **8.29**   7. 3.086 + 6.152 **9.238**   8. 4.7 − 1.9 **2.8**

9. 9.3 − 3.9 **5.4**   10. 5.2 − 1.86 **3.34**   11. 15.98 + 26.37 **42.35**   12. 9.27 + 15.006 **24.276**

13. 5.9 − 2.803 **3.097**   14. 15.7 − 8.923 **6.777**   15. 4.19 − 2.016 **2.174**   16. 14.75 − 6.9264 **7.8236**

Use front-end estimation to estimate each sum.

17. 12 + 0.25 + 4.75 **17**   18. 18.5 + 0.25 + 0.25 **19**   19. 17 + 23 + 10.6 **51**

20. 11.3 + 5.7 **17**   21. 5 + 6.2 + 4.05 **15**   22. 50.6 + 10.4 + 20 **81**

23. 2.1 + 0.6 + 0.3 **3**   24. 14.3 + 16 **30**   25. 4.9 + 0.6 + 4 **10**

Use the table at the right for Exercises 26–28.

26. Find the sum of the decimals given in the chart. What is the meaning of this sum?
1; The sum represents all workers earning hourly pay.

27. What part of the hourly work force is aged 25–44?
0.29 + 0.24 = 0.53

28. Which three age groups combined represent one-fourth of the hourly work force?
16–19, 20–24, and 65 & over; or 20–24, 55–64, and 65 & over

Ages of Workers Earning Hourly Pay

Age of Workers	Part of Work Force
16–19	0.08
20–24	0.15
25–34	0.29
35–44	0.24
45–54	0.14
55–64	0.08
65 & over	0.02

1-7 • Guided Problem Solving **GPS** L3

GPS Student Page 35, Exercise 33:

Population In 2000, the New England states had a total population of about 13.92 million. Find the population of Maine.

State	Population
Connecticut	3.42 million
Maine	?
Massachusetts	6.35 million
New Hampshire	1.24 million
Rhode Island	1.05 million
Vermont	0.61 million

Understand

1. What are you being asked to do?
Determine the population of Maine.

2. How will you use the total population of the New England states to answer the question?
Subtract the population of each state from the total.

Plan and Carry Out

3. Find the sum of the populations of the other states.
12.66 million

4. What is the total population of all the New England states?
13.92 million

5. Write an expression to find the population of Maine.
13.92 − 12.66

6. Evaluate the expression to find the population of Maine.
13.92 − 12.66 = 1.26

7. Find the population of Maine.
1.26 million

Check

8. How can you check your answer?
Add 1.26 million to the total of the other states' population. The total should be 13.92 million.

Solve Another Problem

9. You and a friend calculate your grade for a class. You have an 83.5 and your friend has an 85.65. Who has the higher grade? How much higher is it?
your friend; 85.65 − 83.50 = 2.15; 2.15 points

Use <, =, or > to complete each statement.

29. 0.041 + 0.009 $<$ 0.5

30. 0.315 + 0.14 + 0.05 $>$ 0.5

31. 669.583 + 204.222 $>$ 873.8

32. 665.5 − 281.7 $>$ 373.8

33. Population In 2000, the
GPS New England states had a total
population of about 13.92 million.
Find the population of Maine.
1.26 million

State	Population
Connecticut	3.41 million
Maine	
Massachusetts	6.35 million
New Hampshire	1.24 million
Rhode Island	1.05 million
Vermont	0.61 million

Source: U.S. Census Bureau.
Go to **www.PHSchool.com** for a data update.
Web Code: aqg-9041

T-Shirts and Sweatshirts For Sale

Adult T-shirt
(M-XL) $15.00
(XXL) $17.95

Adult Sweatshirt
(M-XL) $29.50
(XXL) $29.95

34. A series of orders was placed
with a clothing company. Using
the prices at the left, estimate the
total cost of each order.
  a. 2 XXL adult T-shirts and
    1 child sweatshirt   **about $53**
  b. 3 XL adult sweatshirts and
    4 child sweatshirts   **about $158**
  c. 3 child T-shirts, 2 XL adult T-shirts and 2 XXL adult T-shirts
    about $105

Child's T-shirt
$12.50

Child's Sweatshirt
$16.95

35. Choose a Method A hot dog vendor receives a $20 bill for
a $5.25 purchase. Is the vendor most likely to use estimation,
mental math, or a calculator to find the amount of change?
Explain. **Answers may vary. Sample: mental math because it
is quicker**

C **36. Challenge** Find the missing numbers.
  a. 1.2 × ■ = 18 **15**
  b. 2.5 × ■ = 11.25 **4.5**

Test Prep and Mixed Review   **Practice**

Multiple Choice

37. At a baseball game, Ben ordered peanuts for $3.25. He paid
with a $5 bill. How much change did Ben get? **B**
  Ⓐ $1.25   Ⓑ $1.75   Ⓒ $2.25   Ⓓ $2.75

38. Patrick spent $22 on a taxi ride, $48 on a theater ticket, and
$31 on snacks. Which is closest to the total amount he spent? **G**
  Ⓕ $90   Ⓖ $100   Ⓗ $110   Ⓙ $120

39. Which statement about 11.924 and 11.942 is true? **C**
  Ⓐ 11.924 > 11.942
  Ⓑ 11.924 = 11.942
  Ⓒ 11.942 > 11.924
  Ⓓ 11.942 < 11.924

Round each number to the nearest hundred.

40. 287 **300**   **41.** 812 **800**   **42.** 86 **100**   **43.** 1,413 **1,400**   **44.** 6,546 **6,500**

GO for Help

For Exercises	See Lesson
40–44	1-2

---

4. Assess & Reteach

Lesson Quiz

Find each sum or difference.

1. 3.6 + 42.09 + 64 **109.69**

2. 100 − 21.75 **78.25**

3. 1.293 + 50.38 + 257.4 **309.073**

4. 52.7 − 7.002 **45.698**

5. Use front-end estimation and
adjust to estimate the sum.
$5.95 + $3.07 + $2.95 **$12**

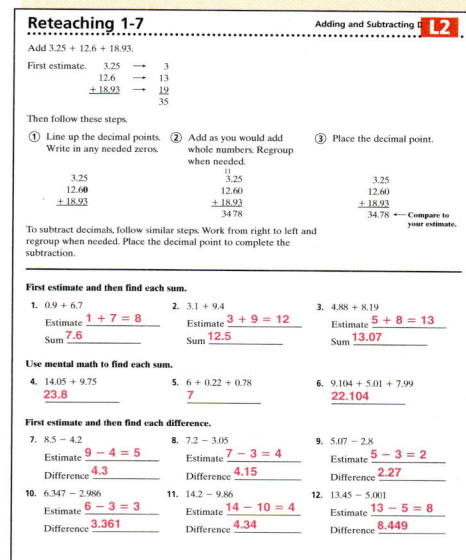

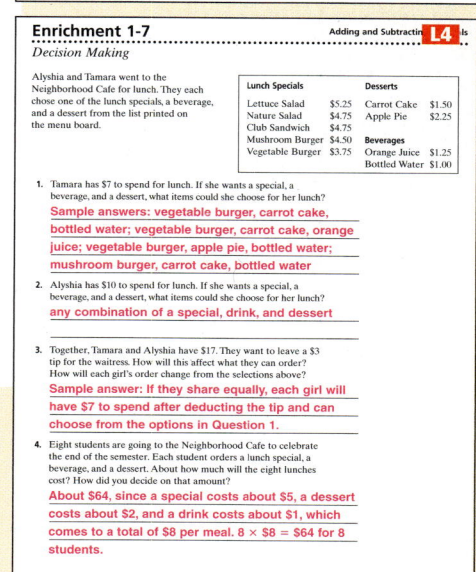

Alternative Assessment

Each student in a pair writes a horizontal decimal
addition and subtraction exercise. Partners
exchange exercises and rewrite them vertically on
graph paper to help them to align the decimals by
place value. Students then estimate and find the
sum or difference for each exercise.

Test Prep

Resources

For additional practice with a variety of test item
formats:
• Test-Taking Strategies, p. 51
• Test Prep, p. 55
• Test-Taking Strategies with Transparencies

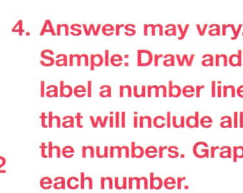

High-Use Academic Words

Vocabulary Builder

High-Use Academic Words

Students learn a strategy for acquiring vocabulary that will be useful for them in mathematics.

High-use academic words are words that you will see often in textbooks and on tests. These words are not math vocabulary terms, but knowing them will help you to succeed in mathematics.

Guided Instruction

Draw students' attention to the table of words and meanings. Ask which of these words they have seen before and where they have seen them. For example, ask:

- *What would you* explain *in a math problem?* **Sample: how to do a process like front-end estimation**
- *What would you* compare *in mathematics?* **Sample: two decimals to see which is greater**
- *What would you* name *in mathematics?* **Sample: the place value of a digit in a number**

Teaching Tip
Point out the use of these words in lessons in this chapter.

Exercises
Have students work with partners to do Exercises 1–3 and exchange partners to do Exercises 4–6. Assign Exercise 7 as independent work.

Differentiated Instruction

Auditory Learners
Invite students to find one example of each word in their textbooks. Have them read the example aloud and tell how it exemplifies the meaning in the table.

Resources

- Vocabulary and Study Skills Worksheets

Direction Words

Some words tell what to do in a problem. I need to understand what these words are asking so that I give the correct answer.

Word	Meaning
Explain	To give facts and details that make an idea easier to understand
Compare	To tell or show how two things are alike and different
Name	To identify something by stating its name

Exercises

1. Explain how to make a peanut butter and jelly sandwich.
   1–3. Check students' work.

2. Compare a peanut butter and jelly sandwich to a ham and cheese sandwich.

3. Name the ingredients in a peanut butter and jelly sandwich.

4. Explain how to order a group of numbers using a number line.

5. Compare 0.8 and 0.85. **0.8 < 0.85**

6. Name the place and value of each digit in 10.92. **1: tens, 1 ten or 10; 0: ones, 0 ones or 0; 9: tenths, 9 tenths or 0.9; 2: hundredths, 2 hundredths or 0.02**

7. a. **Word Knowledge** Think about the word *reasonable*. Choose the letter that shows how well you know the word. **7a–c. Check students' work.**
   A. I know its meaning.
   B. I have seen it, but I don't know its meaning.
   C. I don't know it.
   b. **Research** Look up and write the definition of *reasonable*.
   c. Use the word in a sentence involving mathematics.

4. Answers may vary. Sample: Draw and label a number line that will include all the numbers. Graph each number.

Modeling Decimal Multiplication

A model can help you to multiply decimals.

EXAMPLES **Multiplying Decimals**

1 **Coin Collecting** A collector buys two 1942 Mercury dimes. Each coin costs $.92. Draw a model to find the total cost.

You want to find 0.92 + 0.92, or 2 × 0.92.

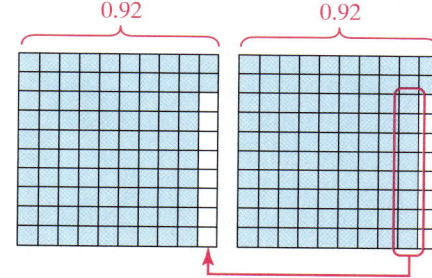

Shade 92 squares in each of two grids.

0.92   0.92

Move 8 hundredths to fill the first grid.

Miss Liberty's winged cap makes her look like the Roman god Mercury, so the coin was called the "Mercury" dime.

Count the shaded squares in the grids.

The shaded area is 1 whole and 84 hundredths, or 1.84. The total cost is $1.84.

2 Draw a model to find the product 0.5 × 0.4.

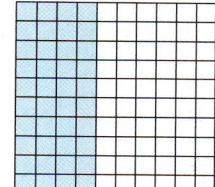

Shade 4 *columns* → of a grid to represent 0.4.

Shade 5 *rows* to → represent 0.5. Use a different color or style.

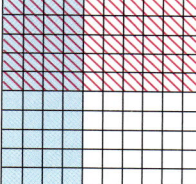

The shadings overlap in 20 squares, representing 20 hundredths, or 0.20. So 0.5 × 0.4 = 0.20.

Exercises

Draw a model to find each product. 1–6. See margin for models.

1. 3 × 0.9 **2.7**
2. 2 × 0.61 **1.22**
3. 0.8 × 0.5 **0.40**
4. 0.7 × 0.2 **0.14**
5. 0.1 × 0.6 **0.06**

6. **Writing in Math** Explain how to use models to find 2.6 × 0.2.

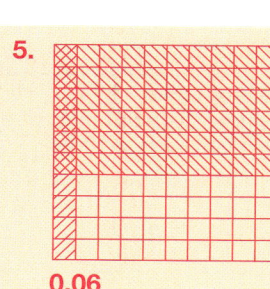

4. 0.14

5. 0.06

6. Answers may vary. Sample: Draw a model showing 1, 1, and 0.6. This is 2.6. Shade 2 rows in each model. The shading overlaps 20 squares, 20 squares, and 12 squares, or 0.52.

Modeling Decimal Multiplication

Students create and shade in grids to model multiplication of a whole number and a decimal. Then they find the product of two decimals.

Guided Instruction

Before beginning the Activity, be sure students understand how tenths and hundredths are represented on a grid. Ask questions, such as:

- *In Example 1, when you move 8 hundredths from the second grid what happens to the first grid?* **It becomes 100 hundredths or 1 whole.**
- *In Example 2, why do you use columns to represent the tenths?* **Each column represents ten hundredths, or one tenth.**
- *What can you use to represent a whole number?* **One complete square represents 1, two complete squares represent 2, and so on.**

Exercises

Ask students to identify which of Exercises 1–5 will have overlapping shadings and to explain why. **Exercises 3–5 because each factor is a decimal less than 1.**

1–3. See back of book.

Resources

- Activity Lab 1-8: Multiplying Decimals
- graph paper
- Classroom Aid 2, 10

37

Objective
To multiply decimals and to solve problems by multiplying decimals

Examples
1   Multiplying by a Decimal
2   Multiplying Decimals
3   Application: Predicting Growth

Math Understandings: p. 2D

Math Background

Multiplying decimals is similar to multiplying whole numbers except for the extra step of correctly placing the decimal point. Simply count the number of decimal places in the factors being multiplied. Then place the decimal point so that the number of decimal places in the product is the same as the total number in the factors. So 2×1.5 results in 3.0, 0.2×1.5 results in 0.30, and 0.2×0.15 results in 0.030.

More Math Background: p. 2D

Lesson Planning and Resources

See p. 2E for a list of the resources that support this lesson.

Bell Ringer Practice

☑ **Check Skills You'll Need**
Use student page, transparency, or PowerPoint. For intervention, direct students to:
Estimating With Whole Numbers
Lesson 1-2
Extra Skills and Word Problems
   Practice, Ch. 1

☑ Check Skills You'll Need

1. **Vocabulary Review**
Are 130 and 5 *compatible* numbers when dividing 130 by 5? Explain.

Estimate using compatible numbers.

2. 21×29 **3.** 59×3

4. $498 \div 5$ **5.** $71 \div 7$

GO for Help
Lesson 1-2

Check Skills You'll Need
1. **Yes; 130 is easy to divide by 5 mentally.**

2. **about 600**

3. **about 180**

4. **about 100**

5. **about 10**

What You'll Learn

To multiply decimals and to solve problems involving decimals

Why Learn This?

Understanding how much a plant will grow over time is important in gardening. You can multiply decimals to estimate how tall a flower or tree will grow.

The model below shows how to find 0.5×1.5. You are finding half of 1.5.

Shade 15 columns to represent 1.5.

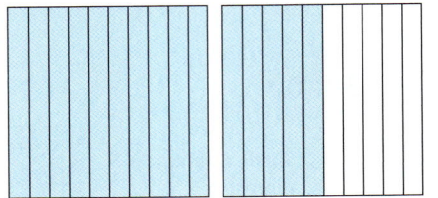

Shade 5 rows of each grid to represent 0.5.

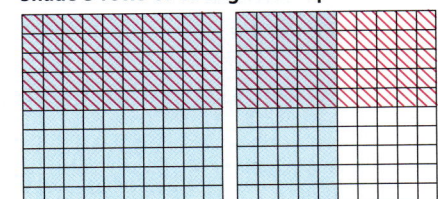

The shadings overlap in 75 squares, or 0.75. So $0.5 \times 1.5 = 0.75$.

The model shows a pattern. To find the number of decimal places in a product, add the number of decimal places in the factors.

EXAMPLE   Multiplying by a Decimal

1 Find the product 0.47×8.

$$
\begin{array}{rl}
0.47 & \leftarrow \quad \text{2 decimal places} \\
\underline{\times\ 8} & \leftarrow \quad +\ \text{0 decimal places} \\
3.76 & \leftarrow \quad \text{2 decimal places}
\end{array}
$$

☑ Quick Check

1. a. Find 6×0.13. **0.78**   **b.** Find 4.37×5. **21.85**

Differentiated Instruction   Solutions for All Learners

Special Needs **L1**
Students will benefit from modeling Examples 1, 2, and 3 on grids before moving on to the multiplication procedure. Using grids that they can color in and overlap is helpful.

learning style: visual

Below Level **L2**
Review the number of decimal places with various decimals such as these.

0.51 **2**	3.4 **1**	8 **0**
0.02 **2**	25 **0**	9.06 **2**

learning style: visual

You can show multiplication in these three ways:

$$0.5 \times 1.5 \qquad 0.5 \cdot 1.5 \qquad 0.5(1.5)$$

Video Tutor Help
Visit: PHSchool.com
Web Code: aqe-0775

EXAMPLE **Multiplying Decimals**

2 Find the product $1.31 \cdot 2.4$.

$$
\begin{array}{r}
1.31 \\
\times\ 2.4 \\
\hline
524 \\
+\ 262 \\
\hline
3.144
\end{array}
\begin{array}{l}
\leftarrow \text{2 decimal places} \\
\leftarrow +\text{ 1 decimal place} \\
\\
\\
\leftarrow \text{3 decimal places}
\end{array}
$$

Check for Reasonableness It makes sense that a number slightly greater than 1 times a number slightly greater than 2 equals a product of about 3.

✓ **Quick Check**

2. Find each product.
   a. $0.3(0.2)$ **0.06**   b. $1.9 \cdot 5.32$ **10.108**   c. 0.9×0.14 **0.126**

You can also use compatible numbers to estimate with decimals.

EXAMPLE **Application: Predicting Growth**

3 A eucalyptus tree grows 5.45 meters in one year. At that rate, how much does the tree grow in 3.5 years?

Estimate $3.5 \times 5.45 \approx 4 \times 5$, or 20   ← **4 and 5 are compatible numbers.**

$$
\begin{array}{r}
5.45 \\
\times\ 3.5 \\
\hline
2725 \\
+\ 1635 \\
\hline
19.075
\end{array}
\begin{array}{l}
\leftarrow \text{2 decimal places} \\
\leftarrow \text{1 decimal place} \\
\\
\\
\leftarrow \text{3 decimal places}
\end{array}
$$

At that rate, the tree grows about 19.075 meters in 3.5 years.

Check for Reasonableness 19.075 is close to 20, so the answer is reasonable.

The leaves and flowers of eucalyptus trees are the koala's main diet.

✓ **Quick Check**

3. One pound of tomatoes costs $1.29. To the nearest cent, how much do 2.75 pounds of tomatoes cost? **$3.55**

Advanced Learners **L4**
Have students work on decimal multiplications with three factors such as these.

$2.5 \cdot 3.75 \cdot 4.1$ **38.4375**
$88.3 \cdot 6.2 \cdot 5.4$ **2,956.284**

learning style: visual

English Language Learners **ELL**
In Example 3, explain what the phrase *at that rate of growth* means. Make sure students understand that the tree is growing 5.45 meters every year for 3.5 years.

learning style: verbal

---

2. Teach

Activity Lab
Use before the lesson.
Student Edition Activity Lab 1-8a, Modeling Decimal Multiplication, p. 37

All in One Teaching Resources
Activity Lab 1-8: Multiplying Decimals

Guided Instruction

Example 1
Ask: *If you were multiplying 0.47×0.8, how many decimal places would be in the product?* **3**

Example 2
Ask: *What indicates the operation of multiplication in $1.31 \cdot 2.4$?* **The raised dot indicates multiplication.**

Example 3
Ask: *How does estimating the product help you place the decimal point?* **Your estimate was 20, and 19 is close to 20.**

Connection to Science
Eucalyptus trees also grow in the United States. The hot, dry climates of California, Arizona, and Nevada promote the growth of this native Australian tree.

PowerPoint
Additional Examples

1 Find the product 2.73×4.
10.92

2 Find the product $0.6 \cdot 0.42$.
0.252

3 Cameron can read 196 words in a minute. Robert reads 1.6 times as fast. How many words can Robert read in a minute? **313.6, or about 314**

All in One Teaching Resources
- Daily Notetaking Guide 1-8 **L3**
- Adapted Notetaking 1-8 **L1**

Closure

- *How do you multiply decimals?*
  See back of book.

Assignment Guide

Check Your Understanding
Go over Exercises 1–9 in class before assigning the Homework Exercises.

Homework Exercises
A	Practice by Example	10–34
B	Apply Your Skills	35–42
C	Challenge	43
	Test Prep and Mixed Review	44–49

Homework Quick Check
To check students' understanding of key skills and concepts, go over Exercises 16, 29, 36, 41, and 42.

Differentiated Instruction Resources

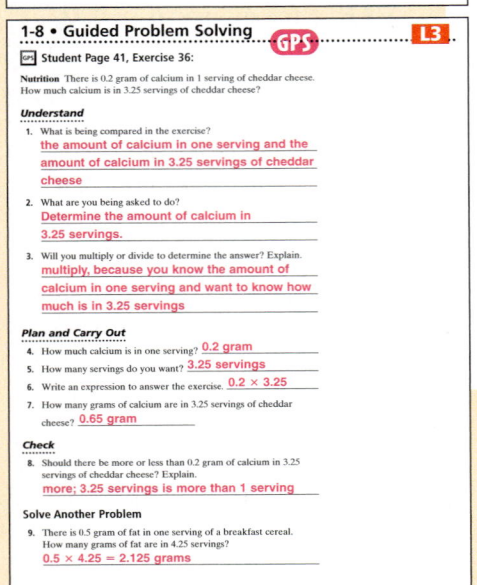

Check Your Understanding

1. 7; there are 3 decimal places in the first number and 4 decimal places in the second number. So 3 + 4 = 7.

2. Answers may vary. Sample: No; I can estimate to check. 20 × 3 = 60 and 60 is not close to 612.8.

3. < 1; 0.5 × 2 = 1 and 0.2 < 0.5, so 0.2 × 2 < 1

4. > 1; 0.5 × 2 = 1 and 0.7 > 0.5, so 2.2 × 0.7 > 1

5. = 1; 0.5 × 2 = 1

1. Reasoning You are multiplying 9.876×5.4321. How many decimal places does the answer have? Explain.

2. Error Analysis A student says $19.8 \times 3.1 = 612.8$. Is this answer correct? Explain how you know. **See left.**

Number Sense Is the product *greater than*, *equal to*, or *less than* 1? Explain your reasoning. **3–5. Explanations may vary. Samples are given at the left.**

3. 2×0.2 **4.** 2.2×0.7 **5.** 2×0.5

Copy each problem. Place the decimal point in the product.

6. 0.403	**7.** 524	**8.** 0.15	**9.** 8.42
$\times$ 5	$\times$ 0.5	$\times$ 0.31	$\times$ 6.7
2015	2620	465	56414
2.015	**262.0**	**0.0465**	**56.414**

Homework Exercises

For more exercises, see Extra Skills and Word Problems.

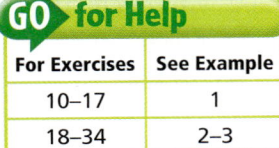

For Exercises	See Example
10–17	1
18–34	2–3

A Find each product.

10. 0.018 **0.072**   **11.** 1.9 **17.1**   **12.** 35 **196.0**   **13.** 39 **2.34**
$\times$ 4 $\times$ 9 $\times$ 5.6 $\times$ 0.06

14. 358 **250.6**   **15.** 0.12 **5.64**   **16.** 53 **2.12**   **17.** 0.25 **23.0**
$\times$ 0.7 $\times$ 47 $\times$ 0.04 $\times$ 92

18. 0.2 **0.14**   **19.** 0.8 **0.32**   **20.** 0.3 **0.15**   **21.** 0.7 **0.63**
$\times$ 0.7 $\times$ 0.4 $\times$ 0.5 $\times$ 0.9

22. 0.12(0.96)   **23.** 0.06(0.18)   **24.** 0.486 · 0.9   **25.** 0.03 · 0.574
    0.1152   **0.0108**   **0.4374**   **0.01722**
26. 4.5(230)   **27.** 1.7 × 3.702   **28.** 3.2 · 4.5   **29.** 8.1 · 1.3
    1,035   **6.2934**   **14.4**   **10.53**
30. 3.3(420)   **31.** 3.2 · 15.5   **32.** 4.25 · 6.18   **33.** 1.2 × 2.065
    1,386   **49.6**   **26.265**   **2.478**

34. A year on Mars is 1.88 times as long as a year on Earth. An Earth year lasts 365.3 days. Find the length of a year on Mars. **686.764 days**

B  **35. Guided Problem Solving** Ham costs $8.79 per pound and turkey costs $9.48 per pound. What is the total cost of 2 pounds of ham and 1.5 pounds of turkey? **$31.80**
  • What is the cost of 2 pounds of ham? 1.5 pounds of turkey?

---

40   Chapter 1   Whole Numbers and Decimals

37–39. Methods may vary. Samples are given.

37. 40; paper and pencil

38. 30; mental math

39. 298.1973; calculator

42. Answers may vary. Sample: In both cases, you multiply the same way; with 0.3 × 0.4, you need to show two decimal places.

Hybrid car
58.0 miles per gallon

Sport utility vehicle (SUV)
13.5 miles per gallon

36. Nutrition There is 0.2 gram of calcium in 1 serving of cheddar cheese. How much calcium is in 3.25 servings of cheddar cheese? **0.65 g**

Choose a Method Find each product. Tell whether you use mental math, paper and pencil, or a calculator. **37–39. See margin.**

37. 16×2.5 **38.** $60(0.5)$ **39.** 56.37×5.29

40. The average fuel rates for a hybrid car and an SUV are shown at the left. How much farther than the SUV can the hybrid car travel using 13 gallons of gas? **578.5 mi**

41. Astronomy Mercury is about 36 million miles from the sun. Jupiter is about 13.43 times that distance. About how far is Jupiter from the sun? **483.48 million mi**

42. Writing in Math Explain how multiplying 0.3×0.4 is like multiplying 3×4. How are the two problems different? **See margin.**

C 43. Challenge Find the value that makes each statement true.
a. ■ ÷ 0.2 = 0.7   **b.** ■ ÷ 0.03 = 0.5
0.14   **0.015**

Test Prep and Mixed Review   **Practice**

Multiple Choice

44. Abby's mother and father take Abby and three of her friends to a water park. Admission is $14 for adults and $11 for children. The steps for finding the total cost are below.
  Step K: Multiply $11 by 4.
  Step L: Add the products.
  Step M: Count two adults and four children.
  Step N: Multiply $14 by 2.

Which list shows the correct order of steps? **B**
  Ⓐ L, M, K, N   Ⓒ K, N, L, M
  Ⓑ M, K, N, L   Ⓓ M, L, N, K

45. Which is a reasonable estimate of the sum $214 + 92 + 56$? **G**
  Ⓕ 300   Ⓖ 350   Ⓗ 400   Ⓙ 450

46. Which statement about 2.315 is NOT true? **D**
  Ⓐ $2.315 > 2.13$ Ⓒ $2.15 < 2.315$
  Ⓑ $2.31 < 2.315$ Ⓓ $2.315 > 2.51$

Find each sum or difference.

47. $7.32 + 4.29$ **11.61**   **48.** $11.07 - 1.2$ **9.87**   **49.** $6.5 - 0.32$ **6.18**

GO for Help

For Exercises	See Lesson
47–49	1-7

---

4. Assess & Reteach

PowerPoint
Lesson Quiz

1. Find 0.51×56. **28.56**

2. Find $0.07(3.92)$. **0.2744**

3. Find $7.29 \cdot 5.08$. **37.0332**

4. Find $0.2(7.3 \times 5)$. **7.3**

5. Apples cost $0.89 for 1 pound. How much do 2.5 pounds of apples cost? **$2.225, or $2.23**

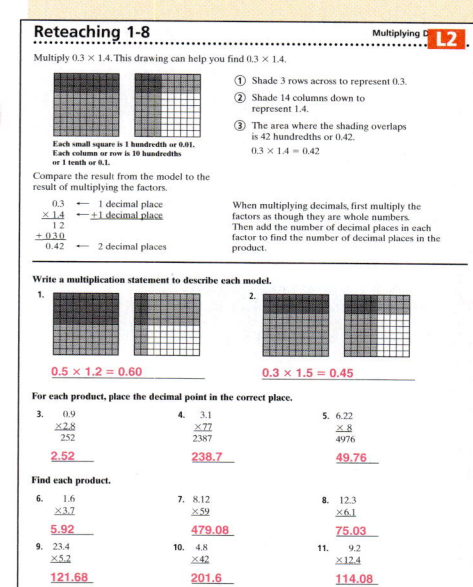

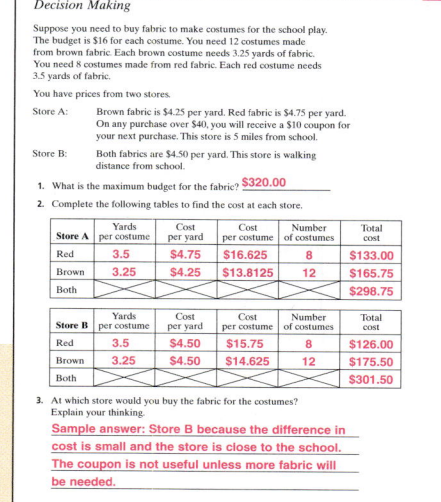

Alternative Assessment

Each student in a pair writes two or three exercises involving decimal multiplication, as in Exercises 10–33. Partners exchange papers. Each partner records the number of decimal places that should occur in the product. Then partners work together to do the multiplication and discuss the results.

Test Prep

Resources
For additional practice with a variety of test item formats:
• Test-Taking Strategies, p. 51
• Test Prep, p. 55
• Test-Taking Strategies with Transparencies

41

Multiplying and Dividing Decimals by 10, 100, and 1,000

Students use a calculator to multiply and divide by 10, 100, and 1,000.

Guided Instruction

Discuss the movement of the decimal point as students multiply or divide by 10, 100, or 1,000. Ask:
- *Predict what will happen if you multiply by 10,000.* **The decimal point will move one place more to the right.**
- *Predict what will happen if you divide by 10,000.* **The decimal point will move one place more to the left.**

Exercises
Have students check Exercises 1–6 using a calculator.

Advanced Learners   **L4**
Have students review Exercises 7a–d to determine how multiplying by 0.1, 0.01, 0.001, and 0.0001 is related to dividing by 10, 100, 1,000, and 10,000.

Resources
- calculator
- Classroom Aid 11

Multiplying and Dividing Decimals by 10, 100, and 1,000

There are shortcuts for multiplying and dividing decimals by 10, 100, and 1,000. You can use these shortcuts to multiply mentally.

ACTIVITY

1. Use a calculator to multiply.

a. $2.6 \times 10 =$ ▦   **26**
$2.6 \times 100 =$ ▦   **260**
$2.6 \times 1,000 =$ ▦   **2,600**

b. $0.45 \times 10 =$ ▦   **4.5**
$0.45 \times 100 =$ ▦   **45**
$0.45 \times 1,000 =$ ▦   **450**

2. a. Patterns What do you notice about the movement of the decimal point in your answer when you multiply by 10? By 100? By 1,000?

b. Write a rule for multiplying a decimal by 10, 100, and 1,000. **2a–b. See margin.**

3. Use a calculator to divide.

a. $2.6 \div 10 =$ ▦   **0.26**
$2.6 \div 100 =$ ▦   **0.026**
$2.6 \div 1,000 =$ ▦   **0.0026**

b. $0.45 \div 10 =$ ▦   **0.045**
$0.45 \div 100 =$ ▦   **0.0045**
$0.45 \div 1,000 =$ ▦   **0.00045**

4. a. Patterns What do you notice about the movement of the decimal point when you divide by 10? By 100? By 1,000?

b. Write a shortcut for dividing a decimal by 10, 100, and 1,000.

4a. When you divide by 10, you move the decimal point to the left 1 place; multiplying by 100 moves the decimal 2 places; by 1,000 moves it 3 places.

b. To divide by 10, 100, or 1,000, move the decimal point to the left by the appropriate number of zeroes.

Exercises

Use mental math to find each answer.

1. 6.2×10 **62**

2. $122.9 \div 10$ **12.29**

3. $161.7 \div 100$ **1.617**

4. $1,000(4.3)$ **4,300**

5. $1.5 \div 100$ **0.015**

6. $1,000 \cdot 0.89$ **890**

7. Use a calculator to multiply.

a. 527×0.1 **52.7**   **b.** 527×0.01 **5.27**   **c.** 527×0.001 **0.527**   **d.** 527×0.0001 **0.0527**

e. Patterns What do you notice about the movement of the decimal point in your answers for parts (a)–(d)?   **Answers may vary. Sample: The number of decimal places in the product is the same as the factor that is not 527.**

2a. When you multiply by 10, you move the decimal point to the right 1 place; multiplying by 100 moves the decimal 2 places; by 1,000 moves the decimal 3 places.

b. To multiply by 10, 100, or 1,000, move the decimal point to the right by the number of zeroes in either 10, 100, or 1,000.

1. Write 12.035 in words. **twelve and thirty-five thousandths**

2. Order the numbers 9, 8.7, 9.31, 8.0, and 8.05 from least to greatest.
   8.0; 8.05; 8.7; 9; 9.31

Round each decimal to the nearest tenth.

3. 7.83 **7.8**   4. 7.98 **8.0**   5. 17.051 **17.1**

Find each sum, difference, or product.

6. 1.25 + 6.07 **7.32**   7. 9.06 − 0.8 **8.26**   8. 5.2 × 6.3 **32.76**   9. 1.7 − 0.28 **1.42**

10. Jo made 7 pounds of cookies. She gave 3.25 pounds to her friends and 0.7 pounds to each of her three brothers. How many pounds did she have left? **1.65 lb**

MATH GAMES

Slide and Score

What You'll Need
- Six note cards with × 10, × 100, × 1,000, ÷ 10, ÷ 100, and ÷ 1,000 written on them
- Two chips to use as decimal points
- Two strips of paper with 4 1 2 3 5 and 5 3 1 4 2 written on them

How To Play
- Place the chips after the first digit in each number. The chips are used as decimal points. Line up the decimal points.
- A player draws a card and performs the operation on one of the numbers. Then the player lines up the decimal points again. The player receives points for any two numbers in a column. In the game below, the player will receive 3 points when the decimal is moved to the left.
- Replace the operation card and shuffle. A player's turn continues until the operation cannot be performed on either number. The winner is the first person to score 11 points.

43

Use this Checkpoint Quiz to check students' understanding of the skills and concepts of Lessons 1–5 through 1–8.

Resources

- All-in-One Teaching Resources Checkpoint Quiz 2
- ExamView Assessment Suite CD-ROM
- Success Tracker™ Online Intervention

MATH GAMES

Slide and Score

This game will help students reinforce their skills multiplying and dividing decimals by 10, 100, and 1,000.

Guided Instruction

Students may play in pairs.

Have students read through the game instructions before they begin to play. You may wish to have a volunteer read the instructions aloud to assist English learners.

If students wish to continue the game, use another set of numbers with the same digits, such as 7 0 6 8 4 and 6 4 0 7 8. You may also change the point total needed to win.

Resources

- 6 note cards
- 2 chips
- 2 strips of paper

1-9

Objective
To divide decimals and to solve problems involving decimals

Examples
1 Dividing by a Whole Number
2 Dividing a Decimal by a Decimal

Math Understandings: p. 2D

Math Background

Long division with decimals is similar to long division with whole numbers with an additional step: multiply both the divisor and dividend by a power of 10 to obtain a whole number divisor. Division by decimals between 0 and 1 gives a quotient greater than the original dividend, confusing some students.

If the division results in a remainder of 0, the decimal is called a *terminating* decimal. If the division does not end and produces a repeating pattern of nonzero remainders, the decimal is called a *repeating decimal*.

More Math Background: p. 2D

Lesson Planning and Resources

See p. 2E for a list of the resources that support this lesson.

PowerPoint

Bell Ringer Practice

☑ **Check Skills You'll Need**
Use student page, transparency, or PowerPoint. For intervention, direct students to:
Dividing Whole Numbers
Skills Handbook, p. 642

1-9 Dividing Decimals

Check Skills You'll Need

1. Vocabulary Review
How is a *dividend* different from a *divisor*?

Simplify.

2. 935 ÷ 5 **187**

3. 296 ÷ 8 **37**

4. 636 ÷ 12 **53**

GO for Help
Skills Handbook
p. 642

Check Skills You'll Need

1. A dividend is the number being divided. A divisor is the number that divides.

Vocabulary Tip

You can indicate division three ways:

15 ÷ 3

3)15

$\dfrac{15}{3}$ ← dividend
← divisor

What You'll Learn

To divide decimals and to solve problems involving decimals

Why Learn This?

Sometimes you want to share costs with your friends. You can divide decimals to find the amount each person should pay.

Dividing decimals is similar to dividing whole numbers.

EXAMPLE Dividing by a Whole Number

1 Transportation and tickets for 12 friends to an amusement park cost $364.20. How much will each person pay?

You are looking for the size of equal groups, so divide.

Estimate 364.20 ÷ 12 ≈ 360 ÷ 12, or 30

$$\begin{array}{r} 30.35 \\ 12\overline{)364.20} \\ -36 \\ \hline 04 \\ -0 \\ \hline 42 \\ -36 \\ \hline 60 \\ -60 \\ \hline 0 \end{array}$$

← Divide as with whole numbers. Place the decimal point in the quotient above the decimal point in the dividend.

Each person will pay $30.35 for transportation and a ticket.

Check for Reasonableness 30.35 is close to 30.

☑ Quick Check

1. a. Find 8)385.6. **48.2** **b.** Find 9.12 ÷ 6. **1.52**

---

44 Chapter 1 Whole Numbers and Decimals

Differentiated Instruction **Solutions for All Learners**

Special Needs **L1**
Help students label the dividend, divisor, and quotient when they are using different division symbols. This will facilitate using all the symbols appropriately.

learning style: visual

Below Level **L2**
Have students perform whole number long divisions that result in decimals such as these.

30 ÷ 4 **7.5** 32 ÷ 5 **6.4**
75 ÷ 2 **37.5** 36 ÷ 8 **4.5**

learning style: visual

One way to think about dividing decimals is to break the dividend into equal groups. The model below shows $0.8 \div 0.2$, or how many groups of 0.2 are in 0.8.

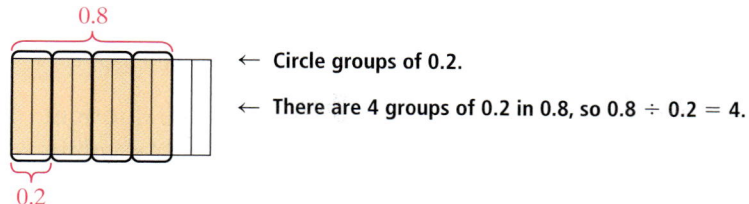

0.8

← Circle groups of 0.2.

← There are 4 groups of 0.2 in 0.8, so $0.8 \div 0.2 = 4$.

0.2

Study the pattern of quotients below.

	Dividend	÷	Divisor	=	Quotient
	0.8	÷	0.2	=	4
Multiply dividend and divisor by 10. →	8	÷	2	=	4
Multiply dividend and divisor by 100. →	80	÷	20	=	4

The pattern shows that when you multiply both the dividend and the divisor by the same number, the quotient remains the same.

> **KEY CONCEPTS** **Dividing Decimals**
>
> To divide a decimal by a decimal, multiply both the dividend and the divisor by 10, 100, or 1,000 so that the divisor is a whole number.

EXAMPLE **Dividing a Decimal by a Decimal**

② **Recipes** You use 0.5 pounds of berries to make one smoothie. How many smoothies can you make with 2.25 pounds of berries?

Multiply 0.5 by 10 to make the divisor a whole number.

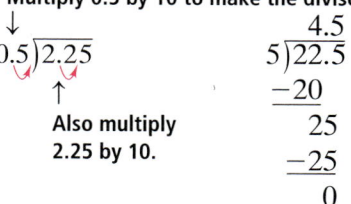

$$0.5\overline{)2.25}$$

Also multiply 2.25 by 10.

$$
\begin{array}{r}
4.5 \\
5\overline{)22.5} \\
-20 \\
\hline
25 \\
-25 \\
\hline
0
\end{array}
$$

← Divide as with whole numbers. Place the decimal point in the quotient above the decimal point in the dividend.

You can make 4.5 smoothies.

✓ **Quick Check**

2. You have $2.75. You want to buy trading cards that cost $.25 each. How many can you buy? **11 trading cards**

Guided Instruction

Example 1
Students sometimes have difficulty translating a division from the horizontal form to the "division-house" form. Suggest that they make a display like the one below in their notebooks.

dividend ÷ divisor = quotient

$$\text{divisor}\overline{)\text{dividend}}^{\text{quotient}}$$

Example 2
Have student describe smoothies. Related fruit and yogurt beverages are enjoyed in many cultures and the subject may create a lively discussion.

PowerPoint
Additional Examples

① A class of 27 students held a picnic. They purchased food and drinks for the picnic for a total cost of $93.15. What was the price for each student's meal? **$3.45**

② Find each quotient.
   a. $0.475 \div 0.05$ **9.5**
   b. $9.674 \div 0.7$ **13.82**
   c. $163.125 \div 2.9$ **56.25**

All in One Teaching Resources
• Daily Notetaking Guide 1-9 **L3**
• Adapted Notetaking 1-9 **L1**

Closure

• *How do you divide a decimal by another decimal?* **Sample: Multiply the dividend and divisor by the same number to make the divisor a whole number. Divide as with whole numbers, placing the decimal point in the quotient above the decimal point in the dividend.**

45

3. Practice

Assignment Guide

Check Your Understanding
Go over Exercises 1–6 in class before assigning the Homework Exercises.

Homework Exercises
A Practice by Example 7–21
B Apply Your Skills 22–33
C Challenge 34
Test Prep and
  Mixed Review 35–38

Homework Quick Check
To check students' understanding of key skills and concepts, go over Exercises 14, 21, 23, 25, and 33.

Differentiated Instruction **Resources**

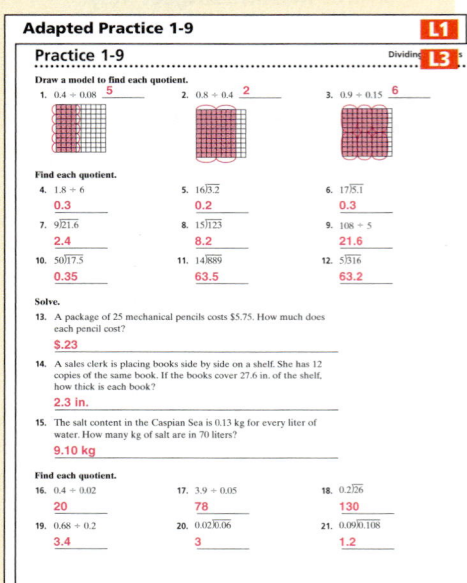

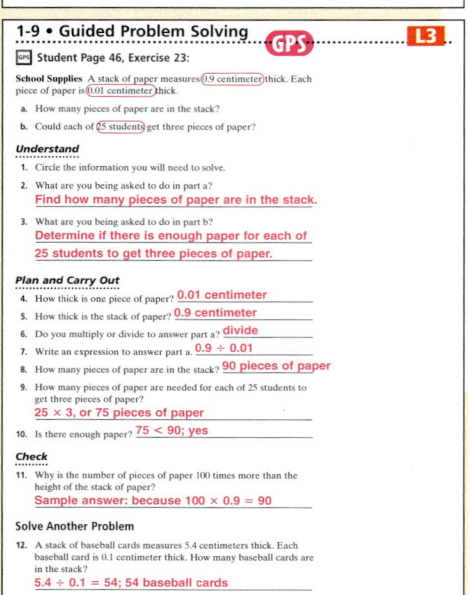

Check Your Understanding

1. **Vocabulary** When you divide both the dividend and the divisor by the same number, the (dividend, divisor, quotient) remains the same. **quotient**

2. **< 3; when you divide a number a little more than 3 by a divisor more than 1, your answer will be less than 3.**

2. **Number Sense** Is the quotient of $3.05 \div 1.25$ *greater than*, *less than*, or *equal to* 3? Explain your reasoning.

3. Draw a model to find $0.6 \div 0.2$. **See left.**

3.
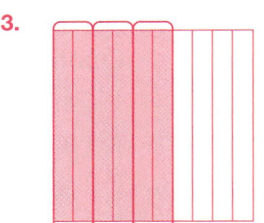
3

Complete each division.

4.
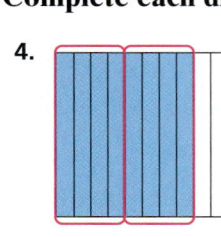

5.
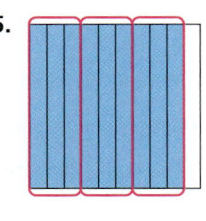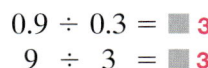

6.
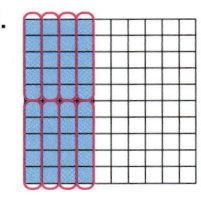

$0.8 \div 0.4 = \blacksquare$ **2** $0.9 \div 0.3 = \blacksquare$ **3** $0.40 \div 0.05 = \blacksquare$ **8**
$8 \div 4 = \blacksquare$ **2** $9 \div 3 = \blacksquare$ **3** $40 \div 5 = \blacksquare$ **8**

Homework Exercises

For more exercises, see Extra Skills and Word Problems.

A Find each quotient.

For Exercises	**See Example**
7–14	1
15–21	2

 **GO for Help**

7. $328.25 \div 13$ **25.25**   8. $7\overline{)255.5}$ **36.5**   9. $237.6 \div 33$ **7.2**

10. $32\overline{)258.24}$ **8.07**   11. $84\overline{)26.46}$ **0.315**   12. $144.54 \div 6$ **24.09**

13. $27\overline{)99.36}$ **3.68**   14. $38.27 \div 43$ **0.89**   15. $29.5 \div 0.4$ **73.75**

16. $8.9\overline{)6.497}$ **0.73**   17. $3.1\overline{)10.261}$ **3.31**   18. $16.8 \div 2.4$ **7**

19. $0.96\overline{)0.144}$ **0.15**   20. $10.54 \div 0.17$ **62**   21. $5.9\overline{)0.649}$ **0.11**

B 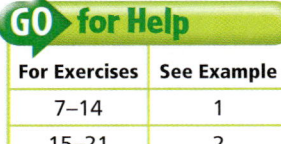 **GPS**

22. **Guided Problem Solving** Seventeen customers bought two movie tickets each. The total cost was $263.50. What was the price per ticket? **$7.75**
   - What was the total number of tickets purchased?
   - What operation should you use to find the price per ticket?

23. **School Supplies** A stack of paper measures 0.9 centimeter **GPS** thick. Each piece of paper is 0.01 centimeter thick.
   a. How many pieces of paper are in the stack? **90 pieces**
   b. Could each of 25 students get three pieces of paper? **yes**

24. **Bridges** The Great Seto Bridge in Japan is 9,368 meters long. A bicyclist riding across the bridge can travel 500 meters in 1 minute. A person walking can travel 100 meters in 1 minute. How many minutes shorter is the bicycle trip than the walk? 74.944 min

25. Five friends share three pizzas that cost $12.75 each. How much does each friend pay? $7.65

Find each quotient. Round to the nearest hundredth.

26. $64.97 \div 3.2$ 20.30
27. $10.126 \div 2.3$ 4.40
28. $3.3\overline{)26.81}$ 8.12
29. $5.637 \div 0.17$ 33.16
30. $6.24\overline{)78.28}$ 12.54
31. $0.12\overline{)1.2542}$ 10.45

GO Online
Homework Video Tutor
Visit: PHSchool.com
Web Code: aqe-0109

32. A utility company charges $.12 for each kilowatt-hour of electricity you use. Your electric bill was $125.10. How many kilowatt-hours did you use? 1,042.5

33. **Reasoning** Which quotient is greater, $127.34 \div 0.673$ or $127.34 \div 0.671$? Explain your reasoning. See left.

33. Answers may vary. Sample: $127.34 \div 0.671$; because 0.671 is smaller, it can go into 127.34 more times.

C 34. **Challenge** You and a friend are paid $38.25 for doing yard work. You work 2.5 hours and your friend works 2 hours. How much should you get for your share of the work? Explain. $21.25

Test Prep and Mixed Review

Practice

Multiple Choice

35. Four friends line up from shortest to tallest. Mac is shorter than Nate and taller than Ben. Charlie is taller than Mac and not on either end of the line. Which friend is first in line? A
   - (A) Ben
   - (B) Charlie
   - (C) Mac
   - (D) Nate

36. Kelly bought a pair of jeans, a pair of sneakers, and four shirts. What missing piece of information is needed to find the total amount Kelly spent? F
   - (F) the price of a shirt
   - (G) the amount of money Kelly has
   - (H) the original prices before the discount
   - (J) the number of shirts Kelly bought

Sale!
Jeans $24.99
Sneakers $34.99
Shirts 2 for the price of 1

GO for Help

For Exercises	See Lesson
37–38	1-6

Order each set of decimals from least to greatest.

37. 8.3, 8.03, 8.308, 8.035
8.03, 8.035, 8.3, 8.308

38. 1.8, 1.18, 1.801, 1.081
1.081, 1.18, 1.8, 1.801

Online lesson quiz, PHSchool.com, Web Code: aqa-0109

4. Assess & Reteach

PowerPoint

Lesson Quiz

Find each quotient.

1. $35.92 \div 8$ 4.49
2. $6.045 \div 7.5$ 0.806
3. $0.84 \div 0.7$ 1.2
4. $3.55 \div 0.5$ 7.1
5. $0.084 \div 0.4$ 0.21

Reteaching 1-9 Dividing D… L2

Find the quotient $1.52 \div 0.4$.

You can use a model to estimate the quotient.

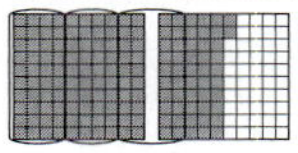

← Draw a model for 1.52.

← Since each square is 0.01, 40 squares represent 0.4. Circle groups of 0.4.

There are close to four groups of 0.4. The quotient is about 4.

① Multiply the dividend and divisor by 10 so that the divisor is a whole number.

$0.4\overline{)1.52}$

② Divide as with whole numbers.

$4\overline{)15.2}$ = 38; −12, 32, −32, 0

③ Place the decimal point in the quotient above its place in the dividend. Insert zeros as placeholders if necessary.

$4\overline{)15.2}$ = 3.8; −12, 32, −32, 0

3.8 is close to 4.

Use the model to find each quotient.

1. 
$0.8 \div$ 0.04 $= 20$

2. 
$0.70 \div 0.1 =$ 7

3. 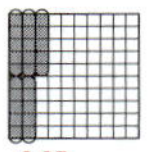
0.25 $\div 0.05 =$ 5

Estimate, then find each quotient.

4. $3\overline{)1.35}$ 0.45
5. $4\overline{)2.68}$ 0.67
6. $8.4 \div 6$ 1.4
7. $8\overline{)27}$ 3.375
8. $12.96 \div 5$ 2.592
9. $3 \div 0.12$ 25
10. $1.5\overline{)84}$ 56
11. $78 \div 15.6$ 5
12. $0.9\overline{)1.35}$ 1.5

Enrichment 1-9 Dividin… L4 …ls

Decision Making

Many food products are packaged in a variety of sizes. The list below gives the sizes and costs of fruit juice drinks at one store.

$1.92 single-serving multi-pack (serves 6)
$1.12 one quart (serves 4)
$2.16 two quarts (serves 8)
$3.52 one gallon (serves 16)

1. Choose two different sizes and give an advantage for buying each.
Sample answer: Single servings are convenient to take in lunches; gallons are better for a large group.

2. What is the cost per serving for each of the fruit juice packages? Which is the least expensive?
single: $.32; quart: $.28; two quarts: $.27; gallon: $.22; a gallon is the least expensive.

3. Suppose you need to have 22 servings of the juice drink. Which size or sizes of containers would you buy? Explain your reasoning.
Sample answer: One gallon and two quarts is the least expensive choice, although there would be 2 servings left over.

4. Choose your favorite breakfast cereal. Go to the grocery store and record the number of ounces, the cost, and the number of servings for each size available. Then compute the cost per serving.

Size (in ounces)	Cost	Number of Servings	Cost per Serving

Check students' answers.

5. Which size is least expensive? Check students' answers.

6. Which size box of cereal would you prefer to buy? Explain your reasoning.
Check students' answers.

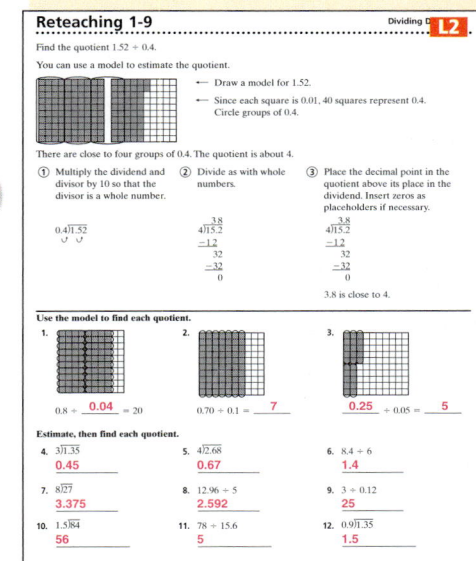

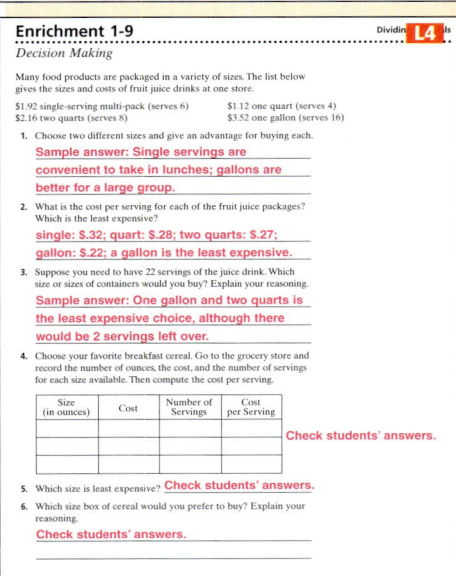

Alternative Assessment

Each student in a pair writes a decimal. Then partners together write two division expressions with their decimals and perform each division. Partners should check their work using multiplication.

Test Prep

Resources

For additional practice with a variety of test item formats:

- Test-Taking Strategies, p. 51
- Test Prep, p. 55
- Test-Taking Strategies with Transparencies

Using Decimals

Students use a table with decimal measures to find information and solve problems.

Guided Instruction

Activity

Discuss the table with students. Point out that there are measures for both male and female bones. Ask:

- *Why do you think scientists multiply male bones by 2.9 and female bones by 2.8?* **Sample: On average, female arm bones represent a greater fraction of total height than male arm bones.**
- *What is the rule for finding the height in inches of a male from an arm bone measured in centimeters?* **Multiply the length of the arm bone by 2.9 and add 70.6. Then divide by 2.54.**

Exercises

Have students work with partners to do Exercises 2–6.

Resources

- centimeter ruler

Using Decimals

Archaeologists are detectives who solve mysteries. The items they unearth provide clues about the people who once lived in a region. For example, archaeologists can measure the length of bones to determine the approximate heights of people.

ACTIVITY

about 67.8 in.

1. The table at the right shows the length of the humerus, or arm bone, for five skeletons from an archaeological dig. Estimate the height of Male 1 in inches. Use the steps below.

Skeleton	Length of Humerus (cm)
Male 1	35
Female 1	32.5
Male 2	31.5
Female 2	■
■	24.5

Male	Female
Step 1 Multiply the length of the humerus by 2.9.	**Step 1** Multiply the length of the humerus by 2.8.
Step 2 Add 70.6 to the result.	**Step 2** Add 74.8 to the result.
Step 3 Divide by 2.54 to find the height in inches.	**Step 3** Divide by 2.54 to find the height in inches.

2. Find the height in inches of Female 1 and Male 2. **about 65.3 in.; about 63.8 in.**

3. Measure the length of your own humerus in centimeters. To do this, measure from your elbow to the edge of your shoulder. Use this value to estimate your height in inches. How accurate is this estimate? **Check students' work.**

4. Suppose that the height of Female 2 is 148 cm. Work backward to estimate the length of her humerus. **about 26.1 cm**

5. The person listed in the bottom row of the chart was 140 cm tall. Is it more likely that this person was a male or a female? **male;** Support your answer with data and calculations. **24.5 × 2.9 + 70.6 = 141.7**

6. **Writing in Math** Write a short paragraph explaining how this technique for estimating a person's height might have been developed. How accurate is it? **Check students' work.**

Choosing the Right Operation

Rubber Band Ball   John Bain made the largest rubber-band ball in the world. The ball was 5 feet tall. It took 550,000 rubber bands, and 4 years, 2 months to put together. About how many rubber bands did Mr. Bain add each month?

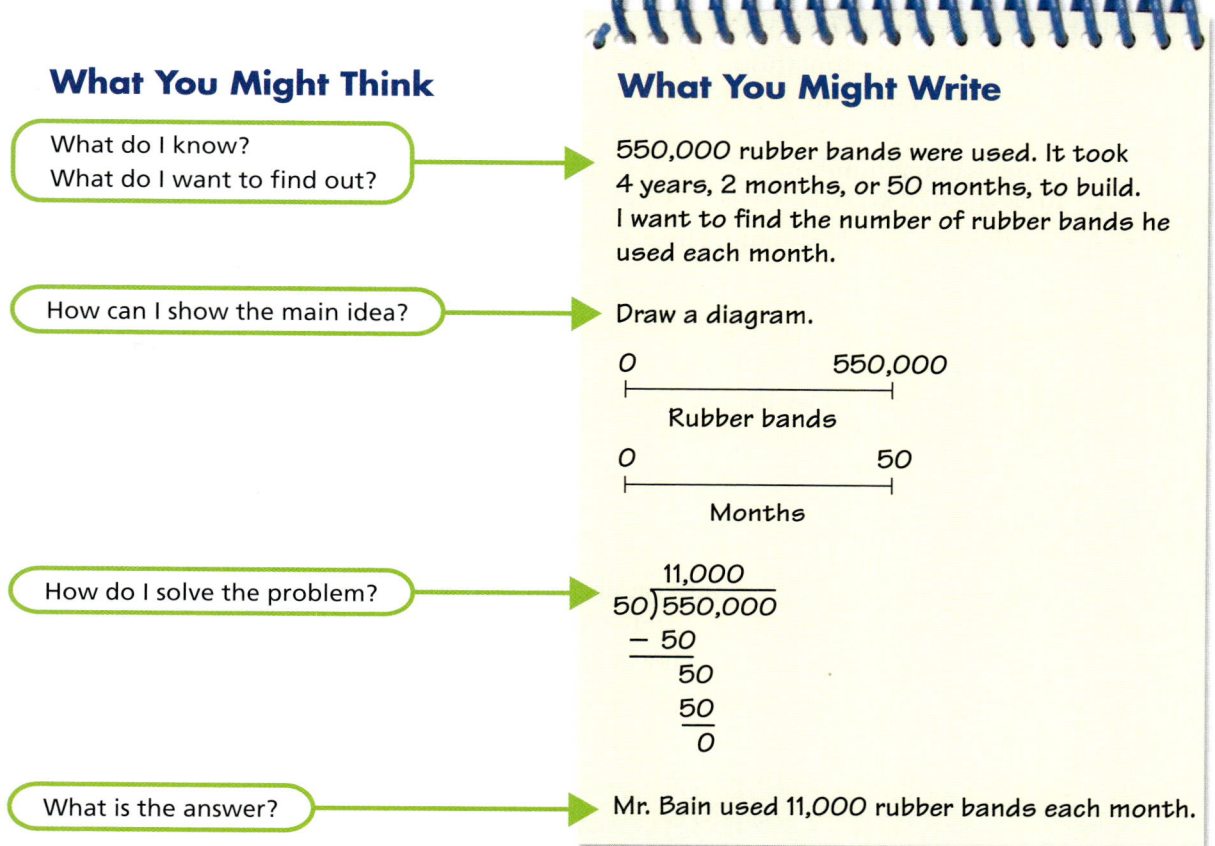

What You Might Think

> What do I know?
> What do I want to find out?

> How can I show the main idea?

> How do I solve the problem?

> What is the answer?

What You Might Write

550,000 rubber bands were used. It took 4 years, 2 months, or 50 months, to build. I want to find the number of rubber bands he used each month.

Draw a diagram.

```
0                        550,000
├─────────────────────────────┤
        Rubber bands

0                          50
├─────────────────────────────┤
          Months
```

```
      11,000
  50)550,000
    − 50
      ─────
       50
       50
       ──
        0
```

Mr. Bain used 11,000 rubber bands each month.

GPS Guided Problem Solving

Choosing the Right Operation

In this feature, students identify what they know and what they are trying to find out. They show the main idea, decide which operation to use, estimate the answer, solve the problem, and check that their answer is reasonable.

Guided Instruction

Discuss with students the need to read the problem carefully. Students need to decide what information is relevant to the problem they are trying to solve. Have a volunteer read the problem aloud. Ask:

- *What information is not needed to solve the problem?* **the dimensions of the ball, 5 feet tall**
- *How can you find the number of months?* **Multiply 4 years by 12 months per year and add the extra two months.**
- *How do you know to divide by 50?* **To find the average number per month, divide the total number by the number of months.**

Think It Through

1. Why does the diagram show 0–550,000 rubber bands on a line the same length as the line for 0–50 months?   **1–3. See margin.**

2. Explain why 4 years, 2 months is the same as $4 \times 12 + 2$ months.

3. **Estimation**   Use estimation to show that the answer is reasonable.

1. The diagram shows 0 to 550,000 rubber bands as the same length as 0 to 5 months because 550,000 rubber bands were used over 50 months.

2. Each year is 12 months, so 4×12 is the number of months in 4 years.

3. I can estimate 4 years and 2 months as 50 months and 550,000 rubber bands as 500,000 rubber bands. I can divide 500,000 by 50 and estimate that he used 10,000 rubber bands per month.

Exercises

4. Suppose Mr. Bain started with 5 packages of rubber bands. The packages cost $1.39, $1.59, $0.89, $1.98, and $1.13. Use front-end estimation to determine about how much he spent to begin his project. **about $7.50**
   a. What do you know?
   b. What are you trying to find out?
   c. Finish this front-end estimation.
      • Add the front-end numbers below.
        $1 + $1 + $0 + $1 + $1
      • Add the decimal numbers.
        $0.39 + $0.59 + $0.89 + $0.98 + $0.13 is about $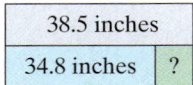.
      • Adjust the front-end estimate. The estimate is then $■.

5. To test the elasticity of the rubber bands, Mr. Bain stretched each rubber band in a package. The farthest a rubber band stretched was 38.5 inches. The shortest a rubber band stretched was 34.8 inches. Use the model below to find the difference in distances. **3.7 inches**

38.5 inches	
34.8 inches	?

6. Mr. Bain spent about $240 each month on his rubber-band ball. What was the total cost of his project? Copy the drawing below. Label the cost at the first ■. Then solve the problem and label the total cost at the second ■. **$12,000**

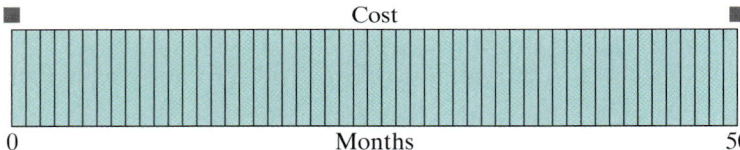

7. You can make a chain 1 mile long using 63,360 paper clips. The world record is a chain 19.62 miles long. How many paper clips were used to make this chain? **1,243,124 paper clips**

8. A teacher made a paper-clip chain using 60,650 paper clips. It took the teacher about 26.75 hours to make the chain. About how many seconds did the teacher spend adding each paper clip? **about 1.59 s**

Test-Taking Strategies

Writing Gridded Responses

Some tests include gridded responses. When you find an answer, write the answer at the top of the grid. Then fill in the matching bubbles.

EXAMPLE **Using the Answer Grid**

A fitness trail is 3.4 miles long. You walk 2.7 miles of the trail. How many more miles must you walk to reach the end of the trail?

$$3.4 \text{ miles} - 2.7 \text{ miles} = 0.7 \text{ mile}$$

You can write the answer as 0.7 or .7. Here are the two ways to enter these answers. You do not include labels in the grid.

Start to grid your answer at the right side of the grid.
↓

Add the 0 to → the left of the decimal point.

← Add the decimal point in the correct place. →

Exercises

Find each answer. If you have a grid, record your answer and fill in the bubbles.

1. A diver received scores of 6.5, 5.5, 6.0, 6.5, and 6.0 in a diving competition. What was his total score? **30.5**

2. Compare each of the decimals. Which decimal is the greatest? 0.23 0.256 0.236 0.26 0.24 **0.26**

3. You bought 2 books for $9 each. You also purchased 3 DVDs for $15 each. You paid with a $100 bill. What was your change in dollars? **37**

4. Lisa bought 32.4 ounces of glue. She used 6.8 ounces to put together a model. How many ounces of glue did Lisa have left? **25.6**

Writing Gridded Responses

This strategy provides students with examples that demonstrate how to correctly answer a gridded-response test question.

Guided Instruction

Example

Emphasize that fully completing a gridded-response test question involves two distinct parts: (1) writing the answer in the top row, one digit or symbol to a column, and (2) filling in the circle in each column that corresponds to the digit or symbol written at the top of that column.

Teaching Tips

Have volunteers explain how to fill in the correct responses. Be sure students place digits correctly around the decimal point provided.

Resources

Test-Taking Strategies with Transparencies
• Transparency 2
• Practice sheet, p. 1

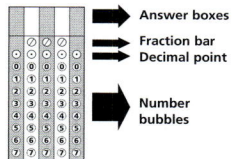

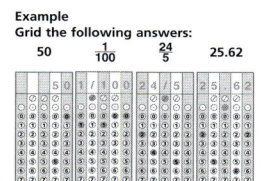

51

Chapter 1 Review

Resources

Student Edition
Extra Skills and Word Problems
    Practice, Ch. 1, p. 612
English/Spanish Glossary, p. 654
Formulas and Properties, p. 652
Tables, p. 648

All in One Teaching Resources
- Vocabulary and Study
  Skills 1F **L3**

Differentiated Instruction

Spanish Vocabulary Workbook
    with Study Skills **ELL**
Interactive Textbook
- Audio Glossary
Online Vocabulary Quiz

Success Tracker™
Online at PHSchool.com

Vocabulary Review

 Associative Property of Addition (p. 12)
Associative Property of Multiplication (p. 13)
Commutative Property of Addition (p. 12)

Commutative Property of Multiplication (p. 13)
compatible numbers (p. 9)
expanded form (p. 23)
expression (p. 16)
front-end estimation (p. 32)

Identity Property of Addition (p. 12)
Identity Property of Multiplication (p. 13)
order of operations (p. 16)
standard form (p. 4)

Go Online
PHSchool.com

For: Vocabulary Quiz
Web Code: aqj-0151

Choose the correct vocabulary term to complete each sentence.

1. An example of the ? is $5 + 0 = 5$. **Ident. Prop. of Add.**

2. Numbers that are easy to compute mentally are called ? .
   compatible numbers

3. The number 0.5830 is written in ? . **standard form**

4. $7 + 4 \times 2$ is a(n) ? . **expression**

5. $5 + (6 + 8) = (5 + 6) + 8$ is an example of the ? .
   Assoc. Prop. of Add.

Skills and Concepts

Lessons 1-1, 1-2, 1-3
- To write and compare whole numbers
- To estimate with whole numbers by rounding and by using compatible numbers
- To understand and use the properties of numbers

You can round each number or use **compatible numbers** to estimate. You can use the **commutative, associative,** and **identity properties** to help you add and multiply mentally.

Write each number in words.

6. 5,000,025 **five million, twenty-five**   7. 5,025 **five thousand, twenty-five**

Write the numbers in order from least to greatest.

8. 1,010; 1,100; 1,001; 1,101
   1,001; 1,010; 1,100; 1,101

9. 2,332; 2,323; 2,322; 2,232
   2,232; 2,322; 2,323; 2,332

Estimate using rounding or compatible numbers.

10. $5,021 + 2,957$
    about 8,000

11. $52 + 29 + 97$
    about 180

12. $597 - 201$
    about 400

13. $8,989 \div 3$
    about 3,000

14. 19×52
    about 1,000

15. $6,012 \div 99$
    about 60

Use mental math to find each sum or product.

16. $1 + 250 + 99$
    350

17. $2 \times 13 \times 5$
    130

18. $16 + 3 + 4 + 7$
    30

Spanish Vocabulary/Study Skills **ELL**

Vocabulary/Study Skills **L3**

1F Vocabulary Review   For use with the Chapter Review

Study Skill Review your class notes as soon as possible. This will help you identify any concepts in which you need additional explanation.

Match the term in Column A with its definition or example in Column B.

Column A	Column B
1. Identity Property of Multiplication **E**	A. decimals that represent the same amount
2. place value **F**	B. $7 + (3 + 9) = (7 + 3) + 9$
3. compatible numbers **C**	C. numbers that are easy to compute mentally
4. equivalent decimals **A**	D. $6 + 8 = 8 + 6$
5. Associative Property of Addition **B**	E. $8.3 \times 1 = 8.3$
6. Commutative Property of Addition **D**	F. value of a digit based on its location in a particular number

Match the term in Column A with its definition or example in Column B.

Column A	Column B
7. Identity Property of Addition **L**	G. $8 \cdot 4 = 4 \cdot 8$
8. Associative Property of Multiplication **K**	H. sum that shows the place and value of each digit
9. Commutative Property of Multiplication **G**	I. a number written using digits
10. expanded form **H**	J. mathematical phrase containing numbers and operations
11. standard form **I**	K. $8(7 \cdot 9) = (8 \cdot 7)9$
12. expression **J**	L. $4 + 0 = 4$

---

52   Chapter 1   Chapter Review

Lesson 1-4

- To use the order of operations to simplify expressions and solve problems

An **expression** is a mathematical phrase that contains numbers and operation symbols. You can use the **order of operations** to find the value of an expression.

Find the value of each expression.

19. $30 - 5 + 4 \times 3$ **20.** $6 - (27 - 9) \div 3$ **21.** $5 \times 8 + 4 \div 2$
   37   0   42

Lessons 1-5, 1-6

- To read, write, and round decimals
- To compare and order decimals using models and place value

You can write decimals in words, in **standard form,** and in **expanded form.** You can compare and order decimals using models, a number line, or place value.

Write each decimal in words. 22–25. See margin.

22. 525.5   **23.** 0.5255   **24.** 5.025   **25.** 50.0025

Round each decimal to the underlined place.

26. 45.1<u>6</u> 45.2   **27.** 98.<u>6</u>45 98.6   **28.** 5.1<u>2</u>5 5.13   **29.** 1.2<u>4</u>6 1.25

30. 0.06; 0.14; 0.4; 0.52

31. 23; 23.03; 23.2; 23.25

Order each set of decimals from least to greatest. 30–31. See left.

30. 0.52, 0.4, 0.14, 0.06   **31.** 23, 23.2, 23.25, 23.03

Lesson 1-7

- To add and subtract decimals and to solve problems involving decimals

You can use estimation to tell whether your answer is reasonable. You can use **front-end estimation** to estimate a sum.

First estimate. Then find each sum or difference. 32–37. See margin.

32. $337.4 + 20.08$ **33.** $1.741 - 0.81$ **34.** $1.6 + 1.8$

35. $9.6 - 7.9$ **36.** $4.12 - 0.253$ **37.** $2.01 + 5.39$

Lessons 1-8, 1-9

- To multiply and divide decimals and to solve problems involving decimals

When multiplying decimals, add the decimal places in the factors to place the decimal point in the product. When dividing decimals, multiply both the dividend and the divisor by the same number so that the divisor is a whole number.

Find each product or quotient. 42–45. See left.

42. 6.94

43. 31.458

44. 10.4

45. 170

38. 1.2×29.5 **39.** $12.12 \div 6$ **40.** $38.4 \div 0.08$ **41.** 0.54×17
      35.4   2.02   480   9.18
42. $27.76 \div 4$ **43.** 3.21×9.8 **44.** 13×0.8 **45.** $8.5 \div 0.05$

22. five hundred twenty-five and five tenths

23. five thousand, two hundred fifty-five ten-thousandths

24. five and twenty-five thousandths

25. fifty and twenty-five ten-thousandths

32–37. Answers may vary. Samples are given.

32. about 357; 357.48

33. about 1; 0.931

34. about 3; 3.4

35. about 2; 1.7

36. about 4; 3.867

37. about 7; 7.4

53

Chapter 1 Test

Go Online
PHSchool.com
For: Online chapter test
Web Code: aqa-0152

Write each number in words. 1–6. See margin.

1. 623.7

2. 2,086,374

3. 89.123

4. 35,743,620,000

5. 172,254

6. 3.024

Use <, =, or > to complete each statement.

7. 26,145 **>** 25,641

8. 32.12 **<** 32.42

9. 9.7 **=** 9.70

10. 1,247 **>** 1,241

Order each set of numbers from least to greatest.

11. 6,425; 6,542; 6,452; 7,642; 6,524
    6,425; 6,452; 6,524; 6,542; 7,642

12. 0.27, 0.56, 0.212, 0.563, 0.276, 0.5
    0.212, 0.27, 0.276, 0.5, 0.56, 0.563

13. 81, 81.1, 80.08, 82, 81.5, 80.3
    80.08, 80.3, 81, 81.1, 81.5, 82

14. 1.63, 1, 1.064, 0.163, 1.036, 2.136, 2
    0.163, 1, 1.036, 1.064, 1.63, 2, 2.136

15. **Estimation** Suppose your savings account has a balance of $238.52. You deposit $42.56. Then you withdraw $92.35. About how much is left in your savings account? **about $190**

Use rounding, front-end estimation, or compatible numbers to estimate each answer. 16–21. Answers may vary. Samples are given.

16. 37 + 42 + 142
    about 220

17. 50.32 × 22.1
    about 1,000

18. 4.63 × 50.491
    about 250

19. 98 ÷ 24
    about 4

20. 1.01 + 2.89
    about 4

21. 62.85 − 24.12
    about 40

22. **DVDs** Five DVDs cost a total of $75. Explain whether the best estimate for the cost of one DVD is greater than or less than $14. **Greater than $14. Answers may vary. Sample: 5 × $14 = $70, and $70 < $75**

Use mental math to find each answer.

23. 829 + 71 **900**

24. 24 + (72 + 64) **160**

25. 25 × 6 × 4 **600**

26. 10 × 7 × 20 **1,400**

27. You buy movie tickets for yourself and three friends. Each ticket costs $7. You pay with two $20 bills. How much change do you get back? **$12**

Find the value of each expression.

28. 16 ÷ (4 × 4) **1**

29. 8 − 4 ÷ 2 **6**

30. 5 + (32 − 16) **21**

31. (9 − 1 × 3) ÷ 2 **3**

First estimate. Then find each sum or difference. 32–35. Answers may vary. Samples are given.

32. 3.89 + 15.3
    about 19; 19.19

33. 4.6 − 2.07
    about 3; 2.53

34. 41.2 − 19.8
    about 20; 21.4

35. 53.7 + 28.6
    about 80; 82.3

Find each product or quotient.

36. 9.063 × 24 **217.512**

37. 0.36(15) **5.4**

38. 21.6 ÷ 0.06 **360**

39. 7 ÷ 0.14 **50**

40. **Pet Food** Zelda spent $6.24 on pet food. The food costs $.24 per cup. How many cups of pet food did Zelda purchase? **26**

41. **Money** There are 40 quarters in a roll of quarters. What is the value of 9 rolls of quarters? **$90**

1. **six hundred twenty-three and seven tenths**

2. **two million, eighty-six thousand, three hundred seventy-four**

3. **eighty-nine and one hundred twenty-three thousandths**

4. **thirty-five billion, seven hundred forty-three million, six hundred twenty thousand**

5. **one hundred seventy-two thousand, two hundred fifty-four**

6. **three and twenty-four thousandths**

Test Prep · Practice

Reading Comprehension

Read each passage below. Then answer the questions based on what you have read.

> **Rainfall** Hilo, Hawaii, usually receives 129.19 inches of rain each year. Compare that to Phoenix, Arizona, which receives 7.66 inches of rain a year. In Hilo, the wettest month is April, with 15.26 inches of rain, while the driest month is June, with 6.2 inches of rain. Phoenix's wettest month is December, with 1 inch, and its driest is May, with 0.12 inch.

1. In Hilo, how many more inches of rain typically fall in April than in June? **C**
- Ⓐ 0.88 inch
- Ⓒ 9.06 inches
- Ⓑ 15.26 inches
- Ⓓ 21.46 inches

2. In July, Phoenix typically gets 0.83 inch of rain. About how many times as much rain falls in July as in May? **G**
- Ⓕ 6
- Ⓖ 7
- Ⓗ 8
- Ⓙ 9

3. How many inches of rain does Hilo receive in a typical ten-year period? **A**
- Ⓐ 1,291.9 inches
- Ⓒ 76.60 inches
- Ⓑ 12.919 inches
- Ⓓ 0.766 inches

4. Hilos yearly rainfall is about how many times the yearly rainfall is Phoenix? **J**
- Ⓕ 1,040 times
- Ⓗ 138 times
- Ⓖ 122 times
- Ⓙ 16 times

> **Coins** Did you know that some coins contain more pure metal than others? American Gold Eagle coins are 0.9166 gold and Canadian Maple Leaf coins are 0.9999 gold. American Silver Eagle coins are 0.999 silver while American Platinum Eagle coins are 0.9995 platinum.

5. How might you write the purity of the American Silver Eagle coin in order to compare it with the other coins? **B**
- Ⓐ 0.99
- Ⓒ 0.0999
- Ⓑ 0.9990
- Ⓓ 0.9999

6. What portion of the American Gold Eagle coin is NOT gold? **G**
- Ⓕ 0.0004
- Ⓗ 0.0034
- Ⓖ 0.0834
- Ⓙ 0.0934

7. Which of the five coins mentioned contains the greatest portion of pure metal? **C**
- Ⓐ American Silver Eagle
- Ⓑ American Gold Eagle
- Ⓒ Canadian Maple Leaf
- Ⓓ American Platinum Eagle

8. How much gold is in an American Gold Eagle coin that weighs 0.1 ounce? **J**
- Ⓕ 9.166 ounces
- Ⓗ 0.9166 ounce
- Ⓖ 0.91660 ounce
- Ⓙ 0.09166 ounce

Resources

Test Prep Workbook

All in One Teaching Resources
- Cumulative Review **L3**

ExamView Assessment Suite CD-ROM
- Standardized Test Practice

Differentiated Instruction

Spanish Assessment Resources
- Spanish Cumulative Review **ELL**

ExamView Assessment Suite CD-ROM
- Special Needs Practice Bank **L1**

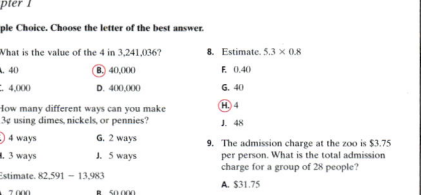

Applying Decimals

Have students look at the shipping cost on the sample order form. Ask:
- *What information is given to calculate the shipping cost?* **6% is given as the cost for shipping**
- *How is the percent used to calculate the cost of shipping?* **6% is changed to its decimal form and multiplied to the total of the items to calculate the cost of shipping**
- *If the items are taxed, how would the sales tax be added to the order?* **The percent of the sales tax is multiplied by the subtotal to calculate the tax cost. Then the tax is added to the subtotal and shipping to calculate the total of the order.**

Activating Prior Knowledge

Have students discuss what they know about early forms of writing—what the marks looked like and how they were used. Explain that Mesopotamia describes the land between the Tigris River and Euphrates River that is now the modern-day country of Iraq.

Guided Instruction

Give students a moment to read the data about cuneiform and about the other early ways to tally data.

Ask:
- *Why do merchants need to keep track of the items they sell and order?* **Answers will vary.**
- *Why is it important to keep track of the money we spend?* **Answers will vary.**

Problem Solving Application

Applying Decimals

That's an Order Ancient Mesopotamians bought and traded grain and other items. They developed a writing system to keep track of their goods and money. Today, we use order forms and receipts to purchase items and record the money we spend.

How Much for That Goat?

This piece of limestone shows part of a business deal including a goat worth one deben of copper, an Ancient Egyptian measure of metal. One deben equals 3 ounces.

Put It All Together

1. Find the five missing values in the sample order form. (*Hint:* Some missing values cannot be found without finding others first.)

2. **Open-Ended** Suppose you have a clothing budget of $500.
   a. **Research** Make a list of items you would like to purchase. Find their prices.
   b. Use an order form like the sample. Complete the Quantity, Description, and Unit Price columns for the items on your list. At least four of the values in the Quantity column should be greater than 1.
   c. Find the total for each row by multiplying the quantity by the unit price. Follow the directions on the order form to fill in the rest of the boxes. Make sure you stay within your budget!
   d. Copy your order form onto another sheet of paper. Leave some boxes blank as in the sample. Trade order forms with another student and find each other's missing values.

Order Form

Quantity	Description	Unit Price	Total
■	20-gallon aquarium	$119.99	$119.99
1	Air pump	$14.95	$14.95
2	Water filter	■	$64.98
3	Tropical fish food	$7.49	$22.47
■	Gravel, one bag	$1.99	■
3	Driftwood decoration	$13.25	$39.75
	Subtotal (Add the totals from above.)		■
	6% Shipping (Multiply subtotal by 0.06.)		$16.44
	Total (Add subtotal and shipping.)		$290.52

Tally Sticks

People have used notched sticks for tallying totals for thousands of years. Larger notches denote greater amounts.

Calculations and More

Handheld calculators, which have taken the place of adding machines, perform many mathematical operations. This one can display graphs.

1. 1; $32.49; 6; $11.94; $274.08

2. Answers may vary. Sample:

a. blue jeans, $39.99; T-shirts, $5.49; winter coat, $117.29; socks, $2.99; sweatshirt, $36.89; winter hat, $14.99; running shoes, $56.79; shorts, $22; boots, $55.99

Napier's Rods

You can use Napier's rods to find products. The rods in the photo show multiples of 4, 7, and 9.

Go Online
PHSchool.com

For: Information about completing order forms
Web Code: aqe-0153

Cuneiform

Ancient Babylonians wrote their numbers in cuneiform, printed with sticks and wedges on clay tablets. The Babylonian number system is sexagesimal, which means it is based on counting 60's. This system remains in our measures of time and angles.

Counting Sheep

The cuneiform characters on this clay tablet are a tally of sheep and goats from an area called Tello, in ancient Mesopotamia.

57

Activity

Help students understand what information each column of the order form shows. For example, ask: *How do you find the unit price for an item?* **Sample: Divide the total price by the quantity.** Have students work in pairs to answer the questions.

Exercises

For Exercise 1, elicit from students that to find the number of gravel bags in this order, they will need to work backward. One way is to first find the total cost of the gravel by adding all the other known totals plus the amount of shipping. Then subtract that total from $290.52. Once they have the gravel cost, they can divide by its unit price to find the quantity.

Geography Connection

Ask students to find Mesopotamia on a map of the ancient Middle East and on a map of the region as it looks today. Have them describe the changes they see.

Differentiated Instruction

Special Needs   **L1**

For Exercises 1–2, provide actual order forms or receipts for students to examine and discuss.

b.   c.   **d. Check students' work.**

Quantity	Description	Unit	Total
2	Blue Jeans	$39.99	$79.98
4	T-shirts	$5.49	$21.96
1	Winter Coat	$117.29	$117.29
6	Socks, pair	$2.99	$17.94
3	Sweatshirt	$36.89	$110.67
1	Winter Hat	$14.99	$14.99
1	Running Shoes, pair	$56.79	$56.79
1	Shorts, pair	$22.00	$22.00
1	Boots, pair	$55.99	$55.99

2 Data and Graphs

Chapter at a Glance

Lesson Titles, Objectives, and Features	Assessment	NCTM Standards	Local Standards
2-1a Activity Lab, Hands On: Exploring the Mean **2-1 Finding the Mean** • To find and analyze the mean of a data set using models and calculations **Vocabulary Builder:** High-Use Academic Words	Lesson Quiz	1, 2, 5, 6, 8, 9, 10	
2-2 Median and Mode • To find and analyze the median and mode of a data set	Lesson Quiz	1, 2, 5, 6, 8, 9, 10	
2-3 Frequency Tables and Line Plots • To analyze a set of data by finding the range and by making frequency tables and line plots	Lesson Quiz	2, 5, 6, 8, 9, 10	
2-4 Bar Graphs and Line Graphs • To make and analyze bar graphs and line graphs **2-4b Activity Lab, Technology:** Making Bar Graphs **Extension:** Double Bar and Line Graphs	Lesson Quiz	2, 5, 6, 8, 9, 10	
2-5 Using Spreadsheets to Organize Data • To use spreadsheets to display data and solve problems **2-5b Activity Lab, Technology:** Spreadsheets and Graphs	Lesson Quiz Checkpoint Quiz 1	2, 5, 6, 8, 9, 10	
2-6 Stem-and-Leaf Plots • To make and analzye stem-and-leaf plots **Guided Problem Solving:** Solving Multiple-Step Problems	Lesson Quiz	2, 5, 6, 8, 9, 10	
2-7 Misleading Graphs and Statistics • To identify misleading graphs and statistics **Extension:** Random Samples and Surveys	Lesson Quiz Checkpoint Quiz 2	5, 6, 7, 8, 9, 10	
Problem Solving Application: Applying Data Analysis			

NCTM Standards 2000

1 Number and Operations	**2** Algebra	**3** Geometry	**4** Measurement	**5** Data Analysis and Probability
6 Problem Solving	**7** Reasoning and Proof	**8** Communication	**9** Connections	**10** Representation

Corrections to Standardized Tests

All content for these tests is contained in *Prentice Hall Math,* Course 1. This chart reflects coverage in this chapter only.

	2-1	2-2	2-3	2-4	2-5	2-6	2-7
Terra Nova CAT6 (Level 16)							
Number and Number Relations							
Computation and Numerical Estimation							
Operation Concepts							
Measurement							
Geometry and Spatial Sense							
Data Analysis, Statistics, and Probability	✔	✔	✔	✔	✔	✔	✔
Patterns, Functions, and Algebra							
Problem Solving and Reasoning	✔	✔	✔	✔	✔	✔	✔
Communication	✔	✔	✔	✔	✔	✔	✔
Decimals, Fractions, Integers, and Percent							
Order of Operations							
Terra Nova CTBS (Level 16)							
Whole Numbers, Decimals, Fractions							
Numeration, Number Theory							
Data Interpretation	✔	✔	✔	✔	✔	✔	✔
Pre-algebra	✔	✔					
Measurement							
Geometry							
ITBS (Level 12)							
Number Properties and Operations							
Algebra							
Geometry							
Measurement							
Probability and Statistics	✔	✔	✔	✔	✔	✔	✔
Estimation							
SAT10 (Int 2 Level)							
Number Sense and Operations							
Patterns, Relationships, and Algebra							
Data, Statistics, and Probability	✔	✔	✔	✔	✔	✔	✔
Geometry and Measurement							
NAEP							
Number Sense, Properties, and Operations							
Measurement							
Geometry and Spatial Sense							
Data Analysis, Statistics, and Probability	✔	✔	✔	✔	✔	✔	✔
Algebra and Functions							

CAT6 California Achievement Test, 6th Ed. **CTBS** Comprehensive Test of Basic Skills **ITBS** Iowa Test of Basic Skills, Form M
SAT10 Stanford Achievement Test, 10th Ed. **NAEP** National Assessment of Educational Progress 2005 Mathematics Objectives

Math Background

Skills Trace

BEFORE Chapter 2

Grade 5 presented graphic displays of data.

DURING Chapter 2

Course 1 reviews and extends the graphical display of data to stem-and-leaf plots and misleading graphs.

AFTER Chapter 2

Throughout this course, students make and interpret graphical displays of data.

2-1 2-2 Finding the Mean, Median, and Mode

Math Understandings

- There are different statistics for describing the "center" of a numerical data set.
- The mean, median, and mode are common measures for the central tendency of a data set.

The **mean** of a set of data is the sum of the data divided by the number of data items. The **median** is the middle number of a set of ordered data. When there is an even number of data items, you can find the median by adding the two middle numbers and dividing by 2. The **mode** is the data item that appears most often. There may be no mode, or one or more modes. If all data items occur the same number of times, there is no mode. An **outlier** is a data item that is far apart from the rest of the data. If a data set has an outlier, then the mean may not describe the data set very well.

Example: For the data set 9, 27, 8, 11, 17, 14, 12, 17, 16, 11 the median is 13. 8, 9, 11, 11, (12, 14), 16, 17, 17, 27 The mean is $\frac{142}{10}$, or 14.2. The two modes are 11 and 17. The data set appears to have an outlier of 27.

2-3 Frequency Tables and Line Plots

Math Understandings

- A frequency table shows how often each data value occurs.
- A line plot visually represents a frequency table on a number line.

A **frequency table** is a table that lists each item in a data set with the number of times the item occurs. A **line plot** is a graph that shows the shape of a data set by stacking X's above each data value on a number line. The **range** of a data set is the difference between the least and greatest values.

DVDs Rental by Each Customer		
Number	Tally	Frequency
One	卌	5
Two	卌 I	6
Three	IIII	4
Four	卌	5
Five	II	2
Six	I	1

DVDs Rented by Each Customer

```
                X
  X    X              X
  X    X    X         X
  X    X    X         X
  X    X    X    X
  X    X    X    X    X    X
  1    2    3    4    5    6
        Number of DVDs
```

2-4 Bar Graphs and Line Graphs

Math Understandings

- You can display numerical information with a bar graph, or a line graph.
- A bar graph shows comparisons.
- A line graph shows trends over time.

A **bar graph** uses vertical or horizontal bars to display numerical information. A **line graph** uses a series of line segments to show changes of one variable compared to another.

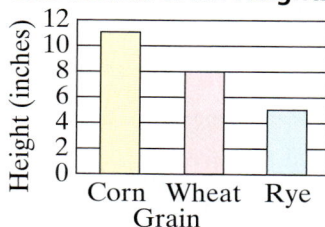

One Month Grain Heights

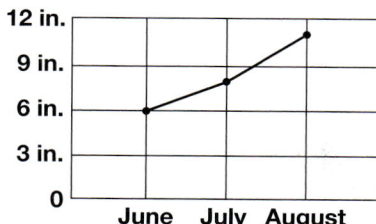

Plant Growth Over 3 Months

One Month Grain Heights	
Grain	Height
Corn	11 in.
Wheat	8 in.
Rye	5 in.

Plant Growth	
Month	Height
June	6 in.
July	8 in.
August	11 in.

2-5 Using Spreadsheets to Organize Data

Math Understandings
- A computer spreadsheet is an electronic workspace that you can use to organize information in cells so that you can use that information in calculations and graphs.
- You can use spreadsheet software and formulas to make repeated calculations that reflect changing data.

A **spreadsheet** is a table made up of rows and columns used to organize data. A **cell** is a box in a spreadsheet where a particular row and column meet.

2-6 Stem-and-Leaf Plots

Math Understandings
- A stem-and-leaf plot shows the distribution of a data set.
- Each stem-and-leaf plot must include a key that shows what the stems and leaves represent for a particular plot.

A **stem-and-leaf** plot is a graph that uses the digits of each number to show the shape of the data. Each data value is broken into a "stem" (digit or digits on the left) and a "leaf" (digit or digits on the right).

**Times to Get Ready
for School (minutes)**

```
2 | 3 3 5 7 8 8
3 | 3 4 5 7 7 7 9
4 | 0 0 2 3 3 5
5 | 8
```
Key: 2 | 3 means 23 min

2-7 Misleading Graphs and Statistics

Math Understandings
- Choices made about the labels, scale intervals, and style of a graph can create a misleading impression.

When you read a graph, make sure the axis scales start at zero and use equal intervals. Otherwise, the graph may be misleading. Statistics such as a mean can also be misleading if the data set contains extreme values, or outliers, that distort the mean.

Additional Professional Development Opportunities

Math Background Notes for Chapter 2: Every lesson has a Math Background in the PLAN section.

Research Overview, Mathematics Strands
Additional support for these topics and more is in the front of the Teacher's Edition.

LessonLab
LessonLab, a Pearson Education company, offers comprehensive, facilitated professional development designed to help teachers to improve student achievement. To learn more, please visit lessonlab.com.

Chapter 2 Resources

Print Resources	2-1	2-2	2-3	2-4	2-5	2-6	2-7	For the Chapter
L3 Practice	●	●	●	●	●	●	●	
L1 Adapted Practice	●	●	●	●	●	●	●	
L3 Guided Problem Solving	●	●	●	●	●	●	●	
L2 Reteaching	●	●	●	●	●	●	●	
L4 Enrichment	●	●	●	●	●	●	●	
L3 Daily Notetaking Guide	●	●	●	●	●	●	●	
L1 Adapted Daily Notetaking Guide	●	●	●	●	●	●	●	
L3 Vocabulary and Study Skills Worksheets	●		●		●	●		●
L3 Daily Puzzles	●	●	●	●	●	●	●	
L3 Activity Labs	●	●	●	●	●	●	●	
L3 Checkpoint Quiz					●			
L3 Chapter Project								●
L2 Below Level Chapter Test								●
L3 Chapter Test								●
L4 Alternative Assessment								●
L3 Cumulative Review								●

Spanish Resources **ELL**	2-1	2-2	2-3	2-4	2-5	2-6	2-7	For the Chapter
L3 Practice	●	●	●	●	●	●	●	
L3 Vocabulary and Study Skills Worksheets	●		●		●	●		●
L3 Checkpoint Quiz					●			
L2 Below Level Chapter Test								●
L3 Chapter Test								●
L4 Alternative Assessment								●
L3 Cumulative Review								●

Transparencies	2-1	2-2	2-3	2-4	2-5	2-6	2-7	For the Chapter
Check Skills You'll Need	●	●	●	●	●	●	●	
Additional Examples	●	●	●	●	●	●	●	
Problem of the Day	●	●	●	●	●	●	●	
Classroom Aid	●			●	●	●		
Student Edition Answers	●	●	●	●	●	●	●	●
Lesson Quiz	●	●	●	●	●	●	●	
Test-Taking Strategies								●

Technology	2-1	2-2	2-3	2-4	2-5	2-6	2-7	For the Chapter
Interactive Textbook Online	●	●	●	●	●	●	●	●
StudentExpress™ CD-ROM	●	●	●	●	●	●	●	●
Success Tracker™ Online Intervention	●	●	●	●	●	●	●	●
TeacherExpress™ CD-ROM	●	●	●	●	●	●	●	●
PresentationExpress™ with QuickTake Presenter CD-ROM	●	●	●	●	●	●	●	●
ExamView® Assessment Suite CD-ROM	●	●	●	●	●	●	●	●
MindPoint® Quiz Show CD-ROM								●
Prentice Hall Web Site: PHSchool.com	●	●	●	●	●	●	●	●

Also available: **Prentice Hall Assessment System**
- Progress Monitoring Assessments
- Skills and Concepts Review
- Test Prep Workbook

Other Resources
Algebra Readiness Tests
All-in-One Student Workbook
All-in-One Student Workbook, Adapted Version
Multilingual Handbook

Solution Key
Math Notes Study Folder
Spanish Cumulative Assessment

Where You Can Use the Lesson Resources

Here is a suggestion, following the four-step teaching plan, for how you can incorporate Differentiated Instruction Resources into your teaching.

	Instructional Resources **L3**	Differentiated Instruction Resources
1. Plan		
Preparation Read the Math Background in the Teacher's Edition to connect this lesson with students' previous experience. **Starting Class** **Check Skills You'll Need** Assign these exercises to review prerequisite skills. **New Vocabulary** Help students pre-read the lesson by pointing out the new terms introduced in the lesson.	**Math Background** **Math Understandings** **Transparencies & PresentationExpress™ with QuickTake Presenter CD-ROM** Check Skills You'll Need Problem of the Day **Resources** Vocabulary and Study Skills	**Spanish Support** **ELL** Vocabulary and Study Skills
2. Teach		
L3 Guided Instruction Use the Activity Labs to build conceptual understanding. Teach each Example. Use the Teacher's Edition side column notes for specific teaching tips, including Error Prevention notes. Use the Additional Examples found in the side column (and on transparency and PowerPoint) as an alternative presentation for the content. After each Example, assign the Quick Check exercise for that Example to get an immediate assessment of student understanding. Use the Closure activity in the Teacher's Edition to help students attain mastery of lesson content.	**Student Edition** Activity Lab **Resources** Daily Notetaking Guide Activity Lab **Transparencies & PresentationExpress™ with QuickTake Presenter CD-ROM** Additional Examples Classroom Aids **ExamView Assessment Suite CD-ROM**	**Teacher's Edition** Every lesson includes suggestions for working with students who need special attention. **L1** Special Needs **L2** Below Level **L4** Advanced Learners **ELL** English Language Learners **Resources** **L1** Adapted Daily Notetaking Guide **Multilingual Handbook**
3. Practice		

Assignment Guide
Check Your Understanding
Use these questions to check students' understanding before you assign homework.
Homework Exercises
Assign homework from these leveled exercises in the Assignment Guide.
  A Practice by Example
  B Apply Your Skills
  C Challenge
  Test Prep and Mixed Review
Homework Quick Check
Use these key exercises to quickly check students' homework.
	Transparencies & PresentationExpress™ with QuickTake Presenter CD-ROM
	Student Answers
	Resources
	Practice
	Guided Problem Solving
	Vocabulary and Study Skills
	Activity Lab
	Daily Puzzles
	ExamView® Assessment Suite CD-ROM
		Spanish Support
		ELL Practice
		ELL Vocabulary and Study Skills
		Resources
		L1 Adapted Practice
		L4 Enrichment

4. Assess & Reteach		
Lesson Quiz Assign the Lesson Quiz to assess students' mastery of the lesson content. **Checkpoint Quiz** Use the Checkpoint Quiz to assess student progress over several lessons.	**Transparencies & PresentationExpress™ with QuickTake Presenter CD-ROM** Lesson Quiz **Resources** Checkpoint Quiz	**Resources** **L2** Reteaching **ELL** Checkpoint Quiz Success Tracker™ Online Intervention **ExamView® Assessment Suite CD-ROM**

KEY **L1** Special Needs **L2** Below Level **L3** For All Students **L4** Advanced, Gifted **ELL** English Language Learners

CHAPTER 2

Data and Graphs

Check Your Readiness

Answers are in the back of the textbook.

For Intervention, direct students to:

Ordering Decimals
Lesson 1–6
Extra Skills and Word
 Problems Practice, Ch. 1

Adding Decimals
Lesson 1-7
Extra Skills and Word
 Problems Practice, Ch. 1

Subtracting Decimals
Lesson 1-7
Extra Skills and Word
 Problems Practice, Ch. 1

Dividing Decimals
Lesson 1-9
Extra Skills and Word
 Problems Practice, Ch. 1

Spanish Vocabulary/Study Skills ELL

Vocabulary/Study Skills L3

2A: Graphic Organizer For use before Lesson 2-1

Study Skill Take notes when your teacher presents new material in class. Organize those notes as a way to study, reviewing them as you go.

Write your answers.

1. What is the chapter title?  Data and Graphs
2. How many lessons are there in this chapter? seven
3. What is the topic of the Test-Taking Strategies page? Answering the Question Asked
4. Complete the graphic organizer below as you work through the chapter.
   - In the center, write the title of the chapter.
   - When you begin a lesson, write the lesson name in a rectangle.
   - When you complete a lesson, write a skill or key concept in a circle linked to that lesson block.
   - When you complete the chapter, use this graphic organizer to help you review.

Check students' diagrams.

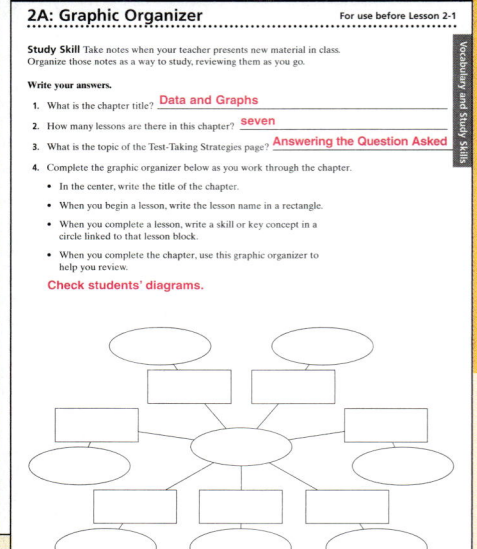

58

What You've Learned

- In Chapter 1, you compared and ordered whole numbers and decimals.
- You used addition, subtraction, multiplication, and division to solve problems involving decimals.
- You used order of operations to simplify expressions.

Check Your Readiness

For Exercises	See Lesson
1–2	1-6
3–9	1-7
10–12	1-9

Ordering Decimals.

Order each set of decimals from least to greatest.

1. $0.12, 0.13, 0.45, 0.35, 0.21$ **0.12, 0.13, 0.21, 0.35, 0.45**

2. $45.1, 44.0, 46.01, 45.01$ **44.0, 45.01, 45.1, 46.01**

Adding Decimals

Find each sum.

3. $13.2 + 23.6 + 26.3$ **63.1**

4. $152.3 + 143.6 + 128$ **423.9**

5. $49.0 + 22.2 + 11.22 + 23.4$ **105.82**

6. $6.09 + 1.5 + 4.68 + 13.6$ **25.87**

Subtracting Decimals

Find each difference.

7. $109.55 - 89.34$ **20.21**

8. $10.42 - 9.36$ **1.06**

9. $75 - 73.2$ **1.8**

Dividing Decimals

Find each quotient.

10. $142.03 \div 10$ **14.203**

11. $361.6 \div 16$ **22.6**

12. $100.75 \div 25$ **4.03**

Chapter 2 Overview

In this chapter, students work with statistics and graphs as they organize, interpret, analyze, display, and evaluate data. They interpret and make bar graphs, line graphs, and stem-and-leaf plots. They conclude the chapter by examining misleading graphs and statistics.

Activating Prior Knowledge

In this chapter, students build on and extend their knowledge of statistics and graphing. They also draw upon their understanding of decimal computations as they find and interpret measures of central tendency. Ask questions such as:
- *What is the sum of 0.4, 12.5, and 0.08?* **12.98**
- *What is (5 + 24 + 12 + 7) ÷ 4?* **12**
- *What is the order of the following decimals from least to greatest? 3.25, 3.2, 4.5, 5.4, 3.15, 3, 2.75* **2.75, 3, 3.15, 3.2, 3.25, 4.5, 5.4**

What You'll Learn Next

- In this chapter, you will find the mean, median, mode, and range of a set of data.

- You will select and use different types of data graphs, including line plots, line graphs, bar graphs, and stem-and-leaf plots.

- You will solve problems by collecting, organizing, displaying, and interpreting data.

🔊 Key Vocabulary

- bar graph (p. 74)
- cell (p. 80)
- frequency table (p. 70)
- line graph (p. 75)
- line plot (p. 71)
- mean (p. 61)
- median (p. 66)
- mode (p. 67)
- outlier (p. 62)
- range (p. 71)
- scatter plot (p. 84)
- spreadsheet (p. 80)
- stem-and-leaf plot (p. 86)

Problem Solving Application On pages 104 and 105, you will work an extended activity on mountain peaks.

Chapter 2   **59**

Exploring the Mean

In Lesson 2-1 that follows, students will learn about one measure of central tendency: the mean. This Activity Lab introduces them to the mean, the measure they are most likely to think of as the "average" of a set of numbers.

Guided Instruction

Teaching Tip

Many students will have an informed or intuitive understanding of the concept of *mean*. Have students suggest reasons why the mean is a useful measure. Ask them to cite instances of its use in the real world.

Differentiated Instruction

Tactile Learners

For a hands-on approach to investigating mean, distribute snap cubes or colored centimeter cubes to groups of students. Have them make rows (trains) of these, corresponding to the length of each name. They compute the mean by adding or removing cubes to form rows that are of the same length.

Resources

- Activity Lab 2-1: Using a Spreadsheet
- marbles, counters, or paper
- Classroom Aid 7

Exploring the Mean

Three friends went apple picking. The friends want to make sure that each person has the same number of apples.

ACTIVITY

1. The diagram below shows the number of apples picked by each friend. Use objects to represent the apples. Make a pile of "apples" for each of the friends.   **Check students' work.**

| Janelle | Ciara | Macario |
| **12 apples** | **6 apples** | **9 apples** |

2. Describe a method you can use to even out the number of apples so that each person has the same number. What is this number?

3. Graph the number of apples each friend picked on the number line. Then draw a small star on the number of apples each friend will get after sharing.

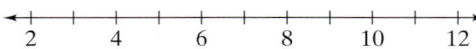

4. **Writing in Math** The value indicated by the star on your number line is called "the mean." Use what you have learned to write a definition for the word *mean*.

5. Make four piles with 13, 16, 18, and 19 "apples." Use the method you described in Step 2 to create four equal piles. What problem did you encounter? How can you solve this problem?   **See margin.**

6. A dance committee is inflating balloons for a dance. The mean number of balloons inflated by each person is 9. Use objects to represent the number of balloons in the table at the right. How many balloons did Eric inflate?

Dance Committee

Name	Number of Balloons
Jamil	12
Ashley	10
Hoshi	4
Eric	■

60   **Activity Lab**   Exploring the Mean

---

2. **9 apples; answers may vary. Sample: You can add to find the total number of apples and then divide by 3.**

3.

4. **Answers may vary. Sample: The mean is the sum of the data divided by the number of data items.**

6. **10 balloons**

5. **Answers may vary. Sample: The sum is not divisible by 4. Since the mean is 16.5, you could cut two apples in half.**

Finding the Mean

What You'll Learn

To find and analyze the mean of a data set using models and calculations

◄) **New Vocabulary** mean, outlier

Why Learn This?

Meteorologists analyze data. They often use a measure, such as the mean, to help describe a set of data.

The **mean** of a set of data is the sum of the data divided by the number of data items. To find the mean of a set of data, you can adjust all of the values so the values are the same.

EXAMPLE   Using a Model to Find the Mean

1 On four days it rained 2 inches, 4 inches, 5 inches, and 1 inch. Find the mean amount of rain.

You can draw a picture or use objects to model the situation.

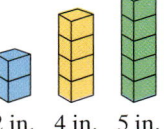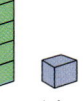

← Model the amount of rain for each day.

2 in. 4 in. 5 in. 1 in.

← Next, move cubes so that the height of each stack is the same.

3 in. 3 in. 3 in. 3 in.

The mean amount of rain is 3 inches.

✔ Quick Check

1. Use a model to find the mean of 3, 6, 3, 4, 2, and 6. **4**

61

Activity Lab

Use before the lesson.
Student Edition Activity Lab,
Hands On 2-1a, Exploring the
Mean p. 60

All in One Teaching Resources

Activity Lab 2-1: Using a
Spreadsheet

Guided Instruction

Example 3
After reviewing the Example, ask:
• *What would happen to the
mean if the outlier is dropped?*
The mean would increase.
• *If there was one more test, what
would raise the mean?* **any
grade greater than the mean**

Technology Tip
For students who use calculators
to find the mean, have them first
find the sum before dividing.

Additional Examples

1 In five days it snowed 3 inches,
7 inches, 2 inches, 2 inches,
and 1 inch at a skiing area.
Find the mean. Draw a picture
to model the situation.

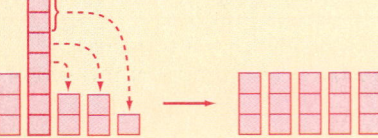

2 Find the mean test score of 78,
85, 94, 88, and 91. **87.2**

3 The number of raisins in each
of five bowls were:

21, 26, 72, 27, 24

What was the outlier? **72**

Find the mean. **34**

How does the outlier affect
the mean? **raises it**

All in One Teaching Resources
• Daily Notetaking Guide 2-1 **L3**
• Adapted Notetaking 2-1 **L1**

Closure

• *How do you find the mean of a
set of data?* **Find the sum of the
data and divide by the number
of data items.**

The thorny lizard survives
high temperatures by
using its spikes to collect
moisture at night.

EXAMPLE **Calculating the Mean**

2 You measure the temperature outside each day during the
week. The temperatures are 95°, 96°, 103°, 99°, and 96°. Find
the mean temperature.

$$95 + 96 + 103 + 99 + 96 = 489 \quad \leftarrow \textbf{Add the temperatures.}$$

$$\frac{489}{5} = 97.8 \quad \leftarrow \textbf{Divide by the number of readings.}$$

The mean temperature is 97.8°.

Check for Reasonableness The mean is between the lowest value,
95, and the greatest value, 103. So, the answer 97.8 is reasonable.

✓ Quick Check

2. You play a word game. Your scores are 12, 23, 13, 32, and 20.
Find your mean score. **20**

An **outlier** is a data item that is much greater or less than the other
data items. If a data set has an outlier, then the mean may not
describe the data very well.

EXAMPLE **Analyzing the Mean**

Quiz Scores		
81	77	92
89	81	87
75	42	81

3 Your quiz scores in science are listed at the left. Find the mean test
score with and without the outlier. What effect does the outlier
have on the mean?

Since 42 is much less than the other scores, the outlier is 42. Find
the mean with and without the outlier.

With the outlier: $\dfrac{81 + 77 + 92 + 89 + 81 + 87 + 75 + 42 + 81}{9}$

≈ 78.333

Without the outlier: $\dfrac{81 + 77 + 92 + 89 + 81 + 87 + 75 + 81}{8}$

$= 82.875$

The outlier reduced the mean quiz score by about 5 points.

✓ Quick Check

3. You keep track of the number of hours you baby-sit for six days:
1.25, 1.50, 1.50, 1.75, 2.0, 5.5. What effect does the outlier have
on the mean? **The outlier increases the value of the mean.**

Advanced Learners **L4**
Ask: *In a set of numbers how does the mean compare
to least and greatest numbers?* **The mean is always
more than or equal to the least number and less
than or equal to the greatest.**

learning style: verbal

English Language Learners **ELL**
Outlier is a word with which many students may not
be familiar. Point out some other words that use *out*
in a similar way such as *outfield.* Have students
explain what each word means.

learning style: verbal

Check Your Understanding

1. Answers may vary. Sample: Add the data and divide the sum by 5.

4. Answers may vary. Sample: An outlier can skew the mean. For example, in the data set 2, 4, 4, 30, the mean is 10, which is not close to any of the data.

1. **Vocabulary** Explain how to find the mean of five test scores.

Use a model to find the mean of each data set.

2. 3, 2, 8, 4, 3 **4**

3. 5, 3, 7, 10, 6, 5 **6**

4. **Open-Ended** Explain why the mean might not be a good measure for a set of data when the set includes outliers. Write a set of data items that supports your explanation. **See left.**

Homework Exercises

For more exercises, see Extra Skills and Word Problems.

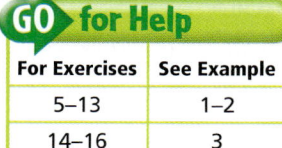

For Exercises	See Example
5–13	1–2
14–16	3

A Find the mean of each data set. You may find a model helpful.

5. 3, 4, 7, 2, 5, 9 **5**

6. 6, 4, 5, 9, 7, 6, 8, 3 **6**

7. 12, 9, 11, 8, 9, 12, 9 **10**

8. 14, 16, 28, 17, 20 **19**

9. 121, 95, 115, 92, 113, 108, 91 **105**

10. 2.4, 1.8, 3.5, 2.3, 6.5 **3.3**

11. 500, 450, 475, 450, 500 **475**

12. 23, 24, 27, 25, 26, 22, 21 **24**

13. You keep track of the time you spend doing homework each evening. You spend 58 minutes, 36 minutes, 44 minutes, and 37 minutes. Find the mean of these times. **43.75 minutes**

For each set of data, identify any outliers. Then determine the effect that the outlier has on the mean.

14. 95, 90, 87, 85, 79, 82, 87, 40, 90, 80 **40; decreases**

15. 8, 7, 10, 12, 8, 11, 8, 6, 9, 50, 8, 10, 7, 7 **50; increases**

16. 200; 225; 3,000; 500; 325; 311; 295; 485; 359; 325 **3,000; increases**

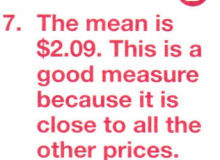

17. The mean is $2.09. This is a good measure because it is close to all the other prices.

18. Check students' work.

B 17. **Guided Problem Solving** The prices for a gallon of milk at four stores are $1.99, $2.29, $2.19, and $1.88. Is the mean a good measure of the price of milk in the four stores? Explain.
- **Understand the Problem** You have to determine whether any outliers affect the mean.
- **Make a Plan** How will you find the mean? **See left.**

18. **Data Collection** Measure the height, in inches, of five different cups in your home. Find the mean height. **See left.**

Assignment Guide

Check Your Understanding
Go over Exercises 1–4 in class before assigning the Homework Exercises.

Homework Exercises
A Practice by Example 5–16
B Apply Your Skills 17–23
C Challenge 24
Test Prep and
　Mixed Review 25–30

Homework Quick Check
To check student's understanding of key skills and concepts, go over Exercises 9, 15, 21, 22, and 23.

Differentiated Instruction Resources

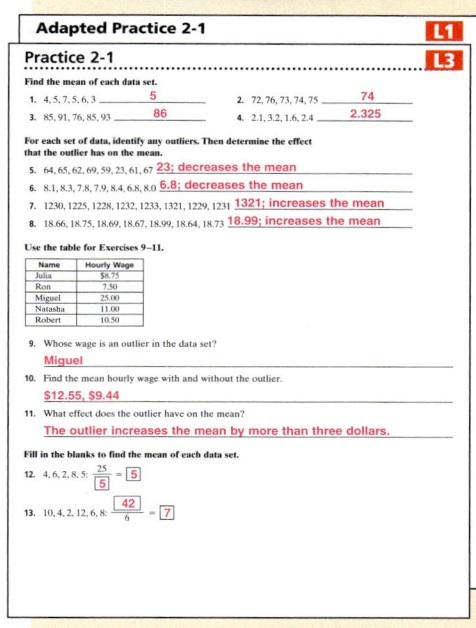

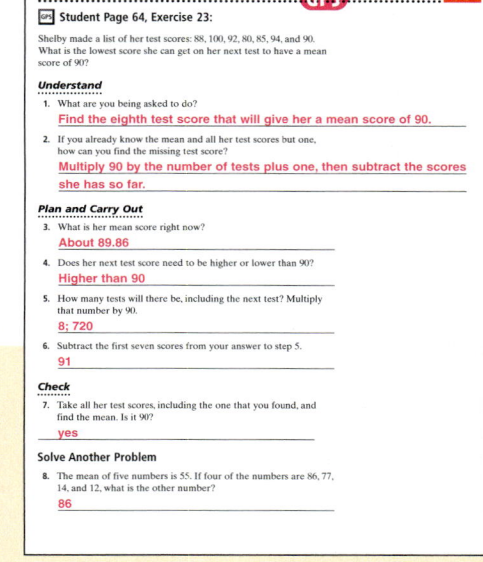

Lesson Quiz

Find the mean of each data set.

1. 65, 47, 93, 100, 65 **74**

2. 115, 200, 95, 200, 45 **131**

3. 90, 48, 120, 48, 72, 90 **78**

Use the data set below.

126, 132, 129, 34, 130

4. What is the outlier? **34**

5. How does it affect the mean? **It lowers the mean.**

Reteaching 2-1 — L2

Math Test Grades

Name	Grade
Sharon	87
Rashid	91
Durrin	88
Nicole	90
Terry	90
Mei-lin	93
Kevin	87
Carlos	110

• The *mean* of a set of data is the sum of the values divided by the number of data items.
87 + 87 + 88 + 90 + 90 + 91 + 93 + 110 = 736
736 ÷ 8 = 92
The mean math test grade is 92.

• An *outlier* is a data item that is much greater or less than the other data items. If a data set has an outlier, then the mean may not describe the data very well.

The outlier in the Math Test Grades set is 110, because it is significantly higher than the other scores. In this case, omitting the outlier from the mean calculation lowers the mean by about 3 points.

87 + 87 + 88 + 90 + 90 + 91 + 93 = 626
626 ÷ 7 = 89.4

Find the mean of each data set.

1. 8, 6, 5, 9, 7, 13 **8**

2. 9, 12, 14, 6, 8, 5 **9**

Identify the outlier in each set of data. What effect does that outlier have on the mean?

3. 94, 77, 37, 80, 74, 94, 87, 85
37; It decreases the mean.

4. 13, 10, 9, 15, 11, 29, 12, 10
29; It increases the mean.

5. 378; 433; 364; 418; 2,877; 408
2,877; It increases the mean.

6. 4,333; 4,290; 4,315; 587; 4,100
587; It decreases the mean.

Enrichment 2-1 — L4

Critical Thinking

Kristen lives in an apartment with central air conditioning. The chart shows how much she spent on electricity from March through August. Study this information and use it to answer the questions below.

Monthly Electric Bill

Month	Bill Amount
March	$125.68
April	$128.35
May	$145.07
June	$137.15
July	$148.94
August	$230.80

1. What is the mean amount of Kristen's electric bill?
$152.66

2. Which piece of data is the *outlier*?
the electric bill amount for August

3. What is the mean *without* the outlier?
$137.03

4. If you subtract the lowest bill amount from the highest bill amount, you will see that the amount Kristen spent changed by about $105.00. Why do you think it was so high some months and so low others?
During the summer she uses the air conditioning, so her electric bill is higher.

5. Does it make sense for Kristen to use the average of her monthly electric bill to budget her money each month? Why or why not?
No, her electric bill changes so much throughout the year that the yearly average would not let her budget her money accordingly.

GO Online
Homework Video Tutor

Visit: PHSchool.com
Web Code: aqe-0201

Find the mean of each data set.

19. 10, 4, 11.7, 30, 7.9, 11, 8.2, 3, 8, 9.2, 14.2, 5.2 **10.2**

20. 2.4, 5.3, 3.5, 2.6, 2.3, 3.5, 2.8, 4.3, 4.5, 3.8 **3.5**

21. The table shows the monthly rainfall for one year in Hilo, Hawaii.
  a. Find the mean amount of rain to the nearest inch.
  b. **Writing in Math** Why are most of the data items less than the mean?
  21a–b. See margin.

22. **Algebra** The mean of 22, 19, 25, and x is 23. Find x. **26**

23. **GPS** Shelby made a list of her test scores: 88, 100, 92, 80, 85, 94, and 90. What is the lowest score she can get on her next test to have a mean score of 90? **91**

C 24. **Challenge** The mean of 22.3, 19.7, 25.4, and another number is 23.4. Find the missing number. **26.2**

Rainfall in Hilo, Hawaii

Month	Rainfall (in.)
January	5
February	1
March	15
April	43
May	9
June	9
July	11
August	11
September	14
October	12
November	36
December	6

SOURCE: *The Weather Almanac*

Dense rain forests are found in Hawaii because of its wet, tropical climate.

Test Prep and Mixed Review — Practice

Multiple Choice

25. Which number is between the two points graphed on the number line? **B**

1.1   1.3   1.5   1.7   1.8

  Ⓐ 1.44   Ⓑ 1.55   Ⓒ 1.63   Ⓓ 1.72

26. Kristi received scores of 5.2 and 2.3 on her two ice-skating routines. What is the difference between these scores? **G**

  Ⓕ 2.1   Ⓖ 2.9   Ⓗ 3.1   Ⓙ 3.9

27. Duke has football practice for 2 hours after school every day. If he goes to practice 5 days, which method can be used to find the total number of hours Duke practices? **C**

  Ⓐ Add 2 and 5.   Ⓒ Multiply 5 by 2.
  Ⓑ Subtract 2 from 5.   Ⓓ Divide 5 by 2.

GO for Help

For Exercises	See Lesson
28–30	1-8

Find each product.

28. 4.2×9.6 **40.32**   **29.** 3.07×6.3 **19.341**   **30.** 4.25×1.04 **4.42**

Test Prep

Resources

For additional practice with a variety of test item formats:
• Test-Taking Strategies, p. 99
• Test Prep, p. 103
• Test-Taking Strategies with Transparencies

Alternative Assessment

Each student in a pair writes five different data sets, each with 4 to 8 numbers. Partners exchange paper and find the mean for each data set. If necessary, students should round the mean to the nearest tenth.

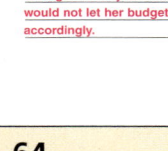

Vocabulary Builder

High-Use Academic Words

High-use academic words are words that you see often in textbooks and on tests. These words are not math vocabulary terms, but knowing them will help you to succeed in mathematics.

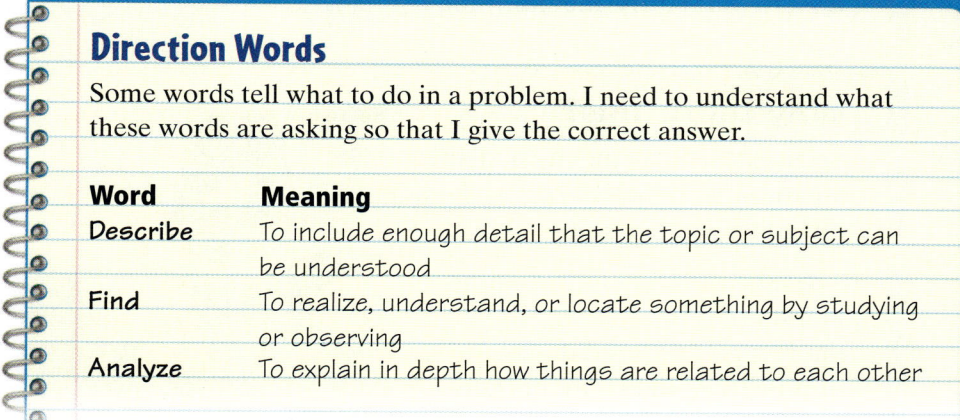

Direction Words

Some words tell what to do in a problem. I need to understand what these words are asking so that I give the correct answer.

Word	Meaning
Describe	To include enough detail that the topic or subject can be understood
Find	To realize, understand, or locate something by studying or observing
Analyze	To explain in depth how things are related to each other

Exercises

Use the activities listed at the right for Exercises 1–2.

1. Describe to your friend how you will spend your Saturday.
   See margin.
2. Find the total time it will take to complete the activities.
   $9\frac{1}{2}$ **hours**

For Exercises 3–5, use the quiz scores 50, 86, 90, 94, and 95.

3. Describe how to calculate your mean score.
   Add 50, 86, 90, 94 and 95 and divide the sum by 5.
4. Find the outlier for the data. **50**

5. Analyze how the outlier affects the mean. **It will decrease the mean.**

6. a. **Word Knowledge** Think about the word *average*. **6a–c. Check students' work.**
   Choose the letter for how well you know the word.
      A. I know its meaning.
      B. I've seen it, but I don't know its meaning.
      C. I don't know it.
   b. **Research** Look up and write the definition of *average*.
   c. Use the word in a sentence involving mathematics.

Saturday Activities	
Clean room	$1\frac{1}{2}$ hours
Do homework	$3\frac{1}{2}$ hours
Watch TV	2 hours
Do chores	2 hours
Prepare lunch	$\frac{1}{2}$ hour

Vocabulary Builder High-Use Academic Words **65**

21a. **14 inches**

   b. **Answers may vary. Sample: The outliers 36 and 43 increase the value of the mean.**

1. **Answers will vary. Sample: I will spend time cleaning, doing chores, watching TV, doing homework, and preparing lunch.**

Vocabulary Builder

High-Use Academic Words

Students learn a strategy for learning words that, while not math vocabulary terms, are important for success in mathematics and on tests.

Guided Instruction

Have students look through their texts for use of the terms: *describe, find,* and *analyze.* Ask:
- *Where do you find the term describe?* **Sample: page 68, Exercise 17**
- *What is another way to say "What is the difference in meters of the heights of the mountains?"* **Sample: Find the difference in meters of the heights of the mountains.**
- *What information could you find by analyzing the graph on page 75?* **Sample: changes in temperature, temperatures at different times**

Teaching Tip
Restate directions given in the text using *describe, find,* and *analyze* as appropriate to familiarize students with these terms.

Differentiated Instruction

English Language Learners **ELL**
Encourage students to write high-use academic words in their native language as needed.

Resources

- Vocabulary and Study Skills Worksheets

65

Objective
To find and analyze the median and mode of a data set

Examples
1 Finding the Median
2 Finding the Mode
3 Analyzing Data

Math Understandings: p. 58C

Math Background

In Lesson 2-1, one measure of central tendency, the mean, was covered. In this lesson, the two other measures of central tendency, median and mode, are covered.

The *median* is especially useful when the data set includes very high or low values that distort the mean. The *mode*, or most often occurring data value, is especially useful when the data are not numerical.

More Math Background: p. 58C

Lesson Planning and Resources

See p. 58E for a list of the resources that support this lesson.

PowerPoint

Bell Ringer Practice

✓ **Check Skills You'll Need**
Use student page, transparency, or PowerPoint. For intervention, direct students to:
Finding the Mean
Lesson 2-1
Extra Skills and Word Problems
   Practice, Ch. 2

2-2 Median and Mode

1. **Vocabulary Review**
   To find the mean of 1, 2, 3, 4, and 5, you add the numbers and divide by __?__. **5**

Find the mean of each set of data.

2. 4, 16, 20, 40 **20**

3. 12, 23, 19, 32, 26 **22.4**

4. 5, 15, 75, 105, 85 **57**

GO for Help
Lesson 2-1

What You'll Learn

To find and analyze the median and mode of a data set

🔊 **New Vocabulary** median, mode

Why Learn This?

Scientists use the mean, median, and mode to describe sets of data, including fish populations.

The **median** is the middle number in a set of ordered data. The median gives a good description of numerical data with outliers.

$$4 \quad 7 \quad 9 \quad 13 \quad 25$$
$$\uparrow$$
$$\text{median}$$

For an even number of data items, you can find the median by adding the two middle numbers and dividing by 2.

EXAMPLE Finding the Median

Test Prep Tip
A griddable answer is not always a decimal.

1 **Gridded Response** A biologist studying the ecology of a river makes a weekly fish count. The results are 19, 18, 22, 23, 20, 24, 23, 20, 34, and 19. Find the median number of fish.

18, 19, 19, 20, 20, 22, 23, 23, 24, 34 ← Order the data. Since there are 10 items, use the two middle values.

$$\frac{20 + 22}{2} = \frac{42}{2}, \text{ or } 21$$ ← Find the mean of 20 and 22.

The median number of fish is 21.

✓ Quick Check

1. Weekly sales of comics at a store are 39, 19, 28, 9, 32, 35, and 17 comics. What is the median number of comics sold? **28**

Differentiated Instruction Solutions for All Learners

Special Needs L1
It may be difficult for students to distinguish all the numbers in a data set and then reorder them without losing track. If so, have them work with a partner to help rewrite and reorder the data sets to find the median.

learning style: visual

Below Level L2
Have students use graph paper to write an evenly-spaced ordered list of the data values in Example 1. They can then fold the paper in half to find the two middle values.

learning style: visual

The **mode** is the data item(s) that appears most often. A data set may have more than one mode. If all data items occur the same number of times, there is no mode. The mode is useful when the data items are repeated or not numerical.

EXAMPLE Finding the Mode

② The list shows the favorite lunches of 15 students. Find the mode.

Group the data.

> pizza, pizza, pizza, pizza, pizza
> hamburger, hamburger, hamburger
> taco, taco, taco, taco
> spaghetti, spaghetti, spaghetti

Favorite Lunch
hamburger, pizza, taco, pizza, spaghetti, taco, spaghetti, hamburger, hamburger, pizza, taco, pizza, pizza, spaghetti, taco

Pizza occurs the most. It is the mode.

✓ Quick Check

2. How many students would have to switch from hamburger to taco as their favorite lunch for taco to be the only mode? **2**

EXAMPLE Analyzing Data

③ Find the mean, median, and mode for the number of minutes spent on the Internet. Does the mean, median, or mode best describe the typical amount of time spent on the Internet?

Amount of Time Spent on Internet (minutes)			
50	276	57	50
62	53	72	71
63	60	22	

mean $\dfrac{50 + 276 + 57 + 50 + 62 + 53 + 72 + 71 + 63 + 60 + 22}{11} = \dfrac{836}{11}$

$= 76$

median 22 50 50 53 57 60 62 63 71 72 276: 60

mode 50

The mode and mean are close to only a few data points. The median is close to most of the data items. So the median best describes the typical amount of time spent on the Internet.

✓ Quick Check

3. The top five women's 1-meter diving scores are 288.75, 261.83, 254.85, 254.1, and 246.8. Does the mean, median, or mode best describe these data? Explain. **See left.**

3. Answers may vary. Sample: The median is the best measure, as 288.75 is an outlier that affects the mean, and there is no mode.

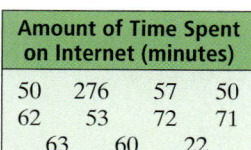

Video Tutor Help
Visit: PHSchool.com
Web Code: aqe-0775

2-2 Median and Mode   **67**

Advanced Learners L4
Ask: *Can a mode be both greater than and less than the median? Explain.* **Yes, a bimodal data set contains two modes; one can be greater than the median and one can be less.**

learning style: verbal

English Language Learners ELL
The language of data can be difficult for many students. Allow them to use index cards and write the terms: *mean, median, mode, outlier* and any others they need along with examples and definitions.

learning style: visual

---

2. Teach

Activity Lab
Use before the lesson.

All in One Teaching Resources
Activity Lab 2-2: Median and Mode

Guided Instruction

Example 2
Ask: *Which measure: mean, median, or mode, is always an actual data value?* **the mode**

Teaching Tip
Help students distinguish between median and mode.
mode - most
median - middle.

PowerPoint
Additional Examples

❶ Find the median of 23, 35, 27, 55, 41, 23, 45, and 69. **38**

❷ Find the mode of the following data: blue, red, blue, yellow, yellow, blue, red, blue, yellow, blue, red, yellow **blue**

❸ The number of emails each of seven students received one day were

17 3 12 14 12 16 15

Does the mean, median, or mode best describe the typical number of emails each received? Explain. **mean**

mean   12.7
mode   12
median 3 12 12 ⑭ 16 16 17

All three measures are close. Since the mean is between the mode and the median, it is probably the best measure.

All in One Teaching Resources
• Daily Notetaking Guide 2-2 L3
• Adapted Notetaking 2-2 L1

Closure

• *How do you find the median of a set of data?* **Write the data values in order and find the middle item in the set of data, or find the mean of the two middle items.**

67

Assignment Guide

Check Your Understanding
Go over Exercises 1–5 in class before assigning the Homework Exercises.

Homework Exercises
A Practice by Example   6–17
B Apply Your Skills   18–25
C Challenge   26
Test Prep and
   Mixed Review   27–31

Homework Quick Check
To check student's understanding of key skills and concepts, go over Exercises 8, 15, 21, 22, and 25.

Differentiated Instruction **Resources**

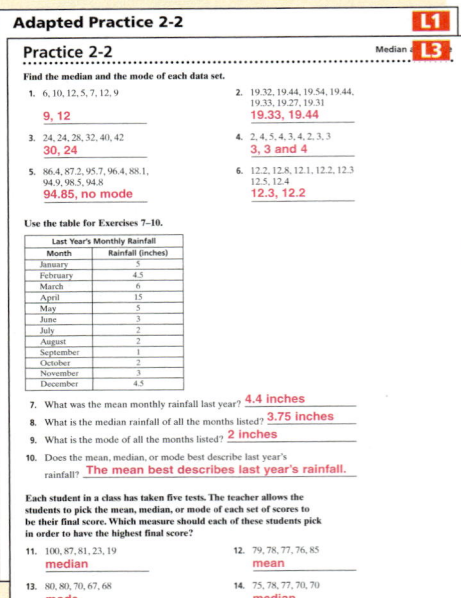

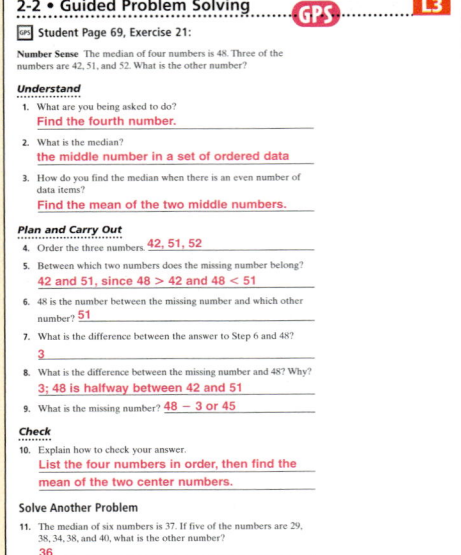

Check Your Understanding

1. **Vocabulary** The (mean, median, mode) of the following data is 4: 1, 2, 2, 4, 7, 9, 20. **median**

2. **Open-Ended** Create a set of data with more than one mode. **Check students' work.**

Vocabulary Tip

The word *median* means "middle."

Find the median and mode(s) of each data set.

3. 5, 7, 8, 8, 8, 10, 12 **8; 8**
4. 1, 1, 1, 2, 3, 4, 5, 5, 5 **3; 1, 5**

5. Add two data items to 40, 20, and 60 so that the median and mode are 60. **Answers may vary. Sample: 60, 100.**

Homework Exercises

For more exercises, see Extra Skills and Word Problems.

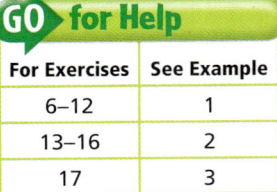

For Exercises	See Example
6–12	1
13–16	2
17	3

Ⓐ Find the median of each data set.

6. 8, 42, 13, 7, 50, 91 **27.5**
7. 0, 1, 1, 1, 0, 1, 1, 0, 0, 0 **0.5**

8. 14.1, 20.7, 24.3, 16.0, 20.8 **20.7**
9. 500, 450, 475, 450, 500 **475**

10. 60.2, 63.5, 62, 62.2, 63.4, 61.1, 60.8 **62**

11. 1,205; 1,190; 1,225; 1,239; 1,187; 1,763 **1,215**

12. **Birds** Here are the number of birds spotted by a bird watcher: 2, 7, 3, 8, 10, and 2. What is the median number of birds? **5**

Find the mode(s) of each data set.

13. 8, 7, 8, 9, 8, 7 **8**
14. sad, glad, glad, mad, sad **sad, glad**

15. 15, 12, 17, 13, 20, 19 **none**
16. 23, 24, 27, 25, 26, 23, 21 **23**

17. **Fitness** For a week you keep track of the number of push-ups you do each morning: 9, 9, 4, 12, 11, 12, and 12. Does the mean, median, or mode best describe the set of data? **median**

18. **Ⓑ GPS Guided Problem Solving** Your homework grades are 92, 87, 74, 96, 83, 88, 91, 82, and 85. What score on your next homework will make the median and the mode equal? **87**
   • List the scores in order from least to greatest.
   • You can use the strategy *Systematic Guess and Check* to help you find the solution.

25a. mean: 6,172.75 m; median: 6,044.5 m

   b. They both increase.
      The mean becomes 6,708.2 m. The median becomes 6,194 m.

Find the mean, median, and mode of each data set.

19. 13.5, 15, 13.5, 11, 13
13.2; 13.5; 13.5

20. 32, 28.3, 26.8, 31, 24.4
28.5; 28.3; none

21. Number Sense The median of four numbers is 48. Three of the numbers are 42, 51, and 52. What is the other number? **45**

22. Writing in Math Your scores on five math tests are 96, 88, 96, 85, and 30. Write a letter to your teacher stating which measure—mean, median, or mode—you think your teacher should use to determine your grade. **Check students' work.**

23. A company is asking students which types of shoe designs they prefer. Which is the best measure for describing the selections, the mean, the median, or the mode? Explain. **See above left.**

24. Books The page lengths of five books are 198, 240, 153, 410, and 374. What is the median? **240**

25. a. Mountains Find the mean and median heights of the peaks listed in the table at the right.
b. The height of Asia's highest peak is 8,850 meters. If you add it to the data, what is the change in the mean? In the median?
25a–b. See margin.

Highest Peaks

Continent	Altitude (meters)
Africa	5,895
Europe	5,642
North America	6,194
South America	6,960

SOURCE: *Time Almanac*

C 26. Challenge Use an example to explain why teachers do not use the median to calculate final grades. **See left.**

23. The mode is the best measure because the types of shoes are not numeric data.

26. Answers may vary. Sample: Median is not a good measure because it doesn't account for how high or low the other scores are.

Careers Shoe designers use survey and research data to decide what features to include in a shoe.

Test Prep and Mixed Review **Practice**

Gridded Response

27. A shoe store recorded the sale of the following shoe sizes: 5, 7, 5, 11, 8, 11, 7, 6, 5, 8, 9, 10, 7, 6, and 7. What is the mode? **7**

28. The height of a tree is 2.7 meters. The height of a second tree is 1.8 meters. What is the difference of the heights in meters? **0.9**

29. A lilac bush is 1 foot tall when you buy it. The bush will grow about 1.5 feet each year. What will be the height of the bush in feet after 6 years? **10**

Find the value of each expression.

30. $10 - 2 \times 4 - 1$ **1**

31. $200 \div (32 - 12) + 5$ **15**

GO for Help

For Exercises	See Lesson
30–31	1-4

Alternative Assessment

Each student in a pair writes five different data sets, each with 4 to 8 numbers. Partners exchange papers and find the median and mode for each data set. If necessary, students should round the median to the nearest tenth.

Test Prep

Resources
For additional practice with a variety of test item formats:
• Test-Taking Strategies, p. 99
• Test Prep, p. 103
• Test-Taking Strategies with Transparencies

Find the median and mode of each data set.

1. 65, 47, 93, 100, 65 **median: 65; mode: 65**

2. 115, 200, 95, 200, 45 **median: 115; mode: 200**

3. 90, 48, 120, 48, 72, 90 **median: 81; mode: 48 and 90**

4. 126, 210, 54, 108, 126, 162 **median: 126; mode: 126**

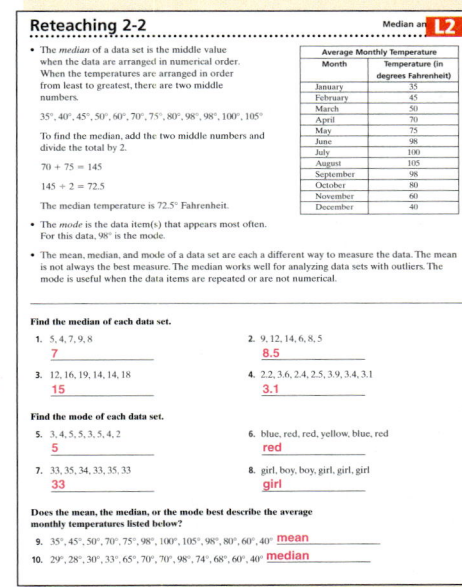

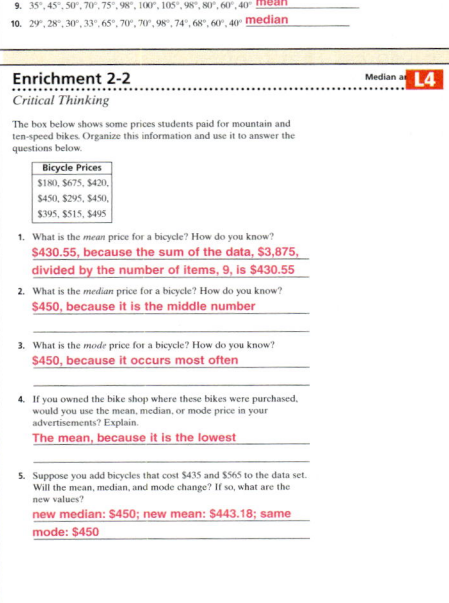

69

Objective
To analyze a set of data by finding the range and by making frequency tables and line plots

Examples
1 Frequency Table
2 Using a Line Plot
3 Find the Range

Math Understandings: p. 58C

Math Background

A *frequency table* lists each item in a data set with the number of times it occurs. A *line* plot shows the frequency distribution of a data set by stacking **✗**'s on a number line to represent each data item. The *range* of a data set is the difference between the least and greatest values.

More Math Background: p. 58C

Lesson Planning and Resources

See p. 58E for a list of the resources that support this lesson.

PowerPoint

Bell Ringer Practice

✓ **Check Skills You'll Need**
Use student page, transparency, or PowerPoint. For intervention, direct students to:
Median and Mode
Lesson 2-2
Extra Skills and Word Problems Practice, Ch. 2

✓ Check Skills You'll Need

1. Vocabulary Review
What is the *mode* of a set of data?
1–3. See below.
Find the mean, median, and mode of each data set.

2. 6, 4, 6, 7, 4, 3, 8, 4

3. 1.5, 0, 3, 0, 2, 8.5, 1

 **for Help**
Lesson 2-2

Check Skills You'll Need

1. The mode is (are) the data item(s) that appear(s) most often.

2. 5.25; 5; 4

3. about 2.29; 1.5; 0

What You'll Learn

To analyze a set of data by finding the range and by making frequency tables and line plots

🔊 **New Vocabulary** frequency table, line plot, range

Why Learn This?

Data, such as your classmates' favorite colors, are easier to read in a table or graph than in a list.

A **frequency table** is a table that lists each item in a data set with the number of times the item occurs.

Favorite Colors

Blue	Blue
Purple	Red
Red	Orange
Blue	Yellow
Blue	Green
Yellow	Blue
Green	Yellow
Purple	Blue

 **Frequency Table**

1 Your classmates' favorite colors are shown above. Organize the data in a frequency table. Find the mode.

Favorite Color

Color	Tally	Frequency
Blue	⊦⊦⊦⊦ I	6
Green	II	2
Orange	I	1
Purple	II	2
Red	II	2
Yellow	III	3

Make a tally mark for each color chosen.

The number of tally marks in each row is the frequency.

Students selected blue most often. So the mode is blue.

✓ Quick Check

1. The first initials of the names of 15 students are listed below. Organize the data in a frequency table. Find the mode.
A J B K L C K D L S T D V P L **See back of book.**

Differentiated Instruction **Solutions for All Learners**

Special Needs **L1**
Students may have a difficult time "stacking" ✗'s in a line plot. Pair up these students with those who can do it. Have these students check the number of ✗'s against the data sets.

learning style: visual

Below Level **L2**
Explain that each tally mark indicates one time that the data value appears. The fifth tally mark is made diagonally through the other 4 marks. This makes it easy to see groups of 5 tally marks.

learning style: visual

A **line plot** is a graph that shows the shape of a data set by stacking ✗'s above each data value on a number line.

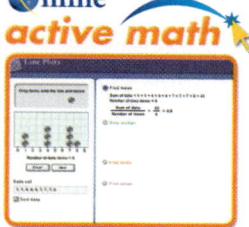

Online active math

For: Line Plots Activity
Use: Interactive Textbook, 2-3

EXAMPLE Using a Line Plot

② **Movies** The number of DVDs each customer rents when he or she visits a video store are 3, 5, 1, 2, 2, 1, 2, 3, 3, 4, 1, 2, 6, 2, 2, 4, 3, 1. Use a line plot to interpret the data.

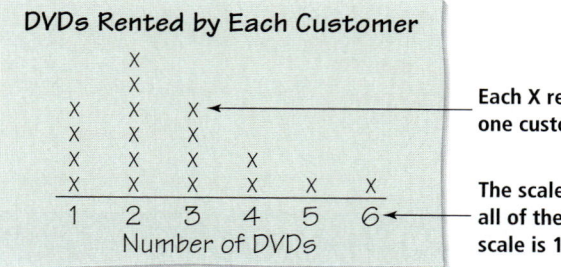

DVDs Rented by Each Customer

Each X represents one customer.

The scale of a graph includes all of the data values. The scale is 1 to 6 in this line plot.

Customers usually rent between one and three DVDs. Most customers rent two DVDs.

✓ **Quick Check**

2. Use a line plot to interpret the number of sales calls made each hour: 2, 3, 0, 7, 1, 1, 9, 8, 2, 8, 1, 2, 8, 7, 1, 8, 6, 1. **See back of book.**

The **range** of a data set is the difference between the least and greatest values.

EXAMPLE Finding the Range

③ **Geography** In 1849 and 1850, six different surveyors made the following measurements of the height of Mount Everest.

28,990 ft; 28,992 ft; 28,999 ft; 29,002 ft; 29,005 ft; 29,026 ft

What is the range of the measurements?

$29,026 - 28,990 = 36$ ← Subtract the least from the greatest value.

The range of the measurements is 36 feet.

✓ **Quick Check**

3. The numbers of pottery items made by students are 36, 21, 9, 34, 36, 10, 4, 35, 30, 7, 5, and 10. Find the range of the data. **32**

2-3 Frequency Tables and Line Plots **71**

Advanced Learners L4
Compare frequency tables and line plots. **Sample: Both show how often each data value occurs. A frequency table is easier to write but does not give as clear a shape of the data.**

learning style: visual

English Language Learners ELL
Make sure students understand the *scale* of 1–6 in the line plot for Example 2. The scale of this graph includes all of the data values. Ask: Where else have you used *scale* in mathematics? **to measure weights; in scale drawings**

learning style: verbal

---

2. Teach

Activity Lab
Use before the lesson.

All in One Teaching Resources
Activity Lab 2-3: Plotting Height

Guided Instruction

Example 3
Help students recognize that range only makes sense for numerical data. Ask: *Can you find the range of favorite colors in Example 1?* **no**

PowerPoint
Additional Examples

❶ The favorite lunch for ten students is: pizza, pizza, chicken, hamburger, chicken, pizza, chicken, pizza, pizza, pizza. Organize the data by making a frequency table. What is the mode? **pizza**

Lunch	Tally	Freq
hamburger	I	1
pizza	ⅧI	6
chicken	III	3

❷ Make a line plot to display the dinner hour for 7 families.
5 7 6 6 8 7 6

Dinner Hours

❸ Find the range for the dinner hour of 7 families.
5 7 6 6 8 7 6 **3 hours**

All in One Teaching Resources
• Daily Notetaking Guide 2-3 L3
• Adapted Notetaking 2-3 L1

Closure

• *What is a frequency table?* **a table that lists each item in a data set with the number of times the data item occurs**
• *What is a line plot?* **a graph that shows the shape of the data set by stacking ✗'s above each data value on a number line**

Assignment Guide

Check Your Understanding
Go over Exercises 1–5 in class before assigning the Homework Exercises.

Homework Exercises
A Practice by Example   6–11
B Apply Your Skills   12–18
C Challenge   19
Test Prep and
Mixed Review   20–24

Homework Quick Check
To check student's understanding of key skills and concepts, go over Exercises 6, 9, 13, and 18.

Differentiated Instruction Resources

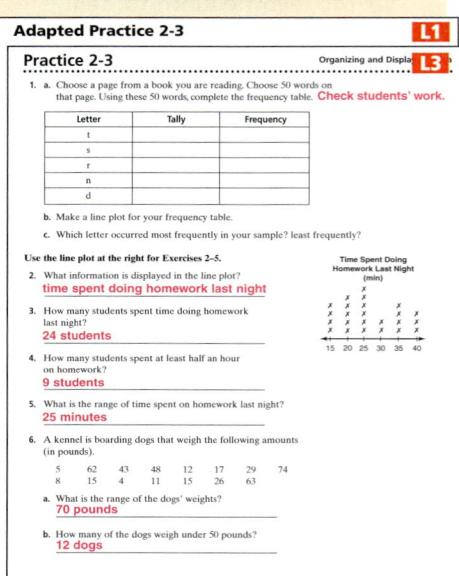

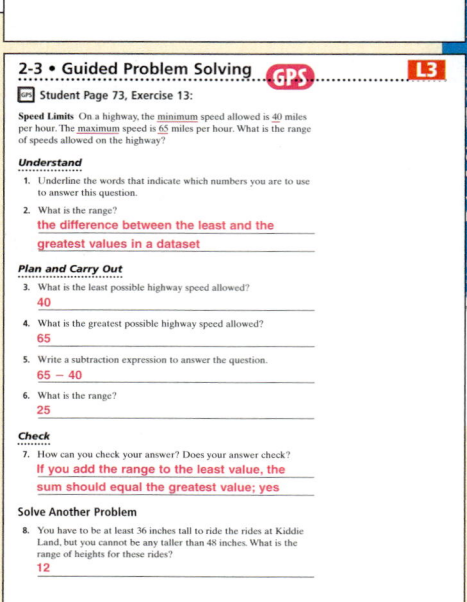

Check Your Understanding

1. Answers may vary. Sample: Both the line plot and frequency table show the data grouped in an easy-to-read way.

4. 3; No; the range shows the spread of the data.

5. Answers may vary. Sample: A line plot immediately shows the mode.

1. **Vocabulary** How is a line plot similar to a frequency table?

The ages for required school attendance in ten states are 6, 7, 6, 5, 7, 6, 8, 6, 5, and 7. Use the data for Exercises 2–5.
2–3. See margin.

2. Make a frequency table.   3. Make a line plot.

4. What is the range of the data? Is this a data point? Explain.
See left.

5. **Reasoning** Describe an advantage of using a line plot rather than a frequency table. See left.

Homework Exercises

For more exercises, see Extra Skills and Word Problems.

A Organize each set of data in a frequency table. Find the mode.
6–7. See back of book.

6. days in each month: 31, 28, 31, 30, 31, 30, 31, 31, 30, 31, 30, 31

7. vehicles in a parking lot:

pickup	compact	compact	mid-size
compact	SUV	mid-size	SUV
mid-size	compact	station wagon	pickup

GO for Help

For Exercises	See Example
6–7	1
8–9	2
10–11	3

8. **Baseball Bat Lengths (in.)**

```
              X
       X      X
       X      X
       X      X
   X   X      X
   X   X   X   X   X
  ---------------------
  28  29  30  31  32
      Length (in.)
```

Use a line plot to interpret each set of data.

8. lengths of baseball bats (inches): Most baseball bats are 29 or 30 inches long.
30 29 31 28 29 29 30 32 30 29 28 30 30

9. word lengths (letters): 7 2 6 1 7 6 9 1 8 4 2 3 10
There are very few words with less than 3 letters.

Find the range for each set of data.

10. the ages of the first ten U.S. presidents when they took office:
57, 61, 57, 57, 58, 57, 61, 54, 68, 51   17 years

11. heights of trees (meters): 2.3, 1.8, 3.4, 2.5, 2.9, 3.1, 3.2, 3.5, 2.8
1.7 m

B GPS 12. **Guided Problem Solving** You spent $44 to purchase two of the least expensive tickets to the ballet. Each ticket you purchased was the same price. The range of the ticket prices is $55. How much is the most expensive ticket? $77
• What is the cost of one of the least expensive tickets?
• How can you use the range to find the cost of the most expensive ticket?

2.

Ages	Tally	Frequency
5	II	2
6	IIII	4
7	III	3
8	I	1

3.
```
          X
       X  X
    X  X  X
    X  X  X  X
   ---------------
    5  6  7  8
```

9. See back of book for line plot.

17. Answers may vary. Sample: Data items 3 and 4 did not occur often but will affect the mean.

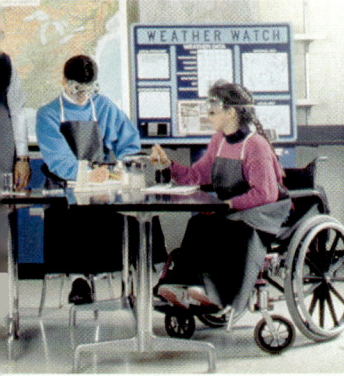

18b. 2; the line plot because it displays the distribution of the data.

13. Speed Limits On a highway, the minimum speed allowed is 40 miles per hour. The maximum speed is 65 miles per hour. What is the range of speeds allowed on the highway? **25 mph**

14. Social Studies A town in Wales, United Kingdom, is named Llanfairpwllgwyngyllgogerychwyrndrobwllllantysiliogogogoch.
a. Make a frequency table for the letters in the town's name.
b. **Writing in Math** Use the mean, median, or mode to describe the data in your table. Explain your choice.
14a–b. See margin.

Nineteen water samples were taken from a river. The number of organisms counted in each sample is shown in the line plot.

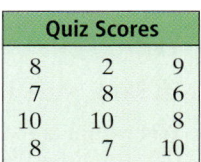

15. What do the numbers represent?
the number of organisms in a sample
16. Find the median and mode.
1; 1
17. Why might you not want to use the mean to describe the data? **See above left.**

18. a. Make a frequency table and a line plot of the quiz scores. **See margin.**

Quiz Scores		
8	2	9
7	8	6
10	10	8
8	7	10

b. Use either the frequency table or line plot to identify any outliers. Which display did you use? Explain your choice.
See left.

C 19. Challenge Make two sets of data with the same range but different means. **Check students' work.**

Test Prep and Mixed Review **Practice**

Multiple Choice

20. Which statement is supported by the graph? **D**
Ⓐ More students received a D than a B.
Ⓑ Six students received a C or better.
Ⓒ Most students received an A or a D.
Ⓓ Two more students received a C than the number who received a B.

Semester Science Grades

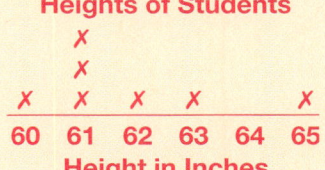

21. Find the median of the numbers. **H**
12, 9, 6, 15, 10, 8, 14, 5, 0, 10, 4, 16, 12, 12, 8
Ⓕ 8   Ⓖ 9   Ⓗ 10   Ⓙ 12

Use mental math to find each sum.

22. 17 + 23 **40**   **23.** 46 + 0 + 14 **60**   **24.** 5 + 32 + 15 **52**

GO for Help

For Exercises	See Lesson
22–24	1-3

14a–b. See back of book.

18a. See back of book.

Test Prep

Resources
For additional practice with a variety of test item formats:
• Test-Taking Strategies, p. 99
• Test Prep, p. 103
• Test-Taking Strategies with Transparencies

---

4. Assess & Reteach

PowerPoint
Lesson Quiz

The heights of several middle school students are: 61, 63, 65, 60, 61, 61, and 62 in.

1. Organize the data by making a frequency table.

Height	60	61	62	63	64	65
Tally	I	III	I	I		I
Freq.	1	3	1	1	0	1

2. Make a line plot for the data.

Heights of Students

```
X
X
X   X   X   X       X
60  61  62  63  64  65
```
Height in Inches

3. Find the range of the data.
5 in.

Alternative Assessment

Each student in a pair writes a numerical data set. Partners exchange data sets. Each student should select an appropriate representation for displaying the data. Students also report the range of the data.

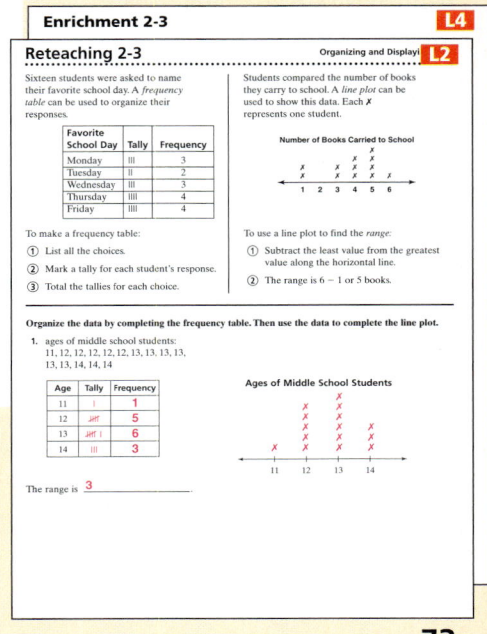

Objective
To make and analyze bar graphs and line graphs

Examples
1 Bar Graph
2 Using a Line Graph
3 Selecting a Type Graph

Math Understandings: p. 58C

Math Background

Graphs visually communicate information. A *bar graph* uses the length of bars to compare numerical amounts.

Line graphs illustrate trends by showing how two quantities relate to one another. There are only three possibilities for change between points on a line (or bars in bar graphs and histograms): an increase, a decrease, or no change.

More Math Background: p. 58C

Lesson Planning and Resources

See p. 58E for a list of the resources that support this lesson.

Bell Ringer Practice

☑ **Check Skills You'll Need**
Use student page, transparency, or PowerPoint. For intervention, direct students to:
Frequency Tables and Line Plots
Lesson 2-3
Extra Skills and Word Problems Practice, Ch. 2

☑ **Check Skills You'll Need**

1. **Vocabulary Review** What is the *range* of a set of data?
1–2. See below.
Make a line plot for each set of data.

2. 5, 6, 7, 8, 6, 5, 8, 7

3. 13, 17, 10, 21, 17
See back of book.

 **for Help**
Lesson 2-3

Check Skills You'll Need

1. The range is the difference between the least and greatest values.

2.
```
X   X   X   X
X   X   X   X
5   6   7   8
```

Vocabulary Tip

An *interval* is the amount of space between the values on the scale.

What You'll Learn

To make and analyze bar graphs and line graphs

 **New Vocabulary** bar graph, line graph

Why Learn This?

To make healthy eating decisions, you need to compare the amounts of nutrients in foods. Graphs help you "see" data by comparing size or showing change.

A **bar graph** uses vertical or horizontal bars to show comparisons.

Calcium Content

Food Item (1 cup)	Calcium (mg)
Milk	300
Yogurt	250
Cottage cheese	150
Ice cream	200
Broccoli	80

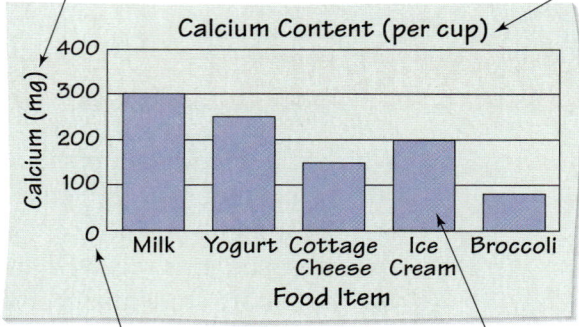

EXAMPLE **Bar Graph**

① **Nutrition** Make a bar graph to display the data above. Compare the amount of calcium in milk to the amount in cottage cheese.

Draw and label the horizontal and vertical axes.   Choose an appropriate title.

[Bar graph: Calcium Content (per cup). Vertical axis: Calcium (mg), 0 to 400 in intervals of 100. Horizontal axis: Food Item — Milk, Yogurt, Cottage Cheese, Ice Cream, Broccoli.]

Choose a scale. The data go from 80 to 300 so use 0 to 400 as the scale. Mark it with intervals of 100.   Draw bars of equal widths. The heights will vary.

The amount of calcium in one cup of milk is twice the amount in one cup of cottage cheese.

☑ **Quick Check**

1. Find the amount of calcium in a cup of milk and a cup of broccoli.
380 mg

Differentiated **Instruction** **Solutions for All Learners**

Special Needs L1
Students may have difficulty plotting points to make a line graph. Have them work with a partner and use a straightedge. Then take turns connecting the points with line segments.

learning style: tactile

Below Level L2
Review simple bar graphs and line graphs. Help students find the value for the height of each bar on the vertical axis; and help students find vertical axis values for specific horizontal axis values in a line graph.

learning style: visual

A **line graph** uses a series of line segments to show changes in data. Usually, a line graph shows changes over time.

EXAMPLE Using a Line Graph

② **Temperature** Use the data at the left to make a line graph. Describe the change in temperature between 10 A.M. and 4 P.M.

Temperatures Throughout the Day	
Time	Temperature
8 A.M.	62°F
10 A.M.	70°F
NOON	78°F
2 P.M.	81°F
4 P.M.	76°F
6 P.M.	74°F

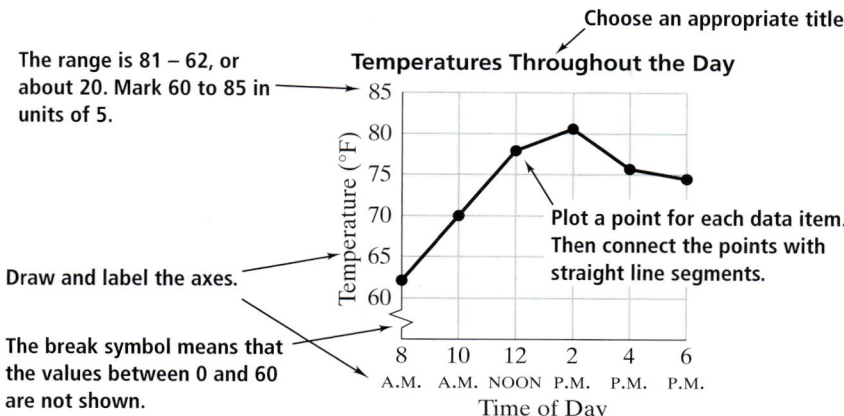

Choose an appropriate title.

The range is 81 – 62, or about 20. Mark 60 to 85 in units of 5.

Plot a point for each data item. Then connect the points with straight line segments.

Draw and label the axes.

The break symbol means that the values between 0 and 60 are not shown.

The temperature increased from 10 A.M. to 2 P.M. Then it began to decrease.

✓ Quick Check

2. Based on the line graph above, is the temperature likely to be greater than or less than 75°F at 8 P.M.? Explain.
   Less than; it is decreasing.

EXAMPLE Selecting a Type of Graph

World's Busiest Airports

Airport	Passengers per Year (millions)
Atlanta	79
Chicago	70
London	63
Tokyo	63
Los Angeles	55

SOURCE: *Time Almanac*

3. Line graph; it shows change over time.

③ **Multiple Choice** Which type of data display is the most appropriate to show a comparison of the data in the table at the left?

Ⓐ organized list   Ⓒ line graph
Ⓑ bar graph   Ⓓ frequency table

Since you want to show comparison, use a bar graph. The correct answer is choice B.

✓ Quick Check

3. Which type of data display is the most appropriate to display the data at the right? Explain. **See left.**

Ticket Sales				
Week	1	2	3	4
Tickets Sold	22	35	33	46

---

2. Teach

Activity Lab
Use before the lesson.

All in One Teaching Resources
Activity Lab 2-4: Making a Bar Graph

Guided Instruction

Example 2
Temperature and time of day are continuous. So, connecting the data points gives the approximate temperature for times between each point.

PowerPoint
Additional Examples

① Make a bar graph of the data.

Students With Jobs

Age	Percent
14	33%
15	60%
16	74%

See back of book for graph.

② Make a line graph of the data.

Running Shoes Sales

Month	Pairs Sold
Feb	54
March	86
April	121
May	115

See back of book for graph.

③ *Which data display is better to show changes in the price of milk over ten years? Why?*
line graph; it shows change over time

All in One Teaching Resources
• Daily Notetaking Guide 2-4 L3
• Adapted Notetaking 2-4 L1

Closure

• *How do you make a bar graph?*
Draw and label each axis. Choose scales and draw bars to proper heights. Write a title.

75

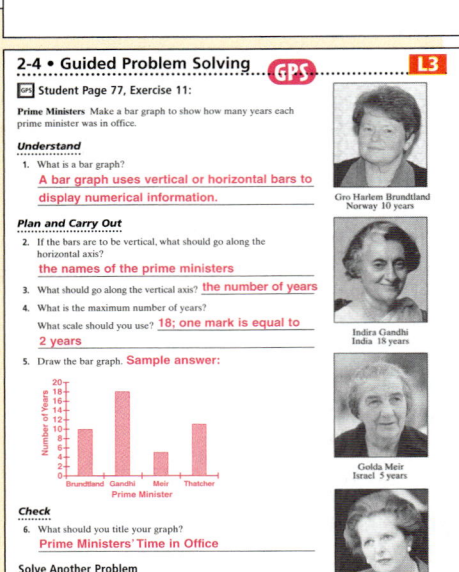

✓ Check Your Understanding

1. **Vocabulary** A (line, bar) graph uses a series of line segments to show changes in data. **line**

Length of Circus Tours

Circus	Number of Days
A	100
B	130
C	160
D	90

Use the table at the left for Exercises 2–4.

2. What type of display is the most appropriate for the data?
bar graph

3. Which information would you choose for the vertical axis?
Number of days

4. Make a graph of the data. Use the graph to compare the number of days Circus D toured to the number of days Circus C toured. **See margin.**

Homework Exercises

For more exercises, see Extra Skills and Word Problems.

GO for Help

For Exercises	See Example
5–6	1
7	2
8	3

A **Budgets** Use the table at the right.

5. Make a bar graph to display the planned budgets. **See left.**

6. Make a bar graph to display the actual budgets. **See margin.**

Monthly Budget

Cost Item	Planned	Actual
Dining Out	$40	$28
Clothes	$35	$42
Concerts	$18	$6
Movies	$22	$22

5.

Planned Monthly Budget

(bar graph with Amount ($) on vertical axis from 0 to 50 and items Dining Out, Clothes, Concerts, Movies on horizontal axis labeled Item)

7. **Hot Lunches** Make a line graph of the data below. **See margin.**

Students Buying Hot Lunch

Day	Mon.	Tue.	Wed.	Thur.	Fri.
Number of Students	125	143	165	48	183

8. Which type of data display is the most appropriate to display the data below? Explain. **Bar graph; it is better for comparing amounts.**

Allowance Each Week

Amount of money ($)	3	4	5	6	7
Number of students	10	21	34	12	6

B **GPS**

9. See margin.

9. **Guided Problem Solving** Make a graph to show how the number of customers changed over the week. Describe the change shown in the graph.
- What type of graph will you use?
- What values will you use for the horizontal and vertical axes?

Music World Customers

Day	Number
Monday	72
Tuesday	94
Wednesday	172
Thursday	106
Friday	181
Saturday	234

4. See back of book.

6–7. See back of book.

9. See back of book.

10. Writing in Math Explain how you can use range when planning to draw a line graph. **See below left.**

11. Prime Ministers Make a bar graph to show how many years **GPS** each prime minister was in office. **See margin.**

**Golda Meir,
Israel, 5 years**

**Indira Gandhi,
India, 18 years**

**Margaret Thatcher,
United Kingdom, 11 years**

**Gro Harlem Brundtland,
Norway, 10 years**

**10. Answers may vary.
Sample: You can
use the range to
help you decide the
intervals you need
on the axis.**

12. Data Collection Make a line graph showing the amount of time you spend on homework each day for one week.
Check students' work.

C 13. Challenge A histogram is a bar graph that shows the frequency of each data value. Histograms often combine data into equal-sized groups. Use the frequency table at the right to make a histogram.
See margin.

Hours of Battery Life

Hours	Tally	Frequency
8–11	III	3
12–15	IIII	4
16–19	II	2
20–23	III	3

Test Prep and Mixed Review **Practice**

Multiple Choice

14. Which statement is supported by the graph below? **A**
  (A) Flu cases increased from September to December.
  (B) The lowest number of flu cases was in October.
  (C) There was a decrease in flu cases.
  (D) The highest number of flu cases was in November.

Total Number of Flu Cases

(graph: Cases vs. Month — Sept., Oct., Nov., Dec.)

15. What is the median price? **G**
$5.95, $2.50, $3.75, $4.95, $8.95, $5.25, $6.95, $4.50
  (F) $4.95   (G) $5.10   (H) $5.25   (J) $5.95

Use <, =, or > to complete each statement.

16. $1.45 \; > \; 1.4$ **17.** $0.75 \; < \; 0.752$ **18.** $3.20 \; = \; 3.2$

GO for Help

For Exercises	See Lesson
16–18	1-6

---

4. Assess & Reteach

PowerPoint
Lesson Quiz

1. The final math grades for all 6th graders were A: 125, B: 200, C: 350, D: 95, and F: 25. Make a bar graph to display this data. **See back of book for graph.**

2. The normal monthly temperatures (in °F) in Portland, OR, from January through December, respectively, are 40, 44, 47, 51, 57, 64, 68, 69, 63, 55, 46, and 40. Make a line graph of data. **See back of book for graph.**

3. Would a line graph or a bar graph be better to compare the times that classmates spent studying for a test? Why? **bar graph; Bar graphs show comparison. There is no change over time.**

11. See back of book.

13. See back of book.

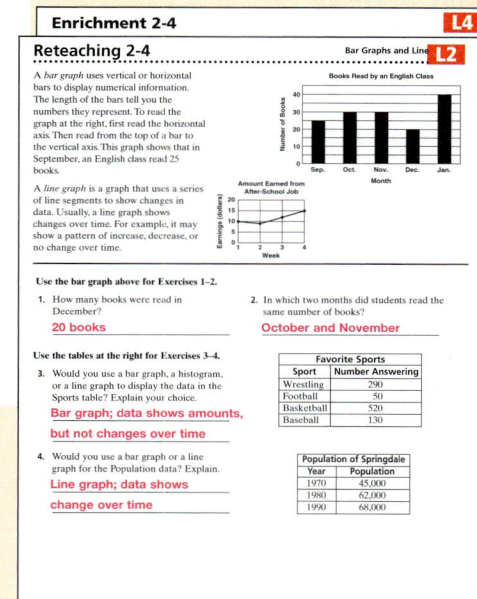

Alternative Assessment

Pairs of students find two sets of real-world data and work together to make a bar graph and a line graph.

Test Prep

Resources
For additional practice with a variety of test item formats:
• Test-Taking Strategies, p. 99
• Test Prep, p. 103
• Test-Taking Strategies with Transparencies

Making Bar Graphs

Students use a graphing calculator to make a bar graph. The data they use is the result of rolling a number cube 15 times so the possible results range from 1 to 6.

Guided Instruction

Activity
Discuss how a graphing calculator differs from other calculations students may be familiar with. Have students compare the screen and the buttons of the calculator.

Have students use their graphing calculations to complete the steps to display the graph. Allow students to compare key strokes with a partner.

Error Prevention!

Be sure students understand the function of each key on the graphing calculator before they begin the steps. Emphasize the importance of Step 1 in preparing and clearing the calculators.

Differentiated Instruction

Below Level **L2**
Allow students who are having difficulty to write the key strokes they will use to make a bar graph. You may want to have them list the keystrokes under headings reflecting Steps 1–4 of the Example.

Resources
- graphing calculator
- Classroom Aid 36

Making Bar Graphs

You can use a graphing calculator to make a bar graph.

EXAMPLE

A number cube was rolled 15 times with the following results: 1, 2, 5, 1, 3, 6, 2, 4, 6, 1, 5, 2, 4, 2, 6. Make a bar graph using the data.

Step 1 Prepare your graphing calculator.
Press [LIST] and delete any data already in the list. Press [2nd] [PLOT] 4: PlotsOff [ENTER] to turn off the plots. Press [Y=] and clear any equations.

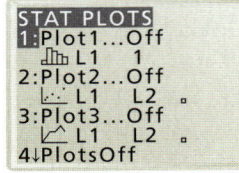

Step 2 Enter the data.
Press [LIST]. Enter each number rolled in the L1 column. Press [ENTER] after typing each number.

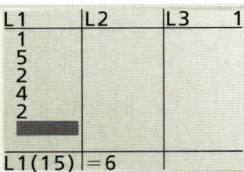

Step 3 Select the type of graph.
Press [2nd] [PLOT] 1 to select the first plot. Highlight On and press [ENTER]. Next, use the arrow keys to select bar graph for the type of graph, L1 for the Xlist, and 1 as the frequency.

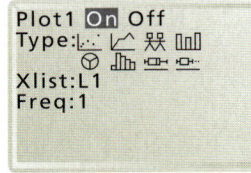

Step 4 Display the graph.
Press [ZOOM] 4: ZQuadrant1 to display the data. This zoom feature selects a window size to view the bar graph.

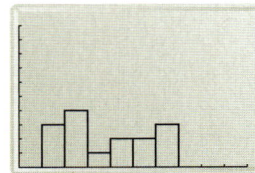

Exercises

1. Roll a number cube 15 times. Combine the results with the data from the Example. Make a new bar graph. **Check students' work.**

2. **Data Collection** Make a bar graph of your classmates' heights on the graphing calculator. **Check students' work.**

Double Bar and Line Graphs

You can plot two data sets on the same graph to compare them easily.

EXAMPLE

A bookstore tracks sales of cooking and travel books. Make a double bar graph and a double line graph of the data at the right.

Use a different color for each data set in the graphs.

Books Sold Each Month

Month	Jan.	Feb.	Mar.	Apr.
Cooking	86	98	112	110
Travel	100	106	88	102

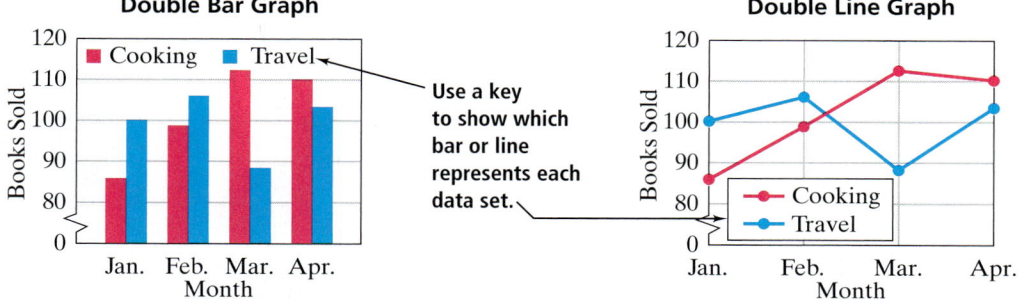

Use a key to show which bar or line represents each data set.

Exercises

Use the example above for Exercises 1 and 2.

1. Which graph shows most clearly how book sales changed from January to February? **double line graph**

2. Which graph shows most clearly the differences in sales between the two types of books? **double bar graph**

Use the table at the right for Exercises 3 and 4.

3. Make a double bar graph. Show the differences between the numbers of endangered plants and animals.
3–4. See margin.

4. Make a double line graph. Show how the numbers of endangered plants and animals have changed over time.

Endangered Species in the United States

Year	1985	1990	1995	2000	2005
Plants	93	179	432	592	599
Animals	207	263	324	379	389

SOURCE: U.S. Fish and Wildlife Service.
Go to **PHSchool.com** for a data update.
Web Code: aqg-9041

3–4. See back of book.

Extension

Double Bar and Line Graphs

In Lesson 2-4, students learned to make bar and line graphs. This feature focuses on making double bar and line graphs by plotting two sets of data on the same graph.

Guided Instruction

Teaching Tip
Remind students that there are only three possible changes between bars or points on a line: an increase, a decrease, or no change.

Exercises
Exercises 1–2 Have students work independently to answer these questions. Make sure students can correctly answer these questions before proceeding to make graphs.

Exercises 3–4 Have students work in pairs to make a double bar graph and a double line graph.

Differentiated Instruction

Visual Learners
Have students examine the double bar graph and ask:
- *Why is it important to use a different color for each data set in the double bar graph?* **Sample: The different colors help you quickly distinguish which set of data each bar belongs to, making comparisons easier.**
- *What significance does the legend have?* **Sample: The legend identifies what each color in the graph represents.**

Resources

- graph paper
- ruler
- Classroom Aid 2

Using Spreadsheets to Organize Data

Objective
To make spreadsheets to display data and solve problems

Examples
1 Reading a Spreadsheet
2 Formulas in a Spreadsheet

Math Understandings: p. 58D

Math Background

A computer *spreadsheet* is an electronic table that organizes data and formulas into columns and rows. The intersection of each column and row identifies a *cell* in a spreadsheet. For example, cell A1 identifies the intersection of column A and row 1.

More Math Background: p. 58D

Lesson Planning and Resources

See p. 58E for a list of the resources that support this lesson.

1. A cell is a box in a spreadsheet where a specific row and column meet.

Bell Ringer Practice

✓ **Check Skills You'll Need**
Use student page, transparency, or PowerPoint. For intervention, direct students to:
Adding Whole Numbers
Skills Handbook, p. 638

✓ Check Skills You'll Need

1. Vocabulary Review
The sum of two whole numbers is (never, usually) greater than either number.
usually

Find each sum.

2. 88 + 71 **159**

3. 424 + 390 **814**

GO for Help
Skills Handbook, p. 638

What You'll Learn

To make spreadsheets to display data and solve problems

🔊 **New Vocabulary** spreadsheet, cell

Why Learn This?

You can use formulas in a spreadsheet to automatically recalculate values when you change an entry.

A **spreadsheet** is a table made up of rows and columns used to organize data. A **cell** is a box in a spreadsheet where a specific row and column meet.

EXAMPLE Reading a Spreadsheet

1 **Music** The spreadsheet below shows the lengths of 15 CDs from five different categories. Identify the value in cell B5. Tell what this number represents.

Column B

	A	B	C	D	E
1	Music Type	Disc 1 (min)	Disc 2 (min)	Disc 3 (min)	Mean Length (min)
2	Rock/Pop	40	44	45	
3	Rap	48	53	55	
4	Country	32	34	30	
5	Classical	45	54	51	
6	Jazz	41	53	44	

Row 5 →

Cell B5

The value in B5 is 45. The first classical CD is 45 minutes long.

✓ Quick Check

1. 30; the minutes of country music on disc 3

1. What is the value in cell D4? What does this number represent?

Differentiated Instruction Solutions for All Learners

Special Needs L1
Help students "find" a cell such as D2, by moving one finger over from 2 to D, and another finger from D down to 2. The point where their fingers meet is cell D2.

learning style: tactile

Below Level L2
Use a local map to introduce the letter and number grid organization of a spreadsheet. Students use the index to identify the location of the school. They then find its location on the map.

learning style: visual

A computer automatically enters a value in a cell of a spreadsheet when you assign a formula to that cell. A formula is a statement of a mathematical relationship. An equal sign (=) tells the computer that an expression is a formula.

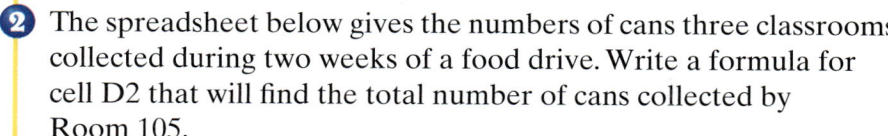 **EXAMPLE**   Formulas in a Spreadsheet

2 The spreadsheet below gives the numbers of cans three classrooms collected during two weeks of a food drive. Write a formula for cell D2 that will find the total number of cans collected by Room 105.

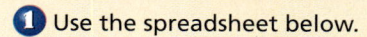

Technology Tip

These operation symbols are used in spreadsheets:

+ addition
− subtraction
* multiplication
/ division

	A	B	C	D
1	Room Number	Week 1 (cans)	Week 2 (cans)	Total (cans)
2	105	389	416	▨ ← D2
3	106	592	462	▨
4	107	481	493	▨
5				▨

Total number
of cans   =   389   +   416
  ↓   ↓   ↓
D2   =   B2   +   C2   ← Write an expression for cell D2.

Here is the formula for cell D2: = B2 + C2.

✓ **Quick Check**

2. For cell D5, write a formula that will calculate the total number of cans collected by all three classrooms. **= D2 + D3 + D4**

✓ **Check Your Understanding**

	A	B
1	Sandals	Pairs
2	Sporty	15
3	Casual	19
4	Total	▨

1. **Vocabulary** How is a cell related to a spreadsheet? **See margin page 80.**

Use the spreadsheet at the left for each matching question.

2. What is the value in cell B3? **D**

3. What is the value in cell B2? **B**

4. What is a formula for cell B4 that adds the values in cells B2 and B3? **F**

5. What is the value in cell B4? **E**

A. = B3 + B4
B. 15
C. Sporty
D. 19
E. 34
F. = B2 + B3

Advanced Learners [L4]
Ask: *How might more than 26 columns be named in a spreadsheet?* **Sample: Use double letters: AA, AB, and so on.**

learning style: verbal

English Language Learners ELL
This lesson may contain language unfamiliar to students. Have them use a printout of a spreadsheet and label a column, a row, a cell, its value, and the spreadsheet itself. They can keep this visual model as they work with spreadsheets.

learning style: visual

---

2. Teach

Activity Lab
Use before the lesson.

All·in·One **Teaching Resources**

Activity Lab 2-5: Constructing a Table of Values

Guided Instruction

Example 1
Have students use index fingers to trace down column B and across row 5 at the same time.

Error Prevention!

Some students may confuse *columns* and *rows*. Have them envision a building with tall columns to remember that columns are vertical.

PowerPoint
💻 **Additional Examples**

1 Use the spreadsheet below.

	A	B	C
1	Date	Phone	Utilities
2	10/15	$68	$118
3	11/15	$55	$143
4	12/15	$72	$159

a. What is the value in cell C3? **$143**

b. Identify the cell(s) that indicate the category *Phone.* **B1, B2, B3, B4**

2 Use the spreadsheet in Question 1. Write a formula for cell D3 that will calculate the total phone and utilities amounts on 11/15. **= B3 + C3**

All·in·One **Teaching Resources**
• Daily Notetaking Guide 2-5 [L3]
• Adapted Notetaking 2-5 [L1]

Closure

• *What is a spreadsheet?* **an electronic table that organizes data using columns and rows**
• *What is a spreadsheet formula?* **a statement of a mathematical relationship that begins with =**

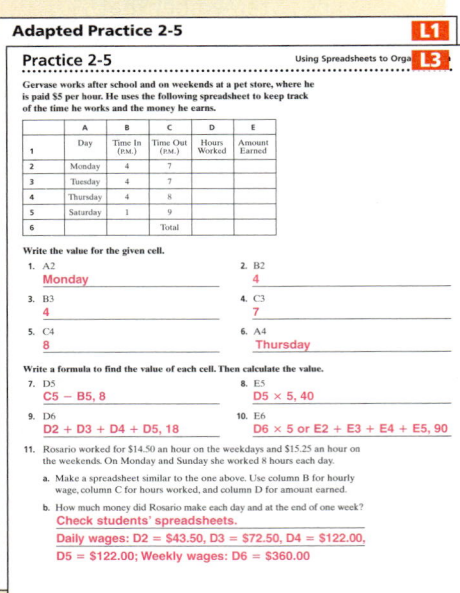

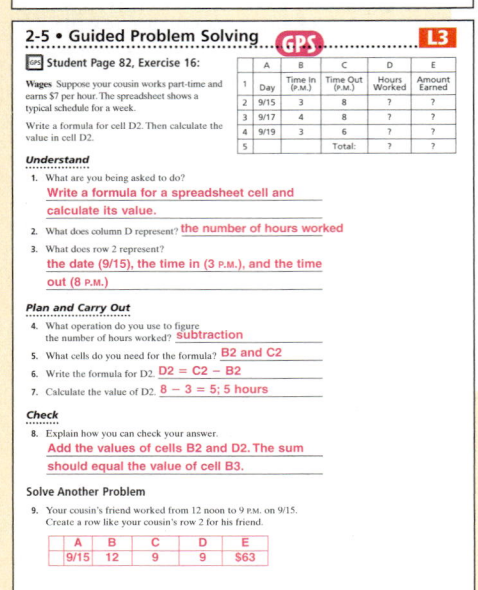

Homework Exercises

For more exercises, see Extra Skills and Word Problems.

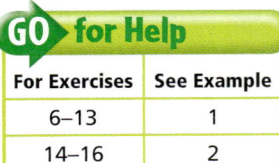

GO for Help

For Exercises	See Example
6–13	1
14–16	2

A Use the spreadsheet below for Exercises 6–15.

Four groups of students made videos. They received scores for originality, effort, and quality.

	A	B	C	D	E	F
1	Group	Originality	Effort	Quality	Total	Mean Score
2	Red	90	85	80	▦	▦
3	Orange	90	90	60	▦	▦
4	Yellow	95	100	75	▦	▦
5	Green	65	80	80	▦	▦

Identify the cell(s) for each category.

6. Effort
C2, C3, C4, C5

7. Mean Score
F2, F3, F4, F5

8. Green
B5, C5, D5, E5, F5

9. Total
E2, E3, E4, E5

Find the value for the given cell.

10. C4 **100**   **11.** C5 **80**   **12.** B4 **95**   **13.** B2 **90**

Write a formula to find each quantity.

14. the total in cell E4
= B4 + C4 + D4

15. the mean score in cell F4
= (B4 + C4 + D4)/3 or = E4/3

Wages Suppose your cousin works part time and earns $7 per hour. The spreadsheet shows a typical schedule for a week.

	A	B	C	D	E
1	Day	Time In (P.M.)	Time Out (P.M.)	Hours Worked	Amount Earned
2	9/15	3	8	▦	▦
3	9/17	4	8	▦	▦
4	9/19	3	6	▦	▦
5			Total:	▦	▦

16. Write a formula for cell D2. Then calculate the value in D2.
= C2 − B2; 5

B **GPS** **17.** **Guided Problem Solving** Refer to the spreadsheet above. How much money did your cousin earn on 9/19? **$21**
  • Use the formula for cell D2 to write a formula for the number of hours worked on 9/19.
  • How can you use the value in D4 in the formula for E4?

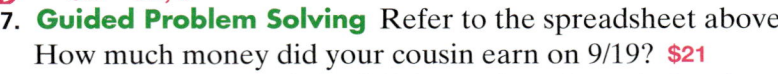

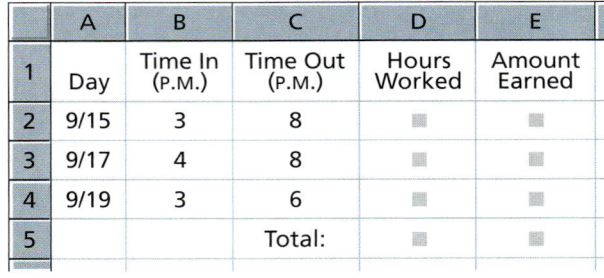

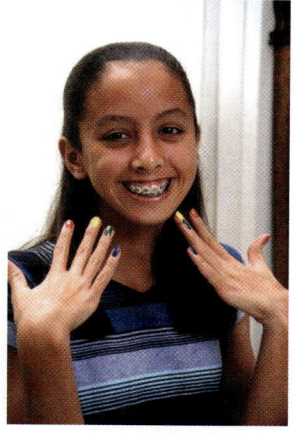

20. Amount Collected (dollars)

As a fundraiser, students sell nail polish for $3 per bottle. Find the value for each cell.

18. A3 Glitter   **19.** B7 5

20. C1 See left.   **21.** C2 24

Use the spreadsheet for Exercises 22–25.

22. Write a formula for cell C2.
= B2*3

23. **a.** Writing in Math Explain how the formula for C2 can be used to calculate the values in cells C3 through C7.
b. Calculate the values in C3 through C7.
23a–b. See margin.

24. Write a formula for cell C8. Then calculate its value.
= C2 + C3 + C4 + C5 + C6 + C7; 168

C 25. Challenge Write a formula that finds the mean amount collected for the six types of nail polish. = C8 ÷ 6

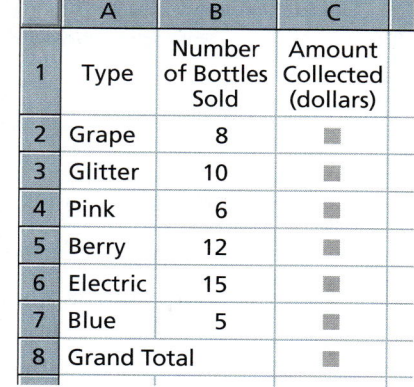

	A	B	C
1	Type	Number of Bottles Sold	Amount Collected (dollars)
2	Grape	8	
3	Glitter	10	
4	Pink	6	
5	Berry	12	
6	Electric	15	
7	Blue	5	
8	Grand Total		

Test Prep and Mixed Review   **Practice**

Multiple Choice

26. The line plot shows the number of slices in loaves of bread. Which statement is NOT supported by the graph? **B**
  Ⓐ 24 different loaves of bread were counted.
  Ⓑ The median value is 18.
  Ⓒ The range of slices is 5.
  Ⓓ The most frequent number of slices is 20.

Slices in Loaves of Bread

```
                X
                X
                X
                X
        X       X   X
        X   X   X   X   X
        X   X   X   X   X   X
        X   X   X   X   X   X
       18  19  20  21  22  23
           Number of Slices
```

27. A student lists her test scores for a quarter: 84, 80, 82, 85, 89, 90, and 92. What is the range of scores? **G**
  Ⓕ 92   Ⓖ 12   Ⓗ 8   Ⓙ 7

28. Estimate each sum. Which is closest to 3,000? **D**
  Ⓐ 612 + 898 + 1,690   Ⓒ 990 + 1,020 + 2,009
  Ⓑ 2,009 + 494 + 708   Ⓓ 1,498 + 898 + 612

GO for Help

For Exercises	See Lesson
29–30	2-2

Find the median of each data set.

29. 5, 4, 7, 8, 3, 4, 11, 3, 7, 8, 7 **7**   **30.** 2.8, 1.6, 0, 0.8, 1, 0 **0.9**

23a. Answers may vary. Sample: The "fill down" function will apply that formula to the entire column of the cell.

b. 30; 18; 36; 45; 15

Test Prep

Resources
For additional practice with a variety of test item formats:
• Test-Taking Strategies, p. 99
• Test Prep, p. 103
• Test-Taking Strategies with Transparencies

---

4. Assess & Reteach

PowerPoint
Lesson Quiz

Use the spreadsheet to answer the questions.

	A	B	C
1	Name	1st Term	2nd Term
2	Eve	85	95
3	Sam	90	96
4	Carl	92	86

1. What are the values of cell C4 and B3? **C4 is 86; B3 is 90**

2. What formula could you write in cell D2 to find Eve's average?
= (B2 + C2)/2

Alternative Assessment

Each student in a pair makes a spreadsheet similar to Example 1. They write several questions that can be answered using their spreadsheets. Partners exchange spreadsheets and questions. Then they answer each other's questions.

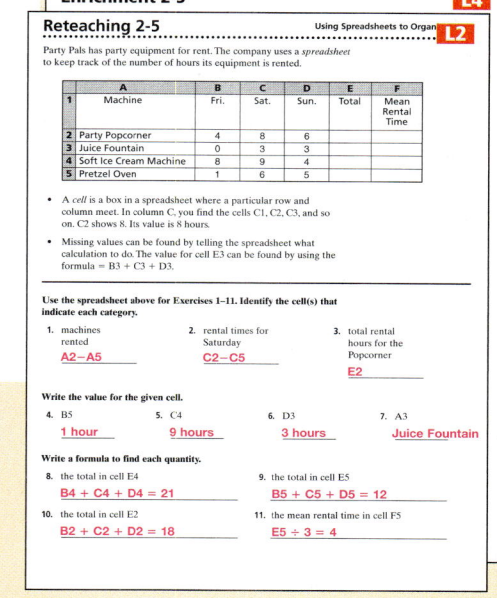

83

Spreadsheets and Graphs

You can use spreadsheet programs to make bar graphs, line graphs, and scatter plots. A scatter plot is a graph that relates two sets of data.

Enter and highlight the data you want to graph. Use the menu to choose the type of graph and the labels. Finally, insert the labels.

EXAMPLE

Sierra makes a table showing the amount of time she studies for each test and the grade she gets on the test. She enters her data in the spreadsheet below. Sierra then chooses a scatter plot because it shows the relationship between sets of data.

	A	B
1	Minutes Studied	Test Score
2	75	89
3	45	92
4	15	65
5	30	75
6	60	90

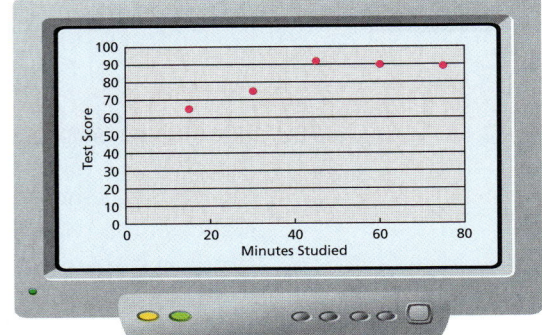

Exercises

Enter the data below in a spreadsheet. Use the program to make a graph of the data. Explain why you chose the type of graph you used.

1. **Allowance Spent at the Mall**   1–2. See margin.

Time in Mall (hours)	2	4	3	1
Amount Spent ($)	$10	$24	$15	$8

2. **How Often People Need to Search for Keys**

Category	Never	Once a year	Once a month	Once a week	Once a day
Number of Responses	31	15	23	9	2

1–2. See back of book.

Use the line plot for Exercises 1–4.

1. Find the mean, the median, and the mode of the data.   **21.07; 21; 21**

2. Find the range of temperatures.   **9**

3. Are there any outliers? Explain.
Yes; 26 is much higher than the majority of the data.

4. Does the mean, median, or mode best describe these data? Explain.
Answers may vary. Sample: The mode represents which high temperature occurred the most.

High Temperatures

```
                  x
                  x   x
         x        x   x        x
  x  x   x   x    x   x        x        x
  17 18  19  20   21  22  23   24   25  26
```
Temperature (°C)

5. Nutrition The grams of fat per serving for 24 breakfast cereals are 0, 1, 3, 1, 1, 2, 2, 0, 3, 1, 3, 2, 0, 1, 0, 2, 1, 1, 0, 0, 0, 2, 1, and 0. Make a frequency table for the data.   **See margin.**

Use the spreadsheet for Exercises 6–8.

6. For cell B6 in the spreadsheet, write a formula to calculate the total collected from the fundraisers.
= B2 + B3 + B4 + B5

7. How much money was collected from the fundraisers?
$800

8. Make a bar graph using the data.   **See margin.**

9. Suppose your bank account balance is $37 in January, $40 in February, $55 in March, and $15 in April. Draw a line graph of the data.   **See margin.**

	A	B
1	Fundraiser	Collected ($)
2	Book sale	200
3	Car wash	125
4	Food stand	325
5	Paper drive	150
6	TOTAL:	▪

MATH AT WORK

Park Ranger

Do you enjoy working outdoors? Are you interested in history? If so, maybe a career as a park ranger is for you. Park rangers use mathematics to predict the number of visitors, measure rainfall and tree growth, plan trails, solve problems involving acid rain or deforestation, and construct timelines.

Go Online
PHSchool.com   **For:** Information on national parks
Web Code: aqb-2031

85

✔ **Checkpoint Quiz**

Use this Checkpoint Quiz to check students' understanding of the skills and concepts of Lessons 2-1 through 2-5.

Resources

- All-in-One Teaching Resources Checkpoint Quiz 1
- ExamView CD-ROM
- Success Tracker™ Online Intervention

MATH AT WORK

Park Ranger

Students may not think that park rangers use much mathematics to do their jobs. Ask students to add to the list of tasks requiring mathematics that a park ranger might do. Other possibilities include planning animal feeding, monitoring the number of visitors, and providing park officials with data.

Guided Instruction

Ask:
- *What would you like about a park ranger's job?* **Sample: working outdoors**
- *What math skills would it be useful for a park ranger to have?* **Sample: ability to present numerical data**

5.

Grams of Fat	Tally	Frequency
0	⊥⊥⊤ |||	8
1	⊥⊥⊤ |||	8
2	⊥⊥⊤	5
3					3

8–9. See back of book.

Objective
To make and analyze stem-and-leaf plots

Examples
1 Interpreting a Stem-and-Leaf Plot
2 Make a Stem-and-Leaf Plot

Math Understandings: p. 58D

Math Background

A *stem-and-leaf plot* uses the digits of the data values to display the shape of a data set. A stem-and-leaf plot separates the digits in each data value into a *stem* and a *leaf*. The stem is recorded once, forming an interval. The leaf lists each data value as often as it appears in the data set.

More Math Background: p. 58D

Lesson Planning and Resources

See p. 58E for a list of the resources that support this lesson.

PowerPoint

Bell Ringer Practice

✓ **Check Skills You'll Need**
Use student page, transparency, or PowerPoint. For intervention, direct students to:
Median and Mode
Lesson 2-2
Extra Skills and Word Problems Practice, Ch. 2

✓ **Check Skills You'll Need**

1. **Vocabulary Review** What is the *median* of a set of data? **See below.**
   Find the median of each data set.

2. 23, 32, 32, 15, 52 **32**

3. 15, 10, 32, 21, 10 **15**

4. 6.7, 4.6, 5.8, 3.8 **5.2**

 **for Help**
Lesson 2-2

Check Skills You'll Need

1. The median of a data set is the middle value when the data are arranged in numerical order.

 **Test Prep Tip**

To read the data in a stem-and-leaf plot, combine the stem with each leaf in the same row.

What You'll Learn

To make and analyze stem-and-leaf plots

◀ **New Vocabulary** stem-and-leaf plot

Why Learn This?

You can use a stem-and-leaf plot to group and interpret data, including how long it takes to get ready for school.

A **stem-and-leaf plot** is a graph that uses the digits of each number to show the shape of the data. Each data value is broken into a "stem" and a "leaf."

stem → 5|8 ← leaf

EXAMPLE **Interpreting a Stem-and-Leaf Plot**

1 The times students take to get ready for school are shown below. How many students take less than 30 minutes? How many take more than 40 minutes?

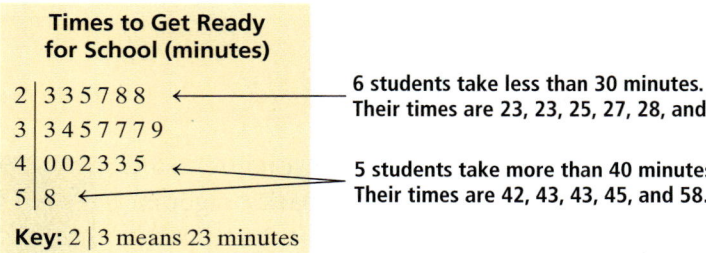

Times to Get Ready for School (minutes)

```
2 | 3 3 5 7 8 8
3 | 3 4 5 7 7 7 9
4 | 0 0 2 3 3 5
5 | 8
```

6 students take less than 30 minutes. Their times are 23, 23, 25, 27, 28, and 28.

5 students take more than 40 minutes. Their times are 42, 43, 43, 45, and 58.

Key: 2 | 3 means 23 minutes

Six students take less than 30 minutes. Five students take more than 40 minutes.

✓ **Quick Check**

1. What is the range of the data? **35**

Differentiated **Instruction** Solutions for All Learners

Special Needs **L1**
Some students have a difficult time making a stem-and-leaf plot. For the data values, 32, 38, 39, and 31, have them draw a stem and mark it 30. Have them draw four leaves on the stem, marking the leaves with the values of 2, 8, 9, and 1.

learning style: visual

Below Level **L2**
Ask: *How is a stem-and-leaf plot similar to a line plot?* Both plots show the shape of the data. Both plots also represent each data value.

learning style: verbal

0–60 Miles per Hour Times (seconds)	
8.2	7.0
7.3	8.9
7.2	8.3
8.0	7.0
7.7	7.6
8.1	8.7
8.1	7.3
7.2	10.5
7.6	8.5
6.5	6.8

EXAMPLE · Making a Stem-and-Leaf Plot

2 Cars The table at the left shows times that it takes compact cars to reach 60 miles per hour. Make a stem-and-leaf plot of the data.

Step 1 Write the stems in order. Use the whole-number part. Draw a vertical line to the right of the stems.

```
stems →   6
          7
          8
          9
         10
```

Step 2 Write the leaves in order. There is no nonzero digit in the hundredths place. So use the values in the tenths place.

```
 6 | 5 8              ← leaves
 7 | 0 0 2 2 3 3 6 6 7
 8 | 0 1 1 2 3 5 7 9
 9 |
10 | 5
```

Step 3 Choose a title and include a key. The key explains what your stems and leaves represent.

```
        0–60 Miles per
      Hour Times (seconds)

 6 | 5 8
 7 | 0 0 2 2 3 3 6 6 7
 8 | 0 1 1 2 3 5 7 9
 9 |
10 | 5

Key: 6 | 5 means 6.5   ← key
```

✓ Quick Check

2. Elections The data below show the numbers of students who voted for class president each year. Make a stem-and-leaf plot.
137, 125, 145, 123, 181, 132, 155, 141, 140, 133, 138, 127, 150, 126, 124, 130, 125, 138, 144, 121, 136   **See above.**
(*Hint:* Use the ones digit for the leaves.)

```
2.  12 | 1 3 4 5 5 6 7
    13 | 0 2 3 6 7 8 8
    14 | 0 1 4 5
    15 | 0 5
    16 |
    17 |
    18 | 1
    Key: 12|3 means 123
```

Closure

- *What is a stem-and-leaf plot?* **a graph that uses the digits of each number to show the shape of the data**

● **More Than One Way**

Your class collected data on how long it takes each student to get to school. The data are below. Use a data display to find the most frequent time.

times, in minutes: 8, 10, 6, 10, 22, 15, 9, 7, 10, 14, 9, 7, 10, 45, 18, 10, 6, 15, 13, 18, 13, 6, 3

Zach's Method

I can use a frequency table.

Time (min)	Tally	Frequency	Time (min)	Tally	Frequency
3	I	1	13	II	2
6	III	3	14	I	1
7	II	2	15	II	2
8	I	1	18	II	2
9	II	2	22	I	1
10	LHT	5	45	I	1

The most frequent time is 10 minutes.

Lauren's Method

I can use a stem-and-leaf plot and choose the time with the most leaves.

Time Spent Traveling to School (minutes)

```
0 | 3 6 6 6 7 7 8 9 9
1 | 0 0 0 0 0 3 3 4 5 5 8 8
2 | 2
3 |
4 | 5
```

Key: 2 | 2 means 22 minutes

The most frequent time is 10 minutes.

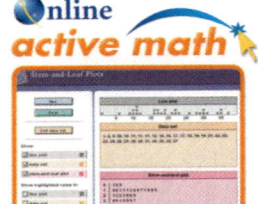

Online active math

For: Stem-and-Leaf Plot Activity
Use: Interactive Textbook, 2-5

Choose a Method

Students are asked how many minutes they think they need for tutoring after school: 30, 45, or 60. The results are shown below. Use a data display to show how long should be set aside for after-school tutoring. Explain why you chose the method you used.
60, 45, 60, 30, 30, 60, 60, 45, 60, 30, 30, 60, 60, 45, 30, 60, 45
See back of book.

Check Your Understanding

4.
```
3 | 6 8 8
4 | 1 1 2 3 4
5 | 0
6 | 2
7 | 5 7 9
8 | 9
```
Key: 3 | 6 means 36 s

5. The stem-and-leaf plot organizes the values from lowest to highest.

1. **Vocabulary** A graph that uses the digits of each number to show the shape of the data is a (line, stem-and-leaf) plot.
stem-and-leaf

Use the stem-and-leaf plot at the right.

2. What do the stem 3 and leaf 8 represent?
30; 8 or 38

3. How many of the times in the plot are greater than 50 seconds?
4

4. Copy the stem-and-leaf plot. Add the following data items: 38 seconds and 89 seconds.
See left.

5. **Writing in Math** What advantage does a stem-and-leaf plot have that a list of values does not have? See left.

```
3 | 6 8
4 | 1 1 2 3 4
5 | 0
6 | 2
7 | 5 7 9
```
Key: 3 | 6 means 36 seconds

Assignment Guide

Check Your Understanding
Go over Exercises 1–5 in class before assigning the Homework Exercises.

Homework Exercises
A Practice by Example   6–10
B Apply Your Skills   11–15
C Challenge   16
Test Prep and
   Mixed Review   17–21

Homework Quick Check
To check student's understanding of key skills and concepts, go over Exercises 8, 10, 13, 14, and 15.

Differentiated Instruction **Resources**

Homework Exercises

For more exercises, see Extra Skills and Word Problems.

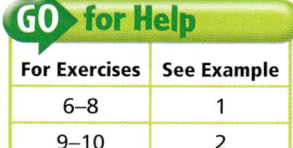

GO for Help

For Exercises	See Example
6–8	1
9–10	2

A Use the stem-and-leaf plot at the right.

6. What does "0 | 8" represent? 8 seconds

7. How many entries have a value of 15?
3 entries

8. How many customers waited less than 9 seconds? 4 customers

Number of Seconds Customers on Hold
```
0 | 7 8 8 8 9 9
1 | 0 2 2 3 4 5 5 5 6 7 7
```
Key: 0 | 7 means 7 seconds

Make a stem-and-leaf plot for each set of data.

9. heights of tomato plants (inches): 27, 40, 31, 33, 35, 33, 26, 36, 41, 29, 30, 36
9–10. See margin.

10. number of jelly beans in a scoop: 47, 28, 38, 47, 58, 34, 76, 35, 32, 45, 53, 43, 35, 27

B 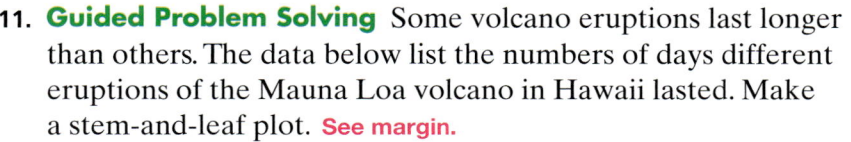 **GPS** 11. **Guided Problem Solving** Some volcano eruptions last longer than others. The data below list the numbers of days different eruptions of the Mauna Loa volcano in Hawaii lasted. Make a stem-and-leaf plot. See margin.

23   24   46   15   39   12   48   16   61   25   16   20   21   15

- How many stems should your plot have?
- How many leaves should your plot have?

9. **Height of Tomato Plants (inches)**
```
2 | 6 7 9
3 | 0 1 3 3 5 6 6
4 | 0 1
```
Key: 2 | 6 means 26 in.

10–11. See back of book.

Adapted Practice 2-6   L1

Practice 2-6   Stem-and-Leaf   L3

Use the stem-and-leaf plot for Exercises 1–6.
1. What is the age of the youngest grandparent? 67
2. How many grandparents are 79 years old? 2
3. How many grandparents are older than 74? 11
4. What is the range of the data? 28
5. What is the median? 79
6. What is the mode? 83

Ages of Grandparents
```
stem | leaf
 6   | 7 8 8
 7   | 0 1 2 3 4 9 9
 8   | 1 3 3 3 4 7
 9   | 0 2 5
```
Key: 6 | 7 means 67

Make a stem-and-leaf plot for each set of data.

7. scores on a history test
84, 93, 72, 87, 86, 97, 68, 74, 86, 91, 64, 83, 79, 80, 72, 83, 76, 90, 77
```
stem | leaf
 6   | 4 8
 7   | 2 2 4 6 7 9
 8   | 0 3 4 6 6 7
 9   | 0 1 3 7
```
Key: 6 | 4 means 67

8. number of badges earned by local scouts
7, 12, 9, 2, 17, 24, 0, 3, 10, 20, 12, 3, 6, 4, 9, 15
```
stem | leaf
 0   | 0 2 3 3 4 6 7 9 9
 1   | 0 2 2 5 7
 2   | 0 4
```
Key: 1 | 0 means 10

9. minutes to travel to a friend's house
12, 31, 5, 10, 23, 17, 21, 12, 8, 33, 3, 11, 10, 25, 9, 16
```
stem | leaf
 0   | 3 5 8 9
 1   | 0 0 1 2 2 6 7
 2   | 1 3 5
 3   | 1 3
```
Key: 3 | 1 means 31

2-6 • Guided Problem Solving   **GPS**   L3

GPS Student Page 90, Exercise 14:

The heights of nine people are below. Use a stem-and-leaf plot to find the median, the mode, and any outliers.

Heights in inches:
```
70    59    64
66    79    67
82    68    61
```

Understand
1. Looking at the data, which numbers should be the stems? Explain.
   the numbers in the tens place, because those numbers are read first

Plan and Carry Out
2. Order the heights from least to greatest.
   59 in., 61 in., 64 in., 66 in., 67 in., 68 in., 70 in., 79 in., 82 in.

3. Write the stems in order. Draw a vertical line next to the stems.   4. Write the leaves in order for each stem.
```
5 |              5 | 9
6 |              6 | 1 4 6 7 8
7 |              7 | 0 9
8 |              8 | 2
```

5. Include a key to explain what the stems and leaves represent.   Key: 5 | 9 means 59 inches

Check
6. How can you check to make sure you used all the data values?
   Make sure the number of leaves matches the number of data items.

Solve Another Problem
7. Eight friends were in a race. Their times in seconds are given below.
108 114 140 118 182 165 150 123
Make a stem-and-leaf plot for the data.   Check students' plots.

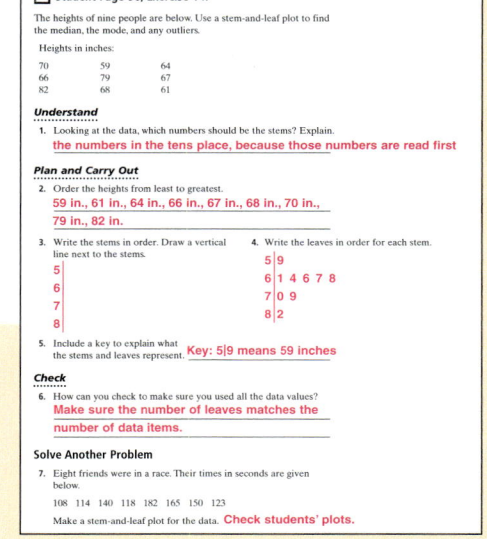

PowerPoint

Lesson Quiz

The Eagles scored the following points in the basketball games they played this season: 67, 59, 75, 49, 68, 72, 84, 59, 71, 69, 81, 55, 68, 83, and 77.

1. Make a stem-and-leaf plot for the data.

Points Scored in a Game

```
4 | 9
5 | 5 9 9
6 | 7 8 8 9
7 | 1 2 5 7   Key:
8 | 1 3 4     8 | 4 means 84
```

Alternative Assessment

Students work in pairs to find real-world data. Partners make a stem-and-leaf plot of the data and then write questions that involve interpreting their plot. Pairs exchange their plots and questions with other pairs and answer the questions.

GO Online

Homework Video Tutor

Visit: PHSchool.com
Web Code: aqe-0206

14. **Heights (in inches)**

```
5 | 9
6 | 1 4 6 7 8
7 | 0 9
8 | 2
```

Key: 5 | 9 means 59 inches

median: 67 in.

mode: none

outliers: 79 in. and 82 in.

Group A		Group B
9 5 3	2	8
	10	
	3	4 7

Key:

means ← 3 | 2 | 8 → means
23   28

---

12. **Population** The table shows the rounded populations of nine states. Make a stem-and-leaf plot. **See margin.**

13. The ages of 18 people are shown below.

21 12 15 13 35 24 16 23 9
40 19 12 15 13 12 20 11 12

a. Make a stem-and-leaf plot and a line plot.

b. Which more clearly shows the number of people in their teens? Explain. **13a–b. See margin.**

14. The heights of nine people are below. **GPS** Use a stem-and-leaf plot to find the median, the mode, and any outliers.

Heights in inches: 70, 59, 64, 66, 79, 67, 82, 68, 61 **See left.**

15. **Data Collection** Choose a paragraph from a book or magazine. Make a stem-and-leaf plot for the number of letters in each word. Use the plot to find the median word length. **Check students' work.**

C 16. **Challenge** The back-to-back stem-and-leaf plot shown at the left displays two sets of data. Make a back-to-back stem-and-leaf plot for the data below. **See margin.**

Group D: 24, 26, 33, 35, 39   Group F: 25, 29, 34, 36, 37

State	Population (millions)
Arizona	5.7
Colorado	4.6
Indiana	6.2
Kentucky	4.1
Maryland	5.6
Minnesota	5.0
Oregon	3.6
Tennessee	5.9
Wisconsin	5.5

SOURCE: U.S. Census Bureau. Go to **PHSchool.com** for a data update. Web Code: aqg-9041

Test Prep and Mixed Review   **Practice**

Multiple Choice

17. Use the stem-and-leaf plot. How many data items are greater than 67? **B**

   Ⓐ 7   Ⓒ 5

   Ⓑ 6   Ⓓ 3

```
4 | 0 9
5 | 2 4 4 5 9
6 | 3 7 7 7 8 8 9
7 | 2 4 6
```

Key: 4 | 0 means 40

18. The favorite activities of eight students are sports, reading, drawing, games, games, drawing, sports, and sports. Find the mode. **H**

  Ⓕ reading   Ⓖ drawing   Ⓗ sports   Ⓙ no mode

19. Which decimal represents $\frac{6}{25}$? **A**

  Ⓐ 0.24   Ⓑ 0.25   Ⓒ 0.30   Ⓓ 0.6

Find the value of each expression.

20. $13 + 5 \times 12 - 4$ **69**
         21. $22 + 44 \div 22 - 11$ **13**

GO for Help

For Exercises	See Lesson
20–21	1-4

---

90   **Chapter 2**   Data and Graphs

Test Prep

Resources

For additional practice with a variety of test item formats:

• Test-Taking Strategies, p. 99
• Test Prep, p. 103
• Test-Taking Strategies with Transparencies

12. See back of book.

13a–b. See back of book.

16. See back of book.

Solving Multiple-Step Problems

The table below shows some gasoline prices. At those prices, how much more would it cost to fill a 22-gallon gas tank in Hawaii than in Georgia?

Gas Prices (dollars per gallon)

Higher Prices		Lower Prices	
Hawaii	2.416	New Jersey	1.872
California	2.302	Texas	1.935
Oregon	2.130	Georgia	1.951

SOURCE: AAA Fuel Gauge Report

What You Might Think

- What do I know?
- What am I trying to find out?
- What diagram can I draw to show the situation?
- What *hidden question* needs to be answered?
- How do I solve the problem?
- What is the answer?

What You Might Write

Hawaii: $2.416 per gal Georgia: $1.951 per gal

I want to know how much more it costs to fill a 22-gallon tank in Hawaii than in Georgia.

Cost of gas in Hawaii	
Cost in Georgia	?

How much more does 1 gallon cost in Hawaii than in Georgia?

$2.416 − $1.951 = $0.465. This is the additional cost per gallon in Hawaii.
$0.465 per gal × 22 gal = $10.23

It costs $10.23 more to fill a 22-gallon tank in Hawaii than in Georgia.

Think It Through

1–3. Answers may vary. Samples are given.

1. How does the diagram show that subtraction is the operation needed to find how much more gas costs in Hawaii? **See right.**

2. **Check for Reasonableness** How can you use rounding to decide whether the answer is reasonable? Check the answer. **2–3. See margin.**

3. **Reasoning** Is there another way to solve the problem? Explain. (*Hint:* Use the total cost to fill a 22-gallon tank.)

1. It shows that the difference is needed to find how much more gas costs.

2. You could round $2.416 to $2.4 and $1.951 to $1.9 and subtract to get 0.5, which is $\frac{1}{2}$. Since $\frac{1}{2}$ of 22 is 11, the answer is reasonable.

3. You could multiply to find the cost of a 22-gallon tank in both states first, and then subtract to find the difference.

Solving Multiple-Step Problems

In this feature, students learn to find and answer hidden questions. After they answer the hidden question, they use the information they have gained to solve the problem.

Guided Instruction

Discuss with students the need to identify a question that relates to the diagram. Be sure they understand that they need to find the difference in Georgia's and Hawaii's gas prices. Ask:
- *What does the question mark in the diagram stand for?* **the difference in price for a gallon of gasoline in Georgia and Hawaii**
- *Why do you multiply by 22?* **to find the additional cost for 22 gallons of gas**

Guided Instruction

Error Prevention!

Be sure students do not stop after finding the difference in price for 1 gallon of gas. Remind them that the problem asks for the difference in price for a 22-gallon tank.

Exercises

Work through Exercise 4 as a class. Then assign students to work with partners to complete Exercises 5–9.

For Exercise 5, ask: *Why was a line graph used to display the data?*
The graph shows changes in prices over time.

Advanced Learners   **L4**

Ask:
Why does the stem-and-leaf plot in Exercise 8 use decimals from 2.3 to 2.9 as stems rather than using just the whole number part, 2? **the leaves would be two-digit**

Exercises

4. How much less does it cost to fill an 18-gallon tank than a 23-gallon tank in Texas? **about $9.68**
   a. What do you know?
   b. What hidden question needs to be answered?
   c. Solve the problem. Decide if the answer is reasonable. Tell how you decided.

5. Use the graph at the right. How much more did a gallon of gas cost in Week 11 than in Week 1? **$0.278**

6. A cab driver filled his car with 15.5 gallons of gasoline at $2.45 per gallon. He then bought snacks for $7.85. Use the diagram below to help you find the total cost. Is your answer reasonable? Explain. **$45.83; explanations may vary.**

Total cost	
Cost of gas	Cost of snacks

7. The tax on a gallon of gasoline in Texas is $.20. If there were no tax on gasoline, what would it cost to fill an 18.5 gallon tank in Texas? Use the diagram below to help answer the hidden question. **$32.10**

$1.935	
$0.20	Cost per gallon without tax

8. Find the mean, median, and mode of the data from the stem-and-leaf plot shown. What would you use for a newspaper headline about the typical gasoline price at these neighborhood stations? Explain your reasoning. **See above right.**

9. Airlines measure the amount of fuel in an airplane in pounds. One gallon of fuel weighs 6.1 pounds. One gallon of water weighs 8.3 pounds. How much less does the fuel in a 5-gallon can weigh than the water in a 5-gallon bucket? **11 lb**

8. **$2.79, $2.80, $2.80; answers may vary. Sample: the mode because that's the price at the most stations.**

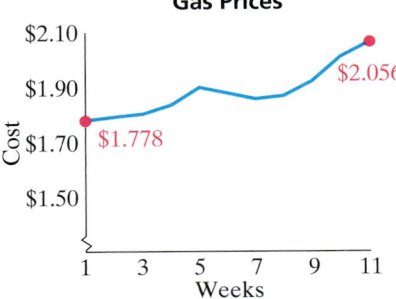

Gas Prices

$2.056

$1.778

Neighborhood Gas Prices

```
2.9 | 1 3 4 5 8
2.8 | 0 0 0 7 7 9 9
2.7 | 0 2 2 8 8
2.6 | 5 7 8
2.5 |
2.4 |
2.3 | 5
```

Key: 2.7 | 2 means $2.72

Misleading Graphs and Statistics

Check Skills You'll Need

1. Vocabulary Review
What is the *mean* of a set of data?
See below.
Find the mean for each set of data.
55.5
2. 21, 25, 52, 81.5, 98
3. 8.5, 9, 11, 19, 20 **13.5**
4. 111, 121, 131, 161
131

GO for Help
Lesson 2-1

Check Skills You'll Need

1. The mean of a set of data values is the sum of the data divided by the number of data values.

What You'll Learn

To identify misleading graphs and statistics

Why Learn This?

Companies often present data in ways that are meant to influence you. You will be able to make better decisions if you carefully analyze the data.

As you look at data displays, consider these questions: Is the information shown accurately? Is the presentation meant to influence you?

Test Prep Tip

A graph can be misleading if the scales have uneven intervals or if the graph does not begin at 0.

EXAMPLE Misleading Line Graphs

① **Multiple Choice** Each month, residents of a town were asked, "Do you think the mayor is doing a good job?" The results are shown. Which statement tells why the graph may be misleading?

Ⓐ The months on the horizontal axis are not consecutive.
Ⓑ The title is misleading.
Ⓒ The vertical scale uses unequal intervals.
Ⓓ The graph does not start at 0.

The graph uses unequal intervals on the vertical scale. The answer is choice C.

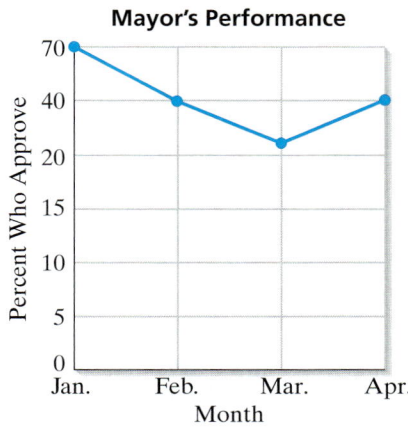

✓ Quick Check

1. Redraw the graph so it is not misleading. **See back of book.**

Objective
To identify misleading graphs and statistics

Examples
1 Misleading Line Graphs
2 Misleading Bar Graphs
3 Identifying Misleading Statistics

Math Understandings: p. 58D

Professional Development

Math Background

Graphs can be misleading if the scale used is unequal or if it does not start at zero. Statistics can also be misleading when they do not accurately reflect the data.

More Math Background: p. 58D

Lesson Planning and Resources

See p. 58E for a list of the resources that support this lesson.

PowerPoint
Bell Ringer Practice

✓ **Check Skills You'll Need**
Use student page, transparency, or PowerPoint. For intervention, direct students to:
Finding the Mean
Lesson 2-1
Extra Skills and Word Problems Practice, Ch. 2

Differentiated Instruction **Solutions for All Learners**

Special Needs **L1**
If students have a difficult time understanding why some of the graphs are misleading, help students redraw them starting at 0, with equal intervals, with data in order so the graphs no longer mislead.

learning style: visual

Below Level **L2**
Review with students the key terms *scale, axis,* and *intervals.* For Example 1, have students find the interval for the scale of the vertical axis, 5, and count by 5s to find where the interval changes. **between 20 and 40**

learning style: visual

Activity Lab
Use before the lesson.

All in One Teaching Resources

Activity Lab 2-7: Misleading Graphs

Guided Instruction

Example 1
Have students look for differences between successive intervals.

PowerPoint
Additional Examples

1 Admission Price

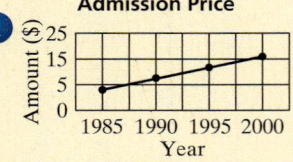

Why is the graph misleading?
The vertical scale has unequal verticals.

2 College Enrollment

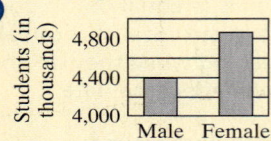

a. What impression is given by the graph? **Sample: The number of females enrolled is more than twice the number of males enrolled.**

b. Why is the graph misleading? **The vertical scale does not start at 0.**

3 Five hourly wages are $5, $8, $7.50, $35, and $7. Why might the mean wage be misleading? **Sample: The mean wage of $12.50 is greater than all wages except the outlier.**

Closure
• *How can graphs be misleading?* **The scale might have unequal intervals or not start at zero.**

All in One Teaching Resources
• Daily Notetaking Guide 2-7 **L3**
• Adapted Notetaking 2-7 **L1**

---

3. Median; the mode is the least data value. It occurs only twice, so its value is really too low to give a good idea of what a typical data value is.

GO for Help

For help with finding the mean, the median, and the mode, go to Lessons 2-1 and 2-2.

A graph can be misleading if the vertical scale does not start at 0.

EXAMPLE Misleading Bar Graphs

2 Advertising An auto dealer made the graph at the right.

a. What impression does the graph give?

It looks like there was a dramatic increase in sales.

b. Why is the graph misleading?

The vertical scale does not begin at 0. So you are looking at just the top of the graph.

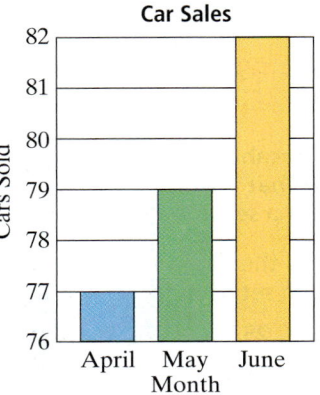

✓ Quick Check

2. Use the graph in Example 2.
a. Compare the height of the bar for June to the height of the bar for May. **It's twice as tall.**
b. How many more cars were sold in June than in May? **3 cars**

Statistics can also be misleading. For example, the mean can be a distorted measure of a data set that contains outliers.

EXAMPLE Identifying Misleading Statistics

3 Five players on a professional basketball team have a mean salary of $2.2 million. Their five salaries are shown at the right. Explain why the mean may not be the best measure for describing the players' salaries.

Only one person makes more than the mean of $2.2 million. The $7.2 million salary is an outlier that greatly increases the mean.

Players' Salaries
$7,200,000
$1,200,000
$1,000,000
$800,000
$800,000

✓ Quick Check

3. In Example 3, which would better describe the basketball players' salaries, the median or the mode? Explain. **See above left.**

Advanced Learners **L4**
Ask: *Can a data set have two outliers but still have a mean that is not distorted?* **Sample: Yes, the outliers can compensate for one another and therefore not distort the mean.**

learning style: verbal

English Language Learners **ELL**
Help students understand the question: *What impression does the graph give in the Check Your Understanding section?* Say: *An impression is what you think when you look at the graph quickly, without carefully analyzing it.*

learning style: verbal

Use the graph for Exercises 1–4.

1. **It looks as if there was a dramatic decrease in sales.**

1. What impression does the graph give? **See left.**

2. How does the height of the bar for Week 1 compare to the height of the bar for Week 4?
It is about four times the height.

3. How many more sales were made in Week 1 than in Week 4?
3 more sales

4. **The vertical scale does not begin at 0. So you are looking at just the top of the graph.**

4. Why is the graph misleading? **See left.**

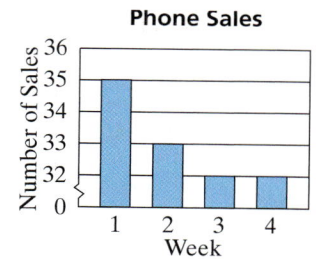

Phone Sales

Homework Exercises

For more exercises, see Extra Skills and Word Problems.

GO for Help

For Exercise	See Example
5	1
6	2
7	3

A **Decide whether each graph is misleading.** If a graph is misleading, what impression does the graph give? Explain why the graph is misleading. Then redraw the graph so it is not misleading.
5–6. See margin.

5.

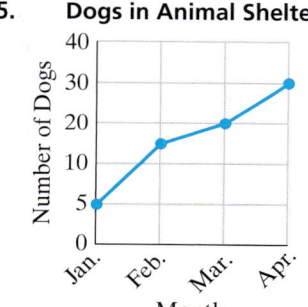

Dogs in Animal Shelter

6.

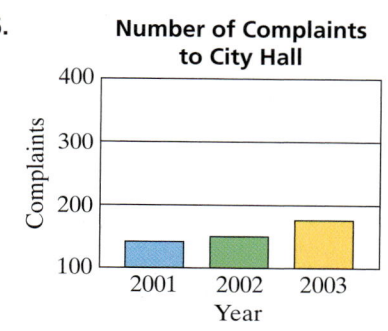

Number of Complaints to City Hall

8. **Answers may vary. Sample: If he is less than fair, he might use the mode, since it has the lowest value and might be most attractive to price-conscious customers.**

7. **Tests** A student scored 100%, 100%, 90%, 70%, and 60% on five quizzes. Which measure makes his grades look best—the mean, the median, or the mode? **mode**

B **GPS** 8. **Guided Problem Solving** The prices of different digital cameras at a store are $138, $138, $138, $179, $189, $198, $219, $249, and $449. Would a salesperson use the mean, median, or mode to encourage you to purchase a digital camera? Explain.
- Does the salesperson want the highest or lowest price to represent the data?
- What are the mean, median, and mode of the prices?
See above left.

🌐line **lesson quiz,** PHSchool.com, **Web Code:** aqa-0207

2-7 Misleading Graphs and Statistics **95**

5–6. See back of book.

3. Practice

Assignment Guide

Check Your Understanding
Go over Exercises 1–4 in class before assigning the Homework Exercises.

Homework Exercises
A Practice by Example   5–7
B Apply Your Skills   8–13
C Challenge   14
Test Prep and
    Mixed Review   15–17

Homework Quick Check
To check student's understanding of key skills and concepts, go over Exercises 5, 7, 9, 10, and 13.

Differentiated Instruction Resources

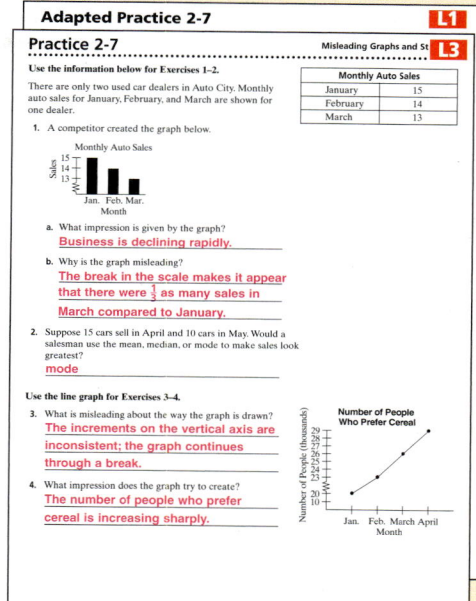

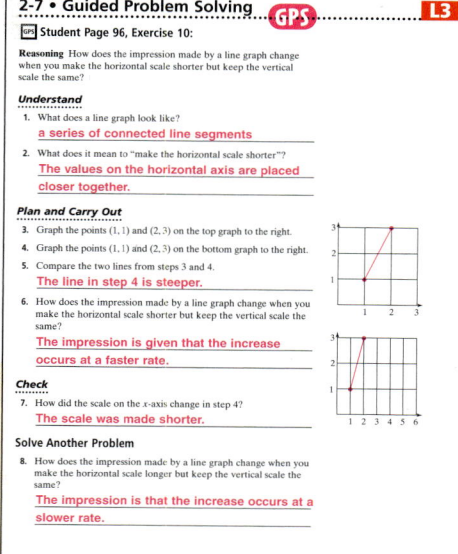

Lesson Quiz

1. Is the graph misleading? Explain.

Video Sales

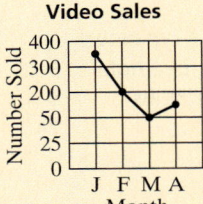

Yes, the scale does not have equal intervals so the drop in sales from January to March does not look as severe as it really is.

2. Five costs for a car wash were $18, $6, $58, $12, and $6. Which measure, the mean, the median, or the mode best represents the costs? **Sample: The median of $12 is most representative of the data.**

3. During the basketball game, the following points were scored: 8, 6, 4, 6, 32, 5. How is the mean score misleading? **Sample: The mean score is greater than all scores except the outlier.**

Enrichment 2-7 · **L4**

Reteaching 2-7 · Misleading Graphs and... **L2**

Data can be displayed on graphs in ways that are misleading.

The horizontal scales make these line graphs seem different.

As the numbers are moved farther apart, it appears that the change over time is less.

A Price of a Slice of Pizza

B Price of a Slice of Pizza

These bar graphs may seem different because of how the vertical scales are drawn.

The break in the vertical scale makes the differences seem greater than they really are.

C Cars on the Road After 10 Years

D Cars on the Road After 10 Years

Use the graphs above for Exercises 1–3.

1. Which graph might be used to convince someone that the price of pizza has risen too quickly over the years?
graph A

2. Which graph would Car Company X use to show that its cars last longer than the competition?
graph D

3. Which graph of cars still on the road after 10 years would Car Company Z prefer?
graph C

4. On a science exam, six students scored a mean of 75. Their scores were 88, 90, 12, 85, 87, and 88. Why might the mean be misleading?
All of the scores except one are well above the mean. The score of 12 is an outlier and greatly decreases the mean.

GO Online

Homework Video Tutor

Visit: PHSchool.com
Web Code: aqe-0207

9. Candidate A: graph I, Candidate B: graph II; the candidate would present a graph to make the results look more favorable.

10. The rises and falls of the values represented on the vertical axis seem more pronounced.

Money Pledged to a Public Radio Station

Year	Amount Pledged
1	$34,096
2	$39,021
3	$41,132
4	$42,209
5	$44,172
6	$45,071
7	$45,759

GO for Help

For Exercise	See Lesson
17	2-6

---

9. Election Results Two graphs of the same election results are shown. Which graph might be preferred by Candidate A? Which might be preferred by Candidate B? Explain.

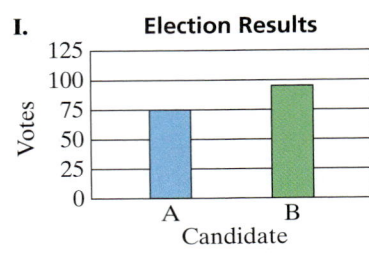

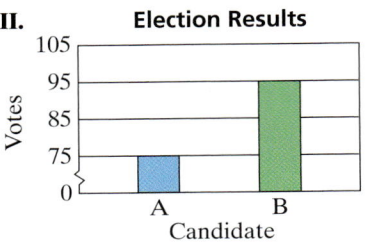

10. Reasoning How does the impression made by a line graph change when you make the horizontal scale shorter but keep the vertical scale the same?

Fundraising Use the table at the left for Exercises 11–13.
11–12. See margin.

11. Draw a bar graph that suggests that the money pledged increased greatly from Year 1 to Year 7.

12. Draw a bar graph that suggests that the money pledged increased slowly from Year 1 to Year 7.

13. Writing in Math If you wanted to summarize the data using a low value, would you use the mean, the median, or the mode? Explain. **See margin.**

C 14. Challenge Which number could you remove from this list to make the mean and the median equal: 2, 7, 12, 14, 17? **14**

Test Prep and Mixed Review · Practice

Multiple Choice

15. Find the median of 4.5, 4, 4.5, 5.5, 6, and 6.5. **C**
- A 4
- B 4.5
- C 5
- D 5.5

16. Which of the following statements is NOT supported by the graph? **F**
- F The initial height was 2 cm.
- G The height was about 7 cm at 3 weeks.
- H The height increased over time.
- J The height was about 8 cm at 4 weeks.

Plant Growth

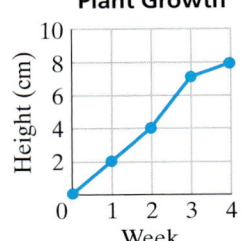

Make a stem-and-leaf plot of the data.

17. 33, 42, 16, 45, 14, 14, 28, 37, 16, 23, 33, 25, 16 **See margin.**

Test Prep

Resources

For additional practice with a variety of test item formats:
- Test-Taking Strategies, p. 99
- Test Prep, p. 103
- Test-Taking Strategies with Transparencies

Alternative Assessment

Each student makes an accurate line graph or bar graph. Then the student redraws the graph to make it misleading.

11–13. See back of book.

17. See back of book.

Random Samples and Surveys

Surveys and polls collect data about a group of people called a *population*. Surveying a large population is difficult. So pollsters select a *sample*, or part of the population. In a *random sample*, each member of the population has the same chance of being selected.

EXAMPLE   Random Samples

1 You want to know the favorite band of students at your school. Which strategy is most likely to result in a random sample?

a. Ask the students in your class.
b. Ask every tenth student who enters the school.
c. Ask the players on the football team.
d. Post a survey on the school bulletin board.

If you limit your survey to your class or to the football team, you are not giving every student in the school the same chance of being selected. A survey on the bulletin board will not get answers from students who do not read the bulletin board.

By asking every tenth student who enters the school, you are most likely getting a random sample, because each student has the same chance of being selected.

Exercises

1. You survey mall customers to find out their favorite store. Is each method likely to give a random sample? Explain.
    a. Survey shoppers in a clothing store.
    b. Walk around the mall and survey shoppers.
    c. Ask your friends where they shop.

2. **Data Collection** Write a survey question on a topic that interests you. Plan and carry out a survey that includes both a random sample and a non-random sample. Use a data display to compare your results. **Check students' work.**

1a–c. Answers may vary. Samples are given.

1a. No; it is more likely the shoppers will name the store they're currently in.

b. Yes; you will survey many different people in different locations.

c. No; your friends probably like most of the same stores.

Extension

Random Samples and Surveys

In Lesson 2-7, students dealt with misleading graphs and statistics. This feature focuses on using random samples to avoid biased or unfair results.

Guided Instruction

Ask students if they have seen advertising that might have been based on biased samples. Have students provide examples of such advertising and explain why it might be biased.

Exercises
Have students work with partners to do Exercise 2. Each should choose a topic and both should identify random and biased samples for the topics after discussion.

Differentiated Instruction
Below Level   L2
The vocabulary in this lesson may be difficult for some students. Be sure they understand why a random sample can produce an unbiased result. Give more examples of random samples for surveys.

Use this Checkpoint Quiz to check students' understanding of the skills and concepts of Lessons 2-6 through 2-7.

Resources

- All-in-One Teaching Resources Checkpoint Quiz 2
- ExamView CD-ROM
- Success Tracker™ Online Intervention

MATH GAMES

Bar Graph Race

In this game, students practice graphing sums rolled on number cubes. Students have the opportunity to fill in six boxes for each sum. The first player to fill in three columns wins.

Guided Instruction

Ask:
- *Do certain sums come up more frequently than others?* **yes**
- *Would you be more likely to fill in the 2 column or the 7 column first? Why?* **For a sum of 2, there is only one possibility, rolling two 1s. For a sum of 7 there are many more possibilities.**

Resources

- three number cubes
- graph for each player labeled as shown on student page
- Classroom Aid 2

 **Checkpoint Quiz 2** **Lessons 2-6 through 2-7**

1. Make a stem-and-leaf plot for test scores: 92, 76, 85, 85, 68, 81, 84, 89, 84, 91, 97, 95, 86, and 64. **See margin.**

Use the stem-and-leaf plot at the right for Exercises 2–5.

2. What is the median life span? **15 years**

3. How many of the animals have a life span greater than 15 years? **8**

4. What is the range of the data? **36**

5. Does the mean, the median, or the mode best describe the data? Explain. **See margin.**

6. A car dealer wants to advertise that its compact car is the roomiest, with 75.6 cubic feet inside. The cars of three competitors have 63.4 cubic feet, 70.1 cubic feet, and 68.7 cubic feet of space. Explain how to make a bar graph that shows a very large difference among the cars.

Life Spans of Different Animals

```
0 | 4 4 5 6 9
1 | 0 0 1 1 3 5 5 5 5 8
2 | 0 0 0 1 2 5
3 |
4 | 0
```

Key: 1 | 8 means 18 years

6. **Answers may vary. Sample: Starting a graph at 60 ft^3 on the vertical axis will make the differences in cars seem very large.**

MATH GAMES

Bar Graph Race

What You'll Need

- three number cubes
- a graph for each player, labeled as shown

How To Play

- Each player takes a turn rolling the three number cubes. The player then chooses two of the numbers rolled and adds them.
- The player fills in one square on the graph in the column labeled with the sum.
- Once any player fills a column completely, no other players may play in that column on their own graphs.
- If a player cannot fill a square, then the player loses a turn.
- The first player to fill in three columns wins.

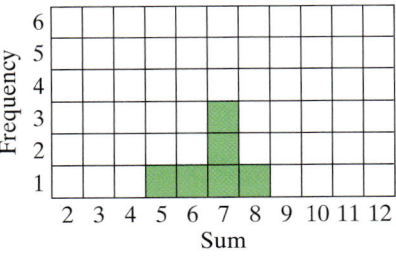

---

1. **Test Scores**

```
6 | 4 8
7 | 6
8 | 1 4 4 5 5 6 9
9 | 1 2 5 7
```

Key: 6 | 4 means 64%

5. **Answers may vary. Sample: Median; an outlier affects the mean.**

Answering the Question Asked

When answering a question, be sure to answer the question that is asked. Read the question carefully and identify the answer that you are asked to find. Some answer choices are answers to related questions, so you have to be careful.

EXAMPLE

1 In Mrs. Sanchez's class, students received the scores shown in the line plot. How many students took the test?

Ⓐ 9   Ⓑ 19   Ⓒ 20   Ⓓ 28

The question asks for the number of students who took the test. The total number of scores is $4 + 4 + 4 + 1 + 6 + 9 = 28$. The correct answer is choice D.

The number of students who scored 20 points is 9. The mode is 20. The median is 19. But none of these is what is asked for.

Student Scores

```
                              X
                              X
                              X
                      X       X
                      X       X
X    X    X           X       X
X    X    X           X       X
X    X    X           X       X
X    X    X    X      X       X
15   16   17   18    19      20
              Score
```

EXAMPLE

2 The stem-and-leaf plot shows the heights of 11 students in inches. What is the median height?

Ⓕ 60 in.   Ⓖ 62 in.   Ⓗ 63 in.   Ⓙ 64 in.

The question asks for the median height. For eleven data items, the sixth is the median. The sixth height is 62 in. The correct answer is choice G.

The mode is 60 in. The mean is 63 in. Answer J is the average of 57 in. and 71 in., or 64 in. But none of these is what is asked for.

Heights of Students

5	7 8
6	0 0 1 2 3 4 7
7	0 1

Key: 5 | 8 means 58 inches

Exercises

1. In Example 2, how tall is the tallest student who is less than 70 in. tall? **B**

Ⓐ 60 in.   Ⓑ 67 in.   Ⓒ 70 in.   Ⓓ 71 in.

2. In Example 2, what is the range of data? **F**

Ⓕ 14 in.   Ⓖ 57 in.   Ⓗ 64 in.   Ⓙ 71 in.

Test-Taking Strategies

Answering the Question Asked

This feature alerts students to the importance of reading test questions carefully to make sure that they are answering the question asked.

Guided Instruction

Review the distinction between these statistics: range, mean, median, and mode. Review the features of stem-and-leaf plots and line plots.

Teaching Tips

Discuss with students that test questions are written to include answer choices that are correct given a *misreading* of the question asked. Emphasize the importance of reading the question very carefully in order to avoid this trap.

Resources

Test-Taking Strategies with Transparencies
• Transparency 8
• Practice sheet, p. 2

Test-Taking Strategies with Transparencies

Test-Taking Strategies: Answering the Question Asked

Incorrect choices may answer related questions.

Example Midori owes $20 on a restaurant bill, and wants to tip the server 15%. How much should Midori pay altogether?

A. $3   B. $15   C. $20   D. $23

Calculate the tip: $0.15 \times 20 = \$3$

Choice A is $3, but this is how much Midori should leave for a tip, not how much to pay altogether.

Calculate the total bill: $20 + 3 = 23$

The answer is $23, or choice D.

Answer the question asked. Explain your reasoning.

1. Clarisse earns $10 per hour and works about 25 hours per week. How much could she earn in a year?

A. $250   B. $1,000   C. $3,000   D. $13,000

2. Find the area of the triangle.

F. 84 units^2 G. 56 units^2 H. 186 units^2 J. 4,200 units^2

Transparency 8

Chapter 2 Review

Vocabulary Review

 bar graph (p. 74)
cell (p. 80)
frequency table (p. 70)
line graph (p. 75)
line plot (p. 71)

mean (p. 61)
median (p. 66)
mode (p. 67)
outlier (p. 62)

range (p. 71)
scatter plot (p. 84)
spreadsheet (p. 80)
stem-and-leaf plot (p. 86)

Choose the correct vocabulary term to complete each sentence.

1. A(n) __?__ lists each item in a data set with the number of times it occurs. **C**

2. The __?__ of a data set is the sum of the values divided by the number of values. **A**

3. A(n) __?__ of a data set is much greater or much less than the other data values. **G**

4. On the computer, you can use a(n) __?__ to organize data in a table. **F**

5. A(n) __?__ typically shows changes over time. **E**

A. mean
B. mode
C. frequency table
D. median
E. line graph
F. spreadsheet
G. outlier

Go **Online**
PHSchool.com
For: Vocabulary quiz
Web Code: aqj-0251

Skills and Concepts

Lessons 2-1 and 2-2
• To find and analyze the mean of a data set using models and calculations
• To find and analyze the median and mode of a data set

The **mean** of a set of data is the sum of the values divided by the number of data items. The **median** is the middle value when data are arranged in numerical order. The **mode** is the value or item that appears most often.

Find the mean, median, and mode of each data set.

6. 34, 49, 63, 43, 50, 50, 26   *45, 49, 50*

7. 3, 7, 1, 9, 9, 5, 8   *6, 7, 9*

Lesson 2-3
• To analyze a set of data by finding the range and by making frequency tables and line plots

A **frequency table** lists each item in a data set with the number of times the item occurs. A **line plot** displays a data set by stacking ✗'s above each data value on a number line.

8. Make a frequency table showing the number of times each vowel occurs in the paragraph above. Consider y a vowel.
8–9. See margin.

9. Make a line plot showing the number of times the words *the, and, a,* and *of* appear in the paragraph above.

100   **Chapter 2**   Chapter Review

8–9. See back of book.

Lesson 2-4

- To make and analyze bar graphs and line graphs

A **bar graph** is used to compare amounts. A **line graph** shows how an amount changes over time.

Tickets Use the table at the right.

10. Make a line graph of the data. **See below left.**

11. Make a bar graph of the data. **See margin.**

12. Is a line graph or bar graph more appropriate for the ticket price data? Explain.
Line graph; it shows changes over time.

Ticket Prices

Year	Price
1985	$10
1990	$15
1995	$20
2000	$25
2005	$30

Lesson 2-5

- To use spreadsheets to display data and solve problems

You can use a **spreadsheet** to organize and analyze data. A **cell** is the spreadsheet box where a row and column meet. A formula is a statement of a mathematical relationship.

10.

Ticket Prices

	A	B	C	D	E
1	Date	Kite Sales ($)	String Sales ($)	Book Sales ($)	Total Sales ($)
2	9/9	50	8	145	▨
3	9/10	75	6	125	▨

13. Which cells are for kite sales? **B2, B3**

14. What is the value of B3? **75**

15. Write the formula for cell E2. **= B2 + C2 + D2**

Lessons 2-6 and 2-7

- To make and analyze stem-and-leaf plots
- To identify misleading graphs and statistics

A **stem-and-leaf plot** uses digits to show the shape of data.

16. Make a stem-and-leaf plot of the data: 507, 301, 479, 367, 543, 388, 512, 479, 483, 379, 548, 341, 399, 465. **See margin.**

Which measure best describes the data—mean, median, or mode?

17. 72, 67, 62, 77, 82 **mean or median, since they are the same**

18. 1, 1.5, 4.5, 8, 4.5, 12 **median or mode**

19. win, loss, tie, tie, tie, loss **mode**

20. 0, 3, 39, 2, 1, 7, 4, 9, 5 **median**

21. See margin.

21. Every week you take a math quiz. The data in Exercise 18 show the scores of your first 5 quizzes. Explain how you would graph the data to show a very small difference in scores.

11. See back of book.

16. See back of book.

21. Answers may vary. Sample: Start the vertical axis at zero and use intervals of 10.

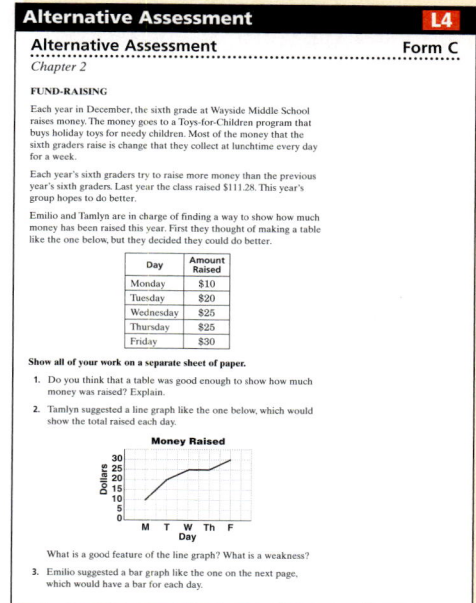

Chapter 2 Test

Go Online
PHSchool.com
For: Online chapter test
Web Code: aqa-0252

Resources

- ExamView Assessment Suite CD-ROM
  - Ch. 2 Ready-Made Test
  - Make your own Ch. 2 test
- MindPoint Quiz Show CD-ROM
  - Chapter 2 Review

Differentiated Instruction

All in One Teaching Resources
- Below Level Chapter 2 Test **L2**
- Chapter 2 Test **L3**
- Chapter 2 Alternative Assessment **L4**

Spanish Assessment Resources **ELL**
- Below Level Chapter 2 Test **L2**
- Chapter 2 Test **L3**
- Chapter 2 Alternative Assessment **L4**

ExamView Assessment Suite CD-ROM
- Special Needs Test **L1**
- Special Needs Practice Bank **L1**

Online Chapter 2 Test at www.PHSchool.com **L3**

---

1. Find the mean, median, mode, and range of the data set: 31, 20, 31, 51, 27. **32, 31, 31, 31**

The numbers of children in 15 families are 1, 3, 2, 1, 3, 1, 2, 6, 2, 3, 3, 4, 3, 4, and 5.

2. Find the median, mode, and range. **3; 3; 5**

3. Make a frequency table of the data. **See margin.**

4. Make a line plot of the data. **See margin.**

5. Profits A business has weekly profits of $5,000, $3,000, $2,000, $2,500, and $5,000. Why is using the mode to describe this data set misleading? **The mode is $5,000, but it is the highest value.**

6. The spreadsheet below shows three quiz scores for two students. Write formulas for cells E2 and E3. **= (B2 + C2 + D2)/3; = (B3 + C3 + D3)/3**

	A	B	C	D	E
1	Student	Q 1	Q 2	Q 3	Mean
2	Yori	81	95	88	▨
3	Sarah	78	81	87	▨

7. Make a stem-and-leaf plot for these state-fair pumpkin weights (pounds): 288, 207, 210, 212, 226, 233, 212, 218, 247, 262, 269, 203, 271. **See margin.**

Reading **Twelve people estimated the time, in minutes, they spend reading each day.** Their responses are below.
20, 5, 45, 90, 60, 45, 30, 10, 30, 45, 15, 25

8. Find the mean, median, mode, and range of the data. **35; 30; 45; 85**

9. Which would you use to describe the data—the mean, median, or mode? **mean or median**

10. **Writing in Math** What type of data display would you use for the data? Explain. **See margin.**

11. Enrollment Use the bar graph below. Which grade level has the fewest students enrolled? **Preschool**

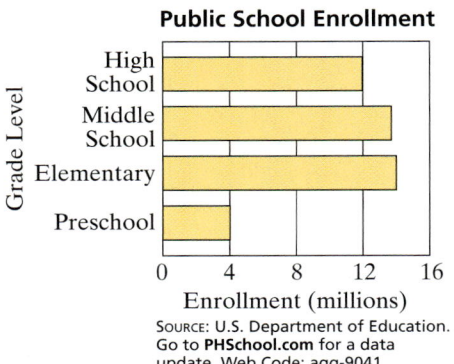

Public School Enrollment

SOURCE: U.S. Department of Education. Go to **PHSchool.com** for a data update. Web Code: aqg-9041

12. Hot Lunches Use the line graph below. What is the median number of students buying lunch? **150**

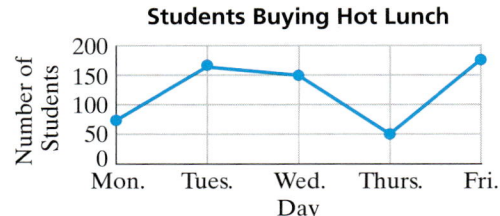

Students Buying Hot Lunch

Use the stem-and-leaf plot below.

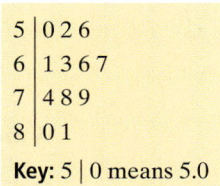

```
5 | 0 2 6
6 | 1 3 6 7
7 | 4 8 9
8 | 0 1
```
Key: 5 | 0 means 5.0

13. How many stems are there? **4**

14. How many leaves are there? **12**

15. Find the range. **3.1**

16. Find the median. **6.65**

3–4. See back of book.

7. See back of book.

10. Answers may vary. Sample: Line plot; it organizes and compares the responses.

Reading Comprehension

Read each passage and answer the questions that follow.

Age of Leadership In 1787 twelve of the original thirteen states sent delegates to Philadelphia to work on forming a government for our new country. In all, 55 delegates attended. You probably know some of their names: James Madison (36 years old), Alexander Hamilton (32), George Washington (55), and Benjamin Franklin (the oldest delegate, at 81).

1. What is the mean age of the delegates mentioned in the passage? **C**
   - A 32
   - B 45
   - C 51
   - D 55

2. What is the median age of the delegates mentioned? **G**
   - F 32
   - G 45.5
   - H 51
   - J 55

3. The mean age of all of the delegates was 42. What was the sum of the ages of all 55 delegates? **B**
   - A 2,106 years
   - C 2,501 years
   - B 2,310 years
   - D 2,525 years

4. Franklin was in poor health and did not attend many of the meetings. Suppose a 60-year-old delegate replaced him. How would that affect the mean and the median ages of the four delegates mentioned in the passage? **F**
   - F The mean would be lower.
   - G The median would be lower.
   - H The mean and median would both be lower.
   - J Neither the mean nor the median would change.

Math in Space The first American astronaut to circle Earth was John Glenn. In 1962, Glenn made three orbits at an average speed of 17,544 miles per hour. He traveled a total distance of 75,679 miles. This was only a short trip into space. Soon astronauts would be looking beyond Earth orbit to the moon, about 240,000 miles away.

5. Based on the passage, about how far did Glenn travel in one orbit around Earth? **C**
   - A 25 miles
   - C 25,000 miles
   - B 17,544 miles
   - D 52,632 miles

6. About how long did an average orbit take? **G**
   - F 1.4 hours
   - H 10 hours
   - G 4.3 hours
   - J 13 hours

7. At Glenn's rate of travel, about how long would it take to reach the moon? **B**
   - A 10 hours
   - C 24 hours
   - B 14 hours
   - D 38 hours

8. *Apollo 11* took about 3 days to go from Earth orbit to moon orbit. About how fast was *Apollo 11*'s average speed? **H**
   - F 80,000 mi/h
   - H 10,000 mi/h
   - G 17,544 mi/h
   - J 3,333 mi/h

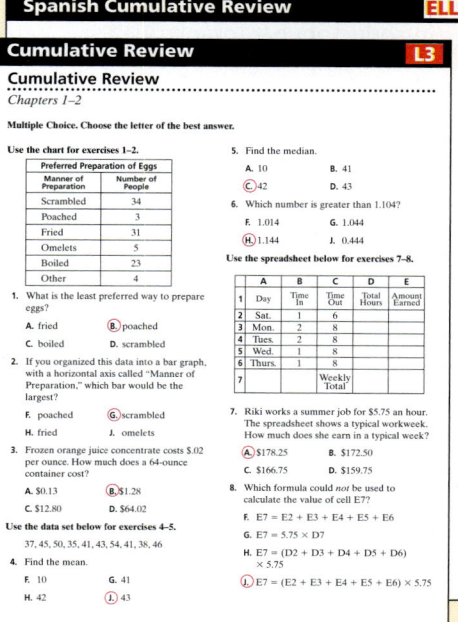

Problem Solving

Applying Data Analysis

Students will use data from these two pages to answer the questions posed in Put It All Together.

Using a world map or globe, invite students to identify on which continents the mountains featured here are located. Ask:

- *How many mountains featured here are found in Europe? Which mountains?* **4: Mt. Vesuvius, Mt. Elbrus, The Matterhorn, and Mount Blanc**
- *Which featured mountains are also volcanoes?* **Mt. Kilimanjaro, Fujiyama, Mt. St. Helens, and Mt. Vesuvius**

Materials
- World map or globe

Activating Prior Knowledge

Have students who have hiked into state or national parks and those who have rock climed share their experiences with the class. Elicit information about special clothing and equipment that are needed for such activities.

Guided Instruction

Have a volunteer read the introductory paragraph. Ask: *Where is Mt. Everest?* **Asia**

Have students find out what the average air pressure is at sea level. **about 1,000 mb (one thousand millibars)** Ask:
- *What is the air pressure at the top of Mt. Everest?* **about 300 mb**
- *What operation do you need to use to solve the question above?* **division**

Applying Data Analysis

A Peak Experience Earth's highest natural features, its great mountains, dwarf even the tallest structures made by humans. The air at the top of Mt. Everest, in the Himalayan mountains, is three times thinner than the air at sea level. Because of the thin air, numbing cold, and unpredictable weather, it takes even the most experienced climbers many weeks to reach the top of Mt. Everest.

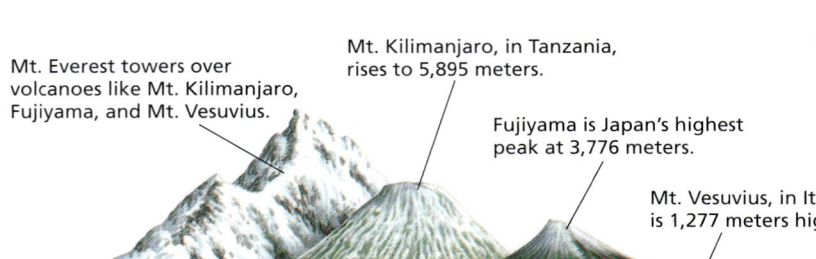

Mt. Everest towers over volcanoes like Mt. Kilimanjaro, Fujiyama, and Mt. Vesuvius.

Mt. Kilimanjaro, in Tanzania, rises to 5,895 meters.

Fujiyama is Japan's highest peak at 3,776 meters.

Mt. Vesuvius, in Italy, is 1,277 meters high.

Mt. Aconcagua is the highest peak in South America at 6,960 meters.

Mt. Elbrus is Europe's highest peak at 5,642 meters.

It's All Relative
Although Kilimanjaro is 2,955 meters shorter than Everest, it is still 40 times as tall as the Great Pyramid in Egypt.

Volcanic Storm
Mount St. Helens, a volcano in Washington state, erupted on May 18, 1980, throwing huge clouds of ash into the sky. Before the eruption, the summit was 2,950 meters high. Afterward, it was about 400 meters lower.

Mt. Cook is New Zealand's highest peak at 3,754 meters.

Mt. St. Helens: 2,550 meters

Put It All Together

Data File Use the information on these two pages and on page 650 to answer these questions.

1. **a.** Write the names of the mountain peaks in the table on page 650 in order from highest to lowest elevation.
   b. Graph the data (in meters) on a number line. Label each point with the name of the mountain.
   c. Insert data points and labels for New Zealand's highest mountain, Mt. Cook, and the Matterhorn, in the European Alps.
2. How tall is Hawaii's Mauna Kea?

1a. **Everest**
Aconcagua
McKinley
Kilimanjaro
Elbrus
Vinson Massif
Kosciusko

b. **Answers may vary. Sample:**

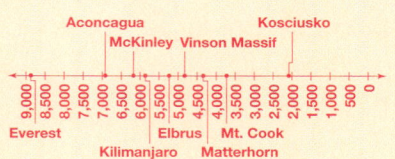

2. **10,202 m**

3. **about 2,550 m**

4. **about 9,288 m**

Mt. Everest: 8,850 meters

Yaks can live at elevations as high as 6,000 meters.

Edmund Hillary and Sherpa Tenzing Norgay, the first people to climb Mt. Everest, pitched their base camp at 5,486 meters.

Mauna Kea   Mt. Everest

Mauna Kea is a volcano in Hawaii. Measured from its base on the ocean floor, Mauna Kea is 1,352 meters taller than Mt. Everest.

Mt. McKinley is the highest peak in North America at 6,194 meters.

Vinson Massif, Antarctica: 4,897 meters

The Matterhorn, in the European Alps, is 4,478 meters above sea level.

Mont Blanc, in the European Alps: 4,810 meters

3. What did the height of Mount St. Helens become after its eruption in 1980?

4. A mountain climber scaled both Mont Blanc and the Matterhorn. How many meters did she climb?

5. a. Estimation About how tall is the Great Pyramid of Egypt?

b. About how many times taller than the Great Pyramid is Mt. Everest?

6. Number Sense Suppose a Sherpa has guided climbers 12 times from a base camp at 5,486 meters to the peak of Mt. Everest. How many kilometers of vertical elevation has he traveled as a guide?

Straight to the Top
Sherpas are people who live in the Himalayas. Many Sherpas act as guides on Mt. Everest.

Go Online
PHSchool.com
For: Information about mountains
Web Code: aqe-0253

105

Activity

Have students work in pairs to make the graphs and answer the questions.

Exercise 1b Have students graph the data using meters as the unit of measure. Have students agree on a range and a scale for the number line, for example, segments of 1,000 m, ranging from 0 through 10,000 m. Elicit the fact that the tics on the number line would be at 0, 1, 2, 3, . . . , 10.

Exercise 6 Ask questions such as:
- *What operation do you need to use to solve this problem?* multiplication
- *What factors do you multiply?* 12 · 5,486
- *How many meters are there in one kilometer?* 1,000 m
- *How do you change meters into kilometers?* Divide the number of meters by 1,000.

Differentiated Instruction
Special Needs L1
Students might benefit from working in small groups in which at least one member is a proficient reader who can assist other team members.

5a. Answers may vary. Accept all reasonable estimates. Sample: about 147 m

b. about 60

6. about 80.736 km

3 Patterns and Variables

Chapter at a Glance

Lesson Titles, Objectives, and Features	Assessment	NCTM Standards	Local Standards
3-1 Describing a Pattern • To find and write rules for number patterns	Lesson Quiz	1, 2, 6, 7, 8, 9, 10	
3-2a Activity Lab, Hands On: Patterns and Expressions **3-2 Variables and Expressions** • To evaluate algebraic expressions	Lesson Quiz	1, 2, 6, 7, 8, 9, 10	
3-3a Activity Lab: Modeling Expressions **3-3 Writing Algebraic Expressions** • To use algebraic expressions to solve problems **3-3b Activity Lab:** Arithmetic Sequences	Lesson Quiz	1, 2, 6, 7, 8, 9, 10	
3-4 Using Number Sense to Solve One-Step Equations • To use mental math to estimate and solve equations **Vocabulary Builder:** High-Use Academic Words	Lesson Quiz Checkpoint Quiz 1	1, 2, 6, 7, 8, 9, 10	
3-5a Activity Lab, Hands On: Modeling Equations **3-5 Solving Addition Equations** • To use subtraction to solve equations	Lesson Quiz	1, 2, 6, 7, 8, 9, 10	
3-6 Solving Subtraction Equations • To use addition to solve equations	Lesson Quiz Checkpoint Quiz 2	1, 2, 6, 7, 8, 9, 10	
3-7a Activity Lab, Hands On: Modeling Division Equations **3-7 Solving Multiplication and Division Equations** • To use multiplication and division to solve equations **Guided Problem Solving:** Writing Equations to Solve Problems	Lesson Quiz	1, 2, 6, 7, 8, 9, 10	
3-8 The Distributive Property • To use the Distributive Property to simplify expressions in problem-solving situations **3-8b Activity Lab, Algebra Thinking:** Understanding Properties	Lesson Quiz	1, 2, 6, 7, 8, 9, 10	
Problem Solving Application: Applying Patterns			

NCTM Standards 2000
1 Number and Operations	**2** Algebra	**3** Geometry	**4** Measurement	**5** Data Analysis and Probability
6 Problem Solving	**7** Reasoning and Proof	**8** Communication	**9** Connections	**10** Representation

Correlations to Standardized Tests

All content for these tests is contained in *Prentice Hall Math*, Course 1. This chart reflects coverage in this chapter only.

	3-1	3-2	3-3	3-4	3-5	3-6	3-7	3-8
Terra Nova CAT6 (Level 16)								
Number and Number Relations	✔	✔	✔	✔	✔	✔	✔	✔
Computation and Numerical Estimation	✔	✔	✔	✔	✔	✔	✔	✔
Operation Concepts	✔	✔	✔	✔	✔	✔	✔	✔
Measurement								
Geometry and Spatial Sense								
Data Analysis, Statistics, and Probability								
Patterns, Functions, Algebra	✔	✔	✔	✔	✔	✔	✔	✔
Problem Solving and Reasoning	✔	✔	✔	✔	✔	✔	✔	✔
Communication	✔	✔	✔	✔	✔	✔	✔	✔
Decimals, Fractions, Integers, Percent	✔	✔	✔	✔	✔	✔	✔	✔
Order of Operations								✔
Terra Nova CTBS (Level 16)								
Whole Numbers, Decimals, Fractions	✔	✔	✔	✔	✔	✔	✔	✔
Numeration, Number Theory	✔	✔	✔	✔	✔	✔	✔	✔
Data Interpretation								
Pre-algebra	✔	✔	✔	✔	✔	✔	✔	
Measurement	✔	✔	✔	✔	✔	✔	✔	✔
Geometry								
ITBS (Level 12)								
Number Properties and Operations	✔	✔	✔	✔	✔	✔	✔	✔
Algebra	✔	✔	✔	✔	✔	✔	✔	✔
Geometry								
Measurement								
Probability and Statistics								
Estimation								
SAT10 (Int 2 Level)								
Number Sense and Operations	✔	✔	✔	✔	✔	✔	✔	✔
Patterns, Relationships, and Algebra	✔	✔	✔	✔	✔	✔	✔	✔
Data, Statistics, and Probability								
Geometry and Measurement								
NAEP								
Number Sense, Properties, and Operations			✔					✔
Measurement								
Geometry and Spatial Sense								
Data Analysis, Statistics, and Probability								
Algebra and Functions	✔	✔	✔	✔	✔	✔	✔	

CAT6 California Achievement Test, 6th Ed. **CTBS** Comprehensive Test of Basic Skills **ITBS** Iowa Test of Basic Skills, Form M
SAT10 Stanford Achievement Test, 10th Ed. **NAEP** National Assessment of Educational Progress 2005 Mathematics Objectives

Math Background

Skills Trace

BEFORE Chapter 3

Grade 5 presented basic algebraic expressions and equations.

DURING Chapter 3

Course 1 extends the study of algebra to solving one-step equations and evaluating algebraic expressions.

AFTER Chapter 3

Throughout this course, students write and solve algebraic equations.

3-1 Describing a Pattern

Math Understandings

- When you continue a pattern, or find the next term in a pattern, you assume that the pattern will continue in the same way.
- You can define or describe a number pattern by giving the first term and a rule that describes how you get from one term to the next.
- You can create and continue patterns of many different types and forms.

Each number in a number pattern is called a *term.* The three dots after the last number tell you that the pattern continues beyond the given terms. A **conjecture** is a prediction about what may happen. You can make a conjecture about how a pattern will continue.

Example: Write a rule for each number pattern.

4, 7, 10, 13, 16, . . .   1, 2, 4, 8, 16, 32, . . .
Start with 4 and add 3.   Start with 1 and multiply by 2.

3-2 Variables and Expressions

Math Understandings

- An algebraic expression differs from an open sentence or equation in that it has no equal sign.
- The value of an algebraic expression can vary depending on the value of the variable.
- Within a single problem, the value of the variable remains the same.

A **numerical expression** is a mathematical phrase with only numbers and operation symbols ($+$, $-$, $\times$, $\div$). A **variable** is a symbol that represents one or more numbers. A mathematical expression with one or more variables is an **algebraic expression.** You can model algebraic expressions using algebra tiles. The smallest tile represents 1. The next smallest tile has a width of 1 and an unknown length to represent x (or another variable).

$5x + 3$  ← 5 green tiles represent $5x$, and three yellow tiles represent 3.

3-3 Writing Algebraic Expressions

Math Understandings

- In order to write a word phrase as an algebraic expression, you translate the words into numbers and operational symbols.

Some examples of key words and their corresponding mathematical operations follow.

Operation	Key Words
Addition	sum, add, plus, increased by, more than
Subtraction	difference, subtract, minus, decreased by, less than
Multiplication	product, multiplied by, times
Division	quotient, divided by

3-4 Using Number Sense to Solve One-Step Equations

Math Understandings

- Until you replace the variable in an open sentence with a number value, the open sentence is neither true nor false.
- All open sentences are equations, but not all equations are open sentences.
- You can estimate solutions to equations using mental math.

An **equation** is a mathematical sentence that has an equal sign. An equation with one or more variables is an **open sentence**. A **solution** of an equation is a value of the variable that makes the equation true.

3-5 Solving Addition, Subtraction,
3-6 Multiplication, and
3-7 Division Equations

Math Understandings

- To solve an equation, use the mathematical properties to get the variable alone on one side of the equation.

PROPERTIES OF EQUALITY	
Arithmetic	**Algebra**
Addition Property of Equality	
$2 \cdot 3 = 6$, so $2 \cdot 3 + 4 = 6 + 4$. If $a = b$, then $a + c = b + c$.	
Subtraction Property of Equality	
$2 \cdot 3 = 6$, so $2 \cdot 3 - 4 = 6 - 4$. If $a = b$, then $a - c = b - c$.	
Multiplication Property of Equality	
$6 \div 2 = 3$, so $(6 \div 2) \times 2 = 3 \times 2$. If $a = b$, then $a \cdot c = b \cdot c$.	
Division Property of Equality	
$4 \times 2 = 8$,	If $a = b$ and $c \neq 0$,
so $4 \times 2 \div 2 = 8 \div 2$.	then $a \div c = b \div c$.

Operations that undo each other, such as addition and subtraction or multiplication and division, are **inverse operations**.

3-8 The Distributive Property

Math Understandings

- You use the Distributive Property to evaluate expressions that have a number multiplied by a sum or difference.
- The Distributive Property can be written and used in several different forms.

The **Distributive Property** shows how multiplication affects an addition or subtraction.

$$8 \times (4 + 6) = (8 \times 4) + (8 \times 6) \quad (6 - 2) \times 7 = (6 \times 7) - (2 \times 7)$$

Additional Professional Development Opportunities

Math Background Notes for Chapter 3: Every lesson has a Math Background in the PLAN section.

Research Overview, Mathematics Strands Additional support for these topics and more is in the front of the Teacher's Edition.

LessonLab LessonLab, a Pearson Education company, offers comprehensive, facilitated professional development designed to help teachers to improve student achievement. To learn more, please visit lessonlab.com.

Chapter 3 Resources

Print Resources

Print Resources	3-1	3-2	3-3	3-4	3-5	3-6	3-7	3-8	For the Chapter
L3 Practice	•	•	•	•	•	•	•	•	
L1 Adapted Practice	•	•	•	•	•	•		•	
L3 Guided Problem Solving	•	•	•	•	•	•		•	
L2 Reteaching	•	•	•	•	•	•		•	
L4 Enrichment	•	•	•	•	•	•		•	
L3 Daily Notetaking Guide	•	•	•	•	•	•		•	
L1 Adapted Daily Notetaking Guide	•	•	•	•	•	•		•	
L3 Vocabulary and Study Skills Worksheets	•		•	•		•		•	•
L3 Daily Puzzles	•	•	•	•	•	•			
L3 Activity Labs	•	•	•	•	•	•			
L3 Checkpoint Quiz				•		•			
L3 Chapter Project									•
L2 Below Level Chapter Test									•
L3 Chapter Test									•
L4 Alternative Assessment									•
L3 Cumulative Review									•

Spanish Resources (ELL)

Spanish Resources	3-1	3-2	3-3	3-4	3-5	3-6	3-7	3-8	For the Chapter
L3 Practice	•	•	•	•	•	•	•		
L3 Vocabulary and Study Skills Worksheets	•		•	•		•		•	•
L3 Checkpoint Quiz				•		•			
L2 Below Level Chapter Test									•
L3 Chapter Test									•
L4 Alternative Assessment									•
L3 Cumulative Review									•

Transparencies

Transparencies	3-1	3-2	3-3	3-4	3-5	3-6	3-7	3-8	For the Chapter
Check Skills You'll Need	•	•	•	•	•	•	•		
Additional Examples	•	•	•	•	•	•	•	•	
Problem of the Day	•	•	•	•	•	•	•		
Classroom Aid			•		•				•
Student Edition Answers	•	•	•	•	•	•	•	•	•
Lesson Quiz	•	•	•	•	•	•	•	•	
Test-Taking Strategies									•

Technology

Technology	3-1	3-2	3-3	3-4	3-5	3-6	3-7	3-8	For the Chapter
Interactive Textbook Online	•	•	•	•	•	•	•	•	•
StudentExpress™ CD-ROM	•	•	•	•	•	•	•	•	•
SuccessTracker™ Online Intervention	•	•	•	•	•	•	•	•	•
TeacherExpress™ CD-ROM	•	•	•	•	•	•	•	•	•
PresentationExpress™ with QuickTake Presenter CD-ROM	•	•	•	•	•	•	•	•	•
ExamView® Assessment Suite CD-ROM	•	•	•	•	•	•	•	•	•
MindPoint® Quiz Show CD-ROM									•
Prentice Hall Web Site: PHSchool.com	•	•	•	•	•	•	•	•	•

Also available: Prentice Hall Assessment System
- Progress Monitoring Assessments
- Skills and Concepts Review
- Test Prep Workbook

Other Resources
Algebra Readiness Tests
All-in-One Student Workbook
All-in-One Student Workbook, Adapted Version
Multilingual Handbook

Solution Key
Math Notes Study Folder
Spanish Cumulative Assessment

Where You Can Use the Lesson Resources

Here is a suggestion, following the four-step teaching plan, for how you can incorporate Differentiated Instruction Resources into your teaching.

	Instructional Resources L3	Differentiated Instruction Resources
1. Plan		
Preparation Read the Math Background in the Teacher's Edition to connect this lesson with students' previous experience. **Starting Class** **Check Skills You'll Need** Assign these exercises to review prerequisite skills. **New Vocabulary** Help students pre-read the lesson by pointing out the new terms introduced in the lesson.	**Math Background** **Math Understandings** **Transparencies & PresentationExpress™ with QuickTake Presenter CD-ROM** Check Skills You'll Need Problem of the Day **Resources** Vocabulary and Study Skills	**Spanish Support** ELL Vocabulary and Study Skills
2. Teach		
L3 **Guided Instruction** Use the Activity Labs to build conceptual understanding. Teach each Example. Use the Teacher's Edition side column notes for specific teaching tips, including Error Prevention notes. Use the Additional Examples found in the side column (and on transparency and PowerPoint) as an alternative presentation for the content. After each Example, assign the Quick Check exercise for that Example to get an immediate assessment of student understanding. Use the Closure activity in the Teacher's Edition to help students attain mastery of lesson content.	**Student Edition** Activity Lab **Resources** Daily Notetaking Guide Activity Lab **Transparencies & PresentationExpress™ with QuickTake Presenter CD-ROM** Additional Examples Classroom Aids **ExamView® Assessment Suite CD-ROM**	**Teacher's Edition** Every lesson includes suggestions for working with students who need special attention. L1 Special Needs L2 Below Level L4 Advanced Learners ELL English Language Learners **Resources** L1 Adapted Daily Notetaking Guide **Multilingual Handbook**
3. Practice		

Assignment Guide
Check Your Understanding
Use these questions to check students' understanding before you assign homework.
Homework Exercises
Assign homework from these leveled exercises in the Assignment Guide.
  A Practice by Example
  B Apply Your Skills
  C Challenge
  Test Prep and Mixed Review
Homework Quick Check
Use these key exercises to quickly check students' homework.
	Transparencies & PresentationExpress™ with QuickTake Presenter CD-ROM
	Student Answers
	Resources
	Practice
	Guided Problem Solving
	Vocabulary and Study Skills
	Activity Lab
	Daily Puzzles
	ExamView® Assessment Suite CD-ROM
		Spanish Support
		ELL Practice
		ELL Vocabulary and Study Skills
		Resources
		L1 Adapted Practice
		L4 Enrichment

4. Assess & Reteach		
Lesson Quiz Assign the Lesson Quiz to assess students' mastery of the lesson content. **Checkpoint Quiz** Use the Checkpoint Quiz to assess student progress over several lessons.	**Transparencies & PresentationExpress™ with QuickTake Presenter CD-ROM** Lesson Quiz **Resources** Checkpoint Quiz	**Resources** L2 Reteaching ELL Checkpoint Quiz Success Tracker™ Online Intervention **ExamView® Assessment Suite CD-ROM**

KEY   L1 Special Needs   L2 Below Level   L3 For All Students   L4 Advanced, Gifted   ELL English Language Learners

CHAPTER 3 Patterns and Variables

Patterns and Variables

 **Check Your Readiness**

Answers are in the back of the textbook.

For intervention, direct students to:

Using the Order of Operations
Lesson 1-4
Extra Skills and Word
   Problems Practice, Ch. 1

Adding and Subtracting Decimals
Lesson 1-7
Extra Skills and Word
   Problems Practice, Ch. 1

Multiplying Decimals
Lesson 1-8
Extra Skills and Word
   Problems Practice, Ch. 1

Dividing Decimals
Lesson 1-9
Extra Skills and Word
   Problems Practice, Ch. 1

What You've Learned

- In Chapter 1, you learned to add, subtract, multiply, and divide decimals.

- You used rounding and compatible numbers to estimate with decimals.

- You used the order of operations to simplify expressions.

Check Your Readiness

GO for Help

For Exercises	See Lesson
1–4	1-4
5–10	1-7
11–13	1-8
14–16	1-9

Using the Order of Operations

Find the value of each expression.

1. $3 \times 8 + 5$ **29**   2. $36 + 6 \div 2$ **39**

3. $48 - 6 \times 5$ **18**   4. $(23 - 18) \times 6$ **30**

Adding and Subtracting Decimals

First estimate. Then find each sum or difference.

5. $36.05 + 6.1$
   about 42; 42.15

6. $36 - 26.5$
   about 9; 9.5

7. $0.05 + 5.05$
   about 5; 5.1

8. $5.2 - 3.04$
   about 2; 2.16

9. $5.12 - 2.85$
   about 2; 2.27

10. $9.8 + 4.56$
    about 15; 14.36

Multiplying Decimals

Find each product.

11. 3.79×5 **18.95**   12. 6.4×3.04 **19.456**   13. 43.7×7.1 **310.27**

Dividing Decimals

Find each quotient.

14. $13.2 \div 4$ **3.3**   15. $85 \div 0.5$ **170**   16. $1.917 \div 2.7$ **0.71**

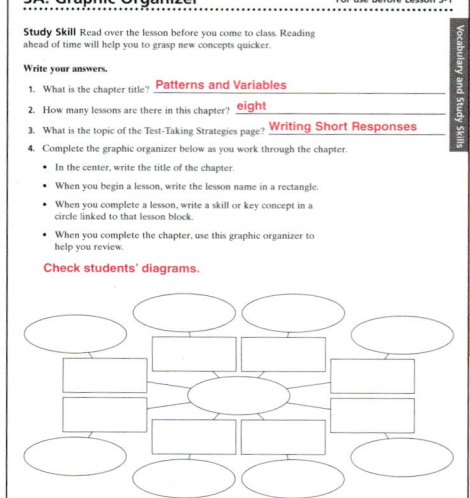

Spanish Vocabulary/Study Skills   **ELL**

Vocabulary/Study Skills   **L3**

3A: Graphic Organizer   For use before Lesson 3-1

Study Skill Read over the lesson before you come to class. Reading ahead of time will help you to grasp new concepts quicker.

Write your answers.

1. What is the chapter title? **Patterns and Variables**

2. How many lessons are there in this chapter? **eight**

3. What is the topic of the Test-Taking Strategies page? **Writing Short Responses**

4. Complete the graphic organizer below as you work through the chapter.
   - In the center, write the title of the chapter.
   - When you begin a lesson, write the lesson name in a rectangle.
   - When you complete a lesson, write a skill or key concept in a circle linked to that lesson block.
   - When you complete the chapter, use this graphic organizer to help you review.

Check students' diagrams.

Chapter 3 Overview

In this chapter, students use algebraic concepts and properties of numbers to investigate patterns, to write and use expressions, and to write and solve one-step equations involving addition, subtraction, multiplication, or division.

Activating Prior Knowledge

In this chapter, students build on and extend their knowledge of algebraic concepts, of patterns, of whole-number operations, and of the properties of whole numbers to work with algebraic expressions, equations and formulas. Ask questions such as:
• *What is 24.4 × 10?* **244**
• *What is (88.5 + 3) ÷ 100?* **0.915**

What You'll Learn Next

• In this chapter, you will learn to use algebraic expressions to describe relationships and patterns.

• You will use mental math to estimate solutions to equations.

• You will use addition, subtraction, multiplication, and division to solve equations.

• You will write equations to solve problems.

 Problem Solving Application On pages 154 and 155, you will work an extended activity on patterns.

🔊 Key Vocabulary

• algebraic expression (p. 113)
• arithmetic sequence (p. 123)
• conjecture (p. 108)
• Distributive Property (p. 144)
• equation (p. 124)
• evaluate (p. 114)
• inverse operations (p. 130)
• numerical expression (p. 113)
• open sentence (p. 125)
• sequence (p. 109)
• solution (p. 125)
• term (p. 108)
• variable (p. 113)

Chapter 3   **107**

Objective
To find and write rules for number patterns

Examples
1 Finding Number Patterns
2 Using a Rule to Write a Pattern
3 Writing a Rule

Math Understandings: p. 106C

Math Background

In an addition/subtraction pattern, each term is derived from the one before it by consistently adding or subtracting the same amount. This type of pattern is called an *arithmetic sequence*.

In a multiplication/division pattern, each term is derived from the one before it by consistently multiplying or dividing by the same amount. Patterns of this type are called *geometric sequences*.

More Math Background: p. 106C

Lesson Planning and Resources

See p. 106E for a list of the resources that support this lesson.

PowerPoint

Bell Ringer Practice

✓ **Check Skills You'll Need**
Use student page, transparency, or PowerPoint. For intervention, direct students to:
Comparing and Ordering Decimals
Lesson 1-6
Extra Skills and Word Problems Practice, Ch. 1

Algebra

3-1 Describing a Pattern

3-1

✓ **Check Skills You'll Need**

1. Vocabulary Review
To order numbers, you compare the place and __?__ of each digit.
value
Order each set of decimals from least to greatest.

2. 3.331, 3.1, 3.31
3.1, 3.31, 3.331
3. 0.105, 0.0105, 10.5
0.0105, 0.105, 10.5

GO for Help
Lesson 1-6

What You'll Learn

To find and write rules for number patterns

🔊 **New Vocabulary** term, conjecture, sequence

Why Learn This?

You can see patterns in nature, art, and music. You can use math to describe the patterns.

The numbers 1, 4, 7, 10, . . . form a number pattern. Each number in the pattern is a **term.** The three dots after the number 10 tell you that the pattern continues.

When you predict terms in a number pattern, you are making a conjecture. A **conjecture** is a prediction about what may happen.

EXAMPLE Finding Number Patterns

1 Decorating Jacob is making a pattern of tiles. The first four designs are shown. How many tiles will be in the fifth and sixth designs?

Count the tiles in each design. You can make a table to display the information. Each design has three more tiles than the one before it.

Design Number	1	2	3	4	5	6
Number of Tiles	1	4	7	10	13	16

← Add 3 to 10 to get the fifth term.
Add 3 to 13 to get the sixth term.

+3 +3

So the fifth and sixth designs have 13 and 16 tiles.

✓ Quick Check

1. The eighth design will go all the way across Jacob's wall. How many tiles will be in the eighth design? **22 tiles**

Differentiated Instruction Solutions for All Learners

Special Needs **L1**
Use a hundreds chart for number patterns that are continued to less than 100. Students can color in the boxes that correspond to each number in the pattern, and then make some conjectures about what the pattern is.

learning style: visual

Below Level **L2**
Have students practice skip-counting by 2, by 3, by 4, and so on. **2, 4, 6, 8, 10, . . . ; 3, 6, 9, 12, 15, . . . ; 4, 8, 12, 16, 20, . . . ; and so on**

learning style: verbal

Sometimes you can use a rule to describe a pattern. A rule states the first term and an explanation of the operations you use to find the next term.

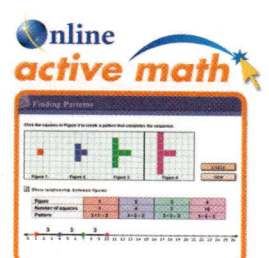

Online active math

For: Exploring Patterns Activity
Use: Interactive Textbook, 3-1

EXAMPLE Using a Rule to Write a Pattern

② Write the first six terms in the number pattern described by this rule: *Start with 1 and multiply by 2 repeatedly.*

The first term is 1.

$\times 2$ $\times 2$ $\times 2$ $\times 2$ $\times 2$

1, 2, 4, 8, 16, 32 ← **Multiply each term by 2 to find the next term.**

✓ Quick Check

2. Write the first six terms in each number pattern.
   a. Start with 90 and subtract 15 repeatedly. **90, 75, 60, 45, 30, 15**
   b. Start with 1 and multiply by 3 repeatedly. **1, 3, 9, 27, 81, 243**

A **sequence** is a set of numbers that follow a pattern.

EXAMPLE Writing a Rule

③ **Multiple Choice** Each number in the sequence below has the same relationship to the number immediately before it.

14.7, 13.4, 12.1, 10.8, . . .

How can you find the next number in the sequence?
Ⓐ By adding 1.3 to the previous number
Ⓑ By subtracting 1.3 from the previous number
Ⓒ By multiplying the previous number by 1.3
Ⓓ By dividing the previous number by 1.3

-1.3 -1.3 -1.3 -1.3

14.7, 13.4, 12.1, 10.8, 9.5 ← **To get from one term to the next, subtract 1.3.**

The rule is *start with 14.7 and subtract 1.3 repeatedly.* The correct answer is choice B.

Test Prep Tip ✎
Always check your answer by testing the answer in the original problem.

3a. **Start with 1.5 and multiply by 3 repeatedly; 121.5, 364.5, 1,093.5.**

b. **Start with 256 and divide by 2 repeatedly; 32, 16, 8.**

✓ Quick Check

3. Write a rule for each pattern. Then write the next three terms.
   a. 1.5, 4.5, 13.5, 40.5, . . . **3a–b. See left.**
   b. 256, 128, 64, . . .

2. Teach

Activity Lab
Use before the lesson.

All in One Teaching Resources
Activity Lab 3-1: Finding Patterns

Guided Instruction

Example 1
After discussing Example 1, ask:
How would the pattern be different if the first term were 2?
Each term would increase by 1; the pattern would be 2, 5, 8, 11, 14, ...

Example 2
After discussing Example 2, ask:
How would the pattern be different if the first term were 2?
It is the same pattern, but without the term 1; the pattern would be 2, 4, 8, 16, 32, ...

PowerPoint
Additional Examples

❶ Write the next two terms in this number pattern.
5, 12, 19, 26, . . . **33, 40**

❷ Write the first six terms in the number pattern described by this rule: *Start with 47 and subtract 3 repeatedly.* **47, 44, 41, 38, 35, 32**

❸ Write the next three terms and write a rule to describe this number pattern.
2.3, 4.4, 6.5, 8.6, . . . **10.7, 12.8, 14.9; rule: Start with 2.3 and add 2.1 repeatedly.**

All in One Teaching Resources
• Daily Notetaking Guide 3-1 **L3**
• Adapted Notetaking 3-1 **L1**

Closure

• *What is a number pattern?*
Sample: a set of numbers in which each number is related to the next number by a rule
• *What is a term of a pattern?* **one of the numbers in the pattern**
• *How do you describe a number pattern?* **Give the first term and the rule.**

Advanced Learners **L4**
Have students create original geometric patterns that represent number patterns, such as the designs in Example 1.

learning style: visual

English Language Learners **ELL**
Students will need a word bank to be able to write rules for the patterns. For example, explain words such as *subsequent, previous, repeatedly,* and *consecutive,* and provide examples so that students can use the words to write rules.

learning style: verbal

Assignment Guide

Check Your Understanding
Go over Exercises 1–4 in class before assigning the Homework Exercises.

Homework Exercises
A Practice by Example 5–15
B Apply Your Skills 16–21
C Challenge 22
Test Prep and
Mixed Review 23–27

Homework Quick Check
To check students' understanding of key skills and concepts, go over Exercises 10, 13, 18, 20, and 21.

Differentiated Instruction Resources

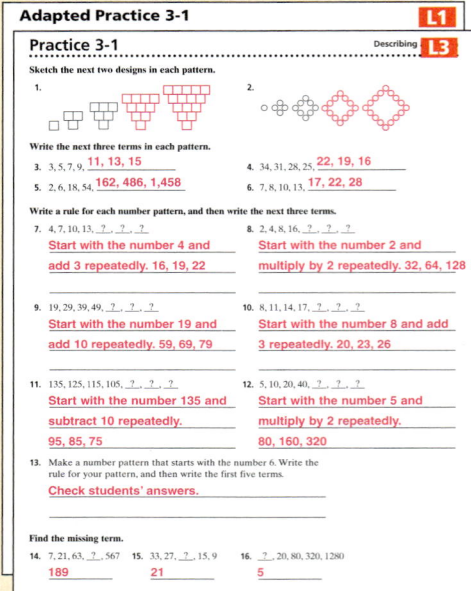

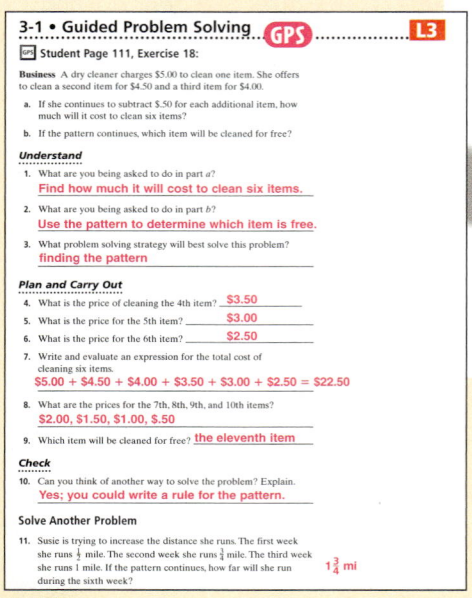

✓ Check Your Understanding

2. **Answers may vary. Sample: The coins increase in size from left to right.**

1. **Vocabulary** A prediction about what may happen is a __?__. conjecture

2. Look at the coins. Describe a pattern that you see.

Write a rule for each number pattern.

3. 53, 49, 45, 41, . . . Start with ■ and subtract ■ repeatedly.
   53 · · · · · · · · · · · 4

4. 2; 10; 50; 250; . . . Start with ■ and multiply by ■ repeatedly.
   2 · · · · · · · · · · · 5

Homework Exercises

For more exercises, see Extra Skills and Word Problems.

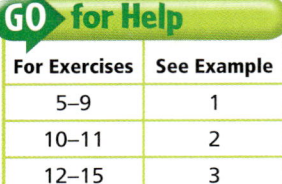

For Exercises	See Example
5–9	1
10–11	2
12–15	3

A Write the next two terms in each number pattern.

5. 2, 6, 10, 14, . . . **18, 22**
6. 99, 88, 77, 66, . . . **55, 44**
7. 1, 5, 25, 125, . . . **625, 3125**
8. 1, 1.4, 1.8, 2.2, . . . **2.6, 3.0**

9. The years 2000, 2004, 2008, and 2012 are leap years. Find the next three leap years. **2016, 2020, 2024**

Write the first six terms in each number pattern.

10. Start with 7 and add 4 repeatedly. **7, 11, 15, 19, 23, 27**

11. Start with 512 and divide by 2 repeatedly. **512, 256, 128, 64, 32, 16**

Write a rule for each pattern. Then write the next three terms.
12–15. See margin.

12. 100, 89, 78, 67, . . .
13. 0.12, 1.2, 12, 120, . . .
14. 600,000; 60,000; 6,000; . . .
15. $2.85, $5.70, $8.55, . . .

B GPS 16. **Guided Problem Solving** You buy 75 pounds of food for your pet llama. You feed her 6.7 pounds of food each day. You will buy more food when you have less than 20 pounds left. After how many days will you buy more llama food? **9 days**

• The rule is *start with* ■ *and subtract* ■ *repeatedly.*

Day	0	1	2	3	4
Amount of Food (lb)	75	68.3	■	■	■

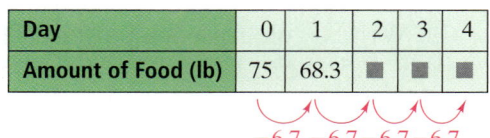
−6.7 −6.7 −6.7 −6.7

12. Start with 100 and subtract 11 repeatedly; 56, 45.
13. Start with 0.12 and multiply by 10 repeatedly; 1,200; 12,000.
14. Start with 600,000 and divide by 10 repeatedly; 600; 60.
15. Start with $2.85 and add $2.85 repeatedly; $11.40; $14.25.

17. Look for a pattern in the table. Find each missing term.

Number of Feet	1	2	3	4	5
Number of Inches	12	24	36	■	■

48 60

18. Business A dry cleaner charges $5.00 to clean one item. She
GPS offers to clean a second item for $4.50 and a third item for $4.00.
  a. If she continues to subtract $.50 for each additional item,
   how much will it cost to clean six items? **$22.50**
  b. If the pattern continues, which item will be cleaned for free?
   11th item

19. Astronomy Edmond Halley (1656–1742) first saw the comet
named for him in 1682. He correctly predicted that it would
return about every 76 years. About how old will you be when
the comet returns next? **Check students' work.**

20. Open-Ended Write a number pattern and its rule. The third
term in your number pattern must equal 12.
Check students' work.

21. Geometry Draw the next design for the pattern. **See margin.**

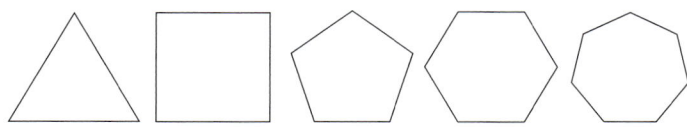

C 22. Challenge Write a rule for 156, 78, 76, 38, 36, 18, 16, . . .
Then write the next three terms in the pattern. **See margin.**

Test Prep and Mixed Review **Practice**

Multiple Choice

23. Each number in the sequence 2, 8, 14, 20, . . . has the same
relationship to the number immediately before it. How can you
find the next number in the sequence? **C**
  Ⓐ Multiply the previous number by 4.
  Ⓑ Divide the previous number by 4.
  Ⓒ Add 6 to the previous number.
  Ⓓ Subtract 6 from the previous number.

24. A gasoline pump shows $2.949 as the price of one gallon of
gasoline. About how much gasoline can you buy for $24? **F**
  Ⓕ 8 gallons   Ⓖ 10 gallons   Ⓗ 14 gallons   Ⓙ 16 gallons

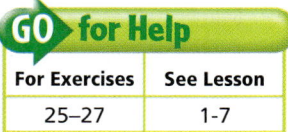
GO for Help

For Exercises	See Lesson
25–27	1-7

First estimate. Then find each sum or difference.
about 12; 12.7   about 4; 4.312   about 11; 10.8
25. $17.2 - 4.5$ **26.** $2.005 + 2.307$ **27.** $8.01 + 1.7 + 1.09$

Alternative Assessment

Each student in a pair writes a number pattern of
four terms that can be extended for at least two
more terms, using one operation. Partners
exchange papers and write the next two terms of
the pattern. Then each student writes a six-term
pattern and erases one of the numbers. Partners
find the missing term in each other's pattern.

Test Prep

Resources
For additional practice with a variety of test item
formats:
• Test-Taking Strategies, p. 149
• Test Prep, p. 153
• Test-Taking Strategies with Transparencies

4. Assess & Reteach

PowerPoint
Lesson Quiz

Write the next two terms and
write a rule for each number
pattern.

1. 3, 9, 15, 21, . . . **27, 33; Start
with 3 and add 6 repeatedly.**

2. 7, 14, 28, 56, . . . **112, 224; Start
with 7 and multiply by 2
repeatedly.**

3. 41.6, 20.8, 10.4, 5.2, . . . **2.6, 1.3;
Start with 41.6 and divide by 2
repeatedly.**

Exercises
Suggest to students that one way
to solve a pattern question, such
as Exercise 17, is to act it out using
objects. In this case, they can use
rulers or string.

21–22. See back of book.

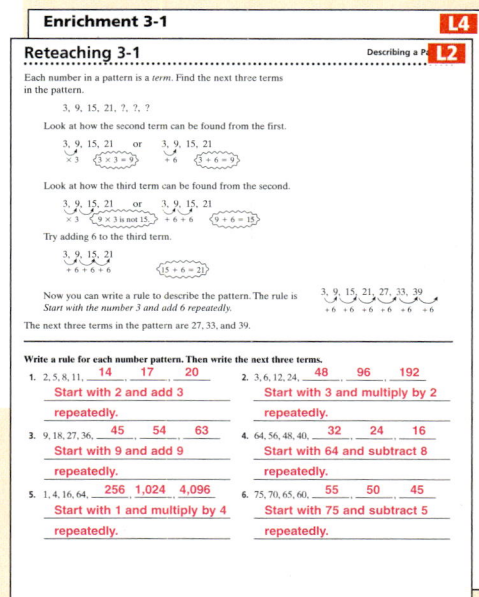

111

Patterns and Expressions

3-2a **Activity Lab**   **Hands On**

Patterns and Expressions

You can use a table to record data as you explore a pattern. A table can help you represent the pattern using symbols.

ACTIVITY

1. The first three designs in a pattern are shown at the right. Continue the pattern. Sketch the fourth and fifth designs on grid paper. **See margin.**

2. How many squares are in the fourth design? In the fifth design? **13 squares; 17 squares**

3. Copy and complete the table.

Design Number	1	2	3	4	5	6	7
Number of Squares	1	5	9	13	17	21	25

4. **Reasoning** Describe how you will find the number of squares in the tenth design of the pattern.

4. Answers may vary. Sample: Multiply (10 − 1), or 9, by 4, and then add 1.

ACTIVITY

5. In each diagram, segments already join point A to the points on the circle. Copy each diagram. Join point A to the other points on the circle. **Check students' work.**

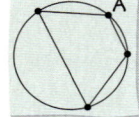 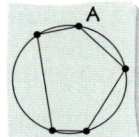 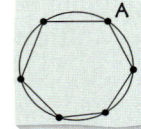

6. Copy and complete the table at the right.

Number of points on circle	4	5	6
Number of segments added to each diagram	1	2	3

7. Extend your table to include 7 and 8 points on a circle. **4; 5**

8. (**Algebra**) How many segments would you draw for n points on a circle? **$n - 3$**

1.

3-2 Variables and Expressions

Check Skills You'll Need

1. Vocabulary Review
What is a mathematical *expression*?
See below.
Find the value of each expression.

2. $40 - 16 \div 2$ **32**

3. $3 \times 5 + 12 \div 3$ **19**

4. $7 \times (95 - 32)$ **441**

for Help
Lesson 1-4

Check Skills You'll Need

1. A mathematical expression is a phrase containing numbers and operation symbols.

Test Prep Tip

The expression 5*d* means "5 times a number *d*." It can also be written as $5 \times d$ and $5 \cdot d$.

What You'll Learn

To evaluate algebraic expressions

🔊 **New Vocabulary** numerical expression, variable, algebraic expression, evaluate

Why Learn This?

You do not know how many people will attend a school fair. You can use a variable to represent the number of people.

A **numerical expression** is a mathematical phrase with only numbers and operation symbols $(+, -, \times, \div)$. An example of a numerical expression is $8 + 5 - 2$.

In the expressions below, $n, d, b,$ and x are variables. A **variable** is a symbol that can represent one or more numbers. A mathematical expression with one or more variables is an **algebraic expression.**

$$n + 2 \qquad 5d \qquad 7b - 2 \qquad 12x \div 3$$

You can use algebra tiles to model algebraic expressions.

🟨 A yellow tile represents 1.

🟩 A green tile represents a variable.

EXAMPLE Modeling With Algebra Tiles

1 Model the expression $5x + 3$ with algebra tiles.

← 5 green tiles represent 5*x*.
3 yellow tiles represent 3.

✓ Quick Check

1. Draw algebra tiles to model the expression $x + 2$. **See left.**

Objective
To evaluate algebraic expressions

Examples
1 Modeling With Algebra Tiles
2 Evaluating an Algebraic Expression
3 Application: Fundraising

Math Understandings: p. 106C

Math Background

Numerical expressions are meaningful combinations of numbers and operation signs.

A *variable* is a letter or other symbol that is a placeholder for an unknown number. An expression that contains at least one variable is called an *algebraic expression.* When each variable in an algebraic expression is replaced by a number, the result is a numerical expression whose value can be calculated. This process is called *evaluating the algebraic expression.*

More Math Background: p. 106C

Lesson Planning and Resources

See p. 106E for a list of the resources that support this lesson.

Bell Ringer Practice

✓ **Check Skills You'll Need**
Use student page, transparency, or PowerPoint. For intervention, direct students to:
Order of Operations
Lesson 1-4
Extra Skills and Word Problems
   Practice, Ch. 1

113

Differentiated Instruction Solutions for All Learners

Special Needs **L1**
Have students model the numerical expression 3 + 2 using objects. Then have them model x + 2 using tiles. Ask what the difference is. **We know the value of 3 in 3 + 2, but we do not know the value of x.**

learning style: tactile

Below Level **L2**
Show students several arrangements of algebra tiles that represent algebraic expressions. Have them write the expression each arrangement represents.

learning style: tactile

Activity Lab

Use before the lesson.
Student Edition Activity Lab, Hands On 3-2a, Patterns and Expressions, p. 112

 **Teaching Resources**

Activity Lab 3-2: Critical Thinking

Guided Instruction

Example 1
Ask: *What does the green tile represent?* **a variable** *What does a yellow tile represent?* **1**

 **Additional Examples**

① Draw algebra tiles to model the expression $2x + 3$.

② Evaluate $8x + 2$ for $x = 3$. **26**

③ The cost to rent a canoe at the lake is a $6 basic fee plus $4 for each hour h the canoe is rented. The expression for the total cost of a canoe rental is $6 + $4h$. Copy and complete the table.

Hours	Total Cost
h	$6 + 4h$
1	▦ **10**
2	▦ **14**
3	▦ **18**

 **Teaching Resources**

- Daily Notetaking Guide 3-2 **L3**
- Adapted Notetaking 3-2 **L1**

Closure

- *What is a variable?* **a symbol that represents an unknown**
- *What is an algebraic expression?* **a mathematical expression with at least one variable**
- *What does it mean to evaluate an algebraic expression?* **to replace each variable with a number and then simplify**

The title screen of a video game usually asks, "How many players?" The number of players is a variable. The game software uses your entry to set up the game.

To **evaluate** an algebraic expression, you replace each variable with a number. Then you use the order of operations to simplify the expression.

EXAMPLE **Evaluating an Algebraic Expression**

② Evaluate $2x - 8$ for $x = 11$.

$$2x - 8 = 2(11) - 8 \quad \leftarrow \text{Replace } x \text{ with 11.}$$
$$= 22 - 8 \quad \leftarrow \text{Multiply 2 and 11.}$$
$$= 14 \quad \leftarrow \text{Subtract.}$$

✓ Quick Check

2. Evaluate each expression for $x = 7$.
   a. $3x + 15$ **36**   **b.** $5x \div 7$ **5**   **c.** $56 - 4x$ **28**

You can evaluate an expression using more than one value. Make a table to organize the different values.

EXAMPLE **Application: Fundraising**

③ You earn $3 for each person who plays the game at your booth at the school fair. The expression $3p$ represents the amount of money you earn, where p is the number of people who play your game. Copy and complete the table for the given number of people.

School Fair Booth Earnings

Number of People	Process	Amount Earned	
p	$3 \times p$	$3p$	← Substitute each number of people for p.
15	$3 \times$ ▪	▪	← $3 \times 15 = 45$
40	$3 \times$ ▪	▪	← $3 \times 40 = 120$
65	$3 \times$ ▪	▪	← $3 \times 65 = 195$

✓ Quick Check

3. How much will you earn from 85 people coming to your booth?   **$255**

Advanced Learners **L4**
Write four algebraic expressions involving the variable z whose value is 9 when z is replaced by 3. **Samples:** $z + 6$; $12 - z$; $3z$; $27 \div z$

learning style: visual

English Language Learners **ELL**
Students often mistake a term like $3p$, where the variable p stands for people, as 3 people. In Example 3, make sure students read $3p$ as *3 times the number of people*.

learning style: verbal

1. **Vocabulary** How are numerical and algebraic expressions different? Give examples. **See margin.**

2. **Number Sense** Will the expression $50 - x$ get *larger, smaller,* or *stay the same* as the value of x increases? **smaller**

Evaluate each expression for $x = 8$.

3. $x + 12$ **20** 4. $80 \div x$ **10** 5. $2x$ **16** 6. $x - 3$ **5**

Homework Exercises

For more exercises, see Extra Skills and Word Problems.

GO for Help

For Exercises	See Example
7–14	1
15–19	2
20–23	3

A **Draw algebra tiles to model each expression.**
7–10. See left.

7. $3x + 5$ 8. $c + 3$ 9. 8 10. $z + 4$

11. $4 + 2x$ 12. $a + 6$ 13. $c + c + c$ 14. $3m + 2$
11–14. See margin.

7.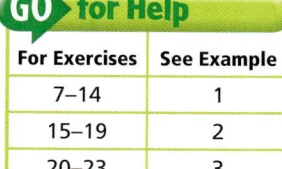

8.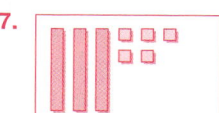

9.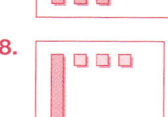

10.

Evaluate each expression.

15. $24 \div d$ for $d = 3$ 16. $p + 8$ for $p = 6$ 17. $3r - 2$ for $r = 65$
8   **14**   **193**

18. $8b - 12$ for $b = 2.1$ 19. $18 - 3y$ for $y = 2.5$
4.8   **10.5**

20. **Biking** The rental fee for a bicycle is $5, plus $2 for each hour h the bike is rented. The expression for the total cost is $5 + 2h$. Copy and complete the table for the given number of hours.

Hour	Rental Fee
h	$5 + 2h$
1	▢ 7
2	▢ 9
3	▢ 11

Copy and complete each table.

21.

x	$x + 6$
1	7
4	▢ 10
7	▢ 13

22.

x	$7x$
2	▢ 14
4	▢ 28
6	▢ 42

23.

x	$100 - x$
20	▢ 80
35	▢ 65
50	▢ 50

B **GPS** 24. **Guided Problem Solving** The formula $P = 2\ell + 2w$ gives the distance around a rectangle with length ℓ and width w. Find P for a rectangle with length 7 cm and width 4 cm. **22 cm**
   • Replace each variable in the formula with the given values.

1. **Answers may vary. Sample: A numerical expression is a mathematical phrase with only numbers and operation symbols. An algebraic expression is a mathematical expression with one or more variables.**

   Example: $8 + 5 \cdot 6$ is a numerical expression. $8 + 5x$ is an algebraic expression.

11–14. See back of book.

3. Practice

Assignment Guide

Check Your Understanding
Go over Exercises 1–6 in class before assigning the Homework Exercises.

Homework Exercises
A Practice by Example   7–23
B Apply Your Skills   24–28
C Challenge   29
Test Prep and
   Mixed Review   30–35

Homework Quick Check
To check students' understanding of key skills and concepts, go over Exercises 12, 18, 20, 27, and 28.

Differentiated Instruction **Resources**

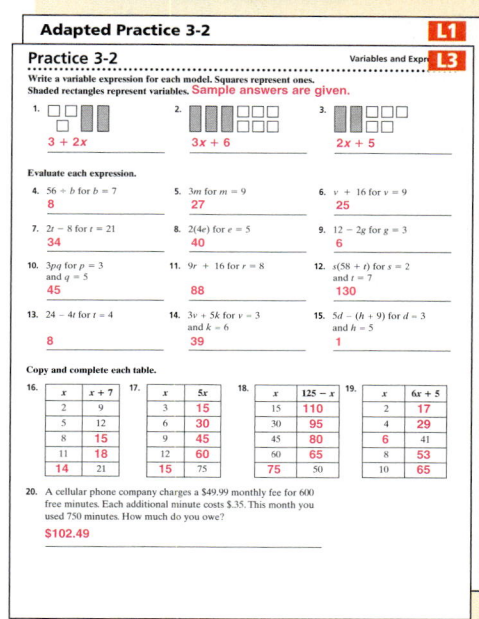

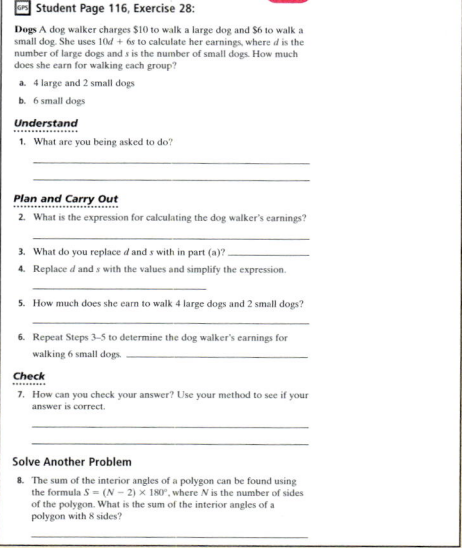

Lesson Quiz

Evaluate each expression for $n = 9$.

1. $n + 15$ **24**

2. $4n - 10$ **26**

3. $3(6 + n)$ **45**

4. $2n \div 3$ **6**

Alternative Assessment

Students work in pairs to write one-step algebraic expressions, such as $x + 4$ or $4x$, for each of the four operations. Together, partners use number sense to decide on a value for the variable in each expression and then evaluate the expression. When students show proficiency in evaluating simple expressions, vary the activity by having them write and evaluate expressions such as $4x - 3$ and $5x \div 4$.

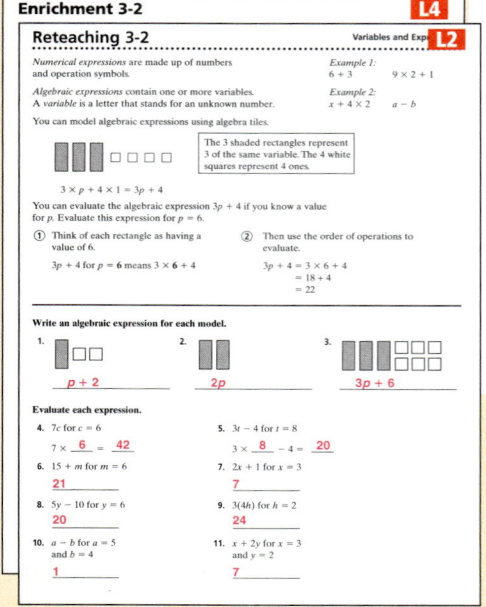

GO Online

Homework Video Tutor

Visit: PHSchool.com
Web Code: aqe-0302

Evaluate each expression.

25. $11t - 6v$ for $t = 9$ and $v = 4$ **26.** $2ab$ for $a = 35$ and $b = 3$
75   **210**

27. The formula $N = 7 \times \ell \times h$ gives the number of bricks needed for a wall of length ℓ feet and height h feet. How many bricks are needed for a wall with length 22 feet and height 30 feet?
4,620 bricks

28. **Dogs** A dog walker charges \$10 to walk a large dog and \$6 to walk a small dog. She uses $10d + 6s$ to calculate her earnings, where d is the number of large dogs and s is the number of small dogs. How much does she earn for walking each group?
a. 4 large and 2 small dogs **\$52**   **b.** 6 small dogs **\$36**

29. **Challenge** Bob plays a game at the school fair. He starts with 0 points. He gets 25 throws. He wins 12 points for hitting the target and loses 8 points for each miss. Bob ends with a score of 0. How many hits and misses does Bob have? **10 hits; 15 misses**

Test Prep and Mixed Review   Practice

Multiple Choice

30. Mr. Vasquez can seat 200 people in his restaurant. He has booths that seat 6 people and tables that seat 4 people. So far tonight, Mr. Vasquez has seated 8 full booths. Which method can he use to figure out how many more people he can seat? **B**
  (A) Add the product of 6 and 8 to 4.
  (B) Subtract the product of 6 and 8 from 200.
  (C) Multiply 4 by the sum of 6 and 8.
  (D) Divide 200 by the sum of 6 and 4.

31. Each number in the sequence has the same relationship to the number immediately before it. **H**

  1; 20; 400; 8,000; . . .

  How can the next number in the sequence be found?
  (F) Add 20.   (H) Multiply by 20.
  (G) Subtract 20.   (J) Divide by 20.

32. Jenice rides her bike 3.4 miles to school. She takes a different route home. The route home is 3.7 miles. How many miles does Jenice ride each day? **D**
  (A) 0.3 miles   (B) 3.5 miles   (C) 6.8 miles   (D) 7.1 miles

GO for Help

For Exercises	See Lesson
33–35	1-8

Find each product.
      29.16   **6.075**   **0.0374**
33. 2.43×12 **34.** 4.05×1.5 **35.** 37.4×0.001

Test Prep

Resources

For additional practice with a variety of test item formats:
• Test-Taking Strategies, p. 149
• Test Prep, p. 153
• Test-Taking Strategies with Transparencies

Enrichment 3-2   **L4**

Reteaching 3-2   Variables and Expr **L2**

Numerical expressions are made up of numbers and operation symbols.

Example 1:
$6 + 3$ $9 \times 2 + 1$

Algebraic expressions contain one or more variables. A *variable* is a letter that stands for an unknown number.

Example 2:
$x + 4 \times 2$ $a - b$

You can model algebraic expressions using algebra tiles.

The 3 shaded rectangles represent 3 of the same variable. The 4 white squares represent 4 ones.

$3 \times p + 4 \times 1 = 3p + 4$

You can evaluate the algebraic expression $3p + 4$ if you know a value for p. Evaluate this expression for $p = 6$.

① Think of each rectangle as having a value of 6.
$3p + 4$ for $p = 6$ means $3 \times 6 + 4$

② Then use the order of operations to evaluate.
$3p + 4 = 3 \times 6 + 4$
$= 18 + 4$
$= 22$

Write an algebraic expression for each model.

1. $p + 2$ **2.** $2p$ **3.** $3p + 6$

Evaluate each expression.

4. $7c$ for $c = 6$
$7 \times$ **6** $=$ **42**

5. $3t - 4$ for $t = 8$
$3 \times$ **8** $- 4 =$ **20**

6. $15 + m$ for $m = 6$
21

7. $2x + 1$ for $x = 3$
7

8. $5y - 10$ for $y = 6$
20

9. $3(4h)$ for $h = 2$
24

10. $a - b$ for $a = 5$ and $b = 4$
1

11. $x + 2y$ for $x = 3$ and $y = 2$
7

Modeling Expressions

You can draw a diagram to help understand a word phrase.

Operation	Word Phrase	Diagram 1	Diagram 2
addition	a number m plus 3.2 the sum of a number m and 3.2 3.2 more than a number m	m 3.2	m 3.2
subtraction	a number p minus 6 the difference of a number p and 6 6 subtracted from a number p	p ? 6	p ? 6
multiplication	4 times a number k the product of 4 and a number k	k k k k	k k k k
division	the quotient of a number z and 5 a number z divided by 5	z ? ? ? ? ?	z ? ? ? ? ?

EXAMPLE

1 Draw a diagram for each word phrase.

a. 2.5 more than x

x 2.5 or x 2.5

b. the product of 3 and w

w w w or w w w

Exercises

Copy and complete the table below. Each line is missing two parts. See margin.

Word Phrase	Diagram 1	Diagram 2
1. Height h divided by 6		
2.		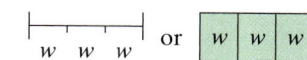 q 8
3.	r r r r r r r	
4. 6.3 smaller than t		

1–4. See back of book.

Modeling Expressions

Students use diagrams to represent word phrases. This will allow students to more easily change words to algebraic expressions in Lesson 3-3.

Guided Instruction

Before beginning the Activity Lab, ask students for examples of diagrams they are familiar with that give a message. Ask questions such as:
- *What diagram indicates a school crossing?* **Sample: a diagram of children crossing a street**
- *What diagram represents a railroad crossing?* **Sample: a diagram of tracks**

Exercises

Have students work in pairs. For each line in Exercises 1–4, one partner can fill in one of the missing parts and the other partner can fill in the other missing part. Have them compare and discuss their work. Then have pairs write their own mathematical word phrase and draw a diagram for it.

Alternative Method

Some students may prefer to use algebra tiles to model word phrases.

Resources

- Activity Lab 3-3: Decision Making
- algebra tiles
- Student Manipulatives Kit
- Classroom Aid 37

Objective
To write algebraic expressions and use them to solve problems

Examples
1 From Words to Expressions
2 Application: Bowling
3 From a Pattern to an Expression

Math Understandings: p. 106C

Math Background

An English phrase is a collection of words that form a cohesive unit, but the unit is less than a complete sentence. In a sense, expressions are the phrases of mathematics. That is, an expression is a collection of numbers, variables, and operation symbols that form a cohesive unit, but these units are less than a complete mathematical sentence.

More Math Background: p. 106C

Lesson Planning and Resources

See p. 106E for a list of the resources that support this lesson.

Bell Ringer Practice

✓ **Check Skills You'll Need**
Use student page, transparency, or PowerPoint. For intervention, direct students to:
Variables and Expressions
Lesson 3-2
Extra Skills and Word Problems
Practice, Ch. 3

✓ **Check Skills You'll Need**

1. Vocabulary Review
What does it mean to *evaluate* an expression?
See below.
Evaluate each expression for $a = 7$.

2. $a + 3$ **10**

3. $7a - 19$ **30**

4. $6 \cdot (a + 1)$ **48**

5. $2 + (2a - 5)$ **11**

 **for Help**
Lesson 3-2

Check Skills You'll Need

1. To evaluate an expression means to replace a variable with a number and simplify it.

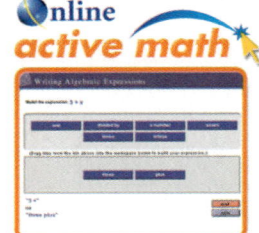

For: Algebraic Expressions Activity
Use: Interactive Textbook, 3-3

What You'll Learn
To write algebraic expressions and use them to solve problems

Why Learn This?
Sometimes you need to find a quantity, cost, or amount. You can use an algebraic expression to model the cost of a night out with your family.

You can write a word phrase as an algebraic expression.

Operation	Word Phrase	Algebraic Expression
addition	a number m plus 45 the sum of a number m and 45 45 more than a number m	$m + 45$
subtraction	a number p minus 6 the difference of a number p and 6 6 subtracted from a number p	$p - 6$
multiplication	4 times a number k the product of 4 and a number k	$4k$
division	the quotient of a number z and 25 a number z divided by 25	$z \div 25, \frac{z}{25}$

EXAMPLE **From Words to Expressions**

① Write an expression for "the product of 7 and k."

$7 \cdot k$, or $7k$ ← *Product* means multiplication.

✓ **Quick Check**

1. Write an expression for "2 more than x." $x + 2$

118 Chapter 3 Patterns and Variables

Differentiated **Instruction** **Solutions for All Learners**

Special Needs **L1**
For Example 3, have students draw some squares with given side lengths, and then describe the pattern they see.

learning style: visual

Below Level **L2**
Have students say word phrases for simple numerical expressions. For example:

$3 + 2$ **3 plus 2, the sum of 3 and 2**
6×5 **6 times 5, the product of 6 and 5**

learning style: verbal

Drawing a diagram can help you write an expression for a real-world situation. Remember to state what the variable represents.

EXAMPLE   Application: Bowling

2 You go bowling and bowl three games. Shoe rental for the day was $1.75. Write an algebraic expression for the total amount you pay.

Let g = the cost of the game. ← Choose a variable to represent the cost of one game.

Total Cost			
g	g	g	1.75

Each g represents the cost of one game.

The total cost is $3g + 1.75$.

✓ Quick Check

2. Brandon is 28 years younger than his father. Write an expression using Brandon's age to describe his father's age.
   Let b = Brandon's age; $b + 28$

You can see the relationship between numbers when they are organized in a table. You can use an algebraic expression to describe this relationship.

EXAMPLE   From a Pattern to an Expression

Perimeter of Squares

Side Length	Perimeter
2 cm	8 cm
3 cm	12 cm
5 cm	20 cm

3 **Multiple Choice** The table at the left shows the length of the sides of three squares and their perimeters. Which expression can you use to find the perimeter of a square with a side s units long?

   Ⓐ $s + 4$ Ⓑ $s - 4$ Ⓒ $4s$ Ⓓ $s \div 4$

Side Length	Process	Perimeter
2 cm	$4 \times 2 = 8$	8 cm
3 cm	$4 \times 3 = 12$	12 cm
5 cm	$4 \times 5 = 20$	20 cm
s cm	$4 \times s = 4s$	$4s$ cm

Look for a relationship between side length and perimeter. It might be "multiply by 4."

Check the rule for the other pairs of numbers.

The expression $4s$ describes the pattern. The correct answer is C.

✓ Quick Check

3. Write an algebraic expression to describe the relationship in the table.

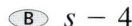

n	▪
2	6
5	9
7	11

$n + 4$

Closure

- *How do you write a word phrase as an algebraic expression?* **Sample: Identify a quantity that can be represented by a variable; look for words or phrases that suggest addition, subtraction, multiplication, or division.**

- *How do you describe an algebraic expression in words?* **Sample: You can write the words you say when you read the expression, or you can use a word or phrase that suggests the operation involved.**

● More Than One Way

A long-distance call costs 10 cents, plus 4.5 cents for each minute. How much will an 8-minute call cost?

Jessica's Method

I can let *m* represent the number of minutes. To find the cost of the call, I can use the algebraic expression $10 + 4.5m$. Then I will evaluate the expression for $m = 8$.

$$10 + 4.5m = 10 + 4.5(8) \quad \leftarrow \text{Replace } m \text{ with 8.}$$
$$= 10 + 36 \quad \leftarrow \text{Multiply 4.5 and 8.}$$
$$= 46 \quad \leftarrow \text{Add 10 to 36.}$$

The telephone call will cost 46 cents.

Luis's Method

If one minute costs 4.5 cents, then a two-minute call will cost 9 cents. A four-minute call will cost 18 cents, and an eight-minute call will cost 36 cents. I need to add the 10 cents. So the total cost is 36 cents + 10 cents, or 46 cents.

Choose a Method

Another long-distance plan charges 5 cents per call, plus 4 cents for each minute. Find how much a 10-minute call costs with this plan. Explain why you chose the method you used.

45 cents; check students' work.

✓ Check Your Understanding

	Total
y	50

1. **Answers may vary. Sample: Your grandfather is 50 years older than you. The expression $y + 50$ relates his age to yours.**

1. **Open-Ended** Write a problem that can be represented using the model at the left. **See left.**

2. **Boating** Renting a paddle boat costs $8 per hour. Write an expression for the cost to rent a paddle boat for *h* hours. **8h**

Write an expression for each word phrase.

3. *m* increased by 4: 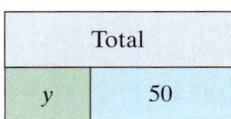 ■ + ■   **m + 4**

4. *y* divided by five: ■ ÷ ■   **y ÷ 5**

5. six times *z*: ■ × ■   **6 × z**

6. 4 subtracted from *m*: ■ − ■   **m − 4**

For more exercises, see Extra Skills and Word Problems.

GO for Help

For Exercises	See Example
7–16	1–2
17–22	3

A **Write an expression for each word phrase.**

7. 34 less than k
$k - 34$

8. 4 plus e
$e + 4$

9. d more than 50
$50 + d$

10. 23 times q
$23q$

11. 7 decreased by b
$7 - b$

12. b divided by 3
$b \div 3$

13. 13 minus d
$13 - d$

14. a times 32
$32a$

15. n less than 19
$19 - n$

16. Jobs Three brothers earn money by doing yardwork. The brothers split the money equally. Write an expression that describes how much money each brother earns. $m \div 3$

Write an expression to describe the relationship in each table.

17. $n - 3$

n	■
10	7
12	9
15	12

18. $7n$

n	■
1	7
2	14
3	21

19. $n + 2$

n	■
3	5
4.5	6.5
7	9

20. $n \div 6$

n	■
42	7
54	9
72	12

21. $11n$

n	■
1	11
2	22
3	33

22. $n - 7$

n	■
30	23
45	38
52	45

B  **23. Guided Problem Solving** The largest pan of lasagna weighed 3,477 pounds. The length of the pan was ten times its width. The lasagna pan was 7 feet wide. Find the length. **70 feet**

• You can use the strategy *Draw a Picture* to help you solve the problem.

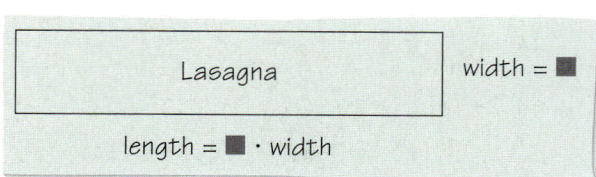

Lasagna   width = ■

length = ■ · width

• The expression is ■. The length is ■.

GO Online
Homework Video Tutor
Visit: PHSchool.com
Web Code: aqe-0303

24. Zoos Admission to the zoo costs $3 per person. A family has a coupon for a discount of $5. There are p people in the family. Write an expression to represent how much the family pays.
$3p - 5$

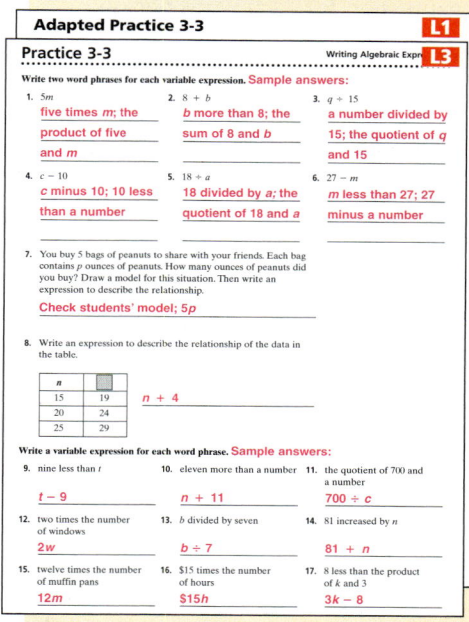

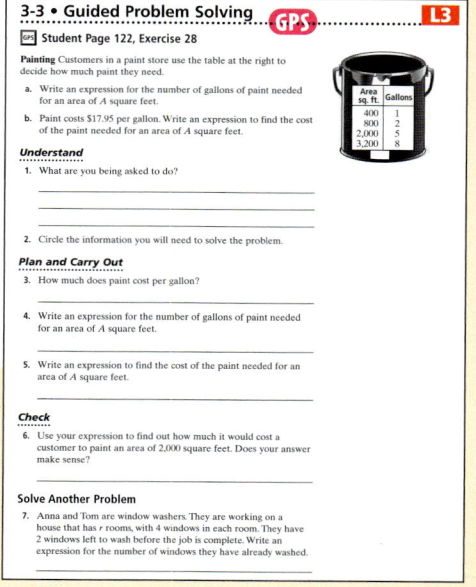

Write an expression for each word phrase.

1. *a* increased by 7 *a* + 7

2. 6 less than *c* *c* − 6

3. 16 cups costs *c* dollars. Write an expression for the cost of one cup. $\frac{c}{16}$

Alternative Assessment

Each student in a pair writes three word phrases similar to those in Exercises 7–15. Partners exchange papers and write the algebraic expression for each word phrase.

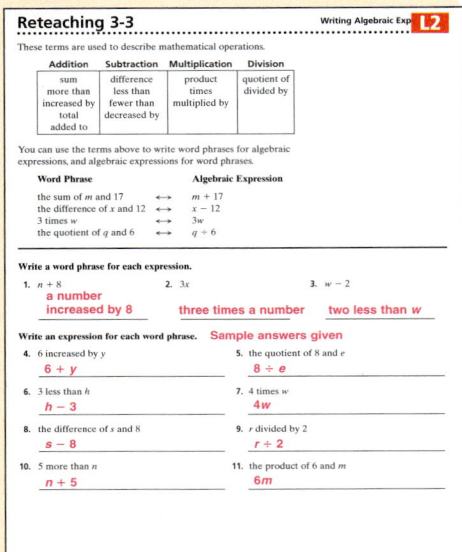

Reteaching 3-3 — Writing Algebraic Expressions **L2**

These terms are used to describe mathematical operations.

Addition	Subtraction	Multiplication	Division
sum	difference	product	quotient of
more than	less than	times	divided by
increased by	fewer than	multiplied by	
total	decreased by		
added to			

You can use the terms above to write word phrases for algebraic expressions, and algebraic expressions for word phrases.

Word Phrase		Algebraic Expression
the sum of *m* and 17	↔	*m* + 17
the difference of *x* and 12	↔	*x* − 12
3 times *w*	↔	3*w*
the quotient of *q* and 6	↔	*q* ÷ 6

Write a word phrase for each expression.

1. *n* + 8 a number increased by 8

2. 3*x* three times a number

3. *w* − 2 two less than *w*

Write an expression for each word phrase. Sample answers given

4. 6 increased by *y* 6 + *y*

5. the quotient of 8 and *e* 8 ÷ *e*

6. 3 less than *h* *h* − 3

7. 4 times *w* 4*w*

8. the difference of *s* and 8 *s* − 8

9. *r* divided by 2 *r* ÷ 2

10. 5 more than *n* *n* + 5

11. the product of 6 and *m* 6*m*

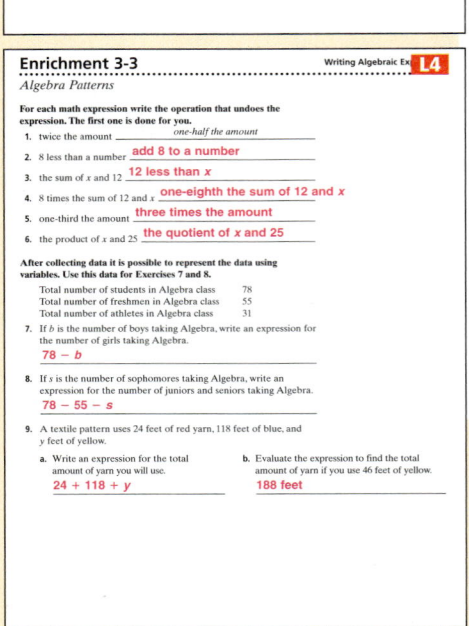

Enrichment 3-3 — Writing Algebraic Expressions **L4**

Algebra Patterns

For each math expression write the operation that undoes the expression. The first one is done for you.

1. twice the amount one-half the amount

2. 8 less than a number add 8 to a number

3. the sum of *x* and 12 12 less than *x*

4. 8 times the sum of 12 and *x* one-eighth the sum of 12 and *x*

5. one-third the amount three times the amount

6. the product of *x* and 25 the quotient of *x* and 25

After collecting data it is possible to represent the data using variables. Use this data for Exercises 7 and 8.

Total number of students in Algebra class   78
Total number of freshmen in Algebra class   55
Total number of athletes in Algebra class   31

7. If *b* is the number of boys taking Algebra, write an expression for the number of girls taking Algebra. 78 − *b*

8. If *s* is the number of sophomores taking Algebra, write an expression for the number of juniors and seniors taking Algebra. 78 − 55 − *s*

9. A textile pattern uses 24 feet of red yarn, 118 feet of blue, and *y* feet of yellow.

a. Write an expression for the total amount of yarn you will use. 24 + 118 + *y*

b. Evaluate the expression to find the total amount of yarn if you use 46 feet of yellow. 188 feet

---

Write an expression for each word phrase.

25. 5 less than the quotient of *m* and *n* *m* ÷ *n* − 5

26. 12 greater than the product of 3 and *j* 3*j* + 12

27. **Space Science** In outer space, gravity has less effect on the human body. After a space flight, an astronaut's height can temporarily be 2 inches greater than her normal height *h*. Write an expression for an astronaut's height at the end of a flight. *h* + 2

28. **Painting** Customers in a paint store use **GPS** the table at the right to decide how much paint they need.

a. Write an expression for the number of gallons of paint needed for an area of *A* square feet. *A* ÷ 400

b. Paint costs $17.95 per gallon. Write an expression to find the cost of the paint needed for an area of *A* square feet. 17.95(*A* ÷ 400)

Careers Astronaut researchers conduct scientific experiments in space.

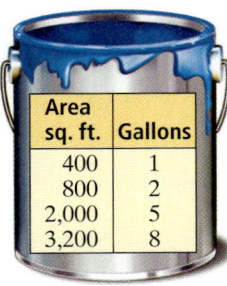

Area sq. ft.	Gallons
400	1
800	2
2,000	5
3,200	8

C 29. **Challenge** A store that personalizes shirts charges $20 for a shirt plus $.75 for each letter. Write an algebraic expression for the cost of *t* shirts using *n* letters each. (20 + 0.75*n*)*t*

 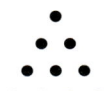 **Test Prep and Mixed Review** **Practice**

Multiple Choice

30. Maria has a box of 20 cookies. She gives 2 cookies to each friend. Which expression shows the number of cookies Maria has left after giving cookies to *m* friends? **B**

Ⓐ 2*m* − 20   Ⓑ 20 − 2*m*   Ⓒ 20*m* − 2   Ⓓ 20 + 2*m*

31. The first four figures in a pattern are shown below.

Which statement best describes the tenth figure in the pattern?

Ⓕ The tenth figure has 10 dots in the bottom row. **F**

Ⓖ The tenth figure has 12 rows of dots.

Ⓗ The tenth figure is 7 cm tall.

Ⓙ The tenth figure has more than 100 dots.

GO for Help

For Exercises	See Lesson
32–34	1-7

Find each sum.

32. 4.432 + 1.009 5.441

33. 2.005 + 12.5 14.505

34. 2.449 + 0.7 3.149

Test Prep

Resources

For additional practice with a variety of test item formats:

• Test-Taking Strategies, p. 149

• Test Prep, p. 153

• Test-Taking Strategies with Transparencies

Arithmetic Sequences

An **arithmetic sequence** is formed by adding a fixed number to or subtracting it from each previous term. You can use an algebraic expression to describe an arithmetic sequence.

EXAMPLE

Consider the sequence modeled in the table at the right. Write an expression to find the term in position n.

Look for a relationship between the position n and the term value.

Position, n	Process	Term Value
1	$1 + 2.5 = 3.5$	3.5
2	$2 + 2.5 = 4.5$	4.5

For the first two positions, you add 2.5 to the position n.

Position, n	Term Value
1	3.5
2	4.5
3	5.5
4	6.5

As the position increases by 1, the term value increases by 1. This can be written as n.

Use the rule to check the remaining values in the table.

Position, n	Process	Term Value
3	$3 + 2.5 = 5.5$	5.5
4	$4 + 2.5 = 6.5$	6.5

The rule applies to all of the number pairs in the table. Write the rule using an algebraic expression.

● The expression for the sequence in the table is $n + 2.5$.

Exercises

Write an algebraic expression for the sequence in each table.

1.

Position, n	Term Value
1	7
3	9
5	11
7	13

$n + 6$

2.

Position, n	Term Value
10	6
11	7
12	8
13	9

$n - 4$

3.

Position, n	Term Value
1	4
2	5
3	6
4	7

$n + 3$

Activity Lab

Arithmetic Sequences

Students use algebraic expressions to describe arithmetic sequences. They look for relationships between pairs in a table and write a rule using an algebraic expression for the terms in the table.

Guided Instruction

Be sure students understand that the expression and rule they choose must work for all pairs in the table. Ask questions such as:
• *In the first Example, how do you know that the expression $3.5 \cdot n$ is not correct?* **Although it works for the first pair, it does not work for the second.**
• *What do you observe about the relationships among term values?* **They differ by 1.**

Have students work independently on the Exercises. Suggest they look at the term values and see how they differ as they attempt to find expressions.

Differentiated Instruction

Advanced Learners **L4**
Have students work in pairs. Each partner makes a table of related pairs and gives it to the other to find the rule. Be sure all number pairs are tested for the rule.

Objective
To use mental math to estimate and solve equations

Examples
1 True Equations and False Equations
2 Using Mental Math
3 Guess, Check, and Revise

Math Understandings: p. 106D

Math Background

An *equation* is a mathematical sentence that contains an equal sign. If both *sides* of an equation are numerical expressions, then the equation can be true or false. If one side is an algebraic expression, then the equation is an *open sentence*; it is neither true nor false. You determine whether a number is a *solution* to such an equation by evaluating when that number replaces the variable. If the resulting statement is true, the number is a solution.

More Math Background: p. 106D

Lesson Planning and Resources

See p. 106E for a list of the resources that support this lesson.

Bell Ringer Practice

✓ **Check Skills You'll Need**
Use student page, transparency, or PowerPoint. For intervention, direct students to:
Adding and Subtracting Decimals
Lesson 1-7
Extra Skills and Word Problems Practice, Ch. 1

✓ **Check Skills You'll Need**

1. **Vocabulary Review** How can you use front-end estimation to add $3.46 + $6.54?

First estimate. Then find each sum or difference.

2. $5.3 + 1.07$

3. $6.1 - 2.4$

4. $8 - 6.3$
1–4. See below.

 for Help
Lesson 1-7

Check Skills You'll Need

1. **Add the whole dollars first and then estimate when adding the cents.**

2. **about 6; 6.37**

3. **about 4; 3.7**

4. **about 2; 1.7**

Vocabulary Tip

Read "1 $\stackrel{?}{=}$ 2" as "Does 1 equal 2?" Read "1 ≠ 2" as "1 does not equal 2."

What You'll Learn

To use mental math to estimate and solve problems
🔊 **New Vocabulary** equation, open sentence, solution

Why Learn This?

Part of the fun of collecting is completing your collection. You can use an equation to find the number of items you still need.

An **equation** is a mathematical sentence that has an equal sign, =. An equation is like a balanced scale.

To be in balance, a scale must have weights with the same total on each side.

$8 + 4 = 3 \times 4$ ← A true equation has equal values on each side of the equal sign.

If each side of the equation does not have the same value, the equation is false. Use ≠ to indicate that an equation is false.

EXAMPLE **True Equations and False Equations**

① Is the equation $6 + 13 = 18$ true or false?

$6 + 13 \stackrel{?}{=} 18$ ← Write the equation.

19 ← Add 6 + 13.

$19 \neq 18$ ← Compare.

The equation is false.

✓ **Quick Check**

1. Tell whether each equation is true or false.
   a. $7 \times 9 = 63$ **true** **b.** $4 + 5 = 45$ **false** **c.** $70 - 39 = 41$ **false**

Differentiated Instruction **Solutions for All Learners**

Special Needs L1
Provide additional equations for students to identify as true or not true. Include some such as 18 = 2 + 16, where the sum or difference is on the left side of the equals sign. Students often think these are "wrong" or untrue.

learning style: visual

Below Level L2
Help students distinguish between an equation and an expression. An expression does not contain an equal sign. Emphasize that both equations and expressions may or may not have a variable.

learning style: visual

An equation with one or more variables is an **open sentence.** A **solution** of an equation is the value of the variable that makes the equation true. For example, $x - 15 = 12$ is an open sentence. Since $27 - 15 = 12$, the value 27 is the solution to $x - 15 = 12$.

You can use mental math to find the solution of some equations.

EXAMPLE   Using Mental Math

② **Baseball Cards** How many baseball cards do you need to add to the 14 cards you already own to have a total of 25 cards? Solve the equation $n + 14 = 25$, which models this situation.

What you think

I need to find a number that I can add to 14 and get 25. Since $11 + 14 = 25$, the solution is 11.

I need 11 more cards.

✓ Quick Check

2. **Mental Math** Solve each equation.
    a. $17 - x = 8$ 9   **b.** $w \div 4 = 20$ 80   **c.** $4.7 + c = 5.9$ 1.2

EXAMPLE   Guess, Check, and Revise

GO for Help

For help with problem solving strategies, go to the Problem Solving Handbook.

③ Use the strategy *Guess, Check, and Revise* to solve $n - 43 = 19$.

Estimate Round the numbers to get a good starting point.

$$n - 43 = 19$$
$$\downarrow \quad \downarrow \quad \downarrow$$
$$n - 40 = 20$$

What you think

Using mental math, I know $60 - 40 = 20$, so n is close to 60.

I can try substituting 60 for n in the equation: $60 - 43 = 17$. The number 17 is too low. I will try $n = 65$: $65 - 43 = 22$. The number 22 is too high. I will try $n = 62$: $62 - 43 = 19$.

Since $62 - 43 = 19$ is true, the solution to $n - 43 = 19$ is 62.

✓ Quick Check

3. Use the strategy *Guess, Check, and Revise* to solve $k + 39 = 82$. 43

Activity Lab
Use before the lesson.

All in One Teaching Resources
Activity Lab 3-4: Exploring Number Squares

Guided Instruction

Example 1
Point out that the equal sign with a question mark above ($\overset{?}{=}$) indicates that you do not yet know whether the equation is true or false.

Example 2
Some students may not know what to do to begin. Encourage them to substitute a value for the variable and see if the result is true by using mental math.

PowerPoint
📖 Additional Examples

① Is the equation $24 - 16 = 8$ true or false? **true**

② Use mental math to solve each equation.
    a. $y - 7 = 15$ **22**
    b. $d \div 9 = 6$ **54**

③ Use the strategy *Guess, Check, and Revise* to solve $r + 27 = 89$. **62**

All in One Teaching Resources
• Daily Notetaking Guide 3-4 **L3**
• Adapted Notetaking 3-4 **L1**

Closure

• *What is an equation?* **a mathematical sentence that contains an equal sign**
• *What is a solution to an equation?* **When an equation contains a variable, a solution is a value of the variable that makes the equation true.**

Advanced Learners **L4**
Have students use number sense or models to solve these equations.

$3r + 1 = 16$ **5**
$2m + 4 = 3m$ **4**

learning style: visual

English Language Learners **ELL**
Some students may be uncomfortable "guessing." Explain to them that sensible guessing is a valid strategy. Focus on the steps that narrow choices—finding a number too high or too low.

learning style: verbal

125

Assignment Guide

Check Your Understanding
Go over Exercises 1–11 in class before assigning the Homework Exercises.

Homework Exercises
A Practice by Example   12–26
B Apply Your Skills   27–29
C Challenge   30
Test Prep and
   Mixed Review   31–33

Homework Quick Check
To check students' understanding of key skills and concepts, go over Exercises 14, 18, 25, 28, and 29.

Differentiated Instruction Resources

Adapted Practice 3-4   **L1**

Practice 3-4   Using Number Sense to Solve One-Step   **L3**

Find the missing number that makes the equation true.
1. $7 + \square = 12$ 2. $\square \times 5 = 30$ 3. $13 - \square = 4$
   5   6   9

Tell whether each equation is true or false.
4. $12 + 10 = 10 + 12$ 5. $31 + 4 = 41 + 3$ 6. $3.5 \times 1 = 1$
  true   false   false
7. $(3 \times 5) \times 4 = 3 \times (5 \times 4)$ 8. $(7 \times 2) + 6 = 7 \times (2 + 6)$ 9. $0 \times a = a$
  true   false   false

Solve each equation. Use either mental math or the strategy *Guess, Check,* and *Revise.*
10. $8b = 72$ 11. $n + 14 = 45$ 12. $h - 3.6 = 8$
  9   31   11.6
13. $w \div 12 = 3$ 14. $53 = z - 19$ 15. $86 = 29 + y$
  36   72   57
16. $153 = 9k$ 17. $4 = m + 24$ 18. $c + 14.7 = 29.8$
  17   96   15.1

19. The winners of a slam dunk basketball competition receive T-shirts. The coach spends $50.40 on shirts for the entire team. Each T-shirt costs $4.20. Solve the equation $(4.20)n = 50.40$ to find the number of team members.
  12 team members

3-4 • Guided Problem Solving   **GPS**   **L3**

GPS Student Page 127, Exercise 29

You have c pounds of cashews and 2.7 pounds of peanuts. You have 6 pounds of nuts altogether. Solve the equation $c + 2.7 = 6$ to find out how many pounds of cashews you have.

Understand
1. What are you being asked to do?

2. How can mental math help you to solve this problem?

Plan and Carry Out
3. What does the equation $c + 2.7 = 6$ mean?

4. What is $6 - 2.7$?
5. How many pounds of cashews do you have?

Check
6. Explain how you can check your answer. Then check your answer.

Solve Another Problem
7. At a school, there are 60 teachers for 1,500 students. Each teacher has the same number of students. Use the equation $60n = 1,500$ to find how many students each teacher has.

Vocabulary Tip
Algebraic is pronounced "al juh BRAY ik."

There are some open sentences that are true for every value you use for the variable. The algebraic equations that illustrate the number properties are true for all values of a, b, and c.

KEY CONCEPTS   **Number Properties**

Identity Properties

The sum of 0 and any number is that number.   The product of 1 and any number is that number.

Arithmetic $0 + 9 = 9$ $1 \times 9 = 9$
Algebra $0 + a = a$ $1 \times a = a$

Commutative Properties   Changing the order of addends or factors does not change the sum or the product.

Arithmetic $9 + 6 = 6 + 9$ $9 \times 6 = 6 \times 9$
Algebra $a + b = b + a$ $a \times b = b \times a$

Associative Properties   Changing the grouping of numbers does not change the sum or the product.

Arithmetic
$9 + (6 + 4) = (9 + 6) + 4$ $9 \cdot (6 \times 4) = (9 \cdot 6) \times 4$
Algebra
$a + (b + c) = (a + b) + c$ $a(bc) = (ab)c$

Check Your Understanding

1. The value(s) of the variable(s) that make(s) the equation true is (are) unknown.

1. **Vocabulary** Why is an equation with one or more variables called an open sentence? **See left.**

2. **Writing in Math** Explain how to use the strategy *Guess, Check, and Revise* to solve $y + 19 = 42$. **See margin.**

3. **Number Sense** Use the balance scale at the left. What value for n will make the equation $n + 3 = 18$ a true equation? **15**

Find the missing number that makes the equation true.

4. $\blacksquare + 3 = 5$ 5. $\blacksquare \times 4 = 12$
   2   3

Tell whether each equation is true or false.
   true   false   false
6. $5 + 14 = 14 + 5$ 7. $0 \times 9 = 9$ 8. $2 \times 5 = 5 + 2$
   true   true   false
9. $0 + 3 = 3$ 10. $1 \cdot y = y$ 11. $x + 1 = x$

126   **Chapter 3**   Patterns and Variables

2. Round 19 to 20 and round 42 to 40. So $n + 20 = 40$. Since you know $20 + 20 = 40$, your starting point is 20. Continue checking numbers close to 20 until you find the value of n which makes the statement true.

Homework Exercises

For more exercises, see Extra Skills and Word Problems.

GO for Help

For Exercises	See Example
12–14	1
15–20	2
21–26	3

A Tell whether each equation is true or false.

12. $3 + 50 = 80$ **false** **13.** $3 + 4 + 2 = 3 + 6$ **true** **14.** $0 \times 5.7 = 5.7$ **false**

Solve each equation. Use either mental math or the strategy *Guess, Check, and Revise*.

15. $x + 5 = 7$ **2**   **16.** $4x = 32$ **8**   **17.** $x + 2 = 6.3$ **4.3**

18. $g \div 4 = 2$ **8**   **19.** $p - 6 = 25$ **31**   **20.** $r + 14 = 23$ **9**

21. $6d = 612$ **102**   **22.** $k + 9 = 28$ **19**   **23.** $p \times 4 = 792$ **198**

24. $588 = 3n$ **196**   **25.** $b - 23 = 68$ **91**   **26.** $w + 13 = 71$ **58**

B  **27. Guided Problem Solving** Suppose you spent $74.95 for a shirt and a jacket. The shirt cost $20.25. Solve the equation $20.25 + j = 74.95$ to find how much you spent on the jacket.
- You can work a simpler problem to estimate an answer. Use number sense to solve $20 + j = 75$.
$54.70

28. Pollution When burned, 18 gallons of gasoline produce about 360 pounds of carbon dioxide. Solve the equation $18n = 360$ to find how much carbon dioxide 1 gallon of gasoline produces.
20 lb

29. You have c pounds of cashews and 2.7 pounds of peanuts. You have 6 pounds of nuts altogether. Solve the equation $c + 2.7 = 6$ to find how many pounds of cashews you have.
3.3 lb

C **30. Challenge** Use estimation to check whether 59.4 is a reasonable solution to $x + 27.6 = 31.8$. Explain your answer.

30. No; $60 + 30 = 90$, which is not close to 31.8.

GO Online
Homework Video Tutor
Visit: PHSchool.com
Web Code: aqe-0304

 **Test Prep and Mixed Review** — **Practice**

Multiple Choice

31. Sue was 30 years old when her daughter Amy was born. If s represents Sue's age, which expression describes Amy's age? **B**
   Ⓐ $s + 30$ Ⓑ $s - 30$ Ⓒ $30 - s$ Ⓓ $30s$

32. A bus has 25 passengers at the beginning of its route. At each stop, 5 people get off the bus and one person gets on. After how many stops will there be one passenger on the bus? **H**
   Ⓕ 4   Ⓖ 5   Ⓗ 6   Ⓙ 10

33. Write the next three terms in the sequence 4, 12, 36, 108, . . .
324; 972; 2,916

GO for Help

For Exercise	See Lesson
33	3-1

Online lesson quiz, PHSchool.com, Web Code: aqa-0304

Alternative Assessment

Each student in a pair writes four equations that contain only numbers. Partners trade papers and identify whether each of the other's equations are true or false.

Test Prep

Resources
For additional practice with a variety of test item formats:
- Test-Taking Strategies, p. 149
- Test Prep, p. 153
- Test-Taking Strategies with Transparencies

---

4. Assess & Reteach

PowerPoint
Lesson Quiz

Tell whether each equation is true or false.

1. $3 + 29 = 32$ **true**

2. $3 + 4 = 4 + 3 - 1$ **false**

Use mental math to solve each equation.

3. $g \div 6 = 8$ **$g = 48$**

4. $h + 20 = 30$ **$h = 10$**

5. Use the strategy *Guess, Check, and Revise* to solve $w - 21 = 78$. **99**

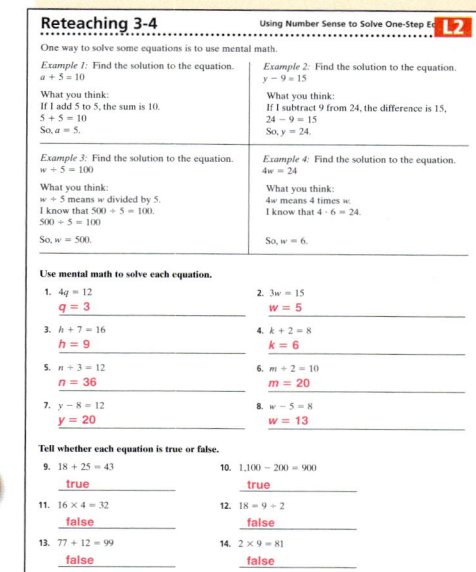

Reteaching 3-4 — Using Number Sense to Solve One-Step Eq... **L2**

One way to solve some equations is to use mental math.

Example 1: Find the solution to the equation.
$a + 5 = 10$
What you think:
If I add 5 to 5, the sum is 10.
$5 + 5 = 10$
So, $a = 5$.

Example 2: Find the solution to the equation.
$y - 9 = 15$
What you think:
If I subtract 9 from 24, the difference is 15,
$24 - 9 = 15$
So, $y = 24$.

Example 3: Find the solution to the equation.
$w \div 5 = 100$
What you think:
$w \div 5$ means w divided by 5.
I know that $500 \div 5 = 100$.
$500 \div 5 = 100$
So, $w = 500$.

Example 4: Find the solution to the equation.
$4w = 24$
What you think:
$4w$ means 4 times w.
I know that $4 \cdot 6 = 24$.
So, $w = 6$.

Use mental math to solve each equation.

1. $4q = 12$ $q = 3$ **2.** $3w = 15$ $w = 5$

3. $h + 7 = 16$ $h = 9$ **4.** $k + 2 = 8$ $k = 6$

5. $n \div 3 = 12$ $n = 36$ **6.** $m + 2 = 10$ $m = 20$

7. $y - 8 = 12$ $y = 20$ **8.** $w - 5 = 8$ $w = 13$

Tell whether each equation is true or false.

9. $18 + 25 = 43$ true   **10.** $1,100 - 200 = 900$ true

11. $16 \times 4 = 32$ false   **12.** $18 = 9 \div 2$ false

13. $77 + 12 = 99$ false   **14.** $2 \times 9 = 81$ false

Enrichment 3-4 — Using Number Sense to Solve One-Step E... **L4**
Critical Thinking

A marathon runner runs 26 miles to complete a race. A marathoner ran a race in the following segments:
- 50 minutes for the first 10 miles
- 48 minutes for the next 8 miles
- 28 minutes for the next 4 miles
- 20 minutes for the final 4 miles

What was the runner's average speed for each segment?

1. To calculate the speed for each race segment, what kind of equation will you use to set up, a multiplication equation or a division equation? Explain.
Sample answer: A division equation; Divide the number of miles by the time to get the speed for each segment.

2. Write an equation you can use to find the speed for each race segment. Make sure you define all variables.
Sample answer: $s = d \div t$, where $d = $ miles for each segment, $s = $ speed, and $t = $ time for each segment

3. Use your equation from Exercise 2 to complete the table for each race segment. Round your answers to the nearest hundredth.

Number of miles	Time per segment	Miles per minute
10	50 minutes	0.20
8	48 minutes	0.17
4	28 minutes	0.14
4	20 minutes	0.20

4. Find the total time, in minutes, it took the runner to run the entire race.
146 minutes

127

Vocabulary Builder

High-Use Academic Words

Vocabulary Builder

Students use a strategy for learning words that, while not math vocabulary terms, are important for success in mathematics and on tests.

Guided Instruction

Have students look through their texts for use of the terms: *identify, list,* and *justify.* Ask the following questions:

- *Where do you find the term justify?* **Sample: page 148**
- *What is another way to say "Order the decimals from least to greatest"?* **Sample: List the decimals in order from least to greatest.**
- *What direction could you write about even and odd numbers using the term* identify? **Sample: Identify each number as even or odd.**

Teaching Tip

Restate directions given in the text using *identify, list,* and *justify* as appropriate to familiarize students with these terms.

Differentiated Instruction

English Language Learners   ELL
Encourage students to write high-frequency academic words in their native language as needed.

Resources

- Vocabulary and Study Skills Worksheets

High-Use Academic Words

High-use academic words are words that you will see often in textbooks and on tests. These words are not math vocabulary terms, but knowing them will help you to succeed in mathematics.

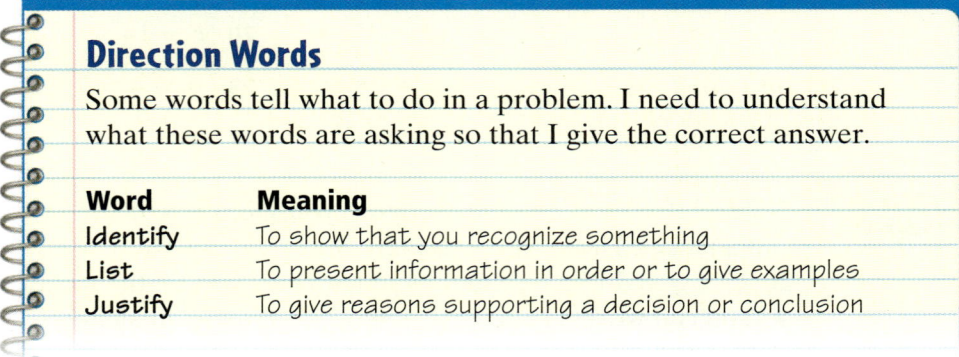

Direction Words

Some words tell what to do in a problem. I need to understand what these words are asking so that I give the correct answer.

Word	Meaning
Identify	To show that you recognize something
List	To present information in order or to give examples
Justify	To give reasons supporting a decision or conclusion

Exercises

1. Identify each animal as a pet or a wild animal.
   a. kitten **pet**   b. elephant **wild animal**   c. dog **pet**   d. crocodile **wild animal**

2. List five animals you could keep as a pet.
   Answers may vary. Sample: dog, cat, fish, bird, hamster

3. Justify your answer to Exercise 2. **Check students' work.**

4. Identify each expression as numerical or algebraic.
   a. $n \div 10$ **algebraic**   b. $5 + (6 - 2) \div 3$ **numerical**   c. $5x - y$ **algebraic**   d. $(1 + 3) \cdot (10 - 3)$ **numerical**

5. List 3 different examples of an algebraic expression. **Check students' work.**

6. Is $10x$ a numerical expression? Justify your answer.
   No; numerical expressions do not contain variables.

7. **Word Knowledge** Think about the word *pattern*. **7a–c. Check students' work.**
   a. Choose the letter for how well you know the word.
      A. I know its meaning.
      B. I've seen it, but I don't know its meaning.
      C. I don't know it.
   b. **Research** Look up and write a definition for *pattern*.
   c. Write a sentence involving mathematics and using the word *pattern*.

Write a rule for each pattern. Then write the next three terms.

1. 1, 6, 36, 216, . . .   **2.** 285, 270, 255, 240, . . .   **3.** 50, 5, 0.5, 0.05, . . .

1–3. See margin.

Algebra **Evaluate each expression for $x = 7$.**

4. $8x$ **56**   **5.** $3 \cdot (x - 4)$ **9**   **6.** $x \cdot (x + 3)$ **70**

Write an expression for each word phrase.

7. d less than 17 **17 − d**   **8.** a times e **ae**   **9.** 14 divided by q **14 ÷ q**

3-5a **Activity Lab**   **Hands On**

Modeling Equations

To solve an equation using models, get the variable by itself on one side.

EXAMPLE **Addition Equations**

Solve $x + 7 = 15$.

$x + 7 = 15$ 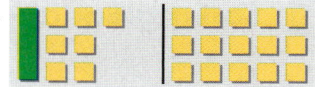   ← Model the equation.

$x + 7 - 7 = 15 - 7$ 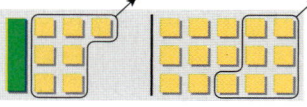   ← Remove 7 tiles from each side. This will keep the equation balanced.

$x = 8$    ← Find the solution.

Exercises

Solve each equation by drawing models or using tiles.

1. $x + 2 = 7$ **x = 5**   **2.** $5 + c = 35$ **c = 30**   **3.** $7 + m = 21$ **m = 14**   **4.** $8 = n + 5$ **3 = n, or n = 3**

129

Use this Checkpoint Quiz to check students' understanding of the skills and concepts of Lessons 3-1 through 3-4.

Resources

- All-in-One Teaching Resources Checkpoint Quiz 1
- ExamView Assessment Suite CD-ROM
- Success Tracker™ Online Intervention

Activity Lab

Modeling Equations

Students use algebra tiles to model and solve equations by subtracting.

Guided Instruction

Example
Go over the solution with students. Ask:
- *Why is 7 the number chosen to be subtracted?* **To get the variable, x, alone on the left side of the equation.**

Exercises
Before doing the exercises, have students identify the number to be subtracted in each.

Resources

- Activity Lab 3-5: Developing Equations I
- algebra tiles
- Student Manipulatives Kit
- Classroom Aid 37

---

1. Start with 1 and multiply by 6 repeatedly; 1,296; 7,776; 46,656.

2. Start with 285 and subtract 15 repeatedly; 225, 210, 195.

3. Start with 50 and divide by 10 repeatedly; 0.005, 0.0005, 0.00005.

Objective
To use subtraction to solve equations

Examples
1. Solving Equations by Subtracting
2. Application: Cats

Math Understandings: p. 106D

Math Background

In Lesson 3-4 students solved equations using number sense. This method is useful in solving relatively simple equations. In this lesson, students will begin to look at algebraic methods that can be used to solve equations. At the heart of these algebraic methods is the concept of *inverse operations*: Addition and subtraction "undo" each other; and multiplication and division "undo" each other.

More Math Background: p. 106D

Lesson Planning and Resources

See p. 106E for a list of the resources that support this lesson.

Bell Ringer Practice

✓ **Check Skills You'll Need**
Use student page, transparency, or PowerPoint. For intervention, direct students to:
Using Number Sense to Solve One-Step Equations
Lesson 3-4
Extra Skills and Word Problems Practice, Ch. 3

Check Skills You'll Need

1. **Vocabulary Review**
   How can you tell that an equation is an *open sentence*?
   See below.
   Use mental math to solve each equation.

   2. $5 = 4 + t$ **1**

   3. $x + 4 = 74$ **70**

   4. $7 + x = 21$ **14**

GO for Help
Lesson 3-4

Check Skills You'll Need

1. It has one or more variables.

GO for Help
For help with evaluating expressions, go to Lesson 3-2, Example 2.

Algebra

3-5 Solving Addition Equations

What You'll Learn

To use subtraction to solve equations

◀》 **New Vocabulary** inverse operations, Subtraction Property of Equality

Why Learn This?

As living things grow, their height and weight change. You can use an equation to find the change.

In the equation $x + 4 = 38$, 4 is added to a variable. To solve the equation, you need to get the variable alone on one side of the equal sign.

To get the variable alone, you *undo* the operation. You undo adding 4 by subtracting 4. Operations that undo each other are **inverse operations.**

EXAMPLE **Solving Equations by Subtracting**

1. Solve $x + 4 = 38$.

   Get x alone on one side of the equation.

   $$x + 4 = 38$$
   $$x + 4 - 4 = 38 - 4 \quad \leftarrow \text{Subtract 4 from each side to undo the addition and get } x \text{ by itself.}$$
   $$x = 34 \quad \leftarrow \text{Simplify.}$$

   Check $x + 4 = 38 \quad \leftarrow$ Check your solution in the original equation.

   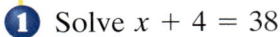

   $34 + 4 \stackrel{?}{=} 38 \quad \leftarrow$ Substitute 34 for x.

   $38 = 38$ ✔

✓ Quick Check

1. Solve $w + 4.3 = 9.1$. Check the solution. **4.8**

Differentiated Instruction **Solutions for All Learners**

Special Needs **L1**
To "undo" an addition or subtraction operation you are getting a number back to zero. Show students $x + 4 - 4$ is the same as $x + 0$. Remind them to use the identity property, which tells them $x + 0$ is really x. This is how to isolate x.

learning style: visual

Below Level **L2**
Give students several addition/subtraction exercises like these to illustrate inverse operations.

$32 + 6$ **38**	$28 - 7$ **21**
$38 - 6$ **32**	$21 + 7$ **28**

learning style: visual

When you solve problems using equations, drawing a diagram may help. The model indicates that the whole = part + part.

Whole	
Part	Part

EXAMPLE Application: Cats

2 When a kitten was brought home it weighed 15 ounces. After two years, the kitten had grown into a cat weighing 120 ounces. How many ounces did the cat gain?

Weight after 2 years	
Original weight	Ounces gained

Let g = the number of ounces gained.

120	
15	g

The equation $15 + g = 120$ models this situation.

$$15 + g = 120$$
$$15 + g - 15 = 120 - 15 \qquad \leftarrow \textbf{Subtract 15 from each side to undo the addition.}$$
$$g = 105 \qquad \leftarrow \textbf{Simplify.}$$

The cat gained 105 ounces.

✓ Quick Check

2. A cat has gained 1.8 pounds in a year. It now weighs 11.6 pounds. Write and solve an equation to find how much it weighed one year ago. Check the solution.
w = the cat's weight last year; 1.8 + w = 11.6; 9.8 lb

When you use inverse operations to solve equations, you are using a mathematical property. The property you use in this lesson is called the **Subtraction Property of Equality.**

Video Tutor Help
Visit: PHSchool.com
Web Code: aqe-0775

KEY CONCEPTS Subtraction Property of Equality

If you subtract the same value from each side of an equation, the two sides remain equal.
Arithmetic $2 \cdot 3 = 6$, so $2 \cdot 3 - 4 = 6 - 4$.
Algebra If $a = b$, then $a - c = b - c$.

Advanced Learners L4
Only one of these equations has a solution. Which equation is it, and what is the solution? *n + n = 2; 1*
$$n + 2 = n$$
$$n + n = 2$$

learning style: visual

English Language Learners ELL
Have volunteers read the word problems in the Exercises before students are asked to work on them. Ask students to work in pairs to identify what they know and what they are trying to find. Have them come up with equations.

learning style: verbal

---

2. Teach

Activity Lab
Use before the lesson.
Student Edition Activity Lab, Hands On 3-5a, Modeling Equations, p. 129

All in One Teaching Resources
Activity Lab 3-5: Developing Equations I

Guided Instruction

Example 1
Some students are better able to visualize the process of subtracting the same number from each side when the subtraction is performed vertically.

$$\begin{aligned} x + 4 &= 38 \\ -\ 4 &= -4 \\ \hline x\quad\ &= 34 \end{aligned}$$

Error Prevention!

Stress the importance of checking a proposed solution by substituting it for the variable *in the original equation.*

PowerPoint
Additional Examples

1 Solve $h + 9 = 14$. **5**

2 Today Anna discovered that she is 4 in. taller than she was last year at this time. Anna's height today is 51 in. What was Anna's height last year at this time? **47 in.**

All in One Teaching Resources
• Daily Notetaking Guide 3-5 **L3**
• Adapted Notetaking 3-5 **L1**

Closure

• *What are inverse operations?* **operations that undo each other, such as addition and subtraction**
• *How do you use subtraction to solve an equation?* **Sample: For an equation like $y + 4 = 20$, subtract 4 from each side to undo the addition; then simplify to get $y = 16$.**

3. Practice

Assignment Guide

Check Your Understanding
Go over Exercises 1–5 in class before assigning the Homework Exercises.

Homework Exercises
A Practice by Example   6–19
B Apply Your Skills   20–29
C Challenge   30
Test Prep and
   Mixed Review   31–34

Homework Quick Check
To check students' understanding of key skills and concepts, go over Exercises 10, 16, 18, 21, and 22.

Differentiated Instruction **Resources**

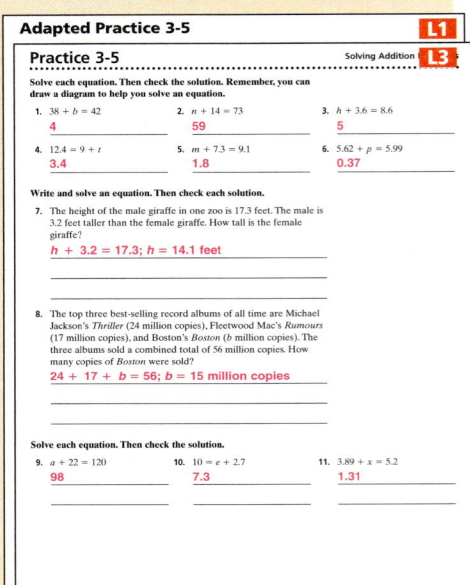

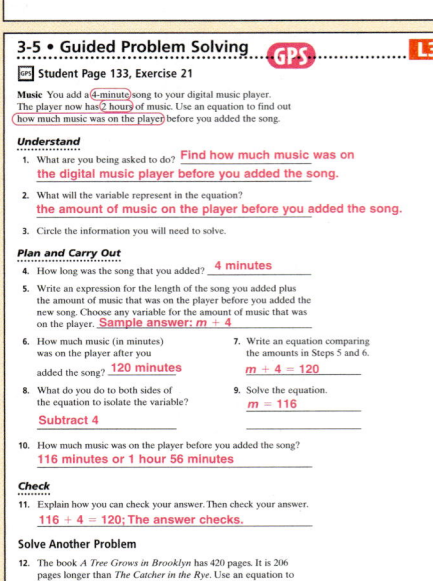

Check Your Understanding

1. **Vocabulary** What is the inverse operation of adding 6?
   subtracting 6

2. **Open-Ended** Write a real-world problem that can be represented using this model.
   Check students' work.

   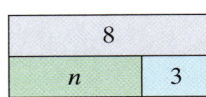

Test Prep Tip
Drawing a diagram can help you model a real-world situation.

Solve each equation.

3. $d + 3 = 21$ **18**
4. $k + 5.1 = 7.4$ **2.3**
5. $x + 4.3 = 7$ **2.7**

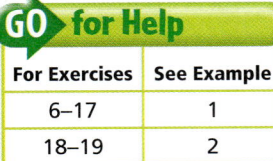

Homework Exercises

For more exercises, see **Extra Skills and Word Problems.**

GO for Help

For Exercises	See Example
6–17	1
18–19	2

A Solve each equation. Check the solution. Remember, you can draw a diagram to help you solve an equation.

6. $x + 46 = 72$ **26**
7. $d + 5 = 53$ **48**
8. $y + 12 = 64$ **52**

9. $n + 17 = 56$ **39**
10. $m + 1.3 = 2.8$ **1.5**
11. $n + 4.5 = 10.8$ **6.3**

12. $14.7 = 5 + f$ **9.7**
13. $31 + y = 82$ **51**
14. $28 + g = 72$ **44**

15. $15 = k + 8.2$ **6.8**
16. $2.7 + g = 8.2$ **5.5**
17. $2.6 = 1.9 + g$ **0.7**

Write and solve an equation. Then check the solution.

18. **m = number of models b**
    $m + 7 = 25$; $m = 18$

18. You build 7 model airplanes during the summer. At the end of the summer, you have 25 model airplanes. How many model airplanes did you have before the summer?

19. **y = the year Mozart was**
    $y + 6 = 1762$; $y = 1756$

19. **Music History** Wolfgang Amadeus Mozart wrote his first piano sonata in 1762, when he was 6 years old. In what year was Mozart born?

B GPS

20. **s = sale price of the j**
    $s + 4.99 = 29.97$;
    $s = \$24.98$

20. **Guided Problem Solving** Jeans that were on sale last week now cost $29.97. The savings were $4.99. Write and solve an equation to find the sale price of the jeans.
    • You can draw a diagram to help you write an equation.

Full price of jeans	
Sale price p	Savings $4.99

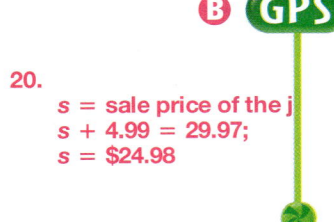

21. Music You add a 4-minute song to your digital music player. **GPS** The player now has 2 hours of music. Use an equation to find how much music was on the player before you added the song. **See margin.**

22. In a number square, the sum of the numbers in each row, column, and main diagonal is the same.
   a. Find the sum for the number square at the right.
   b. Use the sum to write and solve equations to find the values of a, b, and c. **22a–b. See margin.**

a	7	2
1	5	b
8	c	4

23. Biology A hippopotamus can hold its breath for about 15 minutes. It can hold its breath 5 minutes longer than a sea otter. Use an equation to find how long a sea otter can hold its breath. **10 minutes**

Solve each equation. Then check the solution.

24. $y + 13.82 = 24$
10.18

25. $1.5 + x = 9.7$
8.2

26. $0.4 + g = 1.9$
1.5

27. $6.2 = j + 5.91$
0.29

28. $b + 0.87 = 1$
0.13

29. $11.4 = h + 5.9$
5.5

C 30. Challenge A large stepping stone weighs five times as much as a brick. Together, one brick and one stepping stone weigh 30 pounds. Find the weight of the stepping stone. **25 lb**

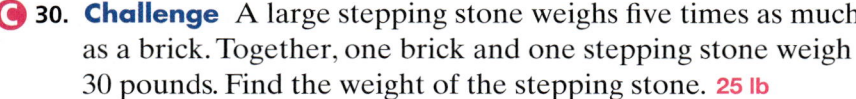
Test Prep and Mixed Review **Practice**

Multiple Choice

31. The table shows the length and perimeter of different rectangles with a width of 3 cm. Which expression can be used to find the perimeter of a rectangle with a length of n units? **D**

Side Length	Perimeter
5 cm	16 cm
10 cm	26 cm
15 cm	36 cm

   Ⓐ $n + 5$ Ⓑ $n + 10$ Ⓒ $n + 11$ Ⓓ $2n + 6$

32. Which of the following does NOT describe 1, 3, 5, 7, 9, . . .? **J**
   Ⓕ List every other whole number, starting with 1.
   Ⓖ Start with 1 and add 2 repeatedly.
   Ⓗ The value of term n in $2n - 1$.
   Ⓙ Start with 1 and add 3 repeatedly.

GO for Help

For Exercises	See Lesson
33–34	3-1

Algebra **Write the first five terms in each number pattern.**

33. Start with 37 and add 3 repeatedly. **37, 40, 43, 46, 49**

34. Start with 3.2 and multiply by 5 repeatedly. **3.2; 16; 80; 400; 2,000**

21. m = number of minutes of music before adding song; $m + 4 = 120$; $m = 116$

22a–b. See back of book.

Test Prep

Resources
For additional practice with a variety of test item formats:
• Test-Taking Strategies, p. 149
• Test Prep, p. 153
• Test-Taking Strategies with Transparencies

4. Assess & Reteach

PowerPoint
Lesson Quiz

Solve each equation.

1. $18 + n = 40$ **22**

2. $m + 3.5 = 6.7$ **3.2**

3. $p + 0.99 = 4.15$ **3.16**

4. $78 = q + 20$ **58**

Alternative Assessment

Provide small groups of students with a balance scale, centimeter cubes, and several addition and subtraction equations that deal with whole numbers. Have students model the equations on the balance. For example, for the equation $x + 9 = 25$, have them place 9 cubes on one pan and 25 on the other. Then have them take away enough cubes from 25 so that the pans balance. Ask students to record the solution to each equation.

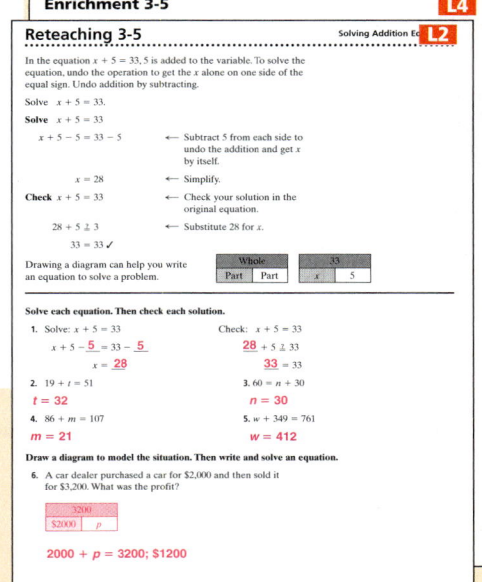

Examples
1 Solving an Equation by Adding
2 Application: Nutrition

Math Understandings: p. 106D

Math Background

See p. 106D for content support.

Lesson Planning and Resources

See p. 106E for a list of the resources that support this lesson.

 **PowerPoint**

Bell Ringer Practice

 **Check Skills You'll Need**
For intervention, direct students to:
Using Number Sense to Solve One-Step Equations
Lesson 3-4
Extra Skills and Word Problems Practice, Ch. 3

2. Teach

Activity Lab

Use before the lesson.

All in One Teaching Resources

Activity Lab 3-6: Developing Equations II

Guided Instruction

Example 2
Stress the importance of always indicating what quantity the variable represents.

134

Algebra

3-6 Solving Subtraction Equations

 **Check Skills You'll Need**

1. **Vocabulary Review**
   Explain why the number 4 is a *solution* to $x + 2 = 6$.
   See below.
   Use mental math to solve each equation.
2. $t - 4 = 10$ **14**
3. $x - 6 = 5$ **11**
4. $p - 7 = 3$ **10**

GO for Help
Lesson 3-4

Check Skills You'll Need

1. It makes the equation true.

What You'll Learn

To use addition to solve equations

◀))) **New Vocabulary** Addition Property of Equality

Why Learn This?

Nutritional information on products can help you decide what you should eat. You can use an equation to find the nutritional contents of foods.

You learned to solve equations by subtracting the same amount from each side of an equation. You can also solve equations by using addition.

KEY CONCEPTS **Addition Property of Equality**

If you add the same value to each side of an equation, the two sides remain equal.

Arithmetic $2 \cdot 3 = 6$, so $2 \cdot 3 + 4 = 6 + 4$.
Algebra If $a = b$, then $a + c = b + c$.

Some equations have a number subtracted on one side. To get the variable by itself, add the same number to each side of the equation.

EXAMPLE **Solving an Equation by Adding**

1 Solve $c - 12 = 43$.

c	
12	43

$$c - 12 + 12 = 43 + 12 \quad \leftarrow \text{Add 12 to each side to undo the subtraction.}$$
$$c = 55 \quad \leftarrow \text{Simplify.}$$

✓ **Quick Check**

● **1. a.** Solve $n - 53 = 28$. **81** **b.** Solve $x - 43 = 12$. **55**

134 Chapter 3 Patterns and Variables

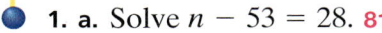
Differentiated Instruction **Solutions for All Learners**

Special Needs **L1**
Model for students what happens if both sides of an equation do not balance. Draw a box for x number of apples and subtract 5 apples. Write $x - 5 = 8$. Then add 5 only on the left and write $x = 8$. Go back and draw 8 apples − 5 apples = 8 apples. That is not a true equation.
learning style: visual

Below Level **L2**
Have students line up problems vertically to solve. Example 1 could be solved as:

$$\begin{array}{r} c - 12 = 43 \\ + 12 = + 12 \\ \hline c = 55 \end{array}$$

learning style: visual

Another way to model a real-world situation is to state the problem as simply as you can. Then use your statement to write an equation.

EXAMPLE **Application: Nutrition**

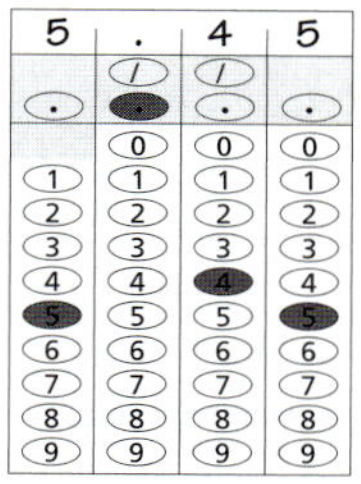

② **Gridded Response** A serving of wheat flakes contains 3.7 mg of zinc. The amount of zinc in wheat flakes is 1.75 mg less than the amount in a breakfast bar. How much zinc is in a breakfast bar?

Words amount in flakes is 1.75 less than amount in bar

Let b = the amount of zinc in a breakfast bar.

Equation 3.7 $=$ b $-$ 1.75

$b - 1.75 = 3.7$ ← Write the equation.

$b - 1.75 + 1.75 = 3.7 + 1.75$ ← Add 1.75 to each side to undo the subtraction.

$b = 5.45$ ← Simplify.

The breakfast bar contains 5.45 mg of zinc.

Test Prep Tip
Verbs such as *is, are, has,* and *was* show you where to place the = sign.

(Gridded response grid showing: 5 . 4 5 filled in)

✓ **Quick Check**

2. **Temperature** The temperature dropped 9°F between 7 P.M. and midnight. It was 54°F at midnight. Use an equation to find the temperature at 7 P.M.
Let t = temperature at 7 P.M.; $t - 9 = 54$; $t = 63$

✓ **Check Your Understanding**

1. She subtracted 4 from each side instead of adding 4 to each side.

1. **Error Analysis** Your friend says the solution to $y - 4 = 24$ is 20. What did your friend do wrong?

2. Sheila is 2 years younger than Javon. Sheila is 10 years old. Write and solve an equation to find Javon's age. 12

Words: Sheila is 2 years younger than Javon.

Let j = Javon's age in years.

Equation: ■ $= j -$ ■
10   2

Match each equation with the correct solution.

3. $x - 3 = 7$ C   A. 15
                          B. 11
4. $x - 4 = 11$ A   C. 10

5. $x - 5 = 6$ B

PowerPoint
Additional Examples

① Solve $p - 22.3 = 5.08$. **27.38**

② The sale price of a CD is $11.49. This is $3.50 less than the regular price. What is the regular price? **$14.99**

All in One Teaching Resources
• Daily Notetaking Guide 3-6 L3
• Adapted Notetaking 3-6 L1

Closure

• *How do you use addition to solve an equation?* **Sample: For an equation like** $m - 9 = 17$, **add 9 to each side to undo the subtraction; then simplify to get** $m = 26$.

3. Practice

Assignment Guide

Check Your Understanding
Go over Exercises 1–5 in class before assigning the Homework Exercises.

Homework Exercises
A Practice by Example   6–18
B Apply Your Skills   19–20
C Challenge   21
Test Prep and
  Mixed Review   22–27

Homework Quick Check
To check students' understanding of key skills and concepts, go over Exercises 9, 13, 15, 18, and 20.

4. Assess & Reteach

PowerPoint **Lesson Quiz**

Solve each equation.

1. $m - 3.2 = 6.7$ **9.9**

2. $z - 3.09 = 8.1$ **11.19**

3. $7.9 = n - 0.35$ **8.25**

Alternative Assessment

Use the Alternative Assessment on page 133 with equations like $n - 7 = 3$.

135

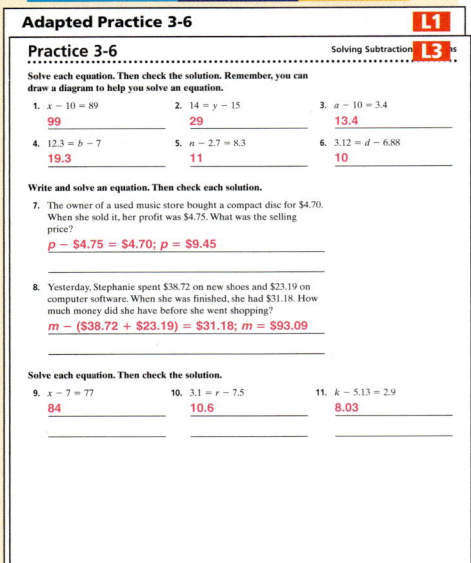

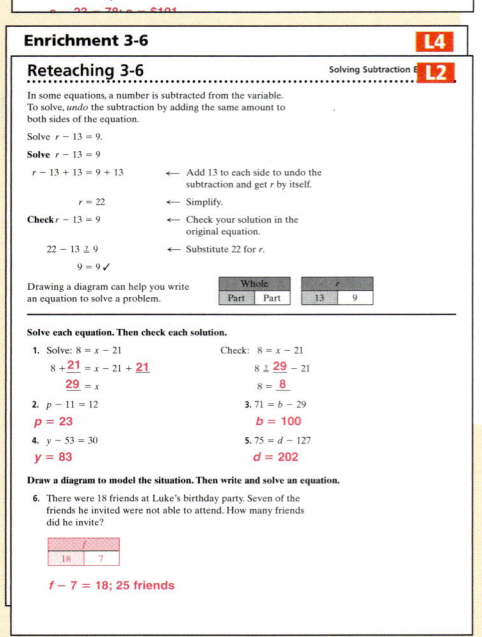

Homework Exercises

For more exercises, see Extra Skills and Word Problems.

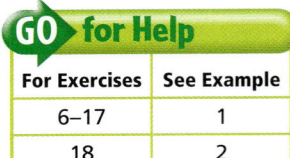
GO for Help

For Exercises	See Example
6–17	1
18	2

(A) Solve each equation. You may find a model helpful.

6. $x - 16 = 72$ **88**
7. $q - 2.4 = 1.8$ **4.2**
8. $n - 297 = 18$ **315**
9. $d - 68 = 40$ **108**
10. $y - 12 = 23$ **35**
11. $k - 56 = 107$ **163**
12. $5.8 = n - 0.35$ **6.15**
13. $0.6 = h - 2.9$ **3.5**
14. $q - 8.2 = 154$ **162.2**
15. $p - 1.23 = 8.77$ **10**
16. $n - 10.5 = 11.7$ **22.2**
17. $x - 5.7 = 5.7$ **11.4**

18. **Geography** The area of Cape Canaveral National Seashore in Florida is about 57,662 acres. That is about 72,772 acres less than the area of Padre Island National Seashore in Texas. Use an equation to find the area of Padre Island National Seashore. **130,434 acres**

19. Let t = temperature when sick; $t - 3.7 = 98.6$; $t = 102.3$.

20. m = money before purchas $m - 18.95 = 7.05$; $m = 26$

(B) GPS 19. **Guided Problem Solving** A healthy person has a normal temperature of about 98.6°F. Suppose a sick person needs to decrease his temperature by 3.7°F to return to normal. Use an equation to find the sick person's temperature. **See above left.**
- What equation will you use to model this problem?
- What operation will you use to solve the equation?

GO Online
Homework Video Tutor
Visit: PHSchool.com
Web Code: aqe-0306

20. You buy several posters. The total cost is $18.95. You have GPS $7.05 left after you pay. Write and solve an equation to find how much money you had before this purchase. **See above left.**

(C) 21. **Challenge** Sue is 2 years older than Mary. Mary is 3 years younger than Bob. Sue is 11 years old. How old is Bob? **12**

Test Prep and Mixed Review
Practice

Gridded Response

22. A store rents DVDs for $2 each, after you pay a membership fee of $10. Jeremy has spent a total of $26. How many DVDs has he rented? **8**

23. The gas tank in the Rivera family car can hold a maximum of 18.2 gallons. After a trip, they filled the tank with 9.6 gallons of gas. How much gas was in the tank before it was filled? **8.6**

GO for Help

For Exercises	See Lesson
24–27	1-4

Find the value of each expression.

24. $24 \div 4 - 2 \times 3$ **0**
25. $24 \div 3 - 2 \times 4$ **0**
26. $24 \div (3 - 2) \times 4$ **96**
27. $(24 \div 3 - 2) \times 4$ **24**

Test Prep

Resources
For additional practice with a variety of test item formats:
- Test-Taking Strategies, p. 149
- Test Prep, p. 153
- Test-Taking Strategies with Transparencies

Solve each equation.

1. $5 + x = 65$ **60**

2. $n - 3.2 = 15$ **18.2**

3. $z + 6 = 8.2$ **2.2**

4. $k - 4 = 3.6$ **7.6**

5. $14 = 3.2 + y$ **10.8**

6. $28 = 1.4 + a$ **26.6**

7. $23 = 16 + y$ **7**

8. $48 = 9.6 + a$ **38.4**

9. You pay for the refreshments at a movie theater with a $10 bill. The refreshments cost $5.73. Write an equation to find how much change you should receive. Solve the equation. **x = change received; $x + 5.73 = 10.00$; $x = \$4.27$**

3-7a Activity Lab

Hands On

Modeling Division Equations

Models can help you understand the steps you need to follow to solve an equation.

EXAMPLE Solving Equations by Dividing

Solve $4x = 12$.

$4x = 12$

← Model the equation.

$4x \div 4 = 12 \div 4$

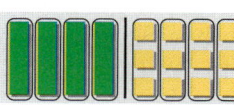

← Divide each side of the equation into 4 equal parts.

$x = 3$

← Find the solution.

Exercises

Solve each equation by drawing a model or using tiles.

1. $2x = 20$ **$x = 10$**

2. $5c = 35$ **$c = 7$**

3. $3g = 12$ **$g = 4$**

4. $7m = 21$ **$m = 3$**

Check students' work.

5. **Reasoning** Explain how you could use a model to solve $6y = 1.8$.

Checkpoint Quiz

Use this Checkpoint Quiz to check students' understanding of the skills and concepts of Lessons 3-5 through 3-6.

Resources

- All-in-One Teaching Resources Checkpoint Quiz 2
- ExamView Assessment Suite CD-ROM
- Success Tracker™ Online Intervention

Activity Lab

Modeling Division Equations

Students use algebra tiles to solve equations by dividing.

Guided Instruction

Example
Go over the solution with students. Ask:
- *Why is the number 4 chosen to divide by?* **To get the variable, x, alone on the left side of the equation**

Exercises
Before solving the equations have students identify the number to divide by in each.

Resources

- Activity Lab 3-7: Solving One-Step Equations
- algebra tiles
- Student Manipulatives Kit
- Classroom Aid 37

Algebra

Solving Multiplication and Division Equations

Objective
To use multiplication and division to solve equations

Examples
1 Solving an Equation by Dividing
2 Application: Photography
3 Solving an Equation by Multiplying

Math Understandings: p. 106D

Math Background

Just as addition and subtraction are a pair of inverse operations, so too are multiplication and division. Students should note the principle that ties together the four properties of equality: If you perform the same operation on each side of an equation, the solution of the resulting equation is the same as the solution of the original equation. Students should also be aware of the restriction to the Division Property of Equality; that is, you cannot divide the sides of an equation by zero.

More Math Background: p. 106D

Lesson Planning and Resources

See p. 106E for a list of the resources that support this lesson.

Bell Ringer Practice

✓ **Check Skills You'll Need**
Use student page, transparency, or PowerPoint. For intervention, direct students to:
Using Number Sense to Solve One-Step Equations
Lesson 3-4
Extra Skills and Word
  Problems Practice, Ch. 3

✓ Check Skills You'll Need

1. **Vocabulary Review**
   How are *equations* different from *expressions*?
   See below.
   Use mental math to solve each equation.

2. $3x = 27$ **9**
3. $6 \div y = 3$ **2**
4. $p \div 3 = 3$ **9**
5. $7x = 21$ **3**

 **for Help**
Lesson 3-4

 **Calculator Tip**
Remember that you can never divide by zero. Your calculator will give you an error message if you try.

Check Skills You'll Need

1. **Answers may vary. Sample: Equations contain equal signs and expressions do not.**

What You'll Learn

To use multiplication and division to solve equations

🔊 **New Vocabulary** Division Property of Equality, Multiplication Property of Equality

Why Learn This?

Many products are sold in groups—cartons, cases, boxes, and bags. You can use an equation to find the cost of a single item.

You can use the **Division Property of Equality** to solve equations involving multiplication.

KEY CONCEPTS **Division Property of Equality**

If you divide each side of an equation by the same nonzero number, the two sides remain equal.

Arithmetic $4 \times 2 = 8$, so $4 \times 2 \div 2 = 8 \div 2$.
Algebra   If $a = b$ and $c \neq 0$, then $a \div c = b \div c$.

You recall that $4n$ means 4 times n. To undo multiplication, you divide by the same number. So $4n \div 4 = n$.

EXAMPLE **Solving an Equation by Dividing**

① Solve $4n = 68$.

$4n \div 4 = 68 \div 4$ ← Divide each side by 4 to undo the multiplication and get n alone.

$n = 17$ ← Simplify.

Check $4(17) \stackrel{?}{=} 68$ ← Check your solution in the original equation. Replace n with 17.

$68 = 68$ ✔

✓ Quick Check

● **1.** Solve $0.8p = 32$. Then check the solution. **40**

Differentiated **Instruction** Solutions for All Learners

Special Needs **L1**
Students may find diagramming the equations helpful. Assist them as needed, or ask them to pair up and generate ideas for useful diagrams before drawing.

learning style: visual

Below Level **L2**
Have students say aloud several multiplication/division exercises like these to illustrate inverse operations.

6 × 9 **54**	88 ÷ 4 **22**
54 ÷ 9 **6**	22 × 4 **88**

learning style: verbal

EXAMPLE Application: Photography

2
You buy a package containing six rolls of film for your camera. The total cost is $38.88. Use an equation to find the cost of one roll of film.

Use a diagram to model the situation.

Let $c =$ the cost of one roll of film. The equation $6c = \$38.88$ models this situation.

$38.88
c c c c c c

$$6c = 38.88 \quad \leftarrow \text{Write the equation.}$$
$$6c \div 6 = 38.88 \div 6 \quad \leftarrow \begin{array}{l}\text{Divide each side by 6 to undo the} \\ \text{multiplication and get } c \text{ alone.}\end{array}$$
$$c = 6.48 \quad \leftarrow \text{Simplify.}$$

The cost of one roll of film is $6.48.

✓ Quick Check

2. A club sells greeting cards for a fundraiser. The profit for each card sold is $.35. The club's total profit is $302.75. Use an equation to find the total number of cards the club sells.
   865 cards

You can use the <mark>Multiplication Property of Equality</mark> to solve equations involving division.

KEY CONCEPTS **Multiplication Property of Equality**

If you multiply each side of an equation by the same number, the two sides remain equal.

Arithmetic $6 \div 2 = 3$, so $(6 \div 2) \times 2 = 3 \times 2$.
Algebra If $a = b$, then $a \cdot c = b \cdot c$.

EXAMPLE Solving an Equation by Multiplying

3 Solve $y \div 6.4 = 8$.

$$y \div 6.4 \times 6.4 = 8 \times 6.4 \quad \leftarrow \begin{array}{l}\text{Multiply by 6.4 to undo the} \\ \text{division and get } y \text{ alone.}\end{array}$$
$$y = 51.2 \quad \leftarrow \text{Simplify.}$$

✓ Quick Check

3. Solve $w \div 1.5 = 10$. Then check the solution. **15**

Activity Lab

Use before the lesson.
Student Edition Activity Lab, Hands On 3-7a, Modeling Division Equations, p. 137

All in One Teaching Resources
Activity Lab 3-7: Solving One-Step Equations

Guided Instruction

Example 1
Present the following solution:

$$4n = 68$$
$$n \cdot 4 = 68$$
$$n \cdot 4 \div 4 = 68 \div 4$$
$$n = 17$$

Error Prevention!

Some students might apply the Division Property of Equality correctly but use the wrong number as the dividend. Suggest that they use this visual aid.

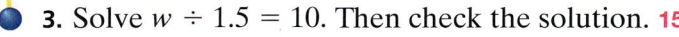

PowerPoint
Additional Examples

1 Solve $6x = 144$. **24**

2 The cost of a pay-per-view concert on television is $39.95. Five friends decide to watch the concert together and split the cost equally. What amount will each friend pay? **$7.99**

3 Solve $x \div 6.3 = 9$. **56.7**

All in One Teaching Resources
• Daily Notetaking Guide 3-7 **L3**
• Adapted Notetaking 3-7 **L1**

Closure

• *How do you use division to solve an equation?* **Divide each side of an equation by the same nonzero number; then simplify.**
• *How do you use multiplication to solve an equation?* **Multiply each side of an equation by the same number; then simplify.**

139

Assignment Guide

Check Your Understanding
Go over Exercises 1–7 in class before assigning the Homework Exercises.

Homework Exercises

A Practice by Example 8–26
B Apply Your Skills 27–35
C Challenge 36
Test Prep and
  Mixed Review 37–42

Homework Quick Check
To check students' understanding of key skills and concepts, go over Exercises 12, 24, 28, 29, and 34.

Differentiated Instruction **Resources**

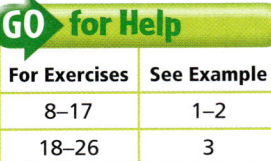

Adapted Practice 3-7 **L1**

Practice 3-7   Solving Multiplication and Division **L3**

State whether the number given is a solution to the equation.

1. $8c = 80; c = 10$ **yes**
2. $b + 7 = 8; b = 56$ **yes**
3. $9m = 108; m = 12$ **yes**
4. $y \div 9 = 17; y = 163$ **no**

5. $9r = 72; r = 7$ **no**
6. $14b = 56; b = 4$ **yes**
7. $48 = y \div 4; y = 12$ **no**
8. $32 = y \div 8; y = 256$ **yes**

9. $17a = 41; a = 3$ **no**
10. $w \div 21 = 17; w = 357$ **yes**
11. $21c = 189; c = 8$ **no**
12. $52 = y \div 6; y = 302$ **no**

Solve each equation. Then check each solution.

13. $905 = 5a$ **181**
14. $6v = 792$ **132**
15. $12 = y \div 12$ **144**
16. $b \div 18 = 21$ **378**

17. $80 = 16b$ **5**
18. $19m = 266$ **14**
19. $d \div 1,000 = 10$ **10,000**
20. $g \div 52 = 18$ **936**

21. $672 = 21f$ **32**
22. $z \div 27 = 63$ **1,701**
23. $43h = 817$ **19**
24. $58 = j \div 71$ **4,118**

Write and solve an equation for each situation. Then check the solution.

25. Lea drove 420 miles and used 20 gallons of gas. How many miles per gallon did her car get?   **21 miles/gallon**

26. Ty spent $15 on folders that cost $3 each. How many folders did he buy?   **5 folders**

27. Julia wants to buy copies of a book to give as presents. How many books can she buy if they are on sale for $12 each, and she has $100 to spend?   **8 books**

3-7 • Guided Problem Solving **GPS** **L3**

GPS Student Page 141, Exercise 29

Biology An adult female elephant's height is about 5.5 times the length of her hind footprint. Use an equation to find the approximate height of an adult female elephant whose hind footprint is 1.5 feet long.

Understand

1. What are you being asked to do?
  Write and solve an equation to find the height of an adult female elephant whose hind footprint is 1.5 feet long.

2. Circle the information you will need to solve.

3. The phrase "5.5 times" tells you to perform what operation?
  It tells you to multiply.

Plan and Carry Out

4. What is the length of the hind footprint of this particular adult female elephant? **1.5 feet**

5. Write an expression to represent the phrase "5.5 times the length of the hind footprint."   **5.5 × 1.5**

6. Write an equation for the height of the elephant.   **$h = 5.5 \times 1.5$**

7. What is the height of the elephant?   **8.25 feet**

Check

8. Explain how you can check your answer. Does your answer check?
  Divide the answer by 5.5 and see if the result is 1.5; the answer checks.

Solve Another Problem

9. Angela makes 1.75 times the amount of money that Janet makes. If Janet makes $38,200, how much does Angela make? Write and solve an equation.   **$1.75 \times 38,200 = \$66,850$**

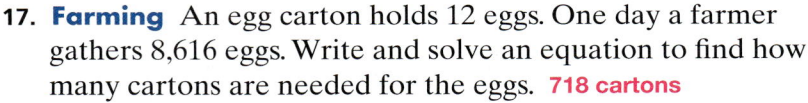
✓ Check Your Understanding

1. The Multiplication Property of Equality states that you can multiply each side of an equation by the same nonzero number and the equation will be the same. The Division Property states the same is true for division.

1. **Vocabulary** How are the Multiplication Property of Equality and the Division Property of Equality different?

Match each equation with the correct model below.

2. $4x = 20$ **C**
3. $x \div 4 = 5$ **B**
4. $5x = 20$ **D**
5. $x \div 5 = 4$ **A**

A.

x				
4	4	4	4	4

B.

x			
5	5	5	5

C.

20			
x	x	x	x

D.

20				
x	x	x	x	x

Solve each equation.

6. $3x = 12.6$ **4.2**
$3x \div \blacksquare = 12.6 \div \blacksquare$

7. $v \div 2 = 7$ **14**
$v \div 2 \cdot \blacksquare = 7 \cdot \blacksquare$

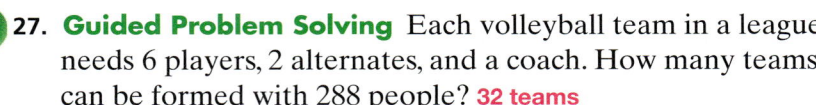
Homework Exercises

For more exercises, see **Extra Skills and Word Problems.**

GO for Help

For Exercises	See Example
8–17	1–2
18–26	3

A Solve each equation. Check the solution. You may find a model helpful.

8. $5a = 100$ **20**
9. $8k = 76$ **9.5**
10. $7n = 11.9$ **1.7**

11. $25h = 450$ **18**
12. $0.4x = 1$ **2.5**
13. $75 = 15c$ **5**

14. $16j = 80$ **5**
15. $2.5g = 17.5$ **7**
16. $10y = 5$ **0.5**

17. **Farming** An egg carton holds 12 eggs. One day a farmer gathers 8,616 eggs. Write and solve an equation to find how many cartons are needed for the eggs. **718 cartons**

Solve each equation. Then check the solution.

18. $q \div 6 = 4$ **24**
19. $a \div 7 = 63$ **441**
20. $n \div 2.5 = 3$ **7.5**

21. $y \div 43 = 1,204$ **51,772**
22. $10 = k \div 20$ **200**
23. $12 = r \div 9$ **108**

24. $n \div 4 = 0.6$ **2.4**
25. $t \div 0.3 = 1.4$ **0.42**
26. $b \div 11 = 87$ **957**

B 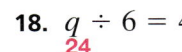 27. **Guided Problem Solving** Each volleyball team in a league needs 6 players, 2 alternates, and a coach. How many teams can be formed with 288 people? **32 teams**
- How many people are needed for each team?
- Draw a diagram to model this situation.

28. Videos A video store charges the same price to rent each movie. The store collected a total of $80.73 for the rentals shown in the line plot. Use an equation to find the cost to rent one movie. **$2.99 per rental**

29. Biology An elephant's height is about **(GPS)** 5.5 times the length of her hind footprint. Use an equation to find the approximate height of an elephant whose hind footprint is 1.5 feet long. **about 8.25 feet**

Number of Movie Rentals

				X
				X
X			X	X
X			X	X
X	X		X	X
X	X	X	X	X
X	X	X	X	X
X	X	X	X	X
M	T	W	T	F

Solve each equation. Check the solution.

30. $y \div 1.6 = 0.256$
0.4096

31. $13 = 65x$
0.2

32. $30 = p \div 30$
900

33. $5.6k = 19.152$
3.42

34. $0.02g = 6$
300

35. $h \div 2.4 = 15$
36

C **36. Challenge** One of the world's largest oil tankers, the *Jahre Viking*, is so long that if 3.5 identical tankers were placed end to end, they would measure about 1 mile long. Estimate the length, in feet, of the *Jahre Viking*. (*Hint*: 1 mile = 5,280 feet)
about 1,508.6 feet

Test Prep and Mixed Review **Practice**

Multiple Choice

37. Tickets to an event cost $25 each. Which equation can you use to find the number of tickets *t* that you can buy with $100? **B**
Ⓐ $4t = 100$
Ⓒ $4 + t = 100$
Ⓑ $25t = 100$
Ⓓ $25 + t = 100$

38. Ashley bought a book for $15.99. She now has $32.12. How much money did Ashley have before she bought the book? **J**
Ⓕ $16.13
Ⓗ $47.11
Ⓖ $17.13
Ⓙ $48.11

39. The table shows a sequence of terms. Which expression can be used to find the value of the term in position *n*? **D**
Ⓐ $n + 2$
Ⓒ $n + 3$
Ⓑ $2n$
Ⓓ $3n$

Position, *n*	Value of Term
1	3
2	6
3	9
n	■

GO for Help

For Exercises	See Lesson
40–42	1-6

Use <, =, or > to complete each statement.

40. 6 ■ 1.6
>

41. 3.4 ■ 3.40
=

42. 8.05 ■ 5.08
>

Alternative Assessment

Provide pairs of students with red pencils. Each partner writes a multiplication and a division equation. Partners exchange papers and solve each other's equations, using the red pencils to write the inverse operations.

Test Prep

Resources
For additional practice with a variety of test item formats:
• Test-Taking Strategies, p. 149
• Test Prep, p. 153
• Test-Taking Strategies with Transparencies

---

4. Assess & Reteach

PowerPoint
Lesson Quiz

Solve each equation.

1. $6x = 156$ **26**

2. $y \div 11 = 15$ **165**

3. $3w = 13.5$ **4.5**

4. $z \div 2.7 = 9$ **24.3**

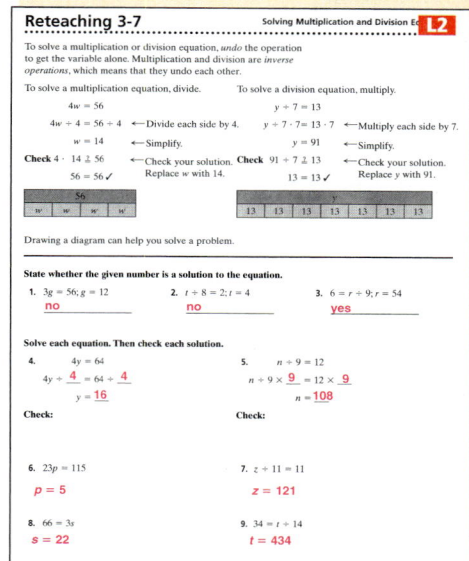

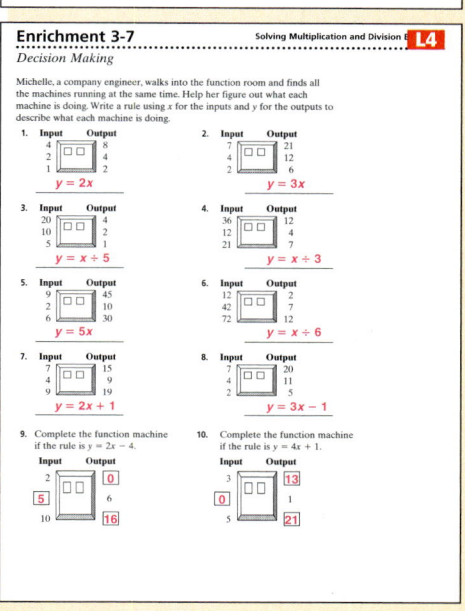

Writing Equations to Solve Problems

GPS Guided Problem Solving

Writing Equations to Solve Problems

Students use diagrams to show the relationships in problems and then write equations to solve the problems.

Guided Instruction

Discuss with students problems found in the real world and the need to solve them. Most real-world problems are posed in words and students must extract information to solve them. They can draw a diagram to show relationships and then write an equation that reflects the same information.

Have a volunteer read the problem aloud. Ask:
- *What are the steps in the Problem-Solving Plan you'll use to solve this problem?* **Understand the Problem; Make a Plan; Carry Out the Plan; Check the Answer**
- *What information will allow you to find how much fuel was used?* **The amount of fuel started with, the amount of fuel lost, and the amount of fuel remaining**

Around the World On March 4, 2005, Steve Fossett set a record by completing a nonstop solo jet flight around the world. He landed with 1,515 pounds of fuel. A fuel leak caused a loss of 2,600 pounds of fuel. He started with 18,100 pounds of fuel. How much fuel did the jet use on the flight?

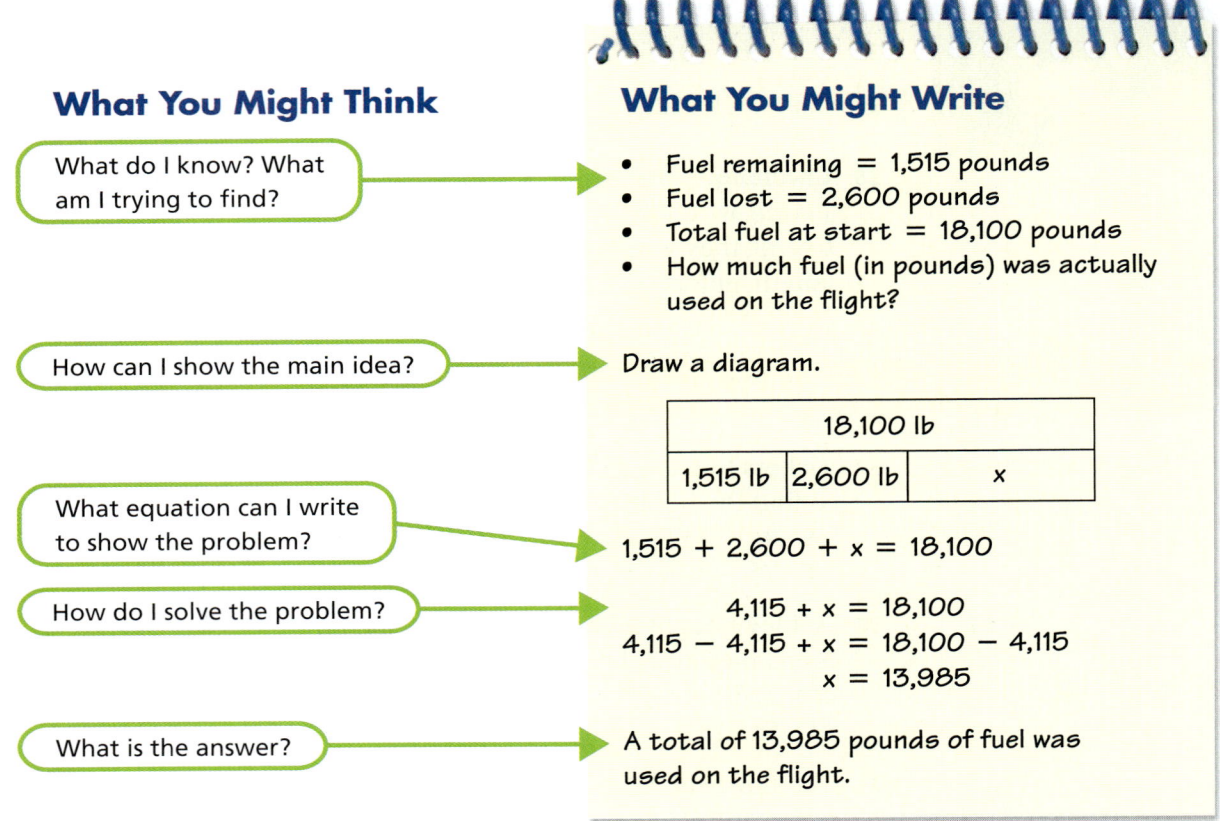

What You Might Think

What do I know? What am I trying to find?

How can I show the main idea?

What equation can I write to show the problem?

How do I solve the problem?

What is the answer?

What You Might Write

- Fuel remaining = 1,515 pounds
- Fuel lost = 2,600 pounds
- Total fuel at start = 18,100 pounds
- How much fuel (in pounds) was actually used on the flight?

Draw a diagram.

18,100 lb		
1,515 lb	2,600 lb	x

$$1{,}515 + 2{,}600 + x = 18{,}100$$

$$4{,}115 + x = 18{,}100$$
$$4{,}115 - 4{,}115 + x = 18{,}100 - 4{,}115$$
$$x = 13{,}985$$

A total of 13,985 pounds of fuel was used on the flight.

Think It Through

1. Is the answer above reasonable? Explain. **See margin.**

2. Refer to the diagram above. How do you know that the section for *x* must be the largest section? **See right.**

3. **Reasoning** Suppose the plane had not lost 2,600 lbs of fuel. How much fuel would have been in the plane when it landed? **4,115 pounds**

2. Answers may vary. Sample: The amount accounted for is less than half of 18,100.

1. Yes; he had about 1,500 pounds left and he lost about 2,500. Since 1,500 + 2,500 = 4,000, he used about 4,000 less than 18,100, which is about 14,000.

Exercises

4. The first flight around the world included stops. It was made by Lowell Smith and Alva Harvey in 1924. How many years passed between their flight and Fossett's flight? **81 years**

  a. What do you know?

  b. What are you trying to find?

  c. Use the diagram below to write and solve an equation.

2005	
1924	x

  d. Decide if the answer is reasonable. Tell how you decided.

5. The first altitude record was set in a hot-air balloon. It rose to 82 feet. Fossett's plane flew at 45,000 feet. How many times higher was Fossett's altitude than that of the hot-air balloon? Use the diagram below to write and solve an equation. Round your answer to the nearest tenth. **about 548.8 times greater**

45,000 ft			
82 ft	82 ft	82 ft	...

6. On October 3, 1967, William Knight flew an X-15 aircraft at 4,520 mph. This is 6.7 times the speed of sound. What is the speed of sound? Use the diagram at the right to help you write and solve an equation. Round your answer to the nearest tenth. **about 674.6 mph**

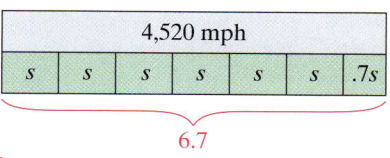

Write and solve an equation for each problem. You can draw a diagram to help you write an equation.

7. At one time the United States had the longest total length of railroad tracks in the world. The 149,129 miles of track could stretch around the world almost six times. What is the distance around the world? **about 24,854.8 miles**

8. In one year, London's Heathrow Airport had 44,262,000 passengers. In the same year, Germany's Frankfurt Airport had 27,546,000 passengers. How many more passengers were there in Heathrow Airport? **16,716,000 passengers**

Error Prevention!

Some students may have difficulty going from diagrams to equations. Review Activity Lab 3-3a on p. 117 with these students. Ask:

• *Why must the three quantities on the bottom of the diagram equal the quantity on the top?* **The used, lost, and remaining fuel must equal the total amount of fuel.**

Exercises

Have students work independently on the exercises. Have them form groups to share and evaluate their answers. Students should adjust their answers to reflect what they learned in the group.

Differentiated Instruction

Below Level   **L2**

Have these students identify the operation they will use for Exercises 4–6 based on the diagrams.

Objective
To use the Distributive Property to simplify expressions in problem-solving situations

Examples
1. Evaluating an Expression
2. Application: Wages

Math Understandings: p. 106D

Math Background

The Distributive Property provides an important alternative when evaluating certain expressions. By the Distributive Property, an expression like $3 \times (10 + 8)$ is equivalent to $3 \times 10 + 3 \times 8$. So the value of $3 \times (10 + 8)$ can be found easily by calculating $3 \times 10 = 30$ and $3 \times 8 = 24$, then performing the simple addition $30 + 24 = 54$.

More Math Background: p. 106D

Lesson Planning and Resources

See p. 106E for a list of the resources that support this lesson.

 **PowerPoint**

Bell Ringer Practice

✓ **Check Skills You'll Need**
Use Student page, transparency, or PowerPoint. For intervention, direct students to:
Adding and Subtracting Decimals
Lesson 1-7
Extra Skills and Word Problems
 Practice, Ch. 1

144

---

1. Vocabulary Review
How are the *associative* and *commutative* properties different?
See below.
Use mental math to find each sum.

2. 15 + 8 + 35 **58**

3. 44 + 73 + 56 **173**

4. 81 + 3 + 99 **183**

 **GO for Help**
Lesson 1-7

Check Skills You'll Need

1. Answers may vary. Sample: The associative property changes the grouping of numbers and the commutative property changes the order of the numbers.

What You'll Learn

To use the Distributive Property to simplify expressions in problem solving situations

🔊 **New Vocabulary** Distributive Property

Why Learn This?

The amount you will earn at a job depends on the number of hours you work. The Distributive Property can help you use mental math to calculate your earnings quickly.

The **Distributive Property** shows how multiplication affects addition or subtraction.

The two rectangles below are drawn on graph paper. One rectangle has 3×5, or 15, squares. The other rectangle has 3×7, or 21, squares.

You can cut out and arrange the rectangles so that the sides with 3 units meet. This forms a rectangle with 3×12, or 36, squares.

Notice that $(3 \times 5) + (3 \times 7) = 3 \times 12 = 3 \times (5 + 7)$. This illustrates the Distributive Property.

$$3 \times (5 + 7) = (3 \times 5) + (3 \times 7)$$
$$= \quad 15 \quad + \quad 21$$
$$= \quad 36$$

Differentiated Instruction **Solutions for All Learners**

Special Needs **L1**
Students may have difficulty understanding how 6.50×8 translates to $(6.00 \times 8) + (0.50 \times 8)$. A model that shows $(6.00 + .50) \times 8$ placed <u>under</u> the 6.50×8 with arrows between corresponding numbers might help students see how the numbers are broken up.

learning style: visual

Below Level **L2**
Give students several exercises like these orally to practice mental computations.

8 × 30 **240**   7 × 800 **5,600**
360 + 12 **372**   350 − 7 **343**

learning style: verbal

KEY CONCEPTS The Distributive Property

Arithmetic	Algebra
$8 \times (4 + 6) = (8 \times 4) + (8 \times 6)$	$a(b + c) = ab + ac$
$7 \times (6 - 2) = (7 \times 6) - (7 \times 2)$	$a(b - c) = ab - ac$

You can use the Distributive Property to multiply mentally.

EXAMPLE Evaluating an Expression

1 Simplify 4×29.

What you think

I can think of 29 as $30 - 1$. Then I multiply both numbers by 4: $4 \times 30 = 120$ and $4 \times 1 = 4$. Now I subtract the two products: $120 - 4 = 116$.

Why it works

$$4 \times 29 = 4 \times (30 - 1) \qquad \leftarrow \text{Write 29 as } 30 - 1.$$
$$= (4 \times 30) - (4 \times 1) \qquad \leftarrow \text{Use the Distributive Property.}$$
$$= 120 - 4 = 116 \qquad \leftarrow \text{Simplify within parentheses and subtract.}$$

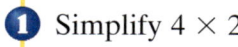
Calculator Tip

Many calculators have a parenthesis key to help you solve problems.

✓ Quick Check

1. Use the Distributive Property to simplify 5×68.

$5 \times (70 - 2) = (5 \times 70) - (5 \times 2) = 350 - 10 = 340$

EXAMPLE Application: Wages

2 A summer job as an assistant camp counselor pays \$6.50 per hour. How much does the counselor earn for working 8 hours?

$$6.50 \times 8 = (6.00 + 0.50) \cdot 8 \qquad \leftarrow \text{Write 6.50 as } 6.00 + 0.50.$$
$$= (6.00 \times 8) + (0.50 \times 8) \qquad \leftarrow \text{Use the Distributive Property.}$$
$$= 48.00 + 4.00 \qquad \leftarrow \text{Simplify within parentheses.}$$
$$= 52.00 \qquad \leftarrow \text{Add.}$$

The counselor earns \$52 for working 8 hours.

✓ Quick Check

2. A local bookstore charges \$2.80 for each used book. What is the charge for 5 used books? **\$14.00**

Advanced Learners L4
Justify whether this statement is true or false.

$a + (b \cdot c) = (a + b) \cdot (a + c)$ **Sample: false;**
$2 + (3 \cdot 4) = 14; (2 + 3) \cdot (2 + 4) = 30;$ so
$2 + (3 \cdot 4) \neq (2 + 3) \cdot (2 + 4)$

learning style: visual

English Language Learners ELL
Have students find the product 6.50×8 two different ways: using the distributive property and multiplying using the traditional algorithm. Discuss which method made it easier to find the product, with less likelihood of errors.

learning style: verbal

---

2. Teach

Activity Lab
Use before the lesson.

All in One Teaching Resources
Activity Lab 3-8: The Distributive Property

Guided Instruction

Teaching Tip
Students might have difficulty with the term *distributive*. Ask: *What happens when a teacher distributes test papers to a class?* The teacher gives one test paper to each student in the class. Point out that, in a similar way, the number outside the parentheses "distributes" itself to each number inside the parentheses.

PowerPoint
Additional Examples

1 Use the Distributive Property to simplify 5×47. **235**

2 A student bought 4 tickets that cost \$5.50. What was the total cost of the tickets? **\$22**

All in One Teaching Resources
• Daily Notetaking Guide 3-8 **L3**
• Adapted Notetaking 3-8 **L1**

Closure

• Explain the Distributive Property. **Sample: When a sum or difference inside parentheses is multiplied by a number outside the parentheses, you can multiply each number inside the parentheses by the number outside, then add or subtract as indicated.**

145

Assignment Guide

Check Your Understanding
Go over Exercises 1–5 in class before assigning the Homework Exercises.

Homework Exercises
A	Practice by Example	6–15
B	Apply Your Skills	16–23
C	Challenge	24

Test Prep and
  Mixed Review   25–29

Homework Quick Check
To check students' understanding of key skills and concepts, go over Exercises 10, 13, 18, 22, and 23.

Differentiated Instruction **Resources**

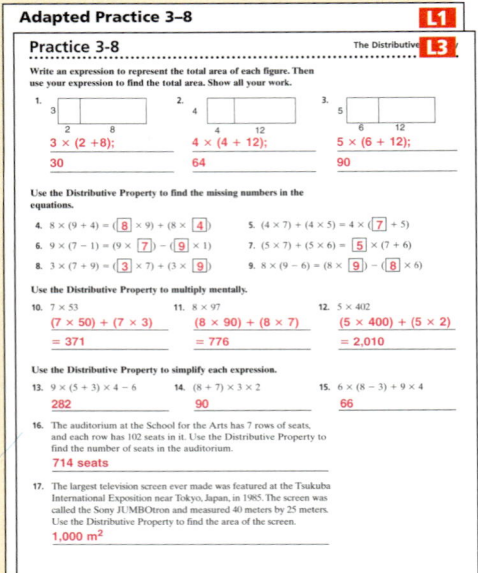

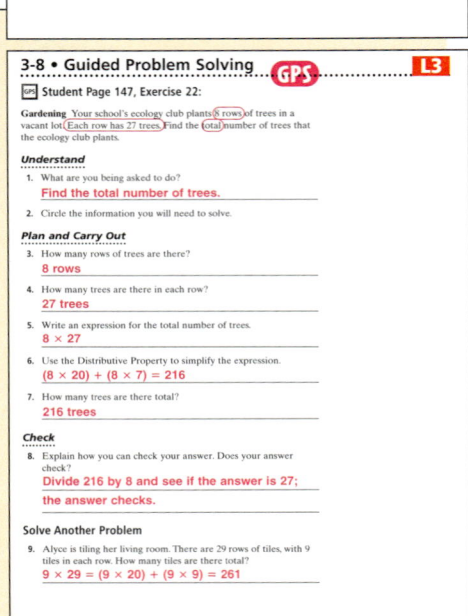

146

✓ Check Your Understanding

1. **Vocabulary** Which property of mathematics tells you that $(4 + 5) \times 7 = (4 \times 7) + (5 \times 7)$? **C**
   - Ⓐ associative
   - Ⓒ distributive
   - Ⓑ commutative
   - Ⓓ identity

2. **Error Analysis** Who simplified $2 \times (3 + 5)$ correctly? Explain.

Thomas	Brian
$(2 \times 3) + (2 \times 5)$	$(2 + 3) \times (2 + 5)$

   2. Thomas; answers may vary. Sample: The Distributive Property multiplies the number outside parentheses by each number inside parentheses.

3. Which of these expressions is NOT equivalent to 19×12? **J**
   - Ⓕ $(19 \times 10) + (19 \times 2)$
   - Ⓗ $(10 \times 12) + (9 \times 12)$
   - Ⓖ $(20 \times 12) - (1 \times 12)$
   - Ⓙ $(10 \times 10) + (9 \times 2)$

   Use the Distributive Property to simplify each expression.

4. $6 \times 52 = 6 \times (50 + 2)$ **312**   5. $4 \times 18 = 4 \times (20 - 2)$ **72**

Homework Exercises

For more exercises, see Extra Skills and Word Problems.

A Use the Distributive Property to simplify each expression.

GO for Help

For Exercises	See Example
6–14	1
15	2

6. 8×28 7. 5×63 8. 4×34

9. 99×6 10. 7×83 11. 3×2.9

12. 9×48 13. 8.7×3 14. 52×6

6–14. See margin.

15. Six students plan to go to a skating rink. The rink charges $4.50 per person. Find the total cost for the group. **$27.00**

B **GPS** 16. **Guided Problem Solving** Mr. Garcia's company pays him 32.5 cents for each mile he drives. How much money does he receive for driving 40 miles? **$13.00**
   - How could you rewrite 32.5 as a sum?

17. **Fundraising** There are 50 people walking in a fundraising event. Each participant walks 5.3 miles. How many miles do the participants walk in all? **265 mi**

18. Answers may vary. Sample: You could add 6.8 and 2, and then multiply the sum by 2.5. You could also multiply 2.5 by 6.8, then by 2, and add the products.

GO Online
Homework Video Tutor
Visit: PHSchool.com
Web Code: aqe-0308

18. **Writing in Math** Describe two ways to find the total area of the rectangle at the right. **See above left.**

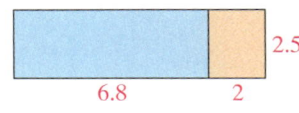

6. $8 \times (20 + 8) = 8 \times 20 + 8 \times 8 = 160 + 64 = 224$

7. $5 \times (60 + 3) = 5 \times 60 + 5 \times 3 = 300 + 15 = 315$

8. $4 \times (30 + 4) = 4 \times 30 + 4 \times 4 = 120 + 16 = 136$

9. $6 \times (100 - 1) = 6 \times 100 - 6 \times 1 = 600 - 6 = 594$

10. $7 \times (80 + 3) = 7 \times 80 + 7 \times 3 = 560 + 21 = 581$

11. $3 \times (3 - 0.1) = 3 \times 3 - 3 \times 0.1 = 9 - 0.3 = 8.7$

12–14. See back of book.

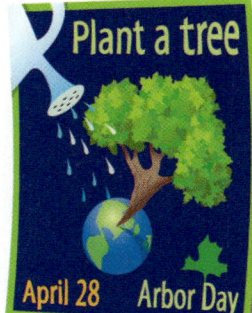
April 28 Arbor Day

Algebra Copy and complete each equation.

19. $4(7 - y) = (4 \cdot 7) - (4 \cdot \blacksquare)$ **20.** $9(a + b) = (\blacksquare \cdot a) + (9 \cdot \blacksquare)$
y 9 b

21. Your class is selling calendars for $2.90 each. How much money does your class collect for selling 8 calendars? **$23.20**

22. Gardening Your school's ecology club plants 8 rows of trees
GPS in a vacant lot. Each row has 27 trees. Find the total number of trees that the ecology club plants. **216 trees**

23. Reasoning Which expression is NOT equivalent to the others?
Ⓐ $(a \times c) + (b \times c)$ Ⓒ $b \times (c + a)$ **C**
Ⓑ $(b + a) \times c$ Ⓓ $(a + b) \times c$

C 24. Challenge Add parentheses to $9 + 8 \times 7 - 6 \times 5 + 4 \times 3 + 2$ so that the value of the expression is 105.
$(9 + 8) \times (7 - 6) \times$

Test Prep and Mixed Review
Practice

Multiple Choice

25. Marissa earned $5 an hour baby-sitting. She worked for 4 hours and spent $8.75 of her earnings. Which equation could be used to determine how much money, m, Marissa had left? **B**
Ⓐ $m = 4 \times (\$5 - \$8.75)$ Ⓒ $m = 4 \times \$5 + \$8.75$
Ⓑ $m = 4 \times \$5 - \$8.75$ Ⓓ $m = 4 \times (\$5 + \$8.75)$

26. Joey asked middle school students to name their favorite type of movie. Which graph correctly displays the data shown in the table? **G**

Student Movie Preference

Movie	Drama	Comedy	Action
Students	140	260	200

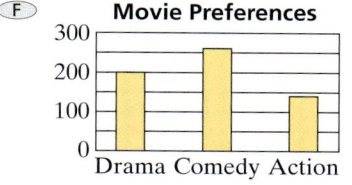
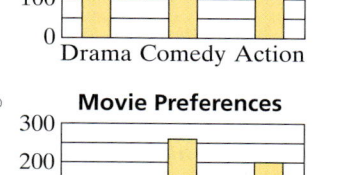
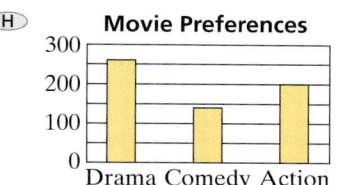
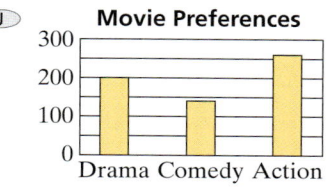

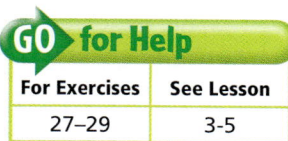
GO for Help

For Exercises	See Lesson
27–29	3-5

Tell whether each equation is true or false.
false   false   true
27. $5 \times 3 = 8$ **28.** $0 \times 9.8 = 9.8$ **29.** $1 \times 6.7 = 6.7$

Online lesson quiz, PHSchool.com, Web Code: aqa-0308   3-8 The Distributive Property **147**

4. Assess & Reteach

PowerPoint
Lesson Quiz

1. Find the missing numbers in $5 \times (70 + 8) = (\blacksquare \times 70) + (5 \times \blacksquare)$. **5; 8**

Rewrite each expression using the Distributive Property and then simplify. **Answers may vary. Samples are given.**

2. 3×24 **$(3 \times 25) - (3 \times 1) = 72$**

3. 7×43
$(7 \times 40) + (7 \times 3) = 301$

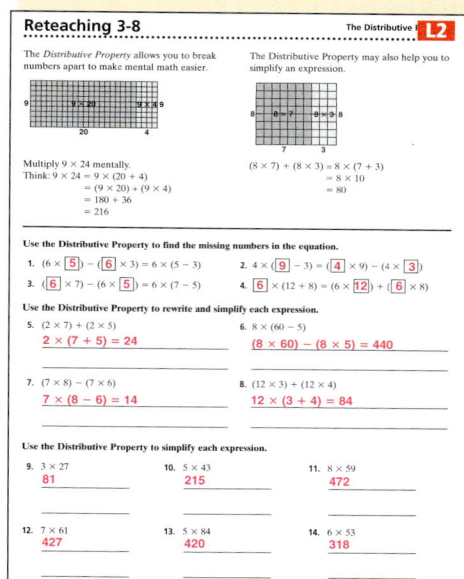
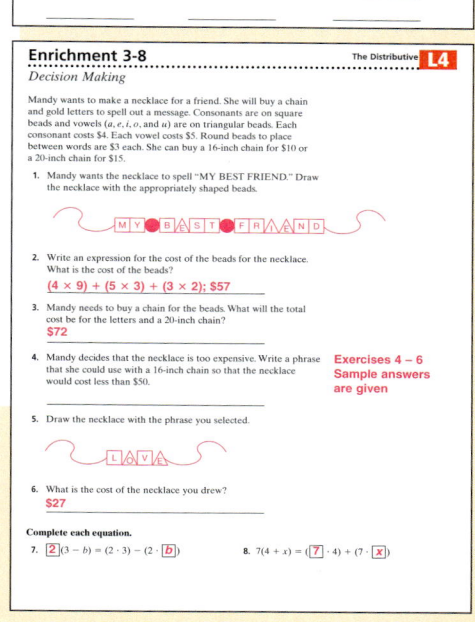

Alternative Assessment
Each student in a pair writes a multiplication problem similar to those in Exercises 6–8. Partners exchange papers and rewrite the expression using the Distributive Property. Students then simplify using mental math.

Test Prep
Resources
For additional practice with a variety of test item formats:
• Test-Taking Strategies, p. 149
• Test Prep, p. 153
• Test-Taking Strategies with Transparencies

147

Understanding Properties

Students use number properties as they learn to "think mathematically." Number properties will help them solve equations.

Guided Instruction

Example

Explain that the numbers are the same in the Example on each side of the equation. Only the order is changed so the equation is true by the Commutative Property of Addition.

Exercises

Work through Exercises 1 and 2 as a class. For Exercise 1, students should note that multiplying by zero always gives 0 as a result. For Exercise 2, students should use the Distributive Property.

Error Prevention!

Have students list the number properties on an index card and keep the list available as they do the Exercises.

Differentiated Instruction

Below Level **L2**

As students do Exercises 7–16, allow them to substitute several sets of numbers for the variables to get an idea of whether the statements are true.

Understanding Properties

Properties become more important as you "think algebraically." Understanding number properties and equality will help you solve algebraic equations.

EXAMPLE

Use a number property or number sense to determine whether the equation $8.8 + 12.5 + 1.2 = 1.2 + 8.8 + 12.5$ is true or false. Justify your reasoning.

$$8.8 + 12.5 + 1.2 = 1.2 + 8.8 + 12.5 \leftarrow$$ The order of the numbers has changed. This is an example of the Commutative Property of Addition.

The equation is true. It uses the Commutative Property of Addition.

Exercises

Determine whether each equation is true or false. Do not compute with paper and pencil. Use number properties and mental math to decide. Justify your reasoning.

1. $3.78 \times 14.95 \times 0 = 388.4 - 300 - 88.4$
   true; Zero Property of Multiplication
2. $15.4 \times 10 = (15 \times 10) + (0.4 \times 10)$
   true; Distributive Property
3. $25.7 - (13 - 10) = (25.7 - 13) - 10$
   false; subtraction is not associative.
4. $16 \times (3.8 \div 3.80) = 2 \times 8$
   true; Multiplicative Identity
5. $60 \times 19.5 = 60 \times 2 - 60 \times 0.5$
   false; $2 - 0.5 \neq 19.5$
6. $321 \times 3 = 300 \times 3 + 21 \times 3$
   true; Distributive Property

Determine whether each statement is true for all numbers a and b. Justify your reasoning.

7. $0 \times a = a$
   false; Zero Property of Multiplication
8. $0 \div a = a$
   false; $0 \div a = 0$
9. $a - b + b = a$
   See margin.
10. $a \div 0 = 0$
    false; cannot divide by 0
11. $a \times b = b \times a$ **11–16. See margin.**
12. $b + a - a = b$
13. $a \times b \div b = a$ (if $b \neq 0$)
14. $a \div b = b \div a$ (if $a, b \neq 0$)
15. $a \div b \times b = a$ (if $b \neq 0$)
16. $a \div a = b \div b$ (if $a, b \neq 0$)

17. **Reasoning** If you use a calculator to compute $0 \div 5$, you will get 0. If you calculate $5 \div 0$, you will get an error message. Use multiplication to explain why $5 \div 0$ is not defined.

    17. You cannot multiply 0 by any number to get 5.

9. True; addition and subtraction are inverse operations.

11. true; Commutative Property of Multiplication

12. True; addition and subtraction are inverse operations.

13. True; division and multiplication are inverse operations.

14. false; division is not commutative.

15. True; division and multiplication are inverse operations.

16. true; $1 = 1$

Writing Short Responses

Short-response questions in this textbook are worth 2 points. To receive full credit, you must give the correct answer with units, if needed, and show your work or explain your reasoning.

EXAMPLE

Measurement Jenny stands on a scale. She weighs 104 pounds. Then she steps on the scale while holding her dog. Now the scale reads 121 pounds. Define a variable. Write and solve an equation to find the weight of the dog.

The problem asks you to define a variable, set up an equation, and solve the equation to find the weight of the dog. Below is a scoring guide that shows the number of points awarded for different answers.

Scoring

[2] The equation and solution are correct and all work is shown. The dog weighs 17 pounds.

[1] There is no equation, but there is a method to show that the dog weighs 17 pounds, OR an equation is written and solved. The response may contain minor errors.

[0] There is no response, no work shown, OR the response is completely incorrect.

Three responses are shown below, with the points each received.

2 points	1 point	0 points
Let d = weight of dog. $104 + d = 121$ $104 + d - 104 = 121 - 104$ $d = 17$ The dog weighs 17 pounds.	$121 - 104 = 17$ 17 pounds	27 pounds

Exercises

Use Example 1 to answer each question. 1–2. See margin.

1. Why did each response receive the indicated number of points?
2. Write a 2-point response for solving the equation $121 - d = 104$.

1–2. Answers may vary. Samples are given.

1. The 2-point response defined the variable, set up an equation, and found the weight of the dog; the 1-point response only showed a method and found the weight of the dog.

2. Let d = weight of the dog.
$$121 - d = 104$$
$$121 - d + d = 104 + d$$
$$121 = 104 + d$$
$$121 - 104 = 104 - 104 + d$$
$$17 = d$$
The dog weighs 17 pounds.

Writing Short Responses

This strategy provides students with a scoring rubric and an example showing how to get full credit for answer to short-response questions.

Guided Instruction

Example

The example suggests subtracting Jenny's weight from the total. Ask:

- *What word expression could you write for the situation?* **Total weight minus Jenny's weight equals dog's weight.**
- *If Jenny weighed 100 pounds, what equation could you use?* **162 − 100 = dog's weight**

Exercises

Have students write word expressions to help.

Resources

Test-Taking Strategies with Transparencies
- Transparency 3
- Practice sheet, p. 3

Test-Taking Strategies with Transparencies

Test-Taking Strategies: Writing Short Responses

Estimate 98.57 × 206. Write your estimate and explain in writing how you got it.

Scoring Guide

2 Explains method, with answer that matches method.

1 Gives estimate with no explanation, OR gives explanation with no answer, OR shows computation, OR rounds first, but not enough to make computation easy.

0 Computes exact answer, then rounds, OR gives incorrect response.

Answer earning 2 points

Round: 98.57 → 100
206 → 200

Estimate = 20,000

First round, then multiply the rounded numbers.

Answer earning 1 point

Estimate:
98.57
206

206
× 99
1854
1854
20394

Answer earning 0 points

98.57
× 206
591 42
19714
20305.42
20305

Transparency 3

Vocabulary Review

 **Addition Property of
Equality** (p. 134)
algebraic expression (p. 113)
arithmetic sequence (p. 123)
conjecture (p. 108)
Distributive Property (p. 144)
Division Property of Equality
(p. 138)

equation (p. 124)
evaluate (p. 114)
inverse operations (p. 130)
**Multiplication Property of
Equality** (p. 139)
numerical expression
(p. 113)

open sentence (p. 125)
sequence (p. 109)
solution (p. 125)
**Subtraction Property of
Equality** (p. 131)
term (p. 108)
variable (p. 113)

Go Online
PHSchool.com
For: Vocabulary quiz
Web Code: aqj-0351

Fill in the blank.

1. Each number in a number pattern is called a(n) __?__. **term**

2. A(n) __?__ contains one or more variables.
   algebraic expression

3. The value of the variable that makes an equation true is a(n) __?__. **solution**

4. A(n) __?__ is a symbol that stands for a number. **variable**

5. A(n) __?__ is a mathematical sentence with an equal sign. **equation**

Skills and Concepts

Lesson 3-1
• To find and write rules
  for patterns

Each number in a number pattern is called a **term**. A **conjecture** predicts how a pattern may continue. You can describe a pattern with a rule.

Write a rule for each pattern. Then write the next three terms.
6–8. See margin.

6. 2, 6, 18, 54, . . .   7. 7, 19, 31, 43, . . .   8. 7, 14, 28, 56, . . .

Lessons 3-2 and 3-3
• To evaluate algebraic
  expressions
• To write algebraic
  expressions and use them to
  solve problems

A **numerical expression** contains only numbers and operation symbols. An **algebraic expression** contains at least one **variable**.

Evaluate each expression.

9. $48 \div x$ for $x = 6$ 10. $c - 7$ for $c = 56$ 11. $14b$ for $b = 3$
   8   **49**   **42**

Write an expression for each word phrase.

12. x divided by 12   13. 2 times b 14. h plus k
    x ÷ 12   **2b**   **h + k**

6. **Start with 2 and multiply by 3 repeatedly; 162; 486; 1,458.**

7. **Start with 7 and add 12 repeatedly; 55, 67, 79.**

8. **Start with 7 and multiply by 2 repeatedly; 112, 224, 448.**

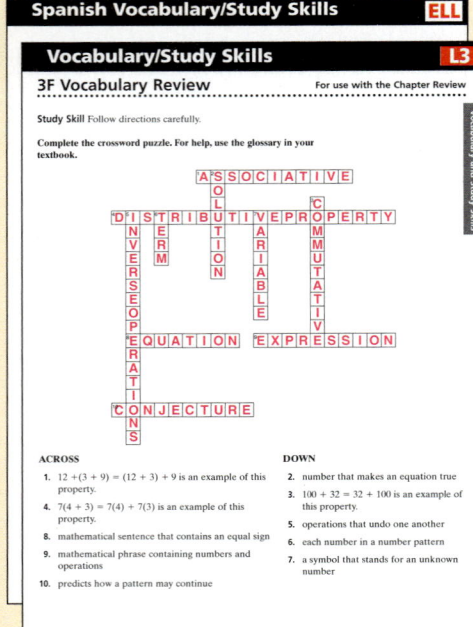

Lesson 3-4

- To use mental math to estimate and solve problems

An **equation** is a mathematical sentence that contains an equal sign. An **open sentence** is an equation that contains one or more variables. A value of the variable that makes an equation true is a **solution.**

Tell whether each equation is true or false.

15. $15 + 25 = 30$
false

16. $21 \div 3 = 7$
true

17. $6 \times 4 = 28$
false

Mental Math Solve each equation.

18. $x + 7 = 12$ **5**

19. $m + 13 = 21$ **8**

20. $4t = 32$ **8**

Lessons 3-5 and 3-6

- To use addition and subtraction to solve equations

You can use the **Addition Property of Equality** and the **Subtraction Property of Equality** to solve equations. Operations that undo each other are **inverse operations.**

Solve each equation.

21. $r - 1,078 = 4,562$ **5,640**

22. $m + 8 = 15$ **7**

23. $5.6 + x = 7$ **1.4**

24. $d - 2.16 = 3.9$ **6.06**

25. Paul is 2.7 pounds heavier than Elizabeth. Paul weighs 132.4 pounds. How much does Elizabeth weigh? **129.7 lb**

Lesson 3-7

- To use multiplication and division to solve equations

You can use the **Multiplication Property of Equality** and the **Division Property of Equality** to solve equations.

Solve each equation.

26. $78x = 4,368$ **56**

27. $t \div 4 = 32$ **128**

28. $1.2h = 3$ **2.5**

29. $7.2 = u \div 1.5$
10.8

30. $v \div 3.2 = 19$
60.8

31. $4.5 = 5n$ **0.9**

32. John has five times as much money as Stuart. John has $83.40. How much money does Stuart have? **$16.68**

Lesson 3-8

- To use the Distributive Property to simplify expressions in problem solving situations

You can use the **Distributive Property** to simplify an expression.

Use the Distributive Property to simplify each expression.
33–35. See margin.

33. 7×28

34. 5×3.4

35. 11×57

Chapter 3 Chapter Review **151**

33. $7(20 + 8) = 140 + 56 = 196$

34. $5(3 + 0.4) = 15 + 2.0 = 17$

35. $(10 + 1)57 = 570 + 57 = 627$

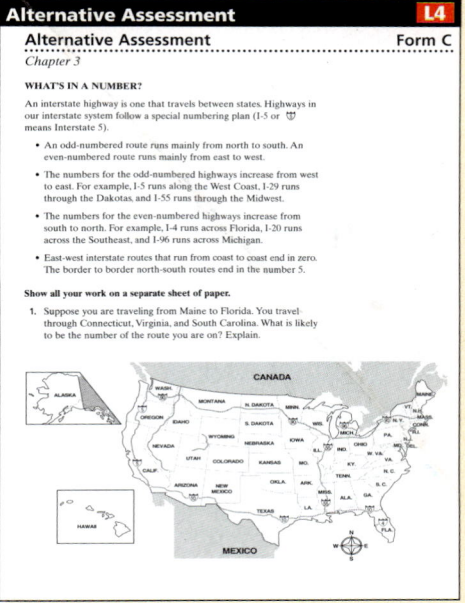
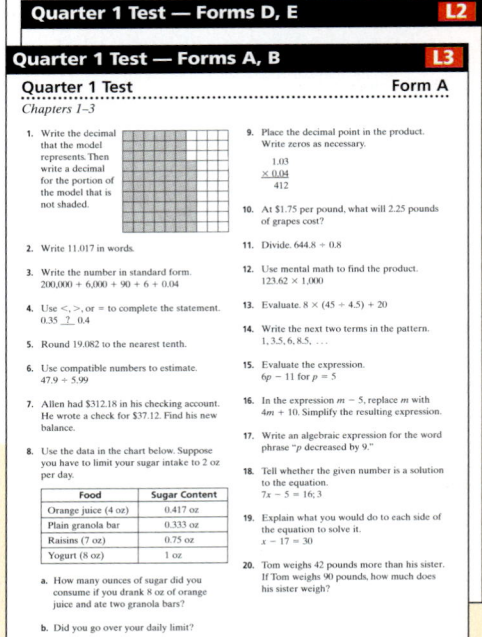

Resources

- ExamView Assessment Suite CD-ROM
  - Ch. 3 Ready-Made Test
  - Make your own Ch. 3 test
- MindPoint Quiz Show CD-ROM
  - Chapter 3 Review

Differentiated Instruction

All in One Teaching Resources
- Below Level Chapter 3 Test **L2**
- Chapter 3 Test **L3**
- Chapter 3 Alternative Assessment **L4**

Spanish Assessment Resources **ELL**
- Below Level Chapter 3 Test **L2**
- Chapter 3 Test **L3**
- Chapter 3 Alternative Assessment **L4**

ExamView Assessment Suite CD-ROM
- Special Needs Test **L1**
- Special Needs Practice Bank **L1**

Online Chapter 3 Test at www.PHSchool.com **L3**

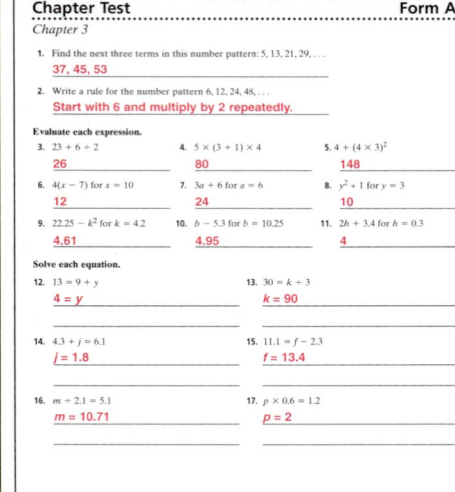

Below Level Chapter Test **L2**

Chapter Test **L3**

Chapter Test   Form A
Chapter 3

1. Find the next three terms in this number pattern: 5, 13, 21, 29, . . .
   37, 45, 53

2. Write a rule for the number pattern 6, 12, 24, 48, . . .
   Start with 6 and multiply by 2 repeatedly.

Evaluate each expression.

3. $23 + 6 \div 2$ 4. $5 \times (3 + 1) \times 4$ 5. $4 + (4 \times 3)^2$
   26   80   148

6. $4(x - 7)$ for $x = 10$ 7. $3a + 6$ for $a = 6$ 8. $y^2 + 1$ for $y = 3$
   12   24   10

9. $22.25 - k^2$ for $k = 4.2$ 10. $b - 5.3$ for $b = 10.25$ 11. $2h + 3.4$ for $h = 0.3$
   4.61   4.95   4

Solve each equation.

12. $13 = 9 + y$ 13. $30 = k + 3$
    4 = y   k = 90

14. $4.3 + j = 6.1$ 15. $11.1 = f - 2.3$
    j = 1.8   f = 13.4

16. $m \div 2.1 = 5.1$ 17. $p \times 0.6 = 1.2$
    m = 10.71   p = 2

Chapter 3 Test

Go Online PHSchool.com   For: Online chapter test   Web Code: aqa-0352

Write the first six terms in each number pattern described.

1. Start with 10 and then multiply by 2 repeatedly.   10, 20, 40, 80, 160, 320

2. Start with 50 and then subtract 4 repeatedly.   50, 46, 42, 38, 34, 30

Write a rule for each number pattern. Then write the next three terms.

3. 6, 10, 14, 18, . . .   4. 64, 32, 16, 8, . . .

5. 78, 69, 60, 51, . . .   6. 4, 12, 36, 108, . . .
   3–6. See margin.

Evaluate each expression for $x = 12$.

7. $500 + (x - 8)$ 504

8. $2x - 3$ 21

9. $8 + x \div 2$ 14

Write an algebraic expression for each model.

10.
   2x + 4

11.
   3x + 2

Use algebra tiles or a drawing to model each equation. Then solve.

12. $v + 3 = 8$ 13. $3g = 15$
    12–13. See margin.

Write an expression for each word phrase.

14. c more than 4   15. 8 less than $3d$
    4 + c   3d − 8

16. Gus is 8 years younger than his brother, Alex. Alex is x years old. Write an algebraic expression that describes how old Gus is.   x − 8

17.  **Writing in Math** Write a word problem that could be described by the expression $d + 4$.   Check students' work.

Tell whether each equation is true or false.

18. $6 + 7 \times 3 = 39$ false

19. $1.5 \times (6 - 4) = 3$ true

Tell whether the given number is a solution to the equation.

20. $x + 1.5 = 32$; 17   no   21. $h - 8 = 2$; 28   no

Solve each equation.

22. $n - 4 = 8.4$ 12.4

23. $25 + b = 138$ 113

24. $k \div 12 = 3$ 36

25. $11t = 99$ 9

26. **Fundraising** A baseball team sold greeting cards to raise money for uniforms. The team received $.40 profit for each card sold. The total profit was $302. How many cards did the team sell?   755 cards

27. **Patterns** Look at the pattern below. How many squares will be in the sixth figure?   13 squares

 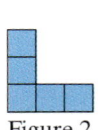 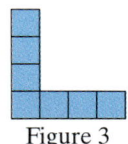

Figure 1   Figure 2   Figure 3

Use the Distributive Property to simplify each expression.   28–31. See margin.

28. 8×39 29. 4×71

30. 6×82 31. 3×98

---

3. **Start with 6 and add 4 repeatedly; 22, 26, 30.**

4. **Start with 64 and divide by 2 repeatedly; 4, 2, 1.**

5. **Start with 78 and subtract 9 repeatedly; 42, 33, 24.**

6. **Start with 4 and multiply by 3 repeatedly; 324; 972; 2916.**

12–13. **See back of book.**

28–31. **See back of book.**

Multiple Choice
Read each question. Then write the letter of the correct answer on your paper.

1. Which decimal is fifty-four hundredths? **B**
   Ⓐ 0.054 Ⓑ 0.54 Ⓒ 5.40 Ⓓ 54.00

2. Which inequality is NOT a true statement? **H**
   Ⓕ 0.04 > 0.01 Ⓗ 0.48 < 0.4798
   Ⓖ 0.014 < 0.02 Ⓙ 29.6 > 29.06

3. Which sentence represents the Commutative Property of Multiplication? **C**
   Ⓐ $5 \times 2 = 10$
   Ⓑ $5 \times (6 + 3) = 5 \times 9$
   Ⓒ $5 \times 9 = 9 \times 5$
   Ⓓ $(5 \times 6) \times 2 = 5 \times (6 \times 2)$

4. For 4 days, Akiko recorded the number of laps she jogged around a track. The numbers she recorded were 7, 11, 15, and 19. If she continues in the same pattern, how many laps will she jog on the sixth day? **J**
   Ⓕ 21 Ⓖ 23 Ⓗ 25 Ⓙ 27

5. Which word phrase does NOT describe the algebraic expression $b - 10$? **C**
   Ⓐ ten less than b Ⓒ b less than 10
   Ⓑ b less ten Ⓓ b minus ten

6. Which expression has a value of 13? **H**
   Ⓕ $(3 + 2)^2$ Ⓗ $3^2 + 2^2$
   Ⓖ $3 + (2)^2$ Ⓙ $3^3 + 2^2$

7. Which operation would you use to get the variable in $x - 15 = 40$ alone on one side of the equation? **C**
   Ⓐ Subtract 15 from each side.
   Ⓑ Subtract x from each side.
   Ⓒ Add 15 to each side.
   Ⓓ Add 40 to each side.

8. What is the value of $2.5c + 2$ when $c = 6$? **G**
   Ⓕ 2.56 Ⓖ 17 Ⓗ 20 Ⓙ 256

9. Which expression is NOT equivalent to the others? **C**
   Ⓐ $13 \times (20 + 2)$
   Ⓑ $13 \times 20 + 13 \times 2$
   Ⓒ $(10 + 13) \times (10 + 12)$
   Ⓓ $22 \times (10 + 3)$

10. Apples cost $.38 each. You have $4.00. What is the greatest number of apples you can buy? **H**
    Ⓕ 5 Ⓖ 9 Ⓗ 10 Ⓙ 11

Gridded Response
Record your answer in a grid.

11. What is the solution of $x \div 0.15 = 1.2$? **0.18**

12. Cod sells for $4.86 per pound. You buy two pieces, which cost a total of $12.15. How many pounds of fish do you buy? **2.5**

13. A sheet of metal has a thickness of 0.004 inches. In inches, how many inches thick is a stack of 100 sheets? **0.4**

Short Response

14. a. Draw the fourth figure in the pattern.
    b. How many white squares will the sixth figure have? **a–b. See margin.**

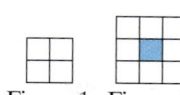 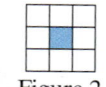 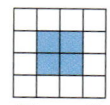

Figure 1   Figure 2   Figure 3

15. How many different sandwiches can you make from the choices of wheat bread, rye bread, or oatmeal bread with a filling of chicken, turkey, cheese, or peanut butter? Explain your method.
    See margin.

Chapter 3   Test Prep   **153**

[1] incorrect figure with correct number of white squares OR correct figure with incorrect number of white squares

15. [2] Draw a tree diagram.

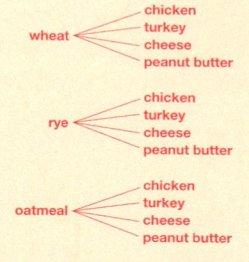

I can make 12 different sandwiches. OR a correct explanation of choices

[1] has correct answer without a correct diagram or explanation OR a correct diagram or explanation without a correct answer

Item	1	2	3	4	5	6	7	8	9	10	11	12	13	14	15
Lesson	1-5	1-6	1-3	3-1	3-3	1-4	3-6	3-2	3-8	1-9	3-7	1-9	1-8	3-1	Problem Solving Handbook

14. [2] a.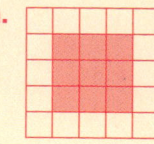

b. The sixth figure will have 7 small squares on each side. In the center, the shaded part will have 5 small squares on each side. The number of white squares will be $7^2 - 5^2 = 49 - 25 = 24$ squares.

Problem Solving

Applying Patterns

Applying Patterns

It's About Time Our day, month, and year are all based on the motion of Earth and the moon. One day is 24 hours long because that's how long it takes Earth to rotate once about its axis. The moon takes one month to orbit Earth, and Earth takes one year to orbit the sun. If we lived on another planet, each of these measures would be different, and we would have different measurements of time.

Earth's Moon
The moon contains almost the same elements, minerals, and rocks as Earth, but it has no water and no atmosphere. The moon orbits Earth in 29 days, 12 hours, 44 minutes, and 3 seconds, on average.

The Last Planet
In 1930, U.S. astronomer Clyde Tombaugh discovered Pluto, the ninth planet in the solar system. During part of Pluto's year, its orbit brings it closer to the sun than Neptune.

Pluto

Jupiter

Uranus

Sun

Venus

Mercury

Saturn

Earth

Mars

154

Measuring Time

The Jantar Mantar observatory, built between 1728 and 1734 in Jaipur, India, includes a giant sundial 27.5 meters high. You climb the steps to read the time, which is accurate to within a few seconds.

Neptune

The Solar System

All nine planets orbit the sun in the same direction (counterclockwise when viewed from above), and most spin around their axes in the same direction, also.

Put It All Together

Planet	Length of Day (Earth hours)	Length of Year (Earth days)
☿ Mercury	1,407.51	87.97
♀ Venus	5,832.61	224.7
⊕ Earth	23.93	365.24
♂ Mars	24.62	686.98
♃ Jupiter	9.93	4,332.71
♄ Saturn	10.23	10,759.3
♅ Uranus	17.23	30,684
♆ Neptune	16.11	60,188.3
♇ Pluto	153.29	90,777.3

SOURCE: *The Cambridge Planetary Handbook*

1. a. How many Mercury years are equivalent to one Earth year? (Give your answer to the nearest whole number.)
   b. If you lived on Mercury, how old would you now be in Mercury years?

2. a. If you lived on Jupiter, how many birthdays would you be likely to celebrate in your lifetime? Explain.
   b. How many birthdays would you celebrate if you lived on Pluto? Explain.

3. Mars has two moons, Phobos and Deimos. Phobos orbits the planet every 7.5 hours, and Deimos every 30.25 hours.
   a. **Writing in Math**  How might you define a "month" on Mars? Explain.
   b. **Reasoning** Do you think a Martian month would be a useful measure of time? Explain.

Go Online
PHSchool.com

For: Information about planets
Web Code: aqe-0353

155

Activity

Make sure students understand what determines a day, a month, and a year. Then have students work in pairs to answer the questions.

Exercise 3 Students' answers to this question should show an understanding that a month is the amount of time it takes a moon to orbit a planet. Mars might have two different months or the orbit of one of its moons might be chosen as the defining month.

Differentiated Instruction
Special Needs   L1
Discuss the terms *orbit* and *axis*. Call on volunteers to demonstrate the meaning of each.

3a. Answers may vary. Sample: a month on Mars could be defined as the time that it takes one of its moons to orbit the planet. This is roughly the definition of one month on Earth.

b. No. Answers may vary. Sample: a Martian month is almost the same as a Martian day.

Chapter at a Glance

Lesson Titles, Objectives, and Features	Assessment	NCTM Standards	Local Standards
4-1 Divisibility and Mental Math • To check for divisibility using mental math and to use divisibility to solve problems	Lesson Quiz	1, 2, 6, 7, 10	
4-2 Exponents • To use exponents and to simplify expressions with exponents	Lesson Quiz	1, 2, 6, 7, 10	
4-3 Prime Numbers and Prime Factorization • To factor numbers and to find the prime factorizaton of numbers	Lesson Quiz Checkpoint Quiz 1	1, 2, 6, 7, 10	
4-4 Greatest Common Factor • To find the GCF of two or more numbers	Lesson Quiz	1, 6, 7, 10	
4-5a Activity Lab, Hands On: Modeling Fractions **4-5 Equivalent Fractions** • To find equivalent forms of fractions **4-5b Activity Lab, Technology:** Simplifying Fractions	Lesson Quiz	1, 2, 6, 7, 10	
4-6a Activity Lab, Hands On: Exploring Improper Fractions **4-6 Mixed Numbers and Improper Fractions** • To use mixed numbers and improper fractions **4-6b Activity Lab, Hands On:** Fractions and Measurement **Vocabulary Builder:** Making Word Lists	Lesson Quiz Checkpoint Quiz 2	1, 3, 4, 6, 7, 10	
4-7 Least Common Multiple • To find the LCM of two or more numbers	Lesson Quiz	1, 2, 6, 7, 10	
4-8 Comparing and Ordering Fractions • To compare and order fractions **Guided Problem Solving:** Practice Solving Problems	Lesson Quiz	1, 6, 7, 10	
4-9 Fractions and Decimals • To find equivalent forms of fractions and decimals and to order fractions and decimals **4-9b Activity Lab, Data Collection:** Conducting a Survey	Lesson Quiz	1, 6, 7, 10	
Problem Solving Application: Applying Fractions			

NCTM Standards 2000
1 Number and Operations	2 Algebra	3 Geometry	4 Measurement	5 Data Analysis and Probability
6 Problem Solving	7 Reasoning and Proof	8 Communication	9 Connections	10 Representation

Correlations to Standardized Tests

All content for these tests is contained in *Prentice Hall Math,* Course 1. This chart reflects coverage in this chapter only.

	4-1	4-2	4-3	4-4	4-5	4-6	4-7	4-8	4-9
Terra Nova CAT6 (Level 16)									
Number and Number Relations	✔	✔	✔	✔	✔	✔	✔	✔	✔
Computation and Numerical Estimation									
Operation Concepts									
Measurement						✔			
Geometry and Spatial Sense									
Data Analysis, Statistics, and Probability									
Patterns, Functions, Algebra	✔	✔	✔	✔	✔	✔	✔	✔	✔
Problem Solving and Reasoning									
Communication									
Decimals, Fractions, Integers, Percent	✔	✔	✔	✔	✔	✔	✔	✔	✔
Order of Operations									
Terra Nova CTBS (Level 16)									
Whole Numbers, Decimals, Fractions	✔	✔	✔	✔	✔	✔	✔	✔	✔
Numeration, Number Theory	✔	✔	✔	✔	✔	✔	✔	✔	✔
Data Interpretation									
Pre-algebra	✔	✔	✔		✔		✔		
Measurement						✔			
Geometry									
ITBS (Level 12)									
Number Properties and Operations	✔	✔	✔	✔	✔	✔	✔	✔	✔
Algebra	✔	✔	✔	✔	✔	✔	✔	✔	✔
Geometry									
Measurement						✔			
Probability and Statistics									
Estimation									
SAT10 (Int 2 Level)									
Number Sense and Operations	✔	✔	✔	✔	✔	✔	✔	✔	✔
Patterns, Relationships, and Algebra	✔	✔	✔	✔	✔	✔	✔	✔	✔
Data, Statistics, and Probability									
Geometry and Measurement						✔			
NAEP									
Number Sense, Properties, and Operations	✔	✔	✔	✔	✔	✔	✔		
Measurement									
Geometry and Spatial Sense									
Data Analysis, Statistics, and Probability									
Algebra and Functions									

CAT6 California Achievement Test, 6th Ed.
SAT10 Stanford Achievement Test, 10th Ed.
CTBS Comprehensive Test of Basic Skills
NAEP National Assessment of Educational Progress 2005 Mathematics Objectives
ITBS Iowa Test of Basic Skills, Form M

Math Background

Skills Trace

BEFORE Chapter 4

Grade 5 presented basic fractions concepts.

DURING Chapter 4

Course 1 extends fraction concepts and uses basic number theory to find prime factorizations, GCFs, LCMs, and LCDs.

AFTER Chapter 4

Throughout this course, students use fraction concepts and basic number theory.

4-1   Divisibility and Mental Math

Math Understandings
- When you find one whole number that divides a second, you know that all the factors of that whole number also divide the second number.

One whole number is **divisible** by a second whole number if the remainder is 0 when the first number is divided by the second number.

Divisibility of Whole Numbers
A whole number is divisible by • 2 if it ends in 0, 2, 4, 6, or 8. • 3 if the sum of its digits is divisible by 3. • 5 if it ends in 0 or 5. • 9 if the sum of its digits is divisible by 9. • 10 if it ends in 0.

An **even number** is any whole number that ends with a 0, 2, 4, 6, or 8. An **odd number** is a whole number that ends with a 1, 3, 5, 7, or 9.

Example: Test 3,471 for divisibility by 3.
$3 + 4 + 7 + 1 = 15$ and $15 \div 3 = 5$. So 3,471 is divisible by 3.

4-2   Exponents

Math Understandings
- When you write a base with an exponent, you are using a mathematical operation that indicates repeated multiplication.

An exponent tells you how many times a number, or base, is used as a factor.
$$5 \times 5 \times 5 \times 5 = 5^4 \begin{smallmatrix}\text{exponent}\\\text{base}\end{smallmatrix}$$
A number expressed using an exponent is called a **power**. The order of operations can be extended to include exponents.

4-3   Prime Numbers and Prime Factorization

Math Understandings
- Every integer greater than one can be expressed as a product of prime factors in one and only one way, except for the order of the factors.
- Every whole number has at least two factors, 1 and itself.
- The whole numbers 0 and 1 are neither prime nor composite.

A **factor** is a whole number that divides a nonzero whole number with remainder 0. A **composite number** is a whole number greater than 1 with more than two factors. A **prime number** is a whole number with exactly two factors, 1 and the number itself. Writing a composite number as a product of prime numbers gives the **prime factorization** of the number.

4-4   Greatest Common Factor

Math Understandings
- Two or more whole numbers may have several common factors, but they have only one greatest common factor.

A factor that two or more numbers share is a **common factor**. The **greatest common factor (GCF)** of two or more numbers is the greatest factor shared by all the numbers. You can find the GCF for two numbers by listing all the factors, using a division ladder, or using factor trees.

4-5 Equivalent Fractions

Math Understandings
- A fraction is a number representing some part of a whole and may be written in the form $\frac{a}{b}$ where $b \neq 0$.

Equivalent fractions are fractions that name the same amount. A fraction is in **simplest form** when the only common factor of the numerator and denominator is 1. One way to write a fraction in simplest form is to divide both the numerator and denominator by their greatest common factor.

Example: $\frac{12}{16} = \frac{3 \cdot 4}{4 \cdot 4} = \frac{12}{16} \div \frac{4}{4} = \frac{3}{4}$

4-6 Mixed Numbers and Improper Fractions

Math Understandings
- One number can be written in many different forms, all of which are equivalent.
- A fraction has a unique simplest form, which may be an improper fraction or mixed number.

Name	Description	Example
proper fraction	numerator less than its denominator	$\frac{12}{23}$
improper fraction	numerator is greater than or equal to its denominator	$\frac{5}{2}$
mixed number	shows the sum of a whole number and a proper fraction	$2\frac{1}{2}$

Example: Change $5\frac{1}{6}$ to an improper fraction.

$5\frac{1}{6} = \frac{5 \times 6 + 1}{6} = \frac{31}{6}$

4-7 Least Common Multiple

Math Understandings
- Two positive integers have an infinite number of common multiples but only one LCM.

A number that is a multiple of each of two or more numbers is a **common multiple**. The **least common multiple (LCM)** of two numbers is the least multiple that is common to both.

Example: Find the least common multiple of 4 and 6.

Multiples of 4: 4, 8, ⑫ 16, 20, ㉔

Multiples of 6: 6, ⑫ 18, ㉔

The least common multiple is 12.

4-8 Comparing and Ordering Fractions

Math Understandings
- If the denominators of two fractions are the same, the fraction with the greater numerator is greater.
- If the numerators are the same, the fraction with the lesser denominator has the greater value.
- If the denominators of two fractions are different, first rewrite the fractions with common denominators.

The **least common denominator (LCD)** of two or more fractions is the least common multiple (LCM) of their denominators.

4-9 Fractions and Decimals

Math Understandings
- To write a decimal as a fraction, write the fraction as you would say the decimal and simplify.
- When you write fractions as decimals, the decimal may continuously repeat one digit or a set of digits.

A fraction indicates division. To write a fraction as a decimal, divide the numerator by the denominator.

Example: $\frac{5}{6} = 6\overline{)5.000}^{\;.833} = 0.8\overline{3}$

Additional Professional Development Opportunities

Math Background Notes for Chapter 4: Every lesson has a Math Background in the PLAN section.

Research Overview, Mathematics Strands Additional support for these topics and more is in the front of the Teacher's Edition.

LessonLab LessonLab, a Pearson Education company, offers comprehensive, facilitated professional development designed to help teachers to improve student achievement. To learn more, please visit lessonlab.com.

Chapter 4 Resources

	4-1	4-2	4-3	4-4	4-5	4-6	4-7	4-8	4-9	For the Chapter
Print Resources										
L3 Practice	●	●	●	●	●	●	●	●	●	
L1 Adapted Practice	●	●	●	●	●	●	●	●	●	
L3 Guided Problem Solving	●	●	●	●	●	●	●	●	●	
L2 Reteaching	●	●	●	●	●	●	●	●	●	
L4 Enrichment	●	●	●	●	●	●	●	●	●	
L3 Daily Notetaking Guide	●	●	●	●	●	●	●	●	●	
L1 Adapted Daily Notetaking Guide	●	●	●	●	●	●	●	●	●	
L3 Vocabulary and Study Skills Worksheets	●		●		●		●		●	●
L3 Daily Puzzles	●	●	●	●	●	●	●	●	●	
L3 Activity Labs	●	●	●	●	●	●	●	●	●	
L3 Checkpoint Quiz			●			●				
L3 Chapter Project										●
L2 Below Level Chapter Test										●
L3 Chapter Test										●
L4 Alternative Assessment										●
L3 Cumulative Review										●
Spanish Resources ELL										
L3 Practice	●	●	●	●	●	●	●	●	●	
L3 Vocabulary and Study Skills Worksheets	●		●		●		●		●	●
L3 Checkpoint Quiz			●			●				
L2 Below Level Chapter Test										●
L3 Chapter Test										●
L4 Alternative Assessment										●
L3 Cumulative Review										●
Transparencies										
Check Skills You'll Need	●	●	●	●	●	●	●	●	●	
Additional Examples	●	●	●	●	●	●	●	●	●	
Problem of the Day	●	●	●	●	●	●	●	●	●	
Classroom Aid						●				
Student Edition Answers	●	●	●	●	●	●	●	●		●
Lesson Quiz	●	●	●	●	●	●	●	●	●	
Test-Taking Strategies										●
Technology										
Interactive Textbook Online	●	●	●	●	●	●	●	●	●	●
StudentExpress™ CD-ROM	●	●	●	●	●	●	●	●	●	●
Success Tracker™ Online Intervention	●	●	●	●	●	●	●	●	●	●
TeacherExpress™ CD-ROM	●	●	●	●	●	●	●	●	●	●
PresentationExpress™ with QuickTake Presenter CD-ROM	●	●	●	●	●	●	●	●	●	●
ExamView® Assessment Suite CD-ROM										●
MindPoint® Quick Show CD-ROM										●
Prentice Hall Web Site: PHSchool.com	●	●	●	●	●	●	●	●	●	●

Also available: Prentice Hall Assessment System
- Progress Monitoring Assessments
- Skills and Concepts Review
- Test Prep Workbook

Other Resources
Algebra Readiness Tests
All-in-One Student Workbook
All-in-One Student Workbook, Adapted Version
Multilingual Handbook

Solution Key
Math Notes Study Folder
Spanish Cumulative Assessment

Where You Can Use the Lesson Resources

Here is a suggestion, following the four-step teaching plan, for how you can incorporate Differentiated Instruction Resources into your teaching.

	Instructional Resources **L3**	**Differentiated Instruction Resources**
1. Plan		
Preparation Read the Math Background in the Teacher's Edition to connect this lesson with students' previous experience. **Starting Class** **Check Skills You'll Need** Assign these exercises to review prerequisite skills. **New Vocabulary** Help students pre-read the lesson by pointing out the new terms introduced in the lesson.	**Math Background** **Math Understandings** **Transparencies & PresentationExpress™ with QuickTake Presenter CD-ROM** Check Skills You'll Need Problem of the Day **Resources** Vocabulary and Study Skills	**Spanish Support** **ELL** Vocabulary and Study Skills
2. Teach		
L3 Guided Instruction Use the Activity Labs to build conceptual understanding. Teach each Example. Use the Teacher's Edition side column notes for specific teaching tips, including Error Prevention notes. Use the Additional Examples found in the side column (and on transparency and PowerPoint) as an alternative presentation for the content. After each Example, assign the Quick Check exercise for that Example to get an immediate assessment of student understanding. Use the Closure activity in the Teacher's Edition to help students attain mastery of lesson content.	**Student Edition** Activity Lab **Resources** Daily Notetaking Guide Activity Lab **Transparencies & PresentationExpress™ with QuickTake Presenter CD-ROM** Additional Examples Classroom Aids **ExamView® Assessment Suite CD-ROM**	**Teacher's Edition** Every lesson includes suggestions for working with students who need special attention. **L1** Special Needs **L2** Below Level **L4** Advanced Learners **ELL** English Language Learners **Resources** **L1** Adapted Daily Notetaking Guide **Multilingual Handbook**
3. Practice		

Assignment Guide
Check Your Understanding
Use these questions to check students' understanding before you assign homework.
Homework Exercises
Assign homework from these leveled exercises in the Assignment Guide.
  A Practice by Example
  B Apply Your Skills
  C Challenge
  Test Prep and Mixed Review
Homework Quick Check
Use these key exercises to quickly check students' homework.
	Transparencies & PresentationExpress™ with QuickTake Presenter CD-ROM
	Student Answers
	Resources
	Practice
	Guided Problem Solving
	Vocabulary and Study Skills
	Activity Lab
	Daily Puzzles
	ExamView® Assessment Suite CD-ROM
		Spanish Support
		ELL Practice
		ELL Vocabulary and Study Skills
		Resources
		L1 Adapted Practice
		L4 Enrichment

4. Assess & Reteach		
Lesson Quiz Assign the Lesson Quiz to assess students' mastery of the lesson content. **Checkpoint Quiz** Use the Checkpoint Quiz to assess student progress over several lessons.	**Transparencies & PresentationExpress™ with QuickTake Presenter CD-ROM** Lesson Quiz **Resources** Checkpoint Quiz	**Resources** **L2** Reteaching **ELL** Checkpoint Quiz Success Tracker™ Online Intervention **ExamView® Assessment Suite CD-ROM**

KEY **L1** Special Needs **L2** Below Level **L3** For All Students **L4** Advanced, Gifted **ELL** English Language Learners

Number Theory and Fractions

For intervention, direct students to:

Reading and Writing Decimals
Lesson 1-5
Extra Skills and Word
  Problems Practice, Ch. 1

Comparing and Ordering Decimals
Lesson 1-6
Extra Skills and Word
  Problems Practice, Ch. 1

Dividing Decimals
Lesson 1-9
Extra Skills and Word
  Problems Practice, Ch. 1

Spanish Vocabulary/Study Skills ELL

Vocabulary/Study Skills L3

4A: Graphic Organizer For use before Lesson 4-1

Study Skill: As you read over the material in the chapter, keep a paper and pencil handy to write down notes and questions that you have.

Write your answers.
1. What is the chapter title? Number Theory and Fractions
2. How many lessons are there in this chapter? 9
3. What is the topic of the Test-Taking Strategy page? Writing Extended Responses
4. Complete the graphic organizer below as you work through the chapter.
  • In the center, write the title of the chapter.
  • When you begin a lesson, write the lesson name in a rectangle.
  • When you complete a lesson, write a skill or key concept in a circle linked to that lesson block.
  • When you complete the chapter, use this graphic organizer to help you review.
  Check students' diagrams.

What You've Learned

• In Chapter 1, you compared and ordered whole numbers and decimals.

• You solved problems involving whole numbers and decimals.

• In Chapter 3, you wrote and simplified expressions using variables.

Check Your Readiness

Reading and Writing Decimals
Write each decimal in words. 1–6. See margin.

1. 0.4
2. 0.37
3. 1.8
4. 0.205
5. 20.88
6. 0.150

GO for Help

For Exercises	See Lesson
1–6	1-5
7–10	1-6
11–16	1-9

Comparing and Ordering Decimals
Order the decimals from least to greatest.

7. 4.2, 4.02, 4.21 **4.02, 4.2, 4.21**
8. 0.3, 0.33, 0.033 **0.033, 0.3, 0.33**
9. 6.032, 6.302, 6.203 **6.032, 6.203, 6.302**
10. 9.013, 9.103, 9.031 **9.013, 9.031, 9.103**

Dividing Decimals
Find each quotient.

11. $1.6 \div 2$ **0.8**
12. $3.85 \div 7$ **0.55**
13. $7.6 \div 0.4$ **19**
14. $290.4 \div 8$ **36.3**
15. $211.2 \div 1.6$ **132**
16. $583 \div 11$ **53**

156 Chapter 4

1. four tenths
2. thirty-seven hundredths
3. one and eight tenths
4. two hundred five thousandths
5. twenty and eighty-eight hundredths
6. one hundred fifty thousandths

What You'll Learn Next

- In this chapter, you will use divisibility rules, prime numbers, and factors to solve problems.

- You will write and simplify expressions using exponents.

- You will compare and order fractions and decimals.

- You will also convert between fractions and decimals.

Problem Solving Application On pages 208 and 209, you will work an extended activity involving levers.

🔊 Key Vocabulary

- base (p. 162)
- common factor (p. 171)
- common multiple (p. 188)
- divisible (p. 158)
- equivalent fractions (p. 176)
- exponent (p. 162)
- factor (p. 166)
- improper fraction (p. 182)
- mixed number (p. 182)
- multiple (p. 188)
- prime factorization (p. 167)
- prime number (p. 166)
- proper fraction (p. 182)
- simplest form (p. 177)

Chapter 4 **157**

Chapter 4 Overview

In this chapter on fractions, students focus on several fraction concepts and properties in preparation for computing with fractions. They use divisibility and mental math skills to investigate prime numbers and prime factorization. They work with concepts of greatest common factor (GCF) and least common multiple (LCM) as they find equivalent fractions, simplify fractions, convert mixed numbers and improper fractions, and express fractions in simplest form.

Activating Prior Knowledge

In this chapter, students build on and extend their knowledge of number theory, of decimals, and of properties of fractions in order to simplify fractions, to find equivalent fractions, and to express fractions as decimals. Ask questions such as:

- *What do the following numbers have in common: 3, 11, 29, and 41?* Sample: each is odd; each is divisible only by itself and 1; each is prime.

- *What do these numbers have in common: 12, 18, 20, and 52?* Sample: each is an even number; each is a multiple of 2; each is divisible by 2.

Objective
To check for divisibility using mental math and to use divisibility to solve problems

Examples
1 Using Mental Math for Divisibility
2 Divisibility by 2, 3, 5, and 10
3 Divisibility by 9

Math Understandings: p. 156C

Math Background

The branch of mathematics that deals with the properties of the whole numbers is called *number theory*. Perhaps the most fundamental concern of number theory is *divisibility*. That is, when one whole number is divided by another, is there a remainder? In this lesson, students learn several methods for determining divisibility. These methods are often called *divisibility tests*.

More Math Background: p. 156C

Lesson Planning and Resources

See p. 156E for a list of the resources that support this lesson.

Bell Ringer Practice

☑ **Check Skills You'll Need**
Use student page, transparency, or PowerPoint. For intervention, direct students to:
Solving Multiplication and Division Equations
Lesson 3-7
Extra Skills and Word Problems Practice, Ch. 3

☑ Check Skills You'll Need

1. **Vocabulary Review**
What is the *inverse operation* of multiplication?
division
Solve each equation. Check the solution.
2. $10x = 490$ **49**
3. $5x = 205$ **41**
4. $0.6x = 30$ **50**

 **for Help**
Lesson 3-7

GO for Help

For help with multiplying whole numbers, go to Skills Handbook, p. 640.

What You'll Learn

To check for divisibility using mental math and to use divisibility to solve problems

🔊 **New Vocabulary** divisible, even number, odd number

Why Learn This?

When you plan an event, you can use divisibility rules to find how many tables you will need for your guests.

A whole number is **divisible** by a second whole number if the first number can be divided by the second number with a remainder of 0. You can use multiplication facts to test for divisibility.

EXAMPLE **Using Mental Math for Divisibility**

1 **a.** Is 56 divisible by 7?

Think Since $56 = 8 \times 7$, 56 is divisible by 7.

b. Is 56 divisible by 4?

Think Since $56 = 8 \times 7$, and $4 \times 2 = 8$, 56 is divisible by 4.

☑ Quick Check

1. a. Is 64 divisible by 6? **no**

b. Is 93 divisible by 3? **yes**

You can test for divisibility using the rules below.

KEY CONCEPTS **Divisibility of Whole Numbers**

A whole number is divisible by
- 2, if the number ends in 0, 2, 4, 6, or 8.
- 3, if the sum of the number's digits is divisible by 3.
- 5, if the number ends in 0 or 5.
- 9, if the sum of the number's digits is divisible by 9.
- 10, if the number ends in 0.

Differentiated Instruction **Solutions for All Learners**

Special Needs L1
Have students use a multiplication chart until they become comfortable with divisibility. This will help them make the connection between multiplication and division, and help them calculate quickly as needed.

learning style: visual

Below Level L2
Review remainders by giving students several pairs of divisions like these.

35 ÷ 5 **7 R0**   90 ÷ 6 **15 R0**
36 ÷ 5 **7 R1**   94 ÷ 6 **15 R4**

learning style: visual

An **even number** is a whole number that ends with a 0, 2, 4, 6, or 8.
An **odd number** is a whole number that ends with a 1, 3, 5, 7, or 9.

EXAMPLE Divisibility by 2, 3, 5, and 10

② Test 715 for divisibility by 2, 3, 5, and 10.

  2: 715 is not an even number. So 715 is not divisible by 2.

  3: Find the sum of the digits in 715.

   $7 + 1 + 5 = 13$ ← **Add the digits.**

   The sum of the digits of 715 is 13, which is not divisible by 3.
   So 715 is not divisible by 3.

  5: 715 ends in a 5. So 715 is divisible by 5.

  10: 715 does not end in 0. So 715 is not divisible by 10.

So 715 is divisible by 5, but not by 2, 3, or 10.

✓ Quick Check

2a. divisible by 2, 3, 5, and 10

  b. divisible by none of these

  c. divisible by 2 and 3

2. Test each number for divisibility by 2, 3, 5, and 10. **See left.**
  a. 150   **b.** 1,021   **c.** 2,112

To test a number for divisibility by 9, you start by finding the sum of the number's digits—just as you did with divisibility by 3.

EXAMPLE Divisibility by 9

③ **Planning** There are 163 people signed up to play softball. Each team will have exactly 9 players. Will everyone who has signed up have a spot on one of the 9-person teams?

If 163 is divisible by 9, then everyone will have a spot on a team.

  $1 + 6 + 3 = 10$ ← **Find the sum of the digits in 163.**

  $10 \div 9$ has a remainder of 1.   ← **The sum is not divisible by 9.**

163 is not divisible by 9. Not everyone will have a spot on a team.

✓ Quick Check

3. **Music** A high school marching band has 126 members. Each row in the band formation on the field has 9 musicians. Will everyone in the band fit in a nine-person row?
  yes

Activity Lab

Use before the lesson.

All in One Teaching Resources

Activity Lab 4-1: Prime and Composite Numbers

Guided Instruction

Error Prevention!

Students might believe that a number is divisible by 2, 5, or 10 if the sum of the digits is divisible by 2, 5, or 10. Stress that the sum-of-the-digits divisibility method applies only to 3 and 9.

PowerPoint
Additional Examples

① Is the first number divisible by the second? Use mental math.

  a. 46 by 3 **no**

  b. 63 by 7 **yes**

② Test each number for divisibility by 2, 3, 5, or 10.

  a. 580 **divisible by 2, 5, and 10**

  b. 3,042 **divisible by 2 and 3**

③ A baker sells muffins in boxes that contain exactly 9 muffins each. Can the baker place 576 muffins in boxes of 9 with none left over? **yes**

All in One Teaching Resources
• Daily Notetaking Guide 4-1 **L3**
• Adapted Notetaking 4-1 **L1**

Closure

• Describe the tests for divisibility by 2, 5, and 10. **Sample: If a number is even, it is divisible by 2; if a number ends in 5 or 0, it is divisible by 5; if a number ends in 0, it is divisible by 10.**

Advanced Learners **L4**
Find all the even numbers between 1,000 and 2,000 that are divisible by 5 and also by 9. **1,080; 1,170; 1,260; 1,350; 1,440; 1,530; 1,620; 1,710; 1,800; 1,890; 1,980**

learning style: visual

English Language Learners **ELL**
Have each student rewrite the divisibility rules on an index card and write examples using symbols next to each rule. Next to the explanation of divisibility by 3, for example, show $51 \div 3$; Yes, $5 + 1 = 6$.

learning style: visual

Assignment Guide

Check Your Understanding
Go over Exercises 1–5 in class before assigning the Homework Exercises.

Homework Exercises

A	Practice by Example	6–25
B	Apply Your Skills	26–33
C	Challenge	34
	Test Prep and Mixed Review	35–41

Homework Quick Check
To check students' understanding of key skills and concepts, go over Exercises 12, 24, 30, 31, and 32.

Differentiated Instruction Resources

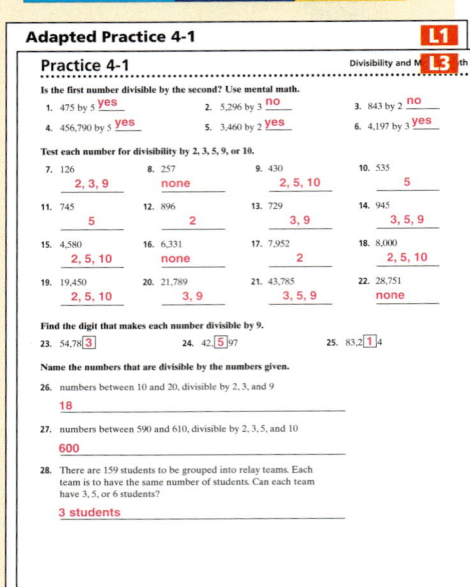

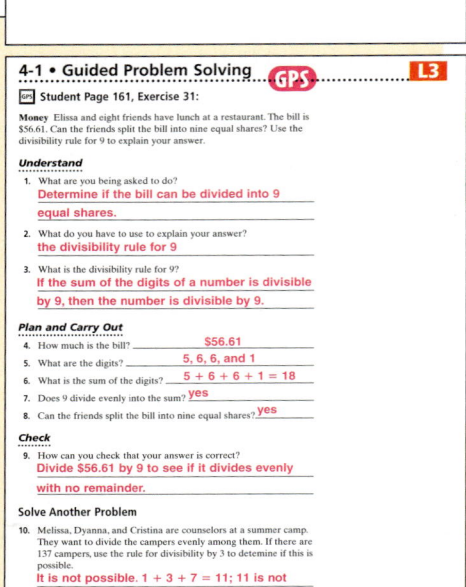

Check Your Understanding

1. If the number is divisible by 2, then the number is even; otherwise, the number is odd.

1. **Vocabulary** How can you tell whether a number is odd or even?

2. **Number Sense** Since 54 is divisible by 6, 54 is also divisible by 2 and 3. Explain. **6 is divisible by 2 and 3.**

Match each number with its divisibility numbers.

3. 60 **C**

4. 48 **B**

5. 81 **A**

    A. 3, 9

    B. 2, 3

    C. 2, 3, 5, 10

Homework Exercises

For more exercises, see Extra Skills and Word Problems.

GO for Help

For Exercises	See Examples
6–9	1
10–22	2
23–25	3

10. **2, 3, 5, and 10**
14. **2, 3, 5, and 10**

(A) Is the first number divisible by the second? Use mental math.

6. 48 by 4 **yes**   7. 46 by 4 **no**   8. 63 by 7 **yes**   9. 122 by 6 **no**

Test each number for divisibility by 2, 3, 5, and 10.

10. 48,960   11. 2,385 **3 and 5**   12. 928 **2**

13. 672 **2 and 3**   14. 202,470   15. 53,559 **3**

16. 57 **3**   17. 92 **2**   18. 171 **3**

19. 962 **2**   20. 1,956 **2 and 3**   21. 11,160 **2, 3, 5, and 10**

22. A total of 114 people have signed up to play in a basketball tournament. There are 3 people on each team. Will everyone who has signed up have a spot on a 3-person team? Explain. **yes; 114 ÷ 3 = 38**

Test each number for divisibility by 9.

23. 1,187 **no**   24. 2,187 **yes**   25. 17,595 **yes**

(B) GPS 26. **Guided Problem Solving** A theater group has 84 members. In how many different ways can the director split the group into teams of equal size? **10 ways**
- Is there more than one way to divide the group?
- How can you use divisibility rules to solve this problem?

What digit makes each number divisible by 9?

27. 9,0■5
4

28. ■7,302
6

29. 2■6,555
4

30. Time The number 60 is convenient for timekeeping because it can be easily divided by many numbers. Is 60 divisible by 2, 3, 4, 5, 6, 7, 8, 9, or 10? **60 is divisible by 2, 3, 4, 5, 6, and 10.**

31. Money Elissa and eight friends have lunch at a restaurant. **GPS** The bill is $56.61. Can the friends split the bill into nine equal shares? Use the divisibility rule for 9 to explain your answer. **See margin.**

32. Patterns A number pattern begins 6, 12, 18, 24, . . .
 a. Write the next four numbers in the pattern.
 b. Which of the eight numbers are divisible by both 2 and 3?
 c. Writing in Math Write a rule for divisibility by 6.
 32a–c. See margin.

33. You have $17 to spend on rides that cost $2 each. If you go on as many rides as you can afford, how much money will you have left? **$1.00**

C 34. Challenge Write all the three-digit numbers containing a 1, 2, and 3. Which of these numbers are divisible by 4? Explain.
123, 132, 213, 231, 312, 321; 132 and 312

Test Prep and Mixed Review
Practice

Multiple Choice

35. Rosa plants rows of flowers with exactly the same number in each row. Each row has more than one flower. She has 28 flowers. What is the largest number of rows she can make?
 Ⓐ 4   Ⓑ 7   Ⓒ 12   Ⓓ 14 **D**

36. Ben must buy all the equipment on the list. He estimates the total cost by rounding each price. Which is the closest to the amount Ben will spend? **J**
 Ⓕ $77   Ⓗ $79
 Ⓖ $78   Ⓙ $80

Soccer Equipment	
Item	**Price($)**
Ball	14.98
Cleats	18.99
Shin guards	11.75
Team socks	6.25
Team jersey	28.50

37. A centimeter is one hundredth of a meter. Which measurement is equal to a centimeter? **B**
 Ⓐ 0.1 m   Ⓑ 0.01 m   Ⓒ 0.001 m   Ⓓ 0.0001 m

GO for Help

For Exercises	See Lesson
38–41	3-2

Evaluate each expression.

38. $2(a - 1)$ for $a = 2$ **2**

39. $1 + 7a$ for $a = 5$ **36**

40. $6(b + 2)$ for $b = 3$ **30**

41. $3b - 2$ for $b = 3$ **7**

31. Yes; 5 + 6 + 6 + 1 = 18 and 18 is divisible by 9, so 5661, or $56.61, is divisible by 9.

32a. 30, 36, 42, 48

 b. All are divisible by 2 and 3.

 c. Any number that is divisible by both 2 and 3 is also divisible by 6.

Test Prep

Resources

For additional practice with a variety of test item formats:
• Test-Taking Strategies, p. 203
• Test Prep, p. 207
• Test-Taking Strategies with Transparencies

PowerPoint
Lesson Quiz

Test each number for divisibility by 2, 3, 5, 9, and 10.

1. 18,520 **2, 5, 10**

2. 270 **2, 3, 5, 9, 10**

3. 5,625 **3, 5, 9**

4. 100,000 **2, 5, 10**

Alternative Assessment

Have students work in pairs. Partners write a list of the whole numbers from 1 to 100. Using a colored pencil, they circle each digit in the ones place and write 2, 5, and/or 10 to the left of each number by which that number is divisible. Next, they write the sum of the digits of the numbers at the right. For each, they determine whether the number is divisible by 3 and/or 9, and use a second color to indicate whether this is so.

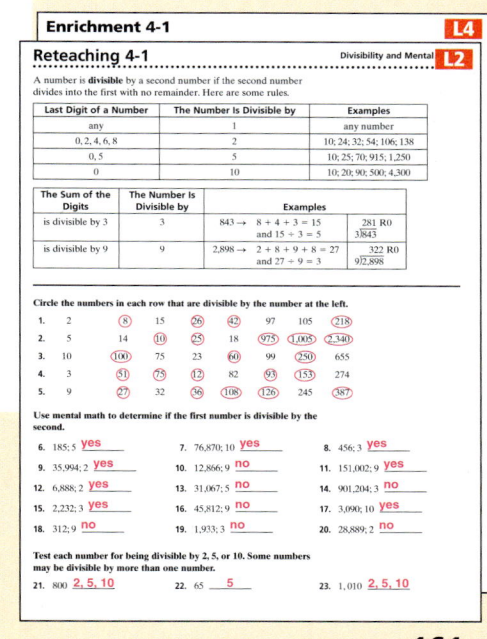

Objective
To use exponents and to simplify expressions with exponents

Examples
1 Using an Exponent
2 Simplifying a Power
3 Simplifying an Expression

Math Understandings: p. 156C

Math Background

Exponents are a mathematical "shorthand" for some calculations:

$$\underbrace{a \times a \times a \times \cdots \times a}_{n \text{ factors}} = a^n$$

In the expression a^n, a is the *base* and n is the *exponent*. When a is a nonzero number, the value of a^0 is defined to be 1. ($5^0 = 1$; $9^0 = 1$)

This lesson completes the development of the order of operations by establishing the position of exponents in the sequence: parentheses; exponents; multiplication, division, addition, and subtraction.

More Math Background: p. 156C

Lesson Planning and Resources

See p. 156E for a list of the resources that support this lesson.

Bell Ringer Practice

✓ **Check Skills You'll Need**
Use student page, transparency, or PowerPoint. For intervention, direct students to:
Order of Operations
Lesson 1-4
Extra Skills and Word Problems Practice, Ch. 1

✓ Check Skills You'll Need

1. Vocabulary Review
A mathematical phrase containing numbers and symbols is an ___?___ .
expression
Find the value of each expression.

2. $3 \times 3 + 4 \times 4$ **25**

3. $1 \times 3 - 1 \times 3$ **0**

4. $1 + 1 \times 2 - 1$ **2**

 **for Help**
Lesson 1-4

Vocabulary Tip
You read 5^4 as "5 to the fourth power."

1a. 3.94^2; 3.94; 2
 b. 7^4; 7; 4
 c. x^3; x; 3

What You'll Learn
To use exponents and to simplify expressions with exponents

🔊 **New Vocabulary** exponent, base, power

Why Learn This?

Exponents are used to represent numbers. You need exponents to write large numbers like the number of stars in a galaxy.

You can write 625 as a product of factors.

$$625 = \underbrace{5 \times 5 \times 5 \times 5}_{\text{factors}}$$

The number 5 is used as a factor four times. An **exponent** tells you how many times a number, or **base,** is used as a factor.

$$5 \times 5 \times 5 \times 5 = 5^4 \quad \leftarrow \text{exponent}$$
$$\uparrow$$
$$\text{base}$$

5^4 is a power. A **power** is a number that can be expressed using an exponent.

EXAMPLE Using an Exponent

① Write $3 \times 3 \times 3 \times 3$ using an exponent. Name the base and the exponent.

$$3 \times 3 \times 3 \times 3 = 3^4 \quad \leftarrow 3^4 \text{ means that 3 is used as a factor 4 times.}$$

The base is 3, and the exponent is 4.

✓ Quick Check

1. Write each expression using an exponent. Name the base and the exponent. **See left.**
 a. 3.94×3.94 **b.** $7 \times 7 \times 7 \times 7$ **c.** $x \cdot x \cdot x$

---

162 **Chapter 4** Number Theory and Fractions

Differentiated Instruction **Solutions for All Learners**

Special Needs **L1**
Have students draw a 3×4 array. Ask them to count the squares. Next have them draw a 3×3 array. Ask: *How much is 3×3 or 3^2?* **9** Then have them draw a 9×3 array, writing $3 \times 3 \times 3$ next to it, and show that 3^3 is greater than 3×4.

learning style: visual

Below Level **L2**
Have students evaluate several pairs of powers like these.

2^3, 3^2 **8; 9** 5^2, 2^5 **25; 32**
3^4, 4^3 **81; 64** 7^3, 3^7 **343; 2,187**

learning style: verbal

The area of the square is 3×3, or 3^2. You read 3^2 as "three squared."

The volume of the cube is $4 \times 4 \times 4$, or 4^3. You read 4^3 as "four cubed."

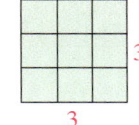
3
3

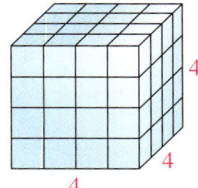
4
4
4

EXAMPLE   Simplifying a Power

② **Science** You have 2^5 bones in your hand and arm. What is the value of 2^5?

$$2^5 = 2 \times 2 \times 2 \times 2 \times 2 = 32 \quad \leftarrow \text{The base 2 is used as a factor 5 times.}$$

The value of 2^5 is 32.

✓ Quick Check

2. Astronomy Phobos, the largest of Mars's moons, has a diameter of 3^3 kilometers. What is the value of 3^3? **27**

The order of operations can be extended to include exponents.

> ### KEY CONCEPTS   Order of Operations
>
> 1. Do all operations within parentheses first.
> 2. Do all work with exponents.
> 3. Multiply and divide in order from left to right.
> 4. Add and subtract in order from left to right.

EXAMPLE   Simplifying an Expression

③ Simplify $3 \times (7^2 + 18 \div 2)$.

$3 \times (49 + 18 \div 2)$ ← Simplify within parentheses. Simplify 7^2.

$3 \times (49 + 9)$ ← In parentheses, simplify $18 \div 2$.

$3 \times (58)$ ← In parentheses, add $49 + 9$.

174 ← Multiply 3 and 58.

Video Tutor Help
Visit: PHSchool.com
Web Code: aqe-0775

GO **●**nline

✓ Quick Check

3. a. Simplify $2^3 - 6 \div 3$. **6**   **b.** Simplify $5 + (2 + 1)^2$. **14**

Advanced Learners **L4**
Fill in the boxes with whole numbers to make a true statement. Find as many answers as possible.
$\square^{\square} = 64$ **2^6, 4^3, 8^2, 64^1**

English Language Learners **ELL**
Write $3 \times 3 \times 3 \times 3$ and ask: *What number do you see?* **3** That is the base. *How many times do you see the 3?* **4** That is the exponent. Write 3 to the fourth power together. Explain that this is the same as saying 3 is used as a factor 4 times.

learning style: visual   **learning style: verbal**

---

2. Teach

Activity Lab
Use before the lesson.

All in One Teaching Resources
Activity Lab 4-2: Understanding Exponents

Guided Instruction

Example 1
Some students with visual impairments might find it difficult to distinguish exponents from bases. For instance, they might see the expression 3^4 as 34. Suggest that these students align the edge of a ruler with the bottom of the expression and look for that part of the expression that does not touch the ruler. This will be the exponent.

PowerPoint
■ Additional Examples

① Write $5 \times 5 \times 5 \times 5$ using an exponent. Name the base and the exponent. **5^4; the base is 5 and the exponent is 4.**

② Simplify each expression.
  a. 6^3 **216**
  b. 3^5 **243**
  c. 2.7^4 **53.1441**

③ Simplify the expression:
$24 - (8 - 1.2 \times 5)^2$. **20**

All in One Teaching Resources
• Daily Notetaking Guide 4-2 **L3**
• Adapted Notetaking 4-2 **L1**

Closure

• *How do you evaluate a base raised to an exponent?* **Sample: Perform a multiplication in which the base is used as a factor the number of times indicated by the exponent.**
• *What is the order of operations in an expression that includes exponents?* **Sample: Do operations within parentheses first; do all work with exponents; multiply and divide in order from left to right; add and subtract in order from left to right.**

163

3. Practice

Assignment Guide

Check Your Understanding
Go over Exercises 1–7 in class before assigning the Homework Exercises.

Homework Exercises
A Practice by Example   8–26
B Apply Your Skills   27–34
C Challenge   35
Test Prep and
    Mixed Review   36–39

Homework Quick Check
To check students' understanding of key skills and concepts, go over Exercises 12, 23, 28, 32, and 33.

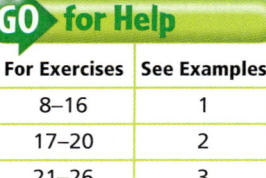

Adapted Practice 4-2   **L1**

Practice 4-2   **L3**

Write each expression using an exponent. Name the base and the exponent.

1. $3 \times 3 \times 3 \times 3$ 2. $7 \times 7 \times 7 \times 7 \times 7 \times 7$ 3. $9 \times 9 \times 9$
   3^4; 3 is the base, 7^6; 7 is the base, 9^3; 9 is the base,
   4 is the exponent   6 is the exponent   3 is the exponent

Write each number in expanded form using powers of 10.

4. 98,364   5. 20,351,401   6. 875,020
   $9 \times 10^4 + 8 \times 10^3 +$ $2 \times 10^7 + 3 \times 10^5 +$ $8 \times 10^5 + 7 \times 10^4 +$
   $3 \times 10^2 + 6 \times 10^1 +$ $5 \times 10^4 + 1 \times 10^3 +$ $5 \times 10^3 + 2 \times 10^1$
   4×1 $4 \times 10^2 + 1 \times 1$

Simplify each expression.

7. 9^2 81   8. 6^4 1,296   9. 5^3 125
10. $156 + (256 \div 8^2)$ 160   11. $32 + 64 \div 2^3$ 104   12. $53 + 64 \div 2^3$ 61
13. $(3 \times 4)^2$ 144   14. $60 \div (8 + 7) + 11$ 15   15. $2^2 \times 5^2 + 106$ 206
16. $4 + 7 \times 2^3$ 60   17. $60 \div (5 \times 4^3) + 2^2 \times 55$ 600   18. $7^2 + 4$ 53
19. $7^2 - 7 \times 2$ 35   20. $48 \div 4 \times 5 - 2 \times 5$ 50   21. $(4^2 - 4) \times 10$ 120
22. $(4 + 3) \times (2 + 1)$ 21   23. $2^4 \times 2^5$ 512   24. $12 \times (30 + 37)$ 804
25. $(3 + 2) \times (6^2 - 7)$ 145   26. $5 \times (9 + 4) + 362 \div 2$ 246   27. $3^4 + 405 + 81$ 86

4-2 • Guided Problem Solving   **GPS**   **L3**

Student Page 165, Exercise 33:

Biology A single-celled animal splits in two after one hour. Each new cell also splits in two after one hour. How many cells will there be after eight hours? Write your answer using an exponent.

Understand
1. What are you being asked to do?
   Find how many cells there will be after 8 hours.
2. Explain what it means to write a number with an exponent.
   It means the number is multiplied by itself the number of times shown in the exponent.

Plan and Carry Out
3. How many cells are there after 3 hours? Write the number using an exponent.
   2^3 cells
4. How many cells are there after 4 hours? Write the number using an exponent.
   2^4 cells
5. How many cells are there after 6 hours? Write the number using an exponent.
   2^6 cells
6. How many cells are there after 8 hours? Write the number using an exponent.
   2^8 cells

Check
7. Why is the exponent 8?
   because the cell doubled eight times

Solve Another Problem
8. An organism divides into 3 different organisms after the first hour. Each of those 3 organisms divide into 3 different organisms after the second hour. If this pattern continues, how many organisms are there after 4 hours? Write the number using an exponent.
   3^4 organisms

✓ Check Your Understanding

1. **Vocabulary** How are exponents used to represent factors?
   The exponent tells how many times the base is used as a factor.
2. **Number Sense** Does 5^4 have the same value as 5×4? Explain.
   No; $5^4 = 5 \times 5 \times 5 \times 5 = 625$ and $5 \times 4 = 5 + 5 + 5 + 5 = 20$.

Write each expression below using an exponent.

3. $3 \times 3 = 3^{\blacksquare}$ 4. $2 \times 2 \times 2 = \blacksquare^3$ 5. $9 \times 9 \times 9 = 9^{\blacksquare}$
   3^2 2^3 9^3

Fill in each blank.

6. $4^2 = 4 \times 4 = \blacksquare$ 7. $2^3 = \blacksquare \times \blacksquare \times \blacksquare = 8$
   16   2   2   2

Homework Exercises

For more exercises, see **Extra Skills and Word Problems.**

A Write each expression using an exponent. Name the base and the exponent. 8–13. See margin.

GO for Help

For Exercises	See Examples
8–16	1
17–20	2
21–26	3

8. $1 \times 1 \times 1 \times 1$ 9. 29 10. $3 \times 3 \times 3 \times 3$

11. $25 \times 25 \times 25$ 12. $2.5 \times 2.5 \times 2.5$ 13. $100 \times 100 \times 100$

14. $r \cdot r$ r^2; r; 2   15. $b \cdot b \cdot b \cdot b \cdot b$ 16. $25 \cdot n \cdot n \cdot n \cdot n$
                          b^5; b; 5 $25n^4$; n; 4

17. A small plane needs 5^3 meters to take off or land. What is the value of 5^3?   125

Simplify each expression.

18. 5^2 25   19. 4^3 64   20. 2.5^2 6.25

21. $(2 + 3)^2$ 25   22. $(3^2 - 1)^2$ 64   23. $(9 - 7)^3 \times 6$ 48

24. $(9 + 1)^2 - 1^3$ 99   25. $15^2 - (1 + 13^2)$ 26. $(10 - 8)^4 \times 3.5$
                                55   56

GPS 27. **Guided Problem Solving** A band of cumulus clouds is located
B   at 10^4 feet. A commercial jet is traveling at 38,000 feet. What is the difference between the altitude of the clouds and the altitude of the jet?   28,000 ft
    • How many feet is 10^4 feet?

28. **Geography** The population of Australia is more than 20,000,000 people. You can write 20,000,000 as $2 \times 10,000,000$. Write 10,000,000 using exponents. 10^7

8. 1^4; 1; 4   11. 25^3; 25; 3

9. 29^1; 29; 1   12. 2.5^3; 2.5; 3

10. 3^4; 3; 4   13. 100^3; 100; 3

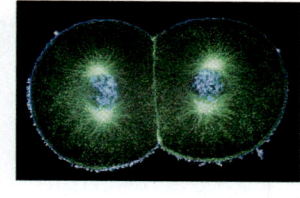
(Algebra) **Evaluate each expression for $j = 2$ and $g = 4$.**

29. j^6 **64**

30. $(j + g)^3$ **216**

31. $(j + g)^2 + 4$ **40**

32. Patterns Copy the table. **32a–d. See margin.**
  a. Fill in the missing values.
  b. **Writing in Math** Explain how the number of zeros in the standard form of a power of 10 relates to the exponent.
  c. Extend the table to 10^8.
  d. Write a rule for the number pattern.

Power	Standard Form
10^1	10
10^2	100
10^3	1,000
10^4	■
■	■

33. Biology A single-celled animal splits in two after one hour.
GPS Each new cell also splits in two after one hour. How many cells will there be after eight hours? Write your answer using an exponent. **2^8 cells**

34. Reasoning Does the expression $2^2 \cdot 3^2 - 2^3 - 1$ have the same value as $2^2 \cdot (3^2 - 2^3) - 1$? Explain. **See margin.**

C 35. Challenge In the equation $d = s^2$, d equals 32. Between what two whole numbers is the value of s? **5 and 6**

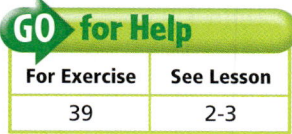
Test Prep and Mixed Review **Practice**

Multiple Choice

36. Yoel has 3 fewer coins than Selena. Selena has 15 coins. Which equation can be used to find k, the number of coins Yoel has?
  Ⓐ $k = 3 \cdot 5$
  Ⓑ $k = 15 \div 3$
  Ⓒ $k = 15 - 3$
  Ⓓ $k = 15 + 3$
  C

37. Karen and her son share 30 grapes. Karen eats twice as many grapes as her son. How many grapes does Karen eat? **H**
  Ⓕ 10
  Ⓖ 15
  Ⓗ 20
  Ⓙ 30

38. The table shows the relationship between side length and volume of a cube. If the side length is n, what is the volume of the cube? **D**
  Ⓐ $2n$
  Ⓑ n^2
  Ⓒ $3n$
  Ⓓ n^3

Side Length, n	Volume
1	1
2	8
3	27
n	■

39. The data below show lengths, in inches, of lake trout. Make a line plot using the data. **See margin.**

13 21 16 15 16 11 15 19 13 16 14 16 15 14 12

32a. 10,000; 10^5; 100,000

  b. The exponent tells the number of 0's in standard form.

  c. 10^6; 1,000,000; 10^7; 10,000,000; 10^8; 100,000,000

  d. 10^n represents 1 followed by n zeros.

Test Prep

Resources
For additional practice with a variety of test item formats:
• Test-Taking Strategies, p. 203
• Test Prep, p. 207
• Test-Taking Strategies with Transparencies

4. Assess & Reteach

PowerPoint
Lesson Quiz

Write each expression using an exponent.

1. 6×6 **6^2**   **2.** $8 \times 8 \times 8$ **8^3**

Simplify each expression.

3. 5^4 **625**   **4.** 3.2^2 **10.24**

5. $2^3 + (10 - 5)$ **13**

6. $3^2 \times (9 - 2) + 1$ **64**

Alternative Assessment

Provide pairs of students with two sets of 1–9 digit cards. Pairs shuffle each set and place them face down in separate stacks, designating one stack as the base and one as the exponent. Partners work together to turn over one card from each stack. They then evaluate the expression and record each base, exponent, and result.

34. See back of book.

39. See back of book.

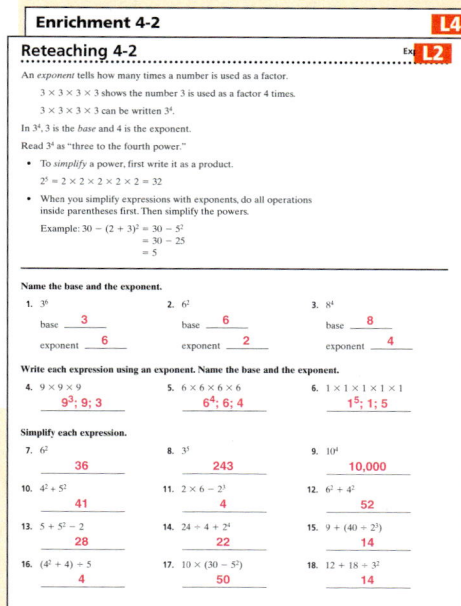

Objective
To factor numbers and to find the prime factorization of numbers

Examples
1 Finding Factors
2 Prime or Composite?
3 Prime Factorization

Math Understandings: p. 156C

Math Background

When one whole number is divisible by a second, the second number is said to be a *factor* of the first. If a whole number greater than 1 has exactly two factors, 1 and the number itself, it is called a *prime number*. If a whole number greater than 1 has more than two factors, it is called a *composite number*. Writing a whole number as a product of prime factors is called the *prime factorization* of the number. Every whole number greater than 1 has exactly one prime factorization.

More Math Background: p. 156C

Lesson Planning and Resources

See p. 156E for a list of the resources that support this lesson.

Bell Ringer Practice

✓ **Check Skills You'll Need**
Use student page, transparency, or PowerPoint. For intervention, direct students to:
Divisibility and Mental Math
Lesson 4-1
Extra Skills and Word Problems Practice, Ch. 4

✓ **Check Skills You'll Need**

1. Vocabulary Review
Is a number *divisible* by 5 always divisible by 10?
1–5. See below.
Test each number for divisibility by 2, 3, 5, 9, and 10.

2. 990   3. 901

4. 800   5. 2,080

 **for Help**
Lesson 4-1

Check Skills You'll Need

1. **No; 25 is divisible by 5 but not divisible by 10.**

2. **2, 3, 5, 9, 10**

3. **divisible by none of these**

4. **2, 5, and 10**

5. **2, 5, and 10**

What You'll Learn

To factor numbers and to find the prime factorization of numbers

◀)) **New Vocabulary** factor, composite number, prime number, prime factorization

Why Learn This?

Using factors, you can organize items or people in rows.

Divisibility rules can help you find factors. A **factor** is a whole number that divides a nonzero whole number with remainder 0.

EXAMPLE **Finding Factors**

① An instructor plans a dance routine for 20 dancers in rows. Each row has the same number of dancers. What are the arrangements the instructor can use?

Look for pairs of factors for 20 to find the possible arrangements.

1×20 ← Write each pair of factors. Start with 1.
$2 \times 10, \ 4 \times 5$ ← 2 and 4 are factors. Skip 3, since 20 is not divisible by 3.
5×4 ← Stop when you repeat factors.

The arrangements are 1×20, 2×10, and 4×5.

✓ **Quick Check**

1. A gift box must hold the same number of pears in each row. You have 24 pears. What arrangements can you use?
$1 \times 24, 2 \times 12, 3 \times 8, 4 \times 6$

A **composite number** is a whole number greater than 1 with more than two factors. A **prime number** is a whole number with exactly two factors, 1 and the number itself. The numbers 0 and 1 are neither prime nor composite.

166   Chapter 4   Number Theory and Fractions

Differentiated Instruction **Solutions for All Learners**

Special Needs [L1]
For Example 1, pair students to draw possible arrays for the 20 desks in the classroom. Provide graph paper, which can be cut out and glued, and ask students to write a multiplication equation next to each array.

learning style: visual

Below Level [L2]
Give students several missing-factor exercises like these.

$34 = 2 \times \blacksquare$ **17** $161 = 7 \times \blacksquare$ **23**
$65 = 5 \times \blacksquare$ **13** $63 = 3 \times 3 \times \blacksquare$ **7**

learning style: verbal

EXAMPLE **Prime or Composite?**

② Is the number prime or composite? Explain.

a. 51

Composite: 51 is divisible by 3. So 51 has more than two factors.

b. 53

Prime: 53 has only two factors, 1 and 53.

✓ **Quick Check**

2a. composite; $39 = 3 \times 13$

b. Prime; it has only two factors, 1 and 47.

c. composite; $63 = 3 \times 21$ or $63 = 7 \times 9$

2. Is the number prime or composite? Explain. **See left.**

a. 39　　　　　　b. 47　　　　　　c. 63

To write the **prime factorization** of a composite number, you write the number as a product of prime numbers. Each composite number has only one prime factorization.

When a factor repeats, use exponents to write your answer. You can use a division ladder or a factor tree to find the prime factorization of a number.

EXAMPLE **Prime Factorization**

③ Write the prime factorization of 84 using exponents.

Method 1 Use a division ladder.

$2\overline{)84}$　← Divide 84 by the prime number 2. Work down.
$2\overline{)42}$　← The result is 42. Since 42 is even, divide by 2 again.
$3\overline{)21}$　← The result is 21. Divide by the prime number 3.
　　7　← The prime factorization is 2 × 2 × 3 × 7.

Online active math

For: Prime Factorization Activity
Use: Interactive Textbook, 4-3

Method 2 Use a factor tree.

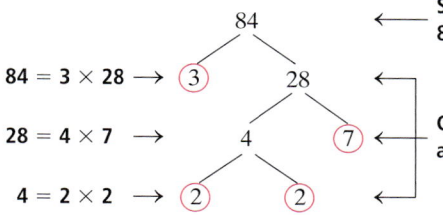

Since the sum of the digits of 84 is 12, 84 is divisible by 3.

$84 = 3 \times 28 \rightarrow$　84

$28 = 4 \times 7 \rightarrow$　28

$4 = 2 \times 2 \rightarrow$

Circle the prime numbers as you find them.

The prime factorization of 84 is $2 \times 2 \times 3 \times 7$, or $2^2 \times 3 \times 7$.

✓ **Quick Check**

3. Find the prime factorization of 27. **3^3**

---

2. Teach

Activity Lab

Use before the lesson.

All in One Teaching Resources

Activity Lab 4-3: Critical Thinking

Guided Instruction

Example 3
Be sure students understand that whether they divide 84 by 2 or 3 first, the prime factorization will be the same.

PowerPoint

Additional Examples

① List the factors of each number.

a. 24 **1, 2, 3, 4, 6, 8, 12, 24**

b. 35 **1, 5, 7, 35**

② Tell whether each number is prime or composite. Explain.

a. 61 **61 is prime. There are only two factors: 1 and 61.**

b. 65 **65 is composite. 5 is a factor of 65.**

③ Find the prime factorization of 90. **2 × 3² × 5**

All in One Teaching Resources

• Daily Notetaking Guide 4-3 **L3**
• Adapted Notetaking 4-3 **L1**

Closure

• *What is the prime factorization of a number?* **an expression that shows the number as a product of prime numbers**

Advanced Learners **L4**
Find all the whole numbers less than 50 whose only prime factors are 2 or 3. **2, 3, 4, 6, 8, 9, 12, 16, 18, 24, 27, 32, 36, 48**

learning style: visual

English Language Learners **ELL**
Ensure students can explain why in Example 3, you start with 2 as a divisor. Explain that it is easier to find prime factors if you get one of the prime factors out of the way in the first division or first multiplication on the factor tree.

learning style: verbal

167

3. Practice

Assignment Guide

Check Your Understanding
Go over Exercises 1–4 in class before assigning the Homework Exercises.

Homework Exercises
A Practice by Example   5–25
B Apply Your Skills   26–32
C Challenge   33
Test Prep and
   Mixed Review   34–38

Homework Quick Check
To check students' understanding of key skills and concepts, go over Exercises 11, 23, 28, 30, and 31.

Differentiated Instruction Resources

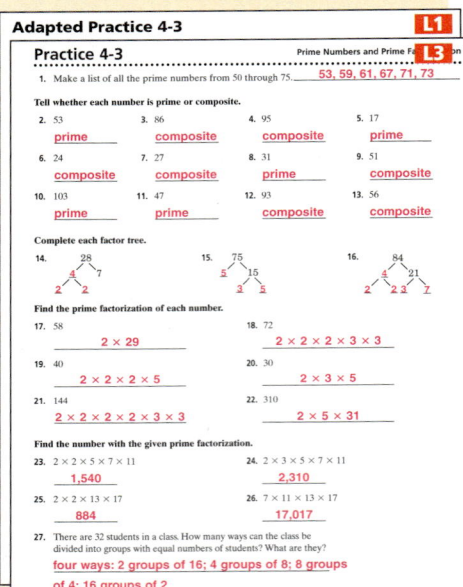

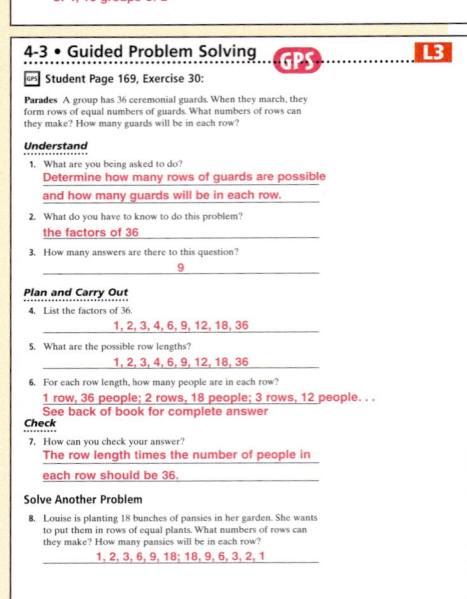

Check Your Understanding

1. **Vocabulary** How is a prime number different from a composite number? **A prime number has exactly two factors and a composite number has more than two factors.**

2. Find two prime numbers between 10 and 20, with a difference of 2. **11 and 13, 17 and 19**

3. **7; 7 has just two factors, 1 and 7.**

3. Which number is not a composite number? Explain. **See left.**

55	51	82	7

4. **Number Sense** Can two numbers have the same prime factorization? Explain. **No. Each number has only one prime factorization.**

Homework Exercises

For more exercises, see Extra Skills and Word Problems.

GO for Help

For Exercises	See Examples
5–13	1
14–17	2
18–25	3

A List the factors of each number. **5–12. See margin.**

5. 28   6. 21   7. 17   8. 60

9. 48   10. 37   11. 144   12. 450

13. **Earth Science** For a science project, you want to display 36 rocks in rows, with the same number of rocks in each row. Find the arrangements that you can use.
$1 \times 36, 2 \times 1$

Is each number *prime* or *composite*? Explain. **14–17. See Left.**

14. **Prime; the only factors are 1 and 19.**

15. **Prime; the only factors are 1 and 67.**

16. **composite; $57 = 3 \times 19$**

17. **composite; $91 = 7 \times 13$**

14. 19   15. 67   16. 57   17. 91

Find the prime factorization of each number.

18. 32 2^5 19. 42 $2 \times 3 \times 7$ 20. 75 3×5^2 21. 400 $2^4 \times 5^2$

22. 15 3×5 23. 45 $3^2 \times 5$ 24. 450 $2 \times 3^2 \times 5^2$ 25. 10,000 $2^4 \times 5^4$

B **GPS** 26. **Guided Problem Solving** The yearbook editor must arrange 48 student photos on a page. Each row must have the same number of photos. What arrangements can she make?
- **Make a Plan** What method can you use to find the factor pairs for 48?
- **Check the Answer** How do you know that you have found all the factor pairs? **$1 \times 48; 2 \times 24; 3 \times 16; 4 \times 12; 6 \times 8$**

5. 1, 2, 4, 7, 14, 28

6. 1, 3, 7, 21

7. 1, 17

8. 1, 2, 3, 4, 5, 6, 10, 12, 15, 20, 30, 60

9. 1, 2, 3, 4, 6, 8, 12, 16, 24, 48

10. 1, 37

11. 1, 2, 3, 4, 6, 8, 9, 12, 16, 18, 24, 36, 48, 72, 144

12. 1, 2, 3, 5, 6, 9, 10, 15, 18, 25, 30, 45, 50, 75, 90, 150, 225, 450

Calculator Find the number with the given prime factorization.

27. $7 \times 11 \times 13$ **1,001**

28. $2^3 \times 5^2 \times 7 \times 11$ **15,400**

29. A clerk arranges 81 apples in a square crate. Each row has the same number of apples. How many rows does he make? **9 rows**

30. Parades A group has 36 ceremonial guards. When they march, they form rows of equal numbers of guards. What numbers of rows can they make? How many guards will be in each row? **1 × 36; 2 × 18; 3 × 12; 4 × 9; 6 × 6**

31. (Algebra) Suppose p is a prime number greater than 2. Does $p + 1$ represent a prime or a composite number? Explain. **See margin.**

32. Landscaping A homeowner buys 116 square tiles to build a rectangular patio. The same number of tiles are in each row. What are the arrangements of tiles that he can make? **1 × 116; 2 × 58; 4 × 29**

C 33. Challenge Find the pairs of prime numbers with a difference of two, between 1 and 100. **3, 5; 5, 7; 11, 13; 17, 19; 29, 31; 41, 43; 59, 61; 71, 73**

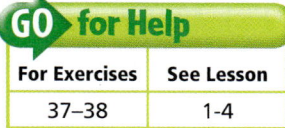
Test Prep and Mixed Review **Practice**

Multiple Choice

34. What is the prime factorization of 48? **D**
Ⓐ $12 \cdot 4$ Ⓑ $6 \cdot 2^4$ Ⓒ $3 \cdot 2 \cdot 2^2$ Ⓓ $2^4 \cdot 3$

35. The graph below shows the results of a student survey. Which statement is supported by the graph? **F**
Ⓕ More students prefer pop or rock than jazz.
Ⓖ More students prefer jazz than country.
Ⓗ About half of the students prefer country and jazz.
Ⓙ 100 students prefer pop or rock.

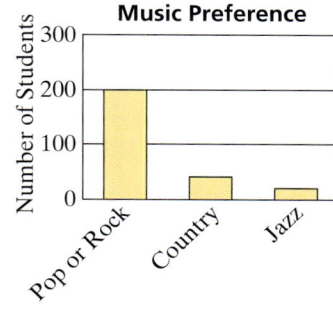

36. Which number is NOT a common factor of 12 and 30? **C**
Ⓐ 2   Ⓑ 3   Ⓒ 5   Ⓓ 6

GO for Help

For Exercises	See Lesson
37–38	1-4

Use <, =, or > to complete each statement.

37. $(8 + 10) \div 2 \ \blacksquare\ 14 \div (2 + 5)$ **>**

38. $3.5 + 2.5 \times 2 \ \blacksquare\ 24 \div 4 + 3$ **<**

31. If $p > 2$ and prime, then p is always odd. So $p + 1$ is even and always composite.

---

4. Assess & Reteach

PowerPoint

Lesson Quiz

Write the prime factorization for each number.

1. 36 $2^2 \times 3^2$

2. 150 $2 \times 3 \times 5^2$

3. 99 $3^2 \times 11$

4. 225 $3^2 \times 5^2$

Alternative Assessment

Provide student pairs with several composite numbers such as 40, 72, 90, and 500. They are to find the prime factorization using factor trees. For 72, they might start with $8 \cdot 9$. One partner writes the factors for the first branch, 8, and the other writes the factors for the second branch, 9. Partners work together to write the prime factorization.

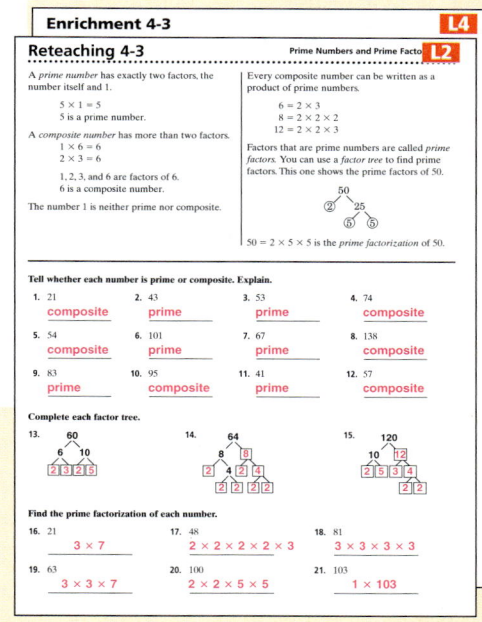

Test Prep

Resources

For additional practice with a variety of test item formats:
• Test-Taking Strategies, p. 203
• Test Prep, p. 207
• Test-Taking Strategies with Transparencies

169

Use this Checkpoint Quiz to check students' understanding of the skills and concepts of Lessons 4-1 through 4-3.

Resources

- All-in-One Teaching Resources Checkpoint Quiz 1
- ExamView CD-ROM
- Success Tracker™ Online Intervention

MATH GAMES

Triple Prime Time

This game will help students identify prime factors.

Guided Instruction

Students play in groups of three or four. Have students read through the instructions before they begin to play.

Differentiated Instruction

English Language Learners **ELL**
You may wish to have a volunteer read the instructions aloud to assist English language learners.

Resources

- 4-by-4 grids
- slips of paper
- container

Checkpoint Quiz 1

Lessons 4-1 through 4-3

Test each number for divisibility by 2, 3, 5, 9, and 10.

1. 375 **3, 5**

2. 1,402 **2**

3. 240 **2, 3, 5, 10**

Simplify each expression.

4. 4^3 **64**

5. $5 + (2^3 - 3)$ **10**

6. 5^5 **3,125**

7. $(6 + 2)^2$ **64**

Find the prime factorization of each number.

8. 42 **2 × 3 × 7**

9. 80 **2^4 × 5**

10. 1,000 **2^3 × 5^3**

11. A photographer is arranging 105 students in rows for a class picture. She wants the same number of students in each row. What are the different arrangements of students she can make? **1 × 105, 3 × 35, 5 × 21, 7 × 15**

MATH GAMES

Triple Prime Time

Getting Started

- Draw a 4-by-4 grid.
- Arrange the following numbers on your grid. Put each number in any square on the grid.
  12, 18, 20, 28, 30, 42, 45, 50, 63, 66, 70, 75, 105, 110, 154, 165
- The host writes the prime numbers **2, 3, 5, 7,** and **11** on slips of paper and puts the slips in a container.

How to Play

- The host draws a prime number, calls it out, and replaces it.
- Find a number on your grid that has the chosen prime number as a factor. Write the prime factor in that square. Each number on your grid has three prime factors.
- The host continues to draw slips and call numbers.
- When you record all three prime factors for a number, cross out the square. For example, you can cross out the square with 28 when you record 2, 2, and 7.
- The first player to cross out four squares in a row wins.

20	154	66	30
2, 2, 7 2̶8̶	18	5 50	165
63	110	12	2 42
70	75	45	105

Greatest Common Factor

Check Skills You'll Need

1. **Vocabulary Review**
   Write a sentence about math using the words *factor* and *product*.
   See below.
   Find the prime factorization.

2. 45 $3^2 \times 5$

3. 21 3×7

4. 99 $3^2 \times 11$

GO for Help
Lesson 4-3

Check Skills You'll Need

1. **Answers may vary.
   Sample: Multiply two factors together to find the product.**

What You'll Learn

To find the GCF of two or more numbers

🔊 **New Vocabulary** common factor, greatest common factor (GCF)

Why Learn This?

A stamp club president distributes equally one set of 18 stamps and another set of 30 stamps to members present at a meeting. No stamps are left over. You can use factors to find the greatest possible number of club members at the meeting.

To find the greatest possible number of club members, you can find the factors that 18 and 30 share. A factor that two or more numbers share is a **common factor**.

The **greatest common factor (GCF)** of two or more numbers is the greatest factor shared by all the numbers. You can find the GCF of two numbers by listing their factors.

EXAMPLE   **Using Lists of Factors**

① Find the greatest common factor of 18 and 30.

List the factors of 18 and the factors of 30. Then circle the common factors.

Factors of 18: ①, ②, ③, ⑥, 9, 18
Factors of 30: ①, ②, ③, 5, ⑥, 10, 15, 30

← The common factors are 1, 2, 3, and 6.

The greatest common factor (GCF) is 6.

Quick Check

1a–c. See back of book.
1. List the factors to find the GCF of each pair of numbers.
   a. 6, 21   b. 18, 49   c. 14, 28

Objective
To find the GCF of two or more numbers

Examples
1   Using Lists of Factors
2   Using a Division Ladder
3   Using Factor Trees

Math Understandings: p. 156C

Math Background

If two numbers are each divisible by a third number, the third number is a *common factor* of the other two. In this lesson, students learn three methods for identifying the *greatest common factor,* or the *GCF.*

More Math Background: p. 156C

Lesson Planning and Resources

See p. 156E for a list of the resources that support this lesson.

PowerPoint
🖥 **Bell Ringer Practice**

✓ **Check Skills You'll Need**
Use student page, transparency, or PowerPoint. For intervention, direct students to:
Prime Numbers and Prime Factorization
Lesson 4-3
Extra Skills and Word Problems Practice, Ch. 4

Differentiated Instruction **Solutions for All Learners**

Special Needs L1
Some students may have difficulty drawing factor trees or drawing division ladders. If so, pair them with students who can draw the trees or the division ladders, while they say the numbers.

learning style: visual

Below Level L2
Have students find the GCF of pairs of numbers that are already in factored form. For example:

$2 \times 2 \times 3$ $2 \times 3 \times 3 \times 5$
$2 \times 3 \times 7$ $3 \times 3 \times 5 \times 5$
GFC = 6   GFC = 45

learning style: visual

171

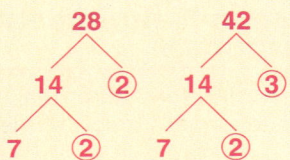
You can also use a division ladder or factor trees to find the greatest common factor of two or more numbers.

EXAMPLE **Using a Division Ladder**

❷ **Gridded Response** Find the GCF of 42 and 56. Use a division ladder.

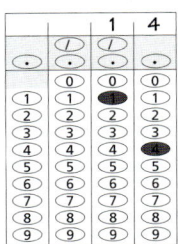

2)42   56   ← **Divide by 2, a common factor of 42 and 56.**
7)21   28   ← **Divide by 7, a common factor of 21 and 28.**
   3   4   ← **3 and 4 have no common factors.**
— **Multiply the common factors: 2 × 7 = 14.**

The GCF of 42 and 56 is 14.

Test Prep Tip
You can use one of the two methods shown in the examples to find the GCF. Then check your answer using the other method.

✓ **Quick Check**

2. You want to cut two ribbons into equal lengths with nothing left over. The ribbons are 18 and 42 inches long. What is the longest possible length of ribbon you can cut? **6 in.**

EXAMPLE **Using Factor Trees**

❸ A volunteer divides 18 adults, 27 girls, and 36 boys into groups to clean up the park. He divides the adults, girls, and boys equally among the groups. What is the largest possible number of groups he can make?

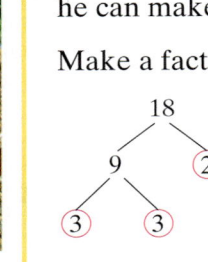

Make a factor tree for each number.

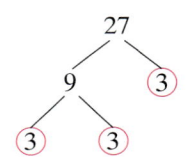
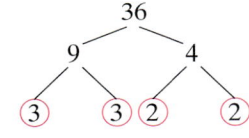

$18 = \boxed{3} \times \boxed{3} \times 2$ ← **Write the prime factorization**
$27 = \boxed{3} \times \boxed{3} \times 3$ **for each number.**
$36 = \boxed{3} \times \boxed{3} \times 2 \times 2$

— **Identify common factors.**

The GCF of 18, 27, and 36 is 9. The largest number of groups is 9.

✓ **Quick Check**

3. Use a factor tree to find the GCF. **3a–b. See back of book.**
   a. 48, 80, 128 **16**   **b.** 36, 60, 84 **12**

✓ Check Your Understanding

1. **Vocabulary** Explain why the GCF of two numbers is sometimes 1. **When two numbers have 1 as their only common factor, then the GCF = 1.**

2. **Open-Ended** Write two numbers with a GCF of 4. **Answers may vary. Sample: 12 and 8**

Match each pair of numbers to the GCF.

3. 18, 3 **B**

4. 8, 12 **C**

5. 22, 110 **A**

A. 22
B. 3
C. 4

Homework Exercises

For more exercises, see Extra Skills and Word Problems.

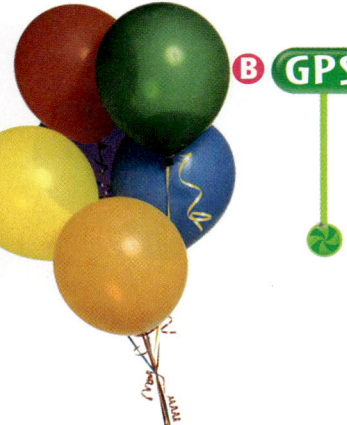

GO for Help

For Exercises	See Examples
6–11	1
12–17	2
18–23	3

A **List the factors to find the GCF of each set of numbers.**
6–11. See margin for lists.

6. 14, 35 **7**
7. 24, 45 **3**
8. 26, 34 **2**

9. 30, 35 **5**
10. 48, 88 **8**
11. 36, 63 **9**

Use a division ladder to find the GCF of each set of numbers.
12–17. See margin for division ladders.

12. 10, 18 **2**
13. 24, 60 **12**
14. 11, 23 **1**

15. 27, 30 **3**
16. 12, 16, 28 **4**
17. 33, 55, 132 **11**

Use factor trees to find the GCF of each set of numbers.
18–23. See margin for factor trees.

18. 20, 60 **20**
19. 54, 84 **6**
20. 72, 120 **24**

21. 64, 125 **1**
22. 117, 130 **13**
23. 45, 150 **15**

B **GPS** 24. **Guided Problem Solving** You want to make bouquets of balloons. You choose 18 yellow, 30 blue, and 42 red balloons. Each bouquet will have the same number of each color. What is the greatest possible number of bouquets you can make?
- What method can you use to find the GCF?
- What is the GCF? How many bouquets can you make? **6 bouquets**

25. Three groups of friends go to a movie. Each ticket costs the same amount. Each group spends a different total amount for tickets. The amounts are $27, $36, and $81. At most how much does each ticket cost? **$9**

○nline lesson quiz, PHSchool.com, Web Code: aqa-0404

4-4 Greatest Common Factor **173**

6–23. See back of book.

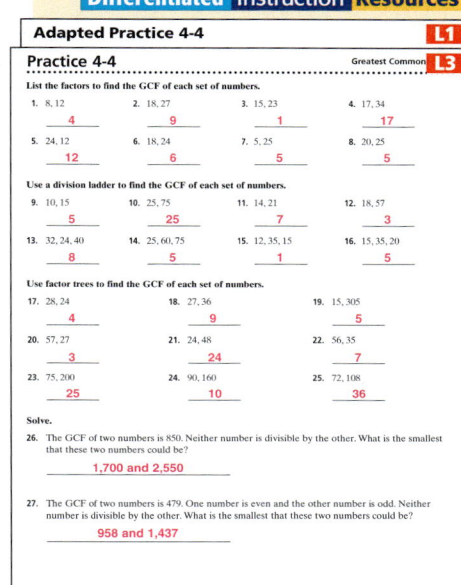
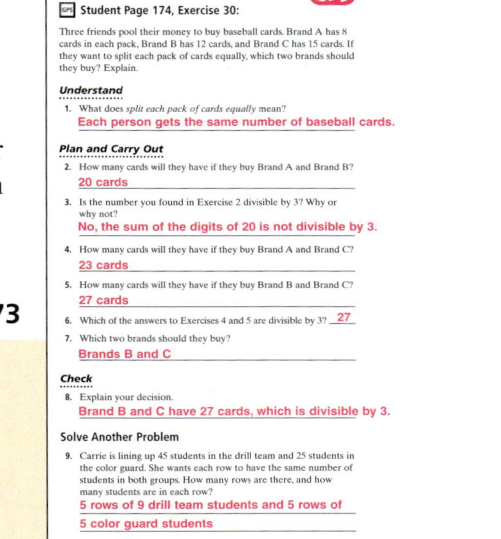

GO Online
Homework Video Tutor
Visit: PHSchool.com
Web Code: aqe-0404

PowerPoint
Lesson Quiz

Find the GCF of each set of numbers.

1. 60, 80 **20**

2. 24, 57 **3**

3. 36, 48 **12**

4. 115, 70, 200 **5**

30. See back of book.

32. See back of book.

Find the GCF of each set of numbers.

26. 300, 450 **150**   27. 280, 420 **140**   28. 200, 300, 400 **100**

29. **Writing in Math** Nine people plan to share equally 24 stamps from one set and 36 stamps from another set. Explain why 9 people cannot share the stamps equally.
Nine is not a common factor of 24 and 36.

30. Three friends pool their money to buy baseball cards. Brand A has 8 cards in each pack, Brand B has 12 cards, and Brand C has 15 cards. If they want to split each pack of cards equally, which two brands should they buy? Explain. **See margin.**

31. **Summer Camp** A camp director splits 14 counselors and 77 campers into activity groups. Each group should have the same number of counselors and the same number of campers. At most how many groups can she make? How many campers are in each group? **7 groups; 2 counselors; 11 campers**

32. **Reasoning** Which number less than 50 has the most factors? Justify your answer. **See margin.**

C 33. **Challenge** There are four two-digit numbers that end with 6 and are less than 50. Find the GCF of the numbers. **2**

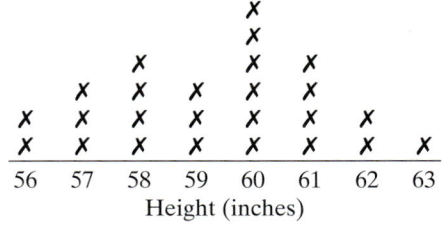

Test Prep and Mixed Review   Practice

Gridded Response

34. You have 36 photos from a trip and 54 photos from a party. What is the GCF of 36 and 54? **18**

35. The line plot shows the height, in inches, of students in a sixth-grade class. How many students are exactly 58 inches tall? **4**

Sixth-Grade Students' Heights

```
                            X
                            X
                X           X    X
           X    X    X      X    X
      X    X    X    X      X    X    X
      X    X    X    X      X    X    X    X
      56   57   58   59    60   61   62   63
```
Height (inches)

GO for Help

For Exercise	See Lesson
36	1-8

36. You buy 3 packs of notebook paper for $1.25 each and a binder for $1.50. Write an expression for the total cost of the items. Then find the total cost. **3 × $1.25 + $1.50 = $5.25**

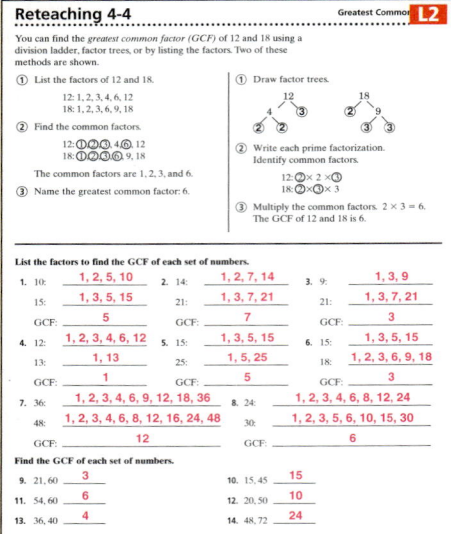

Reteaching 4-4   Greatest Common **L2**

You can find the *greatest common factor (GCF)* of 12 and 18 using a division ladder, factor trees, or by listing the factors. Two of these methods are shown.

① List the factors of 12 and 18.
   12: 1, 2, 3, 4, 6, 12
   18: 1, 2, 3, 6, 9, 18
② Find the common factors.
   12: ①②③4⑥, 12
   18: ①②③⑥, 9, 18
   The common factors are 1, 2, 3, and 6.
③ Name the greatest common factor: 6.

① Draw factor trees.
② Write each prime factorization. Identify common factors.
   12: ②× 2 ×③
   18: ②×③× 3
③ Multiply the common factors. 2 × 3 = 6. The GCF of 12 and 18 is 6.

List the factors to find the GCF of each set of numbers.

1. 10: **1, 2, 5, 10**   2. 14: **1, 2, 7, 14**   3. 9: **1, 3, 9**
   15: **1, 3, 5, 15**   21: **1, 3, 7, 21**   21: **1, 3, 7, 21**
   GCF: **5**   GCF: **7**   GCF: **3**

4. 12: **1, 2, 3, 4, 6, 12** 5. 15: **1, 3, 5, 15**   6. 15: **1, 3, 5, 15**
   13: **1, 13**   25: **1, 5, 25**   18: **1, 2, 3, 6, 9, 18**
   GCF: **1**   GCF: **5**   GCF: **3**

7. 36: **1, 2, 3, 4, 6, 9, 12, 18, 36**   8. 24: **1, 2, 3, 4, 6, 8, 12, 24**
   48: **1, 2, 3, 4, 6, 8, 12, 16, 24, 48**   30: **1, 2, 3, 5, 6, 10, 15, 30**
   GCF: **12**   GCF: **6**

Find the GCF of each set of numbers.

9. 21, 60 **3**   10. 15, 45 **15**
11. 54, 60 **6**   12. 20, 50 **10**
13. 36, 40 **4**   14. 48, 72 **24**

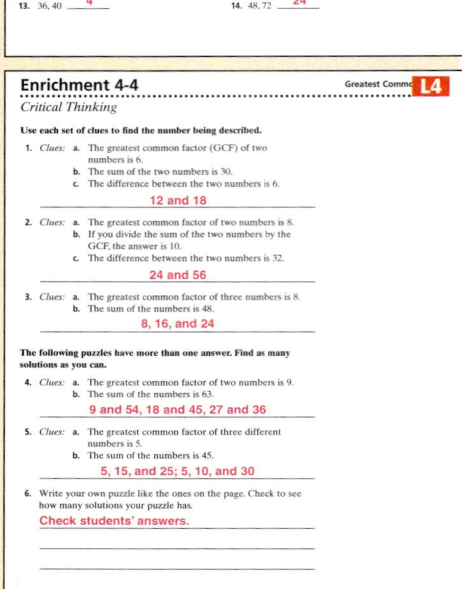

Enrichment 4-4   Greatest Common **L4**
Critical Thinking

Use each set of clues to find the number being described.

1. *Clues:* a. The greatest common factor (GCF) of two numbers is 6.
   b. The sum of the two numbers is 30.
   c. The difference between the two numbers is 6.
   12 and 18

2. *Clues:* a. The greatest common factor of two numbers is 8.
   b. If you divide the sum of the two numbers by the GCF, the answer is 10.
   c. The difference between the two numbers is 32.
   24 and 56

3. *Clues:* a. The greatest common factor of three numbers is 8.
   b. The sum of the numbers is 48.
   8, 16, and 24

The following puzzles have more than one answer. Find as many solutions as you can.

4. *Clues:* a. The greatest common factor of two numbers is 9.
   b. The sum of the numbers is 63.
   9 and 54, 18 and 45, 27 and 36

5. *Clues:* a. The greatest common factor of three different numbers is 5.
   b. The sum of the numbers is 45.
   5, 15, and 25; 5, 10, and 30

6. Write your own puzzle like the ones on the page. Check to see how many solutions your puzzle has.
   Check students' answers.

Test Prep

Resources
For additional practice with a variety of test item formats:
• Test-Taking Strategies, p. 203
• Test Prep, p. 207
• Test-Taking Strategies with Transparencies

Alternative Assessment

Provide pairs of students with pairs of composite numbers such as those in Exercises 6–23. Each partner draws a factor tree to find the prime factorization for one of the composite numbers. Partners then work together to find the GCF of each set of numbers.

Modeling Fractions

A fraction describes a part of a set of items or a part of a whole item.

$\frac{3}{4}$ ← The numerator shows how many parts are being considered.
← The denominator shows the total number of parts.

EXAMPLE Writing Fractions

1 Write a fraction for each situation.

a. What fraction of the flowers are red?

There are 9 red flowers and 16 flowers altogether. So $\frac{9}{16}$ of the flowers are red.

b. What fraction of the pie is left?

The pie had 8 equal pieces. Five are left. So $\frac{5}{8}$ of the pie is left.

c. On the number line, what fraction describes the location of point A?

The segment from 0 to 1 is divided into 5 equal parts. Point A is three sections to the right of 0, so $\frac{3}{5}$ describes the location of point A.

Exercises

Name the fraction represented by each model.

1.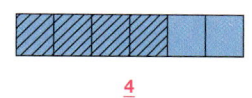
$\frac{4}{6}$

2.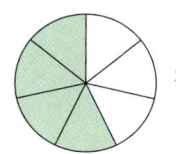
$\frac{4}{7}$

3.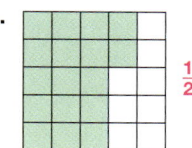
$\frac{17}{25}$

4.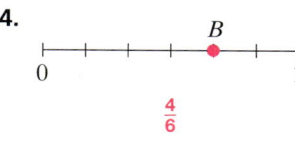
$\frac{4}{6}$

Draw a fraction model for each situation. **5–7. See margin.**

5. $\frac{3}{4}$ as part of a set

6. $\frac{4}{7}$ as part of a rectangle

7. $\frac{5}{8}$ on a number line

8. Number Sense What number is represented when all parts of a fraction model are shaded? When no parts are shaded? **1; 0**

Activity Lab   Modeling Fractions   **175**

Modeling Fractions

In this Activity for use with Lesson 4-5, students model fractions in a variety of ways: as part of a set or whole, on a number line, and with a ruler.

Guided Instruction

After you have worked through Example 1, ask the following questions to check students' understanding:

• *What fraction of flowers is not red?* $\frac{7}{16}$

• *What fraction of the pie is gone?* $\frac{3}{8}$

Error Prevention!

Exercise 1 Students might write a fraction relating the shaded parts to the unshaded parts, such as $\frac{4}{2}$ or $\frac{2}{4}$. Suggest that they write the words *shaded* and *total* next to the numerator and denominator as shown below.

shaded → 4
total → 6

Exercises 5–7 Have students work in pairs or small groups. This helps students who might have difficulty drawing the fraction models.

Resources

• Activity Lab 4-5: Fractions
• inch ruler
• graph paper
• Classroom Aid 2, 12–14

5.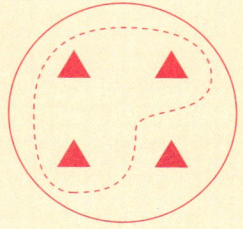

6.

7.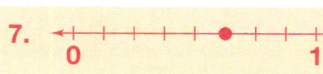

Objective
To find equivalent forms of fractions

Examples
1. Equivalent Fractions
2. Simplify a Fraction Using the GCF
3. Using Prime Factorization

Math Understandings: p. 156D

Math Background

Fractions that name the same amount are called *equivalent fractions*. You can find an equivalent fraction by either multiplying or dividing both numerator and denominator by the same number.

More Math Background: p. 156D

Lesson Planning and Resources

See p. 156E for a list of the resources that support this lesson.

Bell Ringer Practice

✓ **Check Skills You'll Need**
Use student page, transparency, or PowerPoint. For intervention, direct students to:
Greatest Common Factor
Lesson 4-4
Extra Skills and Word Problems Practice, Ch. 4

176

✓ Check Skills You'll Need

1. **Vocabulary Review**
How is a *common factor* different from the GCF?
See below.
Find the GCF of each set of numbers.

2. 20, 25 **5**

3. 12, 30 **6**

4. 5, 18 **1**

GO for Help
Lesson 4-4

Check Skills You'll Need

1. **The GCF is the largest number in the set of common factors.**

4-5 Equivalent Fractions

What You'll Learn

To find equivalent forms of fractions

🔊 **New Vocabulary** equivalent fractions, simplest form

Why Learn This?

Writing equivalent fractions often makes using fractions easier. Both models on the right show the same amount. You can describe the amount as $\frac{2}{3}$ or $\frac{4}{6}$.

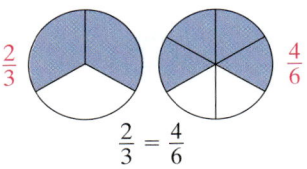
$$\frac{2}{3} = \frac{4}{6}$$

Equivalent fractions are fractions that name the same amount. The fractions $\frac{2}{3}$ and $\frac{4}{6}$ are equivalent fractions.

You form equivalent fractions by multiplying (or dividing) the numerator and denominator of a fraction by the same nonzero number.

EXAMPLE Equivalent Fractions

1. Write two fractions equivalent to $\frac{6}{8}$.

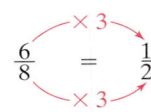
$$\frac{6}{8} = \frac{18}{24}$$
← Multiply the numerator and denominator by 3.

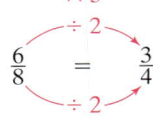
$$\frac{6}{8} = \frac{3}{4}$$
← Divide the numerator and denominator by 2.

So $\frac{3}{4} = \frac{6}{8} = \frac{18}{24}$.

✓ Quick Check

1a–b. Answers may vary. Samples are given.
1. Write two fractions equivalent to each fraction.

a. $\frac{4}{10}$ $\frac{2}{5}, \frac{8}{20}$

b. $\frac{5}{8}$ $\frac{10}{16}, \frac{15}{24}$

Differentiated Instruction Solutions for All Learners

Special Needs L1
For Example 3, help students make an organized list of the types of pet foods with the inventory of each type, and then add the numbers in column form. This makes it clear that you are looking at a comparison of cat food to total number of pet foods.

learning style: visual

Below Level L2
Have students identify groups of equivalent fractions represented by a set of fraction bars. For example:

$$\frac{1}{2} = \frac{2}{4} = \frac{3}{6} = \frac{4}{8} = \frac{5}{10} = \frac{6}{12}; \ \frac{2}{3} = \frac{4}{6} = \frac{8}{12}$$

learning style: visual

A fraction is in **simplest form** when the only common factor of the numerator and denominator is 1. One way to write a fraction in simplest form is to divide both the numerator and the denominator by their greatest common factor.

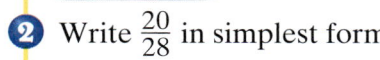 **EXAMPLE**   **Simplify a Fraction Using the GCF**

2 Write $\frac{20}{28}$ in simplest form.

The GCF of 20 and 28 is 4.

$$\frac{20}{28} = \frac{20 \div 4}{28 \div 4} \quad \leftarrow \text{Divide the numerator and the denominator by the GCF.}$$
$$= \frac{5}{7} \quad \leftarrow \text{Simplify.}$$

The fraction $\frac{20}{28}$ written in simplest form is $\frac{5}{7}$.

 **Quick Check**

2. Write $\frac{24}{32}$ in simplest form. $\frac{3}{4}$

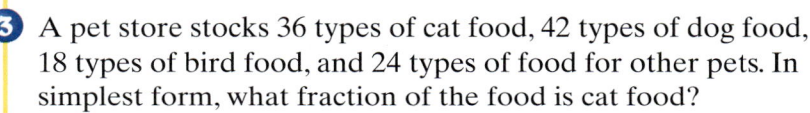 **EXAMPLE**   **Using Prime Factorization**

3 A pet store stocks 36 types of cat food, 42 types of dog food, 18 types of bird food, and 24 types of food for other pets. In simplest form, what fraction of the food is cat food?

Find the total number of food types.

$$36 + 42 + 18 + 24 = 120 \quad \leftarrow \begin{array}{l}\text{Add the number of food types to find} \\ \text{the denominator.}\end{array}$$

$$\frac{36}{120} \quad \begin{array}{l}\leftarrow \text{number of cat food types} \\ \leftarrow \text{total number of food types}\end{array}$$

$$\frac{36}{120} = \frac{2 \cdot 2 \cdot 3 \cdot 3}{2 \cdot 2 \cdot 2 \cdot 3 \cdot 5} \quad \leftarrow \begin{array}{l}\text{Write the prime factorizations of the} \\ \text{numerator and the denominator.}\end{array}$$

$$= \frac{\overset{1}{\cancel{2}} \cdot \overset{1}{\cancel{2}} \cdot \overset{1}{\cancel{3}} \cdot 3}{\underset{1}{\cancel{2}} \cdot \underset{1}{\cancel{2}} \cdot 2 \cdot \underset{1}{\cancel{3}} \cdot 5} \quad \leftarrow \text{Divide the common factors.}$$

$$= \frac{3}{10} \quad \leftarrow \text{Simplify.}$$

So $\frac{3}{10}$ of the food is cat food.

 **Quick Check**

3. In simplest form, what fraction of the food is dog food? $\frac{7}{20}$

---

2. Teach

Activity Lab

Use before the lesson.
Student Edition Hands On Activity 4-5a, Modeling Fractions, p. 175

All in One Teaching Resources
Activity Lab 4-5: Fractions

Guided Instruction

Example 1
Relate the word *equivalent* to the word *equal*. Equivalent fractions are fractions that name *equal* amounts.

Error Prevention!

Some students might multiply or divide the numerator and denominator of a fraction by different numbers. Encourage them to write the number by which they are multiplying or dividing.

 **PowerPoint**
Additional Examples

1 Write three fractions equivalent to $\frac{6}{9}$. **Samples:** $\frac{12}{18}, \frac{18}{27}, \frac{2}{3}$

2 Write $\frac{16}{40}$ in simplest form. Use prime factorization to solve. $\frac{2}{5}$

3 A store stocks 12 types of blue pens, 6 types of black pens, and 2 types of red pens. In simplest form, what fraction of the pens are blue? $\frac{3}{5}$

All in One Teaching Resources
- Daily Notetaking Guide 4-5 **L3**
- Adapted Notetaking 4-5 **L1**

Closure

- *What are equivalent fractions?* fractions that name the same amount
- *When is a fraction in simplest form?* when the only common factor of the numerator and denominator is 1

Assignment Guide

Check Your Understanding
Go over Exercises 1–5 in class before assigning the Homework Exercises.

Homework Exercises
A Practice by Example 6–22
B Apply Your Skills 23–30
C Challenge 31
Test Prep and
 Mixed Review 32–38

Homework Quick Check
To check students' understanding of key skills and concepts, go over Exercises 8, 15, 28, 29, and 30.

Differentiated Instruction **Resources**

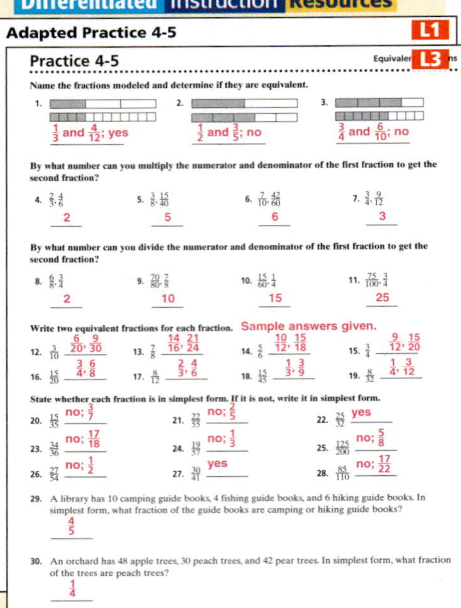

Check Your Understanding

1. **Vocabulary** If the GCF of the numerator and the denominator is 1, then the fraction is in __?__.
   simplest form

2. Name each of the fractions modeled on the right. Are they equivalent? $\frac{8}{12}$ and $\frac{3}{5}$; no

Match each fraction with an equivalent fraction.

3. $\frac{9}{27}$ A   A. $\frac{1}{3}$

4. $\frac{5}{20}$ C   B. $\frac{2}{5}$

5. $\frac{6}{15}$ B   C. $\frac{1}{4}$

Homework Exercises

For more exercises, see Extra Skills and Word Problems.

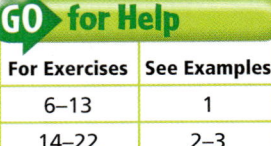

GO for Help

For Exercises	See Examples
6–13	1
14–22	2–3

6–13. Answers may vary. Samples are given.

A Write two fractions equivalent to each fraction.

6. $\frac{2}{4}$ $\frac{1}{2}$, $\frac{4}{8}$ 7. $\frac{6}{7}$ $\frac{12}{14}$, $\frac{24}{28}$ 8. $\frac{12}{18}$ $\frac{2}{3}$, $\frac{4}{6}$ 9. $\frac{3}{16}$ $\frac{6}{32}$, $\frac{9}{48}$

10. $\frac{3}{10}$ $\frac{6}{20}$, $\frac{9}{30}$ 11. $\frac{3}{9}$ $\frac{1}{3}$, $\frac{6}{18}$ 12. $\frac{1}{20}$ $\frac{2}{40}$, $\frac{3}{60}$ 13. $\frac{15}{20}$ $\frac{3}{4}$, $\frac{30}{40}$

Write each fraction in simplest form.

14. $\frac{4}{6}$ $\frac{2}{3}$ 15. $\frac{10}{35}$ $\frac{2}{7}$ 16. $\frac{10}{20}$ $\frac{1}{2}$ 17. $\frac{40}{50}$ $\frac{4}{5}$

18. $\frac{15}{45}$ $\frac{1}{3}$ 19. $\frac{6}{8}$ $\frac{3}{4}$ 20. $\frac{12}{18}$ $\frac{2}{3}$ 21. $\frac{9}{21}$ $\frac{3}{7}$

22. **Sports** Over the last three seasons, a school football team has won 15 out of 25 games. In simplest form, what fraction of the games has the team won? $\frac{3}{5}$

B **GPS** 23. **Guided Problem Solving** A store orders 105 greeting cards. The order includes 50 birthday cards, 30 get-well cards, and some anniversary cards. In simplest form, what fraction of the cards are anniversary cards? $\frac{5}{21}$
   • You can draw a picture to model the situation.

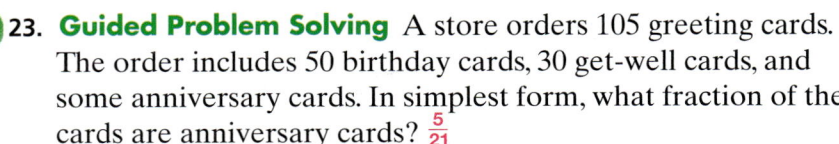

■ cards in all		
50 birthday	30 get-well	■ anniversary

30. To write a fraction in simplest form, divide the numerator and the denominator by their GCF.

State whether each fraction is in simplest form. If the fraction is not, write it in simplest form.

24. $\frac{3}{6}$ no; $\frac{1}{2}$ **25.** $\frac{1}{7}$ yes   **26.** $\frac{15}{18}$ no; $\frac{5}{6}$ **27.** $\frac{17}{51}$ no; $\frac{1}{3}$

28. Traffic Planning Two traffic engineers are writing about the
GPS average driving time between two towns. One engineer writes
the time as 45, but the other writes it as $\frac{3}{4}$. What could explain
the difference? The first engineer is measuring time in minutes.
The second engineer is measuring time in fractions of an hour.

29. On a chessboard, 32 of the squares are white. At the start of a
game, each player places half of her 16 pieces on white squares.
What fraction of the white squares have pieces on them? $\frac{1}{2}$

30. Writing in Math How can you use the GCF of the numerator
and the denominator to write a fraction in simplest form?
See margin.

C 31. Challenge Evaluate $\frac{2a}{3a}$ for a = 1, 2, 5, and 10.
  a. Write each result as a fraction. $\frac{2}{3}, \frac{4}{6}, \frac{10}{15}, \frac{20}{30}$
  b. When a is a nonzero whole number, what do you think is the
  simplest form for $\frac{2a}{3a}$? Explain. $\frac{2}{3}$; when you divide the numerator
and the denominator by the common factor a, the result is in simplest form.

Test Prep and Mixed Review   **Practice**

Multiple Choice

32. What fraction of an hour is 40 minutes? C
  Ⓐ $\frac{3}{4}$ Ⓑ $\frac{5}{6}$ Ⓒ $\frac{2}{3}$ Ⓓ $\frac{2}{5}$

33. On a field day, 84 girls and 78 boys will be split into teams.
Each team will have the same number of girls and the same
number of boys. At most how many teams are possible? G
  Ⓕ 2   Ⓗ 13
  Ⓖ 6   Ⓙ 14

34. At a leadership conference, 96 students divide into discussion
groups of equal sizes. Which method can you use to find the
ways of forming the groups? A
  Ⓐ Find the factors of 96.
  Ⓑ Find the multiples of 96.
  Ⓒ Find the greatest common factor of 4 and 96.
  Ⓓ Find the least common multiple of 96.

GO for Help

For Exercises	See Examples
35–38	4-4

Find the GCF of each pair of numbers.

35. 48, 56 8   **36.** 15, 21 3   **37.** 42, 72 6   **38.** 300, 450
150

Alternative Assessment

Each student in a pair writes a fraction and
exchanges it with their partner. Partners state
whether or not the fraction is in simplest form.
If not, they rename the fraction in simplest form.
After several turns, students should discuss how
they made their decisions and explain their
methods.

Test Prep

Resources
For additional practice with a variety of test item
formats:
• Test-Taking Strategies, p. 203
• Test Prep, p. 207
• Test-Taking Strategies with Transparencies

---

4. Assess & Reteach

Lesson Quiz

Write each fraction in simplest
form.

1. $\frac{55}{100}$ $\frac{11}{20}$ **2.** $\frac{9}{12}$ $\frac{3}{4}$

3. $\frac{18}{20}$ $\frac{9}{10}$ **4.** $\frac{36}{72}$ $\frac{1}{2}$

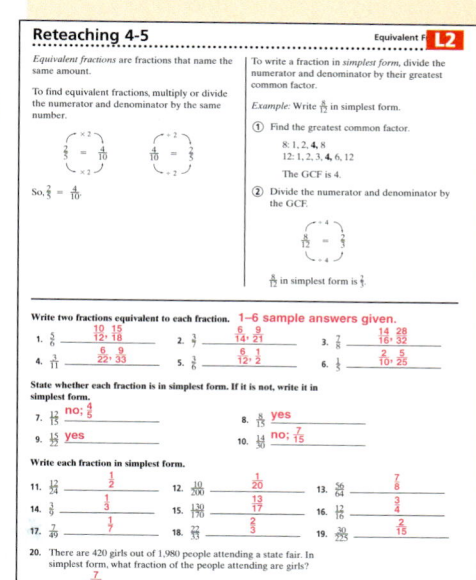

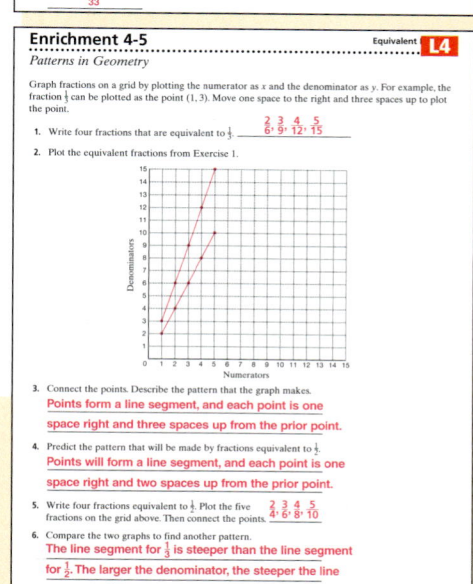

Simplifying Fractions

Simplifying Fractions

You can use a fraction calculator to simplify a fraction. The calculator divides the numerator and denominator by a common factor and rewrites the fraction.

EXAMPLE

Use a fraction calculator to simplify $\frac{9}{27}$.

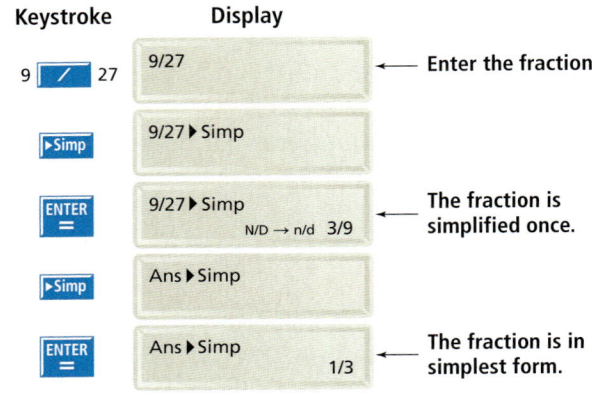

Keystroke	Display	
9 / 27	9/27	← Enter the fraction.
▶Simp	9/27 ▶ Simp	
ENTER =	9/27 ▶ Simp N/D → n/d 3/9	← The fraction is simplified once.
▶Simp	Ans ▶ Simp	
ENTER =	Ans ▶ Simp 1/3	← The fraction is in simplest form.

In simplest form, $\frac{9}{27} = \frac{1}{3}$.

16. Answers may vary. Sample: Use the fraction $\frac{12}{42}$ as a test. If the calculator simplifies $\frac{12}{42}$ to $\frac{2}{7}$ in one step, then it is using the GCF.

Exercises

Use a fraction calculator to simplify each fraction.

1. $\frac{18}{51}$ $\frac{6}{17}$

2. $\frac{21}{49}$ $\frac{3}{7}$

3. $\frac{102}{387}$ $\frac{34}{129}$

4. $\frac{35}{56}$ $\frac{5}{8}$

5. $\frac{20}{65}$ $\frac{4}{13}$

6. $\frac{17}{68}$ $\frac{1}{4}$

7. $\frac{12}{15}$ $\frac{4}{5}$

8. $\frac{28}{32}$ $\frac{7}{8}$

9. $\frac{12}{30}$ $\frac{2}{5}$

10. $\frac{45}{75}$ $\frac{3}{5}$

11. $\frac{12}{96}$ $\frac{1}{8}$

12. $\frac{92}{132}$ $\frac{23}{33}$

13. $\frac{39}{117}$ $\frac{1}{3}$

14. $\frac{126}{324}$ $\frac{7}{18}$

15. $\frac{200}{385}$ $\frac{40}{77}$

16. **Writing in Math** How do you know from the calculator procedures shown in the example that the calculator does not use the greatest common factor (GCF) when simplifying? **See above.**

Exploring Improper Fractions

You can use pattern blocks to name fractions that are equal to or greater than a whole.

EXAMPLES

1 The hexagon represents one whole. Use the pattern blocks to find what part of the whole two trapezoids represent.

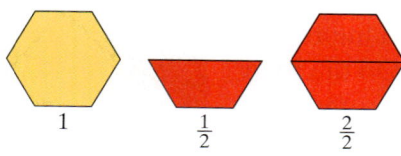

Each trapezoid is $\frac{1}{2}$ of the hexagon. So two trapezoids represent $\frac{2}{2}$ of the whole.

2 What part of the whole do three trapezoids represent?

 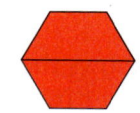 

Three trapezoids represent $\frac{3}{2}$ of the hexagon.

The trapezoids also represent one whole hexagon and half of a second hexagon.

Pattern Blocks

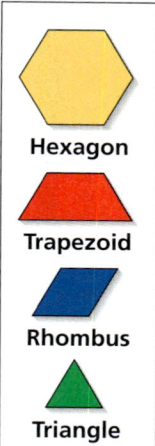

Hexagon

Trapezoid

Rhombus

Triangle

Exercises

1. Use pattern blocks to complete the table at the right. A hexagon represents one whole. **See margin.**

2. **Reasoning** Can an improper fraction be written as a mixed number? Can a mixed number be written as an improper fraction? Explain. **Yes; yes; an improper fraction can represent the same amount as a mixed number.**

3. Use pattern blocks to show that $\frac{4}{4}$ is equivalent to 1. **Check students' work.**

Fractional Parts	Fraction Name for One Part	Two Numbers for All Parts
4 blue rhombuses	$\frac{1}{3}$	$\frac{4}{3}$ and $1\frac{1}{3}$
8 green triangles		
7 green triangles		

Exploring Improper Fractions

In this Activity, using pattern blocks to name improper fractions will increase students' understanding for Lesson 4-6.

Guided Instruction

Ask: How does comparing the numerator to the denominator show whether a fraction is less than, equal to, or greater than 1?

Error Prevention!

If students have difficulty with the terms *trapezoid* and *hexagon*, you can simplify the activity by using circles and half circles. The important idea to get across is that improper fractions represent quantities greater than 1.

Exercises

You may wish to have students work in pairs to complete the table. One student can write the improper fraction while the other writes the mixed number.

Differentiated Instruction

Below Level L2

Make sure students understand that each circle represents 1. If the model for a fraction involves more than one complete circle, the fraction must be greater than 1.

Resources

- Activity Lab 4-6: Writing Mixed Numbers
- inch ruler

1.

Part	Fraction Name of One Part	Two Numbers for All Parts
4 blue rhombuses	$\frac{1}{3}$	$\frac{4}{3}$ and $1\frac{1}{3}$
8 green triangles	$\frac{1}{6}$	$\frac{8}{6}$ and $1\frac{1}{3}$
7 green triangles	$\frac{1}{6}$	$\frac{7}{6}$ and $1\frac{1}{6}$

181

Objective
To use mixed numbers and improper fractions

Examples
1 Writing an Improper Fraction
2 Application: Engines
3 Writing a Fraction as a Mixed Number

Math Understandings: p. 156D

Math Background

A *mixed number* is a "mixture" of two types of numbers: a whole number and a fraction. It represents one or more identical whole quantities, plus some fractional part of the whole. It is possible to rewrite any mixed number as a single fraction, which is called an *improper fraction*.

More Math Background: p. 156D

Lesson Planning and Resources

See p. 156E for a list of the resources that support this lesson.

Bell Ringer Practice

☑ **Check Skills You'll Need**
Use student page, transparency, or PowerPoint. For intervention, direct students to:
Equivalent Fractions
Lesson 4-5
Extra Skills and Word Problems
   Practice, Ch. 4

☑ Check Skills You'll Need

1. Vocabulary Review
Explain how you can tell whether a fraction is in *simplest form*.
See below.
Write each fraction in simplest form.

2. $\frac{9}{27}$ $\frac{1}{3}$

3. $\frac{18}{27}$ $\frac{2}{3}$

4. $\frac{20}{64}$ $\frac{5}{16}$

GO for Help
Lesson 4-5

Check Skills You'll Need

1. when the only common factor of the numerator and denominator is 1

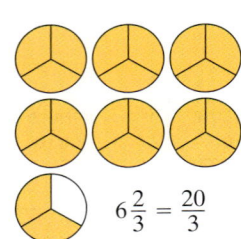

$6\frac{2}{3} = \frac{20}{3}$

You can also use a model to find the answer.

What You'll Learn

To use mixed numbers and improper fractions

🔊 **New Vocabulary** proper fraction, improper fraction, mixed number

Why Learn This?

You can use mixed numbers and improper fractions to describe distances. On the road sign at the right, the distance is written using the mixed number $2\frac{1}{2}$.

A **proper fraction** has a numerator that is less than its denominator. Example: $\frac{3}{8}$

An **improper fraction** has a numerator that is greater than or equal to its denominator. Example: $\frac{11}{8}$

A **mixed number** shows the sum of a whole number and a proper fraction, such as $2 + \frac{1}{2}$. Example: $2\frac{1}{2}$

EXAMPLE Writing an Improper Fraction

❶ Write $6\frac{2}{3}$ as an improper fraction.

Method 1 $6\frac{2}{3} = 6 + \frac{2}{3}$

$= \frac{18}{3} + \frac{2}{3}$ ← Write 6 as $\frac{18}{3}$.

$= \frac{20}{3}$ ← Add.

Method 2 $6\frac{2}{3} = \frac{(3 \times 6) + 2}{3}$ ← Multiply the denominator times the whole number. Then add the numerator.

$= \frac{20}{3}$ ← The denominator stays the same.

☑ Quick Check

1. Write $3\frac{4}{7}$ as an improper fraction. $\frac{25}{7}$

Differentiated Instruction **Solutions for All Learners**

Special Needs L1
Help students break down Example 1 further. Write a row of $\frac{3}{3}$ six times on the board, with the numeral 1 underneath each. Then write $\frac{2}{3}$. Ask students to add the thirds ($\frac{20}{3}$). Ask them to check against the more conventional procedure.
                                          learning style: visual

Below Level L2
Review division involving whole-number remainders using several exercises like these.

$9 \div 5$ **1 R4** $11 \div 5$ **2 R1**
$30 \div 4$ **7 R2** $29 \div 12$ **2 R5**

                                          learning style: verbal

EXAMPLE **Application: Engines**

2 A mechanic needs $3\frac{1}{4}$ gallons of oil for a diesel engine. How many quarts does the mechanic need? (*Hint:* 1 quart $= \frac{1}{4}$ gallon)

Since there are 4 quarts in a gallon, you find the number of quarts by finding the number of fourths in $3\frac{1}{4}$ gallons.

$$3\frac{1}{4} = \frac{13}{4} \quad \leftarrow \text{Change } 3\frac{1}{4} \text{ to an improper fraction.}$$

There are 13 fourths in $3\frac{1}{4}$, so the mechanic needs 13 quarts of oil.

✓**Quick Check**

2. To clean a fish tank you need $2\frac{1}{4}$ gallons of fresh water every two weeks. How many quarts do you need? **9 qt**

You can write an improper fraction greater than 1 as a mixed number. To do this, divide the numerator by the denominator.

EXAMPLE **Writing a Fraction as a Mixed Number**

3 Each orange slice is $\frac{1}{6}$ of an orange. How many oranges are represented by 9 slices?

Write $\frac{9}{6}$ as a mixed number. Begin by dividing 9 by 6.

$$\begin{array}{r} 1 \\ 6\overline{)9} \\ -6 \\ \hline 3 \end{array}$$

$\leftarrow$ The quotient represents one whole orange.

$\leftarrow$ The remainder represents three slices.

Write the remainder 3 as a fraction $\frac{3}{6}$.

$$\frac{9}{6} = 1\frac{3}{6}$$
$$= 1\frac{1}{2} \quad \leftarrow \text{Simplify.}$$

Nine slices represent $1\frac{1}{2}$ oranges.

✓**Quick Check**

3. Write each improper fraction as a mixed number in simplest form.

a. $\frac{40}{9}$ $4\frac{4}{9}$

b. $\frac{32}{6}$ $5\frac{1}{3}$

c. $\frac{23}{4}$ $5\frac{3}{4}$

4-6 Mixed Numbers and Improper Fractions **183**

2. Teach

Activity Lab

Use before the lesson.
Student Edition Hands On Activity 4-6a, Exploring Improper Fractions, p. 181

All in One Teaching Resources
Activity Lab 4-6: Writing Mixed Numbers

Guided Instruction

Example 1
Ask your students to evaluate the effectiveness of using the model or Method 1 to communicate how to write improper fractions.

Example 2
Students can act out this problem using water in quart and gallon measuring jars or pitchers.

PowerPoint
Additional Examples

1 Write $4\frac{3}{5}$ as an improper fraction. $\frac{23}{5}$

2 A chef needs $2\frac{3}{4}$ quarts of water to make soup. How many cups will the chef need? (*Hint:* 1 cup $= \frac{1}{4}$ quart) **11 cups**

3 Write $\frac{42}{9}$ as a mixed number in simplest form. $4\frac{2}{3}$

All in One Teaching Resources
• Daily Notetaking Guide 4-6 **L3**
• Adapted Notetaking 4-6 **L1**

Closure

• How do you write a mixed number as an improper fraction? **Sample: Multiply the denominator by the whole number. Then add this product to the numerator.**
• How do you write an improper fraction as a whole or mixed number? **Divide the numerator by the denominator. The remainder over the denominator is the fractional part of the mixed number, if not equal to zero.**

Advanced Learners **L4**
Fill in the boxes with the numbers 4, 8, 12, 24, and 36 to make a true statement. Use each number exactly once.

▦ = ▪▦ $\frac{36}{8} = 4\frac{12}{24}$

learning style: visual

English Language Learners **ELL**
For Example 2, show students a picture of an engine that marks $3\frac{1}{2}$ gallons at the fill line. Write $\frac{1}{4}$ *gallon = 1 quart* to the side. The students can mentally check their calculations against the visual.

learning style: visual

3. Practice

Assignment Guide

Check Your Understanding
Go over Exercises 1–5 in class before assigning the Homework Exercises.

Homework Exercises
A Practice by Example 6–22
B Apply Your Skills 23–34
C Challenge 35
Test Prep and
  Mixed Review 36–41

Homework Quick Check
To check students' understanding of key skills and concepts, go over Exercises 9, 18, 30, 31, and 34.

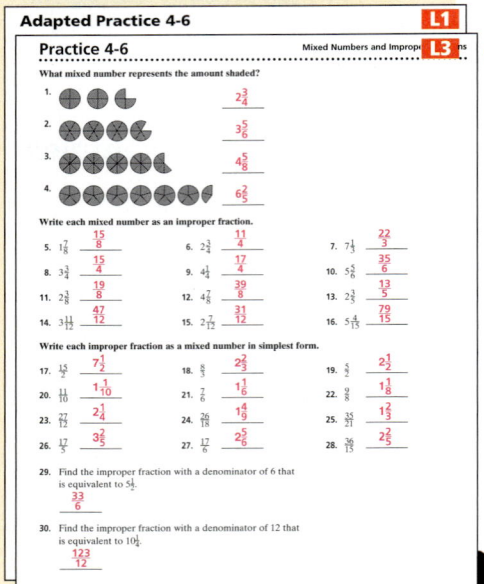

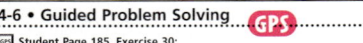

Check Your Understanding

Vocabulary Match each fraction to the fraction type.

1. $\frac{7}{8}$ C
2. $2\frac{4}{5}$ A
3. $\frac{7}{4}$ B

A. mixed number
B. improper fraction
C. proper fraction

Write a mixed number and an improper fraction for each model.

4.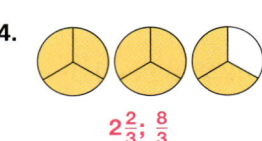

$2\frac{2}{3}; \frac{8}{3}$

5.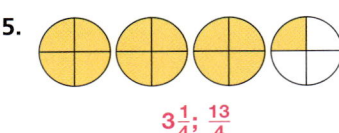

$3\frac{1}{4}; \frac{13}{4}$

Homework Exercises

For more exercises, see Extra Skills and Word Problems.

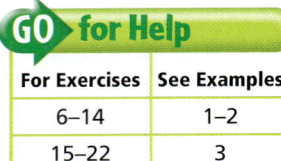
GO for Help

For Exercises	See Examples
6–14	1–2
15–22	3

A Write each mixed number as an improper fraction. You may find a model helpful.

6. $1\frac{4}{5}$ $\frac{9}{5}$
7. $3\frac{1}{7}$ $\frac{22}{7}$
8. $5\frac{1}{4}$ $\frac{21}{4}$
9. $5\frac{1}{2}$ $\frac{11}{2}$

10. $1\frac{3}{11}$ $\frac{14}{11}$
11. $3\frac{3}{8}$ $\frac{27}{8}$
12. $2\frac{1}{16}$ $\frac{33}{16}$
13. $21\frac{1}{3}$ $\frac{64}{3}$

14. **Cooking** A recipe for cookies calls for $2\frac{2}{3}$ cups of flour. You have only a $\frac{1}{3}$-cup scoop for measuring. How many times must you fill the scoop to make the cookies? **8 times**

Write each improper fraction as a mixed number in simplest form.

15. $\frac{17}{5}$ $3\frac{2}{5}$
16. $\frac{10}{4}$ $2\frac{1}{2}$
17. $\frac{27}{12}$ $2\frac{1}{4}$
18. $\frac{9}{4}$ $2\frac{1}{4}$

19. $\frac{21}{14}$ $1\frac{1}{2}$
20. $\frac{18}{11}$ $1\frac{7}{11}$
21. $\frac{21}{10}$ $2\frac{1}{10}$
22. $\frac{16}{12}$ $1\frac{1}{3}$

B **GPS** 23. **Guided Problem Solving** You estimate that 150 people will go to a picnic. Each person will drink about 2 cans of juice. Cans are sold in cases of 24. How many cases do you need?
  • **Make a Plan** Find how many cans you need. Then find how many groups of 24 are in the total number of cans. **13 cases**
  • **Check the Answer** Should your answer be a whole number?

Visit: PHSchool.com
Web Code: aqe-0406

Write each number as an improper fraction and as a mixed number.

24. 33 halves $\frac{33}{2}$; $16\frac{1}{2}$ **25.** 7 fifths $\frac{7}{5}$; $1\frac{2}{5}$ **26.** 106 fourths $\frac{106}{4}$; $26\frac{1}{2}$

27. 2 and 3 fifths $\frac{13}{5}$; $2\frac{3}{5}$ **28.** 8 and 7 ninths $\frac{79}{9}$; $8\frac{7}{9}$ **29.** 6 and 2 thirds $\frac{20}{3}$; $6\frac{2}{3}$

30. Catering A caterer plans to serve two slices of melon to each of 50 guests. She estimates getting 12 slices from each melon. Write the number of melons she will use as a mixed number. How many whole melons does she need? $8\frac{1}{3}$; 9 melons

31. A teacher needs at least 250 school T-shirts to raise money for the music program. The shirts come in boxes of 30. Each box costs $150. How much does the order cost? 9 boxes; $1,350

32. Open-Ended Find a number between $\frac{6}{4}$ and $\frac{7}{4}$. Write your answer as an improper fraction and as a mixed number.
Answers may vary. Sample: $\frac{13}{8} = 1\frac{5}{8}$

Find the length of each segment below. Use mixed numbers.

33. $1\frac{5}{8}$ in.; $1\frac{13}{16}$ in.

34. $\frac{3}{4}$ in.; $1\frac{1}{8}$ in.

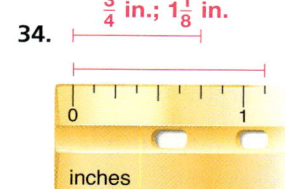

C 35. Challenge You cut $\frac{1}{2}$-inch squares of colored paper to make a mosaic. Each sheet of paper is $8\frac{1}{2}$ inches by 11 inches. How many squares can you make from each sheet? 374 squares

Test Prep and Mixed Review
Practice

Multiple Choice

36. A music teacher ordered 6 pizzas. Each pizza had 8 slices. There were 20 slices left. How many pizzas were left? **C**

  Ⓐ $2\frac{1}{4}$ Ⓑ $3\frac{1}{4}$ Ⓒ $2\frac{1}{2}$ Ⓓ $3\frac{1}{2}$

37. What is the prime factorization of 650? **H**

  Ⓕ $2^2 \cdot 5 \cdot 13$ Ⓖ $2^2 \cdot 5^3$ Ⓗ $2 \cdot 5^2 \cdot 13$ Ⓙ $2^2 \cdot 5^2 \cdot 7$

38. Which number is NOT a factor of 60? **C**

  Ⓐ 20   Ⓑ 15   Ⓒ 8   Ⓓ 5

State whether each equation is true or false.

For Exercises	See Lesson
39–41	1-9

39. $48 \div 6 = 8$ true   **40.** $12.6 \div 2 = 6.2$ false   **41.** $1.8 = 5.4 \div 3$ true

Test Prep

Resources
For additional practice with a variety of test item formats:
• Test-Taking Strategies, p. 203
• Test Prep, p. 207
• Test-Taking Strategies with Transparencies

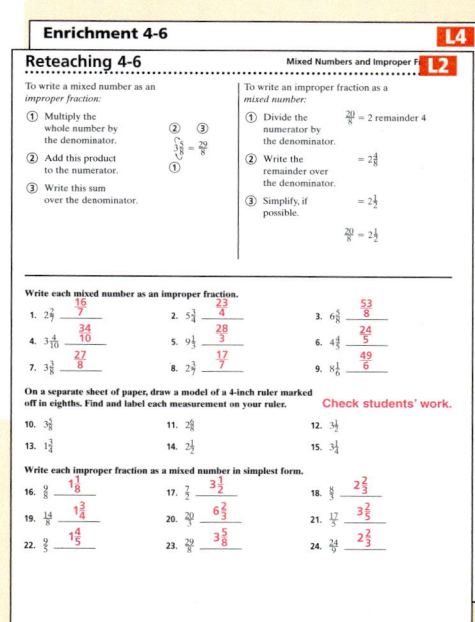

185

Fractions and Measurement

Guided Instruction

Be sure that students align their rulers correctly at the 0 before beginning to measure. Ask:
- *Why is the zero mark not placed at the edge of the ruler?* **Sample: The edges of rulers can be easily "rounded," making it difficult to measure accurately if zero were at the edge.**
- *Does a ruler marked in $\frac{1}{16}$ inches or one marked in $\frac{1}{8}$ inches give you a closer measurement?* **one marked in $\frac{1}{16}$ inches**

Activity

Have students work in pairs to do Exercise 4–9. Each student measures independently but compares and discusses the length he or she measured with a partner. Partners decide on a common answer.

Resources

- ruler ($\frac{1}{16}$ of an inch)

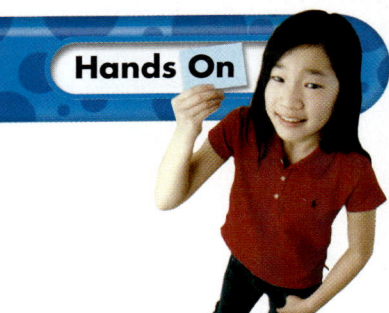

4-6b Activity Lab

Hands On

Fractions and Measurement

The marks on an inch ruler are based on fractions.

EXAMPLE **Fractions on a Ruler**

Biology Find the length for each insect shown below.

a.

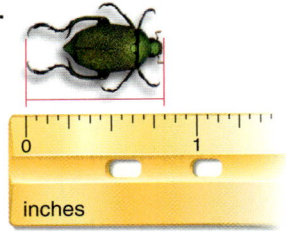

The ruler is marked every $\frac{1}{16}$ inch. The insect is the size of thirteen $\frac{1}{16}$-inch spaces.

So the length of the insect is $\frac{13}{16}$ inch.

b.

The ruler is marked every $\frac{1}{8}$ inch. The insect extends $\frac{1}{8}$ inch past 1 inch.

So the length of the insect is $1\frac{1}{8}$ inches.

Exercises

Find the length of each segment below.

1.

inches

$\frac{6}{8}$ in. = $\frac{3}{4}$ in.

2.

inches

$\frac{13}{16}$ in.

3.

inches

$\frac{3}{16}$ in.

Use a ruler to measure the length of each segment or object below. Measure to the nearest sixteenth of an inch.

4. _____ $\frac{1}{2}$ in.

5. _____ $\frac{3}{4}$ in.

6. _____ $\frac{15}{16}$ in.

7. 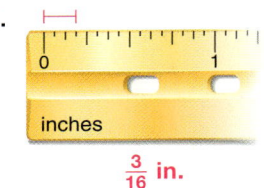 $\frac{3}{8}$ in.

8. $\frac{7}{8}$ in.

9. $\frac{5}{8}$ in.

Making Word Lists

You can learn new vocabulary by making a word list using index cards.

- Write the term. Then write the definition.
- Include any math symbols related to the term.
- Give an example of the term.
- Give a nonexample showing how the term might *not* apply.

> **Greatest Common Factor (GCF)**
>
> **Definition:** The GCF of two or more numbers is the greatest factor shared by all the numbers.
>
> **Example:** The GCF of 12 and 20 is 4.
>
> **Nonexample:** 2 is a common factor of 12 and 20, but 2 is not the GCF.

For the vocabulary terms on page 157, make a word list with cards like the one shown above.

 Checkpoint Quiz 2   Lessons 4-4 through 4-6

Find the GCF of each set of numbers.

1. 45, 80 **5**   **2.** 24, 72 **24**   **3.** 9, 18, 51 **3**   **4.** 18, 48 **6**

Write each mixed number as an improper fraction. Write each improper fraction as a mixed number in simplest form.

5. $3\frac{1}{5}$ **$\frac{16}{5}$**   **6.** $\frac{13}{8}$ **$1\frac{5}{8}$**   **7.** $2\frac{2}{3}$ **$\frac{8}{3}$**

8. You are filling 8 bags with party favors, including small toys, balloons, and bags of peanuts. Each bag has the same number of toys, of balloons, and of bags of peanuts. You have 16 toys, 48 balloons, and 96 bags of peanuts. How many of each item will be in a bag? **2 toys, 6 balloons, 12 bags of peanuts**

Vocabulary Builder

Making Word Lists

Students who grasp the precision of math vocabulary will improve their ability to fully comprehend and share mathematical ideas. This feature guides students to create an index-card word list to help them learn new math vocabulary.

Guided Instruction

Go over all the parts of the sample card and the samples of everyday meanings of the words. Discuss the advantages of including symbols and nonexamples of the defined terms on the cards.

Encourage students to refer to the English/Spanish Illustrated Glossary (p. 654) and the Table of Symbols (p. 649) to help build their vocabulary cards.

Resources

- Vocabulary and Study Skills Worksheets

 **Checkpoint Quiz**

Use this Checkpoint Quiz to check students' understanding of the skills and concepts of Lessons 4-4 through 4-6.

Resources

- All-in-One Teaching Resources Checkpoint Quiz 2
- ExamView CD-ROM
- Success Tracker™ Online Intervention

187

Objective
To find the LCM of two or more numbers

Examples
1 Finding the LCM Using Lists of Multiples
2 Using Prime Factorization

Math Understandings: p. 156D

Math Background

A *multiple* of a number is a product of that number and a nonzero whole number. You can make a list of multiples to find the *least common multiple*, or *LCM*, of a set of numbers. You can also use prime factorizations to find the LCM.

More Math Background: p. 156D

Lesson Planning and Resources

See p. 156E for a list of the resources that support this lesson.

Bell Ringer Practice

✓ **Check Skills You'll Need**
Use student page, transparency, or PowerPoint. For intervention, direct students to:
Prime Numbers and Prime Factorization
Lesson 4-3
Extra Skills and Word Problems Practice, Ch. 4

188

✓ **Check Skills You'll Need**

1. Vocabulary Review
How can you use a factor tree to find the *prime factorization* of a number?
1–5. See below.
Find the prime factorization of each number.

2. 80   3. 32

4. 208   5. 500

 **for Help**
Lesson 4-3

Check Skills You'll Need

1. A factor tree helps you write a number as a product of prime factors.

2. $2^4 \times 5$

3. 2^5

4. $2^4 \times 13$

5. $2^2 \times 5^3$

What You'll Learn

To find the LCM of two or more numbers

🔊 **New Vocabulary** multiple, common multiple, least common multiple (LCM)

Why Learn This?

You can use common multiples to make coordinating schedules easier.

Carmen gets her hair cut every four weeks. Maria gets her hair cut every six weeks. They both had their hair cut last week. How long will it be before they both get their hair cut again in the same week?

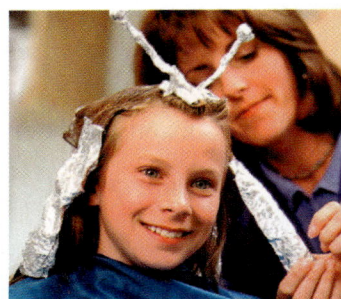

You can list multiples of 4 and 6 to answer this question. A **multiple** of a number is the product of that number and a nonzero whole number.

Multiples of 6
$6 \times 1 = 6$
$6 \times 2 = 12$
$6 \times 3 = 18$
$6 \times y = 6y$

A number that is a multiple of each of two or more numbers is a **common multiple**. The **least common multiple (LCM)** of two or more numbers is the least multiple that is common to all the numbers.

EXAMPLE **Find the LCM Using Lists of Multiples**

① Find the least common multiple of 4 and 6.

multiples of 4: 4, 8, ⑫, 16, 20, ㉔   ← List multiples of each number. 12 and 24 are common multiples.
multiples of 6: 6, ⑫, 18, ㉔

The least common multiple is 12.

✓ **Quick Check**

1. List multiples to find the LCM.
   a. 10, 12 **60**   b. 7, 10 **70**

Differentiated Instruction **Solutions for All Learners**

Special Needs L1
Some students may need to write the multiplication facts to list the multiples of a number. For example, for 4, they may write $4 \times 1 = 4$, $4 \times 2 = 8$, and so on. Suggest that they write the facts in a column, circling the list of products.

learning style: visual

Below Level L2
Have students find the LCM of pairs of numbers that are already in factored form. For example:

$2 \times 2 \times 7$ $2 \times 3 \times 3 \times 5$
$2 \times 3 \times 7$ $2 \times 2 \times 3 \times 5$
LCM = 84   **LCM = 180**

learning style: verbal

REGULAR SERVICE

EVERY

YELLOW LINE 8 min
GREEN LINE 10 min
PURPLE LINE 20 min

EXAMPLE **Using Prime Factorizations**

② **Scheduling** A train for each of the train lines shown in the table on the left has just arrived. In how many minutes will a train for each line arrive at the same time again?

Write the prime factorizations for 8, 10, and 20. Then circle each different factor where it appears the greatest number of times.

$8 = \boxed{2 \times 2 \times 2}$ ← **2 appears the most often here (three times).**
$10 = 2 \times \boxed{5}$ ← **5 appears once.**
$20 = 2 \times 2 \times 5$ ← **Don't circle 5 again.**
$2 \times 2 \times 2 \times 5 = 40$ ← **Multiply the circled factors.**

The LCM is 40. The trains will arrive together in 40 minutes.

✓ **Quick Check**

● 2. Use prime factorization to find the LCM of 6, 8, and 12. **24**

● More Than One Way

Find the LCM of 20, 30, and 45.

Michael's Method

I can use prime factorization to find the LCM.

$20 = \boxed{2 \times 2} \times \boxed{5}$ ← **2 appears twice. 5 appears once.**
$30 = 2 \times 3 \times 5$ ← **Don't circle 2 or 5 again.**
$45 = \boxed{3 \times 3} \times 5$ ← **3 appears twice.**

$2 \times 2 \times 3 \times 3 \times 5 = 180$ ← **Multiply the circled factors.**

The LCM of 20, 30, and 45 is 180.

Amanda's Method

The greatest number is 45. I can list the multiples of 45 until I find one that is also a multiple of 20 and 30.

┌──── **90 is a multiple of 30, but not of 20.**
45, 90, 135, 180 ←── **180 is a multiple of both 20 and 30.**

So the LCM of 20, 30, and 45 is 180.

Choose a Method 90; answers may vary. Check students' work.
Find the LCM of 6, 9, and 10. Explain why you chose your method.

Advanced Learners **L4**
The pennies in a jar can be shared equally by 2, 3, 4, 5, 6, 7, 8, 9, or 10 friends, with no pennies left over. What is the least number of pennies in the jar?
2,520 pennies

learning style: verbal

English Language Learners **ELL**
For Example 2, ask students to check the prime factorization of the numbers using factor trees or division ladders. They can use this strategy again in the Quick Check. Have students circle the factors in any method they choose.

learning style: visual

---

2. Teach

Activity Lab

Use before the lesson.

All in One Teaching Resources
Activity Lab 4-7: Investigating LCM and GCF

Guided Instruction

Error Prevention!

Students might confuse LCM with GCF because the two acronyms sound similar. Suggest that they say "least common multiple" softly whenever they encounter *LCM,* and say "greatest common factor" whenever they encounter *GCF.*

PowerPoint
Additional Examples

❶ List multiples to find the LCM of 6 and 9. **18**

6: 6, 12, ⑱, 24, 30, ㊱
9: 9, ⑱, 27, ㊱

❷ Use prime factorizations to find the LCM of each: 6, 9, 15. **90**

$6 = ②\times 3$ $9 = \boxed{3 \times 3}$ $15 = 3 \times ⑤$

All in One Teaching Resources
• Daily Notetaking Guide 4-7 **L3**
• Adapted Notetaking 4-7 **L1**

Closure

• *What is the LCM of two or more numbers?* **the least multiple that is common to all the numbers**
• *How do you find the LCM by using prime factorization?* **Write the prime factorization for each number. Circle each different factor where it appears the most times. Multiply these factors.**

Assignment Guide

Check Your Understanding
Go over Exercises 1–5 in class before assigning the Homework Exercises.

Homework Exercises
A Practice by Example   6–27
B Apply Your Skills   28–36
C Challenge   37
Test Prep and
    Mixed Review   38–42

Homework Quick Check
To check students' understanding of key skills and concepts, go over Exercises 15, 23, 29, 35, and 36.

Differentiated Instruction **Resources**

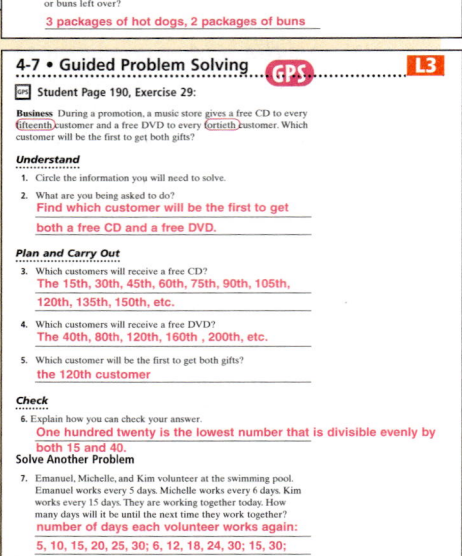

✓ Check Your Understanding

1. **Vocabulary** Use the word *multiple* in a sentence about math.
   Answers may vary. Sample: One number has many multiples.

List four multiples of each number.
Answers may vary. Samples are given.

2. 7 **14, 21, 28, 35**   3. 8 **16, 24, 32, 40**   4. 11 **22, 33, 44, 55**

5. Find the LCM of 16 and 24 using prime factorizations. **48**

Homework Exercises

For more exercises, see Extra Skills and Word Problems.

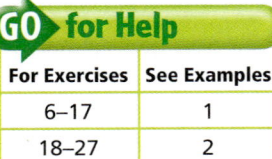

For Exercises	See Examples
6–17	1
18–27	2

Ⓐ List multiples to find the LCM of each set of numbers.

6. 4, 9 **36**   7. 5, 6 **30**   8. 12, 15 **60**

9. 10, 16 **80**   10. 14, 21 **42**   11. 20, 30 **60**

12. 25, 75 **75**   13. 8, 10 **40**   14. 3, 8, 12, 15 **120**

15. 4, 7, 12, 21 **84** 16. 25, 50, 125 **250** 17. 2, 3, 5, 7, 11 **2,310**

Use prime factorizations to find the LCM of each set of numbers.

18. 9, 21 **63**   19. 18, 24 **72**   20. 75, 100 **300**

21. 8, 14 **56**   22. 22, 55 **110**   23. 18, 108 **108**

24. 7, 12 **84**   25. 4, 7, 20 **140**   26. 30, 50, 200 **600**

27. **Shopping** You buy paper plates, napkins, and cups for a party. Plates come in packages of 15. Cups come in packages of 20, and napkins come in packages of 120. You want to have the same number of plates, cups, and napkins. How many packages of each item do you need to buy?
8 packages plates, 6 packages cups, 1 package napkins

Ⓑ **GPS** 28. **Guided Problem Solving** Two ships sail between New York and London. One makes the round trip in 12 days. The other takes 16 days. They both leave London today. In how many days will both ships leave London together again? **48 days**
• How can you use multiples to solve this problem?
• What are the multiples of 12 and 16?

29. **Business** During a promotion, a music store gives a free CD
GPS to every fifteenth customer and a free DVD to every fortieth customer. Which customer will be the first to get both gifts?
120th customer

36. **The LCM will be the product of the two numbers. Examples and explanations may vary. Sample: LCM of 1 and 6 is 6, and 1 × 6 = 6; LCM of 6 and 5 = 30 and 6 × 5 = 30; LCM of 6 and 35 = 210 and 6 × 35 = 210. The rule is true if one or both of the numbers is 1. If neither number is 1, write the prime factorization of each number. The LCM must have all the prime factors of each number. But the numbers will not have any prime factors in common, so you will have to multiply the prime factorizations to get all the factors needed in the LCM.**

Find the LCM of each set of numbers or expressions.

30. 35, 45 **315**   **31.** 6, 8, 16 **48**   **32.** $2^2 \times 7, 2 \times 7^2$
196

33. **Number Sense** A number N has both 8 and 10 as factors.
   a. Name three factors of the number N, other than 1. **2, 4, 5**
   b. What is the smallest number N could be? **40**

34. **Fitness** You lift weights every third day and swim every fourth day. If you do both activities today, in how many days will you do both activities again on the same day? **12 days**

35. (**Algebra**) The LCM of 3 and 6 is 6. The LCM of 5 and 10 is 10. The LCM of x and $2x$ is ■ when x is a nonzero whole number.
2x

36. **Writing in Math** What is the LCM for two numbers that have no common factors greater than 1? Explain your reasoning.
See margin.

C **37.** **Challenge** Find the LCM of $25xy$ and $200xy$. **200xy**

Test Prep and Mixed Review   **Practice**

Multiple Choice

38. What is the least common multiple of 24 and 28? **C**
   Ⓐ 4   Ⓑ 84   Ⓒ 168   Ⓓ 336

39. On January 1, Rosa waters all of her plants. She waters her cactus every 60 days, her fern every 4 days, and her violets every 3 days. How many times in a year will she water all her plants on the same day?
   Step K Find the least common multiple.
   Step L Divide 365 by the least common multiple.
   Step M Find the prime factorizations for 3, 4, and 60.

   Which list shows the steps in the correct order? **G**
   Ⓕ K, M, L   Ⓗ K, L, M
   Ⓖ M, K, L   Ⓙ M, L, K

40. Jon paid a membership fee of $30 to use a skate park. Each time he skated, he paid $2.50. Which equation can be used to find c, the cost of skating for s visits? **A**
   Ⓐ $c = 2.5s + 30$ Ⓒ $c = 30s + 2.5$
   Ⓑ $c = 30(s + 2.5)$ Ⓓ $c = 2.5(s + 30)$

Order each set of decimals on a number line. 41–42. See margin.

41. 0.51, 0.3, 0.49, 0.37, 0.6   **42.** 9.2, 9.28, 9.13, 9.25, 9.26

41–42. See back of book.

PowerPoint
📖 **Lesson Quiz**

Find the LCM of each set of numbers.

1. 3, 7 **21**

2. 12, 18 **36**

3. 5, 6 **30**

4. 4, 9, 12 **36**

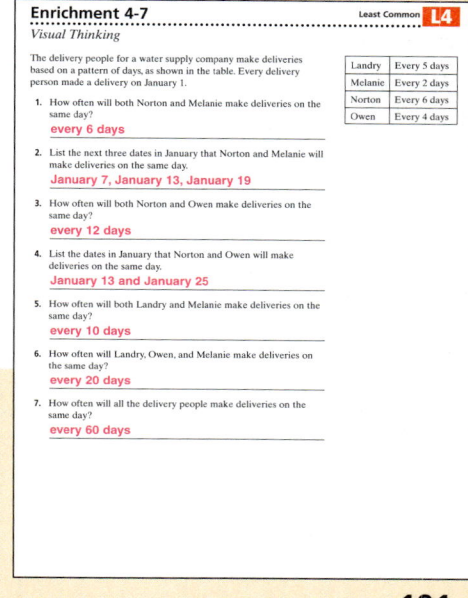

Reteaching 4-7   Least Common M **L2**

Find the *least common multiple (LCM)* of 8 and 12.
① Begin listing multiples of each number.
   8: 8, 16, 24, 32, 40
   12: 12, 24
② Continue the lists until you find the first multiple that is common to both lists. That is the LCM.
The least common multiple of 8 and 12 is 24.

List multiples to find the LCM of each pair of numbers.
1. 4: **4, 8, 12, 16, 20**   2. 6: **6, 12, 18, 24, 30, 36, 42**
   5: **5, 10, 15, 20**   7: **7, 14, 21, 28, 35, 42**
   LCM: **20**   LCM: **42**
3. 9: **9, 18, 27, 36, 45**   4. 10: **10, 20, 30, 40, 50**
   15: **15, 30, 45**   25: **25, 50**
   LCM: **45**   LCM: **50**
5. 8: **8, 16, 24**   6. 8: **8, 16, 24**
   24: **24**   12: **12, 24**
   LCM: **24**   LCM: **24**
7. 4: **4, 8, 12, 16, 20, 24, 28** 8. 15: **15, 30, 45, 60, 75**
   7: **7, 14, 21, 28**   25: **25, 50, 75**
   LCM: **28**   LCM: **75**

Use prime factorization to find the LCM of each set of numbers.
9. 9, 21 **63**   10. 6, 8 **24**
11. 18, 24 **72**   12. 40, 50 **200**

Enrichment 4-7   Least Common **L4**
Visual Thinking

The delivery people for a water supply company make deliveries based on a pattern of days, as shown in the table. Every delivery person made a delivery on January 1.

Landry	Every 5 days
Melanie	Every 2 days
Norton	Every 6 days
Owen	Every 4 days

1. How often will both Norton and Melanie make deliveries on the same day?
   every 6 days
2. List the next three dates in January that Norton and Melanie will make deliveries on the same day.
   January 7, January 13, January 19
3. How often will both Norton and Owen make deliveries on the same day?
   every 12 days
4. List the dates in January that Norton and Owen will make deliveries on the same day.
   January 13 and January 25
5. How often will both Landry and Melanie make deliveries on the same day?
   every 10 days
6. How often will Landry, Owen, and Melanie make deliveries on the same day?
   every 20 days
7. How often will all the delivery people make deliveries on the same day?
   every 60 days

Alternative Assessment

Each student in a pair writes a whole number. Partners exchange numbers and write at least 10 multiples of the number. Working together, partners find the LCM of each set of numbers. Students repeat the activity as time permits.

Test Prep

Resources

For additional practice with a variety of test item formats:
• Test-Taking Strategies, p. 203
• Test Prep, p. 207
• Test-Taking Strategies with Transparencies

Comparing and Ordering Fractions

Examples
1 Comparing Fractions
2 Comparing Mixed Numbers
3 Ordering Fractions and Mixed Numbers

Math Understandings: p. 156D

Math Background

When fractions have like denominators, you compare them by comparing numerators. For instance, $\frac{3}{5} > \frac{2}{5}$ because $3 > 2$.

When fractions have unlike denominators, comparing them involves rewriting the fractions with a common denominator. For instance, $\frac{1}{3} > \frac{1}{4}$ because $\frac{4}{12} > \frac{3}{12}$. Their *least common denominator*, or LCD, is the least common multiple (LCM) of their denominators. So, 12 is the LCM of 3 and 4, and 12 is the LCD of $\frac{1}{3}$ and $\frac{1}{4}$.

More Math Background: p. 156D

Lesson Planning and Resources

See p. 156E for a list of the resources that support this lesson.

Bell Ringer Practice

✓ **Check Skills You'll Need**
Use student page, transparency, or PowerPoint. For intervention, direct students to:
Equivalent Fractions
Lesson 4-5
Extra Skills and Word Problems Practice, Ch. 4

192

✓ Check Skills You'll Need

1. Vocabulary Review
How is writing a fraction in *simplest form* related to finding *equivalent fractions?*
1–5. See below.
Write two fractions equivalent to each given fraction.

2. $\frac{7}{21}$ **3.** $\frac{8}{40}$

4. $\frac{2}{3}$ **5.** $\frac{25}{150}$

GO for Help
Lesson 4-5

Check Skills You'll Need

1. When you write a fraction in simplest form, you are writing an equivalent fraction using division.

2–5. Answers may vary. Samples are given.

2. $\frac{1}{3}, \frac{21}{63}$

3. $\frac{1}{5}, \frac{2}{10}$

4. $\frac{4}{6}, \frac{20}{30}$

5. $\frac{1}{6}, \frac{5}{30}$

What You'll Learn

To compare and order fractions

🔊 **New Vocabulary** least common denominator (LCD)

Why Learn This?

Carpenters, chefs, and musicians all use fractions when comparing measurements.

Models like those below can help you decide whether $\frac{2}{3}$ or $\frac{3}{5}$ is greater.

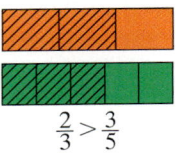

$\frac{2}{3} > \frac{3}{5}$

To compare fractions without using models, use the least common denominator. The <mark>least common denominator (LCD)</mark> of two or more fractions is the least common multiple (LCM) of their denominators.

EXAMPLE   Comparing Fractions

① Compare $\frac{5}{6}$ and $\frac{3}{4}$. Use <, =, or >.

First find the least common denominator. The least common multiple of 6 and 4 is 12, so 12 is the LCD.

$$\frac{5}{6} = \frac{10}{12} \qquad \frac{3}{4} = \frac{9}{12} \qquad \leftarrow \text{Find equivalent fractions and compare.}$$

Then compare fractions. $\frac{10}{12} > \frac{9}{12}$, so $\frac{5}{6} > \frac{3}{4}$.

✓ Quick Check

1. Compare $\frac{6}{8}$ and $\frac{7}{9}$. Use <, =, or >. **<**

Differentiated Instruction **Solutions for All Learners**

Special Needs **L1**
In Example 3, have students change the denominators to compare fractions, help them order the fractions and mixed numbers on a number line. Ask: *Which is closest to 0?* $\frac{1}{4}$ *Which is closest to $\frac{1}{2}$?* $\frac{2}{5}$ *Which is the closest to 2?* $1\frac{7}{9}$

learning style: visual

Below Level **L2**
Review the meanings of the symbols < (is less than), > (is greater than), and = (is equal to). Have students practice using the symbols by asking them to make some simple whole-number comparisons.

learning style: visual

Careers Tailors measure fabric to fit clothing.

Online
active math

For: Ordering Fractions Activity
Use: Interactive Textbook, 4-8

EXAMPLE **Comparing Mixed Numbers**

② **Tailoring** "Measure twice, cut once" is a useful motto for tailors to remember. A tailor needs fabric that is at least $6\frac{27}{32}$ inches wide. Is a $6\frac{3}{4}$-inch piece wide enough?

Since the whole numbers are the same, compare $\frac{27}{32}$ and $\frac{3}{4}$.

$$\frac{27}{32} = \frac{27}{32} \qquad \frac{3}{4} = \frac{24}{32} \qquad \leftarrow \text{Write equivalent fractions. Use the LCD, 32.}$$

$$\frac{27}{32} > \frac{24}{32} \qquad \leftarrow \text{Compare the fractions.}$$

So $6\frac{27}{32} > 6\frac{3}{4}$. The $6\frac{3}{4}$-inch piece is not wide enough.

✓ Quick Check

2. Is a $6\frac{7}{8}$-inch piece of fabric wide enough? Explain.
   Yes; $\frac{7}{8} = \frac{28}{32}$, and $\frac{28}{32} > \frac{27}{32}$. So $6\frac{7}{8} > 6\frac{27}{32}$.

When you order fractions and mixed numbers, compare the two types of numbers separately. The fractions without a whole-number part will be less than the mixed numbers.

EXAMPLE **Ordering Fractions and Mixed Numbers**

③ Order from least to greatest: $1\frac{2}{3}$, $\frac{2}{5}$, $1\frac{7}{9}$, and $\frac{1}{4}$.

Step 1 Order the fractions. Find the LCM of 4 and 5. The LCD of the fractions is 20.

$$\frac{2}{5} = \frac{8}{20} \qquad \frac{1}{4} = \frac{5}{20} \qquad \leftarrow \text{Write equivalent fractions.}$$

$$\frac{5}{20} < \frac{8}{20} \qquad \leftarrow \text{Compare the fractions.}$$

So the order of the fractions is $\frac{1}{4} < \frac{2}{5}$.

Step 2 Order the mixed numbers. Since the whole-number parts are the same, compare $\frac{2}{3}$ and $\frac{7}{9}$.

$$\frac{2}{3} = \frac{6}{9}, \text{ so } \frac{6}{9} < \frac{7}{9}.$$

The order of the mixed numbers is $1\frac{2}{3} < 1\frac{7}{9}$.

Including the fractions first, the order is $\frac{1}{4} < \frac{2}{5} < 1\frac{2}{3} < 1\frac{7}{9}$.

✓ Quick Check

3. Order $2\frac{5}{6}$, $\frac{3}{8}$, $\frac{1}{3}$, $2\frac{4}{5}$, and $1\frac{2}{3}$ from least to greatest. $\frac{1}{3}, \frac{3}{8}, 1\frac{2}{3}, 2\frac{4}{5}, 2\frac{5}{6}$

4-8 Comparing and Ordering Fractions **193**

Assignment Guide

Check Your Understanding
Go over Exercises 1–7 in class before assigning the Homework Exercises.

Homework Exercises

A	Practice by Example	8–29
B	Apply Your Skills	30–37
C	Challenge	38
Test Prep and Mixed Review		39–45

Homework Quick Check
To check students' understanding of key skills and concepts, go over Exercises 17, 24, 34, 35, and 37.

Differentiated Instruction Resources

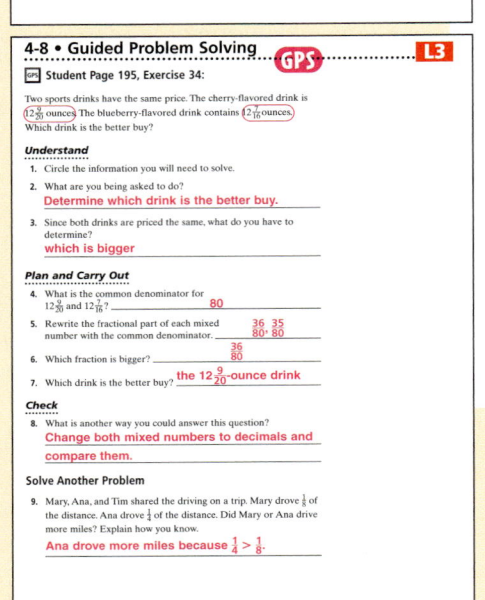

✓ Check Your Understanding

1. Vocabulary What is the LCD for fractions?
It is the LCM of the denominators.

Find the least common denominator for each pair of fractions.

2. $\frac{1}{3}, \frac{1}{4}$ **12**   **3.** $\frac{7}{8}, \frac{1}{2}$ **8**   **4.** $\frac{4}{5}, \frac{1}{6}$ **30**

Mental Math Compare each pair of numbers. Use <, =, or >.

5. $\frac{1}{15} \blacksquare \frac{1}{20}$ **>**   **6.** $\frac{3}{4} \blacksquare \frac{3}{2}$ **<**   **7.** $\frac{2}{45} \blacksquare \frac{1}{30}$ **>**

Homework Exercises

For more exercises, see Extra Skills and Word Problems.

 **for Help**

For Exercises	See Examples
8–16	1
17–23	2
24–29	3

Ⓐ Compare each pair of numbers. Use <, =, or >.

8. $\frac{3}{5} \blacksquare \frac{5}{8}$ **<**   **9.** $\frac{3}{4} \blacksquare \frac{3}{5}$ **>**   **10.** $\frac{1}{2} \blacksquare \frac{7}{16}$ **>**

11. $\frac{3}{5} \blacksquare \frac{12}{20}$ **=**   **12.** $\frac{5}{7} \blacksquare \frac{5}{6}$ **<**   **13.** $\frac{3}{11} \blacksquare \frac{1}{4}$ **>**

14. $\frac{2}{9} \blacksquare \frac{4}{15}$ **<**   **15.** $\frac{15}{16} \blacksquare \frac{7}{8}$ **>**   **16.** $\frac{9}{24} \blacksquare \frac{3}{8}$ **=**

17. $3\frac{1}{8} \blacksquare 3\frac{1}{4}$ **<**   **18.** $7\frac{2}{3} \blacksquare 7\frac{4}{6}$ **=**   **19.** $8\frac{7}{10} \blacksquare 8\frac{3}{5}$ **>**

20. $2\frac{17}{18} \blacksquare 2\frac{13}{16}$ **>**   **21.** $5\frac{4}{6} \blacksquare 5\frac{5}{7}$ **<**   **22.** $3\frac{1}{4} \blacksquare 3\frac{1}{5}$ **>**

23. Tim ran $1\frac{3}{4}$ miles. Naomi ran $1\frac{7}{10}$ miles. Who ran farther? **Tim**

Order each set of numbers from least to greatest. **24–29. See left.**

24. $\frac{2}{3}, \frac{5}{6}, \frac{3}{4}$ **25.** $3\frac{2}{3}, 3\frac{2}{5}, 3\frac{7}{15}$ **26.** $\frac{1}{8}, 2\frac{8}{9}, \frac{3}{10}, 2\frac{5}{6}$

27. $\frac{3}{12}, 2\frac{2}{3}, 3\frac{1}{4}, \frac{1}{2}$ **28.** $\frac{5}{8}, 1\frac{7}{12}, \frac{3}{4}, \frac{1}{2}, 2\frac{2}{3}$ **29.** $6\frac{5}{9}, 6\frac{2}{3}, 8\frac{1}{5}, 8\frac{2}{9}$

24. $\frac{2}{3}, \frac{3}{4}, \frac{5}{6}$

25. $3\frac{2}{5}, 3\frac{7}{15}, 3\frac{2}{3}$

26. $\frac{1}{8}, \frac{3}{10}, 2\frac{5}{6}, 2\frac{8}{9}$

27. $\frac{3}{12}, \frac{1}{2}, 2\frac{2}{3}, 3\frac{1}{4}$

28. $\frac{1}{2}, \frac{5}{8}, \frac{3}{4}, 1\frac{7}{12}, 2\frac{2}{3}$

29. $6\frac{5}{9}, 6\frac{2}{3}, 8\frac{1}{5}, 8\frac{2}{9}$

Ⓑ GPS **30. Guided Problem Solving** Plywood comes in a variety of thicknesses for different uses. Put these thicknesses in order from least to greatest. $\frac{1}{4}, \frac{3}{8}, \frac{1}{2}, \frac{5}{8}, \frac{3}{4}$

$\frac{3}{4}$ inch, $\frac{3}{8}$ inch, $\frac{1}{2}$ inch, $\frac{1}{4}$ inch, $\frac{5}{8}$ inch

• **Make a Plan** Find the least common denominator for the fractions. Then write equivalent fractions.
• **Carry Out the Plan** The least common denominator is $\blacksquare$. Compare the fractions.

31. >; the numerators are equal, so the fraction with the lesser denominator is larger.

32. <; the numerators are equal, so the fraction with the lesser denominator is larger.

33. >; the numerators are equal, so the fraction with the lesser denominator is larger.

35a–b. See back of book.

36–37. See back of book.

Number Sense Without using a common denominator, compare each pair of fractions using <, =, or >. Explain your reasoning.

31. $\frac{3}{7}$ ▦ $\frac{3}{8}$ **32.** $\frac{11}{16}$ ▦ $\frac{11}{12}$ **33.** $\frac{1}{8}$ ▦ $\frac{1}{18}$

31–33. See margin.

34. Ⓖ Two sports drinks have the same price. The cherry flavored drink contains $12\frac{9}{20}$ ounces. The blueberry flavored drink contains $12\frac{7}{16}$ ounces. Which drink is the better buy?

the cherry-flavored drink

35. **Music** Musical notes are based on fractions of a whole note.
  a. Order the fractions shown from greatest to least.
  b. **Patterns** Redraw the note symbols so they are in order. Do the symbols change in a pattern? Explain. 35a–b. See margin.

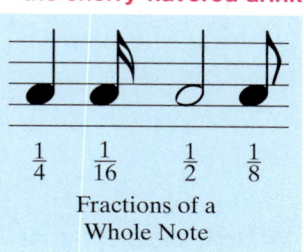

$\frac{1}{4}$ $\frac{1}{16}$ $\frac{1}{2}$ $\frac{1}{8}$

Fractions of a Whole Note

36. **Track** Order the Olympic men's pole vault records below from greatest to least. See margin.

19 ft $1\frac{1}{2}$ in. 19 ft $2\frac{1}{4}$ in. 19 ft 2 in. 18 ft $8\frac{1}{4}$ in. 19 ft $4\frac{1}{4}$ in.

37. **Writing in Math** Explain how to compare two fractions that have the same numerators and different denominators. See margin.

Ⓒ **38.** **Challenge** Find a whole number x such that $\frac{2}{3} < \frac{x}{8} < 1$.
6 or 7

Test Prep and Mixed Review **Practice**

Multiple Choice

39. Which measurement is between $\frac{3}{4}$ inch and $\frac{7}{8}$ inch on a ruler? D

Ⓐ $\frac{5}{8}$ inch   Ⓑ $\frac{6}{8}$ inch   Ⓒ $\frac{12}{16}$ inch   Ⓓ $\frac{13}{16}$ inch

40. Brandon needs to buy equal numbers of hot dogs and buns. Hot dogs come in packages of 10. Hot dog buns come in packages of 8. What is the least number of buns he can buy? H

Ⓕ 20   Ⓖ 24   Ⓗ 40   Ⓙ 80

41. What is the prime factorization of 108? A

Ⓐ $2^2 \cdot 3^3$ Ⓑ $2^3 \cdot 2^2$ Ⓒ $2^3 \cdot 3^3$ Ⓓ $2^2 \cdot 3^2$

GO for Help

For Exercises	See Lesson
42–45	4-5

Write each fraction in simplest form.

42. $\frac{18}{42}$ $\frac{3}{7}$ **43.** $\frac{16}{36}$ $\frac{4}{9}$ **44.** $\frac{36}{132}$ $\frac{3}{11}$ **45.** $\frac{36}{153}$ $\frac{4}{17}$

Alternative Assessment

Provide pairs of students with fraction models. Give them two fractions with unlike denominators such as $\frac{3}{7}$ and $\frac{4}{10}$, or $\frac{2}{5}$ and $\frac{3}{8}$. One partner models one fraction; the other partner models the other fraction. Then partners compare the models to determine which is greater. Students write the comparison using mathematical notation.

Test Prep

Resources

For additional practice with a variety of test item formats:
• Test-Taking Strategies, p. 203
• Test Prep, p. 207
• Test-Taking Strategies with Transparencies

4. Assess & Reteach

PowerPoint
Lesson Quiz

Compare. Use <, =, or >.

1. $\frac{2}{3}$ ▦ $\frac{9}{12}$ <   **2.** $4\frac{3}{8}$ ▦ $4\frac{3}{7}$ <

Order from least to greatest.

3. $\frac{3}{5}$, $\frac{4}{20}$, $\frac{5}{15}$ $\frac{4}{20}$, $\frac{5}{15}$, $\frac{3}{5}$

4. $1\frac{5}{8}$, $1\frac{13}{24}$, $1\frac{5}{16}$ $1\frac{5}{16}$, $1\frac{13}{24}$, $1\frac{5}{8}$

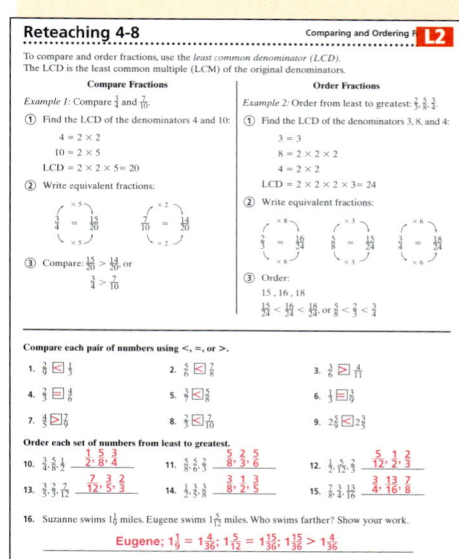

Practice Solving Problems

GPS **Guided Problem Solving**

Practice Solving Problems

In this feature, students use their number sense and knowledge of equivalent fractions to order a set of wrenches by length from shortest to longest.

You can use number sense and equivalent fractions to order fractional amounts.

A set of wrenches falls out of its case. Arrange the wrenches by size from smallest to largest. The sizes, in inches, are $\frac{5}{16}$, $\frac{7}{8}$, $\frac{7}{32}$, $\frac{9}{16}$, $\frac{1}{2}$, $\frac{1}{8}$, and $\frac{21}{32}$.

Guided Instruction

Discuss with students why someone might want to put the wrenches in order by length. Real-world problems such as this one often involve mathematics and since the wrench lengths are given in fractional parts of an inch, the problem involves ordering fractions.

Have a volunteer read the problem aloud. Ask:

- *How can you use number sense to start?* **Sample: Divide the set of wrenches into two parts so the ordering is easier.**
- *Why were some of the fractions changed from fractions with a denominator of 32 to equivalent fractions in the last step?* **so they would be in simplest form**

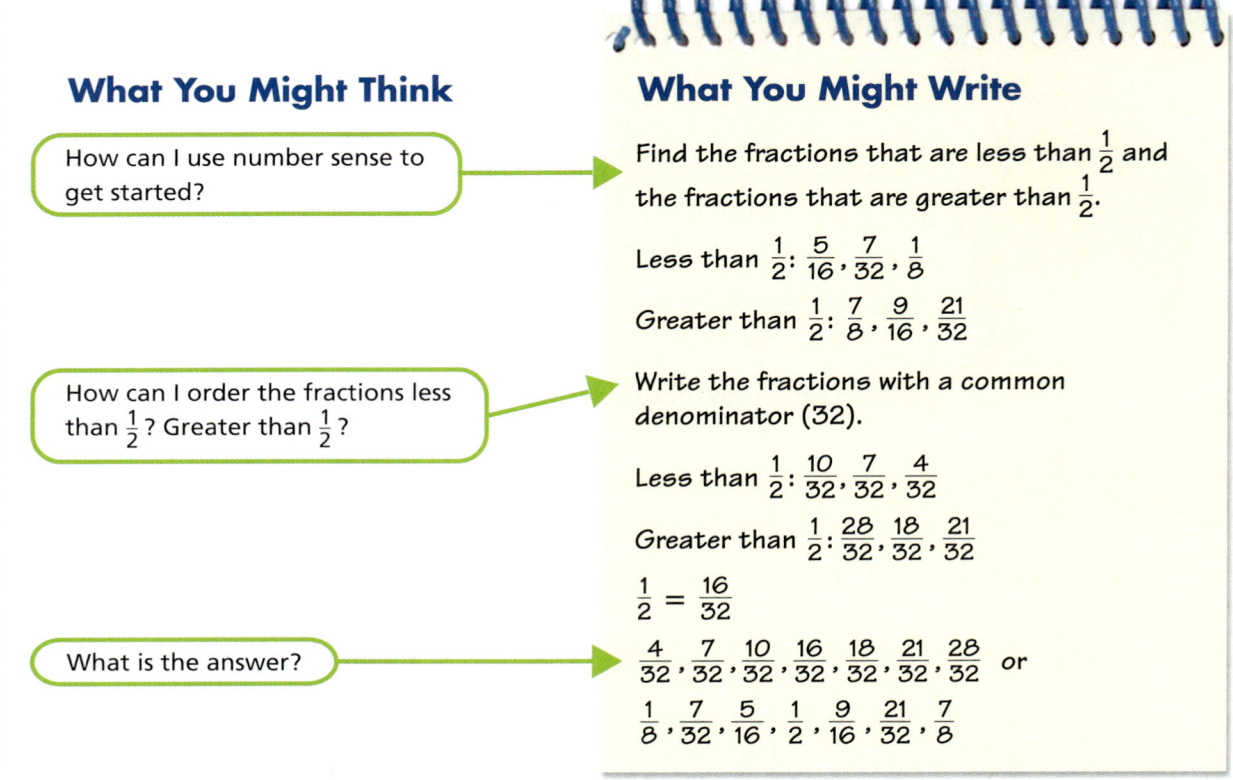

What You Might Think

How can I use number sense to get started?

How can I order the fractions less than $\frac{1}{2}$? Greater than $\frac{1}{2}$?

What is the answer?

What You Might Write

Find the fractions that are less than $\frac{1}{2}$ and the fractions that are greater than $\frac{1}{2}$.

Less than $\frac{1}{2}$: $\frac{5}{16}$, $\frac{7}{32}$, $\frac{1}{8}$

Greater than $\frac{1}{2}$: $\frac{7}{8}$, $\frac{9}{16}$, $\frac{21}{32}$

Write the fractions with a common denominator (32).

Less than $\frac{1}{2}$: $\frac{10}{32}$, $\frac{7}{32}$, $\frac{4}{32}$

Greater than $\frac{1}{2}$: $\frac{28}{32}$, $\frac{18}{32}$, $\frac{21}{32}$

$\frac{1}{2} = \frac{16}{32}$

$\frac{4}{32}$, $\frac{7}{32}$, $\frac{10}{32}$, $\frac{16}{32}$, $\frac{18}{32}$, $\frac{21}{32}$, $\frac{28}{32}$ or

$\frac{1}{8}$, $\frac{7}{32}$, $\frac{5}{16}$, $\frac{1}{2}$, $\frac{9}{16}$, $\frac{21}{32}$, $\frac{7}{8}$

Think It Through

1. **Number Sense** How did you decide which fractions were greater than $\frac{1}{2}$ and which fractions were less than $\frac{1}{2}$? **If a fraction is greater than $\frac{1}{2}$, then its numerator is more than half its denominator.**

2. **Reasoning** Without finding a common denominator, how can you use number sense to tell that $\frac{1}{8}$ is the least fraction and $\frac{7}{8}$ is the greatest fraction? **Using the results of Exercise 1, compare the fractions in each group two at a time.**

Exercises

3. Nail lengths, in inches, are given as mixed numbers. Arrange the nail lengths $2\frac{3}{4}$, $1\frac{3}{4}$, $1\frac{1}{2}$, $3\frac{1}{2}$, $3\frac{1}{4}$, 2, and $3\frac{3}{4}$ in order from least to greatest. (*Hint:* Start by grouping nails with the same whole-number part.) $1\frac{1}{2}$, $1\frac{3}{4}$, 2, $2\frac{3}{4}$, $3\frac{1}{4}$, $3\frac{1}{2}$, $3\frac{3}{4}$

4. **Patterns** Seven drill bits are arranged from smallest to largest in the table. They increase in size following a pattern. Find the diameters of the missing drill bits in simplest form. $\frac{7}{16}$; $\frac{9}{16}$

Drill Bits

Bit Number	Diameter (inches)
1	$\frac{5}{16}$
2	$\frac{3}{8}$
3	■
4	$\frac{1}{2}$
5	■
6	$\frac{5}{8}$
7	$\frac{11}{16}$

5. U.S. presidential elections take place every 4 years. U.S. senators run for election every 6 years. A certain senator is elected in the same year as a presidential election. In how many years will the senator run for reelection in a presidential election year again? **12 years**

6. The thickness and width of two pieces of lumber are given below. Write two true statements comparing the measurements of these pieces of lumber.

   Piece 1: $2\frac{1}{2}$ in. by $5\frac{1}{2}$ in.   Piece 2: $1\frac{1}{4}$ in. by $7\frac{1}{4}$ in.

   6. Answers may vary. Samples: The width of piece 1 is greater than that of piece 2. The length of piece 1 is less than that of piece 2.

7. You want to divide the field below into plots. The plots will be square and be the same size. Each plot will have whole-number side lengths. What is the largest plot size you can use to divide the entire field? **12 ft × 12 ft**

120 feet

84 feet

8. Your dog and cat each eat one can of food every day. Dog food comes in cases of 18 cans. Cat food comes in cases of 16 cans. What is the least number of cases of each type that you must buy so that you have the same number of cans of dog food and cat food? **9 cases cat food; 8 cases dog food**

Objective
To find equivalent forms of fractions and decimals and to order fractions and decimals

Examples
1 Writing a Decimal as a Fraction
2 Writing a Fraction as a Decimal
3 Ordering Numbers

Math Understandings: p. 156D

Math Background

The fraction $\frac{a}{b}$, where a and b are whole numbers and b is not zero, represents $a \div b$. This quotient is the decimal equivalent of $\frac{a}{b}$. For denominators whose only prime factors are 2 or 5—denominators such as 2, 4, 5, 8, 10, 16, 20, 25, 32, 40, 50, and so on—the decimal is a *terminating decimal.*

More Math Background: p. 156D

Lesson Planning and Resources

See p. 156E for a list of the resources that support this lesson.

☑ Check Skills You'll Need

1. Vocabulary Review
When you find $12 \div 3$, you find how many groups of ■ are in ■.
3; 12
Find each quotient.

2. $3 \div 2$ **3.** $2 \div 3$
1.5   **0.6**
4. $8 \div 5$ **5.** $3 \div 10$
1.6   **0.3**

 **for Help**
Lesson 1-9

Vocabulary Tip

Reading 0.225 as "two hundred twenty-five thousandths" can help you write 0.225 as a fraction.

What You'll Learn

To find equivalent forms of fractions and decimals and to order fractions and decimals

🔊 **New Vocabulary** terminating decimal, repeating decimal

Why Learn This?

You can write measurements in different ways—as decimals, as fractions, and as mixed numbers. To compare measurements, write them in the same way.

To write a decimal as a fraction, write the fraction as you would say the decimal. Then simplify.

EXAMPLE   Writing a Decimal as a Fraction

1 Write 0.225 as a fraction in simplest form.

$$0.225 = \frac{225}{1,000} \quad \leftarrow \text{Write "two hundred twenty-five thousandths" as a fraction.}$$

$$\frac{225}{1,000} \overset{\div\,25}{\underset{\div\,25}{=}} \frac{9}{40} \quad \leftarrow \text{Simplify. The GCF of 225 and 1,000 is 25.}$$

So $0.225 = \frac{9}{40}$.

☑ Quick Check

1. Write 5.08 as a mixed number. $5\frac{2}{25}$

A **terminating decimal** is a decimal that stops, or terminates. Examples are 0.5 and 1.25. A **repeating decimal** repeats the same digit or group of digits. A bar is drawn over the digits that repeat. You write $1.\overline{27}$ for $1.2727\ldots$.

Differentiated Instruction   Solutions for All Learners

Special Needs   **L1**
For Example 2, draw a diagram on the board that shows the diameters of the drill bit and of the hole to be drilled. Make sure students understand the hole to be drilled cannot be larger than 0.6 inches in diameter.

learning style: visual

Below Level   **L2**
Have students write the names of several sets of decimals like the following.

0.27   **27 hundredths**   2.7   **2 and 7 tenths**
0.027   **27 thousandths**

learning style: visual

A fraction indicates division. To write a fraction as a decimal, divide the numerator by the denominator.

EXAMPLE **Writing a Fraction as a Decimal**

② **Construction** A construction worker wants to drill a hole with a diameter that is no more than 0.6 in. Can she use a $\frac{5}{8}$-in. drill bit?

To write $\frac{5}{8}$ as a decimal, divide 5 by 8.

Method 1 Use pencil and paper.

$$
\begin{array}{r}
0.625 \\
8\overline{)5.000} \\
-4\,8 \\
\hline
20 \\
-16 \\
\hline
40 \\
-40 \\
\hline
0
\end{array}
$$

← $\frac{5}{8}$ = 0.625

Method 2 Use a calculator.

5 ÷ 8 = 0.625

Since 0.625 > 0.6, the $\frac{5}{8}$-in. drill bit is too big.

✓ Quick Check

2. You answer 35 out of 40 test questions correctly. Your friend answers 0.8 of the questions correctly. Who scores higher? **you**

EXAMPLE **Ordering Numbers**

③ **Multiple Choice** Write 1.6, $1\frac{3}{15}$, 0.9, and $2\frac{2}{9}$ in order from least to greatest.

Ⓐ 0.9, 1.6, $1\frac{3}{15}$, $2\frac{2}{9}$

Ⓒ $2\frac{2}{9}$, 1.6, $1\frac{3}{15}$, 0.9

Ⓑ $2\frac{2}{9}$, $1\frac{3}{15}$, 1.6, 0.9

Ⓓ 0.9, $1\frac{3}{15}$, 1.6, $2\frac{2}{9}$

Write $1\frac{3}{15}$ as a decimal.

$1\frac{3}{15} = 1.2$ ← **Write as a decimal.**

$0.9 < 1.2 < 1.6$ ← **Compare the decimals.**

The order is 0.9, $1\frac{3}{15}$, 1.6, and $2\frac{2}{9}$. The correct answer is choice D.

✓ Quick Check

3. Write $2\frac{2}{3}$, $3\frac{1}{5}$, 1.8, and 2.7 in order from least to greatest.

1.8, $2\frac{2}{3}$, 2.7, $3\frac{1}{5}$

Assignment Guide

Check Your Understanding
Go over Exercises 1–11 in class before assigning the Homework Exercises.

Homework Exercises
A Practice by Example   12–28
B Apply Your Skills   29–39
C Challenge   40
Test Prep and
  Mixed Review   41–47

Homework Quick Check
To check students' understanding of key skills and concepts, go over Exercises 18, 22, 34, 35, and 37.

Differentiated Instruction **Resources**

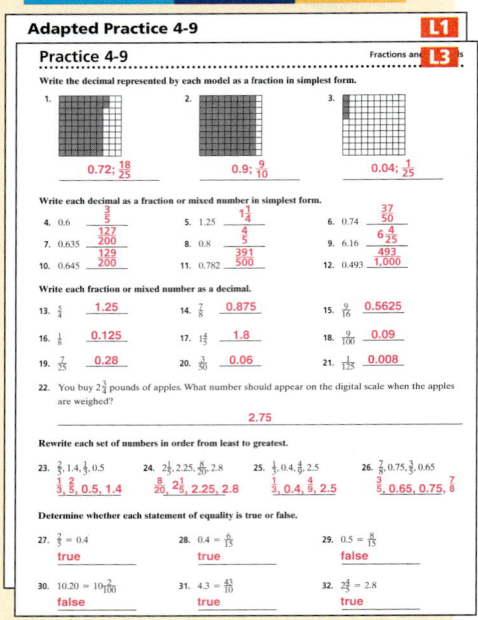

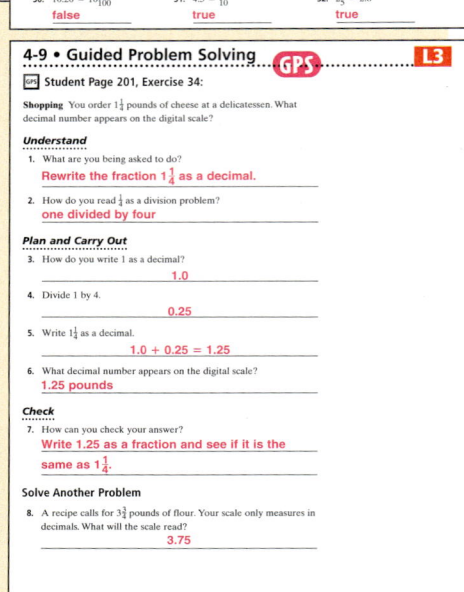

✔ Check Your Understanding

GO for Help

For help with dividing, go to Lesson 1-9, Example 1.

Write each decimal as a fraction in simplest form.

1. 0.3 $\frac{3}{10}$
2. 0.8 $\frac{4}{5}$
3. 0.75 $\frac{3}{4}$
4. 0.04 $\frac{1}{25}$

5. Explain why the mixed number $2\frac{3}{4}$ is the same as 2.75.

Match each fraction to a decimal.
     $2\frac{3}{4} = 2 + \frac{3}{4} = 2 + 0.75$

6. $\frac{2}{5}$ **B**   **A.** 0.75

7. $\frac{3}{4}$ **A**   **B.** 0.40

8. $\frac{3}{8}$ **C**   **C.** 0.375

Write each set of numbers in order from least to greatest.

9. $1.6,\ 1\frac{3}{4},\ 2.3$
    $1.6,\ 1\frac{3}{4},\ 2.3$

10. $2\frac{1}{2},\ 3.7,\ 3.5$
    $2\frac{1}{2},\ 3.5,\ 3.7$

11. $3\frac{3}{8},\ 4\frac{3}{5},\ 3.1$
    $3.1,\ 3\frac{3}{8},\ 4\frac{3}{5}$

Homework Exercises

For more exercises, see Extra Skills and Word Problems.

GO for Help

For Exercises	See Examples
12–19	1
20–28	2–3

A Write each decimal as a fraction or mixed number in simplest form.

12. 0.15 $\frac{3}{20}$
13. 0.17 $\frac{17}{100}$
14. 0.008 $\frac{1}{125}$
15. 5.5 $5\frac{1}{2}$

16. 4.25 $4\frac{1}{4}$
17. 3.149 $3\frac{149}{1,000}$
18. 5.075 $5\frac{3}{40}$
19. 8.32 $8\frac{8}{25}$

Write each fraction or mixed number as a decimal.

20. $\frac{5}{6}$ $0.8\overline{3}$
21. $\frac{7}{15}$ $0.4\overline{6}$
22. $\frac{11}{8}$ 1.375
23. $\frac{10}{9}$ $1.\overline{1}$

24. $4\frac{7}{10}$ 4.7
25. $1\frac{1}{10}$ 1.1
26. $2\frac{7}{12}$ $2.58\overline{3}$
27. $5\frac{3}{20}$ 5.15

28. **Carpentry** The sizes of four wrenches are 0.375, $1\frac{1}{8}$, 0.8125, and $1\frac{1}{16}$ inches. Order the wrench sizes from least to greatest.
See margin.

GPS

B 29. **Guided Problem Solving** A baseball player had 184 hits in 599 at-bats last season. Use a calculator to change the fraction $\frac{184}{599}$ to a decimal. Round to the nearest thousandth.
- What number do you enter first on your calculator?
- List the calculator keys in the order that you will use them.
0.307

28. $0.375,\ 0.8125,\ 1\frac{1}{16},\ 1\frac{1}{8}$

Match each number with its location on the number line below.

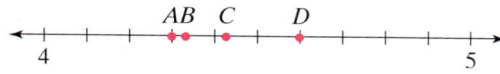

30. $4\frac{3}{5}$ **D**   **31.** 4.3 **A**   **32.** 4.43 **C**   **33.** $4\frac{1}{3}$ **B**

34. Shopping You order $1\frac{1}{4}$ pounds of cheese at a delicatessen.
GPS What decimal number appears on the digital scale? **1.25**

35. Writing in Math Explain the steps you would use to write 0.125 as a fraction in simplest form. **See margin.**

36. Number Sense Change $\frac{2}{3}$, $\frac{3}{3}$, $\frac{4}{3}$, $\frac{5}{3}$, and $\frac{6}{3}$ to decimals. Describe when a denominator of 3 results in a repeating decimal.
$0.\overline{6}$, 1, $1.\overline{3}$, $1.\overline{6}$, 2; when the numerator is not divisible by 3

37. Stocks Until 2001, stock prices were reported as mixed numbers. Find the dollar amounts represented by $6\frac{5}{8}$ and $8\frac{1}{2}$. **$6.625, $8.50**

Write each number as a mixed number and as a decimal.

38. four and three fourths pounds $4\frac{3}{4}$ lb, 4.75 lb

39. five and seven eighths inches $5\frac{7}{8}$ in., 5.875 in.

C **40. Challenge** Use the same digit to make $\frac{\blacksquare 6}{125} = 0.\blacksquare 08$ true.
$\frac{26}{125} = 0.208$

Test Prep and Mixed Review   **Practice**

Multiple Choice

41. Noah wants to write the fraction $\frac{5}{8}$ as a decimal. Which method should he use? **C**
  Ⓐ Write the decimal 0.58.   Ⓒ Divide 5 by 8.
  Ⓑ Write the decimal 0.85.   Ⓓ Divide 8 by 5.

42. Five measuring cups stack inside one another. Which list shows the cup sizes from largest to smallest? **J**
  Ⓕ $\frac{1}{8}$ c, $\frac{1}{4}$ c, $\frac{1}{3}$ c, $\frac{1}{2}$ c, 1 c   Ⓗ 1 c, $\frac{1}{2}$ c, $\frac{1}{4}$ c, $\frac{1}{3}$ c, $\frac{1}{8}$ c

  Ⓖ $\frac{1}{2}$ c, $\frac{1}{4}$ c, $\frac{1}{3}$ c, $\frac{1}{8}$ c, 1 c   Ⓙ 1 c, $\frac{1}{2}$ c, $\frac{1}{3}$ c, $\frac{1}{4}$ c, $\frac{1}{8}$ c

43. Which number is NOT a factor of 144? **C**
  Ⓐ 12   Ⓑ 16   Ⓒ 22   Ⓓ 24

Use the Distributive Property to simplify each expression.

44. 3×42 **126**   **45.** 9×68 **612**   **46.** 7×2.9 **20.3**   **47.** 4×9.1 **36.4**

GO for Help

For Exercises	See Lesson
44–47	3-8

35. Write 0.125 as $\frac{125}{1,000}$. Divide numerator and denominator by 125 to express the fraction in simplest form as $\frac{1}{8}$.

PowerPoint
Lesson Quiz

Write each as a fraction in simplest form.

1. 0.7 $\frac{7}{10}$

2. 0.008 $\frac{1}{125}$

Write as a decimal.

3. $\frac{9}{16}$ **0.5625**

4. Write in order from least to greatest:
  2.4, $2\frac{4}{5}$, 2.25, 2.45
  2.25, 2.4, 2.45, $2\frac{4}{5}$

Alternative Assessment

Each student in a pair writes a decimal. Partners exchange papers and write each other's decimal as a fraction or mixed number in simplest form. Then three groups of partners write their fractions or mixed numbers in order from least to greatest.

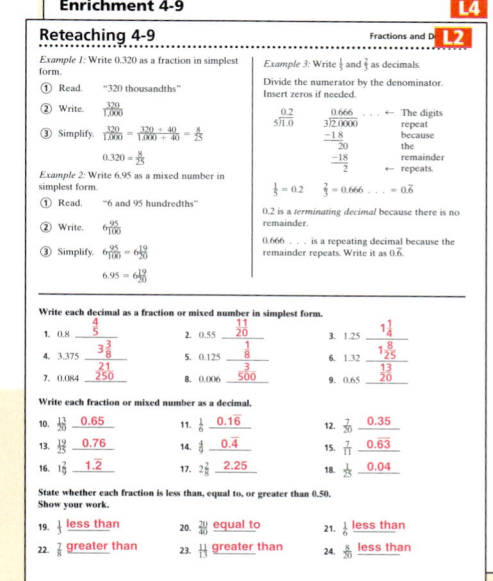

Test Prep

Resources

For additional practice with a variety of test item formats:
• Test-Taking Strategies, p. 203
• Test Prep, p. 207
• Test-Taking Strategies with Transparencies

Conducting a Survey

This Activity helps students understand the difference between a biased and an unbiased survey. After students discover bias in surveys, they learn how to write unbiased survey questions.

Guided Instruction

Ask:
• *Would you be more likely to say that you spent more time on a fun activity or a boring activity? Why?* **Sample: a fun activity because I would not want to spend too much time on something boring**

Exercises

Have students work in two groups on Exercises 1–4. Come back together as a class to do Exercises 5 and 6. Have students form small groups to complete Exercise 7.

Differentiated Instruction

Advanced Learners **L4**
Ask: *Is it more likely that more students will answer survey question A or B? Why?* **Question A because there are more odd days in a year since January, March, May, July, August, October and December all have a 31st (odd) day.**

Conducting a Survey

The way you phrase a survey question can influence the way people answer it. A question that favors one answer over another is biased.

ACTIVITY **1–7. Check students' work.**

1. If your birthday is on an odd day, answer the question in Survey A. If your birthday is on an even day, write your answers to the question in Survey B.

2. Write the fraction of a day that you spend on each of the activities. There are 24 hours in a day.

3. Order your fractions from least to greatest. Write the name of each corresponding activity under each fraction.

4. Find the mean number of hours that students who answered the same survey question as you spend on each activity.

5. **Writing in Math** Compare your results to the results of the students who answered the other survey. Explain how the wording of the two survey questions could lead to differences in the way people responded.

6. Rewrite the question in your survey to remove any bias.

7. **Open-Ended** Choose a topic for a survey question. You might choose study habits, food preferences, favorite movies or books, family life, or computer use.
   a. Write one unbiased and one biased version of your survey question.
   b. **Data Collection** Survey 20 people. Ask 10 people your biased question. Then ask 10 people your unbiased question. Did the bias in your question influence your survey results? Explain.

Survey A
How many hours do you spend each week on these **boring** activities?

• playing an instrument
• playing video games
• watching television
• listening to music
• playing sports
• reading books

Survey B
How many hours do you spend each week on these **fun** activities?

• playing an instrument
• playing video games
• watching television
• listening to music
• playing sports
• reading books

Test-Taking Strategies

Writing Extended Responses

An extended-response question in this book is worth a total of 4 points. To get full credit, you must show your work and explain your reasoning.

EXAMPLE

Mary plans to fence 80 square feet of her backyard for her dog. She wants the length and width to be whole numbers (in feet). What dimensions can she use? Tell how you know that you have found all possible pairs.

Here are four responses with the points each received.

4 points
1 ft by 80 ft, 2 ft by 40 ft, 4 ft by 20 ft, 5 ft by 16 ft, and 8 ft by 10 ft
These are all the pairs because there are no other whole numbers that divide 80 without a remainder.

The 4-point response shows all of the correct whole-number factors of 80 and the student's explanation of why the answer is complete.

2 points
8 ft by 10 ft, 1 ft by 80 ft, 2 ft by 40 ft, 5 ft by 16 ft, and 4 ft by 20 ft

The 2-point response gives all pairs of factors but does not have an explanation.

3 points
8 and 10, 4 and 20, 5 and 14, 2 and 40, 1 and 80
There are no other whole numbers that divide 80 with no remainder, so this must be the answer.

The 3-point response has one error, and the student's explanation of the answer is complete.

1 point
2 and 40, 1 and 80, 8 and 10

The 1-point response is missing some pairs and does not have an explanation.

1. **5 and 14 are not a pair of factors of 80.**

2. **4 and 20, 80 and 10, 5 and 16**

Exercises

1. Read the 3-point response. What error did the student make?

2. Read the 1-point response. Which dimensions are missing?

Test-Taking Strategies

Writing Extended Responses

This feature gives an example for students to see how to receive full credit on extended-response questions.

Guided Instruction

Emphasize to students the importance of providing complete answers to extended-response questions, of showing all work, and of writing a clear and full explanation of their reasoning. Encourage students always to check their work.

Error Prevention

Some students may omit 1 and 80 as dimensions of one of the fenced-in rectangles. Remind them that every number has 1 and itself as factors.

Resources

Test-Taking Strategies with Transparencies
• Transparency 3
• Practice sheet, p. 4

Test-Taking Strategies with Transparencies

Test-Taking Strategies: Writing Extended Responses

1. Draw and label two rectangles of different lengths and widths, each with a perimeter of 20 units.

Scoring Guide

4 Draws 2 rectangles of different lengths and widths, with perimeter 20 units indicated by labels on sides.
3 Draws 2 identical rectangles, with perimeter 20 units, OR draws 2 rectangles of different widths and lengths, only 1 with perimeter 20 units.
2 Draws 1 or 2 rectangles, whose perimeters are not 20 units.
1 Draws 1 or 2 non-rectangles. Does not label the sides.
0 Answers inappropriately or not at all.

2. The Athletic Council is hosting a sports banquet. It costs $300 to rent a hall, plus $8 per person for food. Between 50 and 90 people will attend. What are the least and greatest amounts of money the banquet could cost? Explain.

Scoring Guide

4 Correctly computes least and greatest costs, AND explains adequately.
3 Correctly computes least and greatest costs, but explanation is inadequate.
2 Computes least cost incorrectly, OR computes greatest cost incorrectly, OR explains inadequately.
1 Computes both costs incorrectly, OR computes one cost correctly, but explains inadequately.
0 Answers inappropriately or not at all.

Transparency 4

Chapter 4 Review

Resources

Student Edition

Extra Skills and Word Problems
Practice, Ch. 4, p. 618
English/Spanish Glossary, p. 654
Formulas and Properties, p. 652
Tables, p. 648

All in One Teaching Resources
- Vocabulary and Study
  Skills 4F   **L3**

Differentiated Instruction

Spanish Vocabulary Workbook
with Study Skills   **ELL**
Interactive Textbook
- Audio Glossary
Online Vocabulary Quiz

Success Tracker
Online at PHSchool.com

Vocabulary Review

 base (p. 162)
common factor (p. 171)
common multiple (p. 188)
composite number (p. 166)
divisible (p. 158)
equivalent fractions (p. 176)
even number (p. 159)
exponent (p. 162)

factor (p. 166)
greatest common factor (GCF)
  (p. 171)
improper fraction (p. 182)
least common denominator
  (LCD) (p. 192)
least common multiple (LCM)
  (p. 188)
mixed number (p. 182)

multiple (p. 188)
odd number (p. 159)
power (p. 162)
prime factorization (p. 167)
prime number (p. 166)
proper fraction (p. 182)
repeating decimal (p. 198)
simplest form (p. 177)
terminating decimal (p. 198)

Go Online
PHSchool.com
For: Vocabulary quiz
Web Code: aqj-0451

Choose the correct vocabulary term to complete each sentence.

1. Fractions that represent the same amount are   ? .   **equivalent fractions**

2. The number $5\frac{1}{8}$ is a(n)   ? .   **mixed number**

3. The   ?   of 42 is $2 \times 3 \times 7$.   **prime factorization**

Skills and Concepts

Lesson 4-1
- To check for divisibility
  using mental math and
  to use divisibility to
  solve problems

You can use divisibility rules to solve problems.

Test each number for divisibility by 2, 3, 5, 9, and 10.

4. 207 **3 and 9**   5. 585 **3, 5, and 9**   6. 756 **2, 3, and 9**   7. 3,330 **2, 3, 5, 9, and 10**

Lessons 4-2 and 4-3
- To use exponents and
  to simplify expressions
  with exponents
- To factor numbers and to
  find the prime factorization
  of numbers

You can use an **exponent** to show how many times a number, or **base,** is used as a factor. A number expressed using an exponent is called a **power.**

Simplify each expression.

8. $3^2 + 2^3$ **17**   9. $(15 - 1) - 3^2$ **5**

A **prime number** has exactly two factors, 1 and the number itself. A **composite number** has more than two factors. Writing a composite number as a product of prime numbers gives the **prime factorization** of the number.

Find the prime factorization of each number.

10. 28 $2^2 \times 7$ 11. 51 3×17 12. 100 $2^2 \times 5^2$ 13. 250 2×5^3

Spanish Vocabulary/Study Skills **ELL**

Vocabulary/Study Skills **L3**

4F: Vocabulary Review Puzzle   For use with the Chapter Review

Study Skill Combine clue words and pictures to prompt your memory.

Use the word list below to find hidden words in the puzzle. Once you have found a word, draw a circle around it and cross the word off in the word list. Words can be displayed forwards, backwards, up, down, or diagonally but they are always in a straight line.

divisible	prime factor	improper fraction	factor tree
multiple	composite number	equivalent fractions	least common multiple
mixed number	base	simplest form	common factor
fraction	power		

```
A Z E L P I T L U M N O M M O C T S A E L
C E B A S E W X T Y N U Z N A O G P H O E
O J V G R O T C A F N O M M O C S Q A P Q
M W A G H M L L I F H P F D O P O W E R U
P H P O W E R H E M N O B Q E R Y F Z I I
O I B P E L B I S I V I D C M X A R B M V
S K K G L L C R M E N D B I W C D A P E A
I X J K T S F J L U Q R X V T I V C D F L
T I Y W T D X P K R M E A O P U Y T O A E
E J Z U A E I F G Q J R F A J E I G C N
N I V M E T R F L N Z T Q B C C T O Z T T
U B L X L K W M U I R D K X E Y Z N C O F
M W K U F E C M I E P A H S V B S T U R R
B N M V V O B U E X T J H M R W W N X A A
E U O I N E S D Z Y M U L T I P L E Q G C
R Y L Q R T P M R O F T S E L P M I S Y T
I M P R O P E R F R A C T I O N R S F Z I
K S I R B M T B Q A H O F M D G F H N I O
D A U C E W E N D O Z P V L Q L X A J C N
J T G U H S V G E P I C W R X M Z Y B K S
```

Lesson 4-4
- To find the GCF of two or more numbers

The **greatest common factor (GCF)** of two or more numbers is the greatest factor shared by all the numbers.

Find the GCF of each set of numbers.

14. $18, 28$ **2**   **15.** $12, 62$ **2**   **16.** $25, 35$ **5**   **17.** $16, 40$ **8**

Lessons 4-5 and 4-6
- To find equivalent forms of fractions
- To use mixed numbers and improper fractions

Equivalent fractions are fractions that name the same amount. A fraction is in **simplest form** when the only common factor of the numerator and the denominator is 1. A **mixed number** shows the sum of a whole number and a fraction. An **improper fraction** has a numerator that is greater than or equal to its denominator.

State whether each fraction is in simplest form. If the fraction is not, write the fraction in simplest form. Then write three other equivalent fractions for each fraction. **18–21. See margin.**

18. $\dfrac{5}{20}$ **19.** $\dfrac{4}{6}$ **20.** $\dfrac{1}{3}$ **21.** $\dfrac{2}{9}$

Rewrite each number as an improper fraction or a mixed number.

22. $4\dfrac{2}{3}$ $\dfrac{14}{3}$ **23.** $8\dfrac{1}{5}$ $\dfrac{41}{5}$ **24.** $\dfrac{13}{3}$ $4\dfrac{1}{3}$ **25.** $\dfrac{58}{6}$ $9\dfrac{2}{3}$

Lesson 4-7
- To find the LCM of two or more numbers

A number that is a multiple of each of two or more numbers is a **common multiple.** The **least common multiple (LCM)** of two or more numbers is the least multiple that is common to all the numbers.

Find the LCM of each set of numbers.

26. $12, 22$ **132**   **27.** $10, 20, 35$ **140**

Lessons 4-8, 4-9
- To compare and order fractions
- To find equivalent forms of fractions and decimals and to order fractions and decimals

To compare fractions with unlike denominators, find equivalent fractions that have a common denominator. To write a fraction as a decimal, divide the numerator by the denominator. Write a fraction for a decimal just as you would say the decimal.

Order the numbers from least to greatest. **29–30. See margin.**

28. $\dfrac{1}{2}, \dfrac{1}{4}, \dfrac{1}{6}$ $\dfrac{1}{6}, \dfrac{1}{4}, \dfrac{1}{2}$ **29.** $2\dfrac{4}{15}, 2\dfrac{1}{3}, 2\dfrac{2}{5}$ **30.** $\dfrac{17}{40}, \dfrac{7}{20}, \dfrac{5}{16}$

Write each number as a fraction or mixed number in simplest form or as a decimal.

31. $\dfrac{3}{16}$ **0.1875**   **32.** $6\dfrac{5}{24}$ **6.208$\overline{3}$**   **33.** 0.06 $\dfrac{3}{50}$ **34.** 4.52 $4\dfrac{13}{25}$

18. No; $\frac{1}{4}$; answers may vary. Sample:
$\dfrac{2}{8}, \dfrac{3}{12}, \dfrac{10}{40}$

19. No; $\frac{2}{3}$; answers may vary. Sample:
$\dfrac{10}{15}, \dfrac{8}{12}, \dfrac{20}{30}$

20. Yes; answers may vary. Sample:
$\dfrac{2}{6}, \dfrac{3}{9}, \dfrac{4}{12}$

21. Yes; answers may vary. Sample:
$\dfrac{4}{18}, \dfrac{6}{27}, \dfrac{8}{36}$

29. $2\dfrac{4}{15}, 2\dfrac{1}{3}, 2\dfrac{2}{5}$

30. $\dfrac{5}{16}, \dfrac{7}{20}, \dfrac{17}{40}$

Resources

- ExamView Assessment Suite CD-ROM
  - Ch. 4 Ready-Made Test
  - Make your own Ch. 4 test
- MindPoint Quiz Show CD-ROM
  - Chapter 4 Review

Differentiated Instruction

All in One Teaching Resources
- Below Level Chapter 4 Test **L2**
- Chapter 4 Test **L3**
- Chapter 4 Alternative Assessment **L4**

Spanish Assessment Resources **ELL**
- Below Level Chapter 4 Test **L2**
- Chapter 4 Test **L3**
- Chapter 4 Alternative Assessment **L4**

ExamView Assessment Suite CD-ROM
- Special Needs Test **L1**
- Special Needs Practice Bank **L1**

Online Chapter 4 Test at www.PHSchool.com **L3**

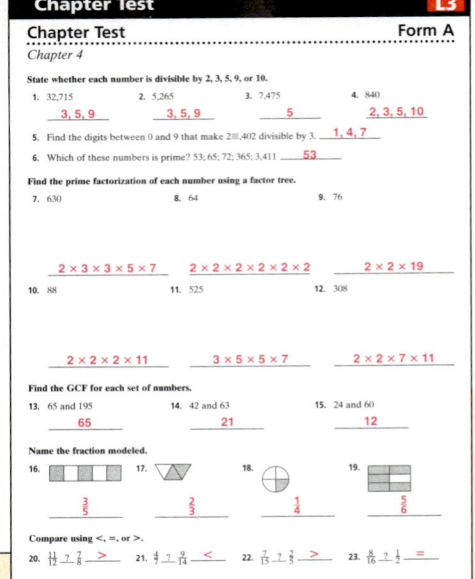

Test each number for divisibility by 2, 3, 5, 9, and 10.

1. 70   **2, 5, and 10**
2. 405   **3, 5, and 9**
3. 628 **2**
4. 837   **3 and 9**

State whether each number is prime or composite.

5. 19 **prime**
6. 39 **composite**
7. 51 **composite**
8. 67 **prime**

Find the prime factorization of each number.

9. 72 $2^3 \times 3^2$
10. 80 $2^4 \times 5$
11. 120 $2^3 \times 3 \times 5$

Find the GCF of each set of numbers.

12. 24, 36 **12**
13. 20, 25, 30 **5**
14. 7, 19 **1**

15. For a writing workshop, 15 coaches and 35 students will be split into groups, each with the same number of coaches and the same number of students. At most how many groups can there be? **5 groups**

16. Find the length of each segment.

    a. $\frac{7}{8}$ in.

    b. $1\frac{5}{16}$ in.

    c. $1\frac{3}{4}$ in.

Write each expression using an exponent. Name the base and the exponent.

17. $10 \times 10 \times 10 \times 10$ **10^4; 10; 4**

18. $p \cdot p \cdot p \cdot p \cdot p \cdot p$ **p^6; p; 6**

Simplify each expression.

19. $4^3 - 1$ **63**
20. 2×3^2 **18**
21. $150 \div 5^2$ **6**
22. $36 - (8 - 6)^4$ **20**

23. **Lawns** Today, two neighbors water their lawns. One neighbor waters her lawn every four days. The other neighbor waters his lawn every three days. In how many days will they water their lawns on the same day again? **12 days**

24. Write two fractions equivalent to each fraction. **24a–d. See margin.**
   a. $\frac{6}{18}$ b. $\frac{9}{24}$ c. $\frac{18}{20}$ d. $\frac{60}{100}$

25. Write $\frac{34}{51}$ in simplest form. **$\frac{2}{3}$**

26. **Writing in Math** Explain how to use prime factorizations to find the LCM of two numbers. Include an example. **See margin.**

Find the LCM for each set of numbers.

27. 4, 8 **8**
28. 6, 11 **66**
29. 10, 12, 15 **60**

Compare each set of numbers using <, =, or >.

30. $1\frac{2}{5} \blacksquare 1\frac{1}{5}$ **>**
31. $\frac{15}{4} \blacksquare \frac{17}{5}$ **>**
32. $\frac{7}{14} \blacksquare \frac{1}{2}$ **=**
33. $2\frac{3}{5} \blacksquare 2\frac{7}{11}$ **<**

34. Order $1\frac{5}{6}$, $1\frac{7}{9}$, $\frac{35}{36}$, and $1\frac{3}{4}$ from least to greatest. **$\frac{35}{36}$, $1\frac{3}{4}$, $1\frac{7}{9}$, $1\frac{5}{6}$**

35. **Fitness** Lee jogged $\frac{1}{2}$ mile, Orlando jogged $\frac{2}{3}$ mile, and Holden jogged $\frac{3}{8}$ mile. Who jogged the longest distance? **Orlando**

Write each decimal as a fraction or mixed number in simplest form. Write each fraction as a decimal.

36. 0.04 **$\frac{1}{25}$**
37. $\frac{17}{40}$ **0.425**
38. 3.875 **$3\frac{7}{8}$**
39. $\frac{8}{9}$ **$0.\overline{8}$**
40. 2.14 **$2\frac{7}{50}$**
41. $\frac{6}{11}$ **$0.\overline{54}$**

24a–d. Answers may vary. Samples:

24a. $\frac{1}{3}$, $\frac{2}{6}$

   b. $\frac{3}{8}$, $\frac{12}{32}$

   c. $\frac{9}{10}$, $\frac{27}{30}$

   d. $\frac{3}{5}$, $\frac{6}{10}$

26. **Answers may vary. Sample:** Write the prime factorization of each number. Circle each different factor where it appears the greatest number of times. Multiply the circled factors.
$12 = 2 \times 2 \times 3$
$8 = 2 \times 2 \times 2$
The LCM of 12 and 8 is $2 \times 2 \times 2 \times 3 = 24$.

Reading Comprehension

Read each passage and answer the questions that follow.

Sum Art Artists have often used mathematics in their work. The artist M.C. Escher used math ideas in many of his drawings. In the early sixteenth century, Albrecht Dürer included a 4 × 4 number square in one of his engravings, *Melancholia*. A number square has numbers arranged so that each row, column, and main diagonal has the same sum. Part of Dürer's number square is shown at the left.

16	3	2	*a*
5	*b*	11	*c*
d	6	7	*e*
f	15	14	1

1. What must be the sum of each row, column, and diagonal in Dürers number square? **C**
- (A) 21
- (B) 23
- (C) 34
- (D) 38

2. What numbers do *a* and *f* represent? **J**
- (F) 13 and 6
- (G) 14 and 4
- (H) 14 and 3
- (J) 13 and 4

3. What is the sum of *b* + *c*? **D**
- (A) 15
- (B) 16
- (C) 17
- (D) 18

4. Two squares next to each other contain the year that Dürer made the engraving. In what year did Dürer engrave *Melancholia*? **J**
- (F) 715
- (G) 911
- (H) 1112
- (J) 1514

Something to Prove One of the most famous unsolved math problems is Goldbach's Conjecture. In 1742, Christian Goldbach made the conjecture that every even number greater than 2 can be written as the sum of two prime numbers. For example, 6 = 3 + 3 and 10 = 3 + 7. Today, mathematicians are still trying to prove Goldbach's Conjecture.

5. To which of the following numbers does Goldbach's Conjecture apply? **D**
- (A) 1
- (B) 2
- (C) 3
- (D) 4

6. Which of the following illustrates Goldbach's Conjecture for 100? **J**
- (F) 100 = 35 + 65
- (G) 100 = 37 + 63
- (H) 100 = 39 + 61
- (J) 100 = 41 + 59

7. Which of the following does NOT illustrate Goldbach's Conjecture for 30? **B**
- (A) 30 = 7 + 23
- (B) 30 = 21 + 9
- (C) 30 = 11 + 19
- (D) 30 = 17 + 13

8. Which of the following odd numbers would NOT be used to illustrate Goldbach's Conjecture? **H**
- (F) 5
- (G) 7
- (H) 9
- (J) 11

Chapter 4 Test Prep **207**

 **Test Prep**

Resources

Test Prep Workbook

All in One Teaching Resources
- Cumulative Review **L3**

ExamView Assessment Suite CD-ROM
- Standardized Test Practice

Differentiated Instruction

Progress Monitoring Assessments
- Benchmark Test 2 **L3**

Spanish Assessment Resources
- Spanish Cumulative Review **ELL**

ExamView Assessment Suite CD-ROM
- Special Needs Practice Bank **L1**

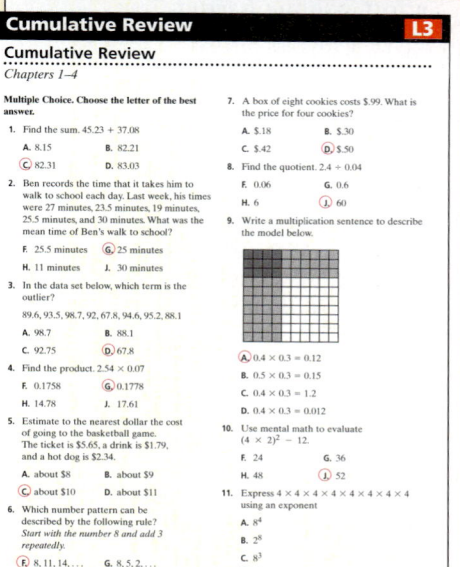

Applying Fractions

Students will use data from these two pages to answer the questions posed in Put It All Together.

Guide students to make sketches of seesaws to help them visually identify the distance, the force, and the weight in each problem of the Activity. Ask:
• *On each seesaw sketch, where would you place the following labels: fulcrum, effort, and load?* **Check students' work.**

Materials
• ruler

Activating Prior Knowledge

Have students share any experiences they have had using levers of all three classes. In particular, ask students to explain the factors involved in trying to balance a seesaw.

Guided Instruction

Have volunteers read the data about levers. Guide them to understand the distinction between the three classes of levers. Elicit that the distinctions have to do with the positioning of three variables: the *load,* the *effort,* and the *fulcrum.* The three classes are a result of the three possible combinations of these elements. Discuss how each example shown fits its classification.

Ask:
• *In which class lever is the load between the effort and the fulcrum?* **Class 2**
• *What is the positioning of the three components for a Class 3 Lever?* **The effort is positioned between the load and the fulcrum.**

Problem Solving Application

Applying Fractions

Lifting With Levers The simplest machines have only a few moving parts and can be powered by hand. For example, you can use a lever like the one in the diagram below to help lift a heavy load. If you know the distances a and b in the diagram, and the weight of a load, you can find the force needed to lift the load.

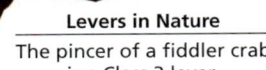

How to Measure Force
force $= \frac{a}{b} \times$ weight of load

Put It All Together

Data File Use the information on these two pages to answer these questions.

1. **a.** Suppose $a = 3$ and $b = 6$. Find the fraction of the load the force will be.
   b. How much force would it take to lift 100 pounds?

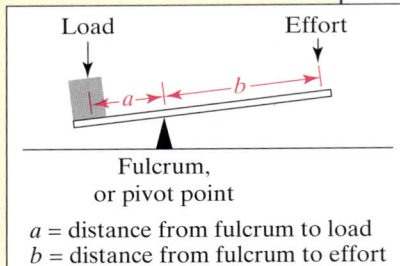

Load   Effort

Fulcrum, or pivot point

a = distance from fulcrum to load
b = distance from fulcrum to effort

Lever	Muscle Multiplier	Great Lifter	Load Lifter	Extra Muscle	Effort Less	Lever Greatness
a	6	4	5	10	8	5
b	10	6	8	15	14	9

2. The table shows the values of a and b in feet for six different levers.
   a. Use the force formula to write the fraction of the load required to work each lever. Write each fraction in simplest form.
   b. List the levers in order from least to most force required. Which levers need the same force?
   c. Convert each of the fractions to a decimal. Round to the nearest hundredth. Use the decimals to check the order of your list.

3. **Open-Ended** Make up your own set of levers.
   a. Choose a and b for six levers (make a less than b).
   b. Make a table to record the data about your levers. Name each lever.
   c. Exchange tables with a classmate. Write the fraction of the load required by each lever (in simplest form). Arrange the levers in order from least to most force required.

4. **Reasoning** For the levers on this page, $a < b$. What would happen if $a > b$? Can you think of a use for such a lever?

5. **Writing in Math** What class of lever is a wrench? Explain.

1a. $\frac{1}{2}$

b. 50 pounds

2a. $\frac{3}{5}, \frac{2}{3}, \frac{5}{8}, \frac{2}{3}, \frac{4}{7}, \frac{5}{9}$

b. Lever Greatness, Effort Less, Muscle Multiplier, Load Lifter, Extra

Muscle, Great Lifter; Extra Muscle and Great Lifter need the same force.

c. 0.56, 0.57, 0.6, 0.63, 0.67, 0.67

3a–c. Check students' work.

4. Answers may vary. Sample: If $a > b$, then the required force is greater than the weight of the load. You could use such a lever to move objects under a microscope.

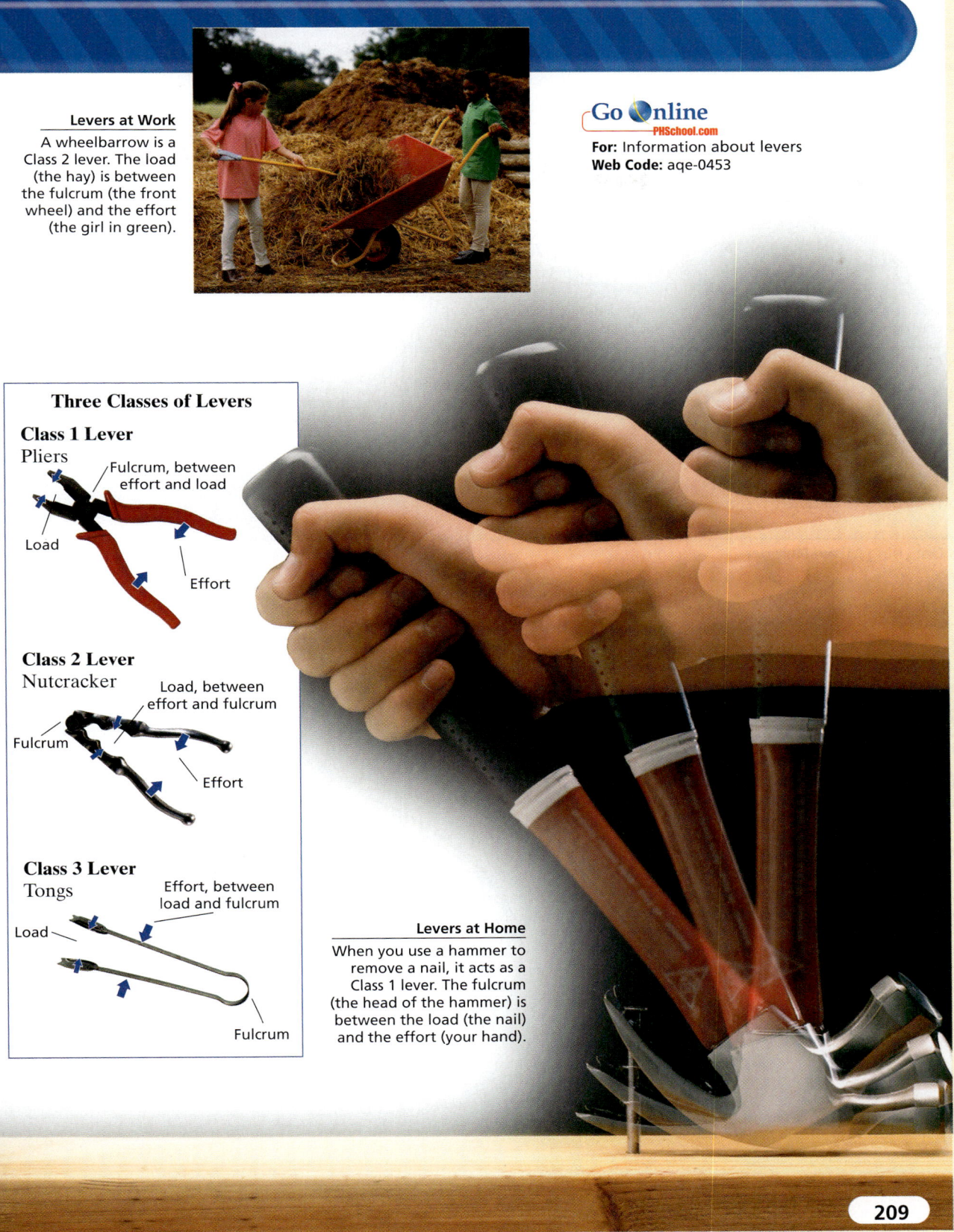

Levers at Work

A wheelbarrow is a Class 2 lever. The load (the hay) is between the fulcrum (the front wheel) and the effort (the girl in green).

Go Online
PHSchool.com

For: Information about levers
Web Code: aqe-0453

Three Classes of Levers

Class 1 Lever
Pliers

Fulcrum, between effort and load

Load

Effort

Class 2 Lever
Nutcracker

Load, between effort and fulcrum

Fulcrum

Effort

Class 3 Lever
Tongs

Effort, between load and fulcrum

Load

Fulcrum

Levers at Home

When you use a hammer to remove a nail, it acts as a Class 1 lever. The fulcrum (the head of the hammer) is between the load (the nail) and the effort (your hand).

209

Activity

Have a volunteer read aloud the paragraph about levers that precedes the data and questions. Point out that each of the names in the table describes a Class-1 lever, like a seesaw. Point out that the use of *force* in the equation refers to *effort* in the diagram. Then have students work in pairs to answer the questions.

Exercise 2 Students can see that levers whose $\frac{a}{b}$ ratios name the same fraction will need the same force.

Science Connection
Have interested students choose another simple machine and find out about its history and how it works. Guide students to look into pulleys, gears, clock mechanisms, wedges, wheels, and screws.

Differentiated Instruction

Special Needs　　L1
Write the formula for force on the board. Then work through Exercise 1 together with students. Provide additional examples to guide them to see that they can use this formula to find any of the variables—force, weight, and either of the distances from the fulcrum.

5. **Class 2; explanations may vary. Sample: The fulcrum is at one end, and the effort is at the other end.**

Chapter at a Glance

Lesson Titles, Objectives, and Features	Assessment	NCTM Standards	Local Standards
5-1 Estimating Sums and Differences • Using benchmarks to estimate sums and differences	Lesson Quiz	1, 2, 4, 6, 7, 8, 9, 10	
5-2a Activity Lab, Hands On: Modeling Fraction Operations			
5-2 Fractions with Like Denominators • Adding and subtracting fractions with like denominators	Lesson Quiz	1, 2, 6, 7, 8, 9, 10	
5-3a Activity Lab: Modeling Unlike Denominators			
5-3 Fractions with Unlike Denominators • Adding and subtracting fractions with unlike denominators using the LCD	Lesson Quiz Checkpoint Quiz 1	1, 2, 6, 7, 8, 9, 10	
5-4a Activity Lab, Hands On: Using Mixed Numbers			
5-4 Adding Mixed Numbers • Adding mixed numbers by adding the parts separately	Lesson Quiz	1, 2, 4, 6, 7, 8, 9, 10	
5-5 Subtracting Mixed Numbers • Subtracting mixed numbers using LCD and renaming whole numbers and mixed numbers	Lesson Quiz Checkpoint Quiz 2	1, 2, 4, 6, 7, 8, 9, 10	
5-5b Activity Lab, Technology: Using a Fraction Calculator			
5-6a Activity Lab, Data Analysis: Using Pictographs			
5-6 Equations with Fractions • Solving equations that include fractions using mental math and the LCD	Lesson Quiz	1, 2, 5, 6, 7, 8, 9, 10	
Guided Problem Solving: Practice Solving Problems			
5-7 Measuring Elapsed Time • Estimating and calculating elapsed time and converting units of time	Lesson Quiz	1, 2, 4, 6, 7, 8, 9, 10	
Problem Solving Application: Applying Mixed Numbers			

NCTM Standards 2000
1 Number and Operations **2** Algebra **3** Geometry **4** Measurement **5** Data Analysis and Probability
6 Problem Solving **7** Reasoning and Proof **8** Communication **9** Connections **10** Representation

Correlations to Standardized Tests

All content for these tests is contained in *Prentice Hall Math*, Course 1. This chart reflects coverage in this chapter only.

	5-1	5-2	5-3	5-4	5-5	5-6	5-7
Terra Nova CAT6 (Level 16)							
Number and Number Relations	✔	✔	✔	✔	✔	✔	✔
Computation and Numerical Estimation	✔	✔	✔	✔	✔	✔	✔
Operation Concepts	✔	✔	✔	✔	✔	✔	✔
Measurement							✔
Geometry and Spatial Sense							
Data Analysis, Statistics, and Probability							
Patterns, Functions, Algebra	✔	✔	✔	✔	✔	✔	✔
Problem Solving and Reasoning	✔	✔	✔	✔	✔	✔	✔
Communication	✔	✔	✔	✔	✔	✔	✔
Decimals, Fractions, Integers, and Percents	✔	✔	✔	✔	✔	✔	✔
Order of Operations							
Terra Nova CTBS (Level 16)							
Whole Numbers, Decimals, Fractions	✔	✔	✔	✔	✔	✔	✔
Numeration, Number Theory	✔	✔	✔	✔	✔	✔	✔
Data Interpretation				✔	✔	✔	✔
Pre-algebra	✔	✔	✔	✔	✔	✔	✔
Measurement							✔
Geometry							
ITBS (Level 12)							
Number Properties and Operations	✔	✔	✔	✔	✔	✔	✔
Algebra	✔	✔	✔	✔	✔	✔	✔
Geometry							
Measurement							✔
Probability and Statistics							
Estimation	✔			✔			✔
SAT10 (Adv 1 Level)							
Number Sense and Operations	✔	✔	✔	✔	✔	✔	✔
Patterns, Relationships, and Algebra	✔	✔	✔	✔	✔	✔	✔
Data, Statistics, and Probability						✔	
Geometry and Measurement							✔
NAEP							
Number Sense, Properties, and Operations	✔	✔	✔	✔	✔		
Measurement							✔
Geometry and Spatial Sense							
Data Analysis, Statistics, and Probability							
Algebra and Functions						✔	

CAT6 California Achievement Test, 6th Ed. **CTBS** Comprehensive Test of Basic Skills **ITBS** Iowa Test of Basic Skills, Form M
SAT10 Stanford Achievement Test, 10th Ed. **NAEP** National Assessment of Educational Progress 2005 Mathematics Objectives

Math Background

Skills Trace

BEFORE Chapter 5
Grade 5 presented fraction addition and subtraction.

DURING Chapter 5
Course 1 reviews and extends adding and subtracting fractions to like and unlike denominators as well as mixed numbers.

AFTER Chapter 5
Throughout this course, students add and subtract fractions to solve problems.

5-1 Estimating Sums and Differences

Math Understandings
- You can find approximate answers by using estimation.
- You can estimate the value of fractions between 0 and 1 by comparing the size of the numerator and denominator.
- You can estimate the sum or difference of two mixed numbers by rounding the mixed numbers to the nearest whole number.

A **benchmark** is a number that is close to a fraction and easy to use when you estimate. The chart below describes when to round to the benchmarks 0, $\frac{1}{2}$, and 1.

Description	Examples	Benchmark
Numerator is close to 0. Denominator is not close to 0.	$\frac{1}{8}, \frac{3}{16}, \frac{2}{25}, \frac{9}{100}$	0
Numerator is about half of denominator.	$\frac{3}{8}, \frac{9}{16}, \frac{11}{25}, \frac{52}{100}$	$\frac{1}{2}$
Numerator and denominator are close to each other.	$\frac{7}{8}, \frac{14}{16}, \frac{23}{25}, \frac{95}{100}$	1

5-2 Fractions With Like Denominators

Math Understandings
- In order to add or subtract fractions, both fractions must be written with the same denominator.

To add fractions with like denominators, add the numerators and keep the same denominator. Then write the sum in simplest form, which may involve writing an improper fraction as a mixed number. To subtract fractions with like denominators, subtract the numerators and keep the same denominator. Write the difference in simplest form.

Example: Find $\frac{5}{6} - \frac{1}{6}$.

$$\frac{5}{6} - \frac{1}{6} = \frac{4}{6} = \frac{2}{3}$$

5-3 Fractions With Unlike Denominators

Math Understandings
- To find the sum or difference of two fractions with different denominators, you must first rewrite each fraction using a common denominator.
- Any common denominator may be used, but using the Least Common Denominator (LCD) may save steps and make it easier to simplify the final answer.
- The product of the denominators will always give a common denominator, but it may not be the lowest common denominator.

To find the sum or difference of two fractions with different denominators, rewrite each fraction using a common denominator, add or subtract numerators, and simplify.

Example: Find $\frac{1}{2} - \frac{1}{3}$.

$$\frac{1}{2} - \frac{1}{3} = \frac{1 \times 3}{2 \times 3} - \frac{1 \times 2}{3 \times 2} = \frac{3}{6} - \frac{2}{6} = \frac{1}{6}$$

5-4 Adding Mixed Numbers

Math Understandings
- To find the sum of two mixed numbers with unlike denominators, you first rewrite each fraction part as an equivalent fraction using a common denominator.

You can find the sum of mixed numbers by adding the whole number and fraction parts separately, and then combining the two parts to find the total. If the sum of the fraction parts is an improper fraction, rename it as a mixed number and simplify.

Example: Find $3\frac{5}{6} + 5\frac{1}{4}$.

$$3\frac{5}{6} \rightarrow 3\frac{10}{12} \leftarrow \text{Rename } \frac{5}{6} \text{ as } \frac{10}{12}.$$
$$+\ 5\frac{1}{4} \rightarrow 5\frac{3}{12} \leftarrow \text{Rename } \frac{1}{4} \text{ as } \frac{3}{12}.$$
$$8\frac{3}{12} = 8 + 1\frac{1}{12} = 9\frac{1}{12}$$

5-5　Subtracting Mixed Numbers

Math Understandings

- To find the difference of two mixed numbers with unlike denominators, you first rewrite each fraction part as an equivalent fraction using a common denominator.
- In order to subtract from a mixed number, it may be necessary to rename the mixed number.

You can find the difference of mixed numbers by subtracting the whole number and fraction parts separately, and then combining the two parts. Sometimes you need to rename whole numbers or fractions in order to subtract from them.

Example: Find $11\frac{1}{6} - 5\frac{2}{3}$.

$$11\frac{1}{6} \rightarrow 10\frac{7}{6} \leftarrow \text{Rename } 11\frac{1}{6} \text{ as } 10\frac{7}{6}.$$
$$-\ 5\frac{2}{3} \rightarrow 5\frac{4}{6} \leftarrow \text{Rename } \frac{2}{3} \text{ as } \frac{4}{6}.$$
$$5\frac{3}{6} = 5\frac{1}{2}$$

5-6　Equations With Fractions

Math Understandings

- You solve an equation with fractions in the same way you solve an equation with whole numbers: you get the variable alone on one side of the equal sign using properties of equality and inverse operations.

You can solve equations with fractions and mixed numbers by applying the addition and subtraction properties of equality and inverse operations. Then write the answer in simplest form.

5-7　Measuring Elapsed Time

Math Understandings

- The standard unit of time is the second.

You can use equivalent units to change from one unit of time to another.

Units of Time	
second (s)	
minute (min)	1 min = 60 s
hour (h)	1 h = 60 min = 3,600 s
day	1 day = 24 h = 1,440 min
week (wk)	1 wk = 7 days = 188 h
year (yr)	1 yr = 52 wk = 365 days

Additional Professional Development Opportunities

Math Background Notes for Chapter 5: Every lesson has a Math Background in the PLAN section.

Research Overview, Mathematics Strands Additional support for these topics and more is in the front of the Teacher's Edition.

LessonLab LessonLab, a Pearson Education company, offers comprehensive, facilitated professional development designed to help teachers to improve student achievement. To learn more, please visit lessonlab.com.

Chapter 5 Resources

Print Resources

	5-1	5-2	5-3	5-4	5-5	5-6	5-7	For the Chapter
L3 Practice	●	●	●	●	●	●	●	
L1 Adapted Practice	●	●	●	●	●	●	●	
L3 Guided Problem Solving	●	●	●	●	●	●	●	
L2 Reteaching	●	●	●	●	●	●	●	
L4 Enrichment	●	●	●	●	●	●	●	
L3 Daily Notetaking Guide	●	●	●	●	●	●	●	
L1 Adapted Daily Notetaking Guide	●	●	●	●	●	●	●	
L3 Vocabulary Worksheets and Study Skills Worksheets	●	●	●	●	●	●	●	●
L3 Daily Puzzles	●	●	●	●	●	●	●	
L3 Activity Labs	●	●	●	●	●	●	●	
L3 Checkpoint Quiz		●			●			
L3 Chapter Project								●
L2 Below Level Chapter Test								●
L3 Chapter Test								●
L4 Alternative Assessment								●
L3 Cumulative Review								●

Spanish Resources ELL

	5-1	5-2	5-3	5-4	5-5	5-6	5-7	For the Chapter
L3 Practice	●	●	●	●	●	●	●	
L3 Vocabulary and Study Skills Worksheets	●		●	●		●	●	●
L3 Checkpoint Quiz			●		●			
L2 Below Level Chapter Test								●
L3 Chapter Test								●
L4 Alternative Assessment								●
L3 Cumulative Review								●

Transparencies

	5-1	5-2	5-3	5-4	5-5	5-6	5-7	For the Chapter
Check Skills You'll Need	●	●	●	●	●	●	●	
Additional Examples	●	●	●	●	●	●	●	
Problem of the Day	●	●	●	●	●	●	●	
Classroom Aid					●			
Student Edition Answers	●	●	●	●	●	●	●	●
Lesson Quiz	●	●	●	●	●	●	●	
Test-Taking Strategies								●

Technology

	5-1	5-2	5-3	5-4	5-5	5-6	5-7	For the Chapter
Interactive Textbook Online	●	●	●	●	●	●	●	●
StudentExpress™ CD-ROM	●	●	●	●	●	●	●	●
Success Tracker™ Online Intervention	●	●	●	●	●	●	●	●
TeacherExpress™ CD-ROM	●	●	●	●	●	●	●	●
PresentationExpress™ with QuickTake Presenter CD-ROM	●	●	●	●	●	●	●	●
ExamView® CD-ROM Assessment Suite	●	●	●	●	●	●	●	●
MindPoint® Quiz Show CD-ROM								●
Prentice Hall Web Site: PHSchool.com	●	●	●	●	●	●	●	●

Also available: Prentice Hall Assessment System
- Progress Monitoring Assessments
- Skills and Concepts Review
- Test Prep Workbook

Other Resources
Algebra Readiness Tests
All-in-One Student Workbook
All-in-One Student Workbook, Adapted Version
Multilingual Handbook

Solution Key
Math Notes Study Folder
Spanish Cumulative Assessment

Where You Can Use the Lesson Resources

Here is a suggestion, following the four-step teaching plan, for how you can incorporate Differentiated Instruction Resources into your teaching.

	Instructional Resources **L3**	Differentiated Instruction Resources
1. Plan		
Preparation Read the Math Background in the Teacher's Edition to connect this lesson with students' previous experience. **Starting Class** **Check Skills You'll Need** Assign these exercises to review prerequisite skills. **New Vocabulary** Help students pre-read the lesson by pointing out the new terms introduced in the lesson.	**Math Background** **Math Understandings** **Transparencies & PresentationExpress™ with QuickTake Presenter CD-ROM** Check Skills You'll Need Problem of the Day **Resources** Vocabulary and Study Skills	**Spanish Support** **ELL** Vocabulary and Study Skills
2. Teach		
L3 Guided Instruction Use the Activity Labs to build conceptual understanding. Teach each Example. Use the Teacher's Edition side column notes for specific teaching tips, including Error Prevention notes. Use the Additional Examples found in the side column (and on transparency and PowerPoint) as an alternative presentation for the content. After each Example, assign the Quick Check exercise for that Example to get an immediate assessment of student understanding. Use the Closure activity in the Teacher's Edition to help students attain mastery of lesson content.	**Student Edition** Activity Lab **Resources** Daily Notetaking Guide Activity Lab **Transparencies & PresentationExpress™ with QuickTake Presenter CD-ROM** Additional Examples Classroom Aids **ExamView® Assessment Suite CD-ROM**	**Teacher's Edition** Every lesson includes suggestions for working with students who need special attention. **L1** Special Needs **L2** Below Level **L4** Advanced Learners **ELL** English Language Learners **Resources** **L1** Adapted Daily Notetaking Guide **Multilingual Handbook**
3. Practice		
Assignment Guide **Check Your Understanding** Use these questions to check students' understanding before you assign homework. **Homework Exercises** Assign homework from these leveled exercises in the Assignment Guide. A Practice by Example B Apply Your Skills C Challenge Test Prep and Mixed Review **Homework Quick Check** Use these key exercises to quickly check students' homework.	**Transparencies & PresentationExpress™ with QuickTake Presenter CD-ROM** Student Answers **Resources** Practice Guided Problem Solving Vocabulary and Study Skills Activity Lab Daily Puzzles **ExamView® Assessment Suite CD-ROM**	**Spanish Support** **ELL** Practice **ELL** Vocabulary and Study Skills **Resources** **L1** Adapted Practice **L4** Enrichment
4. Assess & Reteach		
Lesson Quiz Assign the Lesson Quiz to assess students' mastery of the lesson content. **Checkpoint Quiz** Use the Checkpoint Quiz to assess student progress over several lessons.	**Transparencies & PresentationExpress™ with QuickTake Presenter CD-ROM** Lesson Quiz **Resources** Checkpoint Quiz	**Resources** **L2** Reteaching **ELL** Checkpoint Quiz Success Tracker™ Online Intervention **ExamView® Assessment Suite CD-ROM**

KEY   **L1** Special Needs   **L2** Below Level   **L3** For All Students   **L4** Advanced, Gifted   **ELL** English Language Learners

Adding and Subtracting Fractions

CHAPTER
5
Adding and Subtracting Fractions

 **Check Your Readiness**

Answers are in the back of the textbook.

For intervention, direct students to:

Estimating with Decimals
Lesson 1-5
Extra Skills and Word
　Problems Practice, Ch. 1

Finding Equivalent Fractions
Lesson 4-5
Extra Skills and Word
　Problems Practice, Ch. 4

Writing Mixed Numbers and Improper Fractions
Lesson 4-6
Extra Skills and Word
　Problems Practice, Ch. 4

Finding the Least Common Multiple
Lesson 4-7
Extra Skills and Word
　Problems Practice, Ch. 4

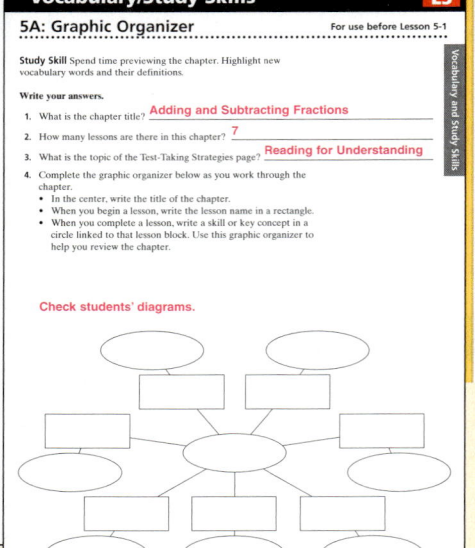

What You've Learned

- In Chapter 1, you used addition and subtraction to solve problems involving decimals.
- In Chapter 3, you solved equations using number sense, models, and the properties of equality.
- In Chapter 4, you compared and ordered fractions and mixed numbers.

 **Check Your Readiness**

GO for Help

For Exercises	See Lesson
1–4	1-5
5–10	4-5
11–13	4-7

Estimating With Decimals
Round each decimal to the nearest hundredth.

1. 2.58796 **2.59**　　　　**2.** 1.98637 **1.99**

3. 6.219054 **6.22**　　　　**4.** 7.654321 **7.65**

Finding Equivalent Fractions
Write each fraction in simplest form.

5. $\frac{5}{10}$ **$\frac{1}{2}$**　　　**6.** $\frac{6}{15}$ **$\frac{2}{5}$**　　　**7.** $\frac{12}{16}$ **$\frac{3}{4}$**

Writing Mixed Numbers and Improper Fractions
Write each improper fraction as a mixed number.

8. $\frac{87}{9}$ **$9\frac{2}{3}$**　　　**9.** $\frac{21}{4}$ **$5\frac{1}{4}$**　　　**10.** $\frac{15}{2}$ **$7\frac{1}{2}$**

Finding the Least Common Multiple
Find the LCM of each pair of numbers.

11. 8, 18 **72**　　　**12.** 5, 16 **80**　　　**13.** 14, 30 **210**

210　Chapter 5

In this chapter, students estimate and find sums and differences of fractions and mixed numbers with the same denominators and with different denominators. They also solve one-step equations involving fractions and solve problems involving elapsed time.

Activating Prior Knowledge

In this chapter, students build on and extend their knowledge of fraction concepts to add and subtract fractions and mixed numbers. They also draw upon their understanding of time measurement to find elapsed time. Ask questions such as:

- *Write the mixed number* $4\frac{4}{6}$ *as an improper fraction in simplest form.* $\frac{14}{3}$
- *What is the GCF of 24 and 18?* **6**
- *What is the LCM of 24 and 18?* **72**
- *Write in order from least to greatest:* $\frac{1}{2}$, *0.8,* $\frac{3}{8}$. $\frac{3}{8}$, $\frac{1}{2}$, **0.8**

What You'll Learn Next

- In this chapter, you will learn to model addition and subtraction problems involving fractions.
- You will use addition and subtraction to solve problems involving fractions.
- You will solve equations with fractions.
- You will use different units of time to solve problems involving elapsed time.

 Problem Solving Application On pages 256 and 257, you will work an extended activity involving speeds.

🔊 Key Vocabulary

- benchmark (p. 212)
- elapsed time (p. 246)

Chapter 5 **211**

Estimating Sums and Differences

Objective
To estimate sums and differences with fractions and mixed numbers

Examples
1 Selecting a Fraction Benchmark
2 Estimating Sums and Differences
3 Estimating With Mixed Numbers

Math Understandings: p. 210C

Math Background

A *benchmark* is a number that is easy to use when you estimate. You can use the benchmark values of 0, $\frac{1}{2}$, and 1 to estimate sums and differences of fractions. For instance, the fraction $\frac{4}{7}$ would have a benchmark estimate of $\frac{1}{2}$ and $\frac{7}{8}$ would have a benchmark of 1. You can estimate the sum $\frac{4}{7} + \frac{7}{8}$ as about $\frac{1}{2} + 1$, or $1\frac{1}{2}$. For mixed numbers, simply round to the nearest whole number when making estimates.

More Math Background: p. 210C

Lesson Planning and Resources

See p. 210E for a list of the resources that support this lesson.

☑ **Check Skills You'll Need**

1. Vocabulary Review What are *compatible numbers*? See below.
Round each number to the nearest ten.

2. 64 **60**   **3.** 146 **150**

4. 895 **900**   **5.** 1,234 **1,230**

GO for Help Lesson 1-2

Vocabulary Tip

You can think of a *benchmark* as a reference point.

Check Skills You'll Need

1. Compatible numbers are numbers that are easy to compute mentally.

inches

What You'll Learn

To estimate sums and differences with fractions and mixed numbers

🔊 **New Vocabulary** benchmark

Why Learn This?

You can use estimation to compare measurements, including heights, lengths, and weights.

A **benchmark** is a convenient number used to replace fractions that are less than 1. The benchmarks 0, $\frac{1}{2}$, and 1 are particularly useful when estimating sums and differences of fractions.

You can use benchmarks to estimate measurements. The following table will help you decide which benchmarks to use.

Description	Examples	Benchmark
Numerator is very small when compared to the denominator.	$\frac{1}{8}, \frac{3}{16}, \frac{2}{25}, \frac{9}{100}$	0
Numerator is about one half of denominator.	$\frac{3}{8}, \frac{9}{16}, \frac{11}{25}, \frac{52}{100}$	$\frac{1}{2}$
Numerator and denominator are close to each other.	$\frac{7}{8}, \frac{14}{16}, \frac{23}{25}, \frac{95}{100}$	1

EXAMPLE **Selecting a Fraction Benchmark**

1 Choose a benchmark for the measurement $\frac{7}{16}$ inch.

7 is about half of 16.

So choose the benchmark $\frac{1}{2}$ inch.

☑ **Quick Check**

1. Choose a benchmark for the measurement $\frac{8}{9}$ inch. **1**

212 Chapter 5 Adding and Subtracting Fractions

Differentiated Instruction **Solutions for All Learners**

Special Needs **L1**
For Example 3, use a vertical number line to show Dave's height. Draw another vertical number line using the same scale, to show Lina's height. Circle the part of Dave's number line that represents the difference in heights.

learning style: visual

Below Level **L2**
Give students fractions with benchmark values of $\frac{1}{2}$ such as $\frac{2}{5}, \frac{6}{10}, \frac{5}{8}$, and $\frac{5}{12}$. Have them shade fraction bars for each fraction.

learning style: visual

You can use the benchmarks 0, $\frac{1}{2}$, and 1 to estimate sums and differences.

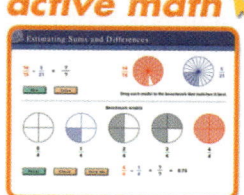

EXAMPLE **Estimating Sums and Differences**

2 Estimate $\frac{7}{12} + \frac{4}{5}$.

$\frac{7}{12} + \frac{4}{5} \approx \frac{1}{2} + 1$ ← Replace each fraction with a benchmark.

$= 1\frac{1}{2}$ ← Add.

✓ Quick Check

2. **a.** Estimate $\frac{5}{6} + \frac{3}{7}$. **1$\frac{1}{2}$**   **b.** Estimate $\frac{12}{13} - \frac{2}{25}$. **1**

You can also round before estimating the sum or difference of two mixed numbers. The diagram below shows how to round $7\frac{9}{16}$ inches and $6\frac{1}{8}$ inches. If a mixed number has a fraction of $\frac{1}{2}$, round up.

EXAMPLE **Estimating With Mixed Numbers**

3 **Measurement** Dave is $62\frac{3}{4}$ inches tall. Lina is $54\frac{1}{4}$ inches tall. Estimate the difference between their heights.

Estimate $62\frac{3}{4} - 54\frac{1}{4}$.

$62\frac{3}{4} \approx 63$ ← Since $\frac{3}{4} > \frac{1}{2}$, round to 63.

$54\frac{1}{4} \approx 54$ ← Since $\frac{1}{4} < \frac{1}{2}$, round to 54.

$63 - 54 = 9$ ← Estimate by finding the difference.

Dave is about 9 inches taller than Lina.

✓ Quick Check

3. It takes $3\frac{3}{4}$ hours to drive to the beach. It takes $8\frac{1}{2}$ hours to drive to the mountains. Estimate the difference in driving times. **about 5 h**

---

2. Teach

Activity Lab

Use before the lesson.

All in One Teaching Resources

Activity Lab 5-1: Estimating Sums and Differences

Guided Instruction

Example 2
For students who have difficulty identifying fractions close to $\frac{1}{2}$, suggest that they change the numerator or denominator to find a fraction that is exactly $\frac{1}{2}$. For example, $\frac{7}{12}$ is close to $\frac{6}{12}$ and to $\frac{7}{14}$.

PowerPoint
Additional Examples

1 Choose a benchmark for the measurement $\frac{3}{8}$ inch. **$\frac{1}{2}$ inch**

2 Estimate each sum or difference. Use the benchmarks 0, $\frac{1}{2}$, and 1.
a. $\frac{5}{6} + \frac{4}{7}$ **1$\frac{1}{2}$**   **b.** $\frac{7}{8} - \frac{1}{9}$ **1**

3 Steven is $13\frac{11}{12}$ years old. Chloe is $9\frac{1}{4}$ years old. Estimate how many years older Steven is than Chloe. **about 5 years**

All in One Teaching Resources
- Daily Notetaking Guide 5-1 **L3**
- Adapted Notetaking 5-1 **L1**

Closure

- *When is 0 a good benchmark value for a fraction?* **Sample: when the numerator is much smaller than the denominator**
- *When is $\frac{1}{2}$ a good benchmark value for a fraction?* **Sample: when the denominator is about twice as large as the numerator**

Advanced Learners **L4**
Write a mixed number that rounds up to 4. Then write five other mixed numbers that are between that number and 4. **Sample:**

$3\frac{7}{8}; 3\frac{9}{10}; 3\frac{29}{32}; 3\frac{15}{16}; 3\frac{39}{40}; 3\frac{319}{320}$

learning style: visual

English Language Learners **ELL**
Ask students to transfer the numbers in the table of benchmark fractions to a number line. This will help them see the fractions' proximity to 0, $\frac{1}{2}$, or 1. Ask them to use the word *about* when estimating.

learning style: visual

3. Practice

Assignment Guide

Check Your Understanding
Go over Exercises 1–6 in class before assigning the Homework Exercises.

Homework Exercises
A Practice by Example   7–25
B Apply Your Skills   26–30
C Challenge   31
Test Prep and
   Mixed Review   32–39

Homework Quick Check
To check students' understanding of key skills and concepts, go over Exercises 9, 17, 27, 28, and 29.

Differentiated Instruction Resources

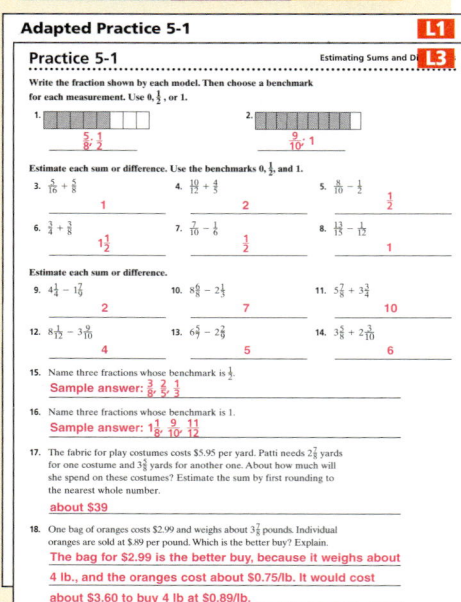

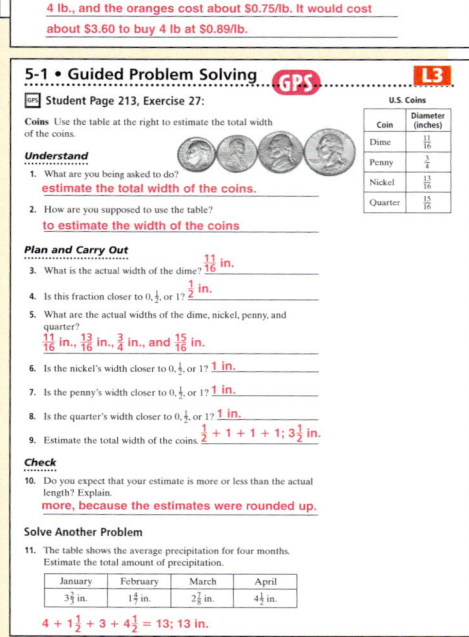

214

✓ Check Your Understanding

Benchmarks are whole numbers or fractions that are easy to use, such as 0, $\frac{1}{2}$, or 1. Rounding uses place value to find approximate values for numbers.

1. **Vocabulary** How are finding a benchmark and rounding similar?

2. **Reasoning** Choose a benchmark for each fraction. Use $0, \frac{1}{2}$, or 1. Which of the fractions has a different benchmark from the others? $\frac{11}{57}$

$$\frac{3}{8} \qquad \frac{7}{15} \qquad \frac{11}{57} \qquad \frac{45}{92}$$

Choose a benchmark for each fraction. Use $0, \frac{1}{2}$, or 1.

3. $\frac{1}{10}$ **0**   4. $\frac{10}{20}$ **$\frac{1}{2}$**   5. $\frac{48}{50}$ **1**   6. $\frac{87}{200}$ **$\frac{1}{2}$**

Homework Exercises

For more exercises, see Extra Skills and Word Problems.

A Choose a benchmark for each measurement. Use $0, \frac{1}{2}$, or 1.

GO for Help

For Exercises	See Example
7–12	1
13–18	2
19–25	3

7. $\frac{1}{8}$ inch **0**   8. $\frac{4}{8}$ inch **$\frac{1}{2}$**

9. $\frac{15}{16}$ inch **1**   10. $\frac{3}{8}$ inch **$\frac{1}{2}$**

11. $\frac{11}{16}$ inch **$\frac{1}{2}$**   12. $\frac{3}{16}$ inch **0**

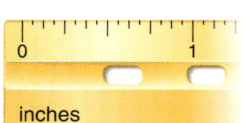

Estimate each sum or difference. Use the benchmarks $0, \frac{1}{2}$, and 1.

13. $\frac{5}{13} + \frac{4}{25}$ **$\frac{1}{2}$**   14. $\frac{17}{19} - \frac{2}{13}$ **1**   15. $\frac{70}{85} + \frac{32}{51}$ **$1\frac{1}{2}$**

16. $\frac{11}{20} - \frac{2}{15}$ **$\frac{1}{2}$**   17. $\frac{9}{16} - \frac{18}{37}$ **0**   18. $\frac{5}{16} + \frac{7}{15}$ **1**

19. $4\frac{2}{9} + 6\frac{13}{27}$ **$10\frac{1}{2}$**   20. $9\frac{7}{15} - 3\frac{1}{2}$ **6**   21. $22\frac{1}{9} - 16\frac{9}{11}$ **5**

22. $22\frac{8}{14} - 17\frac{3}{7}$ **5**   23. $76\frac{6}{23} - 45\frac{1}{5}$ **31**   24. $84\frac{3}{36} + 41\frac{7}{8}$ **126**

25. **Science** A kudzu plant is $1\frac{1}{12}$ feet tall. Over time, the plant grows to $4\frac{5}{6}$ feet. About how much does the plant grow? **about 4 ft**

B  26. **Guided Problem Solving** Your dog weighed $42\frac{3}{4}$ pounds. The dog gained $3\frac{1}{2}$ pounds. You put him on a diet and he lost $6\frac{1}{4}$ pounds. About how much does your dog weigh now?
- You can use the strategy *Draw a Picture* to decide which operations are needed to solve the problem.
- Use a benchmark for each mixed number. **about 40 lb**

214   **Chapter 5**   Adding and Subtracting Fractions

30a. Jocelyn: 0 in.; Carlos: 1 in.;
     Amanda: 2 in.

b. Amanda

28. Answers may vary. Sample: Less than the actual sum; since two of the three fractions are slightly greater than their benchmarks, the estimate will be less than the sum.

29. Answers may vary. Sample: Whole numbers are easier to add and subtract; yes.

Heights (inches)

Person	June	Sept.
Jocelyn	$61\frac{7}{8}$	$62\frac{1}{4}$
Carlos	$60\frac{3}{4}$	$61\frac{5}{8}$
Amanda	$59\frac{1}{8}$	$60\frac{5}{8}$

27. Coins Use the table at the right to **GPS** estimate the total width of the coins.
about $3\frac{1}{2}$ in.

U.S. Coins

Coin	Diameter (inches)
Dime	$\frac{11}{16}$
Penny	$\frac{3}{4}$
Nickel	$\frac{13}{16}$
Quarter	$\frac{15}{16}$

28. Number Sense You estimate $\frac{1}{8} + \frac{9}{16} + \frac{31}{32}$ using the benchmarks $0, \frac{1}{2},$ and 1. Is your estimate less than or greater than the actual sum? Explain. **See left.**

29. Writing in Math Why does it make sense to round a mixed number to the nearest whole number when estimating a sum or difference? Could you round to the nearest $\frac{1}{2}$ instead? Explain.

30. Estimation Use the table at the left.
a. About how much did each person grow during the summer?
b. Who grew the most? **30a–b. See margin.**

C 31. Challenge Use <, =, or > to compare.

$$14\frac{9}{10} - \left(8\frac{1}{7} + 1\frac{8}{9}\right) \; < \; 14\frac{9}{10} - 8\frac{1}{7} + 1\frac{8}{9}$$

Test Prep and Mixed Review   **Practice**

Multiple Choice

32. The length of a sticker is $\frac{3}{4}$ inch. The width is $\frac{7}{8}$ inch more **B** than the length. What is a reasonable estimate for the width?
Ⓐ 1 inches   Ⓑ 2 inches   Ⓒ 3 inches   Ⓓ 4 inches

33. Which weight is nearest to the amount of cheese? **H**

IMPORTED SWISS CHEESE		
Weight	Price per Unit	Total Cost
1.47 lb	$5.29/lb	$7.78

Ⓕ $\frac{1}{2}$ lb   Ⓗ $1\frac{1}{2}$ lb
Ⓖ 1 lb   Ⓙ 2 lb

34. Which statement about $\frac{3}{8}$ and 0.375 is true? **D**
Ⓐ $\frac{3}{8} > 0.375$ Ⓒ $0.375 > \frac{3}{8}$
Ⓑ $\frac{3}{8} < 0.375$ Ⓓ $0.375 = \frac{3}{8}$

Write each fraction as a decimal.

35. $\frac{47}{1,000}$ **36.** $\frac{4}{5}$ **37.** $\frac{3}{500}$ **38.** $\frac{17}{20}$ **39.** $\frac{1}{8}$
   0.047   0.8   0.006   0.85   0.125

GO for Help

For Exercises	See Lesson
35–39	4-9

PowerPoint
Lesson Quiz

Use benchmarks to estimate each sum or difference.

1. $\frac{9}{10} + \frac{1}{8}$ about 1
2. $\frac{7}{8} - \frac{4}{9}$ about $\frac{1}{2}$

Estimate each sum or difference by rounding.

3. $5\frac{3}{4} + 3\frac{4}{5}$ about 10
4. $8\frac{11}{12} - 2\frac{8}{9}$ about 6

Exercise 27
Ask: *Is the estimate for the total width of the coins reasonable? Explain.*

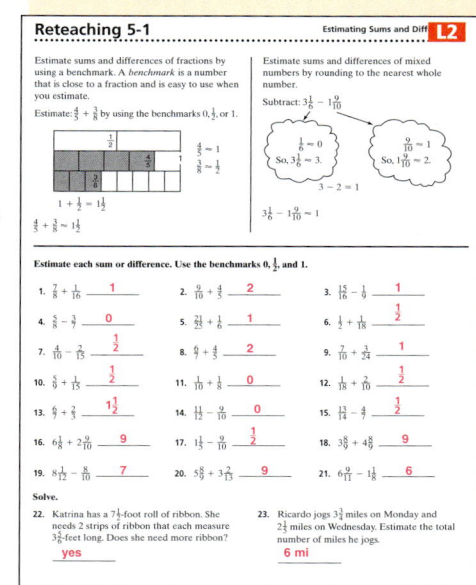

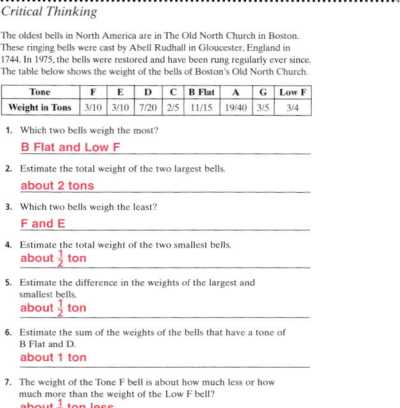

Alternative Assessment

Provide pairs of students with number lines. Partners work together using the number lines to determine whether the given fractions in Exercises 13–18 are closer to 0, $\frac{1}{2}$, or 1.

Test Prep

Resources
For additional practice with a variety of test item formats:
• Test-Taking Strategies, p. 251
• Test Prep, p. 255
• Test-Taking Strategies with Transparencies

215

Modeling Fraction Operations

Students use paper models to help them solve problems involving fractions. This will prepare them for adding and subtracting fractions later in the chapter.

Guided Instruction

Before beginning the Activity, draw a rectangle and divide it into quarters. Ask questions such as:
- *When I shade in one section, what fraction does that represent?* **one quarter**
- *How many sections would I shade to show three quarters?* **3**

Exercises

Before doing the exercises, ask students how many sections their models should be divided into for each question.

Alternative Method

Some students may prefer to use algebra tiles to model fractions.

Resources

- Activity Lab 5-2: Adding and Subtracting Fractions I
- algebra tiles
- Student Manipulatives Kit

Modeling Fraction Operations

You can use a paper model to help you add and subtract fractions.

ACTIVITY

1. Draw and cut out a circle. Fold the circle in half. Then fold it in half three more times. When you unfold the circle, there are 16 sections. Each section represents $\frac{1}{16}$ of the circle. **Check students' work.**

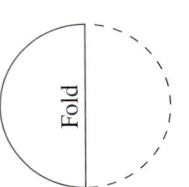 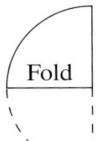  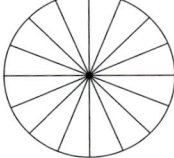

2. From the circle, cut a piece that contains 7 small sections. From the remaining part, cut another piece that contains 5 sections. Put the two pieces together. Use this model to find $\frac{7}{16} + \frac{5}{16}$. **$\frac{12}{16}$**

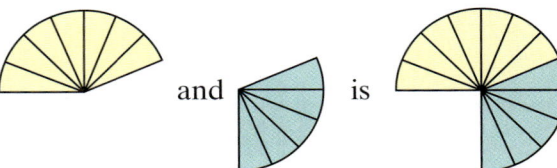

and   is

3. Use new circles to model $\frac{11}{16}$ and $\frac{7}{16}$. Is the sum of $\frac{7}{16}$ and $\frac{11}{16}$ greater than 1? Find the sum of $\frac{7}{16}$ and $\frac{11}{16}$. **$\frac{18}{16}$**

4. Place your model for $\frac{7}{16}$ on top of your model for $\frac{11}{16}$. How much of the $\frac{11}{16}$ model is not covered? Find $\frac{11}{16} - \frac{7}{16}$. **$\frac{4}{16}$**

Exercises

Use models to add or subtract.

1. $\frac{1}{16} + \frac{9}{16}$ **$\frac{10}{16}$**

2. $\frac{6}{8} - \frac{4}{8}$ **$\frac{2}{8}$**

3. $\frac{3}{8} + \frac{7}{8}$ **$\frac{10}{8}$**

4. $\frac{15}{16} - \frac{3}{16}$ **$\frac{12}{16}$**

5. a. **Patterns** Look at the numerators for the exercises that you modeled. What pattern do you see when you add or subtract fractions with the same denominator?

   b. Use the pattern to find $\frac{2}{5} + \frac{3}{5} + \frac{1}{5}$. **$\frac{6}{5}$**

   When you add or subtract fractions with the same denominators, you add or subtract the numerators and leave the denominators.

Fractions With Like Denominators

Check Skills You'll Need

✓ **Check Skills You'll Need**

1. Vocabulary Review
How can you tell when a fraction is in *simplest form*? **See below.**
Write each fraction in simplest form.

2. $\frac{10}{40}$ $\frac{1}{4}$ 3. $\frac{8}{24}$ $\frac{1}{3}$

4. $\frac{20}{24}$ $\frac{5}{6}$ 5. $\frac{12}{28}$ $\frac{3}{7}$

 **for Help**
Lesson 4-5

What You'll Learn

To add and subtract fractions with like denominators

Why Learn This?

At a bake sale, $\frac{4}{12}$ of a cherry pie and $\frac{7}{12}$ of an apple pie are sold. You can find the total amount of pie sold by adding fractions.

To add fractions with like denominators, you add the numerators and do not change the denominators.

Objective
To add and subtract fractions with like denominators

Examples
1 Adding With Like Denominators
2 Sums Greater Than 1
3 Subtracting With Like Denominators

Math Understandings: p. 210C

Math Background

To add and subtract fractions with like denominators, simply add or subtract the numerators and keep the denominator the same. Then write the answer in simplest form.

More Math Background: p. 210C

Lesson Planning and Resources

See p. 210E for a list of the resources that support this lesson.

Vocabulary Tip

Like means "the same."

Check Skills You'll Need

1. A fraction is in simplest form when the GCF of the numerator and denominator is 1.

KEY CONCEPTS **Adding With Like Denominators**

To add fractions with like denominators, add the numerators and keep the same denominator.

Arithmetic	Algebra
$\frac{2}{7} + \frac{3}{7} = \frac{2+3}{7} = \frac{5}{7}$	$\frac{a}{c} + \frac{b}{c} = \frac{a+b}{c}$

EXAMPLE **Adding With Like Denominators**

① Find $\frac{4}{12} + \frac{7}{12}$.

$\frac{4}{12} + \frac{7}{12} = \frac{4+7}{12}$ ← The fractions have like denominators. Add the numerators. The denominator stays the same.

$= \frac{11}{12}$ ← Simplify the numerator.

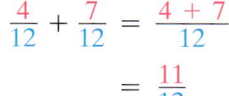

✓ **Quick Check**

● **1. a.** Add $\frac{1}{6} + \frac{1}{6}$. $\frac{1}{3}$ **b.** Add $\frac{10}{21} + \frac{4}{21}$. $\frac{2}{3}$

PowerPoint
Bell Ringer Practice

✓ **Check Skills You'll Need**
Use student page, transparency, or PowerPoint. For intervention, direct students to:
Equivalent Fractions
Lesson 4-5
Extra Skills and Word Problems Practice, Ch. 4

Differentiated Instruction **Solutions for All Learners**

Special Needs **L1**
For Example 2, ask students to draw a model using 9 ninths and to color in 7 of the ninths. Then ask them whether they have enough ninths to color in 5 more. Since they do not, they will have to draw another model using ninths.

learning style: visual

Below Level **L2**
Have students write a new fraction that has the same denominator but a different numerator. **Samples:**

$\frac{1}{4}$ $\frac{3}{4}$ $\frac{5}{8}$ $\frac{3}{8}$ $\frac{7}{12}$ $\frac{5}{12}$

$\frac{2}{9}$ $\frac{4}{9}$ $\frac{2}{3}$ $\frac{1}{3}$ $\frac{6}{10}$ $\frac{9}{10}$

learning style: visual

All in One Teaching Resources

Activity Lab 5-2: Adding and
Subtracting Fractions I

Guided Instruction

Teaching Tip
Write the fractions $\frac{1}{2}$ and $\frac{47}{94}$ on
the board. Have students try to
quickly picture them in their
minds. Then point out that the
quantities are equal. Guide
students to recognize that it is
usually much easier to understand
a fraction when it is written in its
simplest form. Likewise, the mixed
number $4\frac{2}{5}$ is easier to picture
than the improper fraction $\frac{22}{5}$. So
improper fractions should be
changed into mixed numbers for
final answers.

Error Prevention!

Some students have difficulty
writing fractions neatly on their
papers. Provide them with graph
paper and emphasize that the
numerators and denominators
are aligned.

PowerPoint

Additional Examples

1 Find $\frac{2}{9} + \frac{4}{9}$. **$\frac{2}{3}$**

2 Find $\frac{3}{4} + \frac{3}{4}$. **$1\frac{1}{2}$**

3 Find $\frac{7}{8} - \frac{1}{8}$. **$\frac{3}{4}$**

All in One Teaching Resources

- Daily Notetaking Guide 5-2 **L3**
- Adapted Notetaking 5-2 **L1**

Closure

- *How do you add fractions with
  like denominators?* **Add the
  numerators and keep the
  denominator, then simplify.**
- *How do you subtract fractions
  with like denominators?*
  **Subtract the numerators and
  keep the denominator, then
  simplify.**

GO for Help

For help with writing
an improper fraction as
a mixed number, go to
Lesson 4-6, Example 3.

If the sum of fractions results in an improper fraction, rename the
improper fraction as a mixed number.

EXAMPLE **Sums Greater Than 1**

2 Find $\frac{7}{9} + \frac{5}{9}$.

$$\frac{7}{9} + \frac{5}{9} = \frac{7+5}{9} \quad \leftarrow \text{Add the numerators. The denominator remains the same.}$$

$$= \frac{12}{9} \quad \leftarrow \text{Simplify the numerator.}$$

$$= 1\frac{3}{9} \quad \leftarrow \text{Write as a mixed number.}$$

$$= 1\frac{1}{3} \quad \leftarrow \text{Divide the numerator and denominator by the GCF, 3.}$$

✓ Quick Check

2. a. Find $\frac{5}{16} + \frac{13}{16}$. **$1\frac{1}{8}$**   **b.** Find $\frac{11}{20} + \frac{17}{20}$. **$1\frac{2}{5}$**

To subtract fractions with like denominators, subtract the
numerators and keep the same denominator. Write the answer
in simplest form.

EXAMPLE **Subtracting With Like Denominators**

3 **Circus** A circus has ten seating sections. Eight sections are filled
for the first show. Six sections are filled for the second show. How
much more of the entire seating area is filled for the first show?

Eight sections out of ten means $\frac{8}{10}$. Six out of ten means $\frac{6}{10}$.

The difference is $\frac{8}{10} - \frac{6}{10}$.

$$\frac{8}{10} - \frac{6}{10} = \frac{8-6}{10} \quad \leftarrow \text{Subtract the numerators. The denominator remains the same.}$$

$$= \frac{2}{10} \quad \leftarrow \text{Simplify the numerator.}$$

$$= \frac{1}{5} \quad \leftarrow \text{Write the fraction in simplest form.}$$

In the circus, $\frac{1}{5}$ more of the seating area is full for the first show.

✓ Quick Check

3. A board is $\frac{11}{12}$ foot long. You need $\frac{7}{12}$ foot of the board for a
brace. How much is left after you cut off the piece you need?

$\frac{1}{3}$ foot

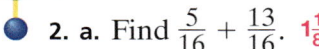

Advanced Learners **L4**
Write five sums, each with a different denominator,
that equal $\frac{2}{3}$ when simplified. **Sample:**
$\frac{7}{12} + \frac{1}{12}$; $\frac{2}{9} + \frac{1}{9} + \frac{2}{9} + \frac{1}{9}$;
$\frac{1}{3} + \frac{1}{3}$; $\frac{3}{6} + \frac{1}{6}$; $\frac{5}{18} + \frac{5}{18} + \frac{2}{18}$

learning style: visual

English Language Learners **ELL**
Be explicit about the meaning of the word "like" in
this chapter. Make sure that students understand that
this means something different from "like" in "I like
you." For like denominators, *like* means *alike,* or
common, or the *same.*

learning style: verbal

1. $\frac{3}{5}$; you do not add the denominators when adding two or more fractions.

1. **Error Analysis** Which solution to $\frac{1}{5} + \frac{2}{5}$ is correct? Explain your reasoning.

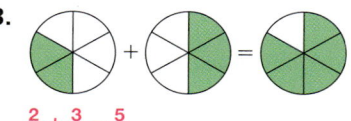

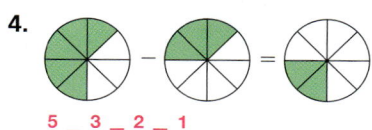

2. You can tell an answer is not in simplest form when the numerator and the denominator have a common factor.

2. **Number Sense** Explain how you can tell when your answer is not in simplest form.

Write an addition or subtraction sentence for each model.

3.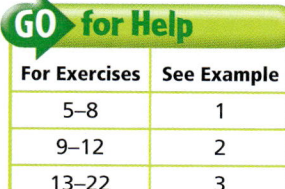

$$\frac{2}{6} + \frac{3}{6} = \frac{5}{6}$$

4.

$$\frac{5}{8} - \frac{3}{8} = \frac{2}{8} = \frac{1}{4}$$

3. Practice

Assignment Guide

Check Your Understanding
Go over Exercises 1–4 in class before assigning the Homework Exercises.

Homework Exercises
A Practice by Example   5–22
B Apply Your Skills   23–30
C Challenge   31
Test Prep and
   Mixed Review   32–38

Homework Quick Check
To check students' understanding of key skills and concepts, go over Exercises 6, 19, 27, 28, and 29.

Differentiated Instruction Resources

Homework Exercises

For more exercises, see Extra Skills and Word Problems.

A **Find each sum. You may find a model helpful.**

GO for Help

For Exercises	See Example
5–8	1
9–12	2
13–22	3

5. $\frac{1}{4} + \frac{1}{4}$ $\frac{1}{2}$

6. $\frac{2}{5} + \frac{3}{5}$ 1

7. $\frac{2}{9} + \frac{4}{9}$ $\frac{2}{3}$

8. $\frac{1}{6} + \frac{3}{6}$ $\frac{2}{3}$

9. $\frac{2}{3} + \frac{2}{3}$ $1\frac{1}{3}$

10. $\frac{9}{10} + \frac{7}{10}$ $1\frac{3}{5}$

11. $\frac{7}{12} + \frac{6}{12}$ $1\frac{1}{12}$

12. $\frac{4}{5} + \frac{3}{5}$ $1\frac{2}{5}$

Find each difference.

13. $\frac{17}{18} - \frac{5}{18}$ $\frac{2}{3}$

14. $\frac{15}{20} - \frac{3}{20}$ $\frac{3}{5}$

15. $\frac{4}{5} - \frac{3}{5}$ $\frac{1}{5}$

16. $\frac{6}{7} - \frac{3}{7}$ $\frac{3}{7}$

17. $\frac{5}{9} - \frac{2}{9}$ $\frac{1}{3}$

18. $\frac{9}{16} - \frac{3}{16}$ $\frac{3}{8}$

19. $\frac{8}{12} - \frac{5}{12}$ $\frac{1}{4}$

20. $\frac{17}{24} - \frac{7}{24}$ $\frac{5}{12}$

21. $\frac{3}{5} - \frac{1}{5}$ $\frac{2}{5}$

22. **Nature Trails** The blue trail at a national park is $\frac{7}{10}$ mile long. The orange trail is $\frac{6}{10}$ mile long. How much longer is the blue trail than the orange trail? $\frac{1}{10}$ mi

B  23. **Guided Problem Solving** You can run $\frac{5}{8}$ of a mile in ten minutes. Your friend can run $\frac{7}{8}$ of a mile in ten minutes. $\frac{1}{2}$ mi
How much farther can your friend run in twenty minutes?
• You can use the strategy *Work a Simpler Problem*. Find how much farther your friend runs in ten minutes.
• How much farther can your friend run in twenty minutes?

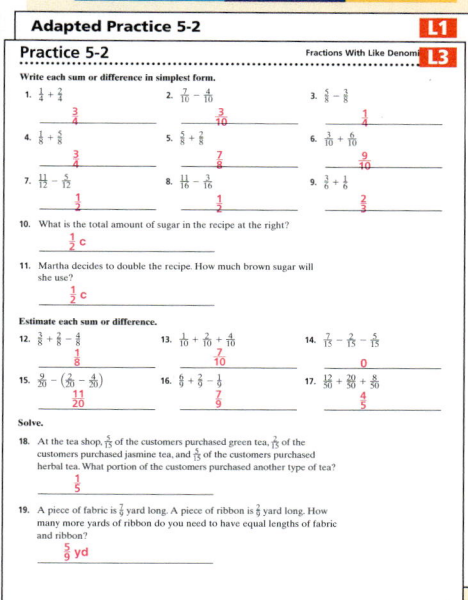

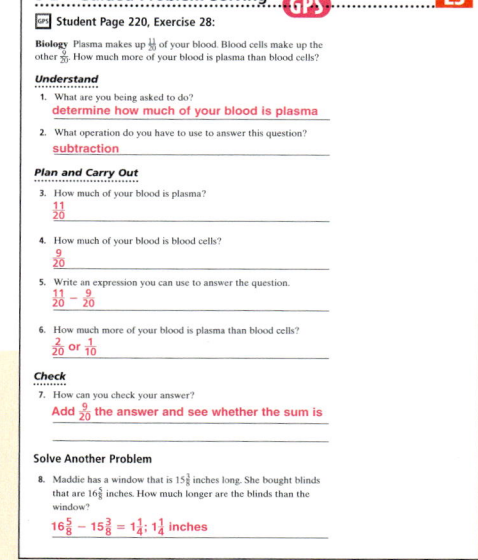

Lesson Quiz

Find each sum or difference.

1. $\frac{3}{8} + \frac{7}{8}$ $1\frac{1}{4}$

2. $\frac{5}{6} - \frac{1}{6}$ $\frac{2}{3}$

3. $\frac{14}{15} - \frac{11}{15}$ $\frac{1}{5}$

4. $\frac{3}{12} + \frac{6}{12}$ $\frac{3}{4}$

Exercises

To model addition and subtraction with words, have students read Exercises 27 and 28 aloud.

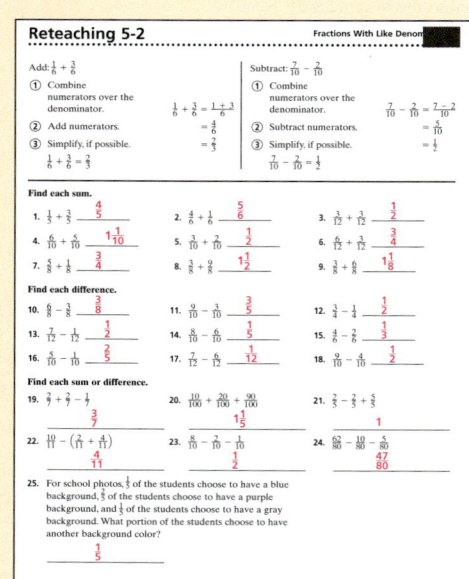

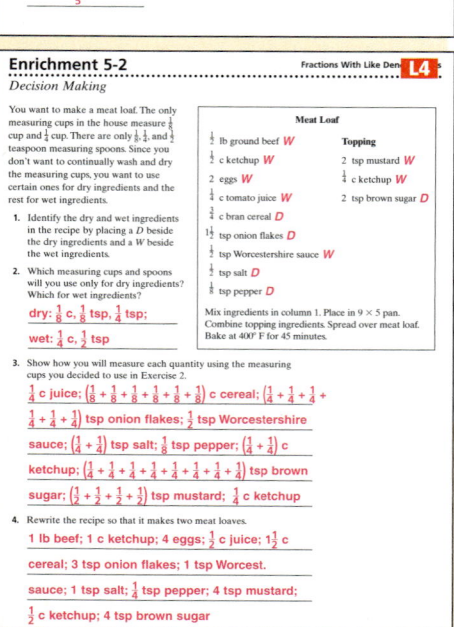

GO Online
Homework Video Tutor
Visit: PHSchool.com
Web Code: aqe-0502

Find each sum.

24. $\frac{1}{20} + \frac{3}{20} + \frac{5}{20}$ $\frac{9}{20}$

25. $\frac{27}{100} + \frac{41}{100} + \frac{3}{100}$ $\frac{71}{100}$

26. $\frac{4}{15} + \frac{1}{15} + \frac{7}{15}$ $\frac{4}{5}$

27. A typical garden spider is $\frac{7}{8}$ inch long. A black widow spider is $\frac{3}{8}$ inch long. How much longer is the garden spider? $\frac{1}{2}$ in.

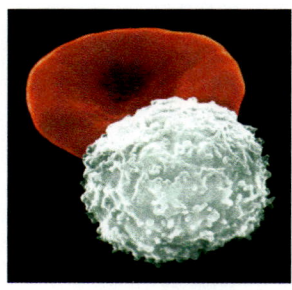

28. **Biology** Plasma makes up $\frac{11}{20}$ of your blood. Blood cells make up the other $\frac{9}{20}$. How much more of your blood is plasma than blood cells? $\frac{1}{10}$

29. **Writing in Math** Explain how to find the sum of $\frac{5}{9}$ and $\frac{7}{9}$. See margin.

30. Suppose it rains $\frac{3}{8}$ inch on Friday and $\frac{7}{8}$ inch on Saturday.
    a. What is the total rainfall during the two days? $1\frac{1}{4}$ in.
    b. What is the difference in rainfall for the two days? $\frac{1}{2}$ in.

C 31. **Challenge** Replace the ■ to make the equation true.
$\frac{7}{12} - \frac{■}{12} = \frac{1}{6}$ 5

Test Prep and Mixed Review
Practice

Multiple Choice

32. Greg nails two boards together. Each board is $\frac{1}{4}$ inch thick. Greg needs to find the total combined thickness. Which process can he use to find the sum $\frac{1}{4} + \frac{1}{4}$? **D**
    Ⓐ Add the denominators and add the numerators.
    Ⓑ Add the denominators and keep the same numerator.
    Ⓒ Keep the same denominator and the same numerator.
    Ⓓ Keep the same denominator and add the numerators.

33. Which measurement is closest to the length of the line? **G**
    Ⓕ $1\frac{3}{4}$ in.   Ⓗ $1\frac{3}{16}$ in.
    Ⓖ $1\frac{7}{8}$ in.   Ⓙ $2\frac{1}{4}$ in.

inches

34. Which expression represents the model? **A**
    Ⓐ $\frac{1}{2} - \frac{1}{6}$ Ⓒ $\frac{3}{4} - \frac{1}{4}$
    Ⓑ $\frac{1}{3} - \frac{1}{6}$ Ⓓ $\frac{3}{5} - \frac{1}{5}$

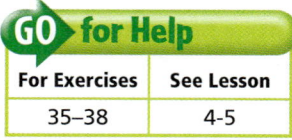

GO for Help

For Exercises	See Lesson
35–38	4-5

Write two fractions equivalent to each fraction. 35–38. Answers may vary. Samples are given.

35. $\frac{3}{8}$ $\frac{6}{16}, \frac{9}{24}$

36. $\frac{1}{6}$ $\frac{2}{12}, \frac{3}{18}$

37. $\frac{2}{5}$ $\frac{4}{10}, \frac{6}{15}$

38. $\frac{7}{10}$ $\frac{14}{20}, \frac{21}{30}$

Test Prep

Resources
For additional practice with a variety of test item formats:
• Test-Taking Strategies, p. 251
• Test Prep, p. 255
• Test-Taking Strategies with Transparencies

Alternative Assessment

Provide pairs of student with fraction bars. Partners work together, using the fraction bars, to model addition and subtraction exercises from Exercises 5–21. Have students record their work.

29. See back of book.

Modeling Unlike Denominators

In Lesson 5-2, you added and subtracted fractions with like denominators. To add or subtract fractions such as $\frac{5}{8}$ and $\frac{1}{4}$, first you must write the fractions with like denominators.

EXAMPLE

Use models to find each sum or difference.

a. $\frac{5}{8} + \frac{1}{4}$

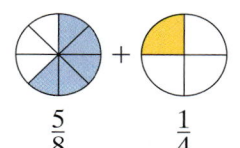

$\frac{5}{8}$ $\frac{1}{4}$

Change the model for $\frac{1}{4}$ so that it has ← the same number of sections as the model for $\frac{5}{8}$.

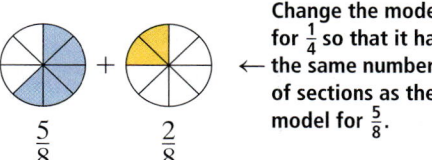

$\frac{5}{8}$ $\frac{2}{8}$

Add $\frac{2}{8}$ to ← the model for $\frac{5}{8}$.

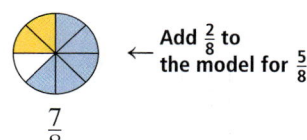

$\frac{7}{8}$

b. $\frac{5}{6} - \frac{2}{3}$

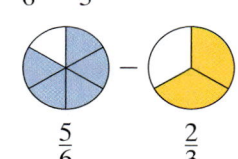

$\frac{5}{6}$ $\frac{2}{3}$

Change the model for $\frac{2}{3}$ so that it has ← the same number of sections as the model for $\frac{5}{6}$.

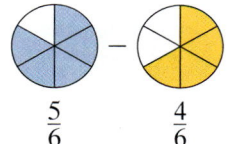

$\frac{5}{6}$ $\frac{4}{6}$

Remove $\frac{4}{6}$ from ← the model for $\frac{5}{6}$.

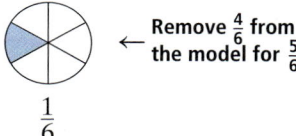

$\frac{1}{6}$

Exercises

Use models to find each sum or difference.

1. 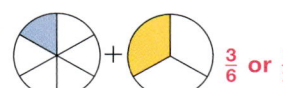 $\frac{3}{6}$ or $\frac{1}{2}$

2. 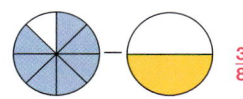 $\frac{3}{8}$

3. 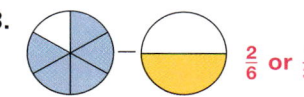 $\frac{2}{6}$ or $\frac{1}{3}$

Use models to find each sum or difference.   4–8. See margin.

4. $\frac{1}{8} + \frac{3}{4}$ 5. $\frac{2}{3} - \frac{1}{6}$ 6. $\frac{1}{2} + \frac{3}{8}$ 7. $\frac{5}{6} - \frac{1}{3}$ 8. $\frac{1}{2} + \frac{1}{3}$

9. **Writing in Math** Explain why you should use a common denominator to add or subtract fractions.   Answers may vary. Sample: A common denominator means that the pieces are all the same size.

 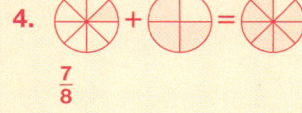
Modeling Unlike Denominators

Students use models to help them solve problems involving fractions with different denominators. This will help them add and subtract fractions with different denominators in Lesson 5-3.

Guided Instruction

Before beginning the Activity, draw two squares on the board and divide one in half and the other in quarters. Ask questions such as:

• *How many quarters of this square are equal to half of the other square?* two

• *How would you say the equivalent of one half in quarters?* two quarters

Exercises

Before doing the Exercises, have students write what fraction each model represents using words.

Alternative Method

Students may prefer to use algebra tiles or other manipulatives to model fractions rather than drawing models. Ask students to evaluate the effectiveness of the model they chose.

Differentiated Instruction

Below Level   L2

Have students identify the denominator they will use for each of Exercises 1–8 before adding or subtracting.

Resources

• Activity Lab 5-3: Adding and Subtracting Fractions II
• algebra tiles
• Student Manipulatives Kit

Objective
To add and subtract fractions with unlike denominators

Examples
1 Adding With Unlike Denominators
2 Application: Surveys
3 Subtracting Fractions

Math Understandings: p. 210C

Math Background

In order to add or subtract fractions, the fractions must have the same denominator, known as a *common denominator*. The least common denominator (LCD) is the smallest denominator that is common to both fractions. So, choosing the LCD may save the step of simplifying the sum or difference. When adding or subtracting fractions with unlike denominators, find a common denominator, write equivalent fractions with that denominator, add or subtract the numerators, and simplify as needed.

More Math Background: p. 210C

Lesson Planning and Resources

See p. 210E for a list of the resources that support this lesson.

Bell Ringer Practice

✓ **Check Skills You'll Need**
Use student page, transparency, or PowerPoint. For intervention, direct students to:
Least Common Multiple
Lesson 4-7
Extra Skills and Word Problems Practice, Ch. 4

222

✓ **Check Skills You'll Need**

1. **Vocabulary Review**
How do you use *factoring* when finding the *LCM*?
See below.
Find the LCM.

2. 6, 9 **18**   3. 5, 24 **120**
4. 30, 75 **150**   5. 4, 6, 15 **60**

for Help
Lesson 4-7

 **nline**

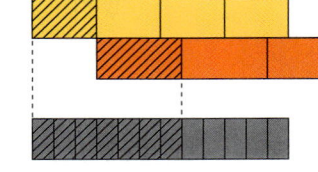

Video Tutor Help
Visit: PHSchool.com
Web Code: aqe-0775

Check Skills You'll Need

1. **Answers may vary. Sample: Write the prime factorization for each number.**

What You'll Learn

To add and subtract fractions with unlike denominators

Why Learn This?

Fractions, such as those used in survey data, sometimes have different denominators. You can use models to add fractions with unlike denominators. You can also write equivalent fractions with the same denominator.

EXAMPLE **Adding With Unlike Denominators**

1 Find $\frac{1}{4} + \frac{1}{3}$.

Method 1 Model $\frac{1}{4} + \frac{1}{3}$.

← Use the fraction model for $\frac{1}{4}$.

← Use the fraction model for $\frac{1}{3}$.

← The LCD is 12. Find a twelfths fraction model with the same amount shaded.

$$\frac{1}{4} + \frac{1}{3} = \frac{7}{12}$$

Method 2 Use a common denominator.

$$\frac{1}{4} \rightarrow \frac{1 \times 3}{4 \times 3} \rightarrow \frac{3}{12}$$
$$+\frac{1}{3} \rightarrow \frac{1 \times 4}{3 \times 4} \rightarrow +\frac{4}{12}$$
$$\frac{7}{12}$$ ← Add the numerators.

The LCD is 12. Write the fractions with the same denominator.

✓ **Quick Check**

1. Find $\frac{3}{5} + \frac{1}{10}$. Use a model or a common denominator. $\frac{7}{10}$

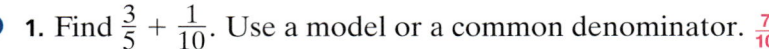

Differentiated Instruction **Solutions for All Learners**

Special Needs **L1**
A fraction model is used in Example 1. Some students will benefit from using fraction models in Examples 2 and 3 as well.

learning style: visual

Below Level **L2**
Read aloud equivalent fractions like these. Have students explain how to find the missing numerator.

$$\frac{3}{4} = \frac{\blacksquare}{12}$$ Multiply 3 by 3; 9.

$$\frac{2}{3} = \frac{\blacksquare}{12}$$ Multiply 2 by 4; 8.

learning style: verbal

EXAMPLE **Application: Surveys**

2 Art students completed a survey about their favorite activity. Ceramics is the favorite of $\frac{2}{5}$ of the students. Drawing is the favorite of $\frac{3}{8}$ of the students. What fraction of the students chose either ceramics or drawing as their favorite activity?

Add $\frac{2}{5}$ and $\frac{3}{8}$ to find the total fraction of the students.

$$\frac{2}{5} \rightarrow \frac{2 \times 8}{5 \times 8} \rightarrow \frac{16}{40}$$
$$+\frac{3}{8} \rightarrow \frac{3 \times 5}{8 \times 5} \rightarrow +\frac{15}{40}$$
$$\frac{31}{40} \quad \leftarrow \text{Add the numerators.}$$

The LCD is 40. Write the fractions with the same denominator.

The favorite activity of $\frac{31}{40}$ of the students is ceramics or drawing.

✓ Quick Check

2. You exercise for $\frac{1}{2}$ hour on Monday and $\frac{1}{3}$ hour on Tuesday. How long did you exercise on Monday and Tuesday? **$\frac{5}{6}$ h**

You can also subtract fractions that have unlike denominators.

EXAMPLE **Subtracting Fractions**

3 **Multiple Choice** A property owner donates $\frac{1}{4}$ acre to a local park. After the donation, the size of the park is $\frac{5}{6}$ acre. Find the area of the park before the donation.

Ⓐ $\frac{1}{3}$ acre   Ⓑ $\frac{2}{5}$ acre   Ⓒ $\frac{1}{2}$ acre   Ⓓ $\frac{7}{12}$ acre

Subtract $\frac{1}{4}$ from $\frac{5}{6}$ to find the original size of the park.

$$\frac{5}{6} \rightarrow \frac{5 \times 2}{6 \times 2} \rightarrow \frac{10}{12}$$
$$-\frac{1}{4} \rightarrow \frac{1 \times 3}{4 \times 3} \rightarrow -\frac{3}{12}$$
$$\frac{7}{12} \quad \leftarrow \text{Subtract the numerators.}$$

The LCD is 12. Write the fractions with the same denominator.

The area of the park was $\frac{7}{12}$ acre. The correct answer is choice D.

Test Prep Tip ✐

When you add or subtract fractions, find equivalent fractions with the same denominator.

✓ Quick Check

3. You have $\frac{2}{3}$ yard of felt. You use $\frac{1}{2}$ yard of the felt for a display. How much felt do you have left? **$\frac{1}{6}$ yd**

2. Teach

Activity Lab

Use before the lesson.
Student Edition Activity Lab 5-3a, Modeling Unlike Denominators, p. 221

All in One Teaching Resources
Activity Lab 5-3: Adding and Subtracting Fractions II

Guided Instruction

Teaching Tips
The greater number of the denominators is often the LCD. For $\frac{1}{2}$ and $\frac{3}{4}$, the LCD is 4.

If the denominators are one number apart, such as 3 and 4, and each of the fractions is in its simplest form, the LCD will be the product of the denominators. For $\frac{1}{4}$ and $\frac{2}{3}$, the LCD is 12.

PowerPoint
Additional Examples

1 Find $\frac{1}{3} + \frac{1}{2}$. **$\frac{5}{6}$**

2 In Ms. DeMarco's class, $\frac{3}{5}$ of the students chose cheese as their favorite pizza topping. Pepperoni was chosen by $\frac{1}{3}$ of the students. What fraction of the students chose either cheese or pepperoni? **$\frac{14}{15}$**

3 Find $\frac{5}{8} - \frac{1}{6}$. **$\frac{11}{24}$**

All in One Teaching Resources
• Daily Notetaking Guide 5-3 **L3**
• Adapted Notetaking 5-3 **L1**

Closure

• *How do you add fractions with unlike denominators?* **Write equivalent fractions with a like denominator. Then add numerators, keep the denominator, and simplify.**
• *How do you subtract fractions with unlike denominators?* **Write equivalent fractions with a like denominator. Then subtract numerators, keep the denominator, and simplify.**

Advanced Learners **L4**
Add a set of parentheses to each equation so that both will equal $\frac{1}{2}$.

$\frac{3}{4} - \left(\frac{1}{6} + \frac{1}{12}\right) = \frac{1}{2}$ $\left(\frac{17}{18} - \frac{2}{3}\right) + \frac{2}{9} = \frac{1}{2}$

learning style: visual

English Language Learners **ELL**
Discuss the prefix "un." Say: *When we see <u>un</u> in front of a word, it means not or the opposite of. Unlike denominators are not like denominators. Since like denominators are common or the same, unlike denominators are different, not the same.*

learning style: verbal

223

3. Practice

Assignment Guide

Check Your Understanding
Go over Exercises 1–4 in class before assigning the Homework Exercises.

Homework Exercises

A	Practice by Example	5–21
B	Apply Your Skills	22–29
C	Challenge	30
	Test Prep and Mixed Review	31–37

Homework Quick Check
To check students' understanding of key skills and concepts, go over Exercises 8, 15, 26, 27, and 28.

Differentiated Instruction Resources

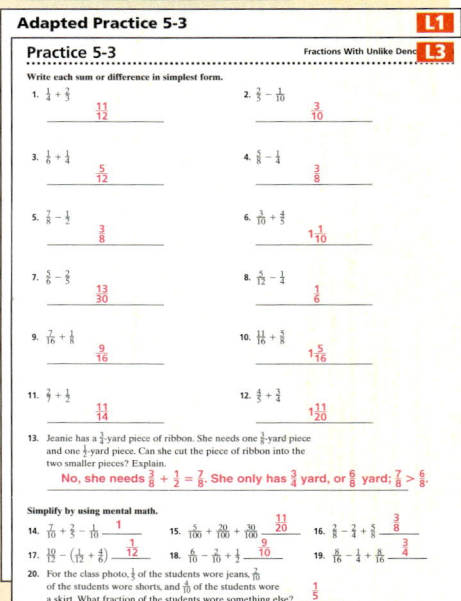

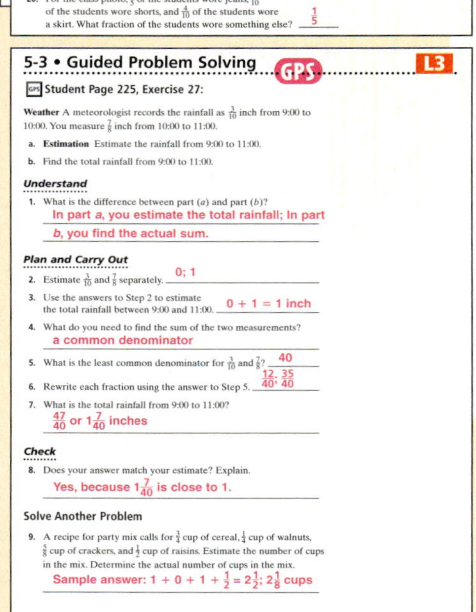

✔ Check Your Understanding

Find each sum or difference.

1. $\frac{2}{5} + \frac{1}{2}$: Use a model.

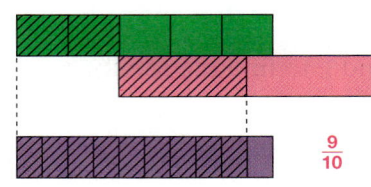

$\frac{9}{10}$

2. $\frac{2}{3} - \frac{5}{12}$: Use a model.

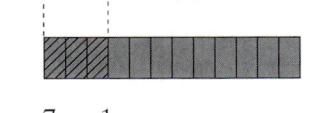

$\frac{1}{4}$

3. $\frac{1}{10} + \frac{2}{5}$: Use the LCD.

$$\frac{1}{10}$$
$$+ \frac{2}{5} \rightarrow \frac{2 \times 2}{5 \times 2} \qquad \frac{1}{2}$$

4. $\frac{7}{9} - \frac{1}{4}$: Use the LCD.

$$\frac{7}{9} \rightarrow \frac{7 \times 4}{9 \times 4}$$
$$- \frac{1}{4} \rightarrow \frac{1 \times 9}{4 \times 9} \qquad \frac{19}{36}$$

Homework Exercises

For more exercises, see **Extra Skills and Word Problems.**

A **Find each sum. You may find a model helpful.**

GO for Help

For Exercises	See Example
5–13	1–2
14–21	3

5. $\frac{1}{3} + \frac{1}{6}$ $\frac{1}{2}$

6. $\frac{1}{6} + \frac{1}{2}$ $\frac{2}{3}$

7. $\frac{8}{9} + \frac{5}{6}$ $1\frac{13}{18}$

8. $\frac{5}{6} + \frac{1}{4}$ $1\frac{1}{12}$

9. $\frac{1}{3} + \frac{2}{5}$ $\frac{11}{15}$

10. $\frac{3}{5} + \frac{3}{20}$ $\frac{3}{4}$

11. $\frac{3}{10} + \frac{1}{4}$ $\frac{11}{20}$

12. $\frac{3}{5} + \frac{1}{3}$ $\frac{14}{15}$

13. **Pets** You have two baby hamsters. One weighs $\frac{1}{4}$ pound and the other weighs $\frac{1}{5}$ pound. How much do they weigh together? $\frac{9}{20}$ lb

GO for Help

For help with writing equivalent fractions, go to lesson 4-5, Example 1.

Find each difference.

14. $\frac{13}{16} - \frac{1}{4}$ $\frac{9}{16}$

15. $\frac{17}{20} - \frac{2}{5}$ $\frac{9}{20}$

16. $\frac{9}{10} - \frac{3}{5}$ $\frac{3}{10}$

17. $\frac{3}{4} - \frac{1}{12}$ $\frac{2}{3}$

18. $\frac{5}{8} - \frac{1}{4}$ $\frac{3}{8}$

19. $\frac{4}{5} - \frac{2}{3}$ $\frac{2}{15}$

20. $\frac{7}{10} - \frac{1}{4}$ $\frac{9}{20}$

21. $\frac{5}{6} - \frac{1}{2}$ $\frac{1}{3}$

B **GPS** 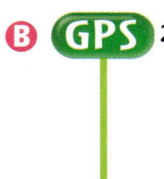 22. **Guided Problem Solving** A roller coaster can hold 48 people. There are 46 people on the ride. Younger adults fill $\frac{1}{3}$ of the seats. Senior citizens fill $\frac{1}{4}$ of the seats. What fraction of the roller coaster is filled by children? $\frac{3}{8}$

- What is the least common denominator?
- What equivalent fractions should you use?

224   **Chapter 5**   Adding and Subtracting Fractions

26. $1\frac{5}{12}$. Answers may vary. Sample: The LCD; the numerators and denominators will be smaller, and the answers will be easier to simplify.

30. $\frac{3}{4}, \frac{7}{8}, \frac{15}{16}$; answers may vary. Sample: The sum will never be greater than 1. Each amount added is smaller and smaller, so that the sum approaches 1 but is never greater than 1.

Use any method to add and subtract.

23. $\frac{5}{8} + \frac{9}{12} + \frac{1}{2}$ $1\frac{7}{8}$

24. $\frac{11}{30} - \frac{1}{5} - \frac{1}{6}$ 0

25. $\frac{2}{5} + \frac{1}{2} - \frac{1}{10}$ $\frac{4}{5}$

26. **Writing in Math** Find $\frac{5}{6} + \frac{7}{12}$ using a model or a common denominator. Explain why you chose the method you used. **See margin.**

27. **Weather** A meteorologist records the rainfall as $\frac{3}{10}$ inch from 9:00 to 10:00. You measure $\frac{7}{8}$ inch of rain from 10:00 to 11:00.
   a. **Estimation** Estimate the rainfall from 9:00 to 11:00. $1\frac{1}{2}$ in.
   b. Find the total rainfall from 9:00 to 11:00. $1\frac{7}{40}$ in.

28. You put $\frac{3}{4}$ cup of paint into a container. You use $\frac{1}{3}$ cup of the paint on a craft project. Later you add another $\frac{1}{2}$ cup of paint to the container. How much paint is in the container? $\frac{11}{12}$ c

29. **Number Sense** You walk $\frac{1}{2}$ mile, $\frac{1}{3}$ mile, and then $\frac{1}{4}$ mile. Is the total distance *greater than, less than,* or *equal to* one mile? **greater than 1 mi**

30. **Challenge** Find $\frac{1}{2} + \frac{1}{4}$. Then find $\frac{1}{2} + \frac{1}{4} + \frac{1}{8}$. Now find $\frac{1}{2} + \frac{1}{4} + \frac{1}{8} + \frac{1}{16}$. If you continue this pattern, when will the sum be greater than 1? Explain.

See margin.

Test Prep and Mixed Review **Practice**

Multiple Choice

31. Sean needs $\frac{2}{3}$ cup of cheese for a casserole and $\frac{1}{4}$ cup of cheese for the topping. How many cups of cheese does Sean need? **C**
   Ⓐ $\frac{3}{12}$ cup Ⓑ $\frac{3}{7}$ cup Ⓒ $\frac{11}{12}$ cup Ⓓ 1 cup

32. Which sum represents the model shown? **F**
   Ⓕ $\frac{1}{6} + \frac{1}{3}$ Ⓗ $\frac{1}{6} + \frac{2}{3}$
   Ⓖ $\frac{1}{8} + \frac{1}{4}$ Ⓙ $\frac{1}{8} + \frac{1}{3}$

33. Anna spends $\frac{1}{2}$ of her savings on a new bike and $\frac{1}{3}$ of her savings on gifts for her family. Which expression gives the fraction of Anna's savings that is left? **C**
   Ⓐ $\frac{1}{2} + \frac{1}{3}$ Ⓒ $1 - \left(\frac{1}{2} + \frac{1}{3}\right)$
   Ⓑ $1 + \frac{1}{2} - \frac{1}{3}$ Ⓓ $1 - \left(\frac{1}{2} - \frac{1}{3}\right)$

List the factors to find the GCF of each pair of numbers.

34. 16, 64 **16** **35.** 33, 121 **11** **36.** 40, 72 **8** **37.** 60, 210 **30**

GO for Help

For Exercises	See Lesson
34–37	4-4

Alternative Assessment

Each student in a pair writes several exercises involving addition and subtraction of fractions with unlike denominators. Students exchange papers and find each sum or difference in simplest form.

Test Prep

Resources

For additional practice with a variety of test item formats:
• Test-Taking Strategies, p. 251
• Test Prep, p. 255
• Test-Taking Strategies with Transparencies

---

4. Assess & Reteach

Lesson Quiz

Find each sum or difference.

1. $\frac{8}{9} - \frac{4}{18}$ $\frac{2}{3}$

2. $\frac{5}{8} + \frac{1}{12}$ $\frac{17}{24}$

3. $\frac{3}{5} - \frac{2}{7}$ $\frac{11}{35}$

4. $\frac{13}{24} + \frac{3}{8}$ $\frac{11}{12}$

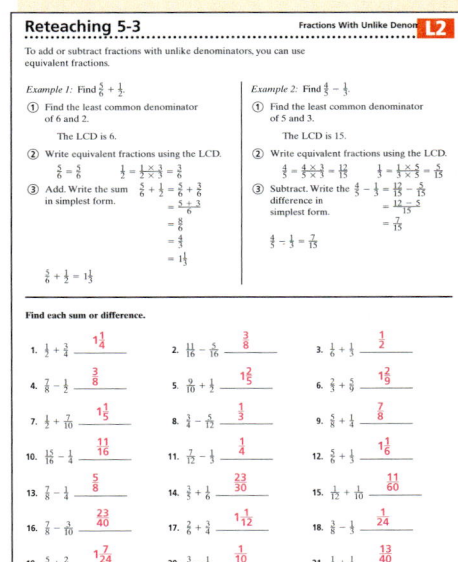

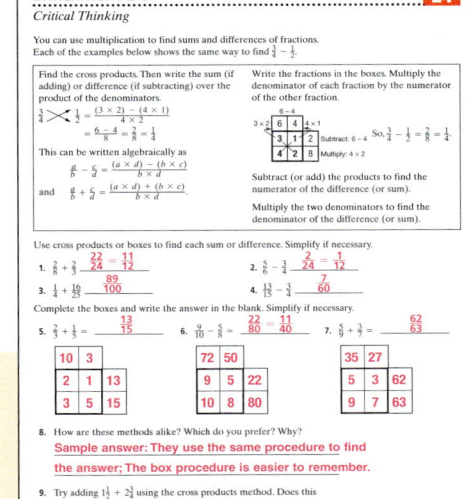

✓ Checkpoint Quiz 1

Estimate each sum or difference. Use the benchmarks 0, $\frac{1}{2}$, and 1.

1. $\frac{8}{9} + \frac{5}{16}$ $1\frac{1}{2}$

2. $\frac{12}{13} - \frac{1}{9}$ 1

3. $\frac{7}{12} + \frac{7}{8}$ $1\frac{1}{2}$

4. $\frac{11}{12} - \frac{5}{6}$ 0

Find each sum or difference. You may find a model helpful.

5. $\frac{3}{10} + \frac{9}{10}$ $1\frac{1}{5}$

6. $\frac{5}{6} - \frac{1}{3}$ $\frac{1}{2}$

7. $\frac{7}{12} + \frac{2}{3}$ $1\frac{1}{4}$

8. $\frac{9}{10} - \frac{1}{3}$ $\frac{17}{30}$

9. $\frac{1}{7} + \frac{5}{14}$ $\frac{1}{2}$

10. $\frac{17}{20} - \frac{3}{20}$ $\frac{7}{10}$

11. In a class, $\frac{1}{6}$ of the students have blue eyes, and $\frac{7}{9}$ of the students have brown eyes. Find how much more of the entire class has brown eyes than blue eyes. $\frac{11}{18}$ **of the class**

12. You are still hungry after eating $\frac{2}{3}$ cup of wheat flakes, so you eat $\frac{1}{2}$ cup of corn flakes. How much cereal do you eat? $1\frac{1}{6}$ **c**

13. You mix $\frac{1}{4}$ gallon of yellow paint with $\frac{1}{8}$ gallon of red paint to make orange paint. How much orange paint do you have? $\frac{3}{8}$ **gal**

MATH AT WORK

Chef

Generally, there are two types of chefs—institutional chefs and restaurant chefs. No matter where a chef works, he or she will measure, mix, and cook meals according to recipes.

The art of cooking requires skill in many areas of mathematics. Knowing how to weigh and measure with both metric and customary measures is essential to following a recipe. A knowledge of estimation, ratios, and proportions will help a chef determine quantities and serving sizes.

Go Online
PHSchool.com **For:** Information on chefs
Web Code: aqb-2031

Using Mixed Numbers

You can use objects to help you understand addition of mixed numbers.

ACTIVITY

Cut string into lengths of $1\frac{3}{8}$ inches, $2\frac{1}{4}$ inches, $1\frac{7}{8}$ inches, $3\frac{1}{8}$ inches, and $3\frac{3}{4}$ inches.

1. Select the strings that measure $1\frac{3}{8}$ inches and $2\frac{1}{4}$ inches in length. Place the two pieces end to end. Estimate the total length of the two pieces. **about 3 in.**

2. Measure the total length of the two pieces of string. **about $3\frac{5}{8}$ in.**

3. Check your measurement by writing an addition equation for the two pieces and finding the sum. Compare the sum to the measured length.
   a. How close was your estimate to the actual length? **3a. Check students' work.**
   b. **Writing in Math** Explain why the measurement of the total length of the string should be the same as the sum of the two lengths. **3b. Answers may vary. Sample: Measuring the two pieces end to end is the same as adding the lengths together.**

4. Repeat Steps 1 through 3 for each pair of strings.

   a. $1\frac{7}{8}$ and $3\frac{3}{4}$ **about 6 in.; $5\frac{5}{8}$ in.; check students' work.**
   b. $2\frac{1}{4}$ and $3\frac{3}{4}$ **about 6 in.; 6 in.; check students' work.**

5. **Number Sense** Will the whole number in your answer always equal the sum of the whole numbers you are adding? Explain. **5. Answers may vary. Sample: No; the fraction parts may add to be a whole number.**

6. **Estimation** Which pairs of pieces of string have a total length between 6 inches and 7 inches? Which pairs have a difference in lengths less than 1 inch? **See margin.**

6. **total length 6 to 7 inches:** $2\frac{1}{4}$ and $3\frac{3}{4}$, and $3\frac{1}{8}$ and $3\frac{3}{4}$; **difference less than 1 inch:** $1\frac{3}{8}$ and $2\frac{1}{4}$, $1\frac{3}{8}$ and $1\frac{7}{8}$, $1\frac{7}{8}$ and $2\frac{1}{4}$, $2\frac{1}{4}$ and $3\frac{1}{8}$, and $3\frac{1}{8}$ and $3\frac{3}{4}$

5-4

Objective
To add mixed numbers with and without renaming

Examples
1   Adding Mixed Numbers
2   Renaming a Sum
3   Application: Music

Math Understandings: p. 210C

Math Background

Adding mixed numbers involves finding a common denominator for the fraction parts, adding the fractions, and then adding the whole numbers separately. If the fraction part of the sum is an improper fraction, you need to change it to a mixed number and add the whole number part to the whole number part of the sum.

More Math Background: p. 210C

Lesson Planning and Resources

See p. 210E for a list of the resources that support this lesson.

Bell Ringer Practice

✓ Check Skills You'll Need
Use student page, transparency, or PowerPoint. For intervention, direct students to:
Mixed Numbers and Improper Fractions
Lesson 4-6
Extra Skills and Word Problems
  Practice, Ch. 4

✓ Check Skills You'll Need

1. **Vocabulary Review**
Explain how you know that $\frac{36}{15}$ is an *improper fraction*.
See below.
Write each fraction as a mixed number in simplest form.

2. $\frac{8}{6}$ $1\frac{1}{3}$ 3. $\frac{15}{6}$ $2\frac{1}{2}$

4. $\frac{7}{4}$ $1\frac{3}{4}$ 5. $\frac{25}{10}$ $2\frac{1}{2}$

 **for Help**
Lesson 4-6

Check Skills You'll Need

1. **The numerator is greater than the denominator.**

What You'll Learn

To add mixed numbers with and without renaming

Why Learn This?

When you say, "I'll be there in an hour and a half," or, "I had band practice until quarter after five," you are using mixed numbers to talk about time.

You can find the sum of mixed numbers by adding the whole number and fraction parts separately. Then you combine the two parts to find the total.

EXAMPLE   Adding Mixed Numbers

① You spent $8\frac{1}{4}$ hours on Saturday and $6\frac{1}{2}$ hours on Sunday working on a science project. How long did you work on the project?

Estimate $8\frac{1}{4} + 6\frac{1}{2} \approx 8 + 7 = 15$

$$8\frac{1}{4} \quad \rightarrow \quad 8\frac{1}{4}$$

$$+6\frac{1}{2} \quad \rightarrow \quad +6\frac{2}{4}$$

The LCD is 4. Write the fractions with the same denominator.

$$14\frac{3}{4} \quad \leftarrow$$ Add the whole numbers.
Then add the fractions.

You work a total of $14\frac{3}{4}$ hours on your science project.

Check for Reasonableness $14\frac{3}{4}$ is close to the estimate of 15. The answer is reasonable.

✓ Quick Check

1. A giant tortoise traveled $2\frac{1}{3}$ yards and stopped. Then it traveled $3\frac{1}{2}$ yards. Find the total distance the giant tortoise traveled.
$5\frac{5}{6}$ **yd**

228   **Chapter 5** Adding and Subtracting Fractions

Differentiated Instruction Solutions for All Learners

Special Needs L1
Before discussing Example 1, show students an analog clock. Ask them to move the minute hand and count every time it goes through an hour, counting on from 8 hours to 14 hours. Then show $\frac{1}{4}$ of an hour, and $\frac{1}{2}$ of an hour and add them.

learning style: tactile

Below Level L2
Have students rewrite mixed number sums with the LCD.
Change to tenths: Change to eighths:
$1\frac{1}{2} + 4\frac{2}{5}$ $5\frac{3}{8} + 2\frac{1}{4}$

$1\frac{5}{10} + 4\frac{4}{10}$ $5\frac{3}{8} + 2\frac{2}{8}$

learning style: visual

The sum of the fraction parts may be an improper fraction. If so, rename the sum as a mixed number.

GO **Online**

Video Tutor Help
Visit: PHSchool.com
Web Code: aqe-0775

EXAMPLE **Renaming a Sum**

② Find $15\frac{5}{6} + 3\frac{1}{2}$.

$$15\frac{5}{6} \quad \rightarrow \quad 15\frac{5}{6}$$

$$+3\frac{1}{2} \quad \rightarrow \quad +3\frac{3}{6} \qquad \leftarrow \text{ The LCD is 6. Write } \frac{1}{2} \text{ as } \frac{3}{6}.$$

$$18\frac{8}{6} \qquad \leftarrow \begin{array}{l}\text{Add the whole numbers.} \\ \text{Then add the fractions.}\end{array}$$

$$= 18 + 1\frac{2}{6} \qquad \leftarrow \text{ Rename } \frac{8}{6} \text{ as } 1\frac{2}{6}.$$

$$= 19\frac{2}{6} \qquad \leftarrow \text{ Add the whole numbers.}$$

$$= 19\frac{1}{3} \qquad \leftarrow \text{ Simplify.}$$

✓ **Quick Check**

● **2. a.** Find $3\frac{5}{6} + 5\frac{11}{12}$. $9\frac{3}{4}$ **b.** Find $7\frac{3}{5} + 13\frac{2}{3}$. $21\frac{4}{15}$

EXAMPLE **Application: Music**

③ **Multiple Choice** A band practiced for $2\frac{1}{2}$ hours on Monday and for $1\frac{3}{4}$ hours on Tuesday. How long did the band practice?

Ⓐ $3\frac{1}{4}$ hours   Ⓑ $3\frac{2}{3}$ hours   Ⓒ $4\frac{1}{4}$ hours   Ⓓ $4\frac{2}{3}$ hours

Find $2\frac{1}{2} + 1\frac{3}{4}$.

$$2\frac{1}{2} \quad \rightarrow \quad 2\frac{2}{4} \qquad \leftarrow \text{ The LCD is 4. Write } \frac{1}{2} \text{ as } \frac{2}{4}.$$

$$+1\frac{3}{4} \quad \rightarrow \quad +1\frac{3}{4}$$

$$3\frac{5}{4} \qquad \leftarrow \begin{array}{l}\text{Add the whole numbers.} \\ \text{Then add the fractions.}\end{array}$$

$$= 3 + 1\frac{1}{4} \qquad \leftarrow \text{ Rename } \frac{5}{4} \text{ as } 1\frac{1}{4}.$$

$$= 4\frac{1}{4} \qquad \leftarrow \text{ Add the whole numbers.}$$

The band practiced for $4\frac{1}{4}$ hours. The correct answer is C.

✓ **Quick Check**

3. Newspapers One advertisement in a newspaper is $1\frac{1}{4}$ inches long. Another advertisement is $2\frac{7}{8}$ inches long. How much space is needed for both advertisements? $4\frac{1}{8}$ in.

Test Prep Tip

Drawing a model can help you solve a problem.

Hours at Practice

Total	
$2\frac{1}{2}$	$1\frac{3}{4}$
Monday	Tuesday

---

2. Teach

Activity Lab

Use before the lesson.
Student Edition Activity Lab, **Hands On 5-4a,** Using Mixed Numbers, p. 227

All in One Teaching Resources
Activity Lab 5-4: Adding Mixed Numbers

Guided Instruction

Example 1
Write or circle the denominators, using the same color to emphasize that they need to be the same.

Error Prevention!

Watch for students who confuse LCD (Least Common Denominator), LCM (Least Common Multiple), and GCF (Greatest Common Factor).

PowerPoint
Additional Examples

❶ Tyler juggled for $1\frac{1}{3}$ hr during the school week. He juggled for $2\frac{1}{4}$ hr over the weekend. How many hours did he juggle in all that week? $3\frac{7}{12}$ hr

❷ Find $5\frac{4}{5} + 3\frac{9}{10}$. $9\frac{7}{10}$

❸ A mother cat weighs $14\frac{5}{8}$ lb. Her kitten weighs $1\frac{1}{2}$ lb. How much do they weigh together? $16\frac{1}{8}$ lb

All in One Teaching Resources
• Daily Notetaking Guide 5-4 **L3**
• Adapted Notetaking 5-4 **L1**

Closure

• *How do you add mixed numbers?* **Add the whole numbers. Then add the fraction parts, finding a common denominator, if needed.**
• *What do you need to do if the sum of mixed numbers includes an improper fraction?* **Change the improper fraction to a mixed number and add the whole numbers.**

Advanced Learners **L4**
Match up A, B, C, and D to the digits 1, 2, 3, and 4 to solve this mystery problem.

$$A\frac{B}{A} + C\frac{C}{D} = 4\frac{11}{12} \qquad A = 3, B = 2, \\ \qquad\qquad\qquad\qquad C = 1, D = 4$$

$$3\frac{2}{3} + 1\frac{1}{4} = 4\frac{11}{12}$$

learning style: visual

English Language Learners **ELL**
For Example 2, ask students what is done in each step. Ask: *What does the 18 represent?* **The sum of the whole numbers** What does $\frac{8}{6}$ represent? **The sum of the fractions** What is $1\frac{1}{3}$? $\frac{8}{6}$ **renamed as a mixed number and simplified**

learning style: verbal

229

Assignment Guide

Check Your Understanding
Go over Exercises 1–5 in class before assigning the Homework Exercises.

Homework Exercises

A	Practice by Example	6–18
B	Apply Your Skills	19–26
C	Challenge	27
	Test Prep and Mixed Review	28–33

Homework Quick Check
To check students' understanding of key skills and concepts, go over Exercises 10, 16, 23, 24, and 26.

Differentiated Instruction Resources

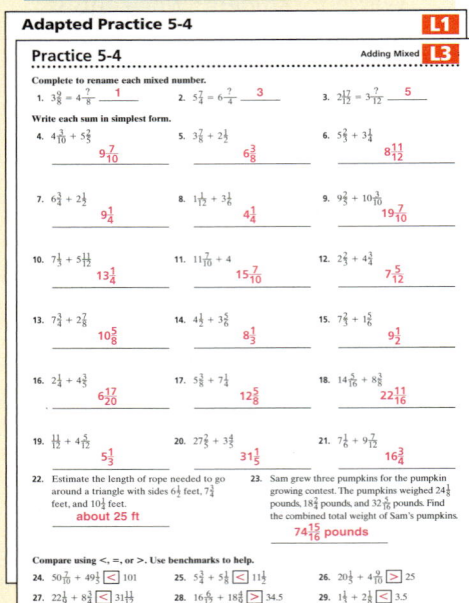

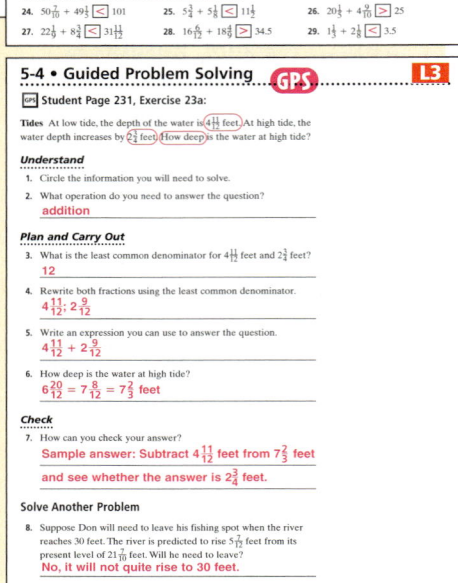

✔ Check Your Understanding

1. **Open-Ended** Write an addition expression. Use two mixed numbers with a sum that is a whole number.
   Answers may vary. Sample: $1\frac{1}{4} + 3\frac{3}{4}$

Mental Math Find each sum.

2. 1
   $+ 2\frac{1}{6}$ $3\frac{1}{6}$

3. $2\frac{2}{3}$
   $+ 4$ $6\frac{2}{3}$

4. $3\frac{5}{7}$
   $+ 1\frac{1}{7}$ $4\frac{6}{7}$

5. $8\frac{1}{5}$
   $+ 3\frac{2}{5}$ $11\frac{3}{5}$

Homework Exercises

For more exercises, see Extra Skills and Word Problems.

GO for Help

For Exercises	See Example
6–9	1
10–18	2–3

Ⓐ Find each sum. You can use a model to help you.

6. $3\frac{1}{9} + 2\frac{2}{3}$ $5\frac{7}{9}$
7. $9\frac{1}{6} + 2\frac{1}{3}$ $11\frac{1}{2}$
8. $2\frac{3}{5} + 7\frac{1}{3}$ $9\frac{14}{15}$

9. $3\frac{1}{2} + 3\frac{1}{5}$ $6\frac{7}{10}$
10. $11\frac{1}{3} + 6\frac{7}{9}$ $18\frac{1}{9}$
11. $8\frac{5}{6} + 2\frac{1}{3}$ $11\frac{1}{6}$

12. $5\frac{2}{3} + 4\frac{1}{2}$ $10\frac{1}{6}$
13. $2\frac{5}{6} + 6\frac{2}{5}$ $9\frac{7}{30}$
14. $2\frac{3}{4} + 1\frac{5}{8}$ $4\frac{3}{8}$

15. $4\frac{5}{8} + 1\frac{3}{4}$ $6\frac{3}{8}$
16. $3\frac{1}{3} + 2\frac{5}{6}$ $6\frac{1}{6}$
17. $1\frac{1}{2} + 3\frac{5}{6}$ $5\frac{1}{3}$

20. No; both recipes need a total of $3\frac{1}{4}$ c milk, so $\frac{1}{4}$ c is still needed.

18. **Soccer** You play $12\frac{1}{6}$ minutes during the first half of a soccer game. Then you play $8\frac{3}{4}$ minutes during the second half. How many minutes do you play in total? $20\frac{11}{12}$ mi

Ⓑ GPS 19. **Guided Problem Solving** You skate $1\frac{1}{4}$ miles from your house to the park. The park has a path that is $2\frac{3}{10}$ miles long. You skate once around the path and then skate home. What is the total distance you skate? $4\frac{4}{5}$ mi

• You can draw a picture to model the problem.

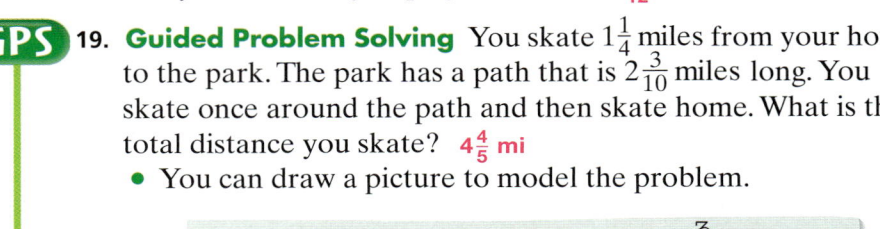

• Which distance do you skate twice?

GO Online
Homework Video Tutor

Visit: PHSchool.com
Web Code: aqe-0504

20. **Reasoning** One recipe uses $1\frac{3}{4}$ cups of milk. Another recipe uses $1\frac{1}{2}$ cups of milk. You have 3 cups of milk at home. Do you have enough milk to make both recipes? Explain.
   See above left.

26. Answers may vary. Sample: Add like fractions: $+$
   Add 2 to the sum of the whole numbers:
   $5 + 3 + 3 + 6 + 2 = 19.$

21. $5\frac{8}{9} + 7\frac{5}{6}$ ▇ 13   **>**

22. $4\frac{5}{13} + 5\frac{4}{9}$ ▇ $10\frac{12}{13}$ **<**

23. a. Tides At low tide, the depth of the water is $4\frac{11}{12}$ feet. At high tide, the water depth increases by $2\frac{3}{4}$ feet. How deep is the water at high tide? **$7\frac{2}{3}$ ft**

    b. The next day, the depth is $5\frac{1}{2}$ feet at low tide. The depth increases the same amount as the day before. What is the water depth at high tide? **$8\frac{1}{4}$ ft**

24. Number Sense Is the sum of two mixed numbers *always*, *sometimes*, or *never* a mixed number? Give examples to support your answer. **Sometimes; check students' work.**

25. Suppose you need the amounts of fabric shown in the table to make a flag. What is the total length of fabric you need? **13 yd**

Fabric Colors	
Color	Length (yards)
Red	$3\frac{1}{4}$
White	$5\frac{1}{2}$
Blue	$4\frac{1}{4}$

26. Writing in Math How can you use mental math to find $5\frac{1}{3} + 3\frac{4}{5} + 3\frac{2}{3} + 6\frac{1}{5}$? **See margin.**

C 27. Challenge Find $7\frac{1}{3} + 7\frac{5}{6} - 7\frac{1}{9}$. **$8\frac{1}{18}$**

Careers Oceanographers study water, plants, and animals from the ocean.

Test Prep and Mixed Review   Practice

Multiple Choice

28. Raul bikes $3\frac{1}{2}$ miles to a movie. Then he bikes $2\frac{3}{4}$ miles to the mall and 5 miles home. How many miles does he bike? **C**

   Ⓐ $10\frac{1}{4}$ mi   Ⓑ $10\frac{3}{4}$ mi   Ⓒ $11\frac{1}{4}$ mi   Ⓓ $11\frac{3}{4}$ mi

29. The tennis team sells pie at a fundraiser. Each pie is cut into 8 slices. The team sells 5 slices of apple pie, 8 slices of lemon pie, 2 slices of peach pie, and 3 slices of pumpkin pie. Which expression can you use to find the total number of pies sold? **G**

   Ⓕ $5 + 8 + 2 + 3$ Ⓗ $8(5 + 8 + 2 + 3)$

   Ⓖ $\frac{5}{8} + \frac{8}{8} + \frac{2}{8} + \frac{3}{8}$ Ⓙ $\frac{5}{8} \times \frac{8}{8} \times \frac{2}{8} \times \frac{3}{8}$

30. Emily uses 30 feet of fencing to make a rectangular dog pen. Which dimensions are NOT possible for the pen? **A**

   Ⓐ 3 ft × 10 ft   Ⓑ 4 ft × 11 ft   Ⓒ 6 ft × 9 ft   Ⓓ 8 ft × 7 ft

Simplify each expression.

31. $2^3 \times 3^2 + 5$ **77**   **32.** $5^3 \times 2^2 \div 10^2$ **5**   **33.** $6^2 \times 10^3$ **36,000**

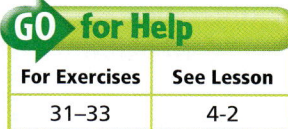

For Exercises	See Lesson
31–33	4-2

PowerPoint

Lesson Quiz

Write each sum.

1. $4\frac{1}{5} + 6\frac{3}{10}$ **$10\frac{1}{2}$**

2. $1\frac{1}{2} + 5\frac{3}{4}$ **$7\frac{1}{4}$**

3. $7\frac{7}{8} + 4\frac{5}{6}$ **$12\frac{17}{24}$**

4. $9\frac{1}{12} + 8\frac{7}{12}$ **$17\frac{2}{3}$**

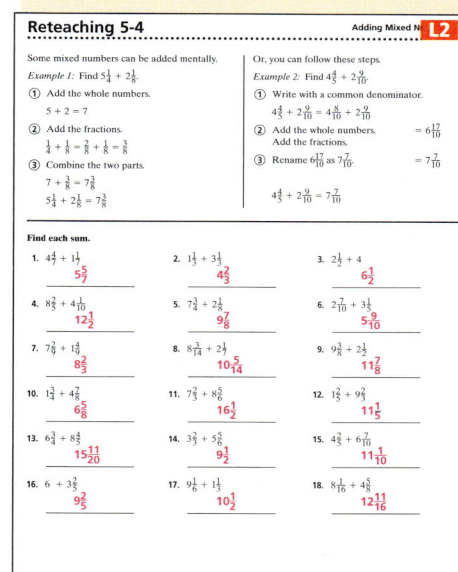

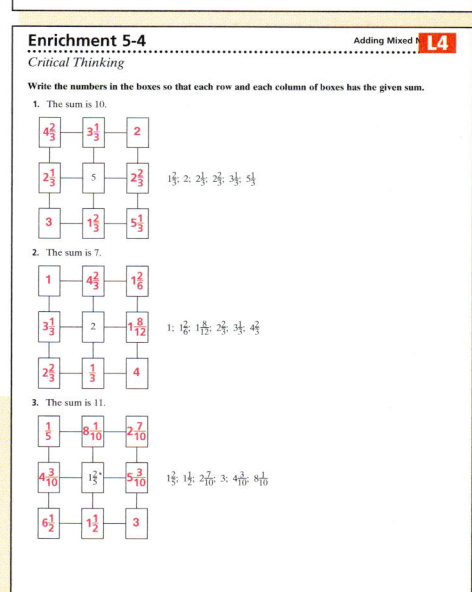

Alternative Assessment

Each student in a pair writes several problems involving addition of mixed numbers. Students exchange papers and write the sums in simplest form. You may wish to allow students to use fraction bars to help them add the fractional parts of the mixed numbers. Have partners record how they found the sums.

Test Prep

Resources

For additional practice with a variety of test item formats:
- Test-Taking Strategies, p. 251
- Test Prep, p. 255
- Test-Taking Strategies with Transparencies

Subtracting Mixed Numbers

Objective
To subtract mixed numbers with and without renaming

Examples
1   Subtracting Mixed Numbers
2   Renaming a Whole Number
3   Renaming a Mixed Number

Math Understandings: p. 210D

Math Background

Subtracting mixed numbers is similar to adding mixed numbers in that whole numbers and fraction parts are dealt with separately and the results are combined. If the fraction being subtracted is greater than the one from which it is being subtracted, you must rename the whole number and the fraction part of the mixed number from which you are subtracting. For instance, in subtracting $4\frac{1}{5} - 2\frac{2}{5}$, you rename $4\frac{1}{5}$ as $3\frac{6}{5}$. First you subtract the fractions. Then you subtract the whole numbers.

More Math Background: p. 210D

Lesson Planning and Resources

See p. 210E for a list of the resources that support this lesson.

☑ Check Skills You'll Need
Use student page, transparency, or PowerPoint. For intervention, direct students to:
Comparing and Ordering Fractions
Lesson 4-8
Extra Skills and Word Problems Practice, Ch. 4

☑ Check Skills You'll Need

1. **Vocabulary Review** Explain how to find the *least common denominator* of $\frac{1}{4}$ and $\frac{1}{6}$.
   1–3. See below.
   Order each set of numbers from least to greatest.
2. $\frac{3}{5}, \frac{7}{10}, \frac{13}{20}$
3. $2\frac{1}{4}, 2\frac{3}{8}, 2\frac{5}{16}, 2\frac{7}{32}$

 **for Help**
Lesson 4-8

Check Skills You'll Need

1. **Answers may vary. Sample: Write multiples of 6 until a multiple is divisible by 4. 12 is divisible by both 6 and 4.**
2. $\frac{3}{5}, \frac{13}{20}, \frac{7}{10}$
3. $2\frac{7}{32}, 2\frac{1}{4}, 2\frac{5}{16}, 2\frac{3}{8}$

🖩 Calculator Tip

You can change mixed numbers to decimals on your calculator. You can rename $2\frac{5}{8}$ by entering
2 ➕ 5 ➗ 8 ＝ .

What You'll Learn

To subtract mixed numbers with and without renaming

Why Learn This?

Some scientists measure plant growth. They use mixed numbers when adding and subtracting the measurements.

When you subtract mixed numbers, you may need to write the fractions with a common denominator. Then you can subtract the whole number and the fraction parts separately.

EXAMPLE Subtracting Mixed Numbers

1 **Science** You grow plants for a science project. One plant is $11\frac{3}{4}$ inches tall. Another plant is $7\frac{5}{8}$ inches tall. Find the difference in the heights of the plants.

To find the difference in heights, find $11\frac{3}{4} - 7\frac{5}{8}$.

$$11\frac{3}{4} \quad \rightarrow \quad 11\frac{6}{8} \quad \leftarrow \text{The LCD is 8. Write } \frac{3}{4} \text{ as } \frac{6}{8}.$$
$$-7\frac{5}{8} \quad \rightarrow \quad -7\frac{5}{8}$$
$$\overline{4\frac{1}{8}} \quad \leftarrow \begin{array}{l}\text{Subtract the whole numbers.}\\ \text{Then subtract the fractions.}\end{array}$$

One plant is $4\frac{1}{8}$ inches taller than the other plant.

☑ Quick Check

1. Another plant is $14\frac{13}{16}$ inches tall. What is the difference between the heights of this plant and the $7\frac{5}{8}$-inch-tall plant? $7\frac{3}{16}$ in.

Differentiated Instruction   **Solutions for All Learners**

Special Needs **L1**
Remind students that they can rewrite any whole number as a fraction, with any denominator. Write examples, such $2 = \frac{4}{2}, \frac{8}{4}$ and so on.

learning style: visual

Below Level **L2**
Have students rename mixed numbers as improper fractions.

$1\frac{2}{3} = \frac{3}{3} + \frac{2}{3} = \frac{5}{3}$ $1\frac{5}{6} = \frac{6}{6} + \frac{5}{6} = \frac{11}{6}$
$1\frac{4}{9} = \frac{9}{9} + \frac{4}{9} = \frac{13}{9}$

learning style: visual

GO for Help

For help writing mixed numbers as improper fractions, go to Lesson 4-6, Example 1.

Sometimes you need to rename whole numbers or fractions so you can subtract. Here is how to rename $3\frac{1}{4}$.

$$3\frac{1}{4} = 2 + 1\frac{1}{4}$$
$$= 2 + \frac{4}{4} + \frac{1}{4}$$
$$= 2\frac{5}{4}$$

$3\frac{1}{4} = 2\frac{5}{4}$

EXAMPLE   **Renaming a Whole Number**

2 Find $7 - 2\frac{5}{8}$.

Write 7 as a mixed number. Use 8 for the denominator since you must subtract $\frac{5}{8}$.

$$7 \rightarrow 6\frac{8}{8} \quad \leftarrow \text{Rename 7 as } 6 + 1 = 6 + \frac{8}{8}, \text{ or } 6\frac{8}{8}.$$
$$-2\frac{5}{8} \rightarrow -2\frac{5}{8}$$
$$\overline{4\frac{3}{8}} \quad \leftarrow \begin{array}{l}\text{Subtract the whole numbers.}\\ \text{Then subtract the fractions.}\end{array}$$

✓ Quick Check

2. a. Find $5 - 3\frac{2}{3}$. $1\frac{1}{3}$ **b.** Find $10 - 4\frac{1}{4}$. $5\frac{3}{4}$

EXAMPLE   **Renaming a Mixed Number**

3 **Lions** One lion cub weighs $7\frac{1}{8}$ pounds. Another cub weighs $5\frac{3}{4}$ pounds. How much more does the heavier cub weigh?

To answer the question, find $7\frac{1}{8} - 5\frac{3}{4}$.

$$7\frac{1}{8} \rightarrow 6\frac{9}{8} \quad \leftarrow \text{Rename } 7\frac{1}{8} \text{ as } 6 + 1\frac{1}{8}, \text{ or } 6\frac{9}{8}.$$
$$-5\frac{3}{4} \rightarrow -5\frac{6}{8} \quad \leftarrow \text{The LCD is 8. Write } \frac{3}{4} \text{ as } \frac{6}{8}.$$
$$\overline{ = 1\frac{3}{8}} \quad \leftarrow \text{Subtract.}$$

The heavier cub weighs $1\frac{3}{8}$ pounds more than the other cub.

✓ Quick Check

3. A picture frame is $1\frac{3}{4}$ feet wide and $3\frac{5}{6}$ feet long. How much longer is the picture frame than it is wide? $2\frac{1}{12}$ ft

---

Closure

- *When do you have to rename when you are subtracting mixed numbers?* **when the fraction being subtracted is greater than the one from which it is being subtracted**
- Explain how you would rename $9\frac{1}{8}$. **Sample: Think of $9\frac{1}{8}$ as $8 + 1 + \frac{1}{8}$. Change the 1 to eighths, or $\frac{8}{8}$. Combine $8 + \frac{8}{8} + \frac{1}{8}$ to get $8\frac{9}{8}$.**

● More Than One Way

Suppose you catch two fish. The first one is $9\frac{1}{8}$ inches long. The second one is $7\frac{1}{4}$ inches long. How much longer is the first fish?

Leon's Method

I need to subtract the lengths. Since $\frac{1}{8} < \frac{1}{4}$, I will rename $9\frac{1}{8}$.

$$
\begin{array}{rll}
9\frac{1}{8} & \quad 8\frac{9}{8} & \leftarrow \text{Rename } 9\frac{1}{8} \text{ as } 8 + 1\frac{1}{8}, \text{ or } 8\frac{9}{8}. \\
-7\frac{1}{4} & \rightarrow \quad -7\frac{2}{8} & \leftarrow \text{The LCD is 8. Write } \frac{1}{4} \text{ as } \frac{2}{8}. \\
& \quad = 1\frac{7}{8} & \leftarrow \text{Find the difference.}
\end{array}
$$

The first fish is $1\frac{7}{8}$ inches longer than the second fish.

Lauren's Method

I need to subtract the lengths. I will change both mixed numbers to improper fractions with the same denominator.

$$
\begin{aligned}
9\frac{1}{8} - 7\frac{1}{4} &= \frac{73}{8} - \frac{29}{4} \quad \leftarrow \text{Write as improper fractions.} \\
&= \frac{73}{8} - \frac{58}{8} \quad \leftarrow \text{Rename as equivalent fractions with a like denominator.} \\
&= \frac{15}{8}, \text{ or } 1\frac{7}{8} \quad \leftarrow \text{Subtract. Write the difference in simplest form.}
\end{aligned}
$$

The first fish is $1\frac{7}{8}$ inches longer than the second fish.

I renamed $10\frac{1}{3}$ as $9\frac{12}{9}$ and subtracted $7\frac{8}{9}$; the difference is $2\frac{4}{9}$.

Choose a Method

Find $10\frac{1}{3} - 7\frac{8}{9}$. Describe your method and explain why it was appropriate.

Answers may vary. See left for sample.

✓ Check Your Understanding

1. **Number Sense** Which mixed number is equal to $4\frac{5}{7}$? **c**

   (A) $3\frac{10}{7}$ (B) $3\frac{11}{7}$ (C) $3\frac{12}{7}$ (D) $3\frac{13}{7}$

Find each difference.

2. $12\frac{3}{4} - 10\frac{1}{4}$ **$2\frac{1}{2}$**

3. $3\frac{4}{4} - 2\frac{3}{4}$ **$1\frac{1}{4}$**

Homework Exercises

For more exercises, see Extra Skills and Word Problems.

GO for Help

For Exercises	See Example
4–13	1
14–16	2
17–21	3

Ⓐ **Find each difference.**

4. $9\frac{4}{7} - 2\frac{3}{14}$ $7\frac{5}{14}$

5. $7\frac{3}{4} - 6\frac{2}{5}$ $1\frac{7}{20}$

6. $2\frac{5}{8} - 1\frac{1}{4}$ $1\frac{3}{8}$

7. $9\frac{4}{5} - 4\frac{4}{15}$ $5\frac{8}{15}$

8. $21\frac{3}{8} - 11\frac{1}{4}$ $10\frac{1}{8}$

9. $15\frac{11}{12} - 11\frac{1}{2}$ $4\frac{5}{12}$

10. $12\frac{1}{4} - 4\frac{1}{8}$ $8\frac{1}{8}$

11. $3\frac{2}{3} - 1\frac{1}{6}$ $2\frac{1}{2}$

12. $19\frac{1}{3} - 7\frac{1}{5}$ $12\frac{2}{15}$

13. You spend $2\frac{2}{3}$ hours reading and $1\frac{1}{2}$ hours watching a movie. How much more time do you spend reading than watching the movie? $1\frac{1}{6}$ h

Find each difference.

14.
$$\begin{array}{r} 8 \\ -\ 2\frac{3}{4} \end{array}\ 5\frac{1}{4}$$

15.
$$\begin{array}{r} 23 \\ -\ 19\frac{5}{8} \end{array}\ 3\frac{3}{8}$$

16.
$$\begin{array}{r} 32 \\ -\ 16\frac{1}{2} \end{array}\ 15\frac{1}{2}$$

17. $10\frac{1}{10} - 3\frac{2}{5}$ $6\frac{7}{10}$

18. $3\frac{3}{8} - 1\frac{3}{4}$ $1\frac{5}{8}$

19. $4\frac{5}{12} - 1\frac{3}{4}$ $2\frac{2}{3}$

20. $6\frac{1}{5} - 2\frac{2}{3}$ $3\frac{8}{15}$

21. **Biology** In one hour, a bee can fly $5\frac{2}{3}$ miles. A moth can fly $11\frac{1}{6}$ miles in one hour. How much farther can the moth fly in one hour than the bee? $5\frac{1}{2}$ miles

Ⓑ  22. **Guided Problem Solving** You have a board that is 12 feet long. You cut two pieces from the board that are both $3\frac{7}{12}$ feet long. How much of the board is left? $4\frac{5}{6}$ ft

- **Make a Plan** Subtract the first piece from 12 feet. Then subtract the second piece from the remaining length.
- **Check the Answer** Draw a picture to determine whether your answer is reasonable.

12-foot board

$3\frac{7}{12}$ feet	$3\frac{7}{12}$ feet	answer

23. **Weather** On Monday, the snowfall in the mountains was $15\frac{3}{4}$ inches. On Tuesday, the snowfall was $18\frac{1}{2}$ inches. How much more snow fell on Tuesday? $2\frac{3}{4}$ in.

Homework Video Tutor
Visit: PHSchool.com
Web Code: aqe-0505

24. **Writing in Math** You are finding $3\frac{1}{6} - 1\frac{5}{6}$. Explain why you would rewrite $3\frac{1}{6}$ as $2\frac{7}{6}$. because $\frac{5}{6}$ is greater than $\frac{1}{6}$

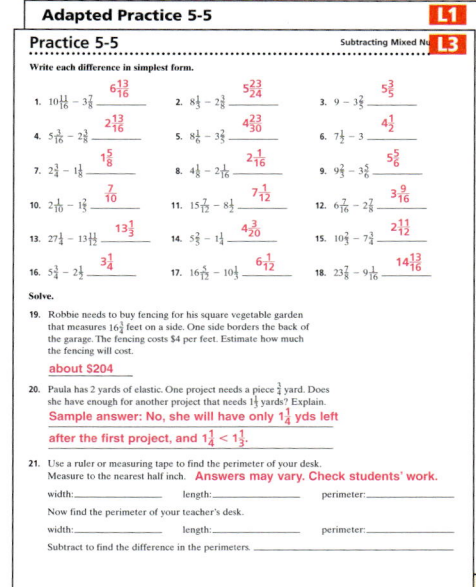
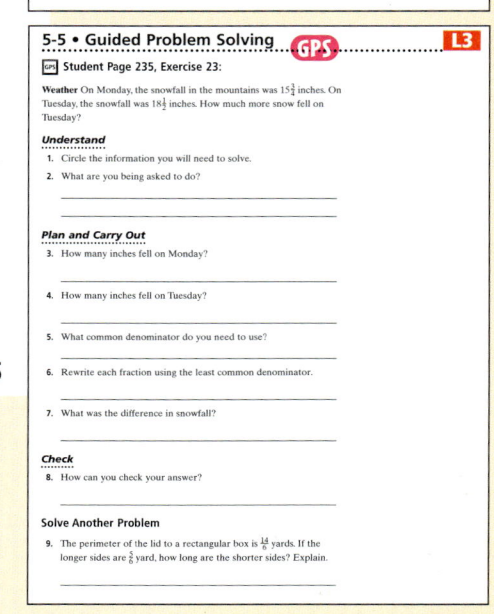

PowerPoint

Lesson Quiz

Find each difference.

1. $7\frac{7}{8} - 4\frac{1}{4}$ $3\frac{5}{8}$

2. $8\frac{2}{5} - 6\frac{8}{10}$ $1\frac{3}{5}$

3. $9\frac{1}{3} - 5\frac{11}{12}$ $3\frac{5}{12}$

4. $14\frac{1}{3} - 6\frac{5}{8}$ $7\frac{17}{24}$

26. $2\frac{9}{10}$; answers may vary. Sample: Rename as improper fractions because the denominators are different.

25. **Gardening** Carlos plants a tree that is $3\frac{1}{2}$ feet tall. A year later the tree is $4\frac{5}{12}$ feet tall. How much has it grown? $\frac{11}{12}$ ft

26. **Choose a Method** Find $6\frac{2}{5} - 3\frac{1}{2}$. Did you subtract the mixed numbers or use improper fractions? Explain your choice. **See left.**

Olympics Use the table for Exercises 27–29.

27. How much farther did Heike Drechsler jump in 1992 than in 2000? **6 in.**

28. Which two jumps were closest in length? **1992 and 1996**

29. Find the difference between the longest and the shortest winning jumps. **1 ft $4\frac{1}{4}$ in.**

Women's Olympic Long Jump Winners

Year	Winner, Country	Distance
1988	Jackie Joyner-Kersee, United States	24 ft $3\frac{1}{2}$ in.
1992	Heike Drechsler, Germany	23 ft $5\frac{1}{4}$ in.
1996	Chioma Ajunwa, Nigeria	23 ft $4\frac{1}{2}$ in.
2000	Heike Drechsler, Germany	22 ft $11\frac{1}{4}$ in.
2004	Tatyana Lebedeva, Russia	23 ft $2\frac{1}{2}$ in.

Source: *ESPN Sports Almanac*

C 30. **Challenge** Solve the equation $x + 1\frac{2}{3} = 3\frac{1}{2}$. $1\frac{5}{6}$

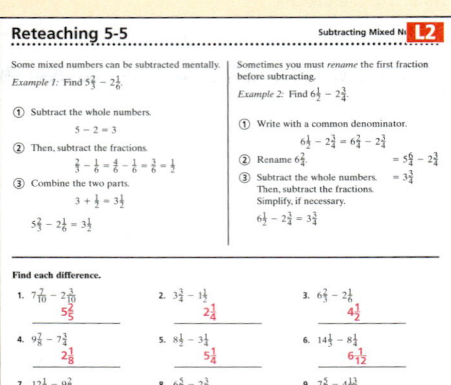

236

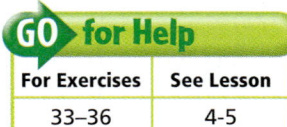

Test Prep and Mixed Review

Practice

Multiple Choice

31. Lauren spent $1\frac{3}{4}$ hours doing math homework and $2\frac{1}{4}$ hours reading. How many more hours did Lauren spend reading? **A**

  Ⓐ $\frac{1}{2}$ hour   Ⓒ $1\frac{1}{2}$ hours

  Ⓑ $\frac{3}{4}$ hour   Ⓓ $1\frac{3}{4}$ hours

32. James will use the following steps to find the sum $6\frac{5}{8} + 3\frac{7}{8}$.

  Step K   Write as a mixed number: $\frac{12}{8} = 1\frac{1}{2}$.

  Step L   Add fraction parts: $\frac{5}{8} + \frac{7}{8} = \frac{12}{8}$.

  Step M   Add whole number and fraction parts: $9 + 1\frac{1}{2} = 10\frac{1}{2}$.

  Step N   Add whole number parts: $6 + 3 = 9$.

  Which list shows the steps in the correct order? **J**

  Ⓕ M, N, L, K   Ⓗ L, N, M, K

  Ⓖ L, K, M, N   Ⓙ N, L, K, M

GO for Help

For Exercises	See Lesson
33–36	4-5

Write each fraction in simplest form.

33. $\frac{15}{25}$ $\frac{3}{5}$ 34. $\frac{16}{56}$ $\frac{2}{7}$ 35. $\frac{36}{54}$ $\frac{2}{3}$ 36. $\frac{8}{4}$ 2

Test Prep

Resources

For additional practice with a variety of test item formats:

• Test-Taking Strategies, p. 251
• Test Prep, p. 255
• Test-Taking Strategies with Transparencies

Alternative Assessment

Have students work in pairs. Refer them to Exercises 14–20. For each exercise, partners must verify with one another that they have found a common denominator and have renamed the mixed number accurately before subtracting. Partners should then compare their answers before moving to the next exercise.

Using a Fraction Calculator

You can use a fraction calculator to add and subtract fractions. Use the **/** key, which indicates division, for the fraction bar.

EXAMPLE

1 Find $\frac{5}{6} - \frac{3}{8}$.

Enter 5 **/** 6 **−** 3 **/** 8 **=** $11/24$.

$\frac{5}{6} - \frac{3}{8} = \frac{11}{24}$

You can also use a fraction calculator to add or subtract mixed numbers. Use the **UNIT** key to enter the whole number part. If you do not use the unit key, the calculator will interpret $1\frac{3}{4}$ as $\frac{13}{4}$.

EXAMPLE

2 Find $1\frac{3}{4} + 3\frac{1}{2}$.

Enter 1 **UNIT** 3 **/** 4 **+** 3 **UNIT** 1 **/** 2 **=** $21/4$.

To rename this number, press **2nd** **a$^{b/c}$** **=** $5\ 1/4$.

In simplest form, $1\frac{3}{4} + 3\frac{1}{2} = 5\frac{1}{4}$.

Exercises

Use a fraction calculator to find each sum or difference.

1. $\frac{3}{4} - \frac{2}{5}$ $\frac{7}{20}$

2. $\frac{8}{9} + \frac{1}{12}$ $\frac{35}{36}$

3. $\frac{11}{12} - \frac{3}{8}$ $\frac{13}{24}$

4. $\frac{4}{5} + \frac{1}{20}$ $\frac{17}{20}$

5. $\frac{3}{10} - \frac{2}{9}$ $\frac{7}{90}$

6. $\frac{22}{25} + \frac{9}{100}$ $\frac{97}{100}$

7. $9\frac{3}{4} + 3\frac{3}{4}$ $13\frac{1}{2}$

8. $6\frac{9}{10} + 2\frac{1}{12}$ $8\frac{59}{60}$

9. $18\frac{5}{12} - 9\frac{1}{2}$ $8\frac{11}{12}$

10. $1\frac{1}{10} + 8\frac{1}{12}$ $9\frac{11}{60}$

11. $13\frac{5}{12} - 5\frac{1}{3}$ $8\frac{1}{12}$

12. $14\frac{3}{10} - 3\frac{1}{2}$ $10\frac{4}{5}$

13. **Writing in Math** How can you use a fraction calculator to simplify an improper fraction? **Answers may vary. Sample: Enter the improper fraction into the calculator. Press** **2nd** **a$^{b/c}$** **=**.

Using a Fraction Calculator

In this Activity, students use a fraction calculator to add and subtract fractions and mixed numbers with different denominators and learn how to express the answers in simplest form.

Guided Instruction

Teaching Tip
Allow students time to familiarize themselves with the special keys, particularly the **SIMP** key, on their fraction calculators.

Example 1

After students have worked through this subtraction, ask: *How can you use the calculator to find the sum of $\frac{5}{6}$ and $\frac{3}{8}$?* **Sample: Use the** **+** **key instead of the** **−** **key.**

Example 2

After students have completed the second example, ask: *How can you use your calculator to check that $5\frac{1}{4}$ is the correct answer?* **Sample: Subtract either addend from $5\frac{1}{4}$ to obtain the other addend.**

Differentiated Instruction

Below Level **L2**
Before beginning the exercises, have students convert all mixed numbers to improper fractions to avoid confusion.

Resources

- fraction calculators
- Classroom Aid II

Checkpoint Quiz 2

Find each sum or difference.

1. $2\frac{1}{2} + 3\frac{1}{8}$ $5\frac{5}{8}$
2. $9\frac{1}{2} - 4\frac{3}{4}$ $4\frac{3}{4}$
3. $6\frac{1}{3} + 8\frac{1}{2}$ $14\frac{5}{6}$
4. $7\frac{5}{9} - 1\frac{2}{3}$ $5\frac{8}{9}$

5. $3\frac{1}{3} + 2\frac{1}{2}$ $5\frac{5}{6}$
6. $2\frac{1}{9} - 1\frac{2}{3}$ $\frac{4}{9}$
7. $4\frac{1}{2} + 5\frac{3}{8}$ $9\frac{7}{8}$
8. $5\frac{2}{3} - 1\frac{1}{2}$ $4\frac{1}{6}$

9. **Music** You spend $1\frac{1}{2}$ hours practicing piano and $2\frac{3}{4}$ hours working on homework. How many total hours have you spent doing both activities? $4\frac{1}{4}$ **hours**

10. **Travel** A road sign says that the next exit is $2\frac{1}{4}$ miles ahead. You travel $1\frac{7}{10}$ miles according to your odometer. How much farther ahead is the next exit? $\frac{11}{20}$ **mile**

MATH GAMES

That's Some Sum!

What You'll Need

- Paper and pencil
- Two pencils or markers of different colors

How To Play

- Draw a square game board and divide it into 16 smaller squares. Write fractions in half of the squares and mixed numbers in the other half.
- Player 1 circles any two numbers and then finds their sum. The sum is added to that player's score.
- Player 2 circles two other numbers, finds the sum, and adds it to his or her score. Players take turns until all numbers have been chosen.
- Any answer may be challenged. If the answer is correct, the challenger loses a turn. If the challenger corrects the answer, that sum is added to the challenger's score. The other player's turn is over without any change to his or her score.
- The player with the greater total score wins.

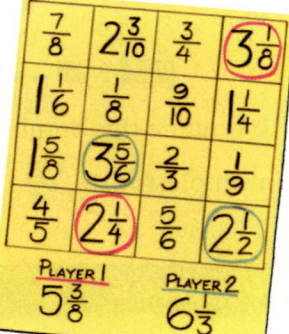

238

Using Pictographs

A pictograph uses pictures or symbols to represent data. Each picture has the same value. The pictograph below shows that $4\frac{1}{2}$ thousand people have attended girls' basketball games.

Basketball Game Attendance

Boys' basketball

Girls' basketball

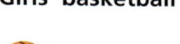 = 1000 people in attendance

Exercises

1. What is the total number of pictures that represent data in the pictograph above? What is the total number of people who have attended girls' and boys' basketball games? **$8\frac{1}{4}$; 8,250 people**

2. The pictograph at the right represents the hits that a player got in one season. How many hits did this player get? **116 hits**

3. For each pictograph below, describe a situation that the pictograph might represent. Then write and solve a mixed-number problem based on the pictograph.

   a. **Pizzas Sold**

   = 10,000 pizzas

   3–5. Check students' work.

   b. **Apartments for Rent**

   = 1,000 apartments

   Number of Hits

   Singles

   Doubles

   Triples

   Home runs

   = 8 hits

4. **Reasoning** Suppose you are making a pictograph in which each picture represents 100 visits to a veterinarian. Why is it easier to use circular or square shapes than to use pictures of people or animals?

5. **Open-Ended** Draw a pictograph for the values $5\frac{3}{10}$ and $3\frac{7}{10}$. Write a problem that could be represented by your pictograph.

Activity Lab

Using Pictographs

Students read symbols in a pictograph used to represent fractions and mixed numbers.

Guided Instruction

Before beginning the Activity, explain to students that each symbol in the pictograph represents 1,000 people. Ask questions such as:
- *If there were $8\frac{3}{4}$ symbols, how many people would that represent?* **8,750**
- *How many symbols would you draw to represent 3,250 people?* **$3\frac{1}{4}$**

Exercises
Before beginning the exercises, have students write out the fraction that each value in the pictographs represents.

Alternative Method
Some students may have difficulty with such large numbers. Provide smaller numbers for them to work with.

Resources

- Activity Lab 5-6: Solving Fraction Equations
- Student Manipulatives Kit

Objective
To solve equations with fractions

Examples
1 Using Mental Math in Equations
2 Solving Equations With Fractions
3 Application: Rainfall

Math Understandings: p. 210D

Math Background

You can solve equations with fractions in a manner similar to that of solving equations with whole numbers. To solve equations involving fractions and mixed numbers, you need to use the Addition Property of Equality or the Subtraction Property of Equality. These properties allow you to add the same number to, or subtract the same number from, both sides of an equation without changing the value of the equation.

More Math Background: p. 210D

Lesson Planning and Resources

See p. 210E for a list of the resources that support this lesson.

Bell Ringer Practice

✓ **Check Skills You'll Need**
Use student page, transparency, or PowerPoint. For intervention, direct students to:
Solving Addition Equations
Lesson 3-5
Extra Skills and Word Problems Practice, Ch. 3

5-6 Equations With Fractions

5-6

✓ **Check Skills You'll Need**

1. **Vocabulary Review**
The *inverse operation* of addition is __?__.
subtraction
Solve each equation.

2. $17 + x = 43$ **26**

3. $4.2 + x = 8$ **3.8**

4. $10.7 = x - 8.2$ **18.9**

GO for Help
Lesson 3-5

What You'll Learn
To solve equations with fractions

Why Learn This?
Weather reports include information such as temperature, humidity, and rainfall. You can use equations with fractions to find rainfall amounts.

Sometimes you can use mental math to solve equations that involve fractions or mixed numbers. Remember, you can also use a model to help you solve equations.

EXAMPLE Using Mental Math in Equations

1 Solve $3\frac{1}{8} + x = 15\frac{7}{8}$ using mental math.

$3 + 12 = 15$ ← Use mental math to find the missing whole number.

$\frac{1}{8} + \frac{6}{8} = \frac{7}{8}$ ← Use mental math to find the missing fraction.

$x = 12\frac{6}{8}$ ← Combine the two parts.

✓ Quick Check

1. Solve each equation using mental math.

   a. $x - 1\frac{3}{8} = 1\frac{3}{8}$ **b.** $14\frac{1}{4} + x = 25\frac{1}{2}$ **c.** $5\frac{5}{6} - x = 2\frac{1}{6}$

        $2\frac{3}{4}$ $11\frac{1}{4}$ $3\frac{2}{3}$

   You can use inverse operations to get the variable alone on one side of the equation.

Differentiated Instruction Solutions for All Learners

Special Needs **L1**
Assist students with different models to solve the equations in this chapter. Algebra tiles or number lines can be useful models.

Below Level **L2**
Write equations with like denominators for students to solve.

$x - \frac{1}{9} = \frac{4}{9}$ $x = \frac{5}{9}$

$x + \frac{4}{8} = \frac{7}{8}$ $x = \frac{3}{8}$

learning style: visual   learning style: visual

EXAMPLE Solving Equations With Fractions

2 Solve $x - \frac{1}{3} = \frac{5}{6}$.

$$x - \frac{1}{3} + \frac{1}{3} = \frac{5}{6} + \frac{1}{3} \quad \leftarrow \text{Add } \frac{1}{3} \text{ to each side.}$$

$$x = \frac{5}{6} + \frac{2}{6} \quad \leftarrow \text{The LCD is 6. Write } \frac{1}{3} \text{ as } \frac{2}{6}.$$

$$x = \frac{7}{6} \quad \leftarrow \text{Add.}$$

$$x = 1\frac{1}{6} \quad \leftarrow \text{Simplify.}$$

GO for Help

For help with adding fractions, go to Lesson 5-3, Example 1.

✓ Quick Check

2. a. Solve $n + \frac{1}{3} = \frac{11}{12}$. $\frac{7}{12}$

b. Solve $\frac{2}{5} + a = \frac{13}{20}$. $\frac{1}{4}$

EXAMPLE Application: Rainfall

3 During the first week of January, a rain gauge collected $\frac{1}{2}$ inch of rain. By the end of January, the total rainfall was $2\frac{3}{5}$ inches. How much rain fell after the first week of January?

Words	rainfall during first week of January	+	rainfall after first week of January	=	total rainfall in January

Let r = the rainfall after the first week of January.

Equation	$\frac{1}{2}$	+	r	=	$2\frac{3}{5}$

$$\frac{1}{2} + r = 2\frac{3}{5}$$

$$\frac{1}{2} + r - \frac{1}{2} = 2\frac{3}{5} - \frac{1}{2} \quad \leftarrow \text{Subtract } \frac{1}{2} \text{ from each side.}$$

$$r = 2\frac{6}{10} - \frac{5}{10} \quad \leftarrow \begin{array}{l}\text{The LCD is 10. Write each fraction}\\ \text{with a denominator of 10.}\end{array}$$

$$r = 2\frac{1}{10} \quad \leftarrow \text{Subtract.}$$

After the first week of January, $2\frac{1}{10}$ inches of rain fell.

The diagram shows a rectangle labeled $2\frac{3}{5}$ on top, split below into $\frac{1}{2}$ and r.

✓ Quick Check

3. You hammer a nail $2\frac{3}{8}$ inches long through a board. The nail pokes $\frac{5}{8}$ inch through the other side. How thick is the board?

$1\frac{3}{4}$ in.

Advanced Learners **L4**

Write two one-step equations that have the solution $x = 5\frac{1}{9}$. **Sample:** $x - 1\frac{1}{3} = 3\frac{7}{9}$, $x + 5\frac{1}{6} = 10\frac{5}{18}$

learning style: visual

English Language Learners **ELL**

A pictorial model for Example 3 would be helpful. For example, a number line can show what is being added to the rainfall after the first week, or the difference between $\frac{1}{2}$ and $2\frac{3}{5}$.

learning style: visual

---

2. Teach

Activity Lab

Use before the lesson.
Student Edition Activity Lab, Data Analysis 5-6a, Using Pictographs, p. 239

All in One Teaching Resources
Activity Lab 5-6: Solving Fraction Equations

Guided Instruction

Teaching Tip
Have students round their ages to the nearest whole number of months. Then have them divide by 12, and write the result as a mixed number in simplest form.

Example 1
Have students share with the class the methods they used to solve the Quick Check exercises.

PowerPoint
Additional Examples

1 Solve $12\frac{7}{9} = x + 3\frac{4}{9}$ using mental math. **$x = 9\frac{1}{3}$**

2 Solve $x - \frac{1}{8} = \frac{3}{4}$. **$x = \frac{7}{8}$**

3 An empty container weighs $\frac{1}{12}$ lb. The same container full of chopped fruit weighs $\frac{7}{8}$ lb. How much does the fruit weigh? **$\frac{19}{24}$ lb**

All in One Teaching Resources
- Daily Notetaking Guide 5-6 **L3**
- Adapted Notetaking 5-6 **L1**

Closure

- *How is solving equations with fractions similar to solving equations with whole numbers?*
  Sample: Both use the properties of equality to get the variable alone on one side of an equation.

3. Practice

Assignment Guide

Check Your Understanding
Go over Exercises 1–5 in class before assigning the Homework Exercises.

Homework Exercises
A Practice by Example 6–24
B Apply Your Skills 25–31
C Challenge 32
Test Prep and
  Mixed Review 33–37

Homework Quick Check
To check students' understanding of key skills and concepts, go over Exercises 7, 18, 27, 29, and 30.

Differentiated Instruction **Resources**

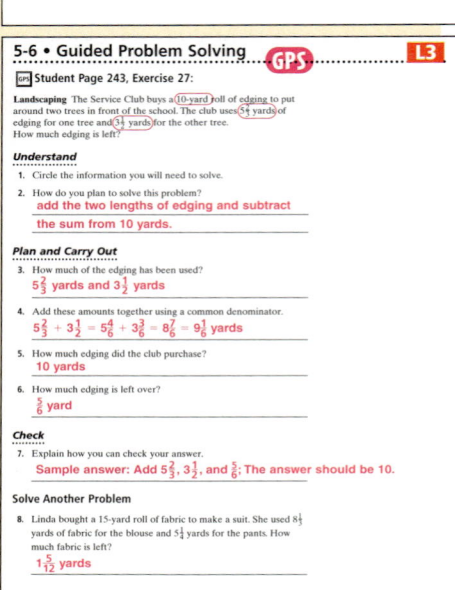

Check Your Understanding

Match each equation with the correct solution.

1. $x - 3\frac{1}{5} = \frac{2}{5}$ **C**   **A.** $3\frac{1}{5}$

2. $x + 4\frac{3}{5} = 8$ **B**   **B.** $3\frac{2}{5}$

3. $x - 2\frac{1}{5} = 1\frac{3}{5}$ **D**   **C.** $3\frac{3}{5}$

4. $x + 4\frac{4}{5} = 8$ **A**   **D.** $3\frac{4}{5}$

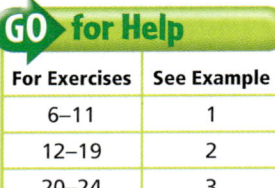

5. Your frog wins second place in a jumping contest. The winning jump of $11\frac{2}{3}$ feet is $\frac{1}{2}$ foot longer than your frog's jump. How far does your frog jump? **$11\frac{1}{6}$ ft**

Homework Exercises

For more exercises, see Extra Skills and Word Problems.

GO for Help

For Exercises	See Example
6–11	1
12–19	2
20–24	3

A **Mental Math** Solve each equation.

6. $x + 4\frac{2}{5} = 7\frac{4}{5}$ **$3\frac{2}{5}$**   7. $a + 6\frac{1}{3} = 20\frac{2}{3}$ **$14\frac{1}{3}$**   8. $c - \frac{3}{10} = 6\frac{9}{10}$ **$7\frac{1}{5}$**

9. $7\frac{4}{5} = 2\frac{3}{5} + n$ **$5\frac{1}{5}$**   10. $4\frac{3}{8} = k - 7\frac{1}{8}$ **$11\frac{1}{2}$**   11. $12\frac{5}{6} = s + 2\frac{5}{6}$ **10**

Solve each equation. You may find a model helpful.

12. $x = \frac{2}{7} + \frac{5}{6}$ **$1\frac{5}{42}$**   13. $\frac{2}{5} - \frac{1}{9} = x$ **$\frac{13}{45}$**   14. $x - \frac{5}{6} = \frac{7}{8}$ **$1\frac{17}{24}$**

15. $\frac{5}{24} + g = \frac{1}{3}$ **$\frac{1}{8}$**   16. $\frac{4}{9} = y - \frac{2}{5}$ **$\frac{38}{45}$**   17. $t - \frac{7}{9} = \frac{1}{3}$ **$1\frac{1}{9}$**

18. $\frac{11}{12} = n + \frac{2}{3}$ **$\frac{1}{4}$**   19. $\frac{5}{8} = a + \frac{1}{3}$ **$\frac{7}{24}$**   20. $3\frac{1}{5} = x - \frac{12}{25}$ **$3\frac{17}{25}$**

21. $y - 2\frac{8}{9} = \frac{5}{6}$ **$3\frac{13}{18}$**   22. $k - 4\frac{5}{6} = 2\frac{1}{4}$ **$7\frac{1}{12}$**   23. $9\frac{7}{8} = b - \frac{3}{4}$ **$10\frac{5}{8}$**

24. **$\frac{5}{8}$ of the book is left or 5 chapters are left**

24. **Reading** A book has 8 chapters. You read $\frac{3}{8}$ of the book in a week. Use an equation to find how much you have left to read. **See left.**

B **GPS** 25. **Guided Problem Solving** You buy 12 pounds of beef for a class picnic. You use $5\frac{1}{2}$ pounds to make burgers and $4\frac{2}{3}$ pounds to make tacos. Use an equation to find how much beef remains.   **$1\frac{5}{6}$ lb left**

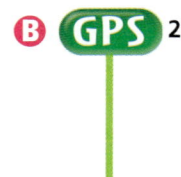

- How much beef have you used in all?
- What equation represents this situation?

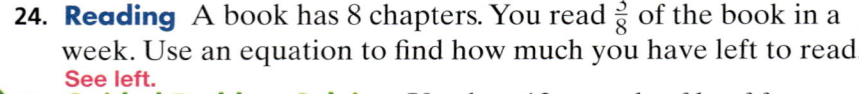

35. $\frac{3}{10}, \frac{1}{2}, \frac{4}{7}, \frac{2}{3}$

36. $\frac{1}{9}, \frac{3}{4}, \frac{11}{12}, \frac{4}{3}$

37. $\frac{0}{5}, \frac{2}{11}, \frac{5}{9}, \frac{8}{7}$

26. Patterns Solve each equation.

a. $\frac{1}{3} + x = \frac{1}{2}$ $\frac{1}{6}$ b. $\frac{1}{4} + x = \frac{1}{3}$ $\frac{1}{12}$ c. $\frac{1}{5} + x = \frac{1}{4}$ $\frac{1}{20}$

d. Predict the solution of $\frac{1}{9} + x = \frac{1}{8}$. $\frac{1}{72}$

27. Landscaping The Service Club buys a 10-yard roll of edging to put around two trees in front of the school. The club uses $5\frac{2}{3}$ yards of edging for one tree and $3\frac{1}{2}$ yards for the other tree. How much edging is left? $\frac{5}{6}$ yd

28. The Golden Gate Bridge in California is about $\frac{4}{5}$ mile long. It is about $\frac{1}{2}$ mile longer than the Brooklyn Bridge in New York. About how long is the Brooklyn Bridge? $\frac{3}{10}$ mi

29. Writing in Math Refer to the table. Did the relay team beat their best total time of 6 minutes for this 1600-meter relay? Explain. **See left.**

30. Your teacher asks your class to name one of the three primary colors. If $\frac{2}{5}$ of the class chooses yellow, and $\frac{1}{3}$ of the class chooses blue, what fraction of the class chooses red? **See left.**

Relay Times (minutes)	
Kim	$1\frac{1}{2}$
Alison	$1\frac{3}{8}$
Laura	$1\frac{3}{4}$
Jamie	$1\frac{1}{4}$

31. Number Sense Which variable, m or n, has the greater value? **n has the greater value.**

$$m - \frac{3}{4} = \frac{37}{50} \qquad n - \frac{4}{5} = \frac{37}{50}$$

C 32. Challenge One girl can eat $\frac{1}{2}$ of an apple in $\frac{1}{3}$ of a minute. At this rate, how many apples can three girls eat in two minutes? **9 apples**

29. Answers may vary.
Sample: Yes; adding each relay time gives $1\frac{1}{2} + 1\frac{3}{8} + 1\frac{3}{4} + 1\frac{1}{4} = 5\frac{7}{8}$, which is faster than 6 min.

30. $\frac{4}{15}$ of the class

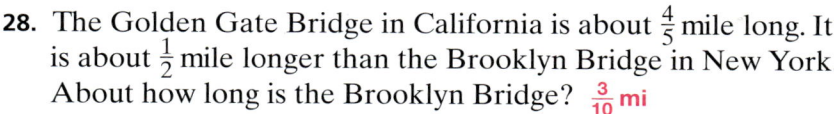

Test Prep and Mixed Review **Practice**

Multiple Choice

33. Greg scores 98, 92, 76, 91, and 98 on 5 math quizzes. What is the median of Greg's quiz scores? **C**

Ⓐ 76   Ⓑ 91   Ⓒ 92   Ⓓ 98

34. The table shows the amount Carla earns baby-sitting. Which expression can you use to find how much Carla earns for baby-sitting h hours? **G**

Ⓕ $2h$ Ⓗ $h + 7$
Ⓖ $8h$ Ⓙ $h + 16$

Baby-sitting Money	
Hours, h	Dollars
1	8
2	16
4	32
h	?

35–37. See margin.
Order each set of numbers from least to greatest.

35. $\frac{1}{2}, \frac{2}{3}, \frac{4}{7}, \frac{3}{10}$ 36. $\frac{3}{4}, \frac{4}{3}, \frac{1}{9}, \frac{11}{12}$ 37. $\frac{2}{11}, \frac{0}{5}, \frac{5}{9}, \frac{8}{7}$

For Exercises	See Lesson
35–37	4-8

Lesson Quiz

Solve each equation.

1. $x + \frac{1}{3} = \frac{14}{15}$ $x = \frac{3}{5}$

2. $x + 10\frac{5}{8} = 16\frac{1}{4}$ $x = 5\frac{5}{8}$

3. $17\frac{3}{4} + x = 18\frac{1}{12}$ $x = \frac{1}{3}$

4. $x - \frac{9}{10} = 3\frac{7}{10}$ $x = 4\frac{3}{5}$

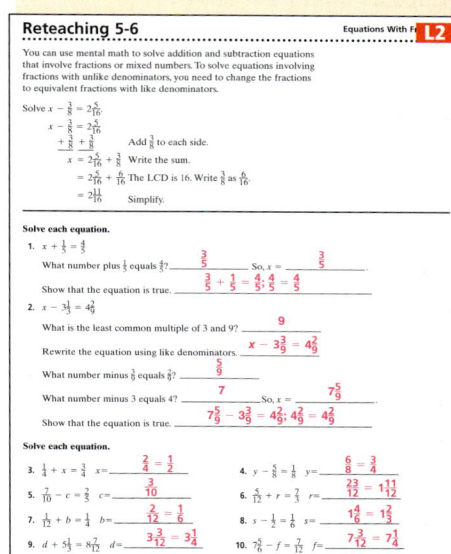

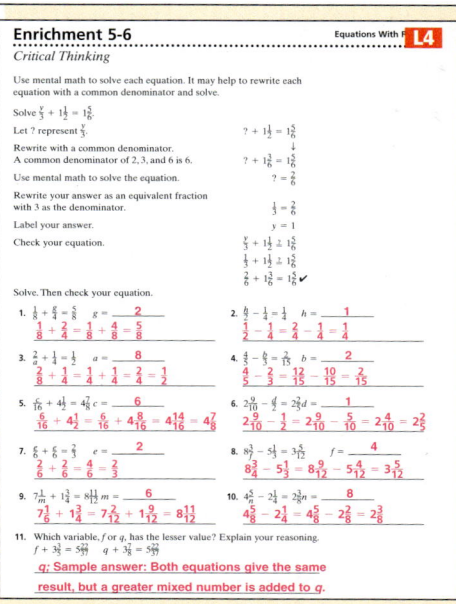

Alternative Assessment

Have students work in pairs. One partner completes Exercises 12, 14, and 16 while the other completes Exercises 13, 15, and 17. Students explain to their partners how they found the solution to each equation.

Test Prep

Resources
For additional practice with a variety of test item formats:
• Test-Taking Strategies, p. 251
• Test Prep, p. 255
• Test-Taking Strategies with Transparencies

Practice Solving Problems

In this feature, students use diagrams to help them visualize the situation in each problem, then write and solve an equation for each problem.

Guided Instruction

Discuss with students that word problems with a lot of information are often difficult to visualize. Explain that drawing a diagram from the given information can make the problem easier to approach.

Have a volunteer read the example aloud. Ask:
- *What would you draw to represent the information in this problem?* **boards of the dimensions described and one board with a variable for its width**
- *What information is necessary to solve the problem?* **the width of both boards, the total width of the wall**
- *How can you find the value of the variable?* **by adding the widths of the first two boards and subtracting that number from the total width**

Practice Solving Problems

Carpentry   You build a garden wall that is 36 inches tall. You place two $1\frac{1}{2}$-inch-by-$11\frac{1}{4}$-inch boards on top of each other. Each board is 5 feet long. How wide does the third board need to be to finish the wall?

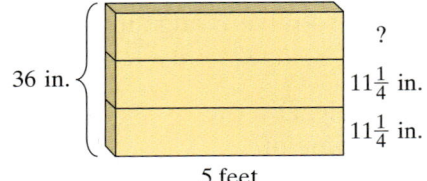

36 in.
?
$11\frac{1}{4}$ in.
$11\frac{1}{4}$ in.
5 feet

What You Might Think

How can I use a diagram to show this situation?

What equation can I write for this situation?

What is the answer?

What You Might Write

36 in.		
$11\frac{1}{4}$ in.	$11\frac{1}{4}$ in.	w

Let w = width of unknown board.

$$11\frac{1}{4} + 11\frac{1}{4} + w = 36$$

$$22\frac{1}{2} + w = 36$$

$$22\frac{1}{2} + w - 22\frac{1}{2} = 36 - 22\frac{1}{2}$$

$$w = 13\frac{1}{2}$$

The third board needs to be $13\frac{1}{2}$ inches wide.

Think It Through

1. Can you solve the equation $11\frac{1}{4} + 11\frac{1}{4} + x = 36$ by subtracting $11\frac{1}{4}$ from each side? Explain.

2. **Check for Reasonableness** How can you use rounding to decide whether the answer is reasonable? **See margin.**

3. **Reasoning** Which strategies can you use to determine which information in the problem is unnecessary? **Check students' work.**

1. Answers may vary. Sample: Yes; you could subtract $11\frac{1}{4}$ from each side of the equation twice to get the variable alone on one side of the equation.

2. Answers may vary. Sample: Each board is about 11 inches wide, so together they are about 22 inches wide. Since $36 - 22 = 14$, and $13\frac{1}{2}$ is close to 14, the answer is reasonable.

Error Prevention!

If students have difficulty seeing the relationship between the word problem and the diagram, review Activity Lab 5-2a on page 216 with them.

Exercises
Have students work on the Exercises independently. Then review the answers as a class. Choose volunteers to give each answer and explain how they arrived at the solution.

Differentiated Instruction

Below Level   L2
Before beginning the Exercises, have students check the answer to the Example and label their diagrams with the value of w.

Exercises

4. Jack Earle starred in the 1924 movie *Jack & the Beanstalk*. He was 8 feet $6\frac{1}{2}$ inches tall. Trijntje Keever (1616–1633) was possibly the tallest woman ever at 8 feet $4\frac{1}{5}$ inches tall. How much shorter was Keever than Earle? $2\frac{3}{10}$ **inches**

5. A textbook is $1\frac{15}{16}$ inches thick. The front and back covers are each $\frac{1}{8}$ inch thick. How thick is the book without its covers? Use the diagram below to write and solve an equation. $1\frac{11}{16}$ **inches**

$1\frac{15}{16}$ in. $\frac{1}{8}$ in.

6. A standard business envelope is $4\frac{1}{8}$ inches high and 9 inches wide as shown at the right. An $8\frac{1}{2}$ inch-by-11 inch sheet of paper is folded and placed in the envelope. How much wider is the envelope than the paper? $\frac{1}{2}$ **inch**

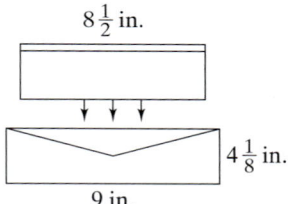

$8\frac{1}{2}$ in.

$4\frac{1}{8}$ in.

9 in.

7. An object needs to be shipped using one of the boxes in the table below. Either box is an appropriate length and width to fit the object. The object is $2\frac{3}{8}$ inches high. Which box would you use? How much extra space would there be?   **the first box;** $\frac{3}{16}$ **inch**

Box Sizes (inches)

Length	Width	Height
$3\frac{3}{4}$	$3\frac{1}{2}$	$2\frac{9}{16}$
$3\frac{5}{8}$	$2\frac{11}{16}$	$2\frac{1}{4}$

8. What is the distance across the inside of the pipe shown at the right? $2\frac{5}{8}$ **inches**

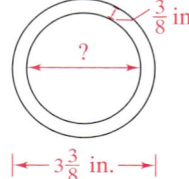

$\frac{3}{8}$ in.

?

$3\frac{3}{8}$ in.

9. An A-10 envelope is 6 inches wide and $9\frac{1}{2}$ inches long. The inside of the envelope is $5\frac{3}{4}$ inches wide and $9\frac{1}{8}$ inches long. What is the difference between an A-10 envelope's outside and inside dimensions? $\frac{1}{4}$ **inch;** $\frac{3}{8}$ **inch**

10. **Writing in Math** Write a word problem that you can solve with the equation $1\frac{1}{2} + 1\frac{1}{2} + d = 10\frac{1}{2}$. Then solve your problem.   **Check students' work;** $7\frac{1}{2}$.

Objective
To add, subtract, and convert between units of time

Examples
1 Adding Units of Time
2 Estimating Elapsed Time
3 Calculating Elapsed Time
4 Reading and Using a Schedule

Math Understandings: p. 210D

Math Background

Elapsed time is the time between two events. To calculate elapsed time, subtract one unit of time from another. Often you need to change from one unit of time to another unit before subtracting. For example, in order to change from years to months, multiply the number of years by 12.

More Math Background: p. 210D

Lesson Planning and Resources

See p. 210E for a list of the resources that support this lesson.

246

✓ **Check Skills You'll Need**

1. Vocabulary Review
Name four different *units of time*.
See below.
Write an equivalent time.

2. 8 hours 2 minutes
482 min
3. 5 days 3 hours
123 hours
4. 3 weeks 5 days
26 days

 **for Help**
Skills Handbook p. 647

Check Skills You'll Need

1. **Answers may vary.**
   Sample: seconds, hours, days, weeks

What You'll Learn
To add, subtract, and convert between units of time

◀)) **New Vocabulary** elapsed time

Why Learn This?

Trains, buses, and airplanes all follow schedules. You can calculate elapsed time to find how long something will last, such as a trip or your school day.

To add units of time, you may need to rewrite some units. You can rewrite 1 minute as 60 seconds, and 1 hour as 60 minutes. You can also rewrite days, weeks, months, and years.

EXAMPLE **Adding Units of Time**

1 An airplane taxis for 12 minutes before taking off. The flight time is 47 minutes. After landing, taxiing to the gate takes 11 minutes. What is the total gate-to-gate time for this flight?

$$12 + 47 + 11 = 70$$

70 minutes = 60 minutes + 10 minutes ← 60 minutes equals one hour.

= 1 hour 10 minutes ← Rewrite your answer using hours and minutes.

The total gate-to-gate time for the flight is 1 hour 10 minutes.

✓ **Quick Check**

1. You study math for 47 minutes and social studies for 39 minutes. What is the total time you spend studying? **1 h 26 min**

The time between two events is called **elapsed time.** To estimate elapsed time, round each time. Then subtract.

Differentiated Instruction **Solutions for All Learners**

Special Needs **L1**
For Example 4, ask students to visualize themselves at a bus stop. Have them notice the schedule. Ask: *How often do buses come?* **Every 30 minutes** Have them look at the schedule to reinforce this.

learning style: visual

Below Level **L2**
Have students say what the time will be 30 minutes later.

10:00 A.M. **10:30 A.M.**
2:07 P.M. **2:37 P.M.**
5:45 A.M. **6:15 A.M.**

learning style: verbal

EXAMPLE Estimating Elapsed Time

2 You begin practice at 1:55 P.M. and end at 5:17 P.M. Estimate the number of hours you practice.

To estimate the elapsed time, round 1:55 and 5:17. Then subtract.

$5:17 \approx 5:00 \quad \rightarrow \quad$ about 5 h after 12:00

$1:55 \approx 2:00 \quad \rightarrow \quad$ about 2 h after 12:00

Since 5:00 is 3 hours past 2:00, the elapsed time is about 3 hours.

✓ Quick Check

2. Estimate the number of hours between 5:25 A.M. and 8:52 A.M.   **4 h**

To find elapsed time, subtract the hours and the minutes. When 12:00 falls between the two times, find the elapsed time between the beginning time and 12:00. Then add the ending time.

EXAMPLE Calculating Elapsed Time

3 **School** How long is a school day that begins at 8:15 A.M. and ends at 3:25 P.M.?

Since 12:00 noon falls between the two times, you first need to find the elapsed time from 8:15 A.M. to noon.

$$12:00 \quad \rightarrow \quad 11 \text{ h } 60 \text{ min} \quad \leftarrow \text{Rename 12:00 as 11 hours 60 minutes.}$$
$$8:15 \quad \rightarrow \quad \underline{- 8 \text{ h } 15 \text{ min}} \quad \leftarrow \text{Subtract the beginning time.}$$
$$3 \text{ h } 45 \text{ min} \quad \leftarrow \text{Subtract.}$$

Then you need to add the ending time to the elapsed time from 8:15 A.M. to noon.

$$3 \text{ h } 45 \text{ min}$$
$$3:25 \quad \rightarrow \quad \underline{+ 3 \text{ h } 25 \text{ min}}$$
$$6 \text{ h } 70 \text{ min}$$

$6 \text{ h } 70 \text{ min} = 7 \text{ h } + 10 \text{ min} \quad \leftarrow \text{Since 70 min is more than 1 h, rename.}$

The school day is 7 h 10 min long.

✓ Quick Check

3. Find the elapsed time from 10:00 A.M. to 7:15 P.M.   **9 h 15 min**

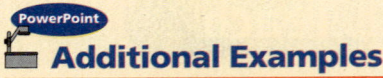
You use elapsed time when reading schedules.

EXAMPLE **Reading and Using a Schedule**

4 **Bus Schedules** You arrive at the Willson Street bus stop 5 minutes after the 11:50 A.M. bus leaves.

a. How long will you wait for the next bus?

The buses run every 30 min. You will wait 30 min − 5 min, or 25 min.

Yellow Bus Line Buses Run Every 30 Minutes Monday–Friday	
Leave Willson St.	Arrive Kagy Blvd.
7:20 A.M.	7:45 A.M.
7:50 A.M.	8:15 A.M.
. . .	. . .
11:20 P.M.	11:45 P.M.

b. How long is the bus ride?

Use the first run, from 7:20 A.M. to 7:45 A.M. Since $45 - 20 = 25$, the elapsed time is 25 min.

c. When will you arrive at Kagy Boulevard?

$11:50 \quad \rightarrow \quad 11\ h\ 50\ min$

$11\ h\ 50\ min + 30\ min = 11\ h\ 80\ min$ ← Find when the next bus leaves.

$\qquad\qquad\qquad\qquad = 12\ h\ 20\ min$ ← Since 80 min is more than 1 h, rename.

The next bus will leave at 12:20 P.M. The trip takes 25 min. Since $20 + 25 = 45$, you will arrive at 12:45 P.M.

✔ Quick Check

4. It is a 50-minute walk from the bus stop on Kagy Boulevard to a gym. You arrive at the bus stop on Willson Street at 5:30 P.M. What time do you get to the gym? **6:20 P.M.**

✔ Check Your Understanding

1. **Vocabulary** The time between two events is called __?__ .
  elapsed time

2. **Reasoning** What is the least possible amount of time that has passed between the times shown on the clocks at the left?
  40 min

3. Draw a clock showing the time 45 minutes after 7:10.
  See margin.

4. Which is equivalent to 205 minutes? **D**
  Ⓐ 2 h 5 min   Ⓑ 2 h 25 min   Ⓒ 3 h 5 min   Ⓓ 3 h 25 min

5. Find 45 min + 30 min + 10 min. **1 h 25 min**

3.

Homework Exercises

For more exercises, see Extra Skills and Word Problems.

GO for Help

For Exercises	See Example
6–9	1
10–13	2
14–17	3
18–20	4

A **Find the total time.**

6. 43 min + 38 min
1 h 21 min

7. 52 min + 25 min
1 h 17 min

8. 58 min + 7 min + 56 min
2 h 1 min

9. 28 min + 49 min + 50 min
2 h 7 min

Estimation Estimate each elapsed time to the nearest hour.

10. from 1:38 A.M. to 4:50 A.M.
3 h

11. from 11:49 A.M. to 7:12 P.M.
7 h

12. from 2:25 P.M. to 3:35 P.M.
2 h

13. from 8:25 A.M. to 10:52 A.M.
3 h

Find the elapsed time for each interval.

14. from 5:25 P.M. to 11:11 P.M.
5 h 46 min

15. from 9:28 A.M. to 11:07 A.M.
1 h 39 min

16. from 11:25 A.M. to 2:45 P.M.
3 h 20 min

17. from 8:30 P.M. to 7:39 A.M.
11 h 9 min

Use the train schedule below for Exercises 18–20.

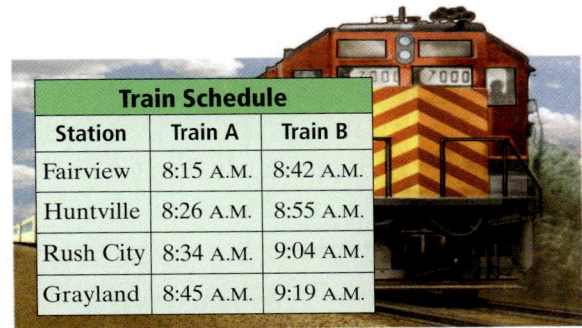

Train Schedule		
Station	**Train A**	**Train B**
Fairview	8:15 A.M.	8:42 A.M.
Huntville	8:26 A.M.	8:55 A.M.
Rush City	8:34 A.M.	9:04 A.M.
Grayland	8:45 A.M.	9:19 A.M.

18. Which train takes less time to go from Fairview to Grayland?
Train A

19. How long do you wait if you get to Rush City at 8:35 A.M.?
29 min

20. How long does Train B take to get to Grayland from Huntville?
24 min

B **GPS** **21.** **Guided Problem Solving** You get home at 1:00 P.M. You make a list of things to do before a party that starts at 4:00 P.M. Make a schedule for your list.
- Which activities must you do in order?
- Can any activities be done at the same time? **See margin.**

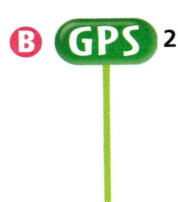

> Decorate room (1 h)
> Mix cake (40 min)
> Bake cake (35 min)
> Cool cake (45 min)
> Frost cake (20 min)
> Shower and dress (25 min)

Online lesson quiz, PHSchool.com, Web Code: aqa-0507

5-7 Measuring Elapsed Time **249**

21. See back of book.

3. Practice

Assignment Guide

Check Your Understanding
Go over Exercises 1–5 in class before assigning the Homework Exercises.

Homework Exercises
A	Practice by Example	6–20
B	Apply Your Skills	21–27
C	Challenge	28
	Test Prep and Mixed Review	29–33

Homework Quick Check
To check students' understanding of key skills and concepts, go over Exercises 8, 16, 25, 26, and 27.

Differentiated Instruction Resources

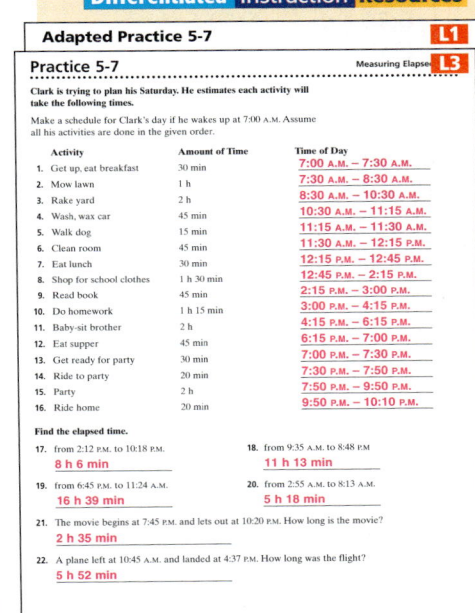

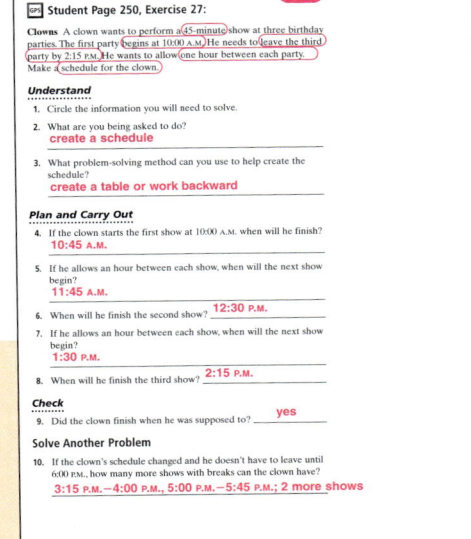

Lesson Quiz

1. David drives 10 minutes to the bus stop and then takes a 40-minute bus ride and a 15-minute subway ride to get to work. How long does it take him to get to work? **1 hour, 5 minutes**

Find the elapsed time.

2. from 8:32 A.M. to 11:30 A.M. **2 h 58 min**

3. from 9:17 A.M. to 7:35 P.M. **10 h 18 min**

Trains Run Every 12 min	
LEAVE K St.	**ARRIVE Q St.**
6:30 A.M.	6:50 A.M.
6:42 A.M.	7:02 A.M.
. . .	. . .

4. How long is the train ride from K St. to Q St.? **20 min**

5. At 8:00 A.M. you arrive at K St. How long is it until the next train to Q St.? **6 min**

GO Online
Homework Video Tutor
Visit: PHSchool.com
Web Code: aqe-0507

26. **Answers may vary. Sample: If it is 1:00 A.M. on a Tuesday in the Eastern time zone, it is 10:00 P.M. on Monday in the Pacific time zone.**

Time Zones The map below shows time zones in the United States. Find the time for each city when it is noon in Denver.

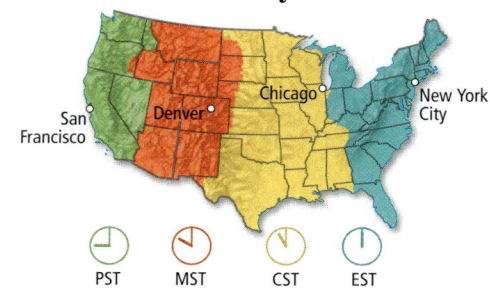

PST MST CST EST

22. Chicago **1:00 P.M.**   23. New York City **2:00 P.M.**   24. San Francisco **11:00 A.M.**

25. (**Algebra**) Write an expression to find the time in New York when the time in San Francisco is x. **$x + 3$**

26. **Writing in Math** It is Monday in one part of the United States and Tuesday in another part. Explain how this is possible. **See left.**

27. **Clowns** A clown wants to perform a 45-minute show at three
GPS birthday parties. The first party begins at 10:00 A.M. He needs to leave the third party by 2:15 P.M. He wants to allow one hour between each party. Make a schedule for the clown. **See margin.**

C 28. **Challenge** Find the elapsed time from Saturday at 7:15 A.M. to Sunday at 3:05 P.M. **31 h 50 min**

Test Prep and Mixed Review — Practice

Multiple Choice

29. Pablo makes a list of things to do before dinner. He leaves school at 3:15. If Pablo eats dinner at 6:00, how many minutes does he have to visit his neighbors? **A**

Ride bike home	20 min
Feed the dog	10 min
Do homework	1 hour
Visit neighbors	▪
Help prepare dinner	35 min

Ⓐ 40 min   Ⓑ 35 min   Ⓒ 30 min   Ⓓ 25 min

30. Miriam made 12.5 cups of soup for her family. After lunch 4.7 cups of soup were left. How many cups of soup did Miriam's family eat for lunch? **J**

Ⓕ 17.2 cups   Ⓖ 16.2 cups   Ⓗ 8.8 cups   Ⓙ 7.8 cups

GO for Help

For Exercises	See Lesson
31–33	3-6

Solve each equation.

31. $23 = d - 16$ **39**

32. $15 = w + 9$ **6**

33. $9.1 - c = 5.3$ **3.8**

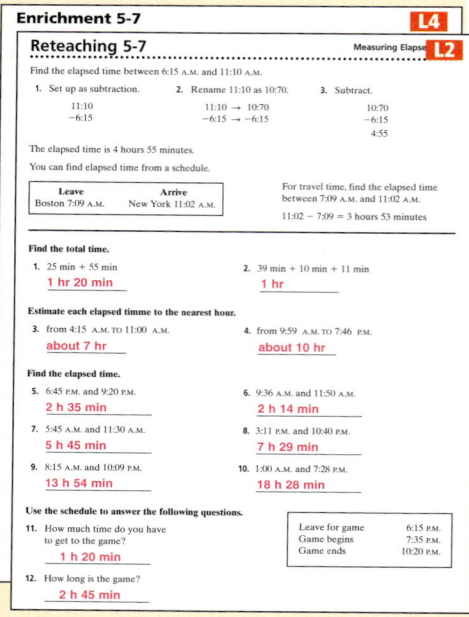

Enrichment 5-7 **L4**

Reteaching 5-7   Measuring Elapse **L2**

Find the elapsed time between 6:15 A.M. and 11:10 A.M.

1. Set up as subtraction.   2. Rename 11:10 as 10:70.   3. Subtract.
   11:10   11:10 → 10:70   10:70
   −6:15   −6:15 → −6:15   −6:15
                                                             4:55

The elapsed time is 4 hours 55 minutes.

You can find elapsed time from a schedule.

Leave	Arrive
Boston 7:09 A.M.	New York 11:02 A.M.

For travel time, find the elapsed time between 7:09 A.M. and 11:02 A.M.

11:02 − 7:09 = 3 hours 53 minutes

Find the total time.

1. 25 min + 55 min   2. 39 min + 10 min + 11 min
   1 hr 20 min   **1 hr**

Estimate each elapsed timme to the nearest hour.

3. from 4:15 A.M. TO 11:00 A.M.   4. from 9:59 A.M. TO 7:46 P.M.
   about 7 hr   **about 10 hr**

Find the elapsed time.

5. 6:45 P.M. and 9:20 P.M.   6. 9:36 A.M. and 11:50 A.M.
   2 h 35 min   **2 h 14 min**

7. 5:45 A.M. and 11:30 A.M.   8. 3:11 P.M. and 10:40 P.M.
   5 h 45 min   **7 h 29 min**

9. 8:15 A.M. and 10:09 P.M.   10. 1:00 A.M. and 7:28 P.M.
   13 h 54 min   **18 h 28 min**

Use the schedule to answer the following questions.

Leave for game	6:15 P.M.
Game begins	7:35 P.M.
Game ends	10:20 P.M.

11. How much time do you have to get to the game? **1 h 20 min**

12. How long is the game? **2 h 45 min**

Test Prep

Resources
For additional practice with a variety of test item formats:
• Test-Taking Strategies, p. 251
• Test Prep, p. 255
• Test-Taking Strategies with Transparencies

Alternative Assessment

Each student in a pair writes a time using A.M. or P.M. Partners designate one time as the starting time and the other as the ending time. They work together to find the elapsed time. Have pairs record their work.

Test-Taking Strategies

Reading for Understanding

Reading comprehension questions are based on a passage that gives facts. Read the directions and questions. Then read the passage. Look for information that helps you answer the questions.

> **Desert Area** Deserts cover about $\frac{1}{5}$ of Earth's land surface. A desert is an area of land where less than 10 inches of precipitation (rain or the equivalent amount of snow) falls per year.
>
> The Sahara is the world's largest desert, covering about $3\frac{1}{2}$ million square miles. The Sahara gets about 8 inches of rain each year.
>
> Antarctica consists largely of desert. It is about 5 million square miles in area. The South Pole lies in the middle of the continent, and gets less than 1 inch of snow each year.

How much larger is Antarctica than the Sahara?

What is the question asking? What is the difference in area between Antarctica and the Sahara?

Identify the information you need. Antarctica is about 5 million square miles in area. The Sahara is about $3\frac{1}{2}$ million square miles in area.

Solve the problem. Find the difference in areas (million square miles).

$$
\begin{array}{c}
5 \\
-3\frac{1}{2} \\
\hline
\end{array}
\quad \rightarrow \quad
\begin{array}{c}
4\frac{2}{2} \\
-3\frac{1}{2} \\
\hline
1\frac{1}{2}
\end{array}
$$

Antarctica is about $1\frac{1}{2}$ million square miles larger than the Sahara.

Exercises

Use the passage above to answer Exercises 1 and 2.

1. In a year, how much more precipitation falls on the Sahara than on the South Pole?   **about 7 in.**

2. Rain forests cover about $\frac{3}{50}$ of Earth's land surface. What fraction of Earth is covered by either desert or rain forest?   **$\frac{13}{50}$**

27.

Activity	Start Time	End Time
1st show	10:00 A.M.	10:45 A.M.
Break	10:45 A.M.	11:45 A.M.
2nd show	11:45 A.M.	12:30 P.M.
Break	12:30 P.M.	1:30 P.M.
3rd show	1:30 P.M.	2:15 P.M.

251

Chapter 5 Review

Go Online PHSchool.com
For: Vocabulary quiz
Web Code: aqj-0551

Vocabulary Review

 benchmark (p. 212)   elapsed time (p. 246)

Choose the vocabulary term that completes each sentence.

1. A(n) __?__ is a value that you use as an estimate for a fraction.
   benchmark
2. The time between two events is called __?__.   **elapsed time**

Skills and Concepts

Lesson 5-1
• To estimate sums
   and differences
   with fractions and
   mixed numbers

A **benchmark** is a whole number or fraction that is easy to use when you estimate. You can use the benchmarks 0, $\frac{1}{2}$, or 1 to estimate sums and differences of fractions. To estimate sums and differences of mixed numbers, round to the nearest whole number.
3–10. Answers may vary. Samples are given.

Estimate each sum or difference. Use the benchmarks 0, $\frac{1}{2}$, and 1.

3. $\frac{8}{9} + \frac{3}{7}$ $1\frac{1}{2}$ 　　4. $\frac{5}{8} - \frac{3}{12}$ 0 　　5. $\frac{4}{5} + \frac{1}{6}$ 1 　　6. $\frac{23}{35} - \frac{4}{7}$ 0

Estimate each sum or difference.

7. $4\frac{1}{7} + 9\frac{7}{14}$ 14 　　　　　　8. $24\frac{11}{16} - 15\frac{1}{4}$ 10

9. $8\frac{5}{6} + 6\frac{3}{8}$ 15 　　　　　　10. $45\frac{33}{35} - 40\frac{2}{7}$ 6

11. You need $1\frac{1}{3}$ cups of lemon juice and $4\frac{3}{4}$ cups of water to make lemonade. Estimate the amount of lemonade you will make.
   about 6 c

Lessons 5-2 and 5-3
• To add and subtract
   fractions with like
   denominators
• To add and subtract
   fractions with unlike
   denominators

To add or subtract fractions, write each fraction using a common denominator. Then add or subtract the numerators.

Find each sum or difference.

12. $\frac{2}{5} + \frac{5}{5}$ $1\frac{2}{5}$ 　13. $\frac{7}{8} - \frac{3}{8}$ $\frac{1}{2}$ 　14. $\frac{3}{20} + \frac{9}{20}$ $\frac{3}{5}$ 　15. $\frac{25}{36} - \frac{5}{36}$ $\frac{5}{9}$

16. $\frac{1}{8} + \frac{3}{4}$ $\frac{7}{8}$ 　17. $\frac{4}{5} - \frac{3}{10}$ $\frac{1}{2}$ 　18. $\frac{17}{24} - \frac{7}{12}$ $\frac{1}{8}$ 　19. $\frac{11}{15} + \frac{1}{2}$ $1\frac{7}{30}$

20. You rode your bicycle $\frac{2}{3}$ mile to school and $\frac{1}{5}$ mile to a friend's house. How far did you ride your bicycle? $\frac{13}{15}$ **mi**

Lesson 5-4

- To add mixed numbers with and without renaming

You can add mixed numbers by first adding the whole numbers and then adding the fraction parts.

Find each sum.

21. $3 + 4\frac{1}{8}$ $7\frac{1}{8}$ 22. $9\frac{8}{9} + 7\frac{4}{9}$ $17\frac{1}{3}$ 23. $35\frac{1}{5} + 28\frac{7}{10}$ $63\frac{9}{10}$

24. Your sister is 10 years old and is $54\frac{1}{3}$ inches tall. Her doctor says she will grow about $2\frac{1}{2}$ inches during the next year and about $2\frac{3}{4}$ inches the year after that. About how tall will your sister be when she is 12 years old?   **about $59\frac{7}{12}$ in.**

Lesson 5-5

- To subtract mixed numbers with and without renaming

You can subtract mixed numbers by first subtracting the whole numbers and then subtracting the fraction parts. Sometimes you need to rename whole numbers or fractions so you can subtract.

Find each difference.

25. $6 - 2\frac{2}{5}$ $3\frac{3}{5}$ 26. $10\frac{7}{8} - 4\frac{1}{2}$ $6\frac{3}{8}$ 27. $25\frac{1}{3} - 8\frac{5}{9}$ $16\frac{7}{9}$

Lesson 5-6

- To solve equations with fractions

You can use mental math or the properties of inverse operations to solve equations involving fractions or mixed numbers.

Solve each equation.

28. $\frac{5}{7} = p + \frac{2}{7}$ $\frac{3}{7}$ 29. $q + \frac{5}{8} = \frac{3}{4}$ $\frac{1}{8}$ 30. $\frac{2}{3} = t - \frac{4}{9}$ $1\frac{1}{9}$

31. $4\frac{2}{3} = x + 1\frac{1}{3}$ $3\frac{1}{3}$ 32. $k - 2\frac{1}{6} = 8\frac{8}{9}$ $11\frac{1}{18}$ 33. $13\frac{3}{5} + h = 20$ $6\frac{2}{5}$

Lesson 5-7

- To add, subtract, and convert between units of time

The time between two events is called **elapsed time.** You may need to rewrite hours and minutes before you can add or subtract time.

Find the elapsed time for each interval.

34. from 8:15 A.M. to 11:56 A.M.   **3 h 41 min**

35. from 9:33 P.M. to 6:21 A.M.   **8 h 48 min**

36. You start doing things on your to-do list at 6:00 P.M. If you take a 25-minute break while doing homework, at what time will you complete your list?
8:10 P.M.

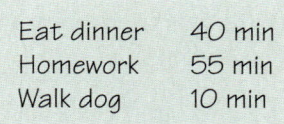

Eat dinner	40 min
Homework	55 min
Walk dog	10 min

Chapter 5   Chapter Review   **253**

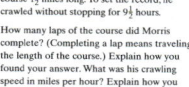

Resources

- ExamView Assessment Suite CD-ROM
  - Ch. 5 Ready-Made Test
  - Make your own Ch. 5 test
- MindPoint Quiz Show CD-ROM
  - Chapter 5 Review

Differentiated Instruction

All in One Teaching Resources
- Below Level Chapter 5 Test L2
- Chapter 5 Test L3
- Chapter 5 Alternative Assessment L4

Spanish Assessment Resources ELL
- Below Level Chapter 5 Test L2
- Chapter 5 Test L3
- Chapter 5 Alternative Assessment L4

ExamView Assessment Suite CD-ROM
- Special Needs Test L1
- Special Needs Practice Bank L1

Online Ch. 5 Test at www.PHSchool.com L3

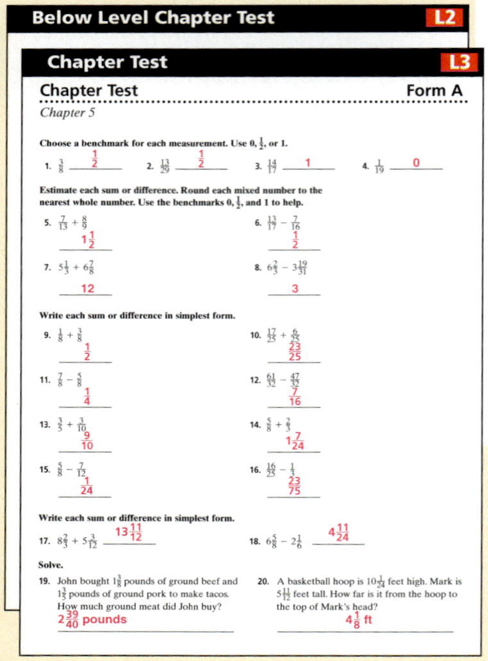
Below Level Chapter Test L2

Chapter Test L3

Chapter Test Form A

Chapter 5

Choose a benchmark for each measurement. Use 0, $\frac{1}{2}$, or 1.

1. $\frac{3}{8}$ $\frac{1}{2}$ 2. $\frac{13}{29}$ $\frac{1}{2}$ 3. $\frac{14}{17}$ 1 4. $\frac{1}{19}$ 0

Estimate each sum or difference. Round each mixed number to the nearest whole number. Use the benchmarks 0, $\frac{1}{2}$, and 1 to help.

5. $\frac{7}{13} + \frac{8}{9}$ $1\frac{1}{2}$
6. $\frac{13}{17} - \frac{7}{16}$ $\frac{1}{2}$
7. $5\frac{1}{3} + 6\frac{7}{8}$ 12
8. $6\frac{2}{3} - 3\frac{19}{31}$ 3

Write each sum or difference in simplest form.

9. $\frac{1}{8} + \frac{3}{8}$ $\frac{1}{2}$
10. $\frac{17}{25} + \frac{6}{25}$ $\frac{23}{25}$
11. $\frac{7}{8} - \frac{5}{8}$ $\frac{1}{4}$
12. $\frac{61}{32} - \frac{47}{32}$ $\frac{7}{16}$
13. $\frac{3}{5} + \frac{3}{10}$ $\frac{9}{10}$
14. $\frac{5}{8} + \frac{2}{3}$ $1\frac{7}{24}$
15. $\frac{5}{8} - \frac{7}{12}$ $\frac{1}{24}$
16. $\frac{16}{25} - \frac{1}{3}$ $\frac{23}{75}$

Write each sum or difference in simplest form.

17. $8\frac{2}{3} + 5\frac{3}{12}$ $13\frac{11}{12}$
18. $6\frac{5}{8} - 2\frac{1}{6}$ $4\frac{11}{24}$

Solve.

19. John bought $1\frac{3}{8}$ pounds of ground beef and $1\frac{3}{5}$ pounds of ground pork to make tacos. How much ground meat did John buy? $2\frac{39}{40}$ pounds
20. A basketball hoop is $10\frac{1}{24}$ feet high. Mark is $5\frac{11}{12}$ feet tall. How far is it from the hoop to the top of Mark's head? $4\frac{1}{8}$ ft

Chapter 5 Test

Go Online PHSchool.com For: Online chapter test Web Code: aqa-0552

Estimate each sum or difference. Use the benchmarks 0, $\frac{1}{2}$, or 1.

1. $\frac{18}{35} + \frac{14}{16}$ $1\frac{1}{2}$
2. $\frac{7}{50} + \frac{9}{16}$ $\frac{1}{2}$
3. $\frac{9}{10} + \frac{2}{26}$ 1
4. How much did Sophia's hair grow during the month of May? $\frac{3}{16}$ in.

Sophia's Hair Length

May 1	$8\frac{1}{8}$ in.
May 31	$8\frac{5}{16}$ in.

Estimate each sum or difference.

5. $6\frac{5}{6} + 2\frac{1}{9}$ 9
6. $11\frac{6}{7} - 3\frac{7}{9}$ 8
7. $10\frac{5}{12} - 5\frac{1}{8}$ 5
8. **Lumber** You need $\frac{3}{8}$ foot of lumber to fix a fence and $\frac{3}{4}$ foot of lumber to fix a shed. How much lumber do you need? about $1\frac{1}{2}$ ft

Find each sum or difference.

9. $\frac{4}{5} + \frac{2}{5}$ $1\frac{1}{5}$
10. $\frac{11}{13} - \frac{7}{13}$ $\frac{4}{13}$
11. $\frac{4}{7} + \frac{6}{7}$ $1\frac{3}{7}$
12. $1\frac{13}{15} - \frac{2}{3}$ $1\frac{1}{5}$
13. $\frac{9}{20} + \frac{4}{5}$ $1\frac{1}{4}$
14. $\frac{3}{4} - \frac{3}{8}$ $\frac{3}{8}$
15. $3\frac{3}{4} - 2\frac{8}{10}$ $\frac{19}{20}$
16. $8\frac{1}{5} + 4\frac{1}{6}$ $12\frac{11}{30}$

Find each sum.

17. $\frac{1}{7} + \frac{2}{7} + \frac{5}{7}$ $1\frac{1}{7}$
18. $\frac{4}{12} + \frac{2}{12} + \frac{5}{12}$ $\frac{11}{12}$
19. Dan ran $\frac{5}{6}$ mile. Sol ran $\frac{7}{8}$ mile.
    a. How much farther than Dan did Sol run? $\frac{1}{24}$ mi
    b. What was their combined distance? $1\frac{17}{24}$ mi
20. **Writing in Math** Explain how you could mentally solve the equation $x - 7\frac{4}{5} = 3\frac{1}{10}$. See margin.

Solve each equation.

21. $\frac{6}{9} = \frac{1}{3} + g$ $\frac{1}{3}$
22. $y - \frac{4}{5} = \frac{11}{20}$ $1\frac{7}{20}$
23. $4\frac{3}{4} + v = 17\frac{1}{8}$ $12\frac{3}{8}$
24. $13\frac{2}{3} = k - 10\frac{7}{9}$ $24\frac{4}{9}$

Use the table for Exercises 25–27.

Spruce Tree	Length of Cone (inches)
White	$1\frac{5}{8}$
Norway	$5\frac{1}{2}$
Black	$\frac{7}{8}$
Red	$1\frac{1}{4}$

25. Find the difference in length between the shortest and longest cones. $4\frac{5}{8}$ in.
26. Which two cones differ in length by about $\frac{1}{2}$ inch? Answers may vary. Sample: white and red
27. What is the difference in length between the red spruce and white spruce tree cones? $\frac{3}{8}$ in.

How many minutes are in each amount of time?

28. 5 h 47 min 347 min
29. 23 h 8 min 1,388 min
30. Find the elapsed time between 6:33 A.M. and 7:20 P.M. 12 h 47 min

20. Answers may vary. Sample: I'd rewrite $7\frac{4}{5}$ as $7\frac{8}{10}$ and then add $3\frac{1}{10}$ to get $10\frac{9}{10}$.

Multiple Choice

Read each question. Then write the letter of the correct answer on your paper.

1. On Venus the length of a day is 243.01 Earth days. On Mercury the length of a day is 58.65 Earth days. How much longer, in Earth days, is a Venus day than a Mercury day? **D**
   - Ⓐ 301.66
   - Ⓒ 195.46
   - Ⓑ 215.64
   - Ⓓ 184.36

2. Suppose you buy a shirt for x dollars with a twenty-dollar bill. The cashier gives you $5.35 back. Which equation can you use to find the cost of the shirt? **G**
   - Ⓕ $5.35x = 20$
   - Ⓗ $x \div 20 = 5.35$
   - Ⓖ $x + 5.35 = 20$
   - Ⓙ $5.35 - x = 20$

3. How much thicker is a quarter than a dime? **C**

 $\updownarrow 1\frac{3}{4}$ mm

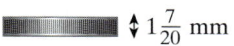 $\updownarrow 1\frac{7}{20}$ mm

   - Ⓐ $\frac{1}{20}$ mm
   - Ⓒ $\frac{2}{5}$ mm
   - Ⓑ $\frac{1}{4}$ mm
   - Ⓓ $\frac{1}{2}$ mm

4. Which equation is NOT an example of the Distributive Property? **J**
   - Ⓕ $12(6.2) + 12(3.8) = 12(6.2 + 3.8)$
   - Ⓖ $0.75(8.8) + 0.25(8.8) = 1(8.8)$
   - Ⓗ $19.1(80) = 19.1(100) - 19.1(20)$
   - Ⓙ $8.1 + 3.5 = 3.5 + 8.1$

5. Which set of numbers has a GCF of 3? **C**
   - Ⓐ 15, 30, 45
   - Ⓒ 24, 36, 9
   - Ⓑ 6, 30, 24
   - Ⓓ 36, 27, 18

6. What is the best estimate for the sum of $12\frac{13}{16}$ and $23\frac{3}{8}$? **H**
   - Ⓕ 30
   - Ⓖ 35
   - Ⓗ 36
   - Ⓙ 37

7. A store sells window glass that is $\frac{7}{32}$ inch, $\frac{3}{16}$ inch, $\frac{5}{16}$ inch, and $\frac{1}{8}$ inch thick. You need glass that is at least $\frac{1}{4}$ inch thick. Which thickness, in inches, should you buy? **C**
   - Ⓐ $\frac{1}{8}$
   - Ⓑ $\frac{3}{16}$
   - Ⓒ $\frac{5}{16}$
   - Ⓓ $\frac{7}{32}$

8. What is the sum of $6\frac{3}{5}$ and $2\frac{4}{5}$? **H**
   - Ⓕ $8\frac{1}{5}$
   - Ⓖ $8\frac{12}{25}$
   - Ⓗ $9\frac{2}{5}$
   - Ⓙ $9\frac{4}{5}$

Gridded Response

Record your answer in a grid.

9. Kerry boards the school bus at 7:48 A.M. and arrives at school at 8:13 A.M. How many minutes does he spend on the bus? **25**

10. What is the solution of $x + \frac{3}{16} = \frac{3}{4}$? Write your answer in simplest form. $\frac{9}{16}$

Short Response

11. What is the least common multiple of 36 and 45? Choose a method of either listing multiples or using prime factorizations. Show the steps you use to find this LCM. **11–12. See margin.**

12. From his home, a jogger runs 1 mile west, $3\frac{1}{2}$ miles north, 1 mile east, and $1\frac{1}{4}$ miles south. How far from home is he? Draw a diagram to help solve the problem. Then solve the problem.

Extended Response

13. At a book fair, a paperback sells for $.35 and a hardcover sells for $1.30. Your friend spends $6.00 on books. She buys three more paperbacks than hardcovers.
   a. Write a list of possibilities for the number of books. **a–b. See margin.**
   b. How many paperbacks does your friend buy?

Item	1	2	3	4	5	6	7	8	9	10	11	12	13
Lesson	1-7	3-5	5-5	3-8	4-4	5-1	4-8	5-4	5-7	5-6	4-7	5-4	Problem Solving Handbook

11. **[2] Methods may vary.**
   $36 = 2^2 \times 3^2$
   $45 = 3^2 \times 5$
   $LCM = 2^2 \times 3^2 \times 5 = 180$

   [1] incorrect LCM OR incorrect method

12. **[2] Drawings may vary.**
   $3\frac{1}{2} - 1\frac{1}{4} = 2\frac{1}{4}$

   [1] incorrect distance OR method

Resources

Test Prep Workbook

All in One Teaching Resources
- Cumulative Review   **L3**

ExamView Assessment Suite CD-ROM
- Standardized Test Practice

Differentiated Instruction

Spanish Assessment Resources
- Spanish Cumulative Review **ELL**

ExamView Assessment Suite CD-ROM
- Special Needs Practice Bank **L1**

13. **[4] a. 1 h, 4 p; 2 h, 5 p; 3 h, 6 p; 4 h, 7 p; . . .**

   b. 3 h, 6 p: 3 × 1.30 + 6 × 0.35 = 6

   [3] appropriate methods, one computational error

   [2] list combinations OR work shown

   [1] correct combination, without work

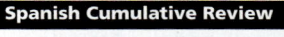

Problem Solving

Applying Mixed Numbers

Students will use data from these two pages to answer the questions posed in the Activity.

Tell students that winning Olympic times in races have been getting faster over the years. Have students find and compare winning times for several races over a number of years. Have students or small groups study different races. Ask:
- *What is one way to display the data that compares the changes in winning times over the years?* **a double line graph could compare the changes of two different years**
- *Have men's or women's times been improving at faster rates?* **Check students' work**

Activating Prior Knowledge

Have students share any experiences they have had watching any of the races described on these pages. Ask them to discuss what the events have in common and how they differ.

Guided Instruction

Have students read aloud about Marion Jones, the Iditarod, Catherine Raney, and the Tour de France. Ask:
- *How could you find the average speed that Raney skated in the 2002 Olympics?* **Sample: Divide the distance Raney skates by her time. Convert distance and time into miles and hours.**
- *About how many miles would you estimate a musher and his or her sled travels per day during the Iditarod?* **about $104\frac{9}{10}$ miles a day**

Applying Mixed Numbers

Fast Fractions People love to race. Some races, like the Iditarod, the Tour de France, and the Paris–Dakar Rally, last days or even weeks. Other races can be over in a flash. The fastest runners can finish a 100-meter race in 10 or 11 seconds.

The Iditarod
The Iditarod is a dog sled race over at least 1,049 miles in Alaska. The fastest sled drivers, or mushers, finish in about 10 days.

Marion Jones
Marion Jones won three gold medals and two bronze medals at the 2000 Olympic Summer Games in Sydney, Australia.

Put It All Together

What You'll Need
- 3 number cubes

How to Play
- Work in a group. The goal of the game is to "run" each of four quarter-mile sections of a one-mile track.
- Roll three number cubes. Write a mixed number that includes a proper fraction. If all three numbers are the same, roll again.
- Take turns until each group member has times in minutes for each quarter-mile section of the track.
- If you roll the same three numbers more than once, you must make a different mixed number with them each time. If that is not possible, roll again.

1. Order your times from least to greatest.
2. **a. Estimation** Estimate the total time for each group member. Who do you think has the fastest time? Explain.
   b. Find your total time. Write your answer in simplest form.
   c. Compare your total to the totals for the others in your group. Who won the race?
3. **Number Sense** The record time for "running" this track is 4.95 minutes. Is it possible to beat this time? Explain.
4. **Data File** Pick one of the animals from page 650. How long would it take the animal to "run" the track? Who runs faster, you or the animal? Explain.

256

1. **Check students' work.**

2. **Check students' work.**

3. **No; your fastest possible time is $1\frac{1}{6} + 1\frac{1}{5} + 1\frac{1}{4} + 1\frac{1}{3}$, which is $4\frac{19}{20}$, or 4.95 min.**

4. **Answers may vary. Sample: A black mamba snake can cover the distance in 3 min. The snake moves faster, because you would take at least 4.95 min.**

Go Online
PHSchool.com

For: Information about racing
Web Code: aqe-0553

Speed Skater
Catherine Raney of the 2002 U.S. Olympic team skated between 20 and 25 miles per hour during the women's 5,000-meter final.

Tour de France
The Tour de France bicycle race lasts about three weeks and covers about 2,000 miles.

257

Activity

Have students work in groups to play the game and then answer the questions.

Teaching Tip
Invite students to formulate and try out their own new versions of the game. Invite them to share their adjustments with other groups. Possibilities include:
- Have students compete for the greatest total.
- Have players wait until they have four sets of three digits before forming the mixed numbers. Have them form mixed numbers to make the *least* total. Ask students to explain how this change affects the strategy they use to win.

Differentiated Instruction

Special Needs L1
Help students understand the rules of the game. Review the meanings of a *mixed number* and an *improper fraction*. Also review how to compare and order fractions and mixed numbers.

Chapter at a Glance

Lesson Titles, Objectives, and Features	Assessment	NCTM Standards	Local Standards
6-1a Activity Lab, Hands On: Modeling Fraction Multiplication **6-1 Multiplying Fractions** • To multiply fractions and to solve problems by multiplying fractions **6-1b Activity Lab, Algebra Thinking:** Understanding Equality	Lesson Quiz	1, 2, 6, 7, 8, 9, 10	
6-2 Multiplying Mixed Numbers • To estimate and find the products of mixed numbers	Lesson Quiz	1, 2, 4, 6, 7, 8, 9, 10	
6-3a Activity Lab, Hands On: Fraction Division **6-3 Dividing Fractions** • To divide fractions and to solve problems by dividing fractions	Lesson Quiz	1, 2, 6, 7, 8, 9, 10	
6-4 Dividing Mixed Numbers • To estimate and compute the quotient of mixed numbers **6-4b Activity Lab, Technology:** Using a Calculator for Fractions	Lesson Quiz Checkpoint Quiz 1	1, 2, 4, 6, 7, 8, 9, 10	
6-5 Solving Fraction Equations by Multiplying • To write fraction equations and solve them by multiplying **Guided Problem Solving:** Practice Solving Problems	Lesson Quiz	1, 2, 4, 6, 7, 8, 9, 10	
6-6 The Customary System • To choose appropriate units and to estimate in the customary system	Lesson Quiz	1, 2, 3, 4, 6, 7, 8, 9, 10	
6-7 Changing Units in the Customary System • To convert between units in the customary system **6-7b Activity Lab, Hands On:** Measuring Objects	Lesson Quiz Checkpoint Quiz 2	1, 2, 3, 4, 6, 7, 8, 9, 10	
Problem Solving Application: Applying Mixed Numbers			

NCTM Standards 2000
1 Number and Operations   2 Algebra   3 Geometry   4 Measurement   5 Data Analysis and Probability
6 Problem Solving   7 Reasoning and Proof   8 Communication   9 Connections   10 Representation

Correlations to Standardized Tests

All content for these tests is contained in *Prentice Hall Math,* Course 1. This chart reflects coverage in this chapter only.

	6-1	6-2	6-3	6-4	6-5	6-6	6-7
Terra Nova CAT6 (Level 16)							
Number and Number Relations	✔	✔	✔	✔	✔	✔	✔
Computation and Numerical Estimation	✔	✔	✔	✔	✔	✔	✔
Operation Concepts	✔	✔	✔	✔	✔	✔	✔
Measurement		✔		✔	✔	✔	✔
Geometry and Spatial Sense						✔	✔
Data Analysis, Statistics, and Probability							
Patterns, Functions, Algebra	✔	✔	✔	✔	✔	✔	✔
Problem Solving and Reasoning	✔	✔	✔	✔	✔	✔	✔
Communication	✔	✔	✔	✔	✔	✔	✔
Decimals, Fractions, Intergers, and Percent	✔	✔	✔	✔	✔	✔	✔
Order of Operations							
Terra Nova CTBS (Level 16)							
Whole Numbers, Decimals, Fractions	✔	✔	✔	✔	✔	✔	✔
Numeration, Number Theory	✔	✔	✔	✔	✔	✔	✔
Data Interpretation							
Pre-algebra	✔	✔	✔	✔	✔	✔	✔
Measurement		✔		✔	✔	✔	✔
Geometry						✔	✔
ITBS (Level 12)							
Number Properties and Operations	✔	✔	✔	✔	✔	✔	✔
Algebra	✔	✔	✔	✔	✔	✔	✔
Geometry						✔	✔
Measurement		✔		✔	✔	✔	✔
Probability and Statistics							
Estimation		✔		✔			
SAT10 (Int 2 Level)							
Number Sense and Operations	✔	✔	✔	✔	✔	✔	✔
Patterns, Relationships, and Algebra	✔	✔	✔	✔	✔	✔	✔
Data, Statistics, and Probability							
Geometry and Measurement		✔		✔	✔	✔	✔
NAEP							
Number Sense, Properties, and Operations	✔	✔	✔	✔			
Measurement						✔	✔
Geometry and Spatial Sense							
Data Analysis, Statistics, and Probability							
Algebra and Functions					✔		

CAT6 California Achievement Test, 6th Ed.   **CTBS** Comprehensive Test of Basic Skills   **ITBS** Iowa Test of Basic Skills, Form M
SAT10 Stanford Achievement Test, 10th Ed.   **NAEP** National Assessment of Educational Progress 2005 Mathematics Objectives

Math Background

Skills Trace

> ### BEFORE Chapter 6
> Grade 5 presented multiplication and division of fractions.
>
> ### DURING Chapter 6
> Course 1 reviews and extends multiplying and dividing fractions to mixed numbers and the solving of equations with fractions.
>
> ### AFTER Chapter 6
> Throughout this course, students multiply and divide fractions to solve real-world problems.

6-1 Multiplying Fractions

Math Understandings
- Finding half of a number is the same as multiplying that number by $\frac{1}{2}$ and as dividing that number by 2.
- The product of two fractions, each less than one, is less than either factor.

You can find the product of two fractions by multiplying the numerators and multiplying the denominators.

Multiplying Fractions	
Arithmetic	Algebra
$\frac{3}{4} \times \frac{1}{2} = \frac{3 \times 1}{4 \times 2} = \frac{3}{8}$	$\frac{a}{b} \times \frac{c}{d} = \frac{ac}{bd}$
	where b and $d \neq 0$.

Sometimes you can simplify before multiplying fractions by dividing out factors common to both numerator and denominator. To multiply a fraction by a whole number, write the whole number as a fraction with a denominator of 1. Then multiply the two fractions.

Example: Find $\frac{5}{6} \times 12$.

$$\frac{5}{6} \times 12 = \frac{5}{\cancel{6}_1} \times \frac{\cancel{12}^2}{1} = \frac{10}{1} = 10$$

6-2 Multiplying Mixed Numbers

Math Understandings
- Multiplying fractions and mixed numbers does not necessarily give a product less than both factors.

To find the product of mixed numbers, write each mixed number as an improper fraction before multiplying.

Example: Find $2\frac{2}{3} \times 3\frac{1}{4}$.

$$2\frac{2}{3} \times 3\frac{1}{4} = \frac{\cancel{8}^2}{3} \times \frac{13}{\cancel{4}_1} = \frac{2 \times 13}{3 \times 1} = \frac{26}{3}, \text{ or } 8\frac{2}{3}$$

6-3 Dividing Fractions
6-4 Dividing Mixed Numbers

Math Understandings
- You can rewrite dividing by a number as multiplying by the reciprocal of that number.
- Two numbers are reciprocals if their product is 1.

The numbers $\frac{2}{3}$ and $\frac{3}{2}$ are **reciprocals**. Notice that the numerators and denominators are switched in fractions that are reciprocals. To divide by a fraction, multiply by the reciprocal of the fraction. You can remember this by thinking "invert and multiply."

Dividing Fractions	
Arithmetic	Algebra
$\frac{5}{8} \div \frac{1}{8} = \frac{5 \times 8}{8 \times 1} = \frac{5}{1}$	$\frac{a}{b} \div \frac{c}{d} = \frac{a}{b} \times \frac{d}{c}$
	where b, c, and $d \neq 0$.

To divide a fraction by a whole number, first write the whole number as an improper fraction with a denominator of 1. You can divide a mixed number by a whole number or another mixed number. Start by writing the numbers as improper fractions.

Example: Find $2\frac{1}{4} \div 3$.

$$2\frac{1}{4} \div 3 = \frac{9}{4} \div \frac{3}{1} = \frac{\cancel{9}^3}{4} \times \frac{1}{\cancel{3}_1} = \frac{3}{4}$$

6-5 Solving Fraction Equations by Multiplying

Math Understandings

- You can use the Multiplication Property of Equality to multiply each side of an equation by the same number to write an equivalent simpler equation.

Multiplication and division are inverse operations that undo each other.

6-6 The Customary System

Math Understandings

- Unlike the metric system, the customary system does not use a base unit and prefixes.

Common customary units of measure with abbreviations follow.

Length	Weight	Capacity
inch (in.)	ounce (oz)	fluid ounce (fl oz)
foot (ft)	pound (lb)	cup (c)
yard (yd)	ton (t)	pint (pt)
mile (mi)		quart (qt)
		gallon (gal)

Example: Choose an appropriate customary unit of measure for each situation.

- weight of a bicycle — pounds
- length of a shoe — inches
- capacity of a bathtub — gallons

6-7 Changing Units in the Customary System

Math Understandings

- To change between customary units, use multiplication or division of equivalent measures.

You can convert between different customary units by using equivalent measures.

Length	Weight	Capacity
12 in. = 1 ft	16 oz = 1 lb	8 fl oz = 1 cup
36 in. = 1 yd	2,000 lb = 1 t	2 cups = 1 pt
3 ft = 1 yd		4 cups = 1 qt
5,280 ft = 1 mi		2 pt = 1 qt
		4 qt = 1 gal

The following rules can help you convert from one unit to another.

Start with	Convert	Get
Many small units $\longrightarrow$	Divide $\longrightarrow$	A few large units
A few large units $\longrightarrow$	Multiply $\longrightarrow$	Many small units

Example: Find the number of gallons in 13 quarts.

$$13 \text{ qt} = (13 \div 4) \text{ gal} \rightarrow 3\tfrac{1}{4} \text{ gal}$$

Chapter 6 Resources

Print Resources

	6-1	6-2	6-3	6-4	6-5	6-6	6-7	For the Chapter
L3 Practice	●	●	●	●	●	●	●	
L1 Adapted Practice	●	●	●	●	●	●	●	
L3 Guided Problem Solving	●	●	●	●	●	●	●	
L2 Reteaching	●	●	●	●	●	●	●	
L4 Enrichment	●	●	●	●	●	●	●	
L3 Daily Notetaking Guide	●	●	●	●	●	●	●	
L1 Adapted Daily Notetaking Guide	●	●		●	●	●		
L3 Vocabulary and Study Skills Worksheets	●		●	●		●		●
L3 Daily Puzzles	●	●	●	●	●	●		
L3 Activity Labs	●	●	●	●	●	●		
L3 Checkpoint Quiz				●			●	
L3 Chapter Project								●
L2 Below Level Chapter Test								●
L3 Chapter Test								●
L4 Alternative Assessment								●
L3 Cumulative Review								●

Spanish Resources ELL

	6-1	6-2	6-3	6-4	6-5	6-6	6-7	For the Chapter
L3 Practice	●	●	●	●	●	●	●	
L3 Vocabulary and Study Skills Worksheets	●		●	●		●	●	●
L3 Checkpoint Quiz				●			●	
L2 Below Level Chapter Test								●
L3 Chapter Test								●
L4 Alternative Assessment								●
L3 Cumulative Review								●

Transparencies

	6-1	6-2	6-3	6-4	6-5	6-6	6-7	For the Chapter
Check Skills You'll Need	●	●	●	●	●	●	●	
Additional Examples	●	●	●	●	●	●	●	
Problem of the Day	●	●	●	●	●	●	●	
Classroom Aid				●				
Student Edition Answers	●	●	●	●		●	●	●
Lesson Quiz	●	●	●	●	●	●	●	
Test-Taking Strategies								●

Technology

	6-1	6-2	6-3	6-4	6-5	6-6	6-7	For the Chapter
Interactive Textbook Online	●	●	●	●	●	●	●	●
StudentExpress™ CD-ROM	●	●	●	●	●	●	●	●
Success Tracker™ Online Intervention	●	●	●	●	●	●	●	●
TeacherExpress™ CD-ROM	●	●	●	●	●	●	●	●
PresentationExpress™ with QuickTake Presenter CD-ROM	●	●	●	●	●	●	●	●
ExamView® Assessment Suite CD-ROM	●	●	●	●	●	●	●	●
MindPoint® Quiz Show CD-ROM								●
Prentice Hall Web Site: PHSchool.com	●	●	●	●	●	●	●	●

Also available: **Prentice Hall Assessment System**
- Progress Monitoring Assessments
- Skills and Concepts Review
- Test Prep Workbook

Other Resources
Algebra Readiness Tests
All-in-One Student Workbook
All-in-One Student Workbook, Adapted Version
Multilingual Handbook

Solution Key
Math Notes Study Folder
Spanish Cumulative Assessment

Where You Can Use the Lesson Resources

Here is a suggestion, following the four-step teaching plan, for how you can incorporate Differentiated Instruction Resources into your teaching.

	Instructional Resources **L3**	Differentiated Instruction Resources
1. Plan		
Preparation Read the Math Background in the Teacher's Edition to connect this lesson with students' previous experience. **Starting Class** **Check Skills You'll Need** Assign these exercises to review prerequisite skills. **New Vocabulary** Help students pre-read the lesson by pointing out the new terms introduced in the lesson.	**Math Background** **Math Understandings** **Transparencies & PresentationExpress™ with QuickTake Presenter CD-ROM** Check Skills You'll Need Problem of the Day **Resources** Vocabulary and Study Skills	**Spanish Support** **ELL** Vocabulary and Study Skills
2. Teach		
L3 Guided Instruction Use the Activity Labs to build conceptual understanding. Teach each Example. Use the Teacher's Edition side column notes for specific teaching tips, including Error Prevention notes. Use the Additional Examples found in the side column (and on transparency and PowerPoint) as an alternative presentation for the content. After each Example, assign the Quick Check exercise for that Example to get an immediate assessment of student understanding. Use the Closure activity in the Teacher's Edition to help students attain mastery of lesson content.	**Student Edition** Activity Lab **Resources** Daily Notetaking Guide Activity Lab **Transparencies & PresentationExpress™ with QuickTake Presenter CD-ROM** Additional Examples Classroom Aids **ExamView® Assessment Suite CD-ROM**	**Teacher's Edition** Every lesson includes suggestions for working with students who need special attention. **L1** Special Needs **L2** Below Level **L4** Advanced Learners **ELL** English Language Learners **Resources** **L1** Adapted Daily Notetaking Guide **Multilingual Handbook**
3. Practice		
Assignment Guide **Check Your Understanding** Use these questions to check students' understanding before you assign homework. **Homework Exercises** Assign homework from these leveled exercises in the Assignment Guide. 　A Practice by Example 　B Apply Your Skills 　C Challenge 　Test Prep and Mixed Review **Homework Quick Check** Use these key exercises to quickly check students' homework.	**Transparencies & PresentationExpress™ with QuickTake Presenter CD-ROM** Student Answers **Resources** Practice Guided Problem Solving Vocabulary and Study Skills Activity Lab Daily Puzzles **ExamView® Assessment Suite CD-ROM**	**Spanish Support** **ELL** Practice **ELL** Vocabulary and Study Skills **Resources** **L1** Adapted Practice **L4** Enrichment
4. Assess & Reteach		
Lesson Quiz Assign the Lesson Quiz to assess students' mastery of the lesson content. **Checkpoint Quiz** Use the Checkpoint Quiz to assess student progress over several lessons.	**Transparencies & PresentationExpress™ with QuickTake Presenter CD-ROM** Lesson Quiz **Resources** Checkpoint Quiz	**Resources** **L2** Reteaching **ELL** Checkpoint Quiz Success Tracker™ Online Intervention **ExamView® Assessment Suite CD-ROM**

KEY   **L1** Special Needs   **L2** Below Level   **L3** For All Students   **L4** Advanced, Gifted   **ELL** English Language Learners

258F

CHAPTER 6 **Multiplying and Dividing Fractions**

Multiplying and Dividing Fractions

What You've Learned

- In Chapter 1, you multiplied and divided decimals and solved problems using multiplication and division.
- In Chapter 4, you simplified and compared fractions. You also learned to express fractions as decimals.
- In Chapter 5, you added and subtracted fractions and mixed numbers.

Check Your Readiness

GO for Help	
For Exercises	**See Lesson**
1–6	3-7
7–12	4-4
13–18	4-5

Solving Equations

Solve each equation.

1. $3a = 12$ **4**
2. $5x = 25$ **5**
3. $p \div 3 = 4$ **12**
4. $14 = x \div 8$ **112**
5. $0.1n = 10$ **100**
6. $2 = g \div 0.3$ **0.6**

Finding the Greatest Common Factor

Find the GCF of each pair of numbers.

7. $12, 24$ **12**
8. $28, 35$ **7**
9. $27, 24$ **3**
10. $80, 100$ **20**
11. $36, 66$ **6**
12. $21, 42$ **21**

Writing Equivalent Fractions

Write each fraction in simplest form.

13. $\frac{15}{35}$ **$\frac{3}{7}$**
14. $\frac{24}{36}$ **$\frac{2}{3}$**
15. $\frac{16}{48}$ **$\frac{1}{3}$**
16. $\frac{24}{64}$ **$\frac{3}{8}$**
17. $\frac{18}{72}$ **$\frac{1}{4}$**
18. $\frac{21}{49}$ **$\frac{3}{7}$**

In this chapter, students continue their study of fractions as they multiply and divide fractions and mixed numbers, and write and solve equations involving multiplication and division of fractions. In addition, students use their knowledge of fraction computation to change units within the customary system of measurement.

Activating Prior Knowledge

In this chapter, students build on and extend their knowledge of fraction computation to multiply and divide fractions. They also draw upon their understanding of common multiples and factors, and of mental math strategies. Ask questions such as:

- *Write $\frac{20}{6}$ as a mixed number in simplest form.* **$3\frac{1}{3}$**
- *What is n in* 3n $= 42$. **$n = 14$**
- *What is the LCM of 4 and 18?* **36**
- *What is the LCM of 12 and 30?* **60**

What You'll Learn Next

- In this chapter you will multiply and divide fractions and mixed numbers.

- You will use multiplication and division to solve problems involving fractions and mixed numbers.

- You will use fractions to change units of measure in the customary system.

◀))) **Key Vocabulary**

- reciprocal (p. 272)

 Problem Solving Application On pages 302 and 303, you will work an extended activity involving carpentry.

Chapter 6   **259**

Modeling Fraction Multiplication

Students use paper models to study multiplication of fractions. The visual representation will help them understand multiplying parts of a whole.

Guided Instruction

Before beginning the Activity Lab, review with students the names of fractions (halves, fourths, eighths). Make sure they understand that the denominator represents the number of parts a whole has been divided into. Then, ask:

- *After you make the third fold, how many sections is the paper divided into?* **eight**
- *If you folded the paper twice lengthwise, what fraction would we divide the paper into?* **thirds**

Exercises

Have students work independently on the Exercises. When they have finished, review the answers as a class and discuss any differences students might have and how to reconcile them.

Alternative Method

Some students may have a better understanding of how the paper is divided if they cut it into sections and shade each piece individually. Provide scissors for these students.

Resources

- Activity Lab 6-1: Multiplying Fractions
- paper
- scissors
- Student Manipulatives Kit

6-1a **Activity Lab** **Hands On**

Modeling Fraction Multiplication

You can use a model to multiply fractions.

ACTIVITY

Use a model to find $\frac{1}{2} \times \frac{3}{4}$.

Step 1 Fold a piece of paper in half. Then fold it in half again.

Step 2 Your paper should be divided into four equal columns. Shade three of the four columns to represent $\frac{3}{4}$.

Step 3 Next, fold the paper in half. Unfold your paper. Shade one of the two rows to represent $\frac{1}{2}$.

1. **a.** How many small rectangles did you make? **8**
   b. How many small rectangles did you shade twice? **3**
   c. What fraction of the small rectangles did you shade twice? **$\frac{3}{8}$**

2. How can you use your answer in Exercise 1 to find the product $\frac{1}{2} \times \frac{3}{4}$? What is $\frac{1}{2} \times \frac{3}{4}$? **Answers may vary. Sample: Since you are shading $\frac{1}{2}$ of the paper and $\frac{3}{4}$ of the paper, the product of $\frac{1}{2}$ and $\frac{3}{4}$ is represented by the fraction of small rectangles shaded twice. $\frac{1}{2} \times \frac{3}{4} = \frac{3}{8}$.**

Exercises

1. Find the product shown in the model. **$\frac{1}{5}$**

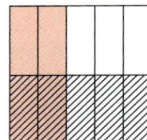

Use a model to find each product.

2. $\frac{1}{2} \times \frac{2}{3}$

3. $\frac{1}{3} \times \frac{1}{4}$

4. $\frac{1}{3} \times \frac{1}{2}$

5. $\frac{1}{6} \times \frac{3}{4}$

2–5. See margin.

6. Write a rule you can use to multiply two fractions without using a model. **Answers may vary. Sample: Multiply the numerators together. Then multiply the denominators together. Then simplify the fraction.**

2. 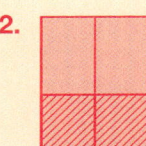 **; $\frac{1}{3}$**

3. 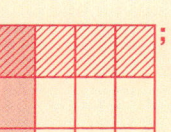 **; $\frac{1}{12}$**

4–5. See back of book.

Multiplying Fractions

Objective
To multiply fractions and to solve problems by multiplying fractions

Examples
1 Multiplying Two Fractions
2 Multiplying a Whole Number

Math Understandings: p. 258C

Check Skills You'll Need

1. **Vocabulary Review**
   Give an example of *equivalent fractions.*
   See below.

   Write each fraction in simplest form.

   2. $\frac{5}{10}$ $\frac{1}{2}$ **3.** $\frac{9}{15}$ $\frac{3}{5}$

   4. $\frac{28}{42}$ $\frac{2}{3}$ **5.** $\frac{90}{100}$ $\frac{9}{10}$

GO for Help
Lesson 4-5

Check Skills You'll Need

1. Answers may vary.
   Sample: $\frac{2}{5}$ and $\frac{4}{10}$

What You'll Learn

To multiply fractions and to solve problems by multiplying fractions

Why Learn This?

Suppose you are building a model. You want to know the length of half of a $\frac{5}{6}$-inch piece of wood. You can multiply fractions to find part of a fractional quantity.

The model below shows $\frac{1}{2} \times \frac{5}{6}$.

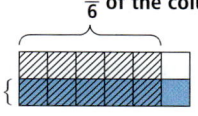

$\frac{5}{6}$ of the columns are shaded with diagonal lines.

$\frac{1}{2}$ the columns are shaded blue.

5 out of 12 of the squares include both types of shading.

So $\frac{1}{2} \times \frac{5}{6} = \frac{5}{12}$. You can also find this product by multiplying the numerators and multiplying the denominators.

Math Background

The familiar rule for multiplying two fractions is $\frac{a}{b} \cdot \frac{c}{d} = \frac{ac}{bd}$, provided that neither b nor d is zero. This rule is, in fact, an algebraic *theorem*. That is, the rule can be justified by a logical argument that is supported by known algebraic properties.

More Math Background: p. 258C

Lesson Planning and Resources

See p. 258E for a list of the resources that support this lesson.

EXAMPLE Multiplying Two Fractions

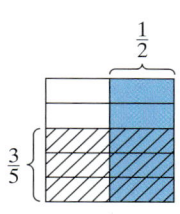

1 Find $\frac{3}{5}$ of $\frac{1}{2}$.

$$\frac{3}{5} \cdot \frac{1}{2} = \frac{3 \cdot 1}{5 \cdot 2} \quad \leftarrow \text{Multiply the numerators.}$$
$$\leftarrow \text{Multiply the denominators.}$$
$$= \frac{3}{10} \quad \leftarrow \text{Simplify.}$$

Quick Check

1. a. Find $\frac{3}{5} \cdot \frac{1}{4}$. $\frac{3}{20}$

   b. Find $\frac{2}{9} \times \frac{5}{7}$. $\frac{10}{63}$

Bell Ringer Practice

✓ **Check Skills You'll Need**
Use student page, transparency, or PowerPoint. For intervention, direct students to:
Equivalent Fractions
Lesson 4-5
Extra Skills and Word Problems Practice, Ch. 4

Differentiated Instruction **Solutions for All Learners**

Special Needs **L1**
Some students may forget to simplify fractions before multiplying. If you notice this occurring, ask students to simplify after they multiply.

learning style: verbal

Below Level **L2**
Give students several blank forms like the one below to use for organizing their work.

learning style: visual

Guided Instruction

Example 1

Students might find it helpful to recite the fraction multiplication rule softly as they perform the steps. In Quick Check 1a, for instance, they can say: "Multiply the numerators—three times one. Multiply the denominators—five times four."

PowerPoint
Additional Examples

1 Find the product $\frac{5}{6} \cdot \frac{3}{8}$. $\frac{5}{16}$

2 There are 30 students in Shari's homeroom. Of these students, $\frac{2}{5}$ worked at the school fair. How many students in Shari's homeroom worked at the school fair? **12 students**

All in One Teaching Resources

- Daily Notetaking Guide 6-1 **L3**
- Adapted Notetaking 6-1 **L1**

Closure

- *How do you multiply fractions?* **Multiply the numerators, multiply the denominators, and simplify.**
- *How do you multiply a fraction by a whole number?* **Write the whole number as a fraction with denominator 1. Then multiply numerators, multiply denominators, and simplify.**

Arithmetic	Algebra
$\frac{3}{4} \times \frac{1}{2} = \frac{3 \times 1}{4 \times 2} = \frac{3}{8}$	$\frac{a}{b} \cdot \frac{c}{d} = \frac{ac}{bd}$, where b and d are not zero.

Vocabulary Tip

The word *of* usually suggests multiplication.

When the numerators and the denominators have a common factor, you can simplify before multiplying fractions.

$$\frac{3}{8} \cdot \frac{2}{5} = \frac{3 \cdot \overset{1}{2}}{\underset{4}{8} \cdot 5} \quad \leftarrow \text{Divide 8 and 2 by their GCF, 2.}$$

$$= \frac{3 \cdot 1}{4 \cdot 5} \quad \leftarrow \text{Multiply the numerators and the denominators.}$$

$$= \frac{3}{20} \quad \leftarrow \text{Simplify.}$$

To multiply a fraction by a whole number, write the whole number as an improper fraction with a denominator of 1.

EXAMPLE   **Multiplying a Whole Number**

2 You are decorating a bulletin board using a piece of green ribbon that is $\frac{5}{6}$ yard long. You also need yellow ribbon that is nine times as long as the green ribbon. How much yellow ribbon do you need?

Draw a picture to help see how these lengths are related.

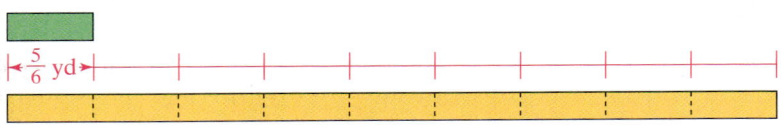

Find the length of the yellow ribbon by multiplying 9 and $\frac{5}{6}$.

$$9 \cdot \frac{5}{6} = \frac{9}{1} \cdot \frac{5}{6} \quad \leftarrow \text{Write 9 as } \frac{9}{1}.$$

$$= \frac{\overset{3}{9}}{1} \cdot \frac{5}{\underset{2}{6}} \quad \leftarrow \text{Divide 9 and 6 by their GCF, 3.}$$

$$= \frac{3 \cdot 5}{1 \cdot 2} \quad \leftarrow \text{Multiply the numerators and denominators.}$$

$$= \frac{15}{2}, \text{ or } 7\frac{1}{2} \quad \leftarrow \text{Simplify. Write as a mixed number.}$$

The yellow ribbon is $7\frac{1}{2}$ yards long.

✓ Quick Check

2. A baby alligator is $\frac{5}{6}$ foot long. An adult alligator is 12 times as long as the baby alligator. How long is the adult alligator? **10 ft**

Advanced Learners **L4**
Find the product. Simplify before you multiply.
$\frac{2}{3} \cdot \frac{9}{10} \cdot \frac{5}{14} \cdot \frac{7}{15}$ $\frac{1}{10}$

learning style: visual

English Language Learners **ELL**
Have students use words, pictures, and symbols to explain why the product is less than the factors when multiplying two fractions. Have them explain why the product is less than only one factor when multiplying a whole number and a fraction.

learning style: verbal, visual

✓ Check Your Understanding

1. **Number Sense** If you multiply 6 by $\frac{1}{2}$, is the answer greater than or less than the result of multiplying 6 by $\frac{1}{3}$? Explain.
Greater; you are multiplying by a greater number.

Match each expression with its product.

2. $\frac{1}{4} \times \frac{1}{3}$ **D**   A. $\frac{3}{8}$

3. $\frac{2}{3} \cdot \frac{2}{5}$ **B**   B. $\frac{4}{15}$

4. $\frac{1}{2} \times \frac{3}{4}$ **A**   C. 6

5. $\frac{6}{7} \cdot 7$ **C**   D. $\frac{1}{12}$

Assignment Guide

Check Your Understanding
Go over Exercises 1–5 in class before assigning the Homework Exercises.

Homework Exercises
A Practice by Example   6–21
B Apply Your Skills   22–30
C Challenge   31
Test Prep and
  Mixed Review   32–38

Homework Quick Check
To check students' understanding of key skills and concepts, go over Exercises 12, 19, 28, 29, and 30.

Differentiated Instruction **Resources**

Homework Exercises

For more exercises, see Extra Skills and Word Problems.

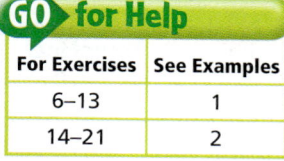

GO for Help

For Exercises	See Examples
6–13	1
14–21	2

A **Find each product. You may find a model helpful.**

6. $\frac{1}{2} \times \frac{3}{8}$ $\frac{3}{16}$ 7. $\frac{5}{11} \times \frac{2}{7}$ $\frac{10}{77}$ 8. $\frac{3}{4} \times \frac{11}{12}$ $\frac{11}{16}$

9. $\frac{2}{9} \times \frac{4}{8}$ $\frac{1}{9}$ 10. $\frac{4}{9} \cdot \frac{3}{10}$ $\frac{2}{15}$ 11. $\frac{3}{5}$ of $\frac{2}{3}$ $\frac{2}{5}$

12. $\frac{4}{11} \cdot \frac{5}{8}$ $\frac{5}{22}$ 13. $\frac{9}{10}$ of $\frac{2}{5}$ $\frac{9}{25}$ 14. $\frac{3}{4} \cdot 20$ 15

15. $\frac{3}{8} \times 5$ $1\frac{7}{8}$ 16. $\frac{11}{14}$ of 28 22   17. $\frac{5}{12} \cdot 30$ $12\frac{1}{2}$

18. $\frac{7}{9}$ of 21 $16\frac{1}{3}$ 19. $\frac{1}{6} \cdot 6$ 1   20. $\frac{3}{10} \times 45$ $13\frac{1}{2}$

22. **You ate more of the popcorn than your friend.**

23. **When you add $\frac{3}{8}$ and $\frac{5}{8}$, you add the numerators and keep the same denominator. When you multiply, you multiply the numerators and multiply the denominators.**

21. **Fitness** In gym class, you run $\frac{3}{4}$ mile. Your gym teacher runs 3 times that distance each day. How far does your teacher run? **$2\frac{1}{4}$ mi**

B  22. **Guided Problem Solving** At the movies, you eat all but $\frac{1}{3}$ of a box of popcorn. Your friend eats $\frac{2}{3}$ of what is left. Who eats more popcorn, you or your friend? **See left.**
   • **Understand the Problem** Draw a picture to help you understand the problem.
   • **Make a Plan** How can you find the answer using your picture?

GO Online
Homework Video Tutor
Visit: PHSchool.com
Web Code: aqe-0601

23. **Reasoning** Adding $\frac{3}{8}$ and $\frac{5}{8}$ is different from multiplying the two fractions. Explain why. **See left.**

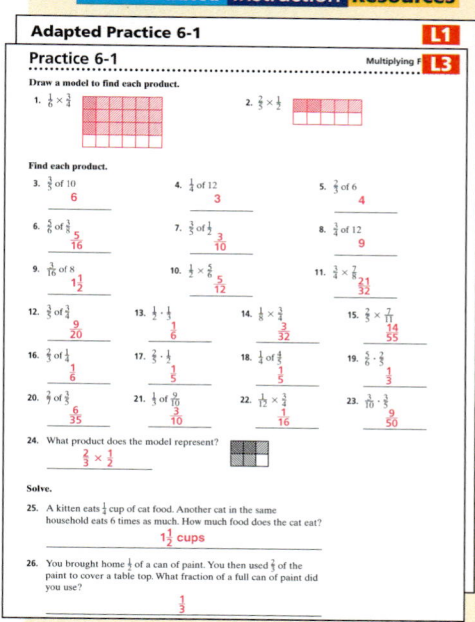

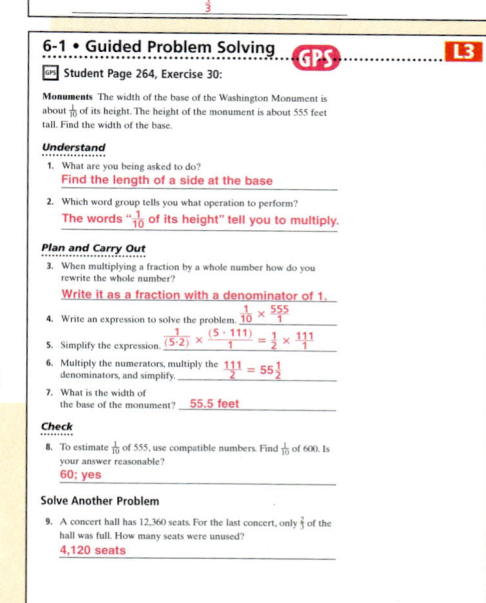

Lesson Quiz

Find each product. Simplify.

1. $\frac{3}{5} \times \frac{5}{8}$ **$\frac{3}{8}$**

2. $8 \times \frac{3}{4}$ **6**

3. $\frac{7}{8}$ of 56 **49**

4. $\frac{4}{5}$ of $\frac{9}{12}$ **$\frac{3}{5}$**

Alternative Assessment

Each student in a pair writes a fraction and a whole number. Partners work together to multiply each of their fractions and to multiply each fraction and whole number, resulting in five fraction multiplications.

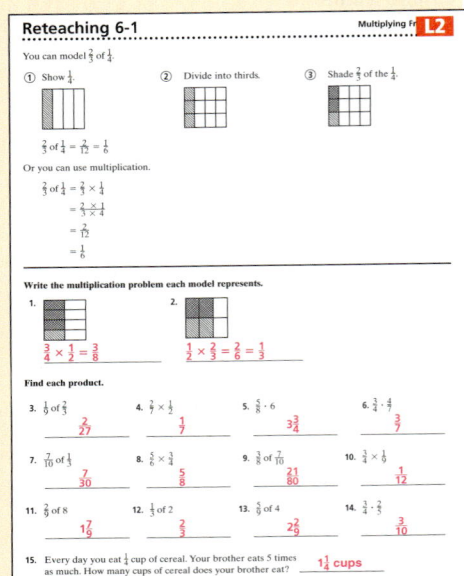

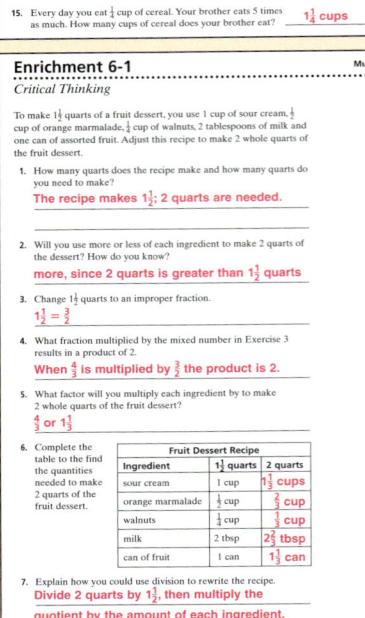

Algebra Evaluate each expression for $x = \frac{2}{3}$.

24. $15x$ **10**

25. $\frac{3}{2}x$ **1**

26. $\frac{9}{10}x$ **$\frac{3}{5}$**

27. $\frac{2}{3}x$ **$\frac{4}{9}$**

28. **Budgets** The graph at the right describes Paul's monthly spending. He makes $2,712 each month. How much does Paul spend each month on his rent and car combined?
$1,017

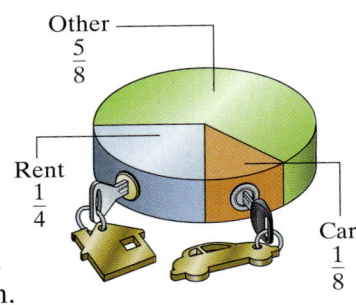

29. **Writing in Math** Is it necessary to have a common denominator when you multiply two fractions? Explain.
See margin.

30. **Monuments** The width of the base of the Washington Monument is about $\frac{1}{10}$ of its height. The height of the monument is about 555 feet tall. Find the width of the base.
about $55\frac{1}{2}$ ft

C 31. **Challenge** Find $8\frac{2}{3} \cdot 7\frac{1}{2}$. **65**

Test Prep and Mixed Review

Practice

Multiple Choice

32. Meg needs 5 yards of fencing to make a pen for her rabbit. She has $\frac{3}{4}$ yard of fencing. Each model below represents 5 yards of fencing. Which model can Meg use to find the amount of fencing she still needs? **B**

Ⓐ
Ⓑ
Ⓒ
Ⓓ

33. What is the prime factorization of 420? **H**
Ⓕ $2^2 \cdot 3 \cdot 3^5$
Ⓗ $2^2 \cdot 3 \cdot 5 \cdot 7$
Ⓖ $2 \cdot 3 \cdot 5 \cdot 7$
Ⓙ $2 \cdot 3 \cdot 5^2 \cdot 7$

34. Julio needs 2 hours to do his homework. He will take one 30-minute break. He wants to finish by 9:30 P.M. What is the latest time that Julio can begin his homework? **C**
Ⓐ 6:00 P.M. Ⓑ 6:30 P.M. Ⓒ 7:00 P.M. Ⓓ 7:30 P.M.

GO for Help

For Exercises	See Lesson
35–38	5-3

Find each sum or difference.

35. $\frac{5}{6} + \frac{1}{3}$ **$\frac{7}{6}$ or $1\frac{1}{6}$**

36. $\frac{4}{5} - \frac{1}{2}$ **$\frac{3}{10}$**

37. $\frac{7}{9} - \frac{3}{5}$ **$\frac{8}{45}$**

38. $\frac{3}{10} + \frac{5}{8}$ **$\frac{37}{40}$**

Test Prep

Resources
For additional practice with a variety of test item formats:
• Test-Taking Strategies, p. 297
• Test Prep, p. 301
• Test-Taking Strategies with Transparencies

29. **No; answers may vary. Sample: Common denominators are not necessary because you are finding part of a fractional amount.**

Reteaching 6-1 Multiplying Fr **L2**

You can model $\frac{2}{3}$ of $\frac{1}{4}$.

① Show $\frac{1}{4}$. ② Divide into thirds. ③ Shade $\frac{2}{3}$ of the $\frac{1}{4}$.

$\frac{2}{3}$ of $\frac{1}{4} = \frac{2}{12} = \frac{1}{6}$

Or you can use multiplication.

$\frac{2}{3}$ of $\frac{1}{4} = \frac{2}{3} \times \frac{1}{4}$
$= \frac{2 \times 1}{3 \times 4}$
$= \frac{2}{12}$
$= \frac{1}{6}$

Write the multiplication problem each model represents.

1. $\frac{3}{4} \times \frac{1}{2} = \frac{3}{8}$

2. $\frac{1}{2} \times \frac{2}{3} = \frac{2}{6} = \frac{1}{3}$

Find each product.

3. $\frac{1}{9}$ of $\frac{2}{3}$ $\frac{2}{27}$
4. $\frac{2}{7} \times \frac{1}{2}$ $\frac{1}{7}$
5. $\frac{5}{8} \cdot 6$ $3\frac{3}{4}$
6. $\frac{3}{4} \cdot \frac{4}{9}$ $\frac{3}{9}$
7. $\frac{7}{10}$ of $\frac{1}{3}$ $\frac{7}{30}$
8. $\frac{5}{6} \times \frac{3}{4}$ $\frac{5}{8}$
9. $\frac{3}{8}$ of $\frac{7}{10}$ $\frac{21}{80}$
10. $\frac{1}{4} \times \frac{1}{3}$ $\frac{1}{12}$
11. $\frac{2}{9}$ of 8 $1\frac{7}{9}$
12. $\frac{1}{3}$ of 2 $\frac{2}{3}$
13. $\frac{5}{9}$ of 4 $2\frac{2}{9}$
14. $\frac{1}{4} \cdot \frac{3}{5}$ $\frac{3}{10}$

15. Every day you eat $\frac{1}{4}$ cup of cereal. Your brother eats 5 times as much. How many cups of cereal does your brother eat? $1\frac{1}{4}$ cups

Enrichment 6-1 Multiplying **L4**

Critical Thinking

To make $1\frac{1}{2}$ quarts of a fruit dessert, you use 1 cup of sour cream, $\frac{2}{3}$ cup of orange marmalade, $\frac{1}{4}$ cup of walnuts, 2 tablespoons of milk and one can of assorted fruit. Adjust this recipe to make 2 whole quarts of the fruit dessert.

1. How many quarts does the recipe make and how many quarts do you need to make?
The recipe makes $1\frac{1}{2}$; 2 quarts are needed.

2. Will you use more or less of each ingredient to make 2 quarts of the dessert? How do you know?
more, since 2 quarts is greater than $1\frac{1}{2}$ quarts

3. Change $1\frac{1}{2}$ quarts to an improper fraction.
$1\frac{1}{2} = \frac{3}{2}$

4. What fraction multiplied by the mixed number in Exercise 3 results in a product of 2.
When $\frac{4}{3}$ is multiplied by $\frac{3}{2}$ the product is 2.

5. What factor will you multiply each ingredient by to make 2 whole quarts of the fruit dessert?
$\frac{4}{3}$ or $1\frac{1}{3}$

6. Complete the table to the find the quantities needed to make 2 quarts of the fruit dessert.

Fruit Dessert Recipe		
Ingredient	$1\frac{1}{2}$ quarts	2 quarts
sour cream	1 cup	$1\frac{1}{3}$ cups
orange marmalade	$\frac{2}{3}$ cup	$\frac{8}{9}$ cup
walnuts	$\frac{1}{4}$ cup	$\frac{1}{3}$ cup
milk	2 tbsp	$2\frac{2}{3}$ tbsp
can of fruit	1 can	$1\frac{1}{3}$ can

7. Explain how you could use division to rewrite the recipe.
Divide 2 quarts by $1\frac{1}{2}$, then multiply the quotient by the amount of each ingredient.

Understanding Equality

A number sentence that uses the = symbol means that the value on the left side is the same as the value on the right side of the symbol. Balance scales may help you think about equality statements.

EXAMPLE   Understanding Equality

Is the equation $7 + 3.1 = 8 + 2.1$ true or false?

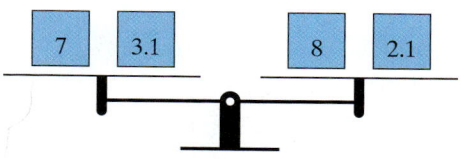

Compare the numbers on the left side to the numbers on the right.

Since 7 is one less than 8, and 3.1 is one more than 2.1, the weights on the left and right are equal. The scale is balanced.

● The equation is true.

Exercises

Find whether each statement is true. Explain your answer using logic and number sense. Do not compute. 1–6. See margin.

1. $525 - 350 = 528 - 353$

2. $48.1 - 28.2 = 38.1 - 18.2$

3. $48.3 + 16 = 38.3 + 6$

4. $13 \times 40 = 130 \times 4$

5. $200 \times \frac{1}{2} = 400 \times \frac{1}{4}$

6. $20 \div 2.4 = 40 \div 4.8$

Use logic and number sense to find the value of the variable that makes the equation true.

7. $4 + 17.3 = 6 + x$ **15.3**

8. $73 - 21.5 = 83 - y$ **31.5**

9. $\frac{1}{3} \times 27 = z \times 9$ **1**

10. $32 \cdot 15 = x \cdot 30$ **16**

11. $75 \div 25 = y \div 50$ **150**

12. $100 \div 20 = 25 \div z$ **5**

Suppose the equation on the left is true. Use logic and number sense to find whether the equation on the right is true or false.

13. $37.4 + 68.8 = 106.2$

Does $(37.4 + 68.8) + 30 = 106.2 + 30$? **Yes**

14. $224 \div 64 = 3.5$

Does $(224 \div 64) - 1.7 = 3.5 - 1.7$? **Yes**

15. $4 \times 6.5 = 26$

Does $(4 \times 6.5) \div 2 = 26 \times 2$? **No**

Activity Lab   Understanding Equality   **265**

1. True; 3 was added to 525, and 3 was subtracted from 350.

2. True; 10 was subtracted from 48.1, and 10 was added to −28.2.

3. False; 10 was subtracted from 48.3 and 16.

4. True; 13 was multiplied by 10, and 40 was divided by 10.

5. True; 200 was multiplied by 2, and $\frac{1}{2}$ was divided by 2.

6. True; 20 and 2.4 were both multiplied by 2.

Activity Lab

Understanding Equality

Students learn to use logic to evaluate number sentences that represent equality and tell whether they are true without computing. This will help them find answers when estimating products of mixed numbers in Lesson 6-2.

Guided Instruction

Discuss " = " with students and review that the numbers on both sides of " = " must be equal to each other for the number sentence to be true.
Ask questions such as:
• *How can we figure out if an equation containing " = " is true, when it contains decimals or fractions?* **by using logic and number sense**
• *How can we use number sense to evaluate an equation containing " = "?* **Compare the numbers on each side using relationships, logic, number sense, and mental math.**

Exercises

Have students work independently on the Exercises. When they have finished, have them trade papers with a partner and discuss any differences in answers. Then compute to find the correct answer.

Differentiated Instruction

Below Level   L2
Have students begin with a few simple problems involving multiples to prove their equality or inequality. For example, $5 + 10 = 5 + 5 + 5$.

Objective
To estimate and find the products of mixed numbers

Examples
1 Estimating Products
2 Multiplying Improper Fractions
3 Application: Skiing

Math Understandings: p. 258C

Math Background

To many students, the task of performing a multiplication such as $2\frac{2}{3} \times 3\frac{1}{4}$ can be intimidating. In this lesson, however, they see how rewriting the mixed numbers as improper fractions transforms a multiplication like this to the familiar form $\frac{a}{b} \cdot \frac{c}{d}$. Then they need only apply the fraction multiplication rule that they learned in Lesson 6-1.

More Math Background: p. 258C

Lesson Planning and Resources

See p. 258E for a list of the resources that support this lesson.

1. See back of book.

Bell Ringer Practice

✓ **Check Skills You'll Need**
Use student page, transparency, or PowerPoint. For intervention, direct students to:

Mixed Numbers and Improper Fractions
Lesson 4-6
Extra Skills and Word Problems Practice, Ch. 4

6-2 Multiplying Mixed Numbers

6-2

✓ Check Skills You'll Need

1. Vocabulary Review
What is the difference between *improper* and *proper* fractions?
See margin.
Write each mixed number as an improper fraction.

2. $3\frac{6}{7}$ $\frac{27}{7}$ **3.** $5\frac{2}{3}$ $\frac{17}{3}$

4. $11\frac{3}{4}$ $\frac{47}{4}$ **5.** $8\frac{7}{9}$ $\frac{79}{9}$

 **for Help**
Lesson 4-6

 **Online active math**

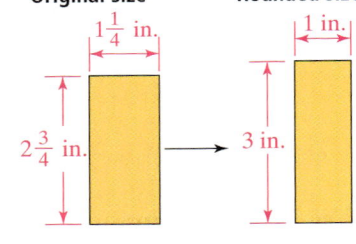

For: Mixed Numbers Activity
Use: Interactive Textbook, 6-2

What You'll Learn

To estimate and find the products of mixed numbers

Why Learn This?

The dimensions of objects are not always expressed as whole numbers. You can multiply mixed numbers to find the area of objects.

To estimate the product of mixed numbers, round the mixed numbers to the nearest whole number. Then multiply. If the fraction in a mixed number is $\frac{1}{2}$ or greater, round up.

EXAMPLE Estimating Products

1 One of the smallest newspapers ever printed had a page size of $1\frac{1}{4}$ inches wide by $2\frac{3}{4}$ inches long. Estimate the area of a page.

Step 1 Round the length and width to the nearest whole numbers.

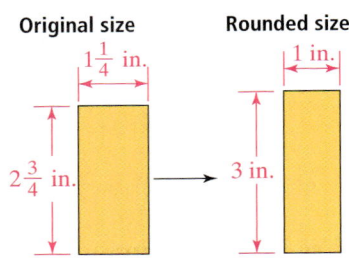

Original size   Rounded size
$1\frac{1}{4}$ in.   1 in.

$2\frac{3}{4}$ in.   3 in.

Step 2 Multiply the whole numbers to estimate the area.

$$\text{area} = \text{length} \times \text{width}$$
$$\approx 3 \times 1$$
$$\approx 3$$

The area of a page was about 3 square inches.

✓ Quick Check

1. a. Estimate $5\frac{5}{6} \times 6\frac{4}{9}$.   **36**

b. Estimate $7\frac{11}{16} \cdot 7\frac{1}{5}$.   **56**

Differentiated Instruction Solutions for All Learners

Special Needs [L1]
Provide number lines with benchmark fractions to help students know when to round up or round down for exercises like Example 1. Some students may still think that a fraction like $\frac{2}{5}$ is greater than $\frac{1}{2}$ unless shown that it is not.

learning style: visual

Below Level [L2]
Have students perform multiplications using improper fractions, such as $\frac{5}{3} \times \frac{3}{2} = \frac{5}{2}$. Then have them rewrite the multiplications using mixed numbers.
$1\frac{2}{3} \times 1\frac{1}{2} = 2\frac{1}{2}$

learning style: visual

To find the product of mixed numbers, write each mixed number as an improper fraction before multiplying.

EXAMPLE   Multiplying Improper Fractions

② Find the product $2\frac{2}{3} \times 3\frac{1}{4}$.

Estimate $2\frac{2}{3} \times 3\frac{1}{4} \approx 3 \times 3$, or 9

$2\frac{2}{3} \times 3\frac{1}{4} = \frac{8}{3} \times \frac{13}{4}$ ← Write the mixed numbers as improper fractions.

$= \frac{\overset{2}{8}}{3} \times \frac{13}{\underset{1}{4}}$ ← Divide 8 and 4 by their GCF, 4.

$= \frac{26}{3}$, or $8\frac{2}{3}$ ← Multiply the numerators and the denominators. Then write the product as a mixed number.

Check for Reasonableness $8\frac{2}{3}$ is near the estimate of 9, so the answer is reasonable.

Test Prep Tip

Estimate first. Then compare your computation to your estimate to decide if your answer is reasonable.

✓ Quick Check

2. a. Find $10\frac{1}{4} \times 2\frac{3}{4}$. **$28\frac{3}{16}$**   b. Find $7\frac{1}{3} \times 3\frac{3}{4}$. **$27\frac{1}{2}$**

EXAMPLE   Application: Skiing

③ A student skis $3\frac{1}{2}$ miles in an hour. An instructor can ski $1\frac{1}{3}$ times as far in an hour. How far does the instructor ski in an hour?

The diagram shows the distance that the student skis in one hour. The instructor skis $1\frac{1}{3}$ times as far as the student skis.

$\boxed{\text{number of miles the instructor skis}} = 1\frac{1}{3} \times \boxed{\text{number of miles the student skis}}$

$= 1\frac{1}{3} \times 3\frac{1}{2}$

$= \frac{4}{3} \times \frac{7}{2}$ ← Write the mixed numbers as improper fractions.

$= \frac{\overset{2}{4}}{3} \times \frac{7}{\underset{1}{2}}$ ← Divide 4 and 2 by their GCF, 2.

$= \frac{14}{3}$, or $4\frac{2}{3}$ ← Multiply the numerators and the denominators. Then write the product as a mixed number.

Student

├── $3\frac{1}{2}$ miles ──┤

Instructor

The instructor skis $4\frac{2}{3}$ miles in one hour.

✓ Quick Check

3. How many miles can the student ski in $\frac{3}{4}$ hour?   **$2\frac{5}{8}$ mi**

Activity Lab

Use before the lesson.

All in One Teaching Resources

Activity Lab 6-2: Multiplying Mixed Numbers

Guided Instruction

Example 1
You might want to review the process of rounding mixed numbers. Ask:
• *Why do you replace $1\frac{1}{4}$ inches with 1 inch?* **Sample: $1\frac{1}{4}$ is closer to 1 than to 2.**
• *Why do you replace $2\frac{3}{4}$ inches with 3 inches?* **Sample: $2\frac{3}{4}$ is closer to 3 than to 2.**

Error Prevention!

In Quick Check 2a, students might calculate $10\frac{1}{4} \times 2\frac{3}{4}$ by multiplying $10 \times 2 = 20$ and $\frac{1}{4} \times \frac{3}{4} = \frac{3}{16}$, then giving the result as $20\frac{3}{16}$. Stress the importance of first rewriting the mixed numbers as improper fractions.

PowerPoint

Additional Examples

① The pages of a book are $5\frac{1}{9}$ inches wide and $8\frac{3}{4}$ inches long. Estimate the area of a page in square inches. **about 45 square inches**

② Find the product $3\frac{3}{8} \times 1\frac{5}{9}$. **$5\frac{1}{4}$**

③ A gear on a machine makes $2\frac{2}{3}$ turns in one minute. How many turns does this gear make in $4\frac{1}{2}$ minutes? **12 turns**

Advanced Learners L4
Find two mixed numbers whose product is $2\frac{1}{10}$.

Sample: $1\frac{1}{2}$ and $1\frac{2}{5}$ ($2\frac{1}{10} = \frac{21}{10} = \frac{3}{2} \cdot \frac{7}{5} = 1\frac{1}{2} \cdot 1\frac{2}{5}$)

learning style: visual

English Language Learners ELL
For Example 3, students may be confused about why the fractions are being multiplied instead of just adding $\frac{1}{3}$ to $3\frac{1}{2}$. Show them the difference when they do both a multiplication and an addition, and alert them to the word *times* in the problem.

learning style: verbal

Closure

- Explain how to multiply mixed numbers. **Write each mixed number as an improper fraction. Then multiply the numerators and multiply the denominators of the fractions. Simplify and rewrite improper fractions as mixed numbers.**

More Than One Way

Answers may vary. Sample: I wrote both numbers as improper fractions and got $\frac{7}{1} \times \frac{17}{5} = \frac{119}{5} = 23\frac{4}{5}$. I didn't see an easy way to multiply mentally.

● More Than One Way

Use the recipe at the right. How should you adjust the amount of tahini if you have $2\frac{2}{3}$ pounds of chickpeas?

HUMMUS
1 lb chickpeas
12 oz tahini
1 tbsp lemon juice
2 cloves garlic
Chop garlic and mix.
Add paprika, salt, cumin to taste.

Lauren's Method

Since I have $2\frac{2}{3}$ times as many pounds of chickpeas, I need $2\frac{2}{3}$ times as much tahini. I will multiply $2\frac{2}{3}$ times 12 ounces.

$2\frac{2}{3} \cdot 12 = \frac{8}{3} \cdot \frac{12}{1}$ ← Write the numbers as improper fractions.

$= \frac{8}{\cancel{3}_1} \cdot \frac{\cancel{12}^4}{1}$ ← Divide 3 and 12 by their GCF, 3.

$= \frac{32}{1}$, or 32 ← Multiply. Then simplify.

I need 32 ounces of tahini.

Luis's Method

I can think of $2\frac{2}{3}$ as more than doubling the original recipe amount of chickpeas.

I need to double the recipe amount by using two 12-ounce jars of tahini. Then I need $\frac{2}{3}$ of another 12-ounce jar of tahini.

12 oz   12 oz $\frac{2}{3}$ full

$2\frac{2}{3} \times 12 = 2 \times 12 + \frac{2}{3} \times 12$

$= 24 + \frac{2}{1} \times 4$

$= 24 + 8$

$= 32$

I need 32 ounces of tahini.

Choose a Method

Find $7 \times 3\frac{2}{5}$. Describe your method and explain why you chose it.

1. **Number Sense** Which product is larger, 3×3 or $3 \times 3\frac{1}{2}$? Justify your answer. $3 \times 3\frac{1}{2}; 3\frac{1}{2}$ is greater than 3.

Change each mixed number to an improper fraction.

2. $1\frac{2}{5}$ $\frac{7}{5}$

3. $3\frac{1}{3}$ $\frac{10}{3}$

4. $2\frac{2}{3}$ $\frac{8}{3}$

Find each product.

5. $\frac{2}{3} \cdot \frac{3}{4}$ $\frac{1}{2}$

6. $2\frac{1}{2} \times 1\frac{2}{3}$ $4\frac{1}{6}$

7. $2\frac{1}{2} \cdot 1\frac{1}{4}$ $3\frac{1}{8}$

Homework Exercises

For more exercises, see Extra Skills and Word Problems.

GO for Help

For Exercises	See Examples
8–14	1
15–21	2–3

A **Estimate each product.**

8. $3\frac{1}{2} \cdot 1\frac{1}{4}$ 4

9. $14\frac{2}{3} \cdot 5\frac{1}{3}$ 75

10. $5\frac{1}{2} \cdot 10\frac{3}{10}$ 60

11. $7\frac{3}{4} \times 9\frac{1}{2}$ 80

12. $15\frac{9}{10} \cdot 3\frac{1}{5}$ 48

13. $2\frac{3}{4} \times 6\frac{1}{8}$ 18

14. Andrew earns $6.25 per hour. He works $4\frac{1}{2}$ hours per day, 5 days per week. Estimate how much money he earns per week. **about $150**

Find each product.

15. $7\frac{1}{2} \cdot 8\frac{2}{3}$ 65

16. $5\frac{1}{3} \times 2\frac{1}{4}$ 12

17. $3\frac{1}{9} \cdot 3\frac{3}{8}$ $10\frac{1}{2}$

18. $2\frac{4}{5} \times 12\frac{1}{2}$ 35

19. $1\frac{1}{3} \cdot 10\frac{1}{2}$ 14

20. $3\frac{1}{5} \cdot 1\frac{7}{8}$ 6

22. No; the carpenter needs $6 \times 3\frac{1}{2}$ ft = 21 ft of wood for the slats; two 10-ft boards are only 20 ft.

21. **Sewing** A quilt pattern has squares with $7\frac{1}{2}$-inch sides. You want to make squares that are $\frac{2}{3}$ of the pattern's size. Find the new dimensions of a square. **5 in. by 5 in.**

B **GPS** 22. **Guided Problem Solving** A carpenter needs six pieces of wood $3\frac{1}{2}$ feet long. The carpenter has two 10-foot boards. Does the carpenter have enough wood? Explain.
   • What is the total length of wood needed?
   • What is the total length of wood the carpenter has? **See left.**

GO Online
Homework Video Tutor
Visit: PHSchool.com
Web Code: aqe-0602

23. **Track and Field** A women's long-jump record is about $1\frac{1}{6}$ the distance of the 15–16-year-old girls' record of $20\frac{13}{24}$ feet. Find the distance of the women's record to the nearest foot. **24 ft**

3. Practice

Assignment Guide

Check Your Understanding
Go over Exercises 1–7 in class before assigning the Homework Exercises.

Homework Exercises
A	Practice by Example	8–21
B	Apply Your Skills	22–31
C	Challenge	32
	Test Prep and Mixed Review	33–35

Homework Quick Check
To check students' understanding of key skills and concepts, go over Exercises 11, 18, 23, 28, and 31.

Differentiated Instruction Resources

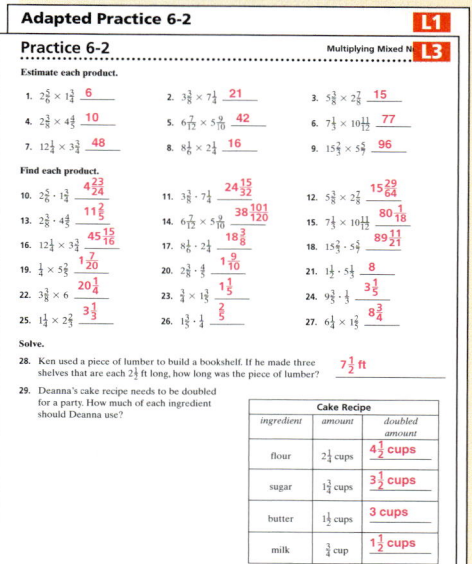

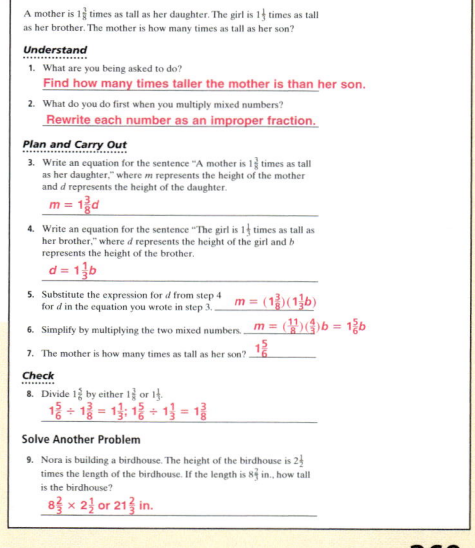

Lesson Quiz

Find each product.

1. $1\frac{2}{3} \times 2\frac{5}{8}$ $4\frac{3}{8}$

2. $3\frac{1}{2} \times 3\frac{3}{5}$ $12\frac{3}{5}$

3. $2\frac{3}{4} \times 8\frac{1}{2}$ $23\frac{3}{8}$

4. $5 \times 2\frac{1}{3}$ $11\frac{2}{3}$

Alternative Assessment

Each student in a pair writes two mixed numbers. Partners work together to multiply each possible pair of their mixed numbers (6 possibilities).

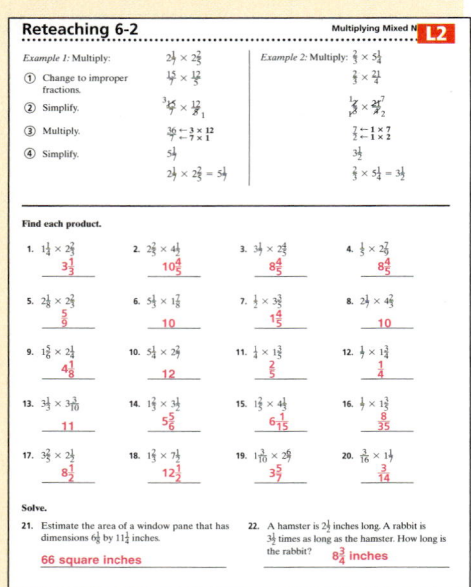

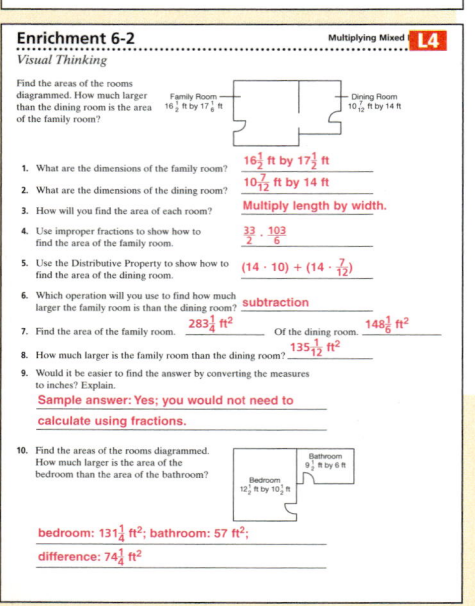

(Algebra) **Evaluate each expression for $x = 5\frac{1}{3}$.**

24. $9x$ **48**

25. $2\frac{5}{8} \cdot x$ **14**

26. $3x + 2$ **18**

27. $7\frac{1}{2}x + 5\frac{1}{4}x$ **68**

28. **GPS** a. A mother is $1\frac{3}{8}$ times as tall as her daughter. The girl is $1\frac{1}{3}$ times as tall as her brother. The mother is how many times as tall as her son? $1\frac{5}{6}$

    b. If the son is 3 feet tall, how tall is his mother? $5\frac{1}{2}$ ft

29. **Design** A painting is $1\frac{3}{4}$ feet by $1\frac{5}{8}$ feet. What size will a copy of the painting be if its length and width are $1\frac{1}{3}$ the size of the original? $2\frac{1}{3}$ ft by $2\frac{1}{6}$ ft

30. You earn \$7.25 per hour. You work $4\frac{1}{2}$ hours each day for 3 days each week. How much money do you earn in two weeks? **\$195.75**

31. **Writing in Math** Describe some items with lengths and widths that are mixed numbers. **Check students' work.**

C 32. **Challenge** Find $\left(2\frac{1}{3}\right) \cdot \left(1\frac{1}{2}\right)^2$. $5\frac{1}{4}$

Test Prep and Mixed Review   **Practice**

Multiple Choice

33. Which measurement is closest to $\frac{1}{2}$ inch? **C**

    Ⓐ $\frac{1}{4}$ inch   Ⓑ $\frac{5}{16}$ inch   Ⓒ $\frac{5}{8}$ inch   Ⓓ $\frac{3}{4}$ inch

34. The length of a credit card is $3\frac{3}{8}$ inches. Its width is $2\frac{1}{8}$ inches. Which expression shows how much greater the length of the card is than the width? **F**

    Ⓕ $3\frac{3}{8} - 2\frac{1}{8}$ Ⓗ $3\frac{3}{8} + 2\frac{1}{8}$

    Ⓖ $3\frac{1}{8} - 2\frac{3}{8}$ Ⓙ $3\frac{1}{8} + 2\frac{3}{8}$

35. Gerry wants to find a number between 90 and 100 that is divisible by 3 and 4. He chooses 92. Why is Gerry's answer incorrect? **B**

    Ⓐ 92 is a prime number.
    Ⓑ 92 is not divisible by 3.
    Ⓒ 92 is divisible by 3 and 4.
    Ⓓ 92 is not divisible by 4.

GO for Help

For Exercises	See Lesson
36–38	5-4

Find each sum.

36. $3\frac{2}{5} + 4\frac{1}{5}$ $7\frac{3}{5}$

37. $2\frac{1}{6} + 1\frac{5}{6}$ **4**

38. $5\frac{3}{8} + 2\frac{1}{4}$ $7\frac{5}{8}$

Test Prep

Resources
For additional practice with a variety of test item formats:

• Test-Taking Strategies, p. 297
• Test Prep, p. 301
• Test-Taking Strategies with Transparencies

Fraction Division

Suppose you divide three large cheese quesadillas into eighths at a party. How many pieces do you have?

You can use a circle model to represent each quesadilla.

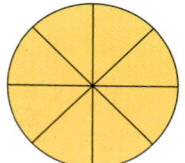 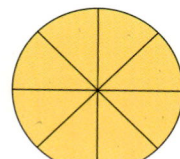 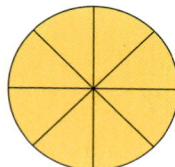

Each circle is divided into eighths. You have 24 pieces. So $3 \div \frac{1}{8} = 24$.

ACTIVITY

1. **a.** Draw three circles and cut them out. Divide each circle in half by cutting it. How many halves are there?   **6 halves**
   b. What is $3 \div \frac{1}{2}$?   **6**

2. Divide four, five, and six circles into halves. Copy and complete the table.   **See margin.**

Number of Circles	Fraction	Number of Pieces	Division Problem
3	$\frac{1}{2}$	■	$3 \div \frac{1}{2} = $ ■
4	$\frac{1}{2}$	■	■
5	$\frac{1}{2}$	■	■
6	$\frac{1}{2}$	■	■

3. **a.** **Patterns** How does the number of pieces relate to the number of circles in the table?   **The number of pieces is twice the number of circles.**
   b. What happens when you divide a number by $\frac{1}{2}$?
   The number is doubled.
4. **Number Sense** How are dividing by $\frac{1}{2}$ and multiplying by 2 related? Explain.   **They produce the same result.**

5. Use circle models to find each quotient.

   a. $4 \div \frac{1}{3}$ **12**   **b.** $5 \div \frac{1}{3}$ **15**   **c.** $4 \div \frac{1}{4}$ **16**

2. See back of book.

Fraction Division

Students model division of a whole number by a fraction in preparation for learning an algorithm for dividing by fractions in Lesson 6-3 that follows.

Guided Instruction

Discuss the three circle models that are each divided into eight equal-sized pieces. Make sure students understand how it represents $3 \div \frac{1}{8}$. Ask: *What can you say about the quotient when you divide a whole number by a fraction?* **The quotient is greater than the whole number.**

Activity

Have students work independently. When they have finished, allow them to compare and discuss their answers with a partner.

Alternative Method

Students with impaired coordination might have difficulty drawing the circles for the first step. Provide them with a sheet containing empty circles that they can use to make the models.

Resources

- Activity Lab 6-3: Calculating with Fractions
- compass
- straightedge

Objective
To divide fractions and to solve problems by dividing fractions

Examples
1 Writing a Reciprocal
2–3 Dividing With Fractions

Math Understandings: p. 258C

Math Background

Algebraically, division is defined in terms of multiplication. The quotient $m \div n$ is defined as $m \times \frac{1}{n}$, when the divisor n is not zero. The number $\frac{1}{n}$ is the *reciprocal* of n. Dividing by a nonzero number is the same as multiplying by the reciprocal of that number. The reciprocal of a fraction $\frac{c}{d}$ is $\frac{d}{c}$. When division involves fractions, use the rule for dividing fractions: $\frac{a}{b} \div \frac{c}{d} = \frac{a}{b} \times \frac{d}{c}$, when b, c, and d are not zero.

More Math Background: p. 258C

Lesson Planning and Resources

See p. 258E for a list of the resources that support this lesson.

Bell Ringer Practice

✓ **Check Skills You'll Need**
Use student page, transparency, or PowerPoint. For intervention, direct students to:
Multiplying Fractions
Lesson 6-1
Extra Skills and Word Problems Practice, Ch. 6

✓ **Check Skills You'll Need**

1. **Vocabulary Review**
How do you find the *greatest common factor* of 4 and 15?
See below.
Find each product.
2. $8 \times \frac{3}{4}$ **6** 3. $\frac{4}{5} \cdot \frac{1}{4}$ $\frac{1}{5}$
4. $\frac{1}{3}$ of $3\frac{3}{7}$ $\frac{1}{7}$ 5. $\frac{10}{11} \cdot \frac{2}{5}$ $\frac{4}{11}$

 **for Help**
Lesson 6-1

 **online**

Video Tutor Help
Visit: PHSchool.com
Web Code: aqe-0775

Check Skills You'll Need

1. List the factors of 4 and 15. Choose the largest number that is a factor of both 4 and 15.

What You'll Learn

To divide fractions and to solve problems by dividing fractions
◀ᵃ **New Vocabulary** reciprocal

Why Learn This?

Suppose you have half of a cake to share. You can find how many eighths you can cut from the cake by dividing by $\frac{1}{8}$.

The model below shows that there are four eighths in $\frac{1}{2}$. So $\frac{1}{2} \div \frac{1}{8} = 4$.

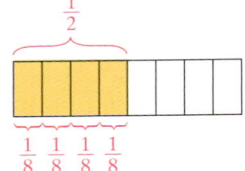

You can also use reciprocals to divide fractions. Two numbers are **reciprocals** if their product is 1. The numerators and denominators are switched in reciprocals such as $\frac{2}{3}$ and $\frac{3}{2}$.

EXAMPLE **Writing a Reciprocal**

① Write the reciprocal of each number.

a. 9
Since $9 \times \frac{1}{9} = 1$, the reciprocal of 9 is $\frac{1}{9}$.

b. $\frac{7}{8}$
Since $\frac{7}{8} \times \frac{8}{7} = 1$, the reciprocal of $\frac{7}{8}$ is $\frac{8}{7}$.

✓ **Quick Check**

1. a. Find the reciprocal of $\frac{3}{4}$.
   $\frac{4}{3}$ or $1\frac{1}{3}$

   b. Find the reciprocal of 7.
   $\frac{1}{7}$

Differentiated Instruction Solutions for All Learners

Special Needs **L1**
It is very easy to make errors when using the procedure for dividing fractions. When possible, allow students to draw a model or picture before they calculate, so they can make sense of their answers.

learning style: visual

Below Level **L2**
Give students several blank forms like the one below to use for organizing their work.

learning style: visual

To divide by a fraction, multiply by the reciprocal of the fraction. You can remember this by thinking "invert and multiply."

KEY CONCEPTS Dividing Fractions

Arithmetic	Algebra
$\dfrac{3}{5} \div \dfrac{1}{3} = \dfrac{3}{5} \cdot \dfrac{3}{1}$	$\dfrac{a}{b} \div \dfrac{c}{d} = \dfrac{a}{b} \cdot \dfrac{d}{c}$, where b, c, and d are not 0.

EXAMPLES Dividing With Fractions

2 Find $\dfrac{5}{10} \div \dfrac{5}{6}$.

$\dfrac{5}{10} \div \dfrac{5}{6} = \dfrac{5}{10} \times \dfrac{6}{5}$ ← Multiply by $\frac{6}{5}$, the reciprocal of $\frac{5}{6}$.

$= \dfrac{\overset{1}{\cancel{5}}}{\underset{5}{\cancel{10}}} \times \dfrac{\overset{3}{\cancel{6}}}{\underset{1}{\cancel{5}}}$ ← Divide the numerator 5 and the denominator 5 by their GCF, 5. Divide 10 and 6 by their GCF, 2.

$= \dfrac{1 \cdot 3}{5 \cdot 1}$ ← Multiply.

$= \dfrac{3}{5}$ ← Simplify.

3 **Feeding Birds** You have 7 cups of birdseed. You use $\frac{2}{3}$ cup of seed each week. How long will your birdseed last?

You want to find how many $\frac{2}{3}$-cup portions are in 7 cups of seed, so divide 7 by $\frac{2}{3}$.

$7 \div \dfrac{2}{3} = \dfrac{7}{1} \div \dfrac{2}{3}$ ← Write 7 as $\frac{7}{1}$.

$= \dfrac{7}{1} \times \dfrac{3}{2}$ ← Multiply by $\frac{3}{2}$, the reciprocal of $\frac{2}{3}$.

$= \dfrac{21}{2}$ ← Multiply.

$= 10\dfrac{1}{2}$ ← Simplify.

The birdseed will last $10\frac{1}{2}$ weeks.

✓ Quick Check

2. a. Find $\dfrac{9}{16} \div \dfrac{3}{4}$. $\frac{3}{4}$

b. Find $\dfrac{4}{5} \div \dfrac{1}{3}$. $2\frac{2}{5}$

3. Your art teacher cuts $\frac{5}{6}$ yard of fabric into five equal pieces. How long is each piece of fabric? $\frac{1}{6}$ **yard**

---

2. Teach

Activity Lab

Use before the lesson.
Student Edition Activity Lab, Hands On 6-3a, Fraction Division, p. 271

All in One Teaching Resources
Activity Lab 6-3: Calculating with Fractions

Guided Instruction

Example 2
Students might find it helpful to recite "invert the second fraction and multiply" procedure softly as they work. In Quick Check 2a, they might say: "nine sixteenths divided by three fourths" as they copy the exercise, then "nine sixteenths multiplied by four thirds" as they write the multiplication.

PowerPoint
Additional Examples

1 Write the reciprocal of each number.
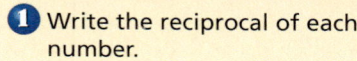
a. $\frac{4}{9}$ $\frac{9}{4}$ **b.** 5 $\frac{1}{5}$

2 Find $\frac{3}{8} \div \frac{7}{12}$. $\frac{9}{14}$

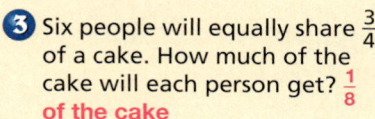

3 Six people will equally share $\frac{3}{4}$ of a cake. How much of the cake will each person get? $\frac{1}{8}$ **of the cake**

All in One Teaching Resources
• Daily Notetaking Guide 6-3 **L3**
• Adapted Notetaking 6-3 **L1**

Closure

• *What does it mean for two numbers to be reciprocals?* **Their product is 1.**
• *How do you use reciprocals when dividing by a fraction?* **To divide by a fraction, you multiply by the reciprocal of that fraction.**

Assignment Guide

Check Your Understanding
Go over Exercises 1–5 in class before assigning the Homework Exercises.

Homework Exercises
A Practice by Example   6–23
B Apply Your Skills   24–32
C Challenge   33
Test Prep and
  Mixed Review   34–39

Homework Quick Check
To check students' understanding of key skills and concepts, go over Exercises 7, 15, 26, 30, and 32.

Differentiated Instruction **Resources**

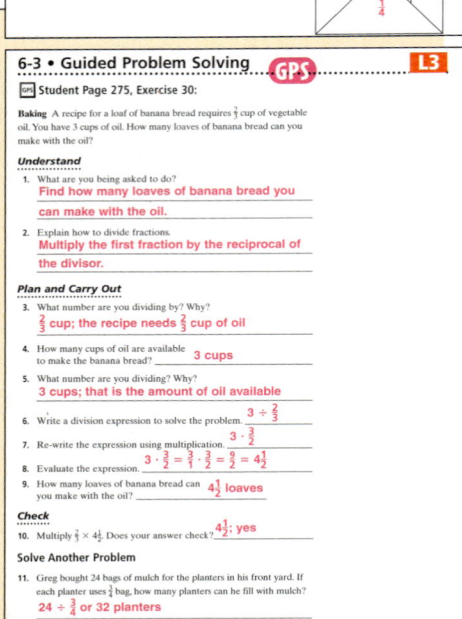

274

✓ Check Your Understanding

2. You need to multiply by the reciprocal of the divisor;
$\frac{11}{9} \times \frac{3}{2} = \frac{33}{18} = 1\frac{5}{6}$.

1. **Vocabulary** The product of reciprocals always equals __?__. **1**

2. **Error Analysis** Find and correct the error in the work at the right.
See left.

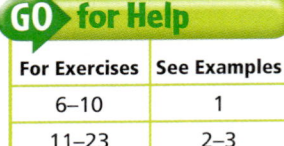

3. **Open-Ended** Write a fraction and its reciprocal. **Answers may vary.**
Sample: $\frac{2}{3}, \frac{3}{2}$

Find each quotient.

4. $5 \div \frac{3}{8}$ $13\frac{1}{3}$

5. $\frac{10}{16} \div \frac{5}{16}$ **2**

Homework Exercises

For more exercises, see Extra Skills and Word Problems.

GO for Help

For Exercises	See Examples
6–10	1
11–23	2–3

Ⓐ **Write the reciprocal of each number.**

6. $\frac{2}{5}$ $\frac{5}{2}$

7. $\frac{1}{7}$ **7**

8. 11 $\frac{1}{11}$

9. $\frac{5}{3}$ $\frac{3}{5}$

10. $\frac{4}{11}$ $\frac{11}{4}$

Find each quotient. You may find a model helpful.

11. $7 \div \frac{3}{5}$ $11\frac{2}{3}$

12. $9 \div \frac{4}{9}$ $20\frac{1}{4}$

13. $6 \div \frac{2}{5}$ **15**

14. $8 \div \frac{3}{7}$ $18\frac{2}{3}$

15. $\frac{8}{9} \div \frac{1}{3}$ $2\frac{2}{3}$

16. $\frac{1}{4} \div \frac{1}{4}$ **1**

17. $\frac{11}{2} \div \frac{3}{4}$ $7\frac{1}{3}$

18. $\frac{1}{5} \div \frac{1}{4}$ $\frac{4}{5}$

19. $\frac{4}{9} \div \frac{2}{3}$ $\frac{2}{3}$

20. $\frac{9}{2} \div \frac{1}{2}$ **9**

21. $\frac{8}{9} \div \frac{4}{5}$ $1\frac{1}{9}$

22. $\frac{3}{4} \div \frac{1}{8}$ **6**

23. A piece of iron $\frac{2}{3}$ yard long is cut into six equal pieces. How long is each piece in feet? $\frac{1}{9}$ **yard**

Ⓑ **GPS** 24. **Guided Problem Solving** A road crew has $\frac{3}{4}$ ton of stone to divide evenly among four sidewalks. How much stone does the crew use for each sidewalk? $\frac{3}{16}$ t
• What amount are you dividing evenly?
• Into how many groups are you dividing the stone?

25. **Measurement** How many $\frac{1}{4}$ inches are in $\frac{1}{2}$ foot? Draw a diagram that models the problem. **See margin.**

26. **Writing in Math** Explain how dividing a number by 2 and dividing a number by $\frac{1}{2}$ are different. Include a diagram.
See margin.

25. 24;
four $\frac{1}{4}$ inches

$1 \quad 2 \quad 3 \quad 4 \quad 5 \quad 6$
inches

26. **See back of book.**

Algebra Evaluate each expression for $a = \frac{1}{2}$, $b = \frac{1}{4}$, and $c = \frac{3}{8}$.

27. $a \div b$ **2**

28. $b \div c$ $\frac{2}{3}$

29. $c \div b$ $\frac{3}{2}$

30. Baking A recipe for a loaf of banana bread requires $\frac{2}{3}$ cup of vegetable oil. You have 3 cups of oil. How many loaves of banana bread can you make with the oil?   **about 4 loaves**

Use the table for Exercises 31–32.

31. How many times as many people live in Argentina as in Peru?
about $1\frac{3}{10}$ times more

32. The population of Brasília, Brazil's capital, is about $\frac{1}{85}$ of the country's population. What fraction of the total population of South America lives in Brasília?
about $\frac{1}{170}$

C 33. Challenge Simplify $\left(\frac{2}{7}\right)^2 \div \left(\frac{1}{7}\right)^2$.
4

South American Population	
Country	**Portion of South America's Population**
Brazil	$\frac{1}{2}$
Colombia	$\frac{1}{9}$
Argentina	$\frac{1}{10}$
Peru	$\frac{1}{13}$

Source: U.S. Census Bureau. Go to PHSchool.com for a data update.
Web Code: aqg-9041

Test Prep and Mixed Review   **Practice**

Multiple Choice

34. You want to buy enough fabric to make three stuffed bears. Each bear requires a certain amount of fabric. You want to know how much the fabric will cost for the three stuffed bears.

Step P Multiply the number of yards needed for each bear by 3.

Step Q Multiply the cost of the fabric by the total number of yards you need.

Step R Identify the cost of the fabric and the amount of fabric needed for each bear.

Which list shows the steps in the correct order for finding how much the fabric for the stuffed bears will cost?   **A**

Ⓐ R, P, Q   Ⓑ R, Q, P   Ⓒ Q, P, R   Ⓓ Q, R, P

35. You buy 2 shirts for $7.99 each and a pair of pants for $19.99. How much do you spend before tax?   **G**

Ⓕ $27.98   Ⓖ $35.97   Ⓗ $39.98   Ⓙ $55.96

Test each number for divisibility by 2, 3, 5, 9, or 10.

36. 1,250   **2, 5, 10**

37. 372   **2, 3**

38. 55,600   **2, 5, 10**

39. 445   **5**

GO for Help

For Exercises	See Lesson
36–39	4-1

---

4. Assess & Reteach

PowerPoint
Lesson Quiz

Find each quotient.

1. $\frac{4}{5} \div \frac{2}{3}$ $1\frac{1}{5}$

2. $\frac{3}{8} \div \frac{5}{6}$ $\frac{9}{20}$

3. $7 \div \frac{3}{10}$ $23\frac{1}{3}$

4. $\frac{7}{12} \div 4$ $\frac{7}{48}$

Alternative Assessment

Each student in a pair writes a fraction and a whole number. Partners work together to divide each of their whole numbers by a fraction (4 possibilities) and each of their fractions by the other fraction (2 possibilities).

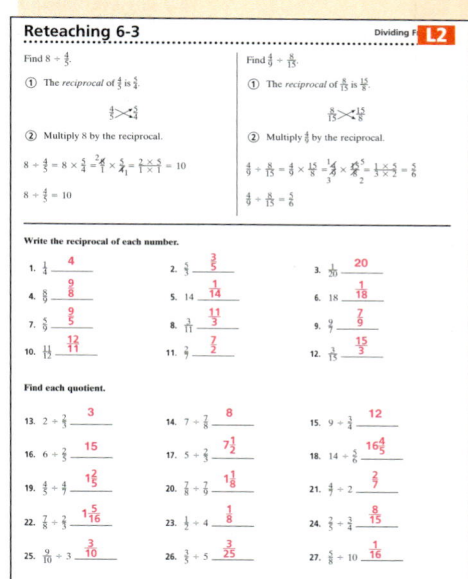

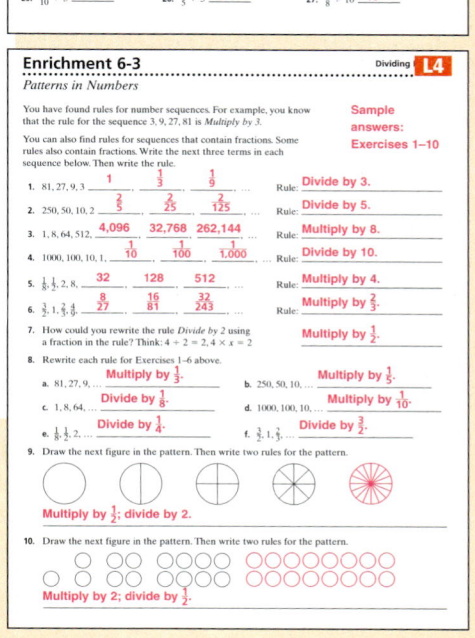

Test Prep

Resources

For additional practice with a variety of test item formats:

• Test-Taking Strategies, p. 297
• Test Prep, p. 301
• Test-Taking Strategies with Transparencies

Objective
To estimate and compute the quotient of mixed numbers

Examples
1 Estimating Quotients
2 Application: Baking
3 Dividing Mixed Numbers

Math Understandings: p. 258C

Math Background

There are two basic models for division. In the *partition model*, the number of groups is given and the size of each group must be found. In the *measurement model*, the size of each group is given and the number of groups must be found. In this lesson, students solve problems related to both models in the context of mixed-number division.

More Math Background: p. 258C

Lesson Planning and Resources

See p. 258E for a list of the resources that support this lesson.

PowerPoint
Bell Ringer Practice

☑ **Check Skills You'll Need**
Use student page, transparency, or PowerPoint. For intervention, direct students to:
Dividing Fractions
Lesson 6-3
Extra Skills and Word Problems Practice, Ch. 6

276

 **Check Skills You'll Need**

1. Vocabulary Review
How do you know that $\frac{5}{7}$ and $\frac{7}{2}$ are *not reciprocals*?
1–5. See below.
Find each quotient.

2. $8 \div \frac{2}{7}$ **3.** $\frac{7}{8} \div \frac{3}{1}$

4. $\frac{2}{3} \div 4$ **5.** $\frac{15}{4} \div \frac{11}{8}$

GO for Help
Lesson 6-3

Online active math

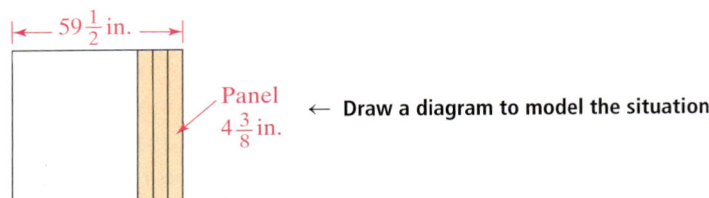

For: Dividing Mixed Numbers Activity
Use: Interactive Textbook, 6-4

Check Skills You'll Need

1. The product of the fractions is not 1.

2. 28

3. $\frac{7}{24}$

4. $\frac{1}{6}$

5. $2\frac{8}{11}$

What You'll Learn
To estimate and compute the quotient of mixed numbers

Why Learn This?
You may need to divide mixed numbers in measurements to make home repairs or change a recipe.

To estimate the quotient of two mixed numbers, round each number to the nearest whole number. Then divide.

EXAMPLE **Estimating Quotients**

1 **Carpentry** A homeowner wants to cover a wall $59\frac{1}{2}$ inches wide with wood panels. Each wood panel is $4\frac{3}{8}$ inches wide. Estimate the number of panels needed to cover the wall.

|← $59\frac{1}{2}$ in. →|

Panel $4\frac{3}{8}$ in.   ← Draw a diagram to model the situation.

$59\frac{1}{2} \div 4\frac{3}{8}$ ← Round each mixed number to the nearest whole number.
↓   ↓
$60 \div 4 = 15$ ← Divide.

About 15 panels are needed to cover the wall.

☑ **Quick Check**
1. a. Estimate $7\frac{2}{5} \div 1\frac{3}{7}$. **about 7**   b. Estimate $14\frac{9}{16} \div 3\frac{8}{19}$. **about 5**

Differentiated Instruction **Solutions for All Learners**

Special Needs L1
Have students continue to make use of number lines to help them round mixed numbers up or down.

learning style: visual

Below Level L2
Have students practice writing reciprocals of several mixed numbers such as the following.

$1\frac{2}{3}$ $\frac{3}{5}$ $4\frac{1}{6}$ $\frac{6}{25}$ $2\frac{5}{7}$ $\frac{7}{19}$

learning style: visual

To divide with mixed numbers, start by writing the numbers as improper fractions.

EXAMPLE **Application: Baking**

2 **Multiple Choice** A baker has $2\frac{1}{4}$ cups of blueberries to make three batches of muffins. How many cups of blueberries should the baker put into each batch?

Ⓐ $\frac{4}{27}$ Ⓑ $\frac{3}{4}$ Ⓒ $\frac{4}{3}$ Ⓓ $6\frac{3}{4}$

Estimate Since $2\frac{1}{4} < 3$, the quotient is less than 1.

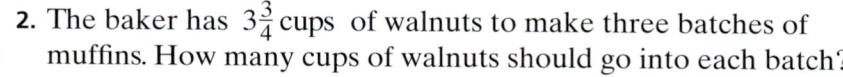

$$\boxed{\text{blueberries}} \div \boxed{\text{batches}} \quad \leftarrow \begin{array}{l}\text{Divide the number of cups by}\\ \text{the number of batches.}\end{array}$$

$$2\frac{1}{4} \quad \div \quad 3 = \frac{9}{4} \div \frac{3}{1} \quad \leftarrow \begin{array}{l}\text{Write the numbers as}\\ \text{improper fractions.}\end{array}$$

$$= \frac{9}{4} \times \frac{1}{3} \quad \leftarrow \text{Multiply by } \frac{1}{3}, \text{ the reciprocal of 3.}$$

$$= \frac{\overset{3}{9}}{4} \times \frac{1}{\underset{1}{3}} \quad \leftarrow \text{Divide 9 and 3 by their GCF, 3.}$$

$$= \frac{3}{4} \quad \leftarrow \text{Multiply.}$$

The baker should put $\frac{3}{4}$ cup of blueberries into each batch. The correct answer is choice B.

✓ Quick Check

2. The baker has $3\frac{3}{4}$ cups of walnuts to make three batches of muffins. How many cups of walnuts should go into each batch?
$1\frac{1}{4}$ cups

EXAMPLE **Dividing Mixed Numbers**

3 Find $10\frac{1}{2} \div 1\frac{3}{4}$.

$$10\frac{1}{2} \div 1\frac{3}{4} = \frac{21}{2} \div \frac{7}{4} \quad \leftarrow \text{Write the mixed numbers as improper fractions.}$$

$$= \frac{21}{2} \times \frac{4}{7} \quad \leftarrow \text{Multiply by } \frac{4}{7}, \text{ the reciprocal of } \frac{7}{4}.$$

$$= \frac{\overset{3}{21}}{\underset{1}{2}} \times \frac{\overset{2}{4}}{\underset{1}{7}} \quad \leftarrow \begin{array}{l}\text{Divide 21 and 7 by their GCF, 7.}\\ \text{Divide 2 and 4 by their GCF, 2.}\end{array}$$

$$= \frac{6}{1} \quad \leftarrow \text{Multiply.}$$

$$= 6 \quad \leftarrow \text{Simplify.}$$

✓ Quick Check

3. a. Find $7 \div 1\frac{1}{6}$. 6   b. Find $6\frac{5}{6} \div 3\frac{1}{3}$. $2\frac{1}{20}$

Video Tutor Help
Visit: PHSchool.com
Web Code: aqe-0775

Advanced Learners L4
Evaluate the expression.

$$3\frac{1}{5} \div 1\frac{1}{4} \div 5\frac{3}{5} \div 4\frac{4}{7} \quad \frac{1}{10}$$

learning style: visual

English Language Learners ELL
Ask students to draw pictures for the word problem in Example 2. That way they can see the division of the blueberries into three batches.

learning style: visual

2. Teach

Activity Lab
Use before the lesson.

All in One Teaching Resources
Activity Lab 6-4: Convert a Recipe

Guided Instruction

Example 2
Have students verify the solution by measuring $2\frac{1}{4}$ cups of rice or sand and dividing it into three portions of $\frac{3}{4}$ cup.

Error Prevention!

In the process of dividing mixed numbers, students can use a checklist to remember the steps.
1. Rewrite the mixed numbers as improper fractions.
2. Change the division to multiplication.
3. Write the reciprocal of the divisor.
4. Multiply the fractions.
5. Simplify the product.

PowerPoint
Additional Examples

1 Paulo wants to put a row of tiles along a wall $72\frac{3}{8}$ inches wide. Each tile is $3\frac{3}{4}$ inches wide. Approximate how many tiles he will need. If each tile costs $7.00, will $100 cover the total cost? **about 18 tiles; $100 will not cover the cost.**

2 Shaleen wants to make cookies with $3\frac{1}{3}$ cups of raisins distributed equally among 5 batches. What amount of raisins should she put into each batch? $\frac{2}{3}$ **cup**

3 Find $6\frac{1}{4} \div 1\frac{7}{8}$. $3\frac{1}{3}$

All in One Teaching Resources
• Daily Notetaking Guide 6-4 L3
• Adapted Notetaking 6-4 L1

Closure

• Explain how to divide mixed numbers. **Write each mixed number as an improper fraction. Find the reciprocal of the divisor and multiply.**

277

Assignment Guide

Check Your Understanding
Go over Exercises 1–3 in class before assigning the Homework Exercises.

Homework Exercises

A	Practice by Example	4–17
B	Apply Your Skills	18–25
C	Challenge	26
	Test Prep and Mixed Review	27–33

Homework Quick Check
To check students' understanding of key skills and concepts, go over Exercises 8, 13, 22, 23, and 24.

Differentiated Instruction **Resources**

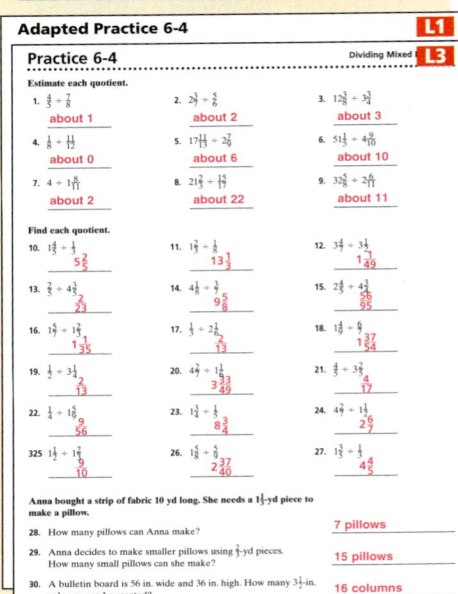

✔ Check Your Understanding

2. Answers may vary. Sample: How many $1\frac{1}{4}$-ton loads of stone are needed to make a total of $2\frac{1}{2}$ tons? $2\frac{1}{2}$ is the total and $1\frac{1}{4}$ is the amount of each part.

1. Estimation Estimate $8\frac{3}{4} \div 3\frac{1}{3}$. **about 3**

2. Open-Ended Write a word problem that you can solve using $2\frac{1}{2} \div 1\frac{1}{4}$. Explain what each number represents. **See left.**

3. Error Analysis Who is correct, Jocelyn or Annie?

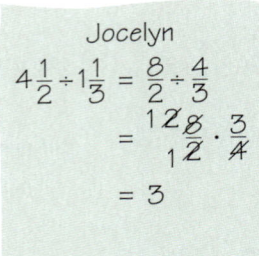

Jocelyn
$$4\frac{1}{2} \div 1\frac{1}{3} = \frac{8}{2} \div \frac{4}{3}$$
$$= \frac{\overset{1}{\cancel{2}}\,\overset{}{\cancel{8}}}{\underset{1}{\cancel{2}}} \cdot \frac{3}{\cancel{4}}$$
$$= 3$$

Annie
$$4\frac{1}{2} \div 1\frac{1}{3} = \frac{9}{2} \div \frac{4}{3}$$
$$= \frac{9}{2} \cdot \frac{3}{4}$$
$$= \frac{27}{8}$$
$$= 3\frac{3}{8}$$

Annie; Jocelyn incorrectly renamed $4\frac{1}{2}$ as $\frac{8}{2}$.

Homework Exercises

For more exercises, see Extra Skills and Word Problems.

GO for Help

For Exercises	See Examples
4–8	1
9–11	2
12–17	3

A **Estimate each quotient.**

4. $50\frac{1}{4} \div 5\frac{3}{16}$ **about 10**

5. $48\frac{8}{10} \div 7\frac{3}{7}$ **about 7**

6. $99 \div 8\frac{2}{3}$ **about 11**

7. During a storm the level of a river rose $10\frac{1}{2}$ inches in $4\frac{1}{2}$ hours. Estimate how many inches per hour the level rose.
about 2 inches per hour

8. The average adult's height is about 8 times the length of the person's head. A man is $6\frac{1}{2}$ feet tall. About how long is his head?
about $\frac{13}{16}$ ft

Find each quotient.

9. $3\frac{1}{6} \div 2$ **$1\frac{7}{12}$**

10. $2\frac{1}{2} \div 7$ **$\frac{5}{14}$**

11. $1 \div 4\frac{1}{2}$ **$\frac{2}{9}$**

12. $3\frac{1}{3} \div 1\frac{1}{2}$ **$2\frac{2}{9}$**

13. $7\frac{1}{3} \div 1\frac{5}{6}$ **4**

14. $3\frac{1}{4} \div 1\frac{1}{2}$ **$2\frac{1}{6}$**

15. $2\frac{1}{2} \div 1\frac{1}{8}$ **$2\frac{2}{9}$**

16. $10\frac{1}{3} \div 3\frac{1}{3}$ **$3\frac{1}{10}$**

17. $2\frac{1}{10} \div 4\frac{2}{3}$ **$\frac{9}{20}$**

Test Prep Tip
Drawing a model may help you solve a problem.

18. about 11 million mi

B **GPS** **18. Guided Problem Solving** Sunlight takes about $8\frac{1}{2}$ minutes to travel approximately 93 million miles from the sun to Earth. How many miles does light travel in one minute? **See left.**

- What operation can you use to find the number of miles light travels in one minute?
- How can you use estimation to check your answer?

Find the number that completes each equation.

19. $2\frac{3}{5} \div 2\frac{1}{2} = \blacksquare$ $1\frac{1}{25}$

20. $2\frac{3}{5} \div \blacksquare = 1$ $2\frac{3}{5}$

21. $\blacksquare \div \frac{1}{2} = 1\frac{3}{4}$ $\frac{7}{8}$

22. Construction An attic ceiling 24 feet wide needs insulation. **GPS** Each strip of insulation is $1\frac{1}{3}$ feet wide. Estimate the number of insulation strips that are needed. **about 24 strips**

23. Gardening A gardener is building a border for a flower garden with a row of red bricks. The row is $136\frac{1}{2}$ inches long. Each brick is $10\frac{1}{2}$ inches long and costs $.35. How much will the border cost? **$4.55**

24. Writing in Math Explain how you can use mental math to find $12 \div \frac{1}{5}$. **Change $12 \div \frac{1}{5}$ to $12 \times \frac{5}{1}$. Since $\frac{5}{1} = 5$, find 12×5 to get 60.**

25. Books A bookstore has a shelf that is $37\frac{1}{2}$ inches long. Each book is $1\frac{1}{4}$ inches thick. How many books can fit on the shelf? **30 books**

C **26. Challenge** Evaluate each expression for $x = 1\frac{1}{3}$.

a. $(x + x) \div \frac{1}{2}$ $5\frac{1}{3}$

b. $(x + 1) \div 1\frac{1}{2}$ $1\frac{5}{9}$

Test Prep and Mixed Review **Practice**

Multiple Choice

27. You serve three different kinds of pizza for dinner. The shaded areas show the amount of pizza left over. How much pizza was eaten? **A**

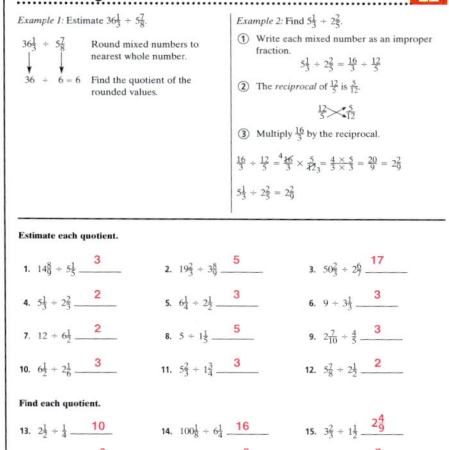

Ⓐ $1\frac{3}{4}$ Ⓑ 2 Ⓒ $2\frac{1}{12}$ Ⓓ $2\frac{1}{8}$

28. Mr. Perez is driving 380 miles home from vacation at an average speed of 60 miles per hour. Which method can Mr. Perez use to find how long it will take him to drive home? **G**

Ⓕ Add 380 and 60.
Ⓖ Divide 380 by 60.
Ⓗ Multiply 380 by 60.
Ⓙ Subtract 60 from 380.

29. Find the greatest common factor of 12 and 20. **C**

Ⓐ 2   Ⓑ 3   Ⓒ 4   Ⓓ 5

Find the prime factorization of each number.

30. 144 $2^4 \times 3^2$ **31.** 98 2×7^2 **32.** 276 $2^2 \times 3 \times 23$ **33.** 5,000 $2^3 \times 5^4$

GO for Help

For Exercises	See Lesson
30–33	4-3

---

4. Assess & Reteach

PowerPoint
Lesson Quiz

Find each quotient.

1. $8 \div 2\frac{1}{2}$ $3\frac{1}{5}$

2. $6\frac{1}{3} \div 9$ $\frac{19}{27}$

3. $10\frac{3}{8} \div 4\frac{1}{6}$ $2\frac{49}{100}$

4. $3\frac{1}{4} \div 5\frac{1}{5}$ $\frac{5}{8}$

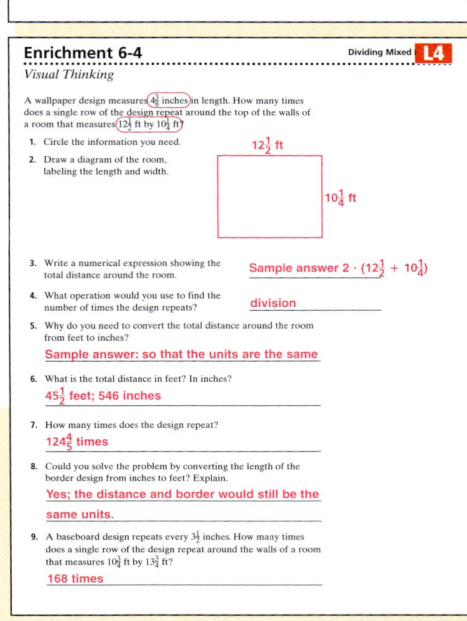

Alternative Assessment

Provide pairs of students with exercises similar to those in Exercises 12–17. For each exercise, one partner renames each mixed number as an improper fraction. The other makes any necessary corrections, writes the reciprocal, and changes the operation sign. Partners work together to find the quotient. Have partners alternate roles for each exercise.

Test Prep

Resources

For additional practice with a variety of test item formats:
• Test-Taking Strategies, p. 297
• Test Prep, p. 301
• Test-Taking Strategies with Transparencies

Using a Calculator for Fractions

Many calculators do not have fraction keys. You can use a calculator without fraction keys to check your computations with fractions by changing the fractions to decimals. The example below is for a calculator that follows the order of operations.

Round repeating decimals to several decimal places. When you compute with rounded decimals, results may be slightly different.

EXAMPLES

1 Check $2\frac{3}{8} \times 4\frac{7}{10} = 11\frac{13}{80}$.

Change the fraction part to a decimal by dividing the numerator by the denominator. Then add the quotient to the whole number.

$$2\frac{3}{8} \qquad \times \qquad 4\frac{7}{10} \qquad \stackrel{?}{=} \qquad 11\frac{13}{80}$$

2 **+** 3 **÷** 8 **=** 2.375   4 **+** 7 **÷** 10 **=** 4.7   11 **+** 13 **÷** 80 **=** 11.1625

2.375 **×** 4.7 **=** 11.1625   ← Use a calculator to find 2.375 × 4.7.

Since $2.375 \div 4.7 = 11.1625$, and $11\frac{13}{80} = 11.1625$, the answer checks.

2 Check $2\frac{2}{7} \div 1\frac{1}{3} = 1\frac{5}{7}$.

Find the decimal equivalent of each fraction. Use three decimal places.

$$2\frac{2}{7} \qquad \div \qquad 1\frac{1}{3} \qquad \stackrel{?}{=} \qquad 1\frac{5}{7}$$

2 **+** 2 **÷** 7 **=** 2.285...   1 **+** 1 **÷** 3 **=** 1.333...   1 **+** 5 **÷** 7 **=** 1.714...

2.285 **÷** 1.333 **=** 1.714   ← Use a calculator to find 2.285 ÷ 1.333.

Since 1.714 is equal to 1.714, the answer $1\frac{5}{7}$ checks.

Exercises

Write a decimal number equation to check each fraction equation. Round repeating decimals to three decimal places.

1. $3\frac{1}{5} \times 1\frac{3}{4} = 5\frac{3}{5}$
3.2 × 1.75 $\stackrel{?}{=}$ 5.6 ✔

2. $9\frac{3}{10} - 3\frac{2}{5} = 5\frac{9}{10}$
9.3 − 3.4 $\stackrel{?}{=}$ 5.9 ✔

3. $6\frac{1}{2} \div 1\frac{3}{5} = 4\frac{1}{16}$
6.5 ÷ 1.6 $\stackrel{?}{=}$ 4.0625 ✔

4. $2\frac{5}{7} + 7\frac{1}{2} = 10\frac{3}{14}$
2.7143 + 7.5 = 10.2143 ✔

Find each product or quotient.

1. $\frac{5}{12}$ of 36   **15**

2. $5\frac{1}{4} \times 4\frac{1}{2}$ **23$\frac{5}{8}$**

3. $24 \div \frac{3}{8}$ **64**

4. $1\frac{1}{9} \div 6\frac{2}{3}$ **$\frac{1}{6}$**

5. $\frac{2}{7} \cdot 5\frac{1}{3}$ **1$\frac{11}{21}$**

6. $2\frac{2}{5} \div 4$ **$\frac{3}{5}$**

7. $8\frac{1}{6} \times 2$ **16$\frac{1}{3}$**

8. $7\frac{4}{9} \div 3\frac{1}{3}$ **2$\frac{7}{30}$**

9. $5\frac{2}{3} \div \frac{1}{6}$ **34**

10. $\frac{3}{5} \cdot 7\frac{1}{2}$ **4$\frac{1}{2}$**

11. $3\frac{3}{10} \div 1\frac{1}{2}$ **2$\frac{1}{5}$**

12. $5\frac{1}{6} \times 3$ **15$\frac{1}{2}$**

13. How tall is a tree that is 9 times as tall as a $4\frac{1}{3}$-foot sapling?   **39 ft**

14. How many $\frac{1}{2}$-inch-thick cookies can you slice from 1 foot of cookie dough? You may find a diagram helpful.   **24 cookies**

15. You must cover a wall $72\frac{3}{8}$ inches wide with wood panels. If each panel is $5\frac{5}{8}$ inches wide, about how many panels will you need?   **about 13**

MATH GAMES

Estimate That Product!

What You'll Need

- 20 cards or paper slips, each with a fraction or mixed number written on it
- fraction calculator (optional)

How To Play

- Three students are needed to play. One student acts as the judge. Two students are the players.
- The judge shuffles the cards and then turns over two cards.
- Players have 10 seconds to write an estimate for the product.
- The judge finds the product. The judge also computes the difference between each estimate and the actual product.
- The player with the estimate closer to the actual product earns one point. If there is a tie, each player gets one point.
- The first player to earn five points wins.

✓ **Checkpoint Quiz**

Use this Checkpoint Quiz to check students' understanding of the skills and concepts of Lessons 6-1 through 6-4.

Resources

- All-in-One Teaching Resources Checkpoint Quiz 1
- ExamView CD-ROM
- Success Tracker™ Online Intervention

MATH GAMES

Estimate That Product!

This game will help students reinforce their multiplication and subtraction skills with fractions.

Guided Instruction

Students play in groups of three.

Have students read through the game instructions before they begin to play. You may wish to have a volunteer read the instructions aloud to assist the English learners.

Resources

- 20 cards or paper slips
- fraction calculator (optional)
- QuickTake CD-ROM

Examples
1. Solving Equations by Multiplying
2. Using Reciprocals to Solve Equations
3. Writing and Solving Equations

Math Understandings: p. 258D

Math Background

In Lesson 3-7, students learned that an equation of the form $x \div a = b$ can be solved by applying the Multiplication Property of Equality. That is, they learned to solve by multiplying each side of the equation by a. Since a fraction bar represents division, the same method can be used to solve an equation that appears in the form $\frac{x}{a} = b$.

More Math Background: p. 258D

Lesson Planning and Resources

See p. 258E for a list of the resources that support this lesson.

PowerPoint

Bell Ringer Practice

✓ **Check Skills You'll Need**
Use student page, transparency, or PowerPoint. For intervention, direct students to:
Solving Multiplication and Division Equations
Lesson 3-7
Extra Skills and Word Problems Practice, Ch. 3

282

✓ Check Skills You'll Need

1. **Vocabulary Review**
   How is the *Division Property of Equality* used to solve $4y = 24$?
   1–5. See below.
   Find each product.
   2. $\frac{1}{3} \cdot \frac{7}{10}$ 3. $\frac{2}{3} \cdot \frac{9}{22}$
   4. $\frac{3}{7} \cdot \frac{14}{15}$ 5. $\frac{9}{10} \cdot \frac{2}{5}$

GO for Help
Lesson 3-7

Check Skills You'll Need

1. Divide each side by 4.
2. $\frac{7}{30}$
3. $\frac{3}{11}$
4. $\frac{2}{5}$
5. $\frac{9}{25}$

What You'll Learn

To write fraction equations and solve them by multiplying

Why Learn This?

Projects, such as making flags from fabric, sometimes require you to solve an equation involving fractions.

The Multiplication Property of Equality states that if you multiply each side of an equation by the same number, the two sides remain equal.

EXAMPLE   Solving Equations by Multiplying

1. **Multiple Choice** Solve $\frac{x}{8} = 20$.

   Ⓐ $2\frac{1}{2}$ Ⓑ 12   Ⓒ 20   Ⓓ 160

   Recall that the fraction $\frac{x}{8}$ can also be written as $x \div 8$.

   $$\frac{x}{8} = 20$$

   $$8 \cdot \frac{x}{8} = 8 \cdot 20 \quad \leftarrow \text{Multiply each side by 8 to undo the division and get } x \text{ by itself.}$$

   $$\frac{\overset{1}{8}}{1} \cdot \frac{x}{\underset{1}{8}} = 160 \quad \leftarrow \text{Write 8 as } \frac{8}{1}.$$

   $$\frac{x}{1} = 160 \quad \leftarrow \text{Multiply the numerators and the denominators.}$$

   $$x = 160 \quad \leftarrow \text{Simplify.}$$

   The solution is 160. The correct answer is choice D.

✓ Quick Check

1. **a.** Solve $\frac{x}{2} = 15$. **30**   **b.** Solve $\frac{n}{6} = 12$. **72**

Differentiated Instruction Solutions for All Learners

Special Needs **L1**
Help students draw a picture for the problem in Example 3. A number line using eighths would be helpful. Have students run their finger along the number line, and count 1 flag every time their finger travels a distance of $\frac{5}{8}$.

learning style: tactile

Below Level **L2**
Review the Multiplication Property of Equality by having students solve several equations such as these.

$$k \div 4 = 9 \quad k = 36$$
$$z \div 6 = 10 \quad z = 60$$

learning style: visual

To solve $\frac{2}{3}x = 8$, multiply each side of the equation by the reciprocal of $\frac{2}{3}$, or $\frac{3}{2}$.

GO for Help

For help multiplying fractions, go to Lesson 6-1, Example 1.

EXAMPLE Using Reciprocals to Solve Equations

2 Solve $\frac{2}{3}x = 8$. Check the solution.

$$\frac{2}{3}x = 8$$

$$\frac{3}{2} \cdot \left(\frac{2}{3}x\right) = \frac{3}{2} \cdot (8) \quad \leftarrow \text{Multiply each side by } \frac{3}{2}, \text{ the reciprocal of } \frac{2}{3}.$$

$$1 \cdot x = 12 \quad \leftarrow \text{Multiply.}$$

$$x = 12 \quad \leftarrow \text{Simplify.}$$

Check $\frac{2}{3}x = 8 \quad \leftarrow \text{Start with the original equation.}$

$$\frac{2}{3} \cdot (12) \stackrel{?}{=} 8 \quad \leftarrow \text{Substitute 12 for } x \text{ in the original equation.}$$

$$8 = 8 \; \checkmark \quad \leftarrow \text{The solution checks.}$$

✓ Quick Check

2. Solve $\frac{7}{8}x = 42$. Check the solution. **48**

EXAMPLE Writing and Solving Equations

3 A volunteer group has 6 yards of material to make flags for Community Day. Each flag uses $\frac{5}{8}$ yard of material. How many flags can the group make?

Words yards per flag × number of flags = total yards

Let b = number of flags

Equation $\quad \dfrac{5}{8} \quad \times \quad b \quad = \quad 6$

GO for Help

For help writing an equation, go to Lesson 3-7, Example 3.

$$\frac{5}{8}b = 6 \quad \leftarrow \text{Write the equation.}$$

$$\frac{8}{5} \cdot \left(\frac{5}{8}b\right) = \frac{8}{5} \cdot \frac{6}{1} \quad \leftarrow \begin{array}{l}\text{Multiply each side by } \frac{8}{5}, \text{ the reciprocal of } \frac{5}{8}.\\ \text{Write 6 as } \frac{6}{1}.\end{array}$$

$$1 \cdot b = \frac{48}{5} \quad \leftarrow \text{Multiply.}$$

$$b = 9\frac{3}{5} \quad \leftarrow \text{Simplify.}$$

The group can make 9 flags.

✓ Quick Check

20 flags

3. How many flags can the group make with 13 yards of material?

Advanced Learners **L4**

Solve mentally.

$\dfrac{m}{12} = 4 \qquad \dfrac{12}{n} = 4 \qquad \dfrac{r}{3} = 6 \qquad \dfrac{3}{s} = 6$

$m = 48 \qquad n = 3 \qquad r = 18 \qquad s = 0.5 \text{ or } \frac{1}{2}$

learning style: visual

English Language Learners **ELL**

Remind students that they want the variable to be "alone," which means there is an implied (1) next to it. Since multiplying by a reciprocal yields a product of 1, they should multiply by the reciprocal to isolate the variable.

learning style: verbal

---

2. Teach

Activity Lab

Use before the lesson.

All in One Teaching Resources

Activity Lab 6-5: Using Fraction Equations to Find Areas

Guided Instruction

Error Prevention!

In Quick Check 1b, students might calculate $12 \div 6 = 2$ and give the solution $x = 2$. Stress the importance of checking the solution in the original equation.

Example 2

Use the reciprocal technique presented in Example 2 to solve Example 1 again. This may help students understand that $\frac{x}{8}$ and $\frac{1}{8}x$ are equivalent expressions.

$$\frac{x}{8} = 20$$

$$\frac{1x}{8} = 20$$

$$\frac{1}{8}x = 20$$

$$\frac{8}{1} \cdot \left(\frac{1}{8}x\right) = \frac{8}{1} \cdot (20)$$

$$1 \cdot x = 8 \cdot 20$$

$$x = 160$$

PowerPoint

Additional Examples

1 Solve $\frac{c}{3} = 14$. **c = 42**

2 Solve $\frac{3}{4}m = 24$. Check the solution. **m = 32**

3 Mai Li worked $7\frac{1}{2}$ hours and earned \$150. What amount did she earn per hour? **\$20 per hour**

All in One Teaching Resources

• Daily Notetaking Guide 6-5 **L3**
• Adapted Notetaking 6-5 **L1**

Closure

• Explain how to solve a fraction equation by multiplying.
  Sample: For an equation like $\frac{a}{5} = 20$, multiply each side by the denominator of the fraction. For an equation like $\frac{4}{5}b = 20$, multiply each side by the reciprocal of the fraction.

283

3. Practice

Assignment Guide

Check Your Understanding
Go over Exercises 1–7 in class before assigning the Homework Exercises.

Homework Exercises
A Practice by Example   8–20
B Apply Your Skills   21–28
C Challenge   29
Test Prep and
   Mixed Review   30–35

Homework Quick Check
To check students' understanding of key skills and concepts, go over Exercises 9, 13, 22, 26, and 28.

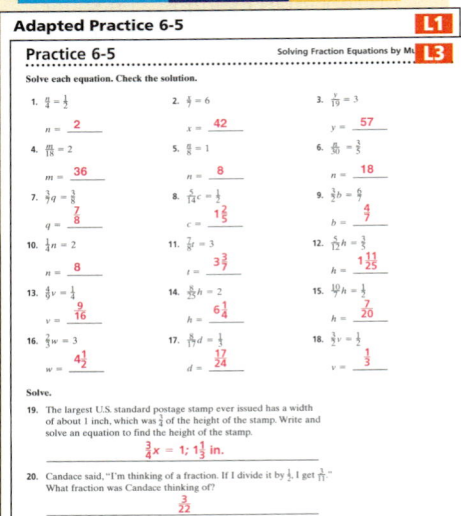

Check Your Understanding

1. **Writing in Math** Without solving the problem, how can you tell that the solution to $\frac{b}{4} = 2.5$ is greater than 8? **Answers may vary.**
   Sample: Let $b = 8$. Since $\frac{8}{4} = 2$, b must be greater than 8.

Name the reciprocal you use to solve each equation.

2. $\frac{m}{3} = 9$ $\frac{3}{1}$ 3. $\frac{2}{5}x = 5$ $\frac{5}{2}$ 4. $\frac{5}{9}z = 30$ $\frac{9}{5}$

Solve each equation. If possible, use mental math.

5. $\frac{v}{4} = 11$ **44**   6. $\frac{s}{5} = 35$ **175**   7. $\frac{4}{5}y = 8$ **10**

Homework Exercises

For more exercises, see **Extra Skills and Word Problems.**

GO for Help

For Exercises	See Examples
8–13	1
14–20	2–3

A Solve each equation. Check the solution.

8. $\frac{x}{3} = 12$ **36**   9. $\frac{a}{7} = 8$ **56**   10. $\frac{j}{12} = 27$ **324**

11. $\frac{x}{15} = 3$ **45**   12. $\frac{t}{2} = 75$ **150**   13. $\frac{r}{12} = 1.5$ **18**

14. $\frac{1}{2}m = 6$ **12**   15. $\frac{2}{3}r = 10$ **15**   16. $\frac{3}{5}n = 9$ **15**

17. $\frac{7}{8}b = 14$ **16**   18. $\frac{3}{20}x = 5$ **$33\frac{1}{3}$**   19. $\frac{3}{4}y = 21$ **28**

20. **Coin Collecting** The value of Gerald's coins is $\frac{7}{12}$ the value of his brother's coins. Gerald's coins are worth $14. What is the value of his brother's coins? Write and solve an equation. **$24**

B GPS 21. **Guided Problem Solving** The Sears Tower in Chicago is 1,450 feet tall. The height of the Sears Tower is $\frac{29}{25}$ of the height of the Empire State Building in New York City. About how tall is the Empire State Building? **1,250 feet**
   - **Understand the Problem** What information do you have? What information do you want to find?
   - **Check the Answer** Estimate the height of the Empire State Building.

22. **Costumes** A costume uses $\frac{5}{6}$ yard of ribbon. You have 9 costumes to make. How many yards of ribbon do you need?
   $7\frac{1}{2}$ yd

284   Chapter 6   Multiplying and Dividing Fractions

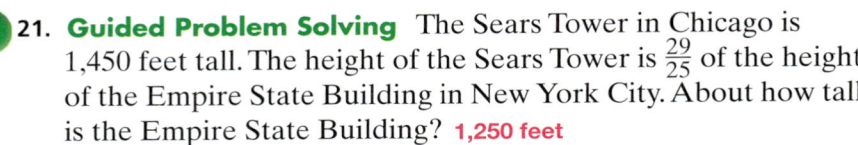
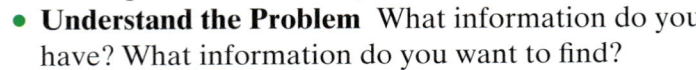

Solve each equation. Check the solution.

23. $2\frac{2}{5}p = 10$ $4\frac{1}{6}$ **24.** $\frac{1}{6}m = \frac{3}{20}$ $\frac{9}{10}$ **25.** $\frac{2}{7}n = \frac{1}{14}$ $\frac{1}{4}$

Write and solve an equation.

26. $\frac{5}{6}p = 12.50$; $15

26. Shopping The price of a shirt is $\frac{5}{6}$ of the price of a pair of
GPS pants. The shirt costs $12.50. How much do the pants cost?

27. A local bike race is broken into 12 stages. Each stage is
$14\frac{1}{2}$ miles. What is the total distance of the bike race?
$\frac{d}{12} = 14\frac{1}{2}$; 174 mi

28. $\frac{2}{5}d = 120$; 300 mi

28. Travel Use the map. The
distance from Cleveland to
Pittsburgh is about $\frac{2}{5}$ of the
distance from Cleveland to
Chicago. About how far is
Cleveland from Chicago?

C 29. Challenge Solve the
equation $2\frac{5}{8}y = 10\frac{1}{2}$.
Check the solution. 4

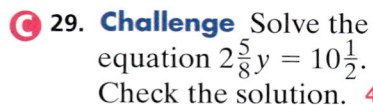
Test Prep and Mixed Review   **Practice**

Multiple Choice

30. Suchin has three pieces of string to tie up newspapers for
recycling. The lengths are 10 feet, 36 feet, and 22 feet. Estimate
the amount of string Suchin has. **C**

Ⓐ 55 ft   Ⓑ 60 ft   Ⓒ 70 ft   Ⓓ 75 ft

31. Enrique mixes $\frac{1}{4}$ pound of peanuts with $\frac{1}{8}$ pound of cashews.
Which strip is shaded to show the total number of pounds he
has? Each strip represents one pound. **H**

Ⓕ
Ⓖ
Ⓗ
Ⓙ

32. Bridget needs $1\frac{1}{4}$ yards of solid fabric and $4\frac{5}{8}$ yards of print
fabric. About how much fabric does Bridget need in all? **B**

Ⓐ 16 yd   Ⓑ 6 yd   Ⓒ 5 yd   Ⓓ 1 yd

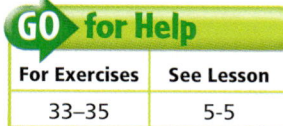
GO for Help

For Exercises	See Lesson
33–35	5-5

Find each difference.

33. $15\frac{6}{9} - 13\frac{5}{12}$ $2\frac{1}{4}$ **34.** $23\frac{2}{3} - 4\frac{1}{2}$ $19\frac{1}{6}$ **35.** $26 - 4\frac{1}{9}$ $21\frac{8}{9}$

PowerPoint
Lesson Quiz

Solve each equation.

1. $\frac{n}{4} = 6$ **24**

2. $\frac{2}{5}p = 30$ **75**

3. $\frac{3}{8}h = \frac{1}{4}$ $\frac{2}{3}$

4. $\frac{1}{6}k = 4$ **24**

Alternative Assessment

Provide pairs of students with
equations similar to those in
Exercises 8–19. Before working
together to solve each equation,
have partners first discuss and list
the steps they will take.

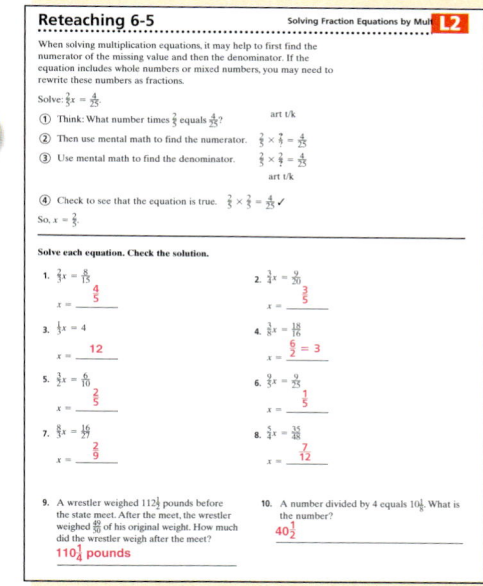

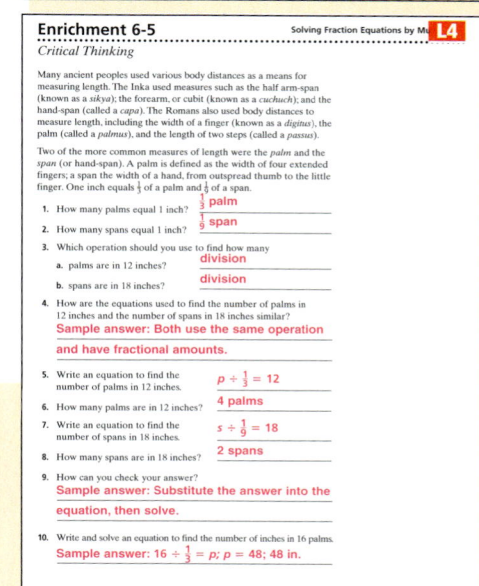

Test Prep

Resources

For additional practice with a variety of test item
formats:
• Test-Taking Strategies, p. 297
• Test Prep, p. 301
• Test-Taking Strategies with Transparencies

GPS **Guided Problem Solving**

Practice Solving Problems

In this feature, students practice solving problems involving multiplying and dividing fractions and mixed numbers.

Guided Instruction

Discuss with students how fractions are important for representing data. Have volunteers give real life examples of using fractions or mixed numbers to compare numbers.

Have a volunteer read the problem aloud. Ask:

- *What information is needed to solve the problem?* **the fractions of the total revenue for each movie**
- *Why do we use division to compare the revenues?* **to discover how many $3\frac{2}{5}$s are in $4\frac{2}{5}$**
- *Will the answer be greater than or less than one? Why?* **greater than one; the divisor is less than the number we are dividing so the quotient will be more than one**

Practice Solving Problems

Movies The table below shows the total earnings for five movies. How many times greater were the earnings for *Shrek 2* than for *Finding Nemo?*

Movie	Earnings ($100 millions)
Shrek 2	$4\frac{2}{5}$
Spider-Man	$4\frac{1}{25}$
Finding Nemo	$3\frac{2}{5}$
Pirates of the Caribbean	$3\frac{1}{20}$
Home Alone	$2\frac{9}{10}$

Source: *U.S. Almanac*

What You Might Think

> How can I use a diagram to show this situation?

> I can use division to find how many times $3\frac{2}{5}$ fits into $4\frac{2}{5}$. What equation can I write and solve?

> What is the answer?

What You Might Write

$$4\frac{2}{5}$$

$$3\frac{2}{5}$$

Let x = the number of times $3\frac{2}{5}$ fits into $4\frac{2}{5}$.

$$x = 4\frac{2}{5} \div 3\frac{2}{5}$$

$$x = \frac{22}{5} \div \frac{17}{5}, \text{ or } \frac{22}{5} \times \frac{5}{17}$$

$$x = \frac{22}{17}, \text{ or } 1\frac{5}{17}$$

The earnings for *Shrek 2* were $1\frac{5}{17}$ times greater than the earnings for *Finding Nemo*.

Think It Through

1. Why should you use division to solve the problem?
   Division is the inverse operation for multiplication.
2. **Number Sense** Before solving the problem, should you expect your answer to be *greater than* or *less than* 1? Explain.
   greater than 1; $3\frac{2}{5}$ goes into $4\frac{2}{5}$ more than one time
3. **Check for Reasonableness** How can you use estimation to decide whether the answer is reasonable? **$4\frac{2}{5}$ is less than twice $3\frac{2}{5}$, so the answer is reasonable.**

286   **Guided Problem Solving**   Practice Solving Problems

Exercises

4. a. **Gas Prices** In the table below, how much greater is the average price of gasoline in the Netherlands than in the United States? **$3.81**

   b. How many times greater is the average price of gas in the Netherlands than in the United States? **about 2.36 times greater**

Gas Prices

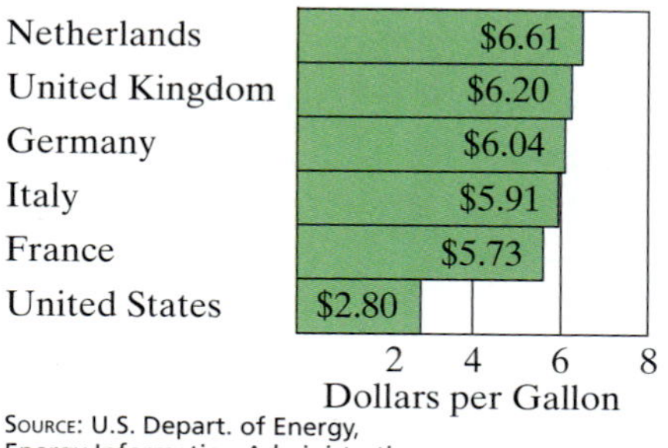

Netherlands	$6.61
United Kingdom	$6.20
Germany	$6.04
Italy	$5.91
France	$5.73
United States	$2.80

2   4   6   8
Dollars per Gallon

SOURCE: U.S. Depart. of Energy,
Energy Information Administration

5. A lap around a motocross track is $\frac{3}{4}$ mile. How many laps do you need to complete to finish a 6-mile race? **8 laps**

6. How high is a stack of 12 pieces of lumber if each piece is $1\frac{1}{4}$ inches thick? **15 in.**

Use the chart below for Exercises 7 and 8.

Minimum Wage

State	Hourly Wage
Alaska	$7.15
New York	$6.75
Texas	$5.15
Kansas	$2.65

SOURCE: U.S. Department of Labor,
Employment Standards Administration

7. How much less would you earn working at minimum wage in a 40-hour week in Texas than in New York? **$64**

8. **Estimation** Estimate the total amount you would earn in Alaska working 8 hours per day for 20 days. **about $1,120**

Guided Problem Solving Practice Solving Problems **287**

Error Prevention!

Students may make mistakes converting mixed numbers to improper fractions. Review this skill with students who are having difficulty. Ask:
• *How do you know your answer is reasonable?* by rounding, 4 is greater than 3, but less than 6, which is 2 times 3, so the answer should be between 1 and 2

Exercises
Have students work independently on the Exercises. Remind them to round and estimate to check the reasonableness of their answers. Allow students to compare answers with a partner when they have finished.

Differentiated Instruction

Advanced Learners   L4
Have students convert the numbers to decimals and check that their answers are correct.

Objective
To choose appropriate units and to estimate in the customary system

Examples
1 Choosing a Unit of Length
2 Choosing a Unit of Weight
3 Choosing a Unit of Capacity

Math Understandings: p. 258D

Math Background

The purpose of this lesson is not so much to teach the customary units of measure as it is to heighten students' awareness of them. Specifically, given an object to be measured, students learn to recognize the type of measurement involved—length, liquid capacity, or weight—and to choose an appropriate unit of that type.

More Math Background: p. 258D

Lesson Planning and Resources

See p. 258E for a list of the resources that support this lesson.

Bell Ringer Practice

✓ **Check Skills You'll Need**
Use student page, transparency, or PowerPoint. For intervention, direct students to:
Comparing and Ordering Fractions
Lesson 4-8
Extra Skills and Word Problems Practice, Ch. 4

✓ **Check Skills You'll Need**

1. **Vocabulary Review**
Describe how to *compare* $\frac{3}{4}$ and $\frac{10}{12}$.
See below.
Compare each pair of numbers. Use $<$, $=$, or $>$.

2. $\frac{1}{2}$ ▨ $\frac{1}{3}$ $>$

3. $\frac{5}{6}$ ▨ $\frac{5}{7}$ $>$

4. 4 ▨ $3\frac{1}{4}$ $>$

 **for Help**
Lesson 4-8

Check Skills You'll Need

1. Answers may vary.
    Sample: Find the least common denominator of 4 and 12 and write equivalent fractions using the LCD to compare.

What You'll Learn

To choose appropriate units and to estimate in the customary system

Why Learn This?

The customary system of measurement is based on units of measurement that have been used since 1824. The United States and a few other countries use this system. Each unit in the customary system has a separate name.

Customary Units of Measure

	Name	Symbol	Approximate Comparison
Length	inch	in.	Length of soda bottle cap
	foot	ft	Length of an adult male's foot
	yard	yd	Length across a door
	mile	mi	Length of 14 football fields
Weight	ounce	oz	Weight of a slice of bread
	pound	lb	Weight of a loaf of bread
	ton	t	Weight of two grand pianos
Capacity	fluid ounce	fl oz	Amount in a mouthful of mouthwash
	cup	c	Amount of milk in a single-serving carton
	pint	pt	Amount in a container of cream
	quart	qt	Amount in a bottle of fruit punch
	gallon	gal	Amount in a large can of paint

You can describe 128 fluid ounces of juice as 16 cups, 8 pints, 4 quarts, or 1 gallon. Using larger units of measure is helpful for larger quantities and estimates.

Quantity	Measurement	Less Helpful Measurement
Weight of a person	160 pounds	2,560 ounces
Distance from home to school	About 1 mile	About 63,360 inches
Amount of water in a swimming pool	About 17,000 gallons	About 272,000 cups

Use smaller units for smaller quantities and where you need to be exact.

Differentiated **Instruction** **Solutions for All Learners**

Special Needs [L1]
If possible, bring in gallon, quart, pint, and cup containers so students can see and touch them. Bring objects of assorted weights so that they can feel them and attach a unit of measure label to them.

learning style: tactile

Below Level [L2]
Give students measures like 2 feet and 2 pounds. Have them identify objects that are described by those measurements. **Samples: 2 feet—width of a student desk; 2 pounds—a textbook**

learning style: tactile

EXAMPLE Choosing a Unit of Length

1 Choose an appropriate customary unit of length to describe the height of a flagpole.

A mile is too large a unit. Use feet or yards.

✓ Quick Check

1a. Inches; pencils are shorter than a foot.

b. Feet or yards; small whales are twice as long as a man.

1. Choose an appropriate unit of length. Explain your choice.
   a. pencil   **b.** adult whale

   1a–b. Answers may vary. See left for samples.

EXAMPLE Choosing a Unit of Weight

2 Which customary unit of weight describes a bag of ice?

The customary units that describe weight are ounces, pounds, and tons. The weight of a bag of ice is best described in pounds.

✓ Quick Check

2. Choose an appropriate unit of weight for a refrigerator.

   Answers may vary. Sample: Pounds; a refrigerator weighs less than a piano.

You use a unit of capacity to describe amounts of liquid.

3a. Gallons; a tanker truck holds more gasoline than can fit in a small bucket.

b. Fluid ounces or cups; a container of yogurt is usually less than a pint.

1 fluid ounce   1 cup   1 pint   1 quart   1 gallon

EXAMPLE Choosing a Unit of Capacity

3 Choose an appropriate customary unit of capacity to describe the amount of liquid a water bottle can hold.

The capacity of a water bottle is not large, so it is best described in fluid ounces.

✓ Quick Check

3. Choose an appropriate unit of capacity. Explain your choice.
   a. a gasoline tanker truck   **b.** container of yogurt

   3a–b. Answers may vary. See left for samples.

Activity Lab

Use before the lesson.

All in One Teaching Resources

Activity Lab 6-6: Customary Measures

Guided Instruction

Error Prevention!

Students often confuse cups, pints, quarts, and gallons. Share this memory device.

lesser unit	→		greater unit
cup	pint	quart	gallon
(3)	(4)	(5)	(6)
fewer letters	→		more letters

PowerPoint Additional Examples

1 Choose an appropriate customary unit of measure to describe the length of an automobile. **feet**

2 Choose an appropriate customary unit of measure to describe the weight of a bag of popcorn. **ounces**

3 Choose an appropriate customary unit of measure to describe the capacity of a household bucket. **gallons**

All in One Teaching Resources

• Daily Notetaking Guide 6-6 **L3**
• Adapted Notetaking 6-6 **L1**

Closure

• *How do you choose an appropriate unit of measure?* **Sample: Choose a unit that roughly matches what you are measuring—a small unit to measure smaller quantities, a large unit to measure larger quantities.**

Advanced Learners **L4**
Have students research the customary units of dry capacity (pint, quart, peck, bucket, bushel) and use them to create problems.

learning style: verbal

English Language Learners **ELL**
Help students use conditional statements when determining a unit of weight. For example, "If I were measuring the distance from one town to another, a whale might be a better unit than a pencil."

learning style: verbal

3. Practice

Assignment Guide

Check Your Understanding
Go over Exercises 1–4 in class before assigning the Homework Exercises.

Homework Exercises
A Practice by Example   5–16
B Apply Your Skills   17–22
C Challenge   23
Test Prep and
   Mixed Review   24–28

Homework Quick Check
To check students' understanding of key skills and concepts, go over Exercises 6, 14, 18, 21, and 22.

Differentiated Instruction Resources

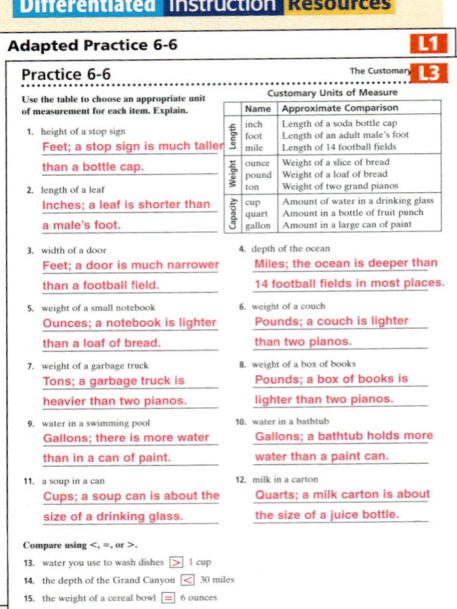

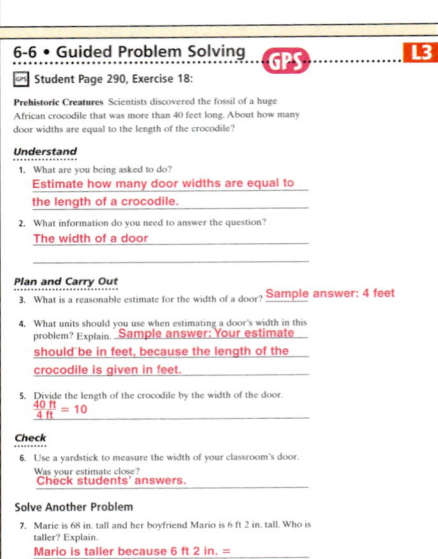

✓ Check Your Understanding

1. **Open-Ended** Give two examples of items in your daily life that you measure using gallons. **Check students' work.**

> **Vocabulary Tip**
> An *attribute* is a quality or characteristic.

Choose an appropriate customary unit of measure for each attribute of the milk carton.

2. height of the carton
   inches
3. amount of milk
   cups
4. weight of full carton
   ounces

Homework Exercises

For more exercises, see Extra Skills and Word Problems.

A Choose an appropriate unit of length. Explain your choice.

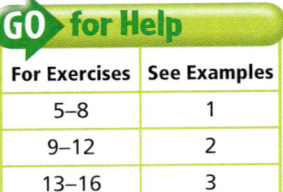

For Exercises	See Examples
5–8	1
9–12	2
13–16	3

5. backyard
6. distance to the moon
7. car's license plate
8. photograph

5–16. Answers may vary. See margin for samples.

Choose an appropriate unit of weight. Explain your choice.

9. bag of oranges
10. package of chewing gum
11. bowling ball
12. pickup truck

Choose an appropriate unit of capacity. Explain your choice.

13. sample shampoo bottle
14. soup bowl
15. lawnmower gasoline tank
16. toothpaste tube

B 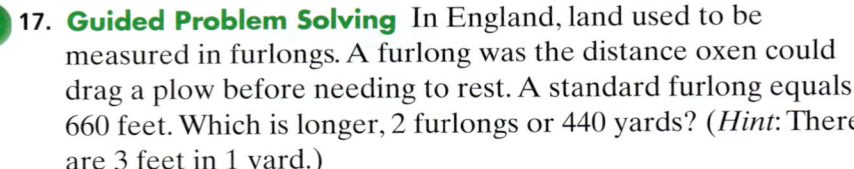 17. **Guided Problem Solving** In England, land used to be measured in furlongs. A furlong was the distance oxen could drag a plow before needing to rest. A standard furlong equals 660 feet. Which is longer, 2 furlongs or 440 yards? (*Hint*: There are 3 feet in 1 yard.)
   - How many feet are in 440 yards?
   - How many feet are in 2 furlongs? **They are equal.**

18. **Prehistoric Creatures** Scientists discovered the fossil of a huge African crocodile that was more than 40 feet long. About how many door widths are equal to the length of the crocodile?
   about 14

5–9. Answers may vary. Samples are given.

5. **Feet; lots are usually measured in feet.**

6. **Miles; any smaller unit would be too small, since the moon is thousands of miles from Earth.**

7. **Inches; a license plate is a little longer than a foot-ruler.**

8. **Inches; width of a photograph is usually measured in inches.**

9. **Pounds; one orange weighs less than a pound, so a bag of oranges would weigh more than a pound.**

10–16. See back of book.

21. Inches are too small to describe walking distances.

Compare, using <, =, or >.

19. weight of a pen ■ 6 oz
    <

20. height of a tree ■ 0.5 mi
    <

21. **Writing in Math** Explain why inches are not an appropriate unit of length for the distance from your home to school.

22. a. Order the heights of the objects in the image below from shortest to tallest. beaker, flask, cylinder
    b. Order the capacities from least to greatest.
       cylinder, flask, beaker

Plastic flask

Glass graduated cylinder

Glass beaker

 23. **Challenge** Jewelers use troy ounces to weigh precious stones. A troy pound contains 12 troy ounces. Each troy ounce equals 480 grains. How many grains will two troy ounces of stones weigh? 960 grains

Test Prep and Mixed Review
Practice

Multiple Choice

24. Which measure of capacity is appropriate to use in describing the amount of milk in a cereal bowl? A
    Ⓐ ounce   Ⓑ cup   Ⓒ quart   Ⓓ gallon

25. Each student pays $12 to go on a field trip. You have collected $108. Which equation can you use to find the number of students s who have paid? F
    Ⓕ $s = 108 \div 12$ Ⓗ $s = 108 + 12$
    Ⓖ $s = 108 \times 12$ Ⓙ $s = 108 - 12$

26. Boris walks $\frac{3}{8}$ of a mile to school. After school he walks $\frac{3}{4}$ mile. Which model can you use to find the total distance Boris walks? C

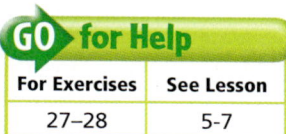
Find the elapsed time for each pair of times.
    1 h 59 min   6 h 15 min
27. 9:30 A.M. and 11:29 A.M.   28. 8:15 A.M. and 2:30 P.M.

PowerPoint
Lesson Quiz

Choose an appropriate customary unit for each item.

1. the length of a pen **in.**
2. the weight of a dog **lb**
3. the capacity of a mug **fl oz**
4. the length of a bed **ft**

Alternative Assessment

Provide pairs of students with customary measuring tools. Partners list four measurable classroom objects and record estimated lengths. Then they measure and record the actual lengths.

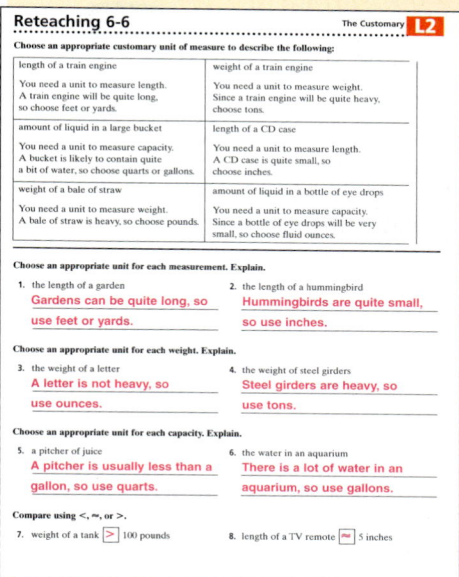

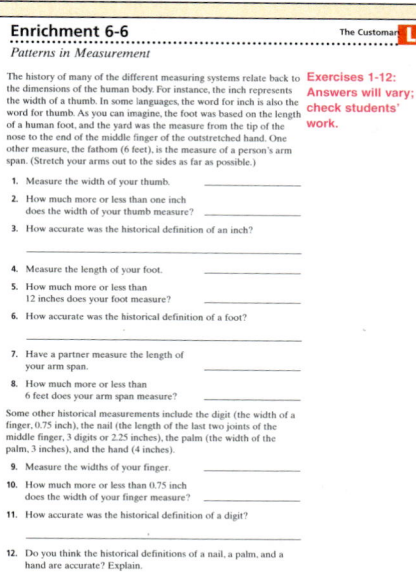

Test Prep

Resources
For additional practice with a variety of test item formats:
• Test-Taking Strategies, p. 297
• Test Prep, p. 301
• Test-Taking Strategies with Transparencies

Objective
To convert between units in the customary system

Examples
1 Larger Units to Smaller Units
2 Smaller Units to Larger Units
3 Renaming Units

Math Understandings: p. 258D

Math Background

To add, subtract, or compare two measurements, the measurements must be expressed in the same units. To convert one of the measurements to a different unit, you can use the following rules:

• *To convert from a larger unit to a smaller unit, you multiply.*
• *To convert from a smaller unit to a larger unit, you divide.*

More Math Background: p. 258D

Lesson Planning and Resources

See p. 258E for a list of the resources that support this lesson.

6-7

Changing Units in the Customary System

✓ Check Skills You'll Need

1. **Vocabulary Review**
What is the difference between a *mixed number* and an *improper fraction*?
See below.
Find each product.

2. $\frac{1}{2} \times 51$ $25\frac{1}{2}$

3. $\frac{5}{6} \times \frac{11}{13}$ $\frac{55}{78}$

4. $\frac{2}{3} \cdot \frac{9}{16}$ $\frac{3}{8}$

5. $\frac{2}{3} \times 1\frac{1}{9}$ $\frac{20}{27}$

 **for Help**
Lesson 6-1

Check Skills You'll Need

1. **An improper fraction has a numerator greater than the denominator. A mixed number is the sum of an integer and a proper fraction.**

Vocabulary Tip

A *quart* is a quarter of a gallon.

What You'll Learn

To convert between units in the customary system

Why Learn This?

Measures in the customary system are often written using more than one unit of measure. To solve problems with more than one unit, you may need to change units.

Length	Weight	Capacity
12 in. = 1 ft	16 oz = 1 lb	8 fl oz = 1 cup
36 in. = 1 yd	2,000 lb = 1 t	2 cups = 1 pt
3 ft = 1 yd		4 cups = 1 qt
5,280 ft = 1 mi		2 pt = 1 qt
		4 qt = 1 gal

To change from a larger unit to a smaller unit, you multiply.

EXAMPLE **Larger Units to Smaller Units**

1 Find the number of quarts in 5 gallons.

$5 \text{ gal} = (5 \times 4) \text{ qt}$ ← Multiply to change to a smaller unit.
$= 20 \text{ qt}$ ← Multiply.

There are 20 quarts in 5 gallons.

✓ Quick Check

1. Find the number of pounds in 2 tons. **4,000 lb**

Differentiated Instruction **Solutions for All Learners**

Special Needs L1
For Example 3, have students draw a number line that has inches and feet on it. It should have twelfths marked off between each foot unit. Then have them travel the distance from 6 feet 11 inches, and 8 feet 7 inches. Have them count the inches, and convert to feet and inches.
learning style: visual

Below Level L2
Review the symbols < and > by giving students true-or-false items about units of time. For example: True or false? 16 days < 2 weeks **false**
learning style: visual

To change from a smaller unit to a larger unit, you divide.

EXAMPLE Smaller Units to Larger Units

2 You need $8\frac{1}{2}$ feet of fabric to make a costume. How many yards of fabric should you buy?

A foot is smaller than a yard, so divide.

$8\frac{1}{2}$ ft $= \left(8\frac{1}{2} \div 3\right)$ yd   ← **3 feet equals 1 yard, so divide $8\frac{1}{2}$ by 3.**

$= \left(\frac{17}{2} \times \frac{1}{3}\right)$ yd   ← **Multiply by $\frac{1}{3}$, the reciprocal of 3.**

$= \frac{17}{6}$ yd, or $2\frac{5}{6}$ yd   ← **Simplify.**

You should buy $2\frac{5}{6}$ yards of fabric.

1 ft
1 ft   } 1 yd
1 ft
$8\frac{1}{2}$ ft
} 1 yd
$\frac{1}{2}$ ft

✓ **Quick Check**

2. You need 5 cups of milk to make hot chocolate. How many quarts of milk should you buy? **$1\frac{1}{4}$ qt**

Sometimes you need to rename units when you add or subtract.

EXAMPLE Renaming Units

3 **Multiple Choice** At age 12, Robert Wadlow was 6 ft 11 in. tall. At age 19, he was 8 ft 7 in. tall. How much did Robert grow from age 12 to age 14?

Ⓐ 1 ft 1 in.   Ⓑ 1 ft 8 in.   Ⓒ 2 ft 3 in.   Ⓓ 2 ft 8 in.

Think: 8 ft 7 in. = 7 ft + 1 ft + 7 in.   ← **Write 8 ft as 7 ft + 1 ft.**

= 7 ft + 12 in. + 7 in.   ← **Rename 1 ft as 12 in.**

= 7 ft 19 in.   ← **Combine 12 in. and 7 in.**

Subtract:

8 ft 7 in.   7 ft 19 in.   ← **Rename 8 ft 7 in. as 7 ft 19 in.**
− 6 ft 11 in.   − 6 ft 11 in.
               1 ft 8 in.   ← **Subtract.**

Robert grew 1 ft 8 in. The correct answer is choice B.

✓ **Quick Check**

3. A baby weighed 6 pounds 8 ounces at birth. She has since gained 1 pound 9 ounces. How much does she weigh now? **8 lb 1 oz**

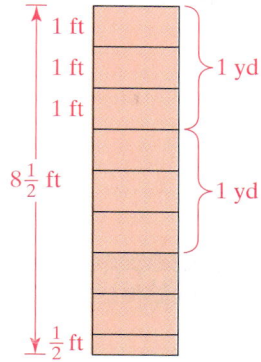

2. Teach

Activity Lab

Use before the lesson.

All in One Teaching Resources
Activity Lab 6-7: Critical Thinking

Guided Instruction

Example 1
Have students softly recite the appropriate conversion rule. In Quick Check 1, they might say: "tons to pounds—larger to smaller—multiply."

Example 2
Some students prefer to use the relationship equation, as shown.

3 ft = 1 yd

1 ft = $\frac{1}{3}$ yd

$8\frac{1}{2}$ ft $= \left(8\frac{1}{2} \times \frac{1}{3}\right)$ yd

The solution then proceeds as indicated in the text.

PowerPoint
Additional Examples

1 Complete each statement.
 a. $4\frac{1}{2}$ lb = ■ oz **72**
 b. 14 ft = ■ yd **$4\frac{2}{3}$**

2 Complete each statement.
 a. 19 cups = ■ qt **$4\frac{3}{4}$**
 b. 111 in. = ■ ft **$9\frac{1}{4}$**

3 A craftsperson is shipping a ceramic vase that weighs 3 lb 12 oz. The weight of the packing crate is 2 lb 6 oz. What is the total weight of the vase and the packing crate? **6 lb 2 oz**

All in One Teaching Resources
• Daily Notetaking Guide 6-7 **L3**
• Adapted Notetaking 6-7 **L1**

Closure

• *When do you need to convert units of measure?* **Samples: when adding or subtracting measures; when comparing measures**

Advanced Learners **L4**
Have students list other relationships that can be derived from the conversion chart on page 292.
Samples:
1,760 yd = 1 mi; 16 fl oz = 1 pt; 8 pt = 1 gal

learning style: visual

English Language Learners **ELL**
Ask students to pair up. One partner must explain why you multiply when changing to a lesser unit, while the other explains why you divide when changing to a greater unit. Listen to their explanations, and help refine as necessary.

learning style: verbal

3. Practice

Assignment Guide

Check Your Understanding
Go over Exercises 1–7 in class before assigning the Homework Exercises.

Homework Exercises
A Practice by Example   8–24
B Apply Your Skills   25–34
C Challenge   35
Test Prep and
   Mixed Review   36–41

Homework Quick Check
To check students' understanding of key skills and concepts, go over Exercises 9, 15, 30, 32, and 33.

Differentiated Instruction Resources

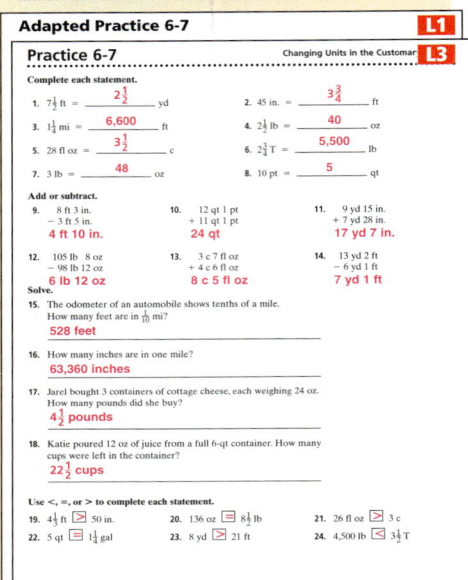

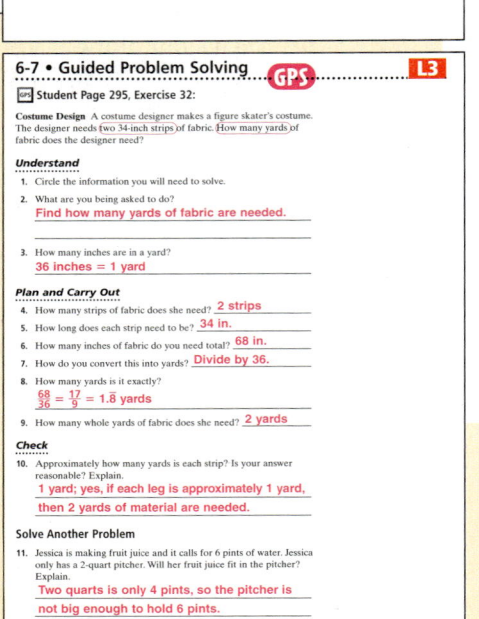

Check Your Understanding

1. *Draw a picture* to show how many yards are in 12 feet.
See margin.

State whether you multiply or divide to change units.

2. pounds to ounces   **3.** feet to yards   **4.** quarts to gallons
    multiply   divide   divide

Is the statement true or false? If false, rewrite the statement to make it true.

5. 6 ft = 3 yd   **6.** 4 c = 32 fl oz   **7.** $2\frac{1}{2}$ t = 4,500 lb
   false; 6 ft = 2 yd   true   false; $2\frac{1}{2}$ t = 5,000 lb

Homework Exercises

For more exercises, see Extra Skills and Word Problems.

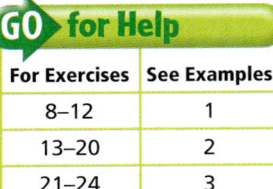

GO for Help

For Exercises	See Examples
8–12	1
13–20	2
21–24	3

A **Complete each statement. You may find a model helpful.**

8. 6 lb = ■ oz   **96**   **9.** 3 mi = ■ ft   **15,840**   **10.** 68 qt = ■ pt   **136**

11. 3 yd = ■ ft   **9**   **12.** 6 qt = ■ pt   **12**   **13.** 40 in. = ■ ft $3\frac{1}{3}$

14. 5,500 lb = ■ t $2\frac{3}{4}$ **15.** $27\frac{1}{4}$ c = ■ pt $13\frac{5}{8}$ **16.** 2,640 ft = ■ mi $\frac{1}{2}$

17. 32 oz = ■ lb   **2**   **18.** 9 fl oz = ■ qt $\frac{9}{32}$ **19.** 24 c = ■ gal $1\frac{1}{2}$

20. You buy 12 ounces of cheese at the store. How many pounds of cheese do you buy? $\frac{3}{4}$ lb

Find the sum or difference.

21.   6 gal 3 qt
   + 4 gal 1 qt
       11 gal

22.   4 ft 8 in.
   − 1 ft 9 in.
     2 ft 11 in.

23.   8 qt 1 cup
   − 6 qt 1 pt
    1 qt 3 cups

24. A female African lion is 5 ft 8 in. long. A male African lion is 7 ft 3 in. long. What is the difference in their lengths?
   1 ft 7 in.

B  **25.** **Guided Problem Solving** The 38,000-foot Mont Blanc Tunnel connects Italy and France through a mountain. The 31-mile Channel Tunnel connects France and England under the English Channel. Which tunnel is longer? **the Channel Tunnel**
   • How many feet are in a mile?
   • Should you change feet to miles, or miles to feet?

26. **Wildlife** The whale shark, the largest fish in the world, can be 50 feet long. How long is the whale shark in inches? **600 in.**

1.   3 ft

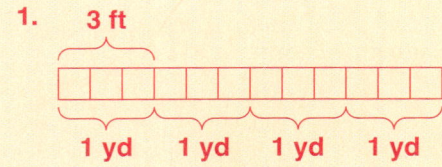

   1 yd   1 yd   1 yd   1 yd

30. Answers may vary.
Sample: When following a recipe, you might need to convert pints to cups or cups to pints.

3. x = yd; y = ft; since 3 ft = 1 yd, to convert 6 feet to yards, you can write $3x = 6$, and $x = 2$. So 6 ft = 2 yd. To convert 9 yards to feet, write $3 \cdot 9 = 27$; 9 yd = 27 ft.

Use <, =, or > to complete each statement.

27. 18 fl oz ▇ 2 c
>

28. $3\frac{1}{2}$ lb ▇ 56 oz
=

29. $1\frac{1}{2}$ t ▇ 4,000 lb
<

30. **Writing in Math** Describe a situation in daily life in which you need to change from one unit of measure to another. **See left.**

31. You have 12 gallons of punch. You estimate that each guest will drink 3 cups. Do you have enough punch for 60 guests? Justify your answer. **Yes. You have 192 cups of punch and you need 180.**

32. **Costume Design** A costume designer makes a figure skater's costume. The designer needs two 34-inch strips of fabric. How many yards of fabric does the designer need? $\frac{17}{18}$ **yd**

33. **(Algebra)** The equation $3x = y$ can be used to convert feet to yards, or yards to feet. Which unit of length is represented by each of the variables x and y? Explain. **See left.**

34. Trucks must weigh 80,000 lb or less to use the highways. In tons, what is the maximum weight allowed for a truck?
40 t

C 35. **Challenge** Use the drawing to find the weight of each block. Explain your reasoning.
A: $5\frac{1}{2}$ lb; B: 9 lb; C: 15 lb

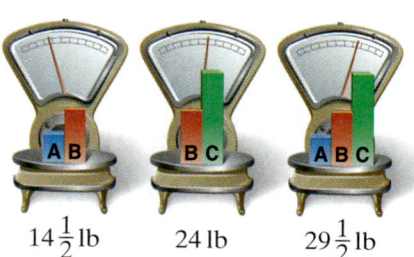

$14\frac{1}{2}$ lb   24 lb $29\frac{1}{2}$ lb

Test Prep and Mixed Review   **Practice**

Multiple Choice

36. Mrs. Kim hired a baby sitter. She paid the babysitter $7 each hour for 3 hours. She spent a total of $55 for the evening. How much did Mrs. Kim spend while she was out? **C**
    Ⓐ $21   Ⓑ $24   Ⓒ $34   Ⓓ $48

37. A football field is 100 yards long. How many lengths of a football field would equal a mile? **G**
    Ⓕ 13.2   Ⓖ 17.6   Ⓗ 26.4   Ⓙ 52.8

38. What is the greatest common factor of 24, 32, and 56? **B**
    Ⓐ 12   Ⓑ 8   Ⓒ 4   Ⓓ 2

Write each difference in simplest form.

39. $8\frac{4}{7} - 3\frac{5}{14}$ $5\frac{3}{14}$ 40. $4\frac{3}{8} - 1\frac{5}{16}$ $3\frac{1}{16}$ 41. $7\frac{2}{9} - 5\frac{5}{6}$ $1\frac{7}{18}$

Lesson Quiz

Use <, =, or > to complete each statement.

1. 6 ft ▇ 74 in. **<**

2. 38 oz ▇ $1\frac{1}{2}$ lb **>**

3. 4 gal ▇ 16 qt **=**

4. Add 1 ft 4 in. and 5 ft 9 in. **7 ft 1 in.**

Alternative Assessment

Provide pairs of students with exercises similar to those in Exercises 8–19 and 27–29. Students make tables of equivalencies for customary units of length, capacity, and weight. Partners work together, referring to their tables, to complete the exercises.

Test Prep

Resources

For additional practice with a variety of test item formats:
• Test-Taking Strategies, p. 297
• Test Prep, p. 301
• Test-Taking Strategies with Transparencies

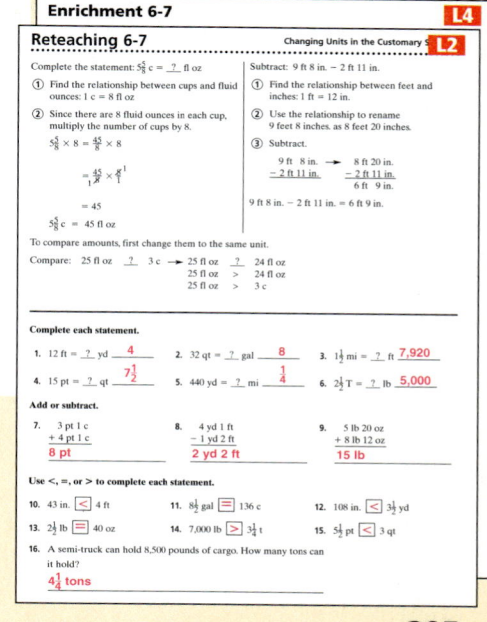

Measuring Objects

Students use customary units to measure objects in the classroom. This will allow them to extend what they learned in Lessons 6-6 and 6-7.

Guided Instruction

Briefly discuss units that you would use to measure different objects in the classroom.

Activity

Ask for volunteers to give answers to Exercises 1–2 and discuss Exercises 3–4 as a class. Allow students to work with a partner on Exercises 5–6. You may wish to assign Exercises 5 and 6 as homework.

Differentiated Instruction

Advanced Learners   L4
Have students work in pairs. Each student should provide one measurement and the area of one surface and ask his or her partner to determine the other measurement.

Resources

- inch ruler
- classroom objects

Checkpoint Quiz

Use this Checkpoint Quiz to check students' understanding of the skills and concepts of Lessons 6-5 through 6-7.

Resources

- All-in-One Teaching Resources Checkpoint Quiz 2
- ExamView CD-ROM
- Success Tracker™ Online Intervention

6-7b   Activity Lab   Hands On

Measuring Objects

You can describe objects using different measures.

ACTIVITY   Check students' work.

1. Examine your textbook. What are some attributes you can use to describe the size of your textbook?

2. Measure the length of your textbook to the nearest $\frac{1}{16}$ inch. Record your measurement. Next, measure the width of your textbook.

3. Compare your measurements to the measurements made by other students in the class.

4. What other attributes can you find to describe your textbook? What tools can you use to measure those attributes?

5. Select a different object in your class or at home. What attributes can you use to describe the object?

6. Measure the attributes of the object. Write them on a card. Hand the card to a classmate. Can your classmate tell what object your measurements describe?

Checkpoint Quiz 2   Lessons 6-5 through 6-7

1. Solve $\frac{2}{3}x = 7$. **$10\frac{1}{2}$**

2. Solve $\frac{1}{3} = \frac{5}{6}h$. **$\frac{2}{5}$**

3. Solve $\frac{1}{2}m = 23$. **46**

4. Solve $\frac{b}{4} = \frac{2}{5}$. **$\frac{8}{5}$ or $1\frac{3}{5}$**

Choose an appropriate unit for each measurement.

5. distance from school to a park **mile**

6. weight of your gym shoes **pound**

7. A 25-mile course has markers at the start, the end, and every $\frac{1}{2}$ mile. How many markers are there? **51 markers**

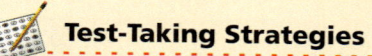
Eliminating Answers

In a multiple-choice problem, you can often eliminate some of the answer choices.

EXAMPLE

A plant that you bought two years ago is 3 feet 2 inches tall. It was 1 foot 11 inches tall when you bought it. How many inches has the plant grown since you bought it?

(A) 3 in.   (B) 11 in.   (C) 15 in.   (D) 61 in.

- The plant is 3 feet 2 inches tall. So it could not have grown 61 inches. Eliminate choice D.

- 3 feet 2 inches is about 3 feet, and 1 foot 11 inches is about 2 feet. So the plant has grown about 1 foot or 12 inches. Eliminate choice A, which is much less than the estimate.

- 11 inches is less than 1 foot. So 11 inches + 1 foot 11 inches is less than 2 feet 11 inches. Eliminate choice B.

- The correct answer is choice C.

Exercises

Identify two choices that you can easily eliminate. Explain why. Then solve the problem.

1. A truck is carrying a load that weighs $15\frac{3}{5}$ tons. The total weight of the truck and the load is $36\frac{1}{2}$ tons. How many tons does the truck weigh? **B**

   (A) $14\frac{9}{10}$ (B) $20\frac{9}{10}$ (C) $21\frac{1}{10}$ (D) $52\frac{1}{10}$

2. The height of a door is 86 inches. A person standing in the doorway is 53 inches tall. Find the approximate distance in feet between the person's head and the top of the door. **H**

   (F) 1 ft   (G) 2 ft   (H) 3 ft   (J) 4 ft

3. You have 2 gallons of juice. How many cups of juice are equivalent to 2 gallons? **B**

   (A) 64 cups   (B) 32 cups   (C) 24 cups   (D) 4 cups

Chapter 6 Review

Go Online
PHSchool.com

For: Vocabulary quiz
Web Code: aqj-0651

Vocabulary Review

 reciprocal (p. 272)

Skills and Concepts

Lessons 6-1 and 6-2
- To multiply fractions and
  to sove problems by
  multiplying fractions
- To estimate and find
  the products of
  mixed numbers

To multiply fractions, multiply the numerators and then multiply
the denominators.

To multiply with mixed numbers, first write the mixed numbers as
improper fractions. Then multiply the fractions.

Estimate each product.

1. $3\frac{1}{3} \times 4\frac{1}{8}$ **12**   2. $5\frac{2}{3} \cdot 1\frac{5}{6}$ **12**   3. $8\frac{3}{8} \times 9\frac{11}{15}$ **80**   4. $7\frac{10}{23} \cdot 12\frac{3}{16}$ **84**

Find each product.

5. $\frac{1}{2} \cdot \frac{3}{5}$ $\frac{3}{10}$ 6. $\frac{12}{13} \times \frac{1}{18}$ $\frac{2}{39}$

7. $\frac{7}{9} \cdot \frac{18}{35}$ $\frac{2}{5}$ 8. $\frac{5}{8} \times 24$ **15**

9. $25 \cdot \frac{7}{10}$ $17\frac{1}{2}$ 10. $5\frac{1}{6} \times \frac{3}{4}$ $3\frac{7}{8}$

11. $3\frac{1}{3} \times 2\frac{2}{25}$ $6\frac{14}{15}$ 12. $4\frac{5}{11} \cdot 4\frac{9}{14}$ $20\frac{15}{22}$

13. **Dessert** A recipe for fruit salad calls for $\frac{2}{3}$ cup peaches. How
    many cups of peaches do you need to make $\frac{1}{2}$ of the original
    recipe? $\frac{1}{3}$ c

Lesson 6-3
- To divide fractions and
  to solve problems by
  dividing fractions

Two numbers are **reciprocals** if their product is 1. The numbers $\frac{2}{3}$
and $\frac{3}{2}$ are reciprocals, as are $\frac{1}{5}$ and 5. To divide by a fraction,
multiply by the reciprocal of the fraction.

Find each quotient.

14. $8 \div \frac{1}{2}$ **16**   15. $4 \div \frac{12}{17}$ $5\frac{2}{3}$ 16. $\frac{3}{11} \div \frac{3}{5}$ $\frac{5}{11}$ 17. $\frac{5}{6} \div \frac{15}{16}$ $\frac{8}{9}$

18. $\frac{4}{7} \div \frac{2}{5}$ $1\frac{3}{7}$ 19. $\frac{18}{25} \div 9$ $\frac{2}{25}$ 20. $3\frac{3}{4} \div \frac{13}{15}$ $4\frac{17}{52}$ 21. $4\frac{1}{7} \div \frac{1}{3}$ $12\frac{3}{7}$

22. You can pick a bucket of tomatoes every $\frac{1}{6}$ hour. How many
    buckets can you pick in $3\frac{1}{3}$ hours? **20 buckets**

Lesson 6-4

• To estimate and compute the quotient of mixed numbers

To divide mixed numbers, first write the numbers as improper fractions. Then multiply by the reciprocal of the divisor.

Estimate each quotient. Then find the quotient.

23. $2\frac{1}{5} \div 2\frac{1}{3}$ **24.** $8\frac{2}{3} \div 3\frac{2}{11}$ **25.** $12\frac{2}{7} \div 3\frac{5}{9}$ **26.** $13\frac{1}{2} \div 7\frac{5}{16}$

$1; \frac{33}{35}$ $3; 2\frac{76}{105}$ $3; 3\frac{51}{112}$ $2; 1\frac{11}{13}$

27. A hair stylist schedules appointments every $\frac{1}{3}$ hour. About how many appointments can a hair stylist schedule in $6\frac{1}{2}$ hours?
about 19 appointments

Lesson 6-5

• To write fraction equations and solve them by multiplying

To solve equations in which a variable is multiplied by a fraction, multiply both sides of the equation by the reciprocal of the fraction. If the variable is multiplied by a mixed number, write the mixed number as an improper fraction. Then solve.

Solve each equation.

28. $\frac{m}{6} = 16$ **96**   **29.** $\frac{2}{5}x = 10$ **25**   **30.** $\frac{3}{8}k = \frac{3}{4}$ **2**   **31.** $\frac{6}{7}y = \frac{9}{14}$ $\frac{3}{4}$

32. $\frac{5}{6}z = 3\frac{1}{3}$ **4**   **33.** $\frac{4}{5}w = 1\frac{3}{5}$ **2**   **34.** $\frac{2}{3}x = 4\frac{4}{5}$ $7\frac{1}{5}$ **35.** $5a = 1\frac{3}{10}$ $\frac{13}{50}$

Lessons 6-6 and 6-7

• To choose appropriate units and to estimate in the customary system
• To convert between units in the customary system

When deciding what unit of measurement to use, first decide whether you are measuring length, weight, or capacity. The table below can help you change measurements.

Length	Weight	Capacity
12 inches = 1 foot	16 ounces = 1 pound	8 fluid ounces = 1 cup
3 feet = 1 yard	2,000 pounds = 1 ton	2 cups = 1 pint
5,280 feet = 1 mile		2 pints = 1 quart
		4 quarts = 1 gallon

Choose an appropriate customary unit for each measurement.

36. weight of a car   **tons**   **37.** capacity of a can of soda
                                                          fluid ounces

Complete each statement.

38. 880 in. $= \blacksquare$ ft   **39.** $2\frac{1}{2}$ gal $= \blacksquare$ c   **40.** $12,000$ lb $= \blacksquare$ t
          $73\frac{1}{3}$ **40**   **6**

41. You are making bows from 50 yards of ribbon. How many feet of ribbon do you have? **150 ft**

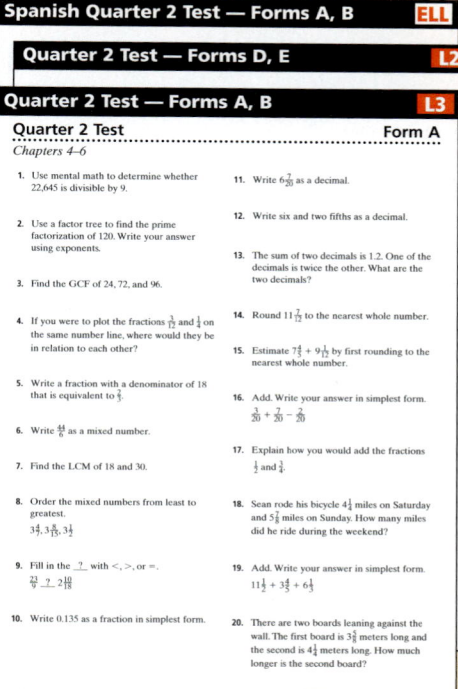

Chapter 6 Test

Go Online PHSchool.com For: Online chapter test Web Code: aqa-0652

Resources

- ExamView Assessment Suite CD-ROM
  - Ch. 6 Ready-Made Test
  - Make your own Ch. 6 test
- MindPoint Quiz Show CD-ROM
  - Chapter 6 Review

Differentiated **Instruction**

All-in-One Teaching Resources
- Below Level Chapter 6 Test **L2**
- Chapter 6 Test **L3**
- Chapter 6 Alternative Assessment **L4**

Spanish Assessment Resources **ELL**
- Below Level Chapter 6 Test **L2**
- Chapter 6 Test **L3**
- Chapter 6 Alternative Assessment **L4**

ExamView Assessment Suite CD-ROM
- Special Needs Test **L1**
- Special Needs Practice Bank **L1**

Online Chapter 6 Test at www.PHSchool.com **L3**

Estimate each product.

1. $4\frac{2}{3} \times 1\frac{2}{7}$ **5**
2. $5\frac{3}{4} \cdot 7\frac{4}{9}$ **42**
3. $2\frac{1}{2} \cdot \frac{11}{19}$ **3**
4. $9\frac{1}{8} \times 2\frac{5}{6}$ **27**

Find each product.

5. $\frac{3}{8}$ of 32 **12**
6. $\frac{5}{6} \cdot \frac{12}{25}$ **$\frac{2}{5}$**
7. $\frac{7}{9} \cdot 5\frac{4}{7}$ **$4\frac{1}{3}$**
8. $3\frac{1}{3} \times 2\frac{3}{4}$ **$9\frac{1}{6}$**

9. **Building Design** A log cabin has walls built with 12 logs lying horizontally on top of one another. If each log is $\frac{3}{4}$ foot thick, how high is each wall? **9 ft**

10. Jolene weighs 96 pounds. Jolene's father weighs $1\frac{7}{8}$ times as much as she does. How much does her father weigh? **180 lb**

Find each quotient.

11. $15 \div \frac{9}{11}$ **$18\frac{1}{3}$**
12. $\frac{2}{5} \div \frac{8}{25}$ **$1\frac{1}{4}$**
13. $\frac{5}{7} \div 25$ **$\frac{1}{35}$**
14. $6\frac{3}{4} \div 4\frac{1}{2}$ **$1\frac{1}{2}$**

Estimate each quotient.

15. $10\frac{4}{17} \div 4\frac{5}{9}$ **2**
16. $30\frac{2}{7} \div 15\frac{1}{10}$ **2**

17. **Encyclopedias** Several volumes of an encyclopedia fill a shelf. Each volume is $1\frac{1}{4}$ inches wide, and the shelf is $27\frac{1}{2}$ inches long. How many volumes are in the encyclopedia? **22 volumes**

Solve for x.

18. $\frac{1}{3}x = 5$ **15**
19. $\frac{2}{3}x = \frac{7}{24}$ **$\frac{7}{16}$**
20. $\frac{1}{3}x = 3\frac{1}{7}$ **$9\frac{3}{7}$**
21. $\frac{x}{3} = 8$ **24**

22. How many miles equal 63,360 inches? **1 mi**

23. How many gallons equal $36\frac{1}{2}$ quarts? **$9\frac{1}{8}$ gal**

24. Instead of walking from school to the grocery store, Scott walks 2 miles from school to the video store. His walk is $\frac{5}{6}$ of the distance to the grocery store. How far from school is the grocery store? **$2\frac{2}{5}$ mi**

25. There are $1\frac{1}{3}$ times as many girls as there are boys at a party. If there are 18 boys, how many people are at the party? **42 people**

Complete each statement.

26. $5\frac{3}{4}$ ft = ■ yd **$1\frac{11}{12}$**

27. 150 lb = ■ oz **2,400**

Use <, =, or > to complete each statement.

28. 15 qt ■ $3\frac{1}{2}$ gal **>**

29. 16 fl oz ■ 1 pt **=**

30. **Writing in Math** Explain how you can use the Distributive Property to find $7\frac{2}{5} \times 5$. **See margin.**

31. Give an appropriate customary unit of measurement for each object.
   a. weight of an airplane **tons**
   b. length of a soccer field **yards**
   c. amount of water in a bathtub **gallons**
   d. amount of mouthwash in one mouthful **fluid ounces**
   e. weight of a mouse **ounces**
   f. length of a child's foot **inches**

---

30. **Answers may vary. Sample: Multiply: $5 \times 7 = 35$ and $5 \times \frac{2}{5} = 2$; $35 + 2 = 37$.**

Below Level Chapter Test **L2**

Chapter Test **L3**

Chapter Test   Form A
Chapter 6
Estimate each product or quotient.
1. $9\frac{3}{4} \times 2\frac{1}{5}$ **20**
2. $11\frac{3}{4} \div 1\frac{5}{6}$ **6**
3. $29\frac{5}{8} \div 5\frac{1}{9}$ **6**
4. $4\frac{1}{8} \times 10\frac{5}{9}$ **44**

Find each product or quotient.
5. $\frac{5}{8} \div \frac{5}{6}$ **$\frac{2}{3}$**
6. $\frac{2}{5}$ of 35 **14**
7. $1\frac{8}{11} \div \frac{1}{3}$ **$5\frac{5}{11}$**
8. $\frac{1}{2} \times \frac{3}{4}$ **$\frac{3}{8}$**
9. $2\frac{1}{5} \times 1\frac{1}{3}$ **$2\frac{14}{15}$**
10. $18 \div \frac{1}{8}$ **144**
11. $7\frac{3}{5} \div 3$ **$2\frac{3}{5}$**
12. $3 \times 4\frac{5}{9}$ **$14\frac{1}{7}$**

Solve.
13. Kisha plans to double a recipe for cookies. The original recipe calls for $1\frac{3}{8}$ cups of flour. How much does she need for the doubled recipe? Write as a mixed number in simplest form. **$2\frac{3}{4}$ cups**
14. Sammy wants to make a half portion of a recipe that calls for $1\frac{1}{3}$ cups of milk. How much milk does she need for the half portion? **$\frac{2}{3}$ cup**
15. You want to cut a 10-foot board into $2\frac{1}{2}$-foot lengths. How many pieces will you have? **4 pieces**

Match the object in the left column with the most appropriate unit of measurement in the right column.
16. length of a person's ear **b** a. tons
17. weight of an elephant **a** b. inches
18. amount of shampoo in a bottle **c** c. fluid ounces
19. length of an airport runway **e** d. ounces
20. weight of a penny **d** e. miles
21. amount of water in a reflecting pool **f** f. gallons

Reading Comprehension

Read each passage and answer the questions that follow.

In the Dough Here is a recipe for making modeling dough.

1 cup flour	$1\frac{1}{2}$ teaspoons cream of tartar
$\frac{1}{2}$ cup salt	1 tablespoon vegetable oil
1 cup water	a few drops of food coloring

Heat the vegetable oil in a pan. Then add the other ingredients. Stir constantly. Let dough cool. Store in an airtight container.

1. How many cups of flour, salt, and water does the recipe call for? **C**

  Ⓐ $1\frac{1}{2}$ cups   Ⓒ $2\frac{1}{2}$ cups

  Ⓑ 2 cups   Ⓓ $2\frac{3}{4}$ cups

2. Suppose you only have enough flour to make half a batch of dough. How much salt would you need? **F**

  Ⓕ $\frac{1}{4}$ cup   Ⓗ $\frac{3}{4}$ cup

  Ⓖ $\frac{1}{2}$ cup   Ⓙ 1 cup

3. Suppose you only have 1 teaspoon of cream of tartar. By what fraction will you need to multiply the other ingredients in order to make dough with the same consistency? **C**

  Ⓐ $\frac{1}{3}$ Ⓑ $\frac{1}{2}$ Ⓒ $\frac{2}{3}$ Ⓓ $\frac{3}{4}$

4. What fraction of a cup of cream of tartar does the recipe call for? (There are 48 teaspoons in 1 cup.) **F**

  Ⓕ $\frac{1}{32}$ Ⓖ $\frac{1}{16}$ Ⓗ $\frac{1}{3}$ Ⓙ $\frac{1}{2}$

Video Value Carlos, Lisa, and Lenny found a box of used computer games at a yard sale. Carlos wanted four of the games, Lisa wanted two of them, and Lenny wanted the other six. The price for the box of computer games was $18. They planned to split the cost according to how many games each person wanted.

5. What fraction of the computer games did Lisa pick? **A**

  Ⓐ $\frac{1}{6}$ Ⓑ $\frac{1}{4}$ Ⓒ $\frac{1}{3}$ Ⓓ $\frac{2}{3}$

6. How much should Lenny pay? **H**

  Ⓕ $4   Ⓖ $6   Ⓗ $9   Ⓙ $12

7. How much should Lisa pay? **A**

  Ⓐ $3   Ⓑ $4   Ⓒ $6   Ⓓ $8

8. What fraction of the computer games did Lenny and Carlos pick together? **H**

  Ⓕ $\frac{2}{3}$ Ⓖ $\frac{3}{4}$ Ⓗ $\frac{5}{6}$ Ⓙ $\frac{7}{8}$

Chapter 6 Test Prep **301**

Test Prep

Resources

Test Prep Workbook

All in One Teaching Resources
- Cumulative Review **L3**

ExamView Assessment Suite CD-ROM
- Standardized Test Practice

Differentiated Instruction

Progress Monitoring Assessments
- Benchmark Test 3 **L3**
- Quarter 2 Test
  - Forms A & B **L3**
  - Forms D & E **L2**

- Mid-Course Test
  - Forms A & B **L3**
  - Forms D & E **L2**

Spanish Assessment Resources
- Spanish Cumulative Review **ELL**
- Spanish Quarter 2 Test
  - Forms A & B **L3**

- Spanish Mid-Course Test
  - Forms A & B **L3**

ExamView Assessment Suite CD-ROM
- Special Needs Practice Bank **L1**

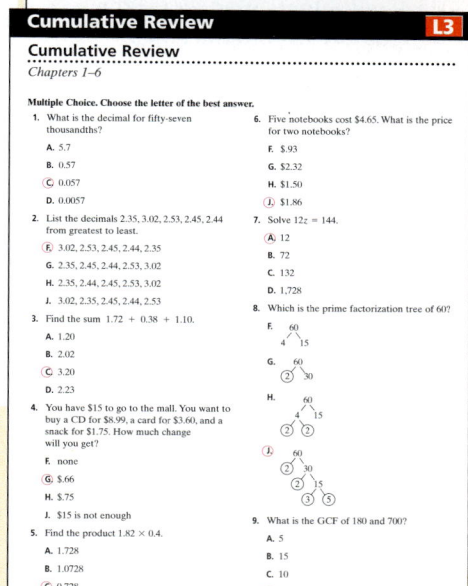

Applying Mixed Numbers

Students will use data from these two pages to answer the questions posed in Put It All Together.

Have students share any experiences they have had swimming and diving. Ask questions such as:

- *How do you swim the breaststroke?*
- *How do you swim the butterfly?*
- *What are other competitive strokes?*

Materials

- Photos or diagrams of correct breaststroke and butterfly form
- Photos or diagrams of regulation-size pool

Activating Prior Knowledge

Invite any students who swim or who are familiar with the sport to talk about the events at a swim meet. Ask them to describe the different types and lengths of races, as well as the size and shape of a regulation-size pool and its lanes.

Guided Instruction

Have volunteers read aloud the data about swimming. Ask questions such as:

- *If a pool has 8 lanes, and each lane is $8\frac{1}{4}$ ft. wide, how wide is the pool?* **66 ft**
- *If there is an extra $\frac{1}{2}$ foot of space on the outside edges of the first and last lanes, how wide is the pool?* **67 ft**
- *If a swimmer has gone $36\frac{1}{2}$ meters in a 50-meter pool, how much farther does he or she have to go to reach the wall?* **$13\frac{1}{2}$ ft**
- *How much farther does he or she have to go if it is a 100-meter race?* **$63\frac{1}{2}$ ft**

DK **Problem Solving Application**

Applying Mixed Numbers

Swimming to Win Suppose you want to build a set of shelves to hold the trophies and photographs for your school's swim team. Knowing how to work with fractions and mixed numbers can help you design and build shelves.

Put It All Together

1. Suppose you are building a trophy case $36\frac{3}{4}$ inches tall with three evenly spaced shelves, each $\frac{3}{4}$ inch thick. Let h represent the height of each shelf. Calculate h.

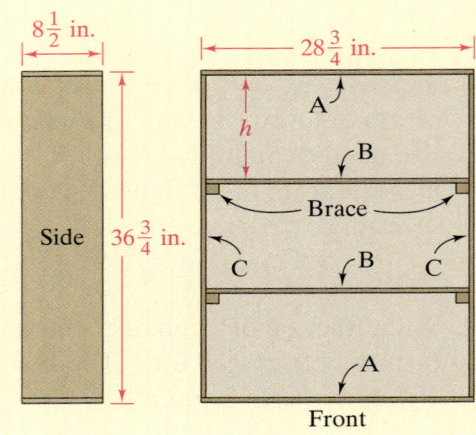

$8\frac{1}{2}$ in.

$28\frac{3}{4}$ in.

Side $36\frac{3}{4}$ in.

A

B

Brace

C B C

A

Front

2. Calculate the length of each of the boards needed to build the trophy case, including the top and bottom (A), the shelves (B), and the sides (C). Sketch each piece with its dimensions labeled.

3. **a.** A lumberyard sells boards that are 8 feet long and boards that are 10 feet long. How many 8-foot boards would you need to buy? How many 10-foot boards would you need? Draw a diagram to support your answers.

   b. The price of the lumber is $3.25 per foot. How much would the lumber for the project cost?

Off the Block

To power your dive off the starting block, grip the block with your hands and toes and put your weight on your back foot. Next, pull hard with your arms and push with your feet.

302

1. $11\frac{1}{4}$ in.

2.

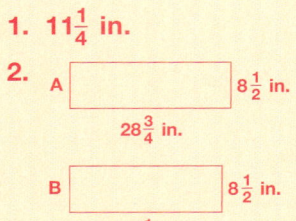

A $8\frac{1}{2}$ in.
$28\frac{3}{4}$ in.

B $8\frac{1}{2}$ in.
$27\frac{1}{4}$ in.

C $8\frac{1}{2}$ in.
$36\frac{3}{4}$ in.

3a. **Answers may vary. Sample: two 8-foot boards cut as shown**

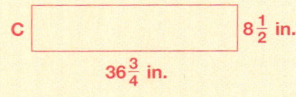

96 in.

C	A	B
$36\frac{3}{4}$ in.	$28\frac{3}{4}$ in.	$27\frac{1}{4}$ in. $3\frac{1}{4}$ in.

b. **$52**

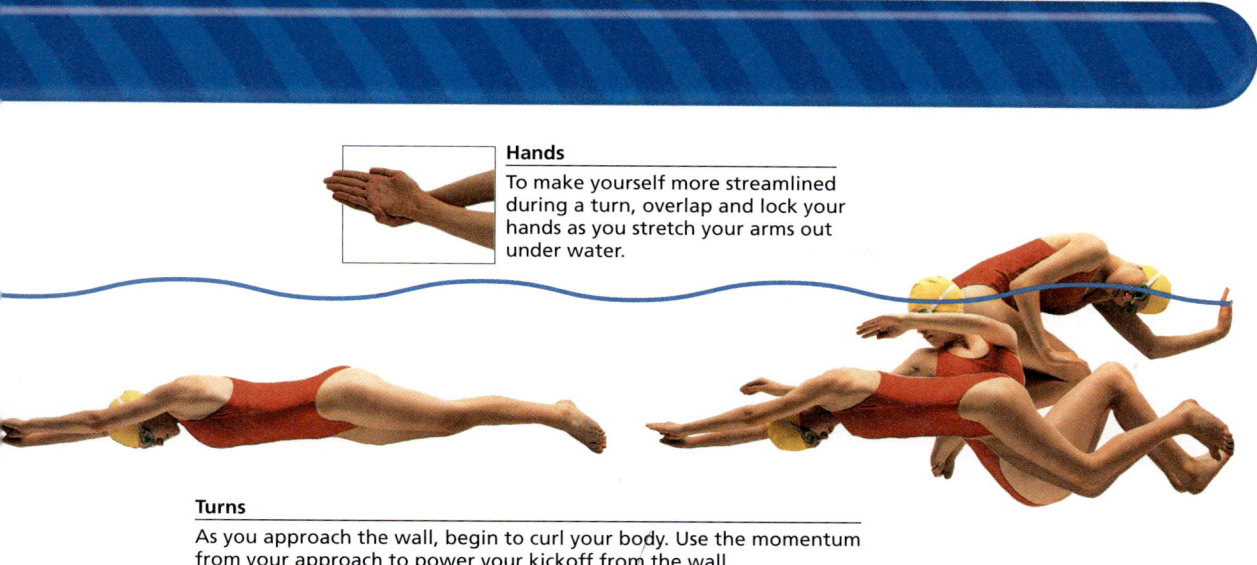

Hands

To make yourself more streamlined during a turn, overlap and lock your hands as you stretch your arms out under water.

Turns

As you approach the wall, begin to curl your body. Use the momentum from your approach to power your kickoff from the wall.

Go Online
PHSchool.com

For: Information about school sports
Web Code: aqe-0653

The Butterfly Stroke

The butterfly was invented in the early 1930s but was considered a form of the breaststroke until 1952. Originally the kick was similar to the breaststroke kick, but now swimmers use the more efficient "dolphin kick."

As your arms sweep backward, raise your head out of the water and take a breath.

303

Activity

Have students share their experiences measuring and building shelves. Ask them to identify any components of the process not included here. Then have students work in pairs to answer the questions.

Exercise 2 Ask students to find the maximum height of a book that can fit on one of these shelves. $11\frac{1}{4}$ **in. high**

Exercise 3 Discuss with students that experienced carpenters know to buy more lumber than they need to account for errors. Have students keep this in mind as they justify their answers.

Differentiated Instruction

Special Needs **L1**

Help students read the diagram and visualize what this shelf looks like. Guide them to understand that a shelf has height, width, and depth, and that the wood itself has thickness. Ask:
- *How deep is this bookshelf?* $8\frac{1}{2}$ **inches**
- *How wide is it?* $28\frac{3}{4}$ **inches wide, or** $27\frac{1}{4}$ **inches of interior space per shelf**

Have students identify some books in the classroom that would fit on this shelf.

Chapter at a Glance

Lesson Titles, Objectives, and Features	Assessment	NCTM Standards	Local Standards
7-1 Ratios • To write ratios to compare real-world quantities **7-1b Activity Lab, Hands On:** Modeling Ratios **Vocabulary Builder:** High-Use Academic Words	Lesson Quiz	1, 2, 6, 7, 8, 9, 10	
7-2 Unit Rates • To find and use unit rates and unit costs	Lesson Quiz	1, 2, 6, 7, 8, 9, 10	
7-3 Understanding Proportions • To understand proportions and determine whether two ratios are proportional	Lesson Quiz	1, 2, 6, 7, 8, 9, 10	
7-4 Solving Proportions • To solve proportions using number sense and cross products **7-4b Activity Lab, Hands On:** Predicting Results	Lesson Quiz Checkpoint Quiz 1	1, 2, 6, 7, 8, 9, 10	
7-5 Scale Drawings • To find the scale of a drawing and to use scales to find actual dimensions	Lesson Quiz	1, 2, 6, 7, 8, 9, 10	
7-6a Activity Lab, Hands On: Modeling Percents **7-6 Percents, Fractions, and Decimals** • To find equivalent forms of fractions, decimals, and percents	Lesson Quiz Checkpoint Quiz 2	1, 2, 5, 6, 7, 8, 9, 10	
7-7 Finding the Percent of a Number • To use percents to find part of a whole	Lesson Quiz	1, 2, 6, 7, 8, 9, 10	
7-8a Activity Lab, Hands On: Exploring Circle Graphs **7-8 Circle Graphs** • To read and make circle graphs to represent real-world data **7-8b Activity Lab, Technology:** Reporting Survey Results **Guided Problem Solving:** Practice Solving Problems	Lesson Quiz	1, 2, 5, 6, 7, 8, 9, 10	
7-9 Estimating with Percents • To use mental math and estimation with percents	Lesson Quiz	1, 2, 6, 7, 8, 9, 10	
Problem Solving Application: Applying Proportions			

NCTM Standards 2000
1 Number and Operations   2 Algebra   3 Geometry   4 Measurement   5 Data Analysis and Probability
6 Problem Solving   7 Reasoning and Proof   8 Communication   9 Connections   10 Representation

Correlations to Standardized Tests

All content for these tests is contained in *Prentice Hall Math*, Course 1. This chart reflects coverage in this chapter only.

	7-1	7-2	7-3	7-4	7-5	7-6	7-7	7-8	7-9
Terra Nova CAT6 (Level 16)									
Number and Number Relations	✔	✔	✔	✔	✔	✔	✔	✔	✔
Computation and Numerical Estimation	✔	✔	✔	✔	✔	✔	✔	✔	✔
Operation Concepts	✔	✔	✔	✔	✔	✔	✔	✔	✔
Measurement									
Geometry and Spatial Sense									
Data Analysis, Statistics, and Probability						✔		✔	
Patterns, Functions, Algebra	✔	✔	✔	✔	✔	✔	✔	✔	✔
Problem Solving and Reasoning	✔	✔	✔	✔	✔	✔	✔	✔	✔
Communication	✔	✔	✔	✔	✔	✔	✔	✔	✔
Decimals, Fractions, Integers, Percent	✔	✔	✔	✔	✔	✔	✔	✔	✔
Order of Operations									
Terra Nova CTBS (Level 16)									
Whole Numbers, Decimals, Fractions	✔	✔	✔	✔	✔	✔	✔	✔	✔
Numeration, Number Theory	✔	✔	✔	✔	✔	✔	✔	✔	✔
Data Interpretation						✔		✔	
Pre-algebra	✔	✔	✔	✔	✔	✔	✔	✔	✔
Measurement									
Geometry									
ITBS (Level 12)									
Number Properties and Operations	✔	✔	✔	✔	✔	✔	✔	✔	✔
Algebra	✔	✔	✔	✔	✔	✔	✔	✔	✔
Geometry									
Measurement									
Probability and Statistics								✔	
Estimation									✔
SAT10 (Adv 1 Level)									
Number Sense and Operations	✔	✔	✔	✔	✔	✔	✔	✔	✔
Patterns, Relationships, and Algebra	✔	✔	✔	✔	✔	✔	✔	✔	✔
Data, Statistics, and Probability						✔		✔	
Geometry and Measurement									
NAEP									
Number Sense, Properties, and Operations	✔	✔	✔	✔	✔	✔	✔	✔	
Measurement					✔				
Geometry and Spatial Sense									
Data Analysis, Statistics, and Probability									
Algebra and Functions									✔

CAT6 California Achievement Test, 6th Ed. **CTBS** Comprehensive Test of Basic Skills **ITBS** Iowa Test of Basic Skills, Form M
SAT10 Stanford Achievement Test, 10th Ed. **NAEP** National Assessment of Educational Progress 2005 Mathematics Objectives

Math Background

Skills Trace

BEFORE Chapter 7

Grade 5 presented fractions, decimals, and percents.

DURING Chapter 7

Course 1 introduces ratios, proportions, and percents with applications such as scale drawings.

AFTER Chapter 7

Throughout this course, students apply proportional reasoning to solve problems.

7-1 Ratios

> **Math Understandings**
> - A ratio compares two similar measures by means of division.
> - All ratios can be written in fraction form.
> - Equivalent ratios can be generated using multiplication or division, just as with fractions.
> - The order of the numbers in a ratio is extremely important.

A **ratio** is a comparison of two numbers by division. Each number in a ratio is called a *term*. Each of the following ratios are read "six to two."

Three Ways to Write a Ratio		
In Words	**With a Symbol**	**As a Fraction**
6 to 2	6 : 2	$\frac{6}{2}$

Two ratios that name the same number are **equivalent ratios.** You can find equivalent ratios by multiplying or dividing each term of a ratio by the same nonzero number.

Example: Write two different ratios equivalent to $\frac{4}{6}$.

$$\frac{4}{6} = \frac{4 \div 2}{6 \div 2} = \frac{2}{3} \text{ and } \frac{4}{6} = \frac{4 \times 3}{6 \times 3} = \frac{12}{18}$$

7-2 Unit Rates

> **Math Understandings**
> - Rates and unit rates are special types of ratios.
> - You can easily make price comparisons for products of different package sizes by finding the unit cost for each.

A **rate** is a ratio that compares two quantities measured in different units. The rate for one unit of a given quantity is called the **unit rate**. A unit rate that gives the cost per unit, such as $1.29 per lb, is a **unit cost.**

Example: Find the unit rate for 370 heart beats in 5 minutes.

$$\frac{\text{beats}}{\text{min}} = \frac{370 \text{ heart beats}}{5 \text{ min}}$$
$$= 74 \text{ beats per min}$$

7-3 Understanding Proportions
7-4 Solving Proportions

> **Math Understandings**
> - In any true proportion, the product of the means equals the product of the extremes. These are called cross products.

A **proportion** is an equation stating that two ratios are equal. You can use the Multiplication Property of Equality to show an important property of proportions.

$$\frac{3}{4} = \frac{15}{20}$$
$$4 \times 20 \times \frac{3}{4} = 4 \times 20 \times \frac{15}{20} \leftarrow \textit{Multiply each side by 4 and 20.}$$
$${}^{1}\!\!\!\!\diagup\!\!4 \times 20 \times \frac{3}{{}_{1}\diagup\!\!4} = 4 \times {}^{1}\!\!\!\!\diagup\!\!20 \times \frac{15}{{}_{1}\diagup\!\!20} \leftarrow \textit{Divide by common factors.}$$
$$20 \times 3 = 4 \times 15$$
$$60 = 60$$

The products 20×3 and 4×15 are called **cross products.** You can find the cross products of two ratios by multiplying the denominator of each ratio by the numerator of the other ratio.

Example: Solve $\frac{x}{32} = \frac{2}{8}$.

$$8x = 32 \cdot 2 \rightarrow x = \frac{64}{8}, \text{ or } 8$$

7-5 Scale Drawings

Math Understandings
- Maps, models, and scale drawings have corresponding quantities that vary proportionally.

A **scale** is the ratio that compares a length in a drawing or model to the length in the original object. The scale of the original envelope to the enlarged envelope is 1 to 3 or $\frac{1}{3}$.

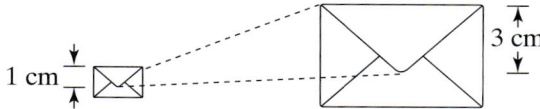

7-6 Percents, Fractions, and Decimals

Math Understandings
- You can represent a percent in different but related ways, such as a ratio, a fraction, and a decimal.
- You can rewrite a decimal that names hundredths directly as the equivalent percent.

A **percent** is a ratio that compares a number to 100. You can write any percent as a decimal. When you write a percent as a fraction, write the fraction in simplest form. To write a decimal as a percent, you multiply by 100, or move the decimal point two places to the right. When the denominator of a fraction is a factor of 100, you can use equal ratios to convert the fraction to an equivalent fraction with denominator of 100 and then to a percent. When the denominator of a fraction is not a factor of 100, convert the fraction to a decimal by dividing, and then write the decimal as a percent.

Examples: $36\% = 0.36 = \frac{36}{100} = \frac{9}{25}$

$\frac{40}{75} = 0.533333\ldots = 53.\overline{3}\%$

7-7 Finding the Percent of a Number

Math Understandings
- Knowing the fraction equivalent of common percents can help you use mental math to calculate with them.

You can find a given percent of a number by rewriting the percent as either a decimal or a fraction and then multiplying.

Example: Find 36% of 112. $0.36 \times 112 = 40.32$

Here are the fraction equivalents of common percents.

Percent	10%	20%	25%	50%	75%
Fraction	$\frac{1}{10}$	$\frac{1}{5}$	$\frac{1}{4}$	$\frac{1}{2}$	$\frac{3}{4}$
Decimal	0.1	0.2	0.25	0.5	0.75

7-8 Circle Graphs

Math Understandings
- You can use a circle graph when the data are in various categories that total 100%.

A **circle graph** is a graph of data where the circle represents the whole. Each wedge in the circle represents a part.

7-9 Estimating With Percents

Math Understandings
- You can estimate percents in daily transactions such as paying sales tax and figuring the tip on a restaurant bill.

Example: Estimate a 15% tip of $14.

First find 10% of $14 ($1.40). Then add half of that amount ($.70) which is 5%. A 15% tip of $14 is $1.40 + $.70, or $2.10.

Additional Professional Development Opportunities

Math Background Notes for Chapter 7: Every lesson has a Math Background in the PLAN section.

Research Overview, Mathematics Strands Additional support for these topics and more is in the front of the Teacher's Edition.

LessonLab LessonLab, a Pearson Education company, offers comprehensive, facilitated professional development designed to help teachers to improve student achievement. To learn more, please visit lessonlab.com.

Chapter 7 Resources

Print Resources

	7-1	7-2	7-3	7-4	7-5	7-6	7-7	7-8	7-9	For the Chapter
L3 Practice	●	●	●	●	●	●	●	●	●	
L1 Adapted Practice	●	●	●	●	●	●	●	●	●	
L3 Guided Problem Solving	●	●	●	●	●	●	●	●	●	
L2 Reteaching	●	●	●	●	●	●	●	●	●	
L4 Enrichment	●	●	●	●	●	●	●	●	●	
L3 Daily Notetaking Guide	●	●	●	●	●	●	●	●	●	
L1 Adapted Daily Notetaking Guide	●	●	●	●	●	●	●	●	●	
L3 Vocabulary and Study Skills Worksheets	●	●	●	●	●	●	●	●	●	●
L3 Daily Puzzles	●	●	●	●	●	●	●	●	●	
L3 Activity Labs	●	●	●	●	●	●	●	●	●	
L3 Checkpoint Quiz				●		●				
L3 Chapter Project										●
L2 Below Level Chapter Test										●
L3 Chapter Test										●
L4 Alternative Assessment										●
L3 Cumulative Review										●

Spanish Resources ELL

	7-1	7-2	7-3	7-4	7-5	7-6	7-7	7-8	7-9	For the Chapter
L3 Practice	●	●	●	●	●	●	●	●	●	
L3 Vocabulary and Study Skills Worksheets	●		●		●		●		●	●
L3 Checkpoint Quiz				●		●				
L2 Below Level Chapter Test										●
L3 Chapter Test										●
L4 Alternative Assessment										●
L3 Cumulative Review										●

Transparencies

	7-1	7-2	7-3	7-4	7-5	7-6	7-7	7-8	7-9	For the Chapter
Check Skills You'll Need	●	●	●	●	●	●	●	●	●	
Additional Examples	●	●	●	●	●	●	●	●	●	
Problem of the Day	●	●	●	●	●	●	●	●	●	
Classroom Aid								●		
Student Edition Answers	●	●	●	●	●	●	●	●	●	●
Lesson Quiz	●	●	●	●	●	●	●	●	●	
Test-Taking Strategies										●

Technology

	7-1	7-2	7-3	7-4	7-5	7-6	7-7	7-8	7-9	For the Chapter
Interactive Textbook Online	●	●	●	●	●	●	●	●	●	●
StudentExpress™ CD-ROM	●	●	●	●	●	●	●	●	●	●
Success Tracker™ Online Intervention	●	●	●	●	●	●	●	●	●	●
TeacherExpress™ CD-ROM	●	●	●	●	●	●	●	●	●	●
PresentationExpress™ with QuickTake Presenter CD-ROM	●	●	●	●	●	●	●	●	●	●
ExamView® Assessment Suite CD-ROM	●	●	●	●	●	●	●	●	●	●
MindPoint® Quiz Show CD-ROM										●
Prentice Hall Web Site: PHSchool.com	●	●	●	●	●	●	●	●	●	●

Also available: **Prentice Hall Assessment System**
- Progress Monitoring Assessments
- Skills and Concepts Review
- Test Prep Workbook

Other Resources
Algebra Readiness Tests
All-in-One Student Workbook
All-in-One Student Workbook, Adapted Version
Multilingual Handbook

Solution Key
Math Notes Study Folder
Spanish Cumulative Assessment

Where You Can Use the Lesson Resources

Here is a suggestion, following the four-step teaching plan, for how you can incorporate Differentiated Instruction Resources into your teaching.

	Instructional Resources `L3`	**Differentiated** Instruction **Resources**
1. Plan		
Preparation Read the Math Background in the Teacher's Edition to connect this lesson with students' previous experience. **Starting Class** **Check Skills You'll Need** Assign these exercises to review prerequisite skills. **New Vocabulary** Help students pre-read the lesson by pointing out the new terms introduced in the lesson.	**Math Background** **Math Understandings** **Transparencies & PresentationExpress™ CD-ROM** Check Skills You'll Need Problem of the Day **Resources** Vocabulary and Study Skills	**Spanish Support** **ELL** Vocabulary and Study Skills
2. Teach		
`L3` **Guided Instruction** Use the Activity Labs to build conceptual understanding. Teach each Example. Use the Teacher's Edition side column notes for specific teaching tips, including Error Prevention notes. Use the Additional Examples found in the side column (and on transparency and PowerPoint) as an alternative presentation for the content. After each Example, assign the Quick Check exercise for that Example to get an immediate assessment of student understanding. Use the Closure activity in the Teacher's Edition to help students attain mastery of lesson content.	**Student Edition** Activity Lab **Resources** Daily Notetaking Guide Activity Lab **Transparencies & PresentationExpress™ CD-ROM** Additional Examples Classroom Aids **ExamView® CD-ROM with QuickTake**	**Teacher's Edition** Every lesson includes suggestions for working with students who need special attention. **L1** Special Needs **L2** Below Level **L4** Advanced Learners **ELL** English Language Learners **Resources** **L1** Adapted Daily Notetaking Guide **Multilingual Handbook**
3. Practice		

Assignment Guide
Check Your Understanding
Use these questions to check students' understanding before you assign homework.
Homework Exercises
Assign homework from these leveled exercises in the Assignment Guide.
  A Practice by Example
  B Apply Your Skills
  C Challenge
  Test Prep and Mixed Review
Homework Quick Check
Use these key exercises to quickly check students' homework.
	Transparencies & PresentationExpress™ CD-ROM
	Student Answers
	Resources
	Practice
	Guided Problem Solving
	Vocabulary and Study Skills
	Activity Lab
	Daily Puzzles
	ExamView® CD-ROM with QuickTake
		Spanish Support
		ELL Practice
		ELL Vocabulary and Study Skills
		Resources
		L1 Adapted Practice
		L4 Enrichment

4. Assess & Reteach		
Lesson Quiz Assign the Lesson Quiz to assess students' mastery of the lesson content. **Checkpoint Quiz** Use the Checkpoint Quiz to assess student progress over several lessons.	**Transparencies & PresentationExpress™ CD-ROM** Lesson Quiz **Resources** Checkpoint Quiz	**Resources** **L2** Reteaching **ELL** Checkpoint Quiz Success Tracker™ Online Intervention **ExamView® CD-ROM with QuickTake**

KEY   **L1** Special Needs   **L2** Below Level   **L3** For All Students   **L4** Advanced, Gifted   **ELL** English Language Learners

CHAPTER 7 **Ratios, Proportions, and Percents**

Ratios, Proportions, and Percents

Check Your Readiness

Answers are in the back of the textbook.

For intervention, direct students to:

Solving Equations
Lesson 3-7
Extra Skills and Word Problems Practice, Ch. 3

Simplifying Fractions
Lesson 4-5
Extra Skills and Word Problems Practice, Ch. 4

Comparing Fractions
Lesson 4-8
Extra Skills and Word Problems Practice, Ch. 4

Multiplying and Dividing Fractions
Lesson 6-3
Extra Skills and Word Problems Practice, Ch. 6

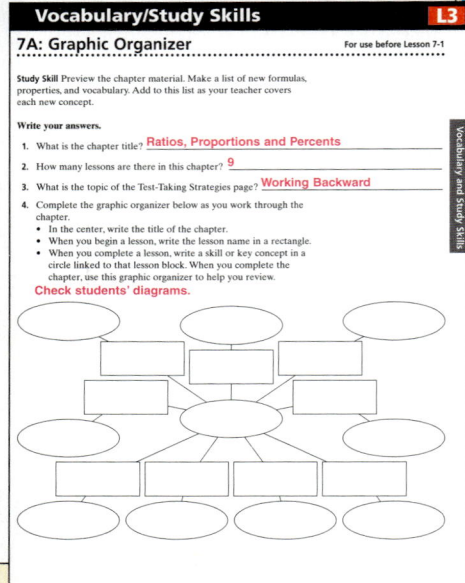

Spanish Vocabulary/Study Skills — **ELL**

Vocabulary/Study Skills — **L3**

7A: Graphic Organizer — For use before Lesson 7-1

Study Skill Preview the chapter material. Make a list of new formulas, properties, and vocabulary. Add to this list as your teacher covers each new concept.

Write your answers.

1. What is the chapter title? Ratios, Proportions and Percents
2. How many lessons are there in this chapter? 9
3. What is the topic of the Test-Taking Strategies page? Working Backward
4. Complete the graphic organizer below as you work through the chapter.
   - In the center, write the title of the chapter.
   - When you begin a lesson, write the lesson name in a rectangle.
   - When you complete a lesson, write a skill or key concept in a circle linked to that lesson block. When you complete the chapter, use this graphic organizer to help you review.

Check students' diagrams.

What You've Learned

- In Chapter 1, you used multiplication and division to solve problems involving decimals.
- In Chapter 5, you solved equations with fractions.
- In Chapter 6, you used multiplication and division to solve problems involving fractions and mixed numbers.

Check Your Readiness

For Exercises	See Lessons
1–4	3-7
5–8	4-5
9–12	4-8
13–16	6-3

Solving Equations

Solve for n.

1. $n \div 8 = 6$ **48**
2. $\frac{n}{7} = 6$ **42**
3. $3 \times n = 72$ **24**
4. $6n = 54$ **9**

Simplifying Fractions

Write each fraction in simplest form.

5. $\frac{10}{25}$ **$\frac{2}{5}$**
6. $\frac{20}{44}$ **$\frac{5}{11}$**
7. $\frac{34}{51}$ **$\frac{2}{3}$**
8. $\frac{27}{81}$ **$\frac{1}{3}$**

Comparing Fractions

Compare. Use <, =, or >.

9. $\frac{7}{9} \ \blacksquare\ \frac{3}{4}$ **>**
10. $\frac{2}{3} \ \blacksquare\ \frac{3}{5}$ **>**
11. $\frac{12}{15} \ \blacksquare\ \frac{12}{9}$ **<**
12. $\frac{24}{48} \ \blacksquare\ \frac{1}{2}$ **=**

Multiplying and Dividing Fractions

Find each product or quotient.

13. $\frac{4}{7} \times \frac{2}{3}$ **$\frac{8}{21}$**
14. $\frac{12}{14} \times \frac{7}{12}$ **$\frac{1}{2}$**
15. $\frac{7}{9} \div \frac{1}{5}$ **$3\frac{8}{9}$**
16. $\frac{11}{12} \div \frac{2}{9}$ **$4\frac{1}{8}$**

In this chapter, students extend their study of numbers and numerical relationships to work with the concepts of ratio and proportion and with related applications such as scale drawings. They then explore the relationship between fractions, decimals, and percents, find percents of numbers, display data on circle graphs, and estimate percents.

Activating Prior Knowledge

In this chapter, students build on and extend their knowledge of simplifying and computing with fractions as they work with ratios and proportions. They also draw upon their understanding of percents and of the relationship between fractions, decimals, and percents. Ask questions such as:

- What is $\frac{10}{35}$ in simplest form? $\frac{2}{7}$
- What is $\frac{6}{10}$ in simplest form? $\frac{3}{5}$
- Which is greater: $\frac{3}{4}$ of 24 or $\frac{8}{10}$ of 24? Explain. Sample: $\frac{8}{10}$ of 24 because $\frac{8}{10}$ is greater than $\frac{3}{4}$.

What You'll Learn Next

- In this chapter, you will use multiplication and division to solve problems involving ratios and rates.

- You will use ratios to describe proportional situations.

- You will use proportions to solve problems, including problems involving scale drawings.

- You will find and estimate percents and use percents to draw circle graphs.

🔊 Key Vocabulary

- circle graph (p. 341)
- cross products (p. 317)
- equivalent ratios (p. 307)
- percent (p. 331)
- proportion (p. 316)
- rate (p. 312)
- ratio (p. 306)
- scale (p. 326)
- unit cost (p. 313)
- unit rate (p. 312)

 Problem Solving Application On pages 358 and 359, you will work an extended activity involving scale.

Chapter 7   **305**

Objective

1 To write ratios to compare real-world quantities

Examples

1 Three Ways to Write a Ratio
2 Writing Equivalent Ratios
3 Writing a Ratio in Simplest Form

Math Understandings: p. 304C

Math Background

A *ratio* is a comparison of two quantities. A ratio can be expressed in three different ways: a to b, $a : b$, and $\frac{a}{b}$. Two ratios that name the same number are *equivalent ratios*. You can find equivalent ratios by multiplying both terms of the ratio by the same non-zero number. Using equivalent ratios, you can write ratios in simplest form.

More Math Background: p. 304C

Lesson Planning and Resources

See p. 304E for a list of the resources that support this lesson.

PowerPoint

Bell Ringer Practice

✓ **Check Skills You'll Need**
Use student page, transparency, or PowerPoint. For intervention, direct students to:
Equivalent Fractions
Lesson 4-5
Extra Skills and Word Problems
  Practice, Ch. 4

7-1 Ratios

7-1

✓ **Check Skills You'll Need**

1. **Vocabulary Review**
How do you know when a fraction is in *simplest* form?
See below.
Write each fraction in simplest form.

2. $\frac{4}{12}$ $\frac{1}{3}$ 3. $\frac{18}{27}$ $\frac{2}{3}$

4. $\frac{14}{63}$ $\frac{2}{9}$ 5. $\frac{3}{48}$ $\frac{1}{16}$

GO for Help
Lesson 4-5

Check Skills You'll Need

1. A fraction is in simplest form when the numerator and denominator have only a common factor of 1.

GO **Online**

Video Tutor Help
Visit: PHSchool.com
Web Code: aqe-0775

What You'll Learn

To write ratios to compare real-world quantities

◀)) **New Vocabulary** ratio, equivalent ratios

Why Learn This?

In recipes, the amounts of the ingredients are related to each other. You can use ratios to compare these amounts.

PARTY MIX
Makes 6 cups
4 cups cereal
2 cups pretzels
3 tbsp Worcestershire
        sauce

A **ratio** is a comparison of two numbers by division. The table below shows three ways to write the ratio of cups of party mix to cups of pretzels. All three ratios are read "six to two."

Statement	Ways to Write a Ratio		
	In Words	With a Symbol	As a Fraction
6 cups party mix to 2 cups pretzels	6 to 2	6 : 2	$\frac{6}{2}$

EXAMPLE   **Three Ways to Write a Ratio**

① **Recipes** Use the party mix recipe above. Write the ratio of cups of cereal to cups of pretzels in three ways.

The recipe calls for 4 cups of cereal and 2 cups of pretzels.

cereal to pretzels →   4 to 2   or   4 : 2   or $\frac{4}{2}$

✓ **Quick Check**

1. Use the recipe above. Write each ratio in three ways.
   a. pretzels to cereal **2 to 4, 2 : 4, $\frac{2}{4}$**
   b. pretzels to party mix **2 to 6, 2 : 6, $\frac{2}{6}$**

Differentiated Instruction **Solutions for All Learners**

Special Needs **L1**
Have students draw 2 bats and 3 balls and circle the picture. Then have them draw the same picture 3 more times. Show them that in the entire diagram there are now 8 bats and 12 balls, but the ratio of 2 to 3 has remained constant in each circle.

learning style: visual

Below Level **L2**
Help students understand that they can form equivalent fractions by multiplying or dividing a fraction by fractional forms of 1, such as $\frac{5}{5}$.

$\frac{3}{4} \times \frac{5}{5} = \frac{15}{20}$ $\frac{15}{20} \div \frac{5}{5} = \frac{3}{4}$

learning style: visual

Two ratios that name the same number are **equivalent ratios.** You can find equivalent ratios by multiplying or dividing each term of a ratio by the same nonzero number.

EXAMPLE Writing Equivalent Ratios

2 Write two different ratios equivalent to 4 : 6.

Divide each term by 2. → $4 : 6$ ÷2 ÷2 → $2 : 3$ $4 : 6$ ×3 ×3 → $12 : 18$ ← Multiply each term by 3.

Two ratios equivalent to 4 : 6 are 2 : 3 and 12 : 18.

✔ Quick Check 2a–c. Answers may vary. Samples are given.

2. Write two different ratios equivalent to each ratio.
   a. $\frac{10}{35}$ **2 to 7, 4 to 14**   b. 12 : 3 **4 to 1, 8 to 2**   c. 8 to 22
   4 to 11, 12 to 33

Just as with fractions, you can write ratios in simplest form. To do this, you can divide the terms of the ratio by their greatest common factor (GCF).

EXAMPLE Writing a Ratio in Simplest Form

3 Write the ratio of bats to balls in simplest form.

There are 8 bats and 12 balls, so the ratio of bats to balls is 8 to 12.

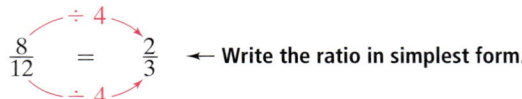

$$\frac{8}{12} = \frac{2}{3}$$ ÷4 ÷4 ← Write the ratio in simplest form.

In simplest form, the ratio of bats to balls is 2 to 3.

✔ Quick Check

3. You use 3 cups of popcorn kernels to make 24 quarts of popcorn. Write the ratio of the amount of kernels to the amount of popcorn in simplest form. **1 : 8**

GO for Help

For help finding the greatest common factor (GCF), go to Lesson 4-4, Example 1.

Assignment Guide

Check Your Understanding
Go over Exercises 1–6 in class before assigning the Homework Exercises.

Homework Exercises
A Practice by Example   7–21
B Apply Your Skills   22–32
C Challenge   33
Test Prep and
   Mixed Review   34–40

Homework Quick Check
To check students' understanding of key skills and concepts, go over Exercises 9, 15, 29, 30, and 31.

Differentiated Instruction **Resources**

Adapted Practice 7-1   **L1**

Practice 7-1   **L3**

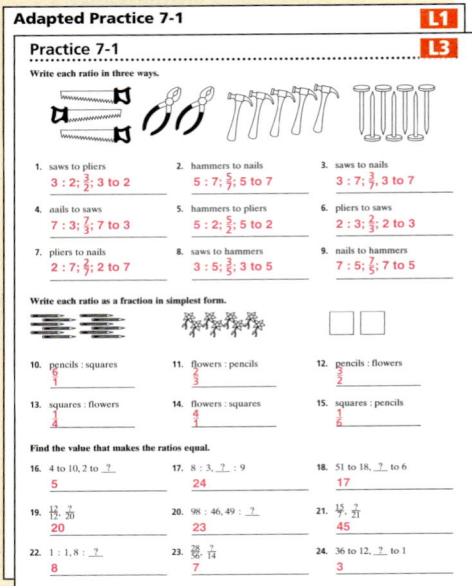

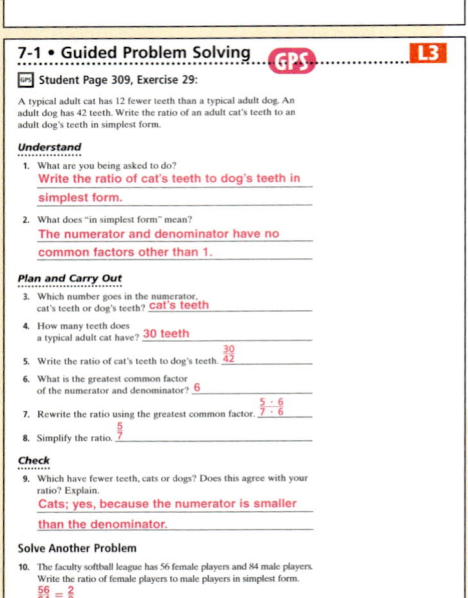

7-1 • Guided Problem Solving   **GPS**   **L3**

✔ Check Your Understanding

1. $\frac{9}{5}$ is a comparison of two numbers by division; $1\frac{4}{5}$ is not.

1. **Vocabulary** Explain why $\frac{9}{5}$ is a ratio and $1\frac{4}{5}$ is not a ratio.

2. Which ratios below are NOT equivalent to 6 : 10?

6 to 10	$\frac{8}{12}$	12 : 20	$\frac{3}{5}$	4 to 8

   $\frac{8}{12}$; 4 to 8

Use the picture at the left. Match each relationship on the left with the correct ratio on the right.

3. cups to bowls   **D**
4. coasters to blue cups   **B**
5. yellow cups to blue bowls   **C**
6. bowls to total number of items   **A**

A. 1 to 3
B. 2 to 1
C. 2 to 3
D. 6 to 5

Homework Exercises

For more exercises, see Extra Skills and Word Problems.

GO for Help

For Exercises	See Examples
7–9	1
10–13	2
14–21	3

A Use the table for Exercises 7–9.
Write each ratio in three ways.

School Play Ticket Sales

Students	35
Adults	24
Seniors	11

7. students to adults
   35 to 24, 35 : 24, $\frac{35}{24}$
8. adults to seniors
   24 to 11, 24 : 11, $\frac{24}{11}$
9. seniors to total number of people
   11 to 70, 11 : 70, $\frac{11}{70}$

Write two different ratios equivalent to each ratio.
10–13. Answers may vary. Samples are given.
10. 6 to 18   11. $\frac{4}{14}$ 12. 8 : 10   13. $\frac{30}{40}$
    3 to 9, 18 to 54, $\frac{2}{7}, \frac{16}{56}, \frac{28}{98}$
    30 to 90
12. 4 : 5, 16 : 20, 24 : 30 $\frac{3}{4}, \frac{6}{8}, \frac{60}{80}$

Write each ratio in simplest form.
14. $\frac{6}{15}$ $\frac{2}{5}$ 15. 40 : 30 4 : 3   16. 42 to 50 21 to 25   17. $\frac{14}{42}$ $\frac{1}{3}$
18. 9 to 81 1 to 9   19. 75 : 15 5 : 1   20. 8 : 36 2 : 9   21. $\frac{18}{12}$ 3 : 2

B  **GPS** 22. **Guided Problem Solving** A jar contains 20 white marbles, 30 black marbles, and some red marbles. Half of the marbles are black. Find the ratio of white marbles to red marbles.
   • How many marbles are in the jar? **2 to 1**
   • How can you find the number of red marbles?

GO Online
Homework Video Tutor

Visit: PHSchool.com
Web Code: aqe-0701

Find the value that makes each pair of ratios equivalent.

23. 6 to 9, ■ to 3 **2**   **24.** 32 : 90, 16 : ■ **45**   **25.** ■ to 96, 4 to 6 **64**

26. $\frac{■}{20}$, $\frac{50}{50}$ **20**   **27.** 50 : 150, 75 : ■ **225**   **28.** $\frac{72}{24}$, $\frac{■}{6}$ **18**

29. **GPS** A typical adult cat has 12 fewer teeth than a typical adult dog. An adult dog has 42 teeth. Write the ratio of an adult cat's teeth to an adult dog's teeth in simplest form. **5 : 7**

30. **Writing in Math** Explain the steps you would use to rewrite 48 : 56 as 6 : 7. **Divide each number by 8.**

31. **Science** You find that 14 students in your class of 20 students choose to make a volcano for a science project. You represent the ratio 14 to 20 using the fraction $\frac{7}{10}$. Does the ratio $\frac{7}{10}$ accurately describe the data? Explain. **Yes; 14 to 20 is equivalent to $\frac{7}{10}$.**

32. **Open-Ended** Write a ratio of the number of vowels to the number of consonants in your first name. **Check students' work.**

C 33. **Challenge** Write $8x : 16x$ in simplest form. **1 : 2**

Test Prep and Mixed Review
Practice

Multiple Choice

34. The table shows participation in three races. Which fraction represents the ratio of the number of 5-km runners to the number of 10-km runners? **B**

Fun Run	
Distance (km)	Number of Runners
10	96
5	128
1	52

Ⓐ $\frac{3}{4}$ Ⓒ $\frac{24}{13}$

Ⓑ $\frac{4}{3}$ Ⓓ $\frac{32}{13}$

35. The final score of a basketball game is 60 to 48. A prize is given to the person in the seat numbered with the least common multiple of 60 and 48. What is the prize-winning seat number?

Ⓕ 12   Ⓖ 120   Ⓗ 240   Ⓙ 480 **H**

36. Anders bought a can of juice labeled "12 fluid ounces." How many cups of juice are in the can? **C**

Ⓐ $\frac{1}{2}$ cup   Ⓑ $\frac{3}{4}$ cup   Ⓒ $1\frac{1}{2}$ cups   Ⓓ $1\frac{3}{4}$ cups

Write each product in simplest form.

37. $\frac{2}{5} \times \frac{3}{7}$ **$\frac{6}{35}$**   **38.** $\frac{3}{4} \times \frac{5}{8}$ **$\frac{15}{32}$**   **39.** $\frac{1}{6}$ of $\frac{3}{5}$ **$\frac{1}{10}$**   **40.** $\frac{3}{16} \cdot \frac{16}{21}$ **$\frac{1}{7}$**

GO for Help

For Exercises	See Lesson
37–40	6-1

Alternative Assessment

Each student in a pair writes five different ratios in words. Partners exchange papers and write each ratio three ways. They then write each ratio in simplest form and write a second equivalent ratio.

Test Prep

Resources
For additional practice with a variety of test item formats:
• Test-Taking Strategies, p. 353
• Test Prep, p. 357
• Test-Taking Strategies with Transparencies

---

4. Assess & Reteach

PowerPoint
Lesson Quiz

A drama club has 14 females and 8 males. Write each ratio in three ways.

1. males to females
8 to 14, 8 : 14, $\frac{8}{14}$

2. females to males
14 to 8, 14 : 8, $\frac{14}{8}$

3. Write two different ratios equivalent to 4 : 8.
Sample answer: 1 : 2; 5 : 10

Write each ratio in simplest form.

4. $\frac{8}{12}$ **$\frac{2}{3}$**   **5.** 10 : 6 **5 : 3**

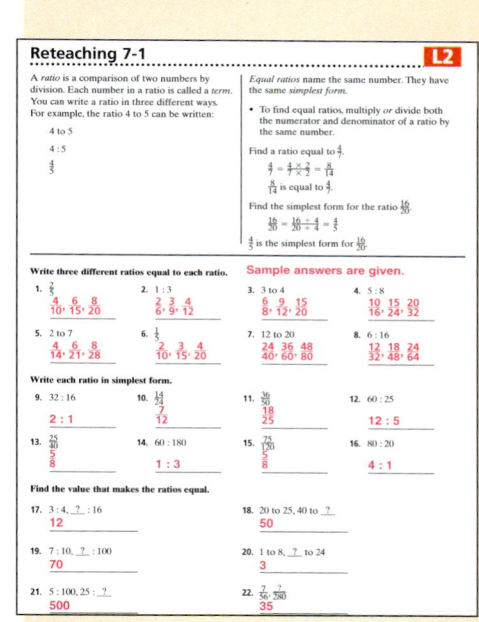

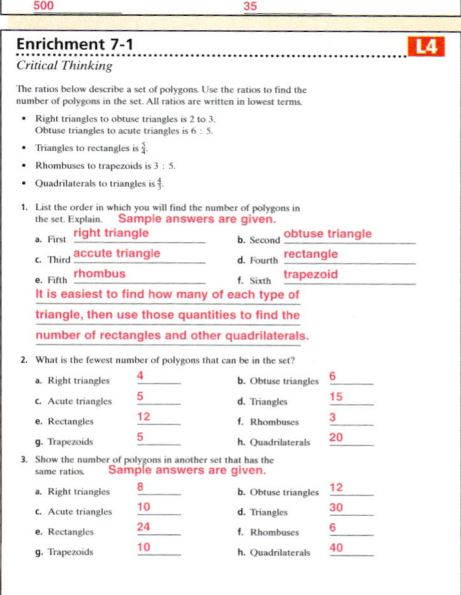

7-1b **Activity Lab**   **Hands On**

Students use paper models to help them understand and compare ratios. They model part-to-part and part-to-whole ratios.

Guided Instruction

Before beginning the activity, ask students to name familiar examples of ratios.
Ask:
- *What is the ratio of boys to girls in this class?* Answers will vary.
- *What is the ratio of girls to boys in this class?* Answers will vary.

Have students work independently on the Exercises. Then have them trade papers with a partner and compare answers. Ask students to comment about the effectiveness of the different representations used to describe ratios.

Differentiated Instruction

Below Level   L2
Make sure students understand which numbers belong in the ratio. Go back over Example 2 and ask:
- *How many students do not walk to school?* 3
- *What would the part-to-part ratio of students who walk to school to students who don't be?* 5 to 3

Resources

- strips of paper of various lengths
- Student Manipulatives Kit

Modeling Ratios

You can use paper strips to model ratios. Cut four strips of paper with equal lengths. Fold and shade the paper strips to represent ratios.

EXAMPLE **Modeling Part to Part**

1 A punch recipe calls for 4 oranges and 2 lemons.

The ratio of oranges to lemons can be written as 4 : 2, 4 to 2, or $\frac{4}{2}$.

EXAMPLE **Modeling Part to Whole**

2 Five out of eight students walk to school.

The ratio of walkers to students can be written as 5 : 8, 5 to 8, or $\frac{5}{8}$.

Exercises

Use paper strips to model each ratio. Write each ratio in three different ways. 1–4. See margin.

1. Three out of five kittens in a litter are male.

2. Seven out of ten high school seniors take a science course.

3. One out of four pairs of shoes sold in the summer are sandals.

4. Use the drawing of the blue jays and goldfinches at the right. Write three different ratios to describe the drawing.

5. **Writing in Math** You are given a part-to-part ratio, as in Example 1. Explain how to find the total number of parts.
Add the parts.

6. **Reasoning** The ratio of girls to boys in a class is 6 to 8. Does this mean there are 14 students in the class? Explain.
No; the ratio may be simplified, so the total could be any multiple of 14.

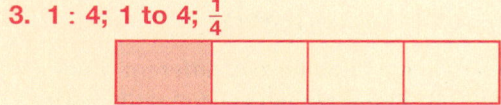

1. 3 : 5; 3 to 5; $\frac{3}{5}$

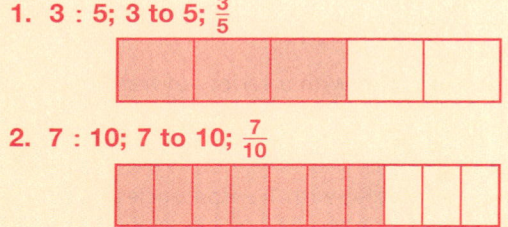

2. 7 : 10; 7 to 10; $\frac{7}{10}$

3. 1 : 4; 1 to 4; $\frac{1}{4}$

4. See back of book.

Vocabulary Builder

High-Use Academic Words

High-use academic words are words that you will see often in textbooks and on tests. These words are not math vocabulary terms, but knowing them will help you to succeed in mathematics.

Direction Words

Some words tell what to do in a problem. I need to understand what these words are asking so that I give the correct answer.

Word	Meaning
Define	To give an accurate meaning with sufficient detail
Classify	To assign things to different groups based on their characteristics
Contrast	To show how two things are different; to include details or examples

Exercises

1. Define *salad*. **Check students' work.**

2. Classify each object as a fruit or a vegetable.
   a. apple **fruit**   b. carrot **vegetable**   c. lettuce **vegetable**   d. banana **fruit**   e. corn **vegetable**

3. Contrast a fruit salad and a vegetable salad. **See margin.**

4. Define *ratio*. **Answers may vary. Sample: A ratio is a comparison of two numbers by division.**

5. Classify each pair of ratios as equal or unequal.

   a. $\frac{1}{2}, \frac{3}{6}$ **equal**   b. $\frac{2}{5}, \frac{4}{10}$ **equal**   c. $\frac{5}{6}, \frac{1}{12}$ **unequal**   d. $\frac{1}{3}, \frac{3}{9}$ **equal**

6. **Word Knowledge** Think about the word *comparison*. **Check students' work.**
   a. Choose the letter for how well you know the word.
      A. I know its meaning.
      B. I've seen it, but I don't know its meaning.
      C. I don't know it.
   b. **Research** Look up and write the definition of *comparison*.
   c. Use the word in a sentence involving mathematics.

3. **Answers may vary. Sample: A fruit salad contains fruits, such as apples and bananas. A vegetable salad contains vegetables, such as lettuce and carrots.**

Vocabulary Builder

High-Use Academic Words

Students become familiar with words that are frequently used in academic contexts.

Guided Instruction

These word are not strictly mathematical but students may find them in texts or tests.

Explain to students why understanding these words is helpful to them when they study math. Ask questions such as:
- *If you wanted to compare fractions and decimals and discuss their differences, what word might you use?* **contrast**
- *How else could you state "What is the meaning of octagon?"* **Sample: Define *octagon*.**

Use these words frequently as you teach to help students become familiar with their meanings.

Differentiated Instruction

Advanced Learners   **L4**
Encourage students to write sentences containing these words that do not relate to math.

Resources

- Vocabulary and Study Skills Worksheet

Objective
To find and use unit rates and unit costs

Examples
1 Finding a Unit Rate
2 Comparing Unit Cost
3 Using a Unit Rate

Math Understandings: p. 304C

Math Background

A *rate* is a special type of ratio that compares two quantities with different units of measure. Speed is a rate that is commonly expressed as a *unit rate,* a rate that compares something to one unit, such as 55 mi/h (miles per "one" hour). You can compare the costs of two sizes of the same product by comparing each cost per unit, or *unit cost.*

More Math Background: p. 304C

Lesson Planning and Resources

See p. 304E for a list of the resources that support this lesson.

PowerPoint

Bell Ringer Practice

✓ **Check Skills You'll Need**
Use student page, transparency, or PowerPoint. For intervention, direct students to:
Ratios
Lesson 7-1
Extra Skills and Word Problems
  Practice, Ch. 7

✓ **Check Skills You'll Need**

1. Vocabulary Review
Which operation is used in a ratio?
See below.
Write each ratio in simplest form.

2. $\frac{48}{12}$ **4**   **3.** $\frac{36}{9}$ **4**

4. $\frac{75}{15}$ **5**   **5.** $\frac{42}{7}$ **6**

GO **for Help**
Lesson 7-1

Check Skills You'll Need

1. division

What You'll Learn

To find and use unit rates and unit costs
🔊 **New Vocabulary** rate, unit rate, unit price

Why Learn This?

Exercise is important for good health. You can use unit rates to find your heart rate.

A **rate** is a ratio involving two quantities in different units. The rate $\frac{150 \text{ heartbeats}}{2 \text{ minutes}}$ compares heartbeats to minutes. The rate for one unit of a given quantity is called the **unit rate.** Its denominator is 1.

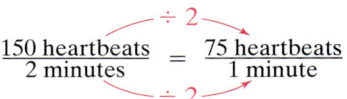

$$\frac{150 \text{ heartbeats}}{2 \text{ minutes}} = \frac{75 \text{ heartbeats}}{1 \text{ minute}}$$

The unit rate is 75 heartbeats per minute.

EXAMPLE **Finding a Unit Rate**

1 A box of wheat crackers contains 6 servings and has a total of 420 Calories. Find the number of Calories in 1 serving.

420 Calories → [model] ← 6 servings

■ Calories → [model] ← 1 serving

The model shows that

total Calories ÷ number of servings = Calories per serving.

Calories → $\frac{420}{6} \div \frac{6}{6} = \frac{70}{1}$ ← Divide by 6 to find the calories in one serving.
servings →

The unit rate is $\frac{70 \text{ Calories}}{1 \text{ serving}}$, or 70 Calories per serving.

✓ **Quick Check**

79 cents per pound
1. Find the unit rate for $2.37 for 3 pounds of grapes.

Differentiated **Instruction** **Solutions for All Learners**

Special Needs **L1**
For Example 3, show a number line labeled from 0 to 1 along the bottom, and from 0–25 along the top. The 1 and 25 should align. Have students extend the number line until 8 is on the bottom and a 200 is on the top to see that the car can travel 200 miles on 8 gallons of gas.
learning style: visual

Below Level **L2**
Have students make a table of Calories for each serving size for the model on page 312.

Serving	1	2	3	4	5	6
Calories	70	140	210	280	350	420

learning style: visual

A unit rate that gives the cost per unit is a **unit cost.** Unit costs help you compare prices.

$1.20

$1.29

EXAMPLE Comparing Unit Cost

2 **Comparison Shopping** Two sizes of sports drink bottles are shown at the left. Which size is the better buy? Round each unit cost to the nearest cent.

Divide to find the unit cost for each size.

$$\frac{\text{price} \rightarrow \$1.20}{\text{size} \rightarrow 24 \text{ oz}} = \$.05 \text{ per fluid ounce}$$

$$\frac{\text{price} \rightarrow \$1.29}{\text{size} \rightarrow 32 \text{ oz}} \approx \$.04 \text{ per fluid ounce}$$

The better buy costs less per fluid ounce. Since $.04 is less than $.05, the 32-ounce bottle is the better buy.

✓ **Quick Check**

2. You can buy 6 ounces of yogurt for $.68, or 32 ounces of yogurt for $2.89. Find each unit cost. Which is the better buy?
   $.11 per ounce; $.09 per ounce; the 32 ounce container

When you know a unit rate, you can use multiplication to solve a problem.

EXAMPLE Using a Unit Rate

3 **Multiple Choice** A car travels about 25 miles on 1 gallon of gas. About how far can the car travel on 8 gallons of gas?

Ⓐ $3\frac{1}{3}$ miles ⓑ 8 miles ⓒ 33 miles ⓓ 200 miles

Write the unit rate as a ratio. Then find an equivalent ratio.

$$\frac{25 \text{ miles}}{1 \text{ gallon}} \overset{\times 8}{\underset{\times 8}{=}} \frac{200 \text{ miles}}{8 \text{ gallons}} \leftarrow \text{Multiply each term by 8.}$$

The car can travel 200 miles on 8 gallons of gas. The correct answer is choice D.

Test Prep Tip
To write a whole number as a fraction, you can write the whole number in the numerator and 1 in the denominator.

✓ **Quick Check**
3a–b. See left.

3. Write the unit rate as a ratio. Then find an equivalent ratio.
   a. You earn $5.25 in 1 hour. How much do you earn in 5 hours?
   b. You can type 25 words in 1 minute. How many words can you type in 10 minutes?

3a. $\frac{\$5.25}{1 \text{ hour}} = \frac{\$26.25}{5 \text{ hours}}$

3b. $\frac{25 \text{ words}}{1 \text{ minute}} = \frac{250 \text{ words}}{10 \text{ minutes}}$

Advanced Learners L4
One office space costs $143,500 and has 1,825 ft². Another office space is $129,799 and has 1,625 ft². Which looks like a better buy? **1,825 ft² office is slightly less per ft²**

learning style: visual

English Language Learners ELL
One common linguistic misconception is that *better* means more or bigger. Make sure students understand that a *better buy* means you get *more* quantity for less money. Sometimes the *better buy* is the smaller quantity.

learning style: verbal

---

2. Teach

Activity Lab
Use before the lesson.

All in One Teaching Resources
Activity Lab 7-2: Find the Better Price

Guided Instruction

Example 3
Show students how multiplying both numerator and denominator by 8 is really multiplication by 1.

$$\frac{25 \text{ mi}}{1 \text{ gal}} \cdot \frac{8}{8} = \frac{25 \text{ mi} \cdot 8}{1 \text{ gal} \cdot 8} = \frac{200 \text{ mi}}{8 \text{ gal}}$$

PowerPoint
Additional Examples

1 Find the unit rate for typing 145 words in 5 minutes.
29 words per min

2 The same brand of pretzels comes in two sizes: a 10-ounce bag for $.99, and an 18-ounce bag for $1.49. Which size is a better buy? Round each unit price to the nearest cent. **10-oz: $.10, 18-oz: $.08; The 18-oz bag is a better buy.**

3 Apples cost $1.49 for 1 pound. How much do 5 pounds of apples cost? **$7.45**

All in One Teaching Resources
• Daily Notetaking Guide 7-2 L3
• Adapted Notetaking 7-2 L1

Closure

• *What is a rate?* **Sample: A rate is a ratio that compares quantities of different units.**

• *How can you compare the cost of two items that are different sizes?* **Sample: Find the unit cost for each item. The lesser unit cost is the better buy.**

Assignment Guide

Check Your Understanding
Go over Exercises 1–6 in class before assigning the Homework Exercises.

Homework Exercises

A	Practice by Example	7–16
B	Apply Your Skills	17–24
C	Challenge	25
	Test Prep and Mixed Review	26–30

Homework Quick Check
To check students' understanding of key skills and concepts, go over Exercises 8, 15, 22, 23, and 24.

Differentiated Instruction Resources

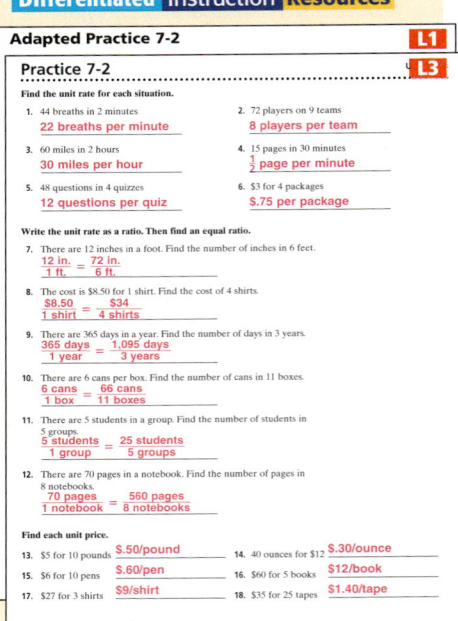

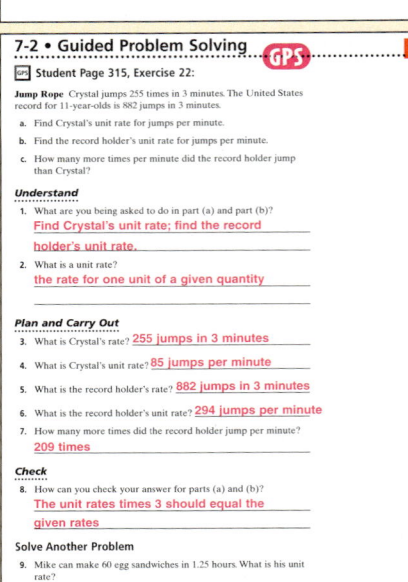

✓ Check Your Understanding

1. $\frac{12 \text{ inches}}{1 \text{ foot}}$ is a unit rate because it has 1 in the denominator.

1. **Vocabulary** Which is a unit rate, $\frac{36 \text{ inches}}{3 \text{ feet}}$ or $\frac{12 \text{ inches}}{1 \text{ foot}}$? Explain.

2. **Health** Find the unit rate for 210 heartbeats in 3 minutes.
70 heartbeats per minute

Match each price to the correct unit cost.

3. peaches: 6 for $3.84 **C**

4. bananas: 4 for $1.96 **A**

5. oranges: 3 for $2.16 **D**

6. pears: 5 for $2.90 **B**

A. $.49 each
B. $.58 each
C. $.64 each
D. $.72 each

Homework Exercises

For more exercises, see **Extra Skills and Word Problems.**

A **Find the unit rate for each situation. You may find a model helpful.**

GO for Help

For Exercises	See Examples
7–10	1
11–13	2
14–16	3

7. 92 desks in 4 classrooms
23 desks per classroom

8. $19.50 for 3 shirts
$6.50 per shirt

9. 45 miles in 5 hours
9 miles per hour

10. $29.85 for 3 presents
$9.95 per present

Comparison Shopping Find each unit cost. Round to the nearest cent. Then determine the better buy. **11–13. See left.**

11. $.15 per oz;
$.16 per oz;
16 oz for $2.39

12. $.04 per oz;
$.05 per oz;
48 oz for $2.07

13. $.63 per lb;
$.79 per lb;
3 lb for $1.89

11. crackers: 16 ounces for $2.39; 20 ounces for $3.19

12. juice: 48 fluid ounces for $2.07; 32 fluid ounces for $1.64

13. apples: 3 pounds for $1.89; 1 pound for $.79

14. A book costs $6.75. Find the cost of 8 books. **$54**

15. There are 3 feet in 1 yard. Find the number of feet in a 15-yard run by a football player. **45 ft**

16. Five buses leave on a field trip. There are about 45 students per bus. About how many students are on the 5 buses? **225 students**

B **GPS** 17. **Guided Problem Solving** You earn $44.55 in 9 hours. Your friend earns $51 in 12 hours. How much do you and your friend earn together if you each work 20 hours? **$184**

• What is your unit rate for earnings? What is your friend's unit rate?

• How can you use unit rates to find the total?

22a. **85 jumps per min**

b. **294 jumps per min**

c. **209 jumps**

For Exercises 18–21, tell which unit rate is greater.

18. Dee reads 60 pages in 2 hours. Teri reads 99 pages in 3 hours. **99 pages in 3 h**

19. Damian types 110 words in 5 minutes. Howard types 208 words in 8 minutes. **208 words in 8 min**

20. Jan bikes 18 miles in 2 hours. Nikki bikes 33 miles in 3 hours. **33 mi in 3 h**

21. Tanya scores 81 points in 9 games. Tamaira scores 132 points in 12 games. **132 points in 12 games**

22. **Jump Rope** Crystal jumps 255 times in 3 minutes. The United
GPS States record for 11-year-olds is 882 jumps in 3 minutes.
a. Find Crystal's unit rate for jumps per minute.
b. Find the record-holder's unit rate for jumps per minute.
c. How many more times per minute did the record-holder jump than Crystal? **22a–c. See above left.**

23. **Estimation** A car travels 279.9 miles on 9.8 gallons of gasoline. Estimate the car's unit rate of miles per gallon. Explain how you found your estimate. **About 28.6 miles per gallon; answers may vary. Sample: I divided 279.9 by 9.8.**

24. **Writing in Math** Explain why the speed limit on a highway is an example of a unit rate. **Answers may vary. Sample: A car's speed is given in miles per hour.**

C 25. **Challenge** An airplane flies 2,750 miles in 5 hours. Find the unit rate in miles per second. Round your answer to the nearest hundredth. **0.15 mi/s**

Test Prep and Mixed Review   **Practice**

Multiple Choice

26. There are 54 students and 18 computers in a classroom. Which ratio accurately compares the number of students to the number of computers? **B**
   (A) 1 : 3   (B) 3 : 1   (C) 3 : 4   (D) 4 : 3

27. Each square below is divided into parts of equal size. In which square is the ratio of shaded to unshaded parts 2 : 1? **H**
   (F)    (G)    (H) 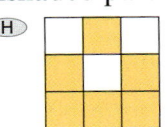   (J)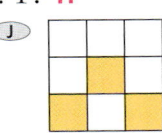

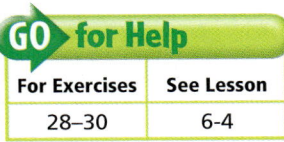

Find each quotient.

28. $4\frac{2}{3} \div 1\frac{3}{4}$ **$2\frac{2}{3}$**
29. $6\frac{1}{4} \div 2\frac{1}{2}$ **$2\frac{1}{2}$**
30. $2\frac{2}{5} \div 7\frac{1}{5}$ **$\frac{1}{3}$**

Alternative Assessment

Each student in a pair writes the size and cost for two different quantities of the same product. Partners exchange papers and find each unit cost to determine the better buy.

Test Prep

Resources
For additional practice with a variety of test item formats:
- Test-Taking Strategies, p. 353
- Test Prep, p. 357
- Test-Taking Strategies with Transparencies

---

4. Assess & Reteach

PowerPoint
Lesson Quiz

Find the unit rate for each situation.
1. 18 in. in 3 years **6 in. per yr**
2. 9 calls in 3 min **3 calls per min**

Find each unit price.
3. 16 oz for $5.28 **$.33 per oz**
4. 5 lb for $6.25 **$1.25 per lb**

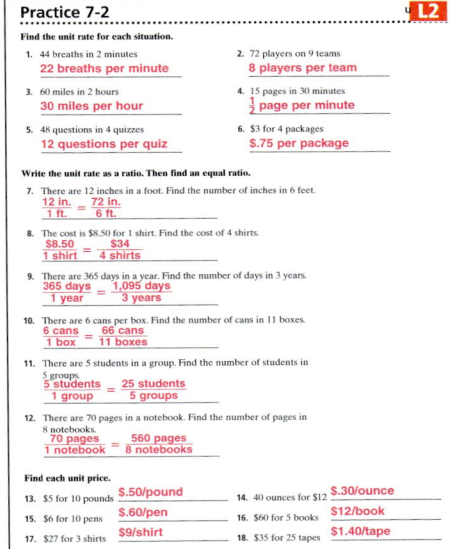

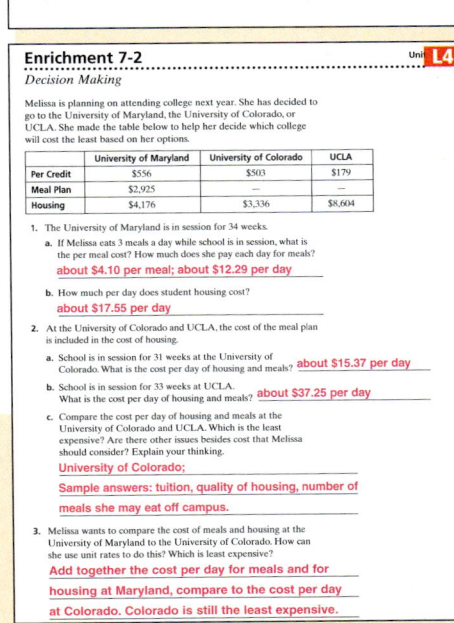

Objective
To understand proportions and to determine whether two ratios are proportional

Examples
1 Identifying Proportions
2 Using Cross Products

Math Understandings: p. 304C

Math Background

A *proportion* is an equation stating that two ratios are equal. You can verify that two ratios form a proportion by writing each ratio in simplest form and checking that they are the same.

In the proportion $\frac{a}{b} = \frac{c}{d}$, ad and bc are called *cross products*. If the cross products of two ratios are equal, then the ratios form a proportion. The converse of this statement is also true: You can use cross products to solve for the missing value in a proportion.

More Math Background: p. 304C

Lesson Planning and Resources

See p. 304E for a list of the resources that support this lesson.

Bell Ringer Practice

✔ **Check Skills You'll Need**
Use student page, transparency, or PowerPoint. For intervention, direct students to:
Comparing and Ordering Fractions
Lesson 4-8
Extra Skills and Word Problems Practice, Ch. 4

7-3 Understanding Proportions

✔ Check Skills You'll Need

1. **Vocabulary Review**
What does it mean to *compare* two quantities such as two fractions?
See below.
Compare each pair of fractions using $<$, $=$, or $>$.

2. $\frac{3}{5} \underset{<}{\blacksquare} \frac{7}{9}$ 3. $\frac{1}{3} \underset{=}{\blacksquare} \frac{5}{15}$

4. $\frac{4}{9} \underset{<}{\blacksquare} \frac{2}{3}$

5. $\frac{14}{35} \underset{<}{\blacksquare} \frac{14}{25}$

GO for Help
Lesson 4-8

What You'll Learn

To understand proportions and to determine whether two ratios are proportional

🔊 **New Vocabulary** proportion, cross products

Why Learn This?

You need 4 scoops of mix and 10 cups of water to make lemonade. Will 12 scoops of mix and 30 cups of water make the same strength lemonade? You can use a proportion to find out.

A **proportion** is an equation stating that two ratios are equal.

One way to show that the ratios $\frac{4 \text{ scoops}}{10 \text{ cups}}$ and $\frac{12 \text{ scoops}}{30 \text{ cups}}$ form a proportion is to show that the ratios are equivalent.

EXAMPLE   Identifying Proportions

Test Prep Tip 🖊
You can use fractions written in simplest form to show that two ratios form a proportion.

Check Skills You'll Need
1. You see whether the two fractions are equal or whether one is greater.

① Do the ratios in each pair form a proportion?

a. $\frac{4}{10}$, $\frac{12}{30}$

$\frac{4}{10} \overset{?}{=} \frac{12}{30}$

$\frac{4}{10} = \frac{12}{30}$ ← Compare ratios →

$\frac{4}{10}$ and $\frac{12}{30}$ form a proportion.

b. $\frac{72}{81}$, $\frac{7}{9}$

$\frac{72}{81} \overset{?}{=} \frac{7}{9}$ ← $72 \div 9 = 8$, not 7

$\frac{72}{81} \neq \frac{7}{9}$

$\frac{72}{81}$ and $\frac{7}{9}$ do *not* form a proportion.

✔ Quick Check

No; $\frac{36}{20}$ cannot reduce to $\frac{8}{5}$.

● 1. Do the ratios $\frac{8}{5}$ and $\frac{36}{20}$ form a proportion? Explain.

Differentiated Instruction Solutions for All Learners

Special Needs L1
Draw two diagonal arrows that intersect at their center. Say: *When you find cross products, you do not multiply straight across, but rather in a diagonal.*

learning style: visual

Below Level L2
Have students make a list of ratios that are equivalent to $\frac{1}{2}$. **Sample:** $\frac{2}{4}$, $\frac{3}{6}$, $\frac{10}{20}$ Ask students what math symbol could be used between any two ratios on the list. $=$

learning style: verbal

 **GO for Help**

For help with the Multiplication Property of Equality, go to Lesson 3-7, Example 3.

You can use the Multiplication Property of Equality to show an important property of proportions.

$$\frac{3}{4} = \frac{15}{20}$$ ← Start with a proportion.

$$\frac{3}{4} \times \frac{4}{1} \times \frac{20}{1} = \frac{15}{20} \times \frac{4}{1} \times \frac{20}{1}$$ ← Multiply each side by the values in the denominators.

$$\frac{3}{4} \times \frac{4^1}{1} \times \frac{20}{1} = \frac{15}{20} \times \frac{4}{1} \times \frac{20^1}{1}$$ ← Divide the common factors.

$$3 \times 20 = 4 \times 15$$ ← Multiply and divide by 1.

$$60 = 60$$ ← The products are equal.

The products 20×3 and 4×15 are called cross products. You can find the **cross products** of two ratios by multiplying the numerator of each ratio by the denominator of the other ratio.

$$\frac{3}{4} = \frac{15}{20}$$ ← Start with a proportion.

$$3 \times 20 = 4 \times 15$$ ← Multiply the numerator of each ratio by the denominator of the other ratio.

$$60 = 60$$ ← The cross products are equal.

KEY CONCEPTS   **Cross Products**

The cross products of a proportion are always equal.

Arithmetic: If $\frac{2}{4} = \frac{3}{6}$, then $2 \times 6 = 4 \times 3$.

Algebra: If $\frac{a}{b} = \frac{c}{d}$, and $b \neq 0$ and $d \neq 0$, then $ad = bc$.

EXAMPLE   **Using Cross Products**

 In one class, 4 of every 12 students have braces. In another class, 5 of every 15 students have braces. Are the ratios equivalent?

students with braces → $\frac{4}{12} \stackrel{?}{=} \frac{5}{15}$ ← students with braces
total students →   ← total students   ← Write a proportion.

$$4 \times 15 \stackrel{?}{=} 5 \times 12$$ ← Write the cross products.

$$60 = 60$$ ← Multiply.

The ratios $\frac{4}{12}$ and $\frac{5}{15}$ are equivalent.

✔ **Quick Check**

2. In a middle school, 1 out of every 12 students has a birthday in June. In a class of 26 students, there are 3 students with a birthday in June. Are these ratios equivalent? Explain.
No; $\frac{1}{12}$ and $\frac{3}{26}$ are not equal.

7-3 Understanding Proportions   **317**

---

2. Teach

Activity Lab

Use before the lesson.

All in One Teaching Resources

Activity Lab 7-3: Checking Proportions

Guided Instruction

Example 1
Students can write each ratio as a decimal by performing the long division and comparing quotients. This method is helpful when fractions are difficult to simplify or when a calculator is available.

Example 2
Make sure students multiply each pair of circled numbers accurately to obtain the correct result—that the circled products are equal for proportions.

 **PowerPoint**

Additional Examples

1 Do the ratios in each pair form a proportion?
a. $\frac{6}{14}$, $\frac{42}{77}$ no   b. $\frac{3}{13}$, $\frac{9}{39}$ yes

2 In one class, 2 out of 16 students' favorite subject is math. In another class, 4 out of 12 students' favorite subject is math. Are these ratios equal? no

All in One Teaching Resources
- Daily Notetaking Guide 7-3 **L3**
- Adapted Notetaking 7-3 **L1**

Closure

- *What is a proportion?* an equation stating that two ratios are equal
- *How can you use cross products to identify proportions?* Sample: Given a pair of ratios, find the cross products; if they are equal the ratios form a proportion.

Advanced Learners **L4**
Have students determine whether the following ratios are equivalent. $\frac{43}{316}$, $\frac{10.2}{75}$ no

learning style: visual

English Language Learners **ELL**
Show students what is meant by the "strength" or concentration of a liquid by drawing pitchers of lemonade with lighter and darker shades of yellow. Explain that the taste is affected by the number of scoops of mix per amount of water which is why proportions are important.

learning style: visual

Assignment Guide

Check Your Understanding
Go over Exercises 1–4 in class before assigning the Homework Exercises.

Homework Exercises

A Practice by Example   5–21
B Apply Your Skills   22–31
C Challenge   32
Test Prep and
   Mixed Review   33–39

Homework Quick Check
To check students' understanding of key skills and concepts, go over Exercises 10, 14, 21, 28, and 30.

Differentiated Instruction Resources

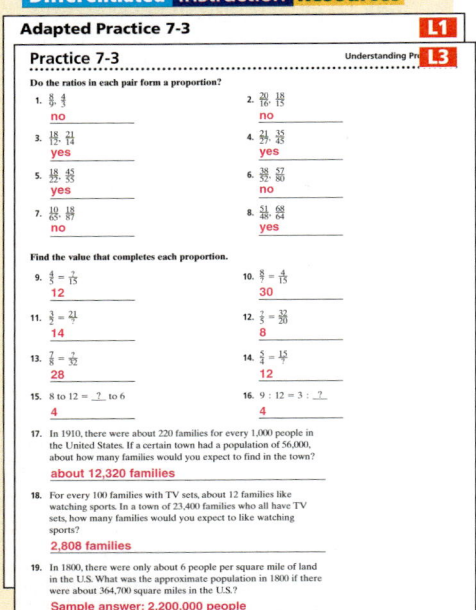

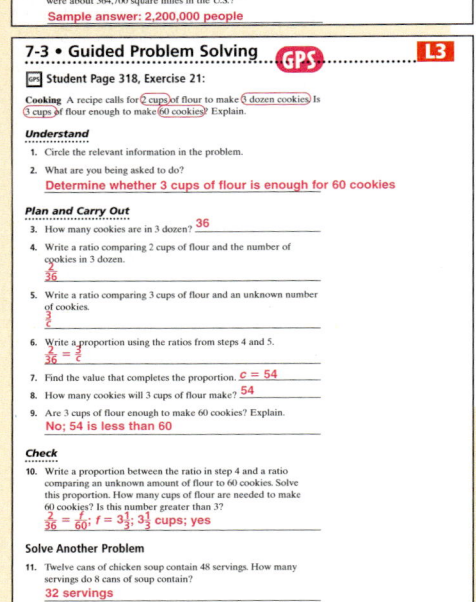

✔ Check Your Understanding

1. The cross products are equal.
2. Answers may vary. Sample: If both fractions are reduced to simplest form, they both equal $\frac{1}{4}$.

1. **Vocabulary** Explain why $\frac{5}{6} = \frac{25}{30}$ is a proportion.

2. **Writing in Math** Explain how you can use fractions in simplest form to tell that $\frac{10}{40}$ and $\frac{25}{100}$ form a proportion. **See left.**

3. Use the numbers below. Write four ratios that are equivalent to $\frac{12}{30}$. **Answers may vary. Sample: $\frac{2}{5}$, $\frac{4}{10}$, $\frac{24}{60}$**

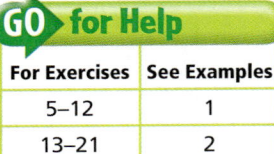
2   4   5   6   10   15   24   60

4. Which ratios do NOT form a proportion? **B**
   (A) $\frac{4}{32}, \frac{1}{8}$ (B) $\frac{9}{4}, \frac{3}{2}$ (C) $\frac{16}{80}, \frac{1}{5}$ (D) $\frac{21}{42}, \frac{9}{18}$

Homework Exercises

For more exercises, see Extra Skills and Word Problems.

GO for Help

For Exercises	See Examples
5–12	1
13–21	2

Ⓐ Does each pair of ratios form a proportion?

5. $\frac{1}{2}, \frac{50}{100}$ **yes**   6. $\frac{10}{20}, \frac{30}{40}$ **no**   7. $\frac{4}{12}, \frac{6}{8}$ **no**   8. $\frac{42}{6}, \frac{504}{72}$ **yes**

9. $\frac{9}{11}, \frac{63}{77}$ **yes**   10. $\frac{72}{27}, \frac{8}{3}$ **yes**   11. $\frac{16}{27}, \frac{4}{9}$ **no**   12. $\frac{3}{2}, \frac{22}{16}$ **no**

13. $\frac{4}{12}, \frac{3}{9}$ **yes**   14. $\frac{32}{80}, \frac{4}{10}$ **yes**   15. $\frac{5}{7}, \frac{8}{10}$ **no**   16. $\frac{6}{2}, \frac{8}{5}$ **no**

17. $\frac{93}{60}, \frac{62}{40}$ **yes**   18. $\frac{18}{9}, \frac{6}{3}$ **yes**   19. $\frac{10}{15}, \frac{3}{5}$ **no**   20. $\frac{10}{16}, \frac{5}{8}$ **yes**

21. no; $\frac{2}{36} \neq \frac{3}{60}$

21. **Cooking** A recipe calls for 2 cups of flour to make 3 dozen **GPS** cookies. Is 3 cups of flour enough to make 60 cookies? Explain. **See left.**

Ⓑ GPS 22. **Guided Problem Solving**
The table shows the results of a survey in different homerooms before a class election. In which homerooms did you receive the same ratio of votes to the total number of votes? **Homerooms A and B**

Student Election Survey

Homeroom	A	B	C
Votes for You	13	10	12
Total Votes	26	20	22

• Use a proportion to compare Homeroom A to Homeroom B.
• Compare Homeroom B to Homeroom C.

23. **Reasoning** Which value makes $\frac{4}{12} = \frac{\blacksquare}{18}$ a proportion?
   (A) 2   (B) 4   (C) 6   (D) 9   **C**

GO Online
Homework Video Tutor

Visit: PHSchool.com
Web Code: aqe-0703

Does each pair of ratios form a proportion?

24. $\frac{3}{1.2}$, $\frac{0.5}{2}$ **no**

25. $\frac{20}{8}$, $\frac{3.5}{1.4}$ **yes**

26. $\frac{8.4}{4.2}$, $\frac{20}{40}$ **no**

27. $\frac{6.1}{3.4}$, $\frac{7.4}{4.7}$ **no**

28. Choose a Method Would you use number sense, simplified fractions, or cross products to show that $\frac{141}{94}$ and $\frac{279}{186}$ form a proportion? Explain. **Answers may vary. Sample: I used cross products because they always give a correct answer.**

29. Architecture In one drawing, a line 4 centimeters long represents a wall 6 feet long. In another drawing, a line 6 centimeters long represents a wall 8 feet long. Do these ratios form a proportion? **no**

30. In a ratio table, each ratio forms a proportion with every other ratio in the table. Copy and complete the ratio table below.

Hours	1	▦	4	6	▦	▦
Pay (Dollars)	5	10	▦	▦	35	50

2; 20; 30; 7; 10

31. (Algebra) Suppose you know that $\frac{a}{b}$ forms a proportion with $\frac{m}{n}$, and $\frac{a}{b}$ does not form a proportion with $\frac{x}{y}$. Does $\frac{m}{n}$ form a proportion with $\frac{x}{y}$? Explain. **See left.**

31. No; answers may vary. Sample: If two ratios are equivalent, a third ratio must be equivalent to both of them or neither of them.

C 32. Challenge You charge $7 to baby-sit for 2 hours. Last night you earned $17.50. How long did you baby-sit? **5 h**

Test Prep and Mixed Review **Practice**

Multiple Choice

33. A team's ratio of wins to losses is 3 to 4. Which of the following could be the team's record? **B**
- Ⓐ 10 wins and 12 losses
- Ⓑ 12 wins and 16 losses
- Ⓒ 9 wins and 16 losses
- Ⓓ 40 wins and 30 losses

34. What is the prime factorization of 200? **F**
- Ⓕ $2^3 \cdot 5^2$
- Ⓖ $2^2 \cdot 5$
- Ⓗ $2^3 \cdot 5$
- Ⓙ $2^2 \cdot 5^2$

35. A class starts at 11:45 A.M. and lasts 85 minutes. At what time does the class end? **C**
- Ⓐ 12:10 P.M.
- Ⓑ 12:40 P.M.
- Ⓒ 1:10 P.M.
- Ⓓ 1:40 P.M.

GO for Help

For Exercises	See Lesson
36–39	5-5

Find each difference.

36. $7\frac{1}{2} - 6\frac{1}{4}$ **$1\frac{1}{4}$** **37.** $7\frac{2}{9} - 5\frac{1}{3}$ **$1\frac{8}{9}$** **38.** $4\frac{1}{4} - 1\frac{1}{2}$ **$2\frac{3}{4}$** **39.** $9\frac{1}{6} - 4\frac{2}{3}$ **$4\frac{1}{2}$**

---

4. Assess & Reteach

PowerPoint
Lesson Quiz

Determine whether each pair of ratios forms a proportion.

1. $\frac{5}{35}$, $\frac{20}{140}$ **yes** **2.** $\frac{24}{72}$, $\frac{1}{3}$ **yes**

3. $\frac{6}{7}$, $\frac{72}{84}$ **yes** **4.** $\frac{26}{65}$, $\frac{2}{7}$ **no**

Alternative Assessment

Have each partner write five pairs of ratios similar to those in Exercises 5–20. Partners exchange papers and determine whether each pair of ratios forms a proportion. If the ratios in each pair do not, have students rewrite one ratio in each pair so that the pairs form a proportion.

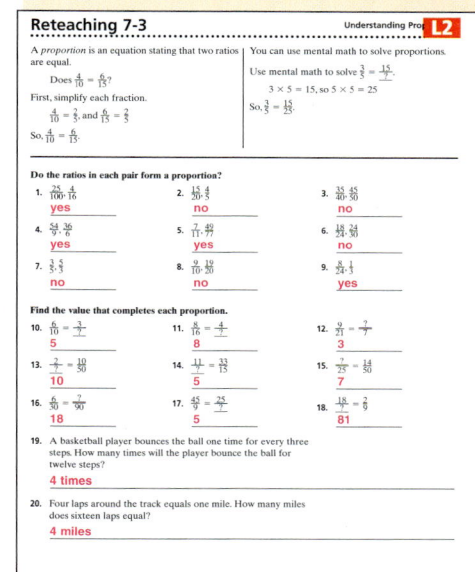

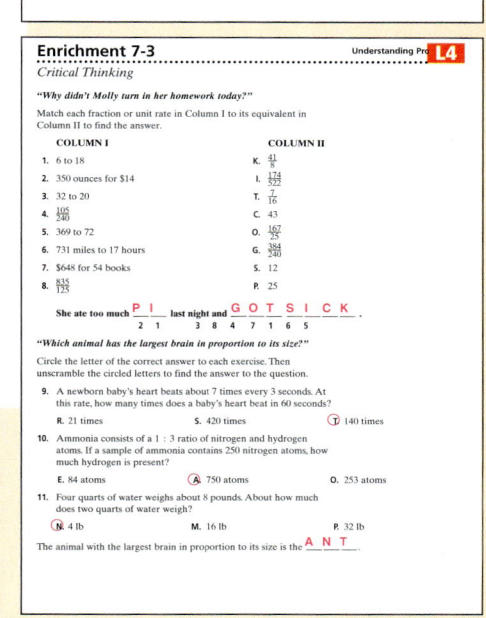

Test Prep

Resources

For additional practice with a variety of test item formats:
- Test-Taking Strategies, p. 353
- Test Prep, p. 357
- Test-Taking Strategies with Transparencies

7-4 Solving Proportions

Objective
To solve proportions using number sense and cross products

Examples
1 Using a Unit Rate
2 Solving a Proportion
3 Using Cross Products

Math Understandings: p. 304C

Math Background

You can solve a proportion in many ways. You can use unit rates to find the missing quantity. You can use number sense and write the ratio in simplest form, then cross-multiply. You can use cross products to solve a proportion.

More Math Background: p. 304C

Lesson Planning and Resources

See p. 304E for a list of the resources that support this lesson.

✓ Check Skills You'll Need

1. Vocabulary Review
Explain why $\frac{2}{3}$ and $\frac{6}{12}$ do not form a *proportion*.
1–2. See below.
Do the ratios form a proportion?

2. $\frac{5}{8}$, $\frac{10}{16}$ **3.** $\frac{4}{12}$, $\frac{6}{14}$
                              no

for Help
Lesson 7-3

Check Skills You'll Need

1. **Answers may vary. Sample:** The ratios do not form a proportion, because their cross products are not equal.

2. **yes**

For: Proportions Activity
Use: Interactive Textbook, 7-4

What You'll Learn

To solve proportions using number sense and cross products

Why Learn This?

You can use a proportion to find missing information or to make a prediction. For example, you can solve a proportion to predict the distance a car can travel.

You can sometimes use a unit rate to complete a proportion.

EXAMPLE   Using a Unit Rate

① Cars A hybrid car can travel 260 miles using 5 gallons of gas. How many miles can the car travel using 8 gallons of gas?

Write a proportion that compares miles driven to gallons of gas.

$$\text{miles} \rightarrow \frac{260}{5} = \frac{\blacksquare}{8} \leftarrow \text{miles}$$
$$\text{gallons} \rightarrow \qquad \qquad \leftarrow \text{gallons}$$

Find a unit rate for 260 miles and 5 gallons.

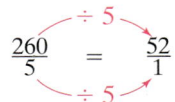
$$\frac{260}{5} = \frac{52}{1} \quad \leftarrow \text{Divide each term by 5 to find the number of miles driven on one gallon of gas.}$$

So the unit rate is 52 miles per gallon.

$$52 \times 8 = 416 \quad \leftarrow \text{Multiply the unit rate by the number of gallons.}$$

The car can travel 416 miles using 8 gallons of gas.

✓ Quick Check

● **1.** Use a unit rate to solve $\frac{12}{4} = \frac{\blacksquare}{5}$.   15

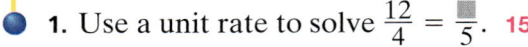

Differentiated Instruction | **Solutions for All Learners**

Special Needs L1
Ask students to draw a picture to solve the More Than One Way example, and compare the picture to the methods Jessica and Michael used. Ask them to decide which method their picture best represents.

learning style: visual

Below Level L2
As students write each cross product, have them say "top value times bottom value" and "bottom value times top value." Also have students use a different color to write each pair of cross products.

learning style: verbal

You can solve some proportions using number sense.

EXAMPLE **Solving a Proportion**

2 Solve $\frac{x}{9} = \frac{4}{6}$.

$\frac{4}{6} = \frac{2}{3}$ ← Write the ratio as a fraction in simplest form.

$\frac{x}{9} = \frac{2}{3}$ ← Since $3 \times 3 = 9$, multiply 2×3 to find x.

$2 \times 3 = 6$, so $x = 6$.

✓ Quick Check

2. a. Solve $\frac{6}{8} = \frac{n}{20}$. **15**   **b.** Solve $\frac{9}{12} = \frac{3}{x}$. **4**

You can also use cross products to solve proportions.

EXAMPLE **Using Cross Products**

3 **Multiple Choice** A student buys 6 drawing pencils for $3.90. Which proportion can you use to find c, the cost of 10 pencils?

Ⓐ $\frac{6}{3.90} = \frac{c}{10}$ Ⓒ $\frac{6}{3.90} = \frac{10}{c}$

Ⓑ $\frac{c}{3.90} = \frac{6}{10}$ Ⓓ $\frac{10}{3.90} = \frac{10}{c}$

Write a proportion. Let $c =$ the cost of 10 pencils.

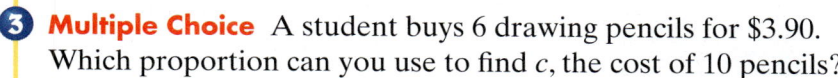

pencils → $\frac{6}{3.90}$ = $\frac{10}{c}$ ← pencils
cost ($) → ← cost ($)   ← Write a proportion.

The correct answer is choice C. You can use cross products to solve the proportion.

$6 \cdot c = 3.90 \cdot 10$ ← Write the cross products.

$6c = 39$ ← Multiply.

$6c \div 6 = 39 \div 6$ ← Division Property of Equality

$c = 6.5$ ← Simplify.

The student pays $6.50 for 10 drawing pencils.

✓ Quick Check

3. If 5 notebooks cost $7.85, how much do 3 notebooks cost? **$4.71**

7-4 Solving Proportions **321**

2. Teach

Activity Lab

All in One Teaching Resources
Activity Lab 7-4: Solving Proportions

Guided Instruction

The method of solving proportions using a common multiplier is sometimes called the "factor of change" method. You can scale a ratio up or down to an equivalent ratio by multiplying its terms by a common multiplier, just as you can generate equivalent fractions by multiplying the numerator and denominator of a fraction by a common multiplier.

Error Prevention!

When using unit rates, make sure students divide the numerator and denominator by the same number.

Example 3
Ask: *How many numbers do you need to solve the proportion using cross products?* **3 numbers**

PowerPoint
Additional Examples

1 Janet earned $31.50 for 5 hours of work. How much does she earn for 7 hours of work at the same rate of pay? **$44.10**

2 Find the value of the variable. $\frac{x}{27} = \frac{7}{21}$ **x = 9**

3 $\frac{14}{26} = \frac{21}{n}$ **n = 39**

Closure

- *How does a unit rate help you solve a proportion?* **Multiplying the unit rate by the other number in the ratio will give you the missing number.**
- *How can you use cross products to solve a proportion?* **Sample: Write the cross products. Isolate the variable and simplify.**

More Than One Way

A package of 50 blank CDs costs $25. However, the store has run out of 50-packs. The manager agrees to sell you packages of 12 at the same unit price. How much should a 12-pack of CDs cost?

Jessica's Method

I'll set up a proportion and use equivalent fractions to solve it.

$$\frac{50 \text{ CDs}}{\$25} = \frac{12 \text{ CDs}}{x \text{ dollars}}$$

$$\frac{2}{1} = \frac{12}{x}$$

$$\frac{2}{1} \underset{\times 6}{\overset{\times 6}{=}} \frac{12}{x}$$

$$x = 6$$

A pack of 12 blank CDs should cost $6.

Michael's Method

I'll find the unit rate for the cost of one CD. Then I'll multiply.

$$\frac{\text{Cost}}{\text{Quantity}} \rightarrow \frac{25 \div 50}{50 \div 50} = \frac{0.5}{1}$$

Each CD costs $.50. Twelve CDs cost $12 \times \$.50 = \$6.00$.

A pack of 12 blank CDs should cost $6.

Choose a Method

An ad says "3 movies for $18." At that rate, what is the cost of 5 movies? Describe your method and explain why you chose it.

$30; answers may vary. Sample: I found that the unit rate was $6 per movie and multiplied it by 5.

Check Your Understanding

1. **Answers may vary. Sample: You could determine whether their cross products are equal or put each ratio in simplest form and see if they are equivalent.**

1. **Writing in Math** Explain two ways that you can use to determine whether the ratios $\frac{45}{50}$ and $\frac{18}{20}$ form a proportion. **See left.**

Solve each proportion. Each solution is either 1, 2, or 3.

2. $\frac{1}{5} = \frac{w}{10}$ **2**   3. $\frac{3}{d} = \frac{12}{4}$ **1**   4. $\frac{n}{3} = \frac{6}{6}$ **3**   5. $\frac{2}{1} = \frac{4}{z}$ **2**

For more exercises, see Extra Skills and Word Problems.

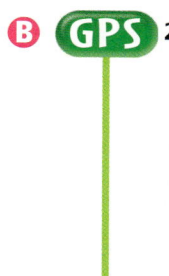

GO for Help

For Exercises	See Examples
6–12	1
13–22	2–3

Ⓐ Solve each proportion.

6. $\dfrac{35}{7} = \dfrac{\blacksquare}{21}$ **105**

7. $\dfrac{12}{4} = \dfrac{\blacksquare}{28}$ **84**

8. $\dfrac{\blacksquare}{57} = \dfrac{38}{19}$ **114**

9. $\dfrac{190}{\blacksquare} = \dfrac{114}{3}$ **5**

10. $\dfrac{20}{\blacksquare} = \dfrac{55}{11}$ **4**

11. $\dfrac{32}{8} = \dfrac{40}{\blacksquare}$ **10**

12. **Groceries** The cost of 3 quarts of milk is $6.75. How much will 7 quarts of milk cost? **$15.75**

Solve each proportion.

13. $\dfrac{20}{6} = \dfrac{c}{12}$ **40**

14. $\dfrac{12}{n} = \dfrac{4}{21}$ **63**

15. $\dfrac{6}{22} = \dfrac{15}{a}$ **55**

16. $\dfrac{16}{27} = \dfrac{4}{m}$ **6.75**

17. $\dfrac{h}{2} = \dfrac{3}{16}$ **0.375**

18. $\dfrac{75}{12} = \dfrac{p}{8}$ **50**

19. $\dfrac{27}{84} = \dfrac{18}{t}$ **56**

20. $\dfrac{k}{17} = \dfrac{20}{68}$ **5**

21. $\dfrac{38}{x} = \dfrac{2}{6}$ **114**

22. **Cooking** A recipe for 10 oz of fondue requires 8 oz of cheese. How much cheese do you need for 36 oz of fondue? **28.8 oz**

Ⓑ GPS 23. **Guided Problem Solving** A photo 5 inches wide and 7 inches long is enlarged. The sides of the new photo are in proportion to the original. The new photo is 14 inches wide. Find the length of the new photo. **19.6 in.**
  - **Understand the Problem** You can draw a picture to see the problem.
  - **Make a Plan** You use a proportion. Write the widths in the numerator and the lengths in the denominator.

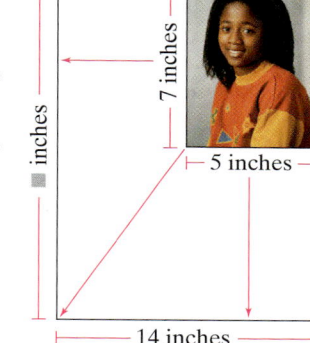

7 inches
inches
5 inches
14 inches

GO Online
Homework Video Tutor
Visit: PHSchool.com
Web Code: aqe-0704

24. **Earth Science** A glacier moves about 12 inches every 36 hours. About how far does the glacier move in 1 week? **56 in.**

25. **Printing** Your friend has a poster
GPS printed from a photograph that is 4 inches wide by 6 inches long. The poster is 22 inches wide and is proportional to the photograph. What is the length of the poster? **33 in.**

26. **Yes; the cross products will be the same.**

26. (**Algebra**) If the ratios $\dfrac{a}{b}$ and $\dfrac{x}{y}$ form a proportion, do the reciprocals $\dfrac{b}{a}$ and $\dfrac{y}{x}$ also form a proportion? Explain. **See left.**

Online lesson quiz, PHSchool.com, Web Code: aqa-0704

3. Practice

Assignment Guide

Check Your Understanding
Go over Exercises 1–5 in class before assigning the Homework Exercises.

Homework Exercises
A Practice by Example 6–22
B Apply Your Skills 23–32
C Challenge 33
Test Prep and
  Mixed Review 34–40

Homework Quick Check
To check students' understanding of key skills and concepts, go over Exercises 7, 13, 25, 30, and 31.

Differentiated Instruction Resources

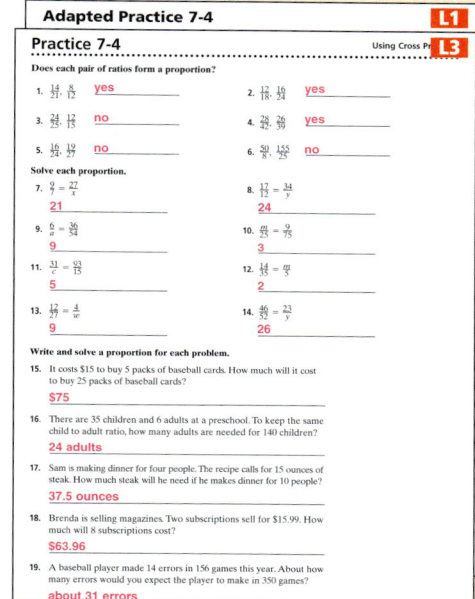

Adapted Practice 7-4 L1

Practice 7-4 Using Cross Pr... L3

Does each pair of ratios form a proportion?

1. $\frac{14}{21}, \frac{8}{12}$ **yes**   2. $\frac{12}{18}, \frac{16}{24}$ **yes**

3. $\frac{24}{25}, \frac{12}{15}$ **no**   4. $\frac{28}{42}, \frac{26}{39}$ **yes**

5. $\frac{16}{24}, \frac{19}{27}$ **no**   6. $\frac{50}{24}, \frac{155}{25}$ **no**

Solve each proportion.

7. $\frac{9}{3} = \frac{27}{x}$ **21**   8. $\frac{17}{24} = \frac{34}{y}$ **24**

9. $\frac{6}{a} = \frac{36}{48}$ **9**   10. $\frac{48}{24} = \frac{9}{15}$ **3**

11. $\frac{31}{c} = \frac{93}{15}$ **5**   12. $\frac{34}{17} = \frac{48}{q}$ **2**

13. $\frac{17}{27} = \frac{4}{w}$ **9**   14. $\frac{48}{24} = \frac{23}{y}$ **26**

Write and solve a proportion for each problem.

15. It costs $15 to buy 5 packs of baseball cards. How much will it cost to buy 25 packs of baseball cards? **$75**

16. There are 35 children and 6 adults at a preschool. To keep the same child to adult ratio, how many adults are needed for 140 children? **24 adults**

17. Sam is making dinner for four people. The recipe calls for 15 ounces of steak. How much steak will he need if he makes dinner for 10 people? **37.5 ounces**

18. Brenda is selling magazines. Two subscriptions sell for $15.99. How much will 8 subscriptions cost? **$63.96**

19. A baseball player made 14 errors in 156 games this year. About how many errors would you expect the player to make in 350 games? **about 31 errors**

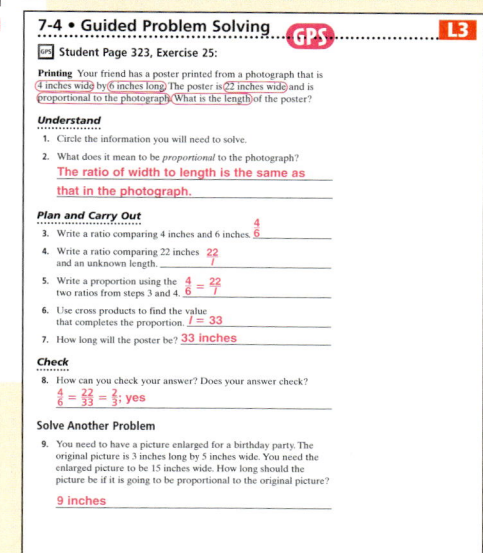

7-4 • Guided Problem Solving **GPS** L3

GPS Student Page 323, Exercise 25:

Printing Your friend has a poster printed from a photograph that is 4 inches wide by 6 inches long. The poster is 22 inches wide and is proportional to the photograph. What is the length of the poster?

Understand
1. Circle the information you will need to solve.
2. What does it mean to be proportional to the photograph? **The ratio of width to length is the same as that in the photograph.**

Plan and Carry Out
3. Write a ratio comparing 4 inches and 6 inches. $\frac{4}{6}$
4. Write a ratio comparing 22 inches and an unknown length. $\frac{22}{l}$
5. Write a proportion using the two ratios from steps 3 and 4. $\frac{4}{6} = \frac{22}{l}$
6. Use cross products to find the value that completes the proportion. $l = 33$
7. How long will the poster be? **33 inches**

Check
8. How can you check your answer? Does your answer check? $\frac{4}{6} = \frac{22}{33} = \frac{2}{3}$; yes

Solve Another Problem
9. You need to have a picture enlarged for a birthday party. The original picture is 3 inches long by 5 inches wide. You need the enlarged picture to be 15 inches wide. How long should the picture be if it is going to be proportional to the original picture?
9 inches

Lesson Quiz

Use unit rates, number sense, or cross products to solve each proportion.

1. $\frac{10}{7} = \frac{a}{56}$ **a = 80**

2. $\frac{b}{3} = \frac{6}{18}$ **b = 1**

3. $\frac{15}{c} = \frac{75}{100}$ **c = 20**

4. $\frac{16}{30} = \frac{8}{d}$ **d = 15**

30b. See back of book.

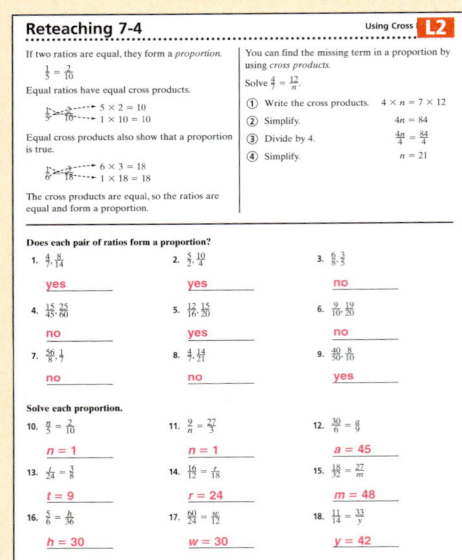

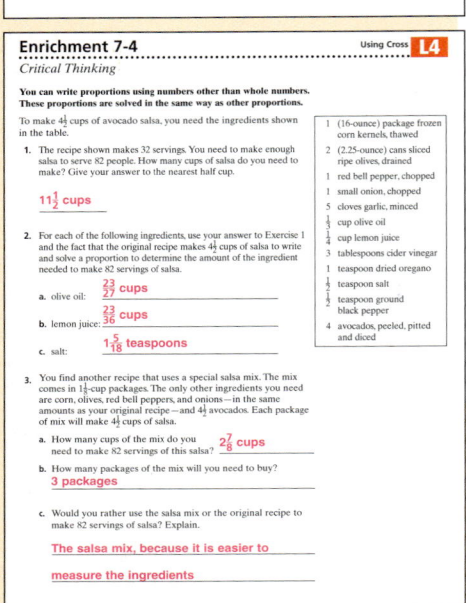

324

Solve each proportion.

27. $\frac{\$1.60}{3} = \frac{d}{12}$ **$6.40**

28. $\frac{3.21}{k} = \frac{6}{8.2}$ **4.387**

29. $\frac{1.5}{3} = \frac{7.5}{h}$ **15**

30. **Sculpture** The carvings at Mount Rushmore National Memorial in South Dakota are 60 feet from chin to forehead.

a. The distance from chin to forehead is typically 9 inches long. The distance between the pupils of the eyes is 2.5 inches long. What is the approximate distance between the pupils in the carving of George Washington's head? **16.7 ft**

b. **Reasoning** Did you need to convert feet to inches or inches to feet before you solved this proportion? Explain.

See margin.

31. **Schools** There are 221 students and 13 teachers at a middle school. To keep the same student-to-teacher ratio, how many teachers are needed for 272 students? **16 teachers**

32. **Choose a Method** A car can travel 54 miles on 3 gallons of gas. Find how far the car can travel on 8 gallons of gas. Explain why you chose the method you used. **See left.**

32. 144 mi; answers may vary. Sample: I found the unit rate and multiplied because this method was quick.

C 33. **Challenge** Solve for x and y in the equation $\frac{x}{3} = \frac{8}{12} = \frac{14}{y}$.

$x = 2$; $y = 21$

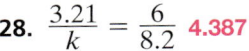

Test Prep and Mixed Review Practice

Multiple Choice

34. Veronica can walk 1 mile every 20 minutes. Which proportion can be used to find m, the number of miles she walks in 1 hour?

A

Ⓐ $\frac{1}{20} = \frac{m}{60}$ Ⓑ $\frac{1}{20} = \frac{60}{m}$ Ⓒ $\frac{1}{20} = \frac{m}{1}$ Ⓓ $\frac{1}{20} = \frac{1}{m}$

35. Matt can type 216 words in 6 minutes. Lya can type 128 words in 4 minutes. Which statement is supported by the information? **F**

Ⓕ Matt can type faster than Lya.

Ⓖ Lya can type faster than Matt.

Ⓗ In 20 minutes, Matt can type 88 more words than Lya.

Ⓙ Matt and Lya typing at the same time need 10 minutes to type 344 words.

36. Chris earns $25 for doing 3 hours of lawn work. About how much would Chris earn for doing 5 hours of lawn work? **B**

Ⓐ $40 Ⓑ $42 Ⓒ $45 Ⓓ $50

Find each quotient.

GO for Help

For Exercises	See Lesson
37–40	6-3

37. $4 \div \frac{4}{5}$ **5**

38. $\frac{4}{5} \div 4$ **$\frac{1}{5}$**

39. $\frac{4}{5} \div \frac{1}{5}$ **4**

40. $\frac{4}{5} \div 5$ **$\frac{4}{25}$**

Test Prep

Resources

For additional practice with a variety of test item formats:

• Test-Taking Strategies, p. 353
• Test Prep, p. 357
• Test-Taking Strategies with Transparencies

Alternative Assessment

Each partner writes four pairs of ratios. Partners exchange papers and use cross products to find whether each pair forms a proportion. Each partner then writes two proportions similar to those in Exercises 13–21. They exchange papers and solve each proportion.

Predicting Results

Last year your school used a spinner in a fundraising booth. Too many players won using the spinner. You make a new spinner to reduce the chance of winning. Your spinner has a ratio of "winning" area to "try again" area of 3 to 9.

ACTIVITY

1–2. See margin.

1. Make a spinner. Divide your spinner into 12 equal sections. Shade 3 sections for the "winning" area. The ratio of "winning" area to "try again" area is 3 to 9.

2. Make another spinner with 4 equal sections. Shade 1 section for the "winning" section.

3. **Reasoning** If you spin your second spinner 60 times, how many times would you expect to win? Justify your prediction.

3. **15; answers may vary. Sample: The ratio of winning area to total area of the spinner is 1 : 4; this is equivalent to 15 : 60.**

4. Spin each of your spinners 60 times. Record your results. Do your data agree with what you expected? Explain. **Check students' work.**

✓ Checkpoint Quiz 1

Lessons 7-1 through 7-4

1. Write 18 : 40 in words and as a fraction. **18 to 40, $\frac{18}{40}$**

2. Cereal costs $.19 per ounce. How much does 15 oz of cereal cost? **$2.85**

3. Two movie tickets cost $15. What is the cost of five tickets? **$37.50**

Does each pair of ratios form a proportion?

4. $\frac{6}{45}, \frac{2}{18}$ **no**

5. $\frac{4}{7}, \frac{30}{42}$ **no**

6. $\frac{8}{12}, \frac{30}{45}$ **yes**

Solve each proportion.

7. $\frac{21}{36} = \frac{7}{n}$ **12**

8. $\frac{54}{c} = \frac{9}{13}$ **78**

9. $\frac{x}{18} = \frac{\$6.30}{7}$ **$16.20**

10. You buy six beverages for $2.97. Find the cost of 16 beverages. **$7.92**

Activity Lab

Predicting Results

Students use ratios to predict the outcome of spinning a spinner many different times.

Guided Instruction

Explain to students that the likelihood of winning is represented by the ratio of winning spaces on the spinner to the total number of spaces on the spinner.

Have students work with partners on the Activity. Compare answers as a class.

Differentiated Instruction

Below Level **L2**
Have students use a straw with a tack through the end to create a spinner with 1 winning space and 3 "try again" spaces. Explain that the ratio of the winning area to the "try again" area is 1 : 3. Students spin the spinner 10 times to test if this is true.

Resources

• paper circles
• pencils
• tacks
• straws
• Student Manipulatives Kit

✓ Checkpoint Quiz

Use this Checkpoint Quiz to check students' understanding of the skills and concepts of Lessons 7-1 through 7-4.

Resources

• All-in-One Teaching Resources Checkpoint Quiz 1
• ExamView CD-ROM
• Success Tracker™ Online Intervention

1.
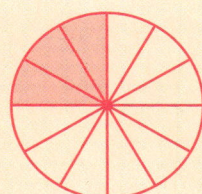

2.
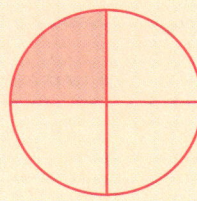

Examples
1 Finding the Scale of a Drawing
2 Finding Distances on a Map
3 Application: Architecture

Math Understandings: p. 304D

Math Background

A *scale drawing* is an enlarged or reduced drawing of an object. The *scale* in a map is the ratio that compares a length on the map to the actual length. Scales are given in simplest form and include the corresponding units.

More Math Background: p. 304D

Lesson Planning and Resources

See p. 304E for a list of the resources that support this lesson.

Bell Ringer Practice

✓ **Check Skills You'll Need**
Use student page, transparency, or PowerPoint. For intervention, direct students to:
Solving Proportions
Lesson 7-4
Extra Skills and Word Problems Practice, Ch. 7

✓ **Check Skills You'll Need**

1. Vocabulary Review
How can you use *equivalent ratios* to solve a proportion?
See below.
Solve each proportion.

2. $\frac{15}{21} = \frac{y}{35}$ **25**

3. $\frac{5}{m} = \frac{12.5}{5}$ **2**

 **for Help**
Lesson 7-4

Check Skills You'll Need

1. Answers may vary.
   Sample: You could rewrite the ratios so the numerators or the denominators are equal.

3 cm

What You'll Learn

To find the scale of a drawing and to use scales to find actual dimensions

🔊 **New Vocabulary** scale

Why Learn This?

Mapmakers and architects make scale drawings. They apply ratios to make drawings that are smaller than the actual size of the objects they represent.

A **scale** is the ratio that compares a length in a drawing or model to the length in the original object. Usually you write a scale as a fraction in simplest form.

EXAMPLE **Finding the Scale of a Drawing**

1 In the drawing at the left, the height of the goat is 3 centimeters. Its actual height is 90 centimeters. What is the scale of the drawing?

Write a ratio to find the scale.

$$\frac{\text{drawing height}}{\text{actual height}} \rightarrow \frac{3 \text{ cm}}{90 \text{ cm}} = \frac{1 \text{ cm}}{30 \text{ cm}} \quad \leftarrow \text{Divide each measure by the GCF, 3.}$$

The scale of the drawing is 1 centimeter to 30 centimeters, or 1 : 30.

✓ **Quick Check**

1. The length of a drawing of an object is 6 inches. The length of the actual object is 84 inches. What is the scale of the drawing?
   1 in. : 14 in.

You can use a scale to calculate actual distances using a map.

Differentiated Instruction **Solutions for All Learners**

Special Needs **L1**
Give students graph paper and ask them to draw rectangles that are longer or shorter using a given scale. For example, ask them to draw a longer rectangle using a scale of 1 : 2 for a rectangle 2 units long. Have them tell how long the sides will be before drawing their rectangles.
learning style: visual

Below Level **L2**
Review the GCF (greatest common factor) and simplifying fractions by using the factors of the numerator and denominator.
$$\frac{10}{25} = \frac{2 \cdot 5}{5 \cdot 5} = \frac{2}{5}$$
learning style: visual

EXAMPLE Finding Distances on a Map

2 Use the map and scale to find the actual distance from Winfield to Auburn.

Step 1 Use a ruler to estimate the map distance from Winfield to Auburn. The distance is about 6 centimeters.

Step 2 Write the scale as a ratio: $\dfrac{1 \text{ centimeter}}{20 \text{ miles}}$.

Step 3 Use a proportion. Let d = the actual distance.

$$\dfrac{1 \text{ cm}}{20 \text{ mi}} = \dfrac{6 \text{ cm}}{d \text{ mi}}$$ ← map distances
← actual distances

$$\dfrac{1}{20} \overset{\times 6}{\underset{\times 6}{=}} \dfrac{6}{d}$$

Since $20 \times 6 = 120$, the distance is about 120 miles.

✓ Quick Check

2. Find the actual distance from Winfield to Montgomery.
about 100 mi

EXAMPLE Application: Architecture

3 You use a scale of 1 inch : 10 feet to build a model of the White House. The White House is 58 feet tall. How tall is your model?

$\dfrac{\text{model (in.)}}{\text{actual (ft.)}} \rightarrow \dfrac{1}{10}$ ← Write a ratio for the scale.

$\dfrac{1}{10} = \dfrac{h}{58}$ ← Use h to represent the model height.
← actual height

$58 = 10h$ ← Write the cross products. Then multiply.

$58 \div 10 = 10h \div 10$ ← Divide each side by 10.

$5.8 = h$ ← Simplify.

Your model is 5.8 inches tall.

✓ Quick Check

17 in.

3. The White House is 170 feet long. How long is your model?

7-5 Scale Drawings **327**

Vocabulary Tip
The scale on a map sometimes uses "=" to indicate the ratio: 1 cm = 20 mi.

GO for Help
For help with cross products, go to Lesson 7-4, Example 3.

2. Teach

Activity Lab
Use before the lesson.

All in One Teaching Resources
Activity Lab 7-5: Designs to Scale

Guided Instruction

Error Prevention!

Point out that both units in the scale are in centimeters. Also point out that the length of the model or map comes first in the scale ratio.

Example 3
Some students may prefer to use the definition of a scale to set up a correct proportion.

$$\text{scale} = \dfrac{1 \text{ in.}}{10 \text{ ft}} = \dfrac{\text{model (in.)}}{\text{actual (ft)}}$$

PowerPoint
Additional Examples

1 The length of a drawing of a kitten is 3 cm. The actual length of the kitten is 27 cm. What is the scale of the drawing? **1 cm : 9 cm**

2 Use a map scale of 1 in. : 20 mi to find the actual distance for 3.4 in. **68 mi**

3 Suppose you are making a model of an 18-meter boat. Use a scale of 1 cm : 2.5 m to find the length of your model boat. **7.2 cm**

All in One Teaching Resources
- Daily Notetaking Guide 7-5 **L3**
- Adapted Notetaking 7-5 **L1**

Closure

- *How do you find the scale of a drawing?* **Sample: Write a ratio of the length of the drawing to the length of the original object; simplify.**
- *How can you use a scale to find actual dimensions of a model?* **Sample: Set up a proportion using the model scale and the given model measure. Solve the proportion.**

Advanced Learners L4
What happens to the volume of a scale model when you double each of its three-dimensions? **The volume is 2 · 2 · 2, or 8 times greater.**

learning style: visual

English Language Learners ELL
Make sure to differentiate between a scale and a scale factor. A scale factor is expressed as 30, for Example 1 (the number you multiply or divide by to get the larger or smaller drawing), whereas the scale is 1 : 30, which means 1 cm for every 30 cm.

learning style: verbal

327

Assignment Guide

Check Your Understanding
Go over Exercises 1–3 in class before assigning the Homework Exercises.

Homework Exercises
A Practice by Example 4–15
B Apply Your Skills 16–22
C Challenge 23
Test Prep and
Mixed Review 24–29

Homework Quick Check
To check students' understanding of key skills and concepts, go over Exercises 5, 11, 15, 21, and 22.

Differentiated Instruction Resources

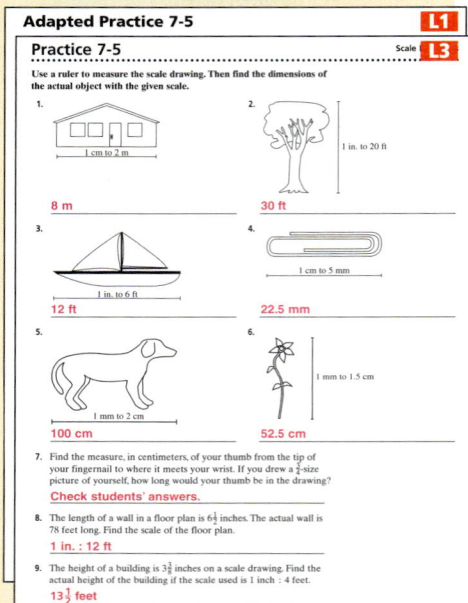

Adapted Practice 7-5 L1

Practice 7-5 Scale L3

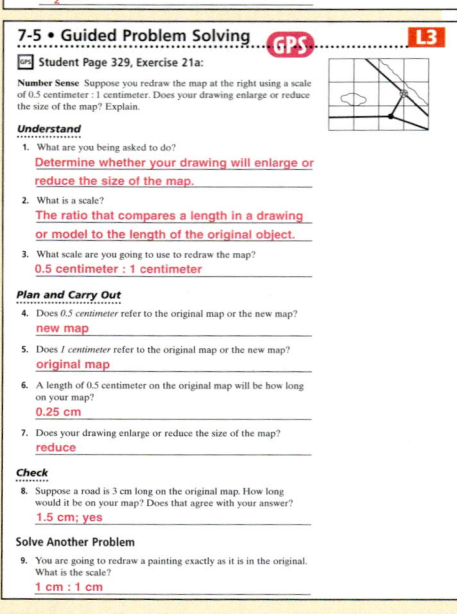

7-5 • Guided Problem Solving GPS L3

✓ Check Your Understanding

1. **Vocabulary** The scale on a map reads "1 in. : 50 miles." Explain what this means. **One inch on the map represents an actual distance of 50 miles.**

2. **Boats** Measure the length of the boat at the left. The scale is 1 cm : 3 m. What is a reasonable length for the actual boat? **D**
   Ⓐ 2.5 cm   Ⓑ 2.5 m   Ⓒ 7.5 cm   Ⓓ 7.5 m

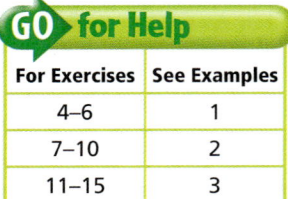

3. **Writing in Math** When you find actual distances on a map, do you expect to get exact or approximate answers? Explain.
Approximate; explanations may vary. Sample: It is very difficult to get exact measurements using a ruler.

Homework Exercises

For more exercises, see Extra Skills and Word Problems.

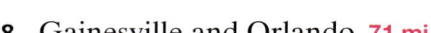

GO for Help

For Exercises	See Examples
4–6	1
7–10	2
11–15	3

Ⓐ **Write each scale as a ratio.**

4. a 10-inch-long drawing of a 40-inch-long table   **1 in. : 4 in.**

5. a 15-foot-long model of a 300-foot-long fence   **1 ft : 20 ft**

6. **Architecture** The height of a wall in a blueprint is 3 inches. The actual wall is 96 inches high. Find the scale of the blueprint.
1 in. : 32 in.

Geography Use the map for Exercises 7–10. Find the actual distance between each pair of cities. Measure with a metric ruler. Round to the nearest mile.
7–10. Answers may vary. Samples are given.

SCALE
1 cm = 31 mi

7. Gainesville and Leesburg   **47 mi**

8. Gainesville and Orlando   **71 mi**

9. Tampa and Daytona Beach   **87 mi**

10. St. Cloud and Daytona Beach   **47 mi**

Suppose you are making a model of each object. Use a scale of 1 inch : 9 inches to find the length or height of your model.

11. A chair is 36 inches tall. **4 in.**   12. A whale is 468 inches long. **52 in.**

13. A lizard is 12 inches long.   14. A stop sign is 117 inches tall.
1⅓ in.   **13 in.**

GO Online
Homework Video Tutor
Visit: PHSchool.com
Web Code: aqe-0705

15. **Toy Design** From head to tail, the length of a *Tyrannosaurus rex* was about 40 feet. You want to design a model with a scale of 1 inch : 8 feet. How long will the model be? **5 in.**

328   Chapter 7   Ratios, Proportions, and Percents

22. See back of book.

B **GPS** 16. **Guided Problem Solving** Suppose you are making a castle for your miniature figures. A 6-foot-tall knight is represented by a figure that is 30 mm tall. Actual castle walls are about 30 feet high. How high should you make the walls of the model? **150 mm**
- **Make a Plan** Use the scale as a ratio to write a proportion.
- **Carry Out the Plan** Solve the proportion $\frac{30 \text{ mm}}{6 \text{ feet}} = \frac{\blacksquare \text{ mm}}{30 \text{ feet}}$.

21a. Reduce. The map is 4 cm wide and 3 cm high. For each centimeter on the map, I would draw 0.5 centimeter on my drawing. My drawing would measure 2 cm wide and 1.5 cm high.

Map Scales Use a map scale of 1 centimeter : 100 kilometers. How many centimeters on the map represent each actual distance?

17. 125 kilometers **1.25 cm**
18. 80 kilometers **0.8 cm**
19. 170 kilometers **1.7 cm**
20. 2,500 kilometers **25 cm**

21. a. **Number Sense** Suppose you redraw the map at the left **GPS** using a scale of 0.5 centimeter : 1 centimeter. Does your drawing enlarge or reduce the size of the map? Explain.
   b. Redraw the map using the scale of 0.5 cm : 1 cm. **See left.**

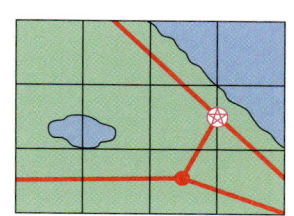

21b.

22. The table shows the measurements of a toy car and the actual car. Copy and complete the table.
See margin.

Part	Toy Size	Actual Size
Car	3 in.	120 in.
Door handle	▧	5 in.
Headlight	▧	8 in.
Front bumper	0.18 ft	▧
Rear window	▧	4.5 ft

C 23. **Challenge** Make a scale drawing of a room in your home. **Check students' work.**

Test Prep and Mixed Review **Practice**

Multiple Choice

24. On a map, 4 inches represents an actual distance of 200 miles. Which ratio best describes the scale of the map? **D**
   (A) 200 mi : 4 in.
   (C) 4 in. : 200 mi
   (B) 50 mi : 1 in.
   (D) 1 in. : 50 mi

25. Jim cut 4 apple pies and 4 cherry pies into slices as shown at the right. He sold 23 slices of apple pie and 29 slices of cherry pie. Which expression shows the number of whole pies Jim sold? **H**

   (F) $\frac{23}{32} + \frac{29}{32}$
   (G) $\frac{23}{12} + \frac{29}{12}$
   (H) $\frac{23}{8} + \frac{29}{8}$
   (J) $\frac{23}{4} + \frac{29}{4}$

Find each product.

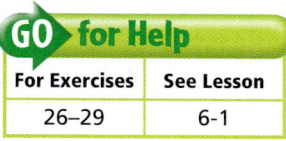
GO for Help

For Exercises	See Lesson
26–29	6-1

26. $\frac{5}{16}$ of 32 **10**
27. $\frac{3}{4} \times 10$ **7$\frac{1}{2}$**
28. $\frac{9}{10} \cdot 55$ **49$\frac{1}{2}$**
29. $\frac{4}{5}$ of 100 **80**

Alternative Assessment

Provide pairs of students with a meter stick and graph paper. Partners work together to make a scale drawing of the dimensions of the classroom, putting in doors and windows as necessary. Remind them to choose an appropriate scale. Have pairs share their scale drawings with the class.

Test Prep

Resources

For additional practice with a variety of test item formats:
- Test-Taking Strategies, p. 353
- Test Prep, p. 357
- Test-Taking Strategies with Transparencies

---

4. Assess & Reteach

PowerPoint
Lesson Quiz

1. The height of a dog in a drawing is 4 centimeters. The actual height of the dog is 80 centimeters. What is the scale of the drawing?
   1 centimeter to 20 centimeters or 1 : 20

Use a scale of 1 cm : 50 km to find each actual distance.

2. 4.2 cm **210 km**
3. 0.8 cm **40 km**
4. Use a scale of 1 in. = 8 ft to find the model length of a 14 ft automobile. **1.75 in.**

Reteaching 7-5 Scale D **L2**

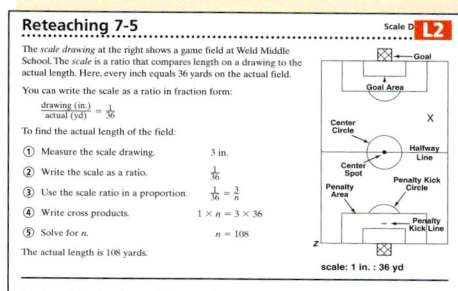

The *scale drawing* at the right shows a game field at Weld Middle School. The *scale* is a ratio that compares length on a drawing to the actual length. Here, every inch equals 36 yards on the actual field.

You can write the scale as a ratio in fraction form:
$\frac{\text{drawing (in.)}}{\text{actual (yd)}} = \frac{1}{36}$

To find the actual length of the field:
① Measure the scale drawing.   3 in.
② Write the scale as a ratio. $\frac{1}{36}$
③ Use the scale ratio in a proportion. $\frac{1}{36} = \frac{3}{n}$
④ Write cross products. $1 \times n = 3 \times 36$
⑤ Solve for n. $n = 108$
The actual length is 108 yards.

scale: 1 in. : 36 yd

Use the scale drawing above to find the actual size.

1. Find the width of the field. **72 yards**
2. Find the perimeter of the field. **360 yards**
3. Find the measure of the shorter side of the penalty area. **18 yards**
4. Find the distance from the center spot to the front of the goal. **54 yards**
5. Brian kicks the ball from the penalty kick line to the opposite goal area. About how far does he kick the ball? **about 90 yards**
6. Kaitlin makes a direct kick from the spot marked X. She scores by getting the ball into the goal nearest her. About how far does she kick the ball? **about 36 yards**

Write each scale as a ratio.

7. a 12-inch model of a 60-foot boat **1 inch to 5 feet**
8. a 6-inch drawing of an 18-inch TV **1 inch to 3 inches**
9. a 4-centimeter model of a 28-centimeter hammer **1 cm to 7 cm**
10. a 9-inch drawing of a 54-foot garden **1 inch to 6 feet**

Enrichment 7-5 Scale Dr **L4**
Visual Thinking

The pep club has been asked to create a school banner with the mascot and the school name printed on the front. The plans are to enlarge the banner so that the football players can run through it at the pep rally and to also reduce the banner so that it fits on hand-held sticks that the students can wave. So that the enlargement and the reduction will be as easy as possible to make, you want to plan the banner to have measurements in whole feet.

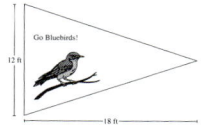

Go Bluebirds!
12 ft
18 in.

1. What is the width-to-length ratio for the large banner that the football players will run through? **12 ft : 18 ft**
2. If the ratios for the large banner and the stick banner are the same, what is the width-to-length ratio for the stick banner? **2 ft : 3 ft**
3. Using the information from Exercise 2, what measures of width and length will you make the banner so that the enlargement and reduction are easy to make? **Sample answer: width of 2 ft, and length of 3 ft**
4. When you enlarge and reduce the banner will you be able to keep the picture and the text in each banner? Explain. **Yes; the picture and the text will both change size proportionally.**
5. What other measure could you make the banner that is greater than the one you just designed? Explain. **Sample answer: width of 4 ft and a length of 6 ft; The banner would still have a ratio of 2 ft : 3 ft.**

329

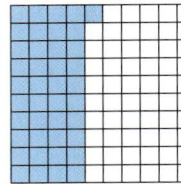

Modeling Percents

In Lesson 4-9, you learned to write a fraction with a denominator of 100 as a decimal. You can also write a fraction and a decimal as a percent.

In the grid model at the right, each small square represents $\frac{1}{100}$ of the whole. Forty-one of the 100 squares are shaded. This can be written as $\frac{41}{100}$, 0.41, or 41%.

Each column contains 10 squares.
Shade 4 columns and 1 additional square.

ACTIVITY

1. On a piece of graph paper, draw a 10-by-10 grid model. **Check students' work**

2. Suppose 50% of students in your school like broccoli. **50 squares** Use your grid model to represent 50%. How many squares will be shaded?

3. Write 50% as a fraction and as a decimal. $\frac{50}{100}$ **or** $\frac{1}{2}$**; 0.50 or 0.5**

4. Make four grid models of the values in the table. Copy the table. Use your models to complete the table.
   See margin.

Fraction	$\frac{5}{100}$	■	■	■
Decimal	■	0.75	■	■
Percent	■	■	37%	100%

Exercises

Model each situation with a grid model. **1–3. See margin.**

1. A basketball player makes 82% of her free throws.

2. 67% of the seats in an auditorium are filled.

3. **Reasoning** Describe a grid model that represents 150%.

4. a. What percent of the grid at the right is shaded? **18%**
   b. What percent of the grid at the right is not shaded? **82%**
   c. **Writing in Math** Explain how you found your answer to part (b). **Subtract 18% from 100%**

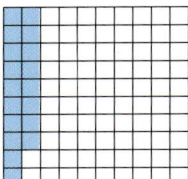

4.

Fraction	$\frac{5}{100}$	$\frac{75}{100}$	$\frac{37}{100}$	$\frac{100}{100}$
Decimal	0.05	0.75	0.37	1.0
Percent	5%	75%	37%	100%

1.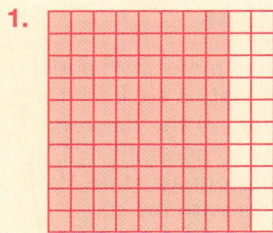

2–3. See back of book.

Percents, Fractions, and Decimals

What You'll Learn

To find equivalent forms of fractions, decimals, and percents

🔊 **New Vocabulary** percent

Why Learn This?

Newspapers use percents, fractions, and decimals to report data. To compare the data, you need to be able to convert from one form to another.

π **Math Times**
Math Test Scores Go Up by 12%

A **percent** is a ratio that compares a number to 100. The symbol for percent is %. You can write a percent as a fraction with a denominator of 100.

EXAMPLES **Representing Percents**

① Write 36% as a fraction. Write your answer in simplest form.

$36\% = \frac{36}{100}$ ← Write the percent as a fraction with a denominator of 100.

$= \frac{9}{25}$ ← Write the fraction in simplest form.

② **Gridded Response** You read 36% of a book. Express this amount as a decimal.

$36\% = \frac{36}{100}$ ← Write the percent as a fraction with denominator 100.

$= 0.36$ ← Write the fraction as a decimal.

✔ **Quick Check**

1. a. Write 55% as a fraction. $\frac{11}{20}$ b. Write 4% as a fraction. $\frac{1}{25}$
2. a. Write 25% as a decimal. **0.25** b. Write 2% as a decimal. **0.02**

To write a decimal as a percent, you write a fraction first.

Objective
To find equivalent forms of fractions, decimals, and percents

Examples
1–2 Representing Percents
3 Writing a Decimal as a Percent
4 Writing a Fraction as a Percent

Math Understandings: p. 304D

Professional Development ★

Math Background

A *percent* is a ratio that compares a number to 100. Percents, fractions, and decimals can all represent parts of a whole. You can convert between percents, fractions, and decimals by using the definition of percent as $\frac{part}{whole} = \frac{percent}{100}$.

To write a decimal as a percent, move the decimal point two places to the right and write the percent sign. To convert a fraction to a percent, divide the numerator by the denominator and convert the resulting decimal to a percent.

More Math Background: p. 304D

Lesson Planning and Resources

See p. 304E for a list of the resources that support this lesson.

PowerPoint

Bell Ringer Practice

✔ **Check Skills You'll Need**
Use student page, transparency, or PowerPoint. For intervention, direct students to:
Equivalent Fractions
Lesson 4-5
Extra Skills and Word Problems Practice, Ch. 4

Activity Lab

Use before the lesson.
Student Edition Activity Lab,
Hands On 7-6a, Modeling
Percents, p. 330

All in One Teaching Resources

Activity Lab 7-6: Fractions,
Decimals, and Percents

Guided Instruction

Example 4
Have students list the factors of
100. **1, 2, 4, 5, 10, 20, 25, 50, 100**

Error Prevention!

Watch for students who
incorrectly move the decimal
point to the left instead of to the
right when they convert decimals
to percents.

PowerPoint

Additional Examples

1 Write 4% as a fraction in
simplest form. $\frac{1}{25}$

2 Write each percent as a
decimal.
   a. 87% **0.87**
   b. 9% **0.09**

3 Write each decimal as a
percent.
   a. 0.16 **16%**
   b. 0.03 **3%**

4 Write $\frac{7}{20}$ as a percent. **35%**

All in One Teaching Resources

- Daily Notetaking Guide 7-6 **L3**
- Daily Notetaking 7-6 **L1**

Closure

- *How do you write a percent as a
fraction?* **Sample: Write the
percent with a denominator of
100 and simplify.**
- *How do you write a decimal as a
percent?* **Sample: Move the
decimal point two places to the
right and write the percent sign.**

EXAMPLE **Writing a Decimal as a Percent**

3 Write 0.07 as a percent.

$$0.07 = \frac{7}{100} = 7\% \quad \leftarrow \text{Write the decimal as a fraction with a denominator of 100.}$$

✓ Quick Check

3. Write each decimal as a percent.
   a. 0.52 **52%**   **b.** 0.05 **5%**   **c.** 0.5 **50%**

You can solve a proportion to convert a fraction to a percent.

EXAMPLE **Writing a Fraction as a Percent**

Careers Physicians
measure heart rate and
blood pressure.

4 **Doctors** According to a news article, 6 of every 25 doctors in the
United States are women. As a fraction, 6 of every 25 is written $\frac{6}{25}$.

Write $\frac{6}{25}$ as a percent.

$$\frac{6}{25} = \frac{p}{100} \quad \leftarrow \text{Write a proportion. Percents have 100 in the denominator.}$$

$$\frac{6}{25} \overset{\times 4}{\underset{\times 4}{=}} \frac{24}{100} \quad \leftarrow \text{Find the fraction with a denominator of 100 equal to } \frac{6}{25}.$$

$$\frac{6}{25} = \frac{24}{100} = 24\% \quad \leftarrow \text{Write using a percent symbol.}$$

In the United States, 24% of the doctors are women.

✓ Quick Check

4. The same article said that 1 of every 20 neurosurgeons in the
United States is a woman. Write the fraction $\frac{1}{20}$ as a percent.
5%

✓ Check Your Understanding

1. **The ratio does not
compare a number to
100.**

$\frac{1}{5}$ 0.02 $\frac{20}{50}$ 0.20 $\frac{4}{12}$

0.2 $\frac{6}{24}$ 0.4 $\frac{20}{100}$ 0.05

1. **Vocabulary** Explain why the ratio 4 : 10 is NOT a percent.

2. Which numbers at the left are equivalent to 20%? $\frac{1}{5}$, **0.2, 0.20,** $\frac{20}{100}$

3. **Open-Ended** Write a fraction and a decimal greater than 80%.
   Answers may vary. Samples: $\frac{5}{6}$ **and 0.85.**

4. **Mental Math** Write 50% as a fraction in simplest form. $\frac{1}{2}$

Advanced Learners **L4**
What percent is 50% of 60% of a number? **30%** If you
increase the original price of an item by 25%, by what
percent do you need to reduce the new price to
obtain the original price? **20%**

learning style: visual

English Language Learners **ELL**
Ask students to *describe* what happens to the decimal
point when you multiply a decimal by 100. Ask them
to *predict* what might happen if they divided by 100.

learning style: verbal

Homework Exercises

For more exercises, see Extra Skills and Word Problems.

GO for Help

For Exercises	See Example
5–14	1
15–25	2
26–30	3
31–36	4

A Write each percent as a fraction in simplest form.

5. 70% $\frac{7}{10}$ **6.** 88% $\frac{22}{25}$ **7.** 5% $\frac{1}{20}$ **8.** 33% $\frac{33}{100}$ **9.** 14% $\frac{7}{50}$

10. 15% $\frac{3}{20}$ **11.** 75% $\frac{3}{4}$ **12.** 18% $\frac{9}{50}$ **13.** 2% $\frac{1}{50}$ **14.** 42% $\frac{21}{50}$

Write each percent as a decimal.

15. 15% **0.15** **16.** 22% **0.22** **17.** 82% **0.82** **18.** 63% **0.63** **19.** 10% **0.1**

20. 40% **0.4** **21.** 3% **0.03** **22.** 7% **0.07** **23.** 12% **0.12** **24.** 100% **1**

25. Quality Control A shipment of radios is packed incorrectly, and 6% arrive damaged. Write this amount as a decimal. **0.06**

Write each decimal as a percent.

26. 0.17 **17%** **27.** 0.08 **8%** **28.** 0.98 **98%** **29.** 0.22 **22%** **30.** 0.44 **44%**

Write each fraction as a percent.

31. $\frac{19}{20}$ **95%** **32.** $\frac{27}{50}$ **54%** **33.** $\frac{1}{4}$ **25%** **34.** $\frac{19}{25}$ **76%** **35.** $\frac{7}{25}$ **28%**

36. School Play Three of every five students who tried out for a play made the cast. Write $\frac{3}{5}$ as a percent. **60%**

B **GPS** **37. Guided Problem Solving** About $\frac{7}{10}$ of Earth's surface is covered by water. What percent of Earth's surface is NOT covered by water? **30%**
- You can draw a picture to model this problem.

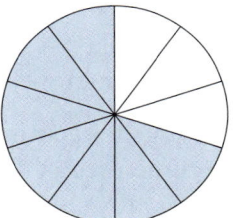

GO Online
Homework Video Tutor
Visit: PHSchool.com
Web Code: aqe-0706

Write the letter of the point on the number line that represents each number.

38. 0.4 **B** **39.** 60% **C** **40.** $\frac{5}{6}$ **D** **41.** 18% **A**

Assignment Guide

Check Your Understanding
Go over Exercises 1–4 in class before assigning the Homework Exercises.

Homework Exercises
A Practice by Example   5–36
B Apply Your Skills   37–50
C Challenge   51
Test Prep and
   Mixed Review   52–58

Homework Quick Check
To check students' understanding of key skills and concepts, go over Exercises 13, 29, 46, 47, and 50.

Differentiated Instruction Resources

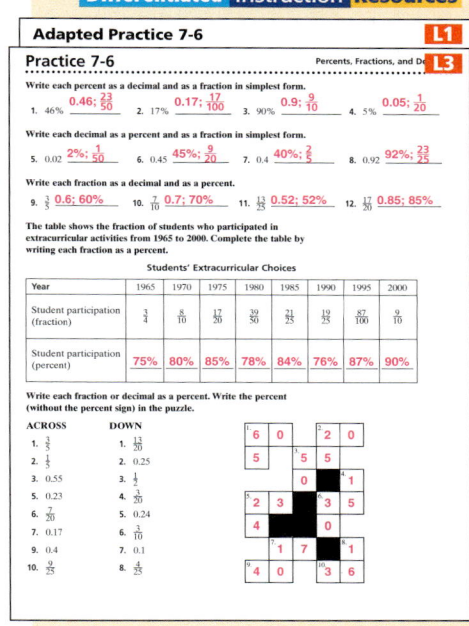

PowerPoint

Lesson Quiz

Write each percent as a decimal and as a fraction in simplest form.

1. 60% **0.60;** $\frac{3}{5}$

2. 38% **0.38;** $\frac{19}{50}$

Write each decimal or fraction as a percent.

3. 0.05 **5%**   **4.** $\frac{3}{20}$ **15%**

47. See back of book.

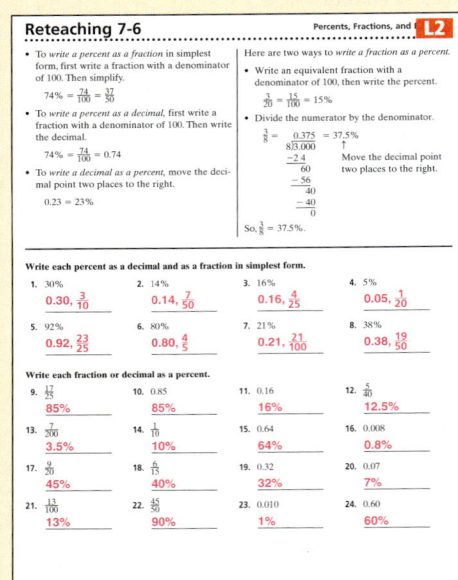

Reteaching 7-6   Percents, Fractions, and **L2**

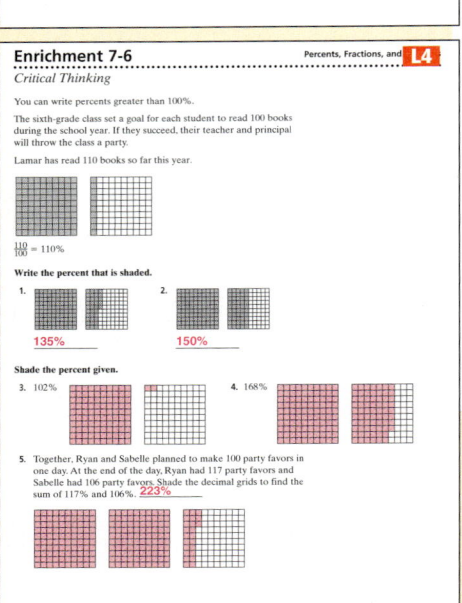

Enrichment 7-6   Percents, Fractions, and **L4**

Critical Thinking

334

Order each set of numbers from least to greatest. 42–45. See left.

42. 46%, $\frac{1}{2}$, 0.53, 5%

43. $\frac{1}{4}$, 22%, 0.24, $\frac{1}{5}$

44. 63%, $\frac{3}{5}$, 0.58, $\frac{31}{50}$

45. $\frac{17}{20}$, 95%, 0.9, $\frac{22}{25}$

46. Biology At least ninety-nine percent of all the kinds of plants and animals that have ever lived are now extinct. Write ninety-nine percent as a fraction and as a decimal. $\frac{99}{100}$, 0.99

GPS

47. Copy and complete the table below. **See margin.**

Fraction	$\frac{11}{50}$	$\frac{39}{50}$	$\frac{22}{25}$	▪	▪	$\frac{4}{5}$
Decimal	▪	0.78	▪	0.45	▪	▪
Percent	22%	▪	▪	▪	42%	▪

48. You answer 32 questions correctly on a 45-question test. You need a score of at least 70% to pass. Do you pass? Explain. yes; $\frac{32}{45} = 0.7\overline{1} \approx 71\%$

49. Fuel Gauge Use the fuel gauge below. What percent of the tank is full? 75%

E   F

50. Writing in Math Explain how to write a decimal as a percent. See left.

C 51. Challenge Find the percent of numbers from 1 to 100 that are prime numbers. 25%

---

42. 5%, 46%, $\frac{1}{2}$, 0.53

43. $\frac{1}{5}$, 22%, 0.24, $\frac{1}{4}$

44. 0.58, $\frac{3}{5}$, $\frac{31}{50}$, 63%

45. $\frac{17}{20}$, $\frac{22}{25}$, 0.9, 95%

50. Answers may vary. Sample: Move the decimal point two places to the right. Round to the nearest whole number. Add a percent sign.

Test Prep and Mixed Review   **Practice**

Gridded Response

52. The formula $i = \frac{127}{50}c$ can be used to convert a measurement from centimeters to inches. Write a decimal equal to $\frac{127}{50}$. **2.54**

53. Eric finishes a swimming race in 51.4 seconds. Bobby finishes the same race in 48.6 seconds. How much faster is Eric's time than Bobby's time, in seconds? **2.8**

54. Billie Jean earns $12 for baby-sitting for 3 hours. How much will she earn in 4 hours, in dollars? **16**

GO for Help

For Exercises	See Lesson
55–58	6-2

Estimate each product.

55. $2\frac{3}{4} \times 5\frac{1}{4}$ **15**

56. $6\frac{1}{8} \times 3\frac{3}{8}$ **18**

57. $4\frac{5}{8} \times 2\frac{2}{3}$ **15**

58. $3\frac{1}{2} \times 5\frac{1}{3}$ **20**

Test Prep

Resources

For additional practice with a variety of test item formats:
- Test-Taking Strategies, p. 353
- Test Prep, p. 357
- Test-Taking Strategies with Transparencies

Alternative Assessment

Each student in a pair writes several percents. Partners exchange papers and write each other's percents as decimals and fractions in simplest form. Next, partners write several fractions and decimals, exchange papers, and write each other's fractions and decimals as percents.

The paradise parrot once lived in Australia. It has been extinct since the early 1900s.

Write each percent as a decimal and as a fraction in simplest form.

1. 74% **0.74, $\frac{37}{50}$**

2. 6% **0.06, $\frac{3}{50}$**

3. 60% **0.6, $\frac{3}{5}$**

Write each fraction as a percent.

4. $\frac{21}{25}$ **84%**

5. $\frac{7}{10}$ **70%**

6. $\frac{1}{20}$ **5%**

Use the map below. Find the distance between each pair of cities.

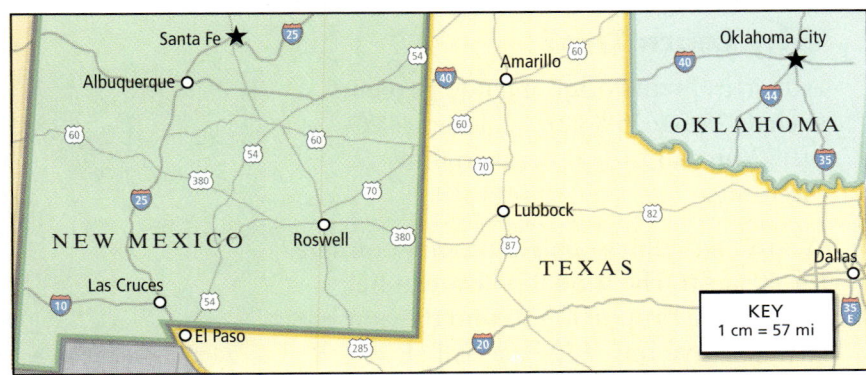

7. Santa Fe and El Paso
   about 268 mi

8. Dallas and Albuquerque
   about 587 mi

9. Dallas and El Paso
   about 570 mi

10. **Advertising** A beverage cup is 6 inches tall. The beverage cup on a restaurant billboard is 18 feet tall. Write the scale of the billboard as a ratio in simplest form. **1 in. : 3 ft**

MATH AT WORK

Help-Desk Technician

Do you enjoy helping your family and friends with their computer-related questions? If so, a career as a help-desk technician might be for you. Help-desk technicians provide support to people who have hardware and software questions.

Help-desk technicians must be able to apply logical reasoning and problem-solving skills in order to assist their customers.

Go Online
PHSchool.com
For: Information on Help-Desk Technicians
Web Code: aqb-2031

335

Objective
To use percents to find part of a whole

Examples
1 Using a Proportion
2 Using a Decimal
3 Using Mental Math

Math Understandings: p. 304D

Math Background

You can find a percent of a number, such as 25% of 60, by performing the multiplication $0.25 \cdot 60$, or $\frac{1}{4} \cdot 60$. You can often use mental math. You can also set up the proportion $\frac{percent}{100} = \frac{part}{whole}$ to solve percent problems.

More Math Background: p. 304D

Lesson Planning and Resources

See p. 304E for a list of the resources that support this lesson.

✓ Check Skills You'll Need
Use student page, transparency, or PowerPoint. For intervention, direct students to:
Solving Proportions
Lesson 7-4
Extra Skills and Word Problems
   Practice, Ch. 7

7-7 Finding the Percent of a Number

✓ Check Skills You'll Need

1. **Vocabulary Review**
How can you use *cross products* to solve a proportion?
See below.
Solve each proportion.

2. $\frac{m}{12} = \frac{6}{9}$ **8**

3. $\frac{6}{45} = \frac{2}{n}$ **15**

4. $\frac{54}{c} = \frac{9}{13}$ **78**

5. $\frac{92}{100} = \frac{q}{250}$ **230**

 **for Help**
Lesson 7-4

Check Skills You'll Need

1. Anwers may vary. Sample: You can set the cross products equal to each other to write and solve an equation.

What You'll Learn
To use percents to find part of a whole

Why Learn This?
Advertisements often include percents such as "Save 25%" or "All items 40% off!" You can use percents to find discounts.

A store has all baseball equipment on sale for 40% off. The model below can help you write a proportion to find the amount you will save on a $32 baseball glove.

$$\frac{n}{32} = \frac{40}{100} \quad \leftarrow \text{The part } n \text{ corresponds to 40% in the diagram.}$$
$$\leftarrow \text{The full price \$32 corresponds to 100%.}$$

EXAMPLE   Using a Proportion

1 **Retail Sales** Find 40% of $32.

$$\begin{array}{l}\text{amount saved} \rightarrow \\ \text{original price} \rightarrow\end{array} \frac{n}{32} = \frac{40}{100} \begin{array}{l}\leftarrow \text{part} \\ \leftarrow \text{whole}\end{array}$$

$$100 \times n = 40 \times 32 \qquad \leftarrow \text{Write the cross products.}$$
$$100n = 1{,}280 \qquad \leftarrow \text{Multiply.}$$
$$n = 12.8 \qquad \leftarrow \text{Divide each side by 100.}$$

You will save $12.80 on the baseball glove.

✓ Quick Check

1. You buy a $40 shirt on sale for 20% off. Find 20% of $40. **$8**

Differentiated Instruction Solutions for All Learners

Special Needs L1
Ask students to draw pictures or use 100 grids to represent the percents shown on the table of percents. Then they have a visual representation to go with the table for Equivalent Expressions for Mental Math.

learning style: visual

Below Level L2
Have students make a horizontal bar model for Quick Check 1 to help them set up their proportions correctly.

learning style: visual

You can find a percent of a number by using a decimal.

EXAMPLE   **Using a Decimal**

② Find 22% of 288.

$$22\% = 0.22$$ ← Write 22% as a decimal.

$$0.22 \times 288 = 63.36$$ ← Multiply.

So 22% of 288 is 63.36.

Quick Check

2. a. Find 12% of 91. **10.92**   **b.** Find 18% of 121. **21.78**

The percents in the table below are found in real-world situations. You can change these to fractions or decimals to use mental math.

Test Prep Tip

Memorizing the values in the table at the right can help you find percents quickly on tests.

Equivalent Expressions for Mental Math

Percent	10%	20%	25%	50%	75%	80%
Fraction	$\frac{1}{10}$	$\frac{1}{5}$	$\frac{1}{4}$	$\frac{1}{2}$	$\frac{3}{4}$	$\frac{4}{5}$
Decimal	0.1	0.2	0.25	0.5	0.75	0.8

EXAMPLE   **Using Mental Math**

③ Suppose 25% of 80 students in a survey vacationed in Florida. Find the number of students who vacationed in Florida.

What you think

$$25\% = \frac{1}{4}; \frac{1}{4} \times 80 = 20.$$

Twenty students vacationed in Florida.

Why it works

$$25\% = \frac{25}{100} = \frac{1}{4}$$ ← Write 25% as a fraction in simplest form.

$$\frac{1}{4} \times 80 = \frac{1}{4} \times \frac{80}{1}$$ ← Multiply $\frac{1}{4}$ by 80. Rewrite 80 as $\frac{80}{1}$.

$$= \frac{80}{4}$$ ← Simplify.

$$= 20$$ ← Divide.

Quick Check

3. Use mental math to find 75% of 12. **9**

---

2. Teach

Activity Lab

Use before the lesson.

All in One Teaching Resources

Activity Lab 7-7: Exploring Percent with a Calculator

Guided Instruction

Example 1
Some students find using the definition of percent helps them set up the correct proportion.

Students write $\frac{\text{part}}{\text{whole}} = \frac{\text{percent}}{100}$ and substitute the given numbers for each term. The remaining term in the proportion becomes the variable.

Error Prevention!

Watch for students who do not write the percent as a decimal before they multiply.

Example 3
Review the fraction equivalents for common percents such as 10%, 20%, 25%, 50%, and 75% found in the table.

PowerPoint

Additional Examples

① Use a proportion to find 60% of 45. **27;** $\frac{n}{45} = \frac{60}{100}$

② Find 88% of 250. **220**

③ Use mental math to find 75% of 84. **63**

All in One Teaching Resources

• Daily Notetaking Guide 7-7 **L3**
• Adapted Notetaking 7-7 **L1**

Closure

• *How can you use a proportion to find a part of a whole?*
  Sample: Set up a proportion using the $\frac{\text{percent}}{100} = \frac{\text{part}}{\text{whole}}$. **Substitute for the percent and the whole; solve for the unknown part using cross products.**

Advanced Learners **L4**
Have students find their favorite sports team's number of wins and games played. Then have them calculate the percent of wins and predict the number of games the team might win for the entire season.

learning style: visual

English Language Learners **ELL**
Encourage students to work Examples 2 and 3 using proportions to make sure they are setting up examples correctly. Have students use language for proportion problems such as "40% is the same as $\frac{40}{100}$. $32 is my whole, or 100%. I need to find part of $32."

learning style: visual

3. Practice

Assignment Guide

Check Your Understanding
Go over Exercises 1–5 in class before assigning the Homework Exercises.

Homework Exercises
A	Practice by Example	6–22
B	Apply Your Skills	23–34
C	Challenge	35
	Test Prep and Mixed Review	36–41

Homework Quick Check
To check students' understanding of key skills and concepts, go over Exercises 10, 20, 28, 29, and 34.

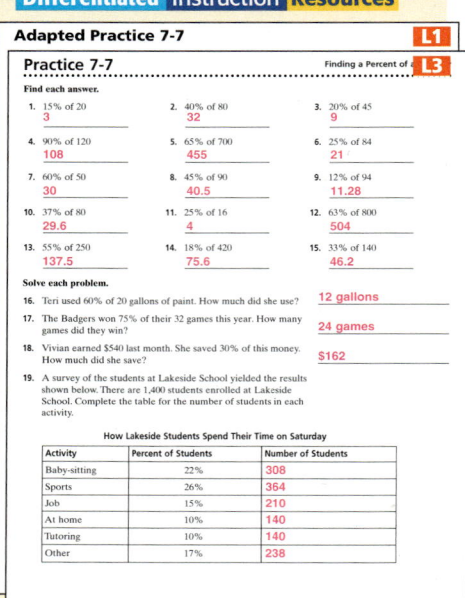

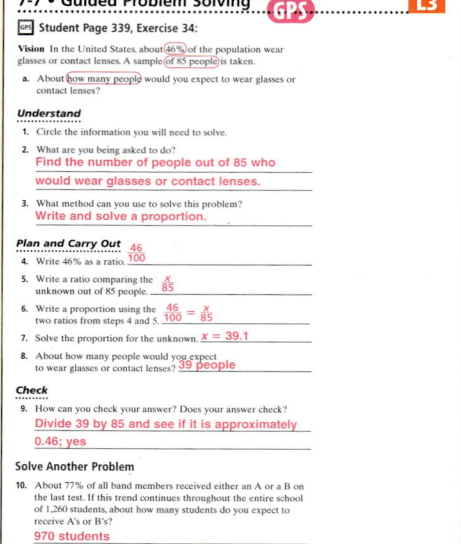

Check Your Understanding

Mental Math Find each answer.

1. 50% of 10 **5**
2. 25% of 40 **10**
3. 3% of 100 **3**

Use the table below for Exercises 4–5.

Frequency of Vowels in Written Passages

Letter	A	E	I	O	U
Frequency	8%	13%	6%	8%	3%

4. Find the number of E's expected in a passage of 100 letters.
13

5. Find the number of I's expected in a passage of 500 letters.
30

Homework Exercises

For more exercises, see Extra Skills and Word Problems.

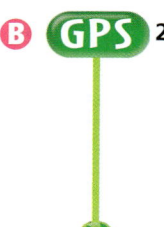
GO for Help

For Exercises	See Examples
6–11	1
12–18	2
19–22	3

A Find each answer. You may find a model useful.

6. 42% of 70 **29.4**
7. 8% of 210 **16.8**
8. 70% of 185 **129.5**
9. 11% of 600 **66**
10. 15% of 90 **13.5**
11. 65% of 240 **156**
12. 7% of 50 **3.5**
13. 18% of 170 **30.6**
14. 44% of 165 **72.6**
15. 43% of 61 **26.23**
16. 55% of 91 **50.05**
17. 30% of 490 **147**

18. **Shopping** You go to a sale where all items are 20% off. Your total clothes bill would have normally cost $80. Find the amount you save. **$16**

Find each answer using mental math.

19. 20% of 180 **36**
20. 80% of 40 **32**
21. 75% of 480 **360**

22. **Dance** Suppose 50% of 180 dancers said they prefer modern dance. How many dancers prefer modern dance? **90 dancers**

B GPS 23. **Guided Problem Solving** You earn $240 for your first paycheck. You pay 22% of it in taxes. You decide to put 40% of the remaining money into savings. How much money will you have left to spend? **$112.32**
- The amount you pay in taxes is ■. The money remaining after taxes is ■.
- Write an expression to find the amount put into savings.

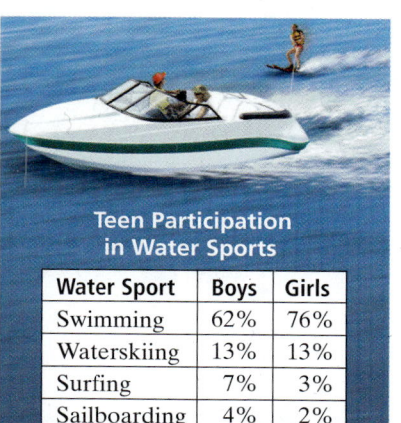

Teen Participation in Water Sports

Water Sport	Boys	Girls
Swimming	62%	76%
Waterskiing	13%	13%
Surfing	7%	3%
Sailboarding	4%	2%

Recreation The results of a survey of 200 boys and 200 girls are shown at the left.

24. How many boys surf? **14**

25. How many girls surf? **6**

26. How many boys swim? **124**

27. How many girls swim? **152**

28. Travel Of 200 students surveyed, 30% said they have visited SeaWorld in Florida. Of those students, 60% saw Shamu. How many students saw Shamu? **36 students**

29. Reasoning You want to buy a game that regularly costs $60. The store has a 40%-off sale. You also have a coupon for 10% off. Is taking 50% off the full price the same as taking 40% off the full price and then 10% off the sale price? Explain. **See left.**

GO Online

Homework Video Tutor

Visit: PHSchool.com
Web Code: aqe-0707

29. No; 50% off is half the price. The 10%-off coupon is applied to a price that is less than $60.

34b. Answers may vary. Sample: I used the equation $x = 0.46 \times 85$, since it is easy to multiply a whole number by a decimal. I rounded down because a fraction of a person is not reasonable.

Money You can find simple interest by multiplying the investment P, the yearly rate r, and the time t. Find the simple interest.

30. $P = \$500$, $r = 1\%$, $t = 2$ **$10**

31. $P = \$1,000$, $r = 3\%$, $t = 4$ **$120**

32. $P = \$895$, $r = 5\%$, $t = 2$ **$89.50**

33. $P = \$4,500$, $r = 2\%$, $t = 3$ **$270**

34. Vision In the United States, about 46% of the population wear glasses or contact lenses. A sample of 85 people is taken.

   a. About how many people would you expect to wear glasses or contact lenses? **about 39 people**

   b. Writing in Math  How did you find your answer to part (a)? **See left.**

C 35. Challenge Store A offers a 60% discount. Store B has a sale for $\frac{2}{3}$ off. Which store gives the greater discount? Explain.

   Store B has a better rate; $\frac{2}{3}$ is equal to $66\frac{2}{3}\%$, which is greater than 60%.

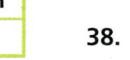

Test Prep and Mixed Review **Practice**

Multiple Choice

36. The blood in a human body accounts for about 7% of total body weight. Which number is equal to 7%? **A**

   A 0.07   **B** 0.7   **C** $\frac{1}{7}$ **D** $\frac{7}{10}$

37. How much of the model is shaded? **H**

   F 54%   **H** 50%
   G 52%   **J** 48%

GO for Help

For Exercises	See Lesson
38–41	7-1

Write each ratio in simplest form.

38. $\frac{10}{45}$ $\frac{2}{9}$

39. $36 : 90$ $\frac{2}{5}$

40. 18 to 21   **6 to 7**

41. $\frac{100}{150}$ $\frac{2}{3}$

Alternative Assessment

One student in a pair writes five percents on separate slips of paper while the partner does the same with whole numbers greater than 20. Students place the slips face down in two stacks. Together they draw a percent and a whole number from each stack. Then they work together to find the percent of the number.

Test Prep

Resources

For additional practice with a variety of test item formats:
• Test-Taking Strategies, p. 353
• Test Prep, p. 357
• Test-Taking Strategies with Transparencies

PowerPoint

Lesson Quiz

Find each answer.

1. 40% of 295 **118**

2. 65% of 340 **221**

3. 18% of 150 **27**

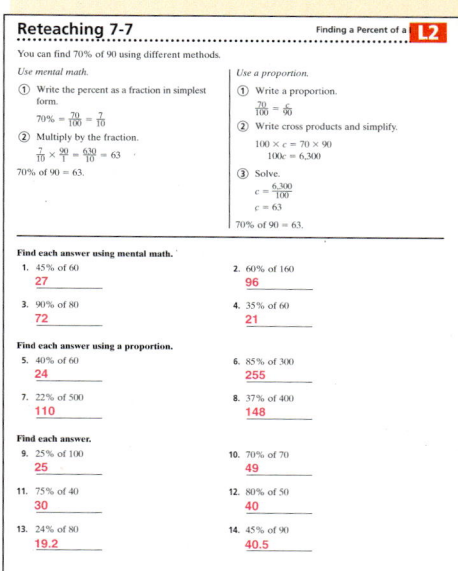

Reteaching 7-7 Finding a Percent of a **L2**

Enrichment 7-7 Finding a Percent of a **L4**

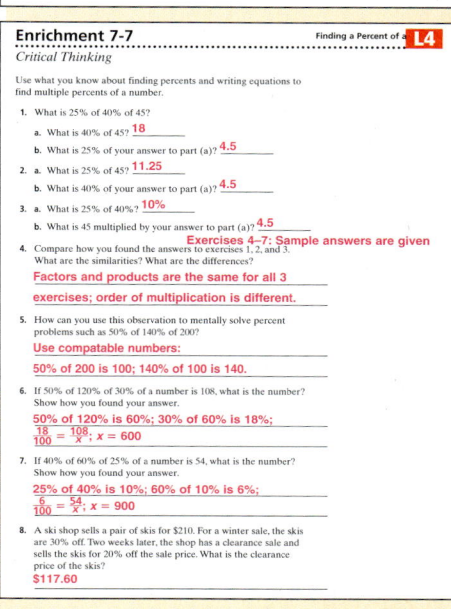

339

Exploring Circle Graphs

You can make a circle graph to display data. You can use a paper strip to help you draw a circle graph.

ACTIVITY

You ask 50 students to name their favorite sport. The results are shown in the table. Make a circle graph to display the data.

1. Cut a strip of paper slightly more than 50 cm long with a tab at the end as shown. Each centimeter represents 1 student.

```
|←————————— 50 cm —————————→|
| 54%          | 20% |10%| 16% |        |←— Tab
|←————————— 100% ——————————→|
```

2. Draw a line 27 cm from the left end of the strip. This section represents the students who prefer football.

3. Draw lines to make sections representing the other sports.

4. Form a ring with the strip. Line up the beginning of the strip with the 50-student line and tape the ends together.

5. Use a compass to draw a circle around your ring. Use your ring to mark sections around the edge of the circle.

6. Connect the marks to the center of the circle. Label each section with the name of the sport it represents.

7. Determine the percent of the students who prefer each sport. Label each section of the circle with the correct percent.

Favorite Sports

Football	27
Basketball	10
Baseball	5
Other	8

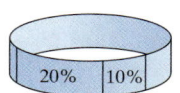

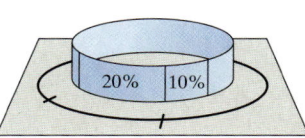

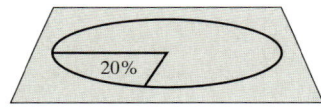

Exercises

Make a circle graph for each table of data. **1–3. See margin.**

1.   **Favorite Colors**

Red	Blue	Green	Yellow
8	6	9	2

2.   **Hours of Sleep Each Night**

Less Than 8	8–10	More Than 10
4	9	7

3.   **Homework on Saturdays**

Usually	Sometimes	Never
12	31	7

1–3. See back of book.

Check Skills You'll Need

1. Vocabulary Review Explain how you can write a ratio as a *percent*.

Find each answer.

2. 35% of 280   **98**

3. 52% of 200   **104**

4. 25% of 384   **96**

GO for Help
Lesson 7-7

ck Skills You'll Need

Answers may vary. Sample: You can write a proportion by setting the ratio equal to $\frac{x}{100}$. Solve the proportion, and write the solution with a percent sign.

What You'll Learn

To read and make circle graphs to represent real-world data

🔊 **New Vocabulary**   circle graph

Why Learn This?

A circle graph is a useful way to represent data. You can use a circle graph to visually compare parts to a whole.

A **circle graph** is a graph of data in which the entire circle represents the whole. Each sector in the circle represents part of the whole.

Where Do All the Apples Go?

Eaten fresh   48%   Processed 39%   13%   Exported

EXAMPLES   Reading a Circle Graph

1 Use the circle graph above. How are 13% of apples used?

The circle graph is divided into three sections. The purple section is labeled 13%. 13% of apples are exported.

2 Use the circle graph above. Describe how many apples are eaten fresh.

A little less than half of the circle is labeled "Eaten fresh." 48% is close to 50%, or $\frac{1}{2}$.

Almost half of apples are eaten fresh.

Vocabulary Tip

A circle graph is often called a pie chart. Each wedge of a circle graph is a "piece of the pie."

✓ Quick Check

1. Using the circle graph above, how are 39% of the apples used?
They are processed.

2. Using the circle graph above, are more apples exported or processed? Justify your answer.
processed; 39% > 13%

Objective
To read and make circle graphs to represent real world data

Examples
1–2 Reading a Circle Graph
3   Sketching a Circle Graph

Math Understandings: p. 304D

Math Background

Circle graphs visually compare parts of a whole. The entire circle represents the whole and each wedge in the circle represents part of that whole. Circle graphs generally use percents and are most dramatic when they use a limited number of wedges. If a circle is divided into too many wedges, it becomes difficult to compare among the many wedges. Bar graphs are more appropriate when a large number of categories are desired.

More Math Background: p. 304D

Lesson Planning and Resources

See p. 304E for a list of the resources that support this lesson.

PowerPoint
Bell Ringer Practice

✓ **Check Skills You'll Need**
Use student page, transparency, or PowerPoint. For intervention, direct students to:
Finding the Percent of a Number
Lesson 7-7
Extra Skills and Word Problems Practice, Ch. 7

Differentiated Instruction   **Solutions for All Learners**

Special Needs   **L1**
Some students may have difficulty dividing the circles or sketching their own graphs. If so, pair these students with a student who can do the sketching. Have them both talk about their reasoning and whether they agree with the relative sizes of the circle sections.

learning style: visual

Below Level   **L2**
Ask: *How can you tell which part of the circle graph represents the greatest amount?* **the widest wedge** *the least amount?* **the narrowest wedge**

learning style: verbal

Guided Instruction

Example 1
Ask:
- *Are the actual numbers of apples given in the graph?* **no**
- *Do circle graphs always give exact data values?* **Sample: No; circle graphs give percents.**

Additional Examples

1 Use the circle graph.

Brands of Jackets Sold

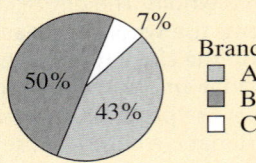

Brand
- ☐ A
- ☐ B
- ☐ C

a. What brand of jacket sold 43%? **Brand A**

b. What percent of Brand C were sold? **7%**

2 Make a circle graph of the data in the table.

Weekly Budget

Savings	$56
Hobbies	$33
Food	$18
Other	$24

See back of book for graph.

All in One Teaching Resources
- Daily Notetaking Guide 7-8 **L3**
- Adapted Notetaking 7-8 **L1**

Closure

- *How do you make a circle graph?* **Sample: Change data to rounded percents of a whole. Draw a circle and divide it into wedges for each percent. Write percents and categories for each wedge and add a title.**

GO Online

Video Tutor Help
Visit: PHSchool.com
Web Code: aqe-0775

EXAMPLE **Sketching a Circle Graph**

3 **Sports** In one season, the Seattle Mariners baseball team stole a total of 174 bases. Sketch a circle graph of the data.

First use a calculator to change the data to percents of the total. Round to the nearest percent.

$$\frac{56}{174} \approx 32\% \qquad \frac{39}{174} \approx 22\%$$

$$\frac{34}{174} \approx 20\% \qquad \frac{45}{174} \approx 26\%$$

Stolen Bases by Seattle Mariners

Player	Total
Ichiro Suzuki	56
Mark McLemore	39
Mike Cameron	34
Other players combined	45
Total number of stolen bases	174

Use number sense to divide the circle.

$32\% \approx \frac{1}{3}$ 22% is slightly less than $\frac{1}{4}$ of the circle.

$26\% \approx \frac{1}{4}$ 20% is the percent left.

Stolen Bases by Seattle Mariners

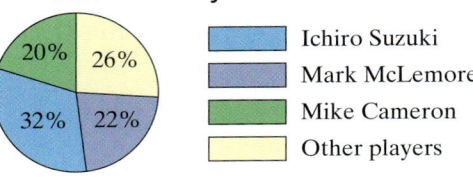

- Ichiro Suzuki
- Mark McLemore
- Mike Cameron
- Other players

Label the divided circle with each percent. Use a different color for each player. Make a key, and add a title.

✓ Quick Check

3. Of 50 students surveyed, 13 bought a hot lunch, 9 packed a lunch, 6 bought a salad, and 22 bought a sandwich. Sketch a circle graph of the data. **See back of book.**

✓ Check Your Understanding

1. **Vocabulary** A circle graph is a graph of data in which the entire circle represents the __?__. **whole**

2. **Music** Use the circle graph at the right. Which instrument do more musicians play than any other? **piano**

The sum of the fractions is not 1.

3. **Reasoning** Explain why you cannot use $\frac{1}{2}$, $\frac{1}{3}$, and $\frac{1}{4}$ to sketch a complete circle graph. **See left.**

Instruments Played by Amateurs

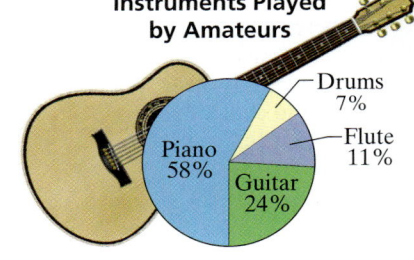

Drums 7%
Flute 11%
Piano 58%
Guitar 24%

Homework Exercises

For more exercises, see Extra Skills and Word Problems.

GO for Help

For Exercises	See Examples
4–7	1–2
8–11	3

Ⓐ Use the circle graph for Exercises 4–7.

Favorite Sport

- 🟩 Tennis
- 🟧 Basketball
- 🟨 Soccer
- 🟦 Baseball
- 🟦 Volleyball

4. Which sport is the least popular?
   tennis

5. Which is more popular, basketball or volleyball? **basketball**

6. List the sports from least to most popular.
   tennis, volleyball, basketball, baseball, soccer

7. Which sport is about twice as popular as basketball?
   baseball

Sketch a circle graph for the given percents. 8–11. See margin.

8. 10%, 40%, 50%

9. 5%, 14%, 33%, 48%

10. 12%, 26%, 62%

11. 12%, 34%, 21%, 33%

Ⓑ GPS 12. **Guided Problem Solving** The table below shows that taxes are a large part of the price of gas. Use two circle graphs to compare the tax a person in each country pays as a percentage of the price of gas. **See margin.**

Taxes on One Gallon of Gasoline

Country	Price (including tax)	Tax
United States	$2.39	$.39
United Kingdom	$6.09	$4.27

- What is the percentage of tax on one gallon of gas in each country?
- Sketch a circle graph for each country. Compare the tax to the price of gasoline in each country.

Sketch a circle graph for each set of fractions. 13–15. See margin.

13. $\frac{1}{2}, \frac{1}{3}, \frac{1}{6}$

14. $\frac{3}{4}, \frac{1}{10}, \frac{1}{10}, \frac{1}{20}$

15. $\frac{3}{8}, \frac{1}{8}, \frac{4}{10}, \frac{1}{10}$

GO Online

Homework Video Tutor

Visit: PHSchool.com
Web Code: aqe-0708

16. **Science** The human body is made up
    GPS of 21 chemical elements. Use the table at the right to make a circle graph.
    See margin.

17. **Data Collection** List the things you do on a Saturday. Estimate the hours you spend on each activity. Write each time as a percent of a 24-hour day. Make a circle graph.
    Check students' graphs.

Human Body Composition

Element	Percent
Oxygen	65
Carbon	18
Hydrogen	10
Nitrogen	3
Other	4

Online lesson quiz, PHSchool.com, Web Code: aqa-0708

7-8 Circle Graphs **343**

8–16. See back of book.

Assignment Guide

Check Your Understanding
Go over Exercises 1–3 in class before assigning the Homework Exercises.

Homework Exercises
A Practice by Example 4–11
B Apply Your Skills 12–18
C Challenge 19
Test Prep and
   Mixed Review 20–25

Homework Quick Check
To check students' understanding of key skills and concepts, go over Exercises 7, 9, 16, 17, and 18.

Differentiated Instruction Resources

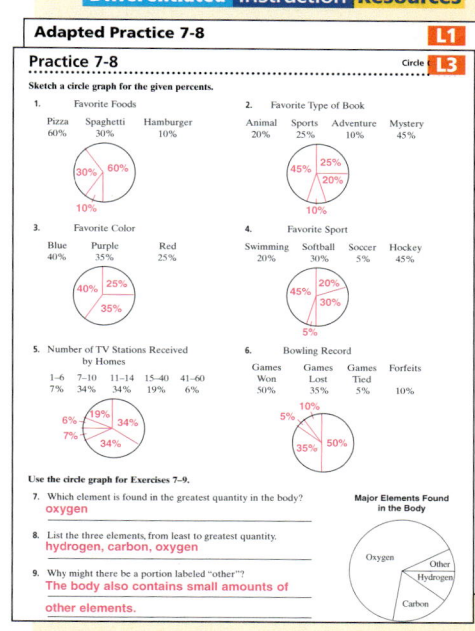

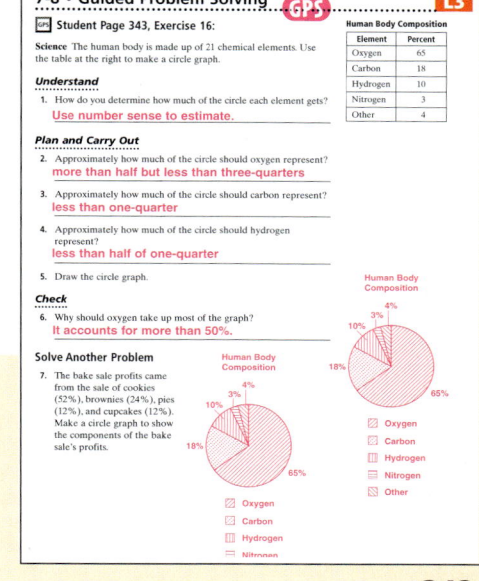

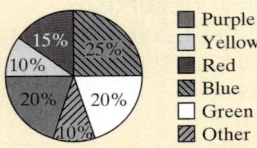

Lesson Quiz

Use the circle graph to answer each question.

Favorite Colors of 250 Students

- 15%
- 25%
- 10%
- 20%
- 20%
- 10%

Legend:
- ▨ Purple
- ☐ Yellow
- ■ Red
- ▨ Blue
- ☐ Green
- ▨ Other

1. What percent of students chose red as their favorite color? **15%**

2. Which color was the favorite of 10% of the students? **yellow**

3. How many students chose green as their favorite color?

50 students

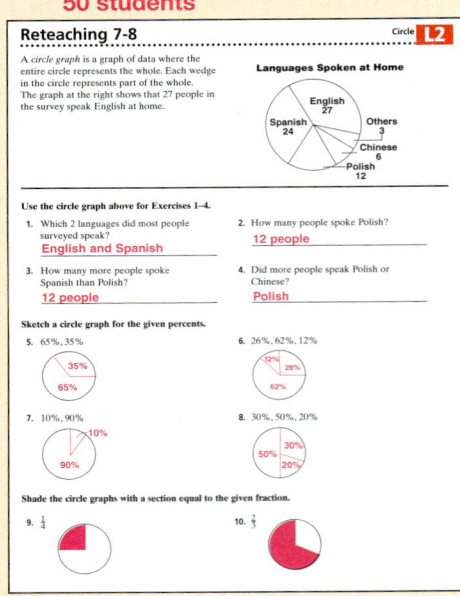

Reteaching 7-8   Circle **L2**

Enrichment 7-8   Circle **L4**

18a. Answers may vary. Sample: The sum is greater than 100%.

Coins Donated

- Quarters — 12%
- Pennies — 25%
- Dimes — 35%
- Nickels — 28%

18. Surveys 100 students were asked how they spend their free time. Of those surveyed, 53% said they like to go to the mall, 80% said they like to watch TV, 72% said they like to spend time outside, and 34% said they like to search the Internet.

a. Writing in Math Explain why you cannot use a circle graph to display the data. **See left.**

b. What kind of graph could you use to compare the data?
bar graph

Ⓒ 19. Challenge A class collected 700 coins for charity. Use the circle graph at the left to find how much money was donated.
$57.05

Test Prep and Mixed Review   Practice

Multiple Choice

20. Of the 100 people Alex surveyed, 18 said spring was their favorite season, 55 said summer, 16 said fall, and 11 said winter. Which circle graph displays the data? **D**

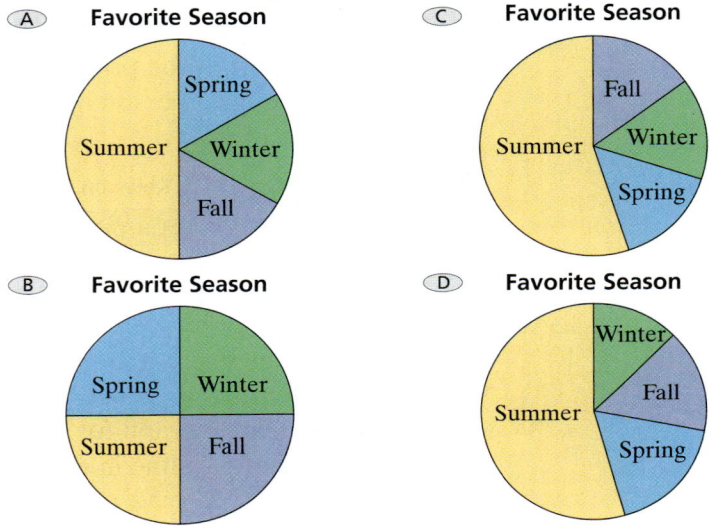

Ⓐ **Favorite Season**
Ⓒ **Favorite Season**
Ⓑ **Favorite Season**
Ⓓ **Favorite Season**

21. Camille earns $14 baby-sitting. She now has $81. Which equation can Camille use to find d, the amount of money she had before baby-sitting? **H**

   Ⓕ $d = 81 \div 14$

   Ⓗ $d = 81 - 14$

   Ⓖ $14 = 81 \times d$

   Ⓙ $14 = 81 + d$

GO for Help

For Exercises	See Lesson
22–25	6-2

Algebra Evaluate each expression for $x = 3\frac{3}{4}$.

22. $8x$ **30**

23. $\frac{2}{5}x$ **$1\frac{1}{2}$**

24. $\frac{4}{3}x$ **5**

25. $x \cdot 2\frac{1}{2}$ **$9\frac{3}{8}$**

Test Prep

Resources

For additional practice with a variety of test item formats:

- Test-Taking Strategies, p. 353
- Test Prep, p. 357
- Test-Taking Strategies with Transparencies

Alternative Assessment

Each student in a pair finds real-world data that can be displayed in a circle graph. Partners exchange data and make circle graphs to display each other's data.

Reporting Survey Results

Sometimes you can combine categories in a survey and choose a data display to support one side of an issue.

ACTIVITY   **1–8. Check Students' work.**

1. Clear your calculator for this activity. Press **LIST** and clear any data already in the list. Press **2nd** [PLOT] 4: PlotsOff to turn off the plots. Press **Y=** and clear any equations.

2. Press **LIST**. Enter "Yes," "Undec," and "No" in the L1 column. Use "Undec" for "Undecided". To type letters, press **2nd** [TEXT] and use the arrow keys. Use quotation marks to begin and end each word. After each word, select Done and press **ENTER**. Press **ENTER** again to add the word to the list.

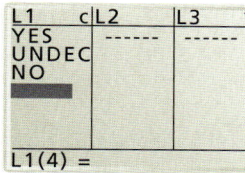

3. Using the table, sort the data into three categories: "Yes," "Undecided," and "No". Enter the totals in the L2 column.

Should the School Change Its Mascot?

Category	Yes	Undecided	No
Number of students	86	28	86
Percent			

4. To make a circle graph, press **2nd** [PLOT] 1: Plot1. Use the arrow keys and the **ENTER** key to select On and Circle Graph. CategList: shows L1, and Data List: shows L2. Then select Percent on the bottom line, and press **ENTER**.

5. Press **GRAPH**. Use **TRACE** and the arrow buttons to display the key on the graph for each category.

6. Combine the "Undecided" and the "No" categories into a new category called "Not Yes." Make a circle graph using the resorted data. Enter the categories "Yes" and "Not Yes."

7. **Writing in Math** Use your graph to explain why the school should not change the mascot.

8. **Reasoning** Use the data above to make a circle graph using two categories different from the categories in Step 6. Show that most people would like to change the mascot.

Reporting Survey Results

Students use their calculators to display data to support one side of an issue. This will help them extend the skills they learned in Lesson 7–8.

Guided Instruction

Before beginning the Activity, have students clear their calculators. This Activity will help students understand how the same data can be used to support two opposing views.
Ask:
- *How does combining the "Undecided" and "No" categories into "Not Yes" help support the idea that the school mascot should not be changed?* **By combining these categories, the vote for no change is greater than for change.**
- *How does combining the "Undecided" and "Yes" categories into "Not No" help support the idea that the school mascot should be changed?* **By combining these categories, the vote for change is greater than for no change.**

Differentiated Instruction

Advanced Learners   **L4**
Have students use their calculators to create graphs to display survey data for a survey with a larger number of possible responses. Ask students to combine categories if possible.

Resources

- Student Manipulatives Kit

345

Practice Solving Problems

GPS **Guided Problem Solving**

Practice Solving Problems

In this feature, students practice solving problems that involve ratios, percents, and circle graphs.

Guided Instruction

Discuss with students how they can use ratios to discover percents for data and then use circle graphs to display the data.

Have a volunteer read the problem aloud.
Ask:

- *What pieces of information are important to solve this problem?* **number of students surveyed, percent of students that worked as a cashier/ grocery clerk**
- *How can you find the number of students that worked as a cashier/grocery clerk?* **Write a proportion with the percent as a fraction and write a fraction with a variable as the numerator and the total number of students as the denominator. Use cross products to find the value of the variable.**
- *How do you know your answer is reasonable?* **The section on the graph is rather small and 26 is a small part of 425.**

Top Jobs A survey identified the four jobs most commonly held by high school sophomores. There were 425 students surveyed. How many students worked as a cashier or a grocery clerk?

Sophomore Job Survey

Job	Percent
Food Service	21
Child Care	13
Cashier or Grocery Clerk	6
Salesperson	4

What You Might Think

> How can I use a diagram to show this situation?

> I can use the diagram to write and solve a proportion.

> What is the answer? Is it reasonable?

What You Might Write

```
0    n                            425
|----+----------------------------|
0%   6%                          100%
```

Let n = the number of students who worked as a cashier or a grocery clerk.

$$\frac{n}{425} = \frac{6}{100}$$

$$n \times 100 = 6 \times 425$$

$$100n = 2{,}550$$

$$\frac{100n}{100} = \frac{2{,}550}{100}$$

$$n = 25.5$$

About 26 sophomores worked as a cashier or a grocery clerk.

10% of 425 is about 42, so 5% is about 21, which is close to 25.5.

Think It Through

Answers may vary. Samples:
$$\frac{n}{6} = \frac{425}{100}; \quad \frac{6}{n} = \frac{100}{425}; \quad \frac{425}{n} = \frac{100}{6}$$

1. Give two other proportions you can write for this situation.

2. **Reasoning** Why is the answer 26, not 25.5? **There cannot be $\frac{1}{2}$ a person.**

3. **Check for Reasonableness** Explain how the estimate was found. **See margin.**

346   Guided Problem Solving   Practice Solving Problems

3. **Answers may vary. Sample: 10% of the people surveyed was found. Then half that number was found since 5% is easier to use than 6%.**

Exercises

4. Use the survey data on the previous page to find how many more students were food service workers than cashiers or grocery clerks. (*Hint*: Find how many students worked in food service.) **63 students**

5. Thirty-seven percent of the students in the survey on the previous page worked 10 hours or less each week. How many of the students worked more than 10 hours each week? Use the diagram below. **about 268 people**

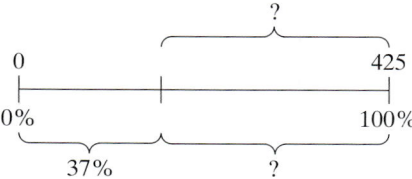

6. Carrie rode her bike a longer distance in less time today than she did yesterday. On which day did she ride faster? Explain. **Today; she went farther in less time.**

7. Suppose an elevator in the Empire State Building takes 80 seconds to travel 950 feet. How far does the elevator travel in 1 minute? **712.5 ft**

8. The distance around the Talladega Motor Speedway track is 2.66 miles. In the drawing below, the backstretch is 1.6 inches. What is the actual length of the backstretch in feet? **4,000 ft**

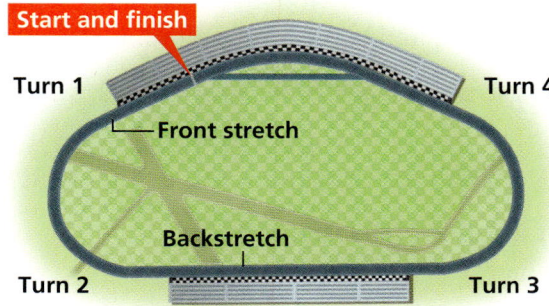

Talladega Motor Speedway

Scale: 1 in. = 2,500 ft

Objective
To use mental math and estimation with percents

Examples
1 Estimating Cost
2 Estimating a Tip
3 Estimating a Sale Price

Math Understandings: p. 304D

Math Background

We commonly estimate percents to calculate dollar amounts for discounted merchandise, sales tax, and tips. You can easily calculate tips of 15% by finding 10% of the bill and adding $\frac{1}{2}$ of this amount (5%).

More Math Background: p. 304D

Lesson Planning and Resources

See p. 304E for a list of the resources that support this lesson.

348

 **Check Skills You'll Need**

1. **Vocabulary Review** How can you use the *Distributive Property* to simplify 3×98? **See below.**

2. Find $5 \times 1{,}003$. **5,015**

3. Find 10.2×4. **40.8**

 **for Help**
Lesson 3-8

Check Skills You'll Need

1. Write 98 as $100 - 2$ and multiply by 3; $3(100 - 2)$.

What You'll Learn

To use mental math and estimation with percents

Why Learn This?

When shopping, you need to know whether you have enough money to buy an item. You can use mental math to estimate prices.

$9.99

$14.99

EXAMPLE **Estimating Cost**

① **Sales Tax** Suppose you buy the scarf above. The sales tax rate is 5%. Estimate the total cost of the scarf to the nearest dollar.

Method 1 Estimate the cost and multiply.

Round the cost of the scarf to $15.

$$5\% \text{ of } 15 = 0.05 \times 15 \quad \leftarrow \textbf{Write 5\% as 0.05.}$$
$$= 0.75 \quad \leftarrow \textbf{Multiply to find the tax.}$$
$$15 + 0.75 = 15.75 \quad \leftarrow \textbf{Find the sum of the price and the tax.}$$

The cost of the scarf including tax is about $16.

Method 2 Estimate the cost and use number sense.

Round the cost of the scarf to $15. 10% of $15 is $1.50.

Since 5% is half of 10%, 5% of $15 is half of $1.50, or $.75. So the tax is about $.75. The total cost is about $15 + $.75 = $15.75.

The cost of the scarf including tax is about $16.

✓ Quick Check

1. Use a 6% tax rate to estimate the total cost for the hat shown with the scarf above. **about $10.60**

Differentiated **Instruction** **Solutions for All Learners**

Special Needs **L1**
Students may need to review how to round dollar amounts to the nearest whole dollar. Also, briefly review how to rewrite percents as decimals in order to help students successfully work through the problems in this lesson.

learning style: verbal

Below Level **L2**
Have students practice finding 15% tips using three steps such as: 10% of $24 = $2.40; 5% of 24 = $\frac{1}{2}$ of $2.40 = $1.20; $2.40 + $1.20 = $3.60, a 15% tip.

learning style: visual

348

EXAMPLE Estimating a Tip

2 **Dining Out** Estimate a 15% tip for a bill of $26.22.

What you think

The bill is about $26. 15% = 10% + 5%.
Since 10% of $26 is $2.60, 5% is half of $2.60, or $1.30.
A 15% tip of $26.22 is about $2.60 + $1.30 = $3.90, or about $4.

Why it works

$15\% \times \$26 = (10\% + 5\%) \times \$26$ ← **Replace 15% with 10% + 5%.**

$= 10\% \times \$26 + 5\% \times \$26$ ← **Distributive Property**

$= \$2.60 + (5\% \times \$26)$ ← **Find 10% × $26.**

$= \$2.60 + \left(\frac{1}{2} \times 10\% \times \$26\right)$ ← **Replace 5% with $\frac{1}{2}$ × 10%.**

$= \$2.60 + \$1.30$ ← **Simplify inside the parentheses.**

$= \$3.90$, or about $4.00   ← **Add.**

✓ Quick Check

2. Estimate a 15% tip for a bill of $41.63. **about $6**

EXAMPLE Estimating a Sale Price

3 **Sales** The regular price for a pair of hiking boots is $57.95. The store is having a 30%-off sale. Estimate the sale price.

Method 1

The regular price is about $60. If the sale price is 30% off, you pay 100% − 30%, or 70% of the regular price.
70% of $60 is $42. The sale price is about $42.

Method 2

The sale price is 30% off the regular cost.

$30\% \times \$60 = 0.3 \times \$60$ ← **Write 30% as 0.3.**

$= \$18$ ← **Simplify.**

Subtract the amount saved from the regular price.
$60 − $18 = $42. The sale price is about $42.

3. about $24

✓ Quick Check See left.

3. Estimate the sale price of a $40.19 baseball glove at 40% off.

7-9 Estimating With Percents **349**

---

2. Teach

Activity Lab

Use before the lesson.

All in One Teaching Resources

Activity Lab 7-9: Estimating with Percents

Guided Instruction

Example 1
Some students may find it easier to work with fractions such as:

$$60\% \times \$90 \rightarrow \frac{60}{100} \times \frac{90}{1} = 54.$$

Error Prevention!

The boots in Example 3 are not 30% *of* the original price but 30% *off*. 30% *off* the regular price is 70% *of* the regular price.

PowerPoint
Additional Examples

1 Using a 5% sales tax, estimate the sales tax and the total cost for a pair of sneakers that costs $34.99. **sales tax: $1.75; total cost: about $36.75**

2 Estimate a 15% tip for a bill of $29.34. **about $4.50**

3 A jacket is on sale for 20% off the regular price of $49.95. Estimate the sale price of the jacket. **about $40.**

All in One Teaching Resources

- Daily Notetaking Guide 7-9 **L3**
- Adapted Notetaking 7-9 **L1**

Closure

- *How do you find the total cost of an item with sales tax?* **Sample: Find and add the sales tax to the cost of the item.**
- *How do you estimate a 15% tip for a bill?* **Sample: Find 10% by moving the decimal one place to the left. Then add to it half of this amount, which is 5%.**

Advanced Learners L4
Give at least two different ways to estimate a 7.5% sales tax. **Sample: Find 15% and divide by 2; or find 10% and then 5% and add.**

learning style: visual

English Language Learners ELL
Encourage students to experiment using their calculators to multiply the cost of the items in Examples 1 and 2 by 105% and 115% (or 1.05 or 1.15). Ask them to *explain* how that calculation gets them the same product as adding 5% or 15% to the original price.

learning style: verbal

349

Assignment Guide

Check Your Understanding
Go over Exercises 1–6 in class before assigning the Homework Exercises.

Homework Exercises
A Practice by Example   7–18
B Apply Your Skills   19–28
C Challenge   29
Test Prep and
   Mixed Review   30–36

Homework Quick Check
To check students' understanding of key skills and concepts, go over Exercises 7, 17, 20, 21, and 25.

Differentiated Instruction Resources

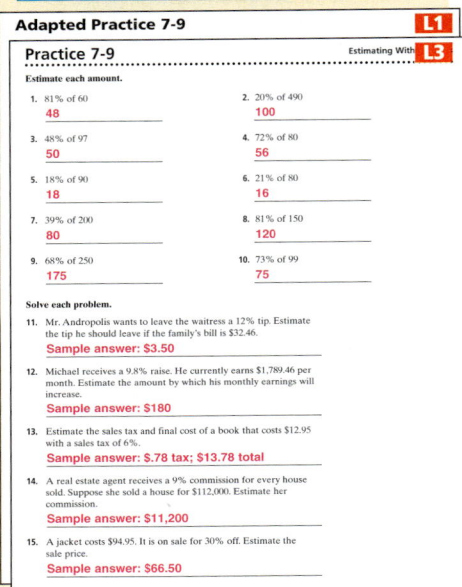

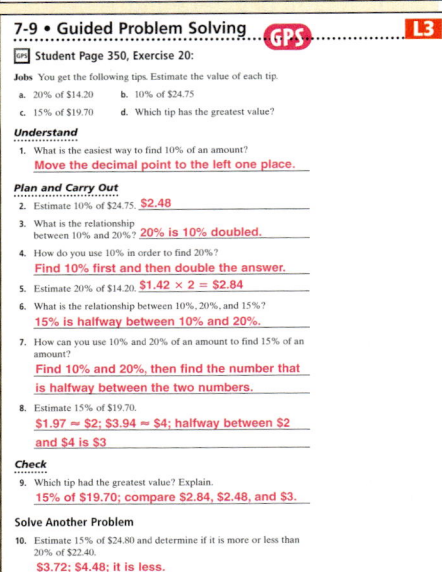

Check Your Understanding

1. **Mental Math** There is a 10% tax on a game priced at $49.99. About how much is the total cost of the game? **about $55**

2. Round up to $35; if you estimate low, you may not have enough money.

2. **Reasoning** When estimating tax, is it better to round a price like $34.48 up to $35 or down to $34? Explain your choice. **See left.**

Write a numerical expression you can use to estimate the amount of tax or discount.

3. cost: $19.99; sales tax: 9%
   $20 × 0.09

4. cost: $499.95; discount: 30%
   $500 × 0.3

5. cost: $39.80; sales tax: 5%
   $40 × 0.05

6. cost: $109.80; discount: 25%
   $110 × 0.25

Homework Exercises

For more exercises, see Extra Skills and Word Problems.

GO for Help

For Exercises	See Example
7–10	1
11–14	2
15–18	3

20a. **$2.80**
  b. **$2.50**
  c. **$3.00**
  d. **15% of $19.70**

A **Use a sales tax rate of 7%. Estimate the total cost for each item.**

7. a game that costs $27.60
   $1.96, $29.96

8. a bicycle that costs $129
   $9.10, $139.10

9. a book that costs $14.59
   $1.05, $16.05

10. a DVD that costs $19.95
    $1.40, $21.40

Estimate a 15% tip for each amount.

11. $41.90
    $6.30

12. $8.60
    $1.35

13. $79.10
    $12

14. $40.60
    $6

Estimate the sale price of each item.

15. 40% off a $42 necklace **$24**

16. 50% off a $789 sofa **$400**

17. 70% off a $16.99 shirt **$5.10**

18. 90% off a $68 jacket **$7**

B **GPS**

19. **Guided Problem Solving** The regular price of a bicycle helmet is $28. You get a discount of 25%. Then you must pay a 6% sales tax. Find the total cost for the bicycle helmet. **$22.26**
   • What is the sale price of the helmet?
   • How much tax will you pay on the sale price?

GO Online
Homework Video Tutor
Visit: PHSchool.com
Web Code: aqe-0709

21. I could round to $4.50 and multiply by 4; I could round to $4.50 and multiply by 3.

20. **Jobs** You get the following tips. Estimate the value of each tip.
   a. 20% of $14.20   b. 10% of $24.75   c. 15% of $19.70
   d. Which tip has the greatest value? **20a–d. See left.**

21. **Writing in Math** Suppose 5% tax on a restaurant bill is $4.36. Explain how you can use this amount to find a 20% tip and a 15% tip. **See left.**

26. Florida: $.05, $.85
    Georgia: $.03, $.83
    Massachusetts: $.04, $.84
    Tennessee: $.06, $.86

27. Florida: $3.90, $68.90
    Georgia: $2.60, $67.60
    Massachusetts: $3.25, $68.25
    Tennessee: $4.55, $69.55

28. Florida: $.30, $5.30
    Georgia: $.20, $5.20
    Massachusetts: $.25, $5.25
    Tennessee: $.35, $5.35

Sale Price
$12.74

Estimate each amount. State whether your answer is an overestimate or an underestimate of the exact answer.

22. 90% of 49
45, overestimate

23. 12% of 302
36, underestimate

24. 1.2% of 490
6, overestimate

25. The snowboard at the left is on sale for $12.74. The snowboard is on sale for 60% off. Find the regular price of the snowboard.
$31.85

Sales Tax Use the sales tax rate table. Estimate the sales tax and the total cost of each item below for each state in the table.
26–28. See margin.

26. erasers: $.79

27. art book: $64.45

28. journal: $5.29

State Sales Tax

State	Tax
Florida	6%
Georgia	4%
Massachusetts	5%
Tennessee	7%

SOURCE: *The World Almanac*

C 29. Challenge By age two, a child's height is usually about 50% of his or her full adult height. Estimate the adult height of a two-year-old whose height is 2 feet 9 inches. **5 ft 6 in.**

Test Prep and Mixed Review

Practice

Multiple Choice

30. Samantha and her friends buy 11 shirts, each priced at $24. About how much do the shirts cost all together? **B**

Ⓐ $200   Ⓑ $250   Ⓒ $300   Ⓓ $350

31. The chart shows the ratio of men to women in the United States population for three age groups. Which statement is best supported by the data? **G**

Age (years)	Ratio (men : women)
55–64	92 : 100
65–74	84 : 100
75 and older	46 : 100

Ⓕ The ratio of men to women increases as age increases.
Ⓖ The ratio of men to women decreases as age increases.
Ⓗ The ratio of men to women decreases as age decreases.
Ⓙ There is no relationship between the ratio and age.

33. 75
34. 130
35. 345
36. 380

32. You read 80% of a book. What fractional part of the book do you have left to read? **A**

Ⓐ $\frac{1}{5}$ Ⓑ $\frac{1}{4}$ Ⓒ $\frac{3}{4}$ Ⓓ $\frac{4}{5}$

How many minutes are in each amount of time? 33–36. See left.

 GO for Help

For Exercises	See Lesson
33–36	5-7

33. 1 h 15 min   **34.** 2 h 10 min   **35.** 5 h 45 min   **36.** 6 h 20 min

Online

Alternative Assessment

Each student in a pair writes several restaurant bill amounts. Partners exchange papers and find a 7% sales tax and the total cost for each bill amount. Partners then estimate a 15% tip for each total amount.

Test Prep

Resources

For additional practice with a variety of test item formats:
• Test-Taking Strategies, p. 353
• Test Prep, p. 357
• Test-Taking Strategies with Transparencies

PowerPoint

Lesson Quiz

1. Using a 6% sales tax, estimate the sales tax and total cost of a $48.95 DVD player. sales tax is about $3; total cost is about $52

2. Estimate a 15% tip for a bill of $51.23. about $7.50

3. Estimate the sale price of a $397 camera on sale for 30% off. about $280

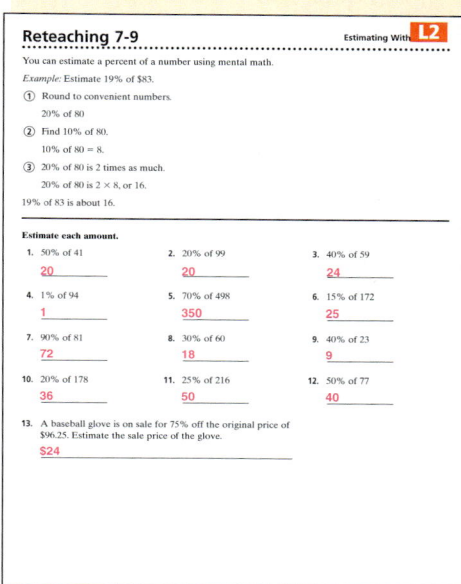

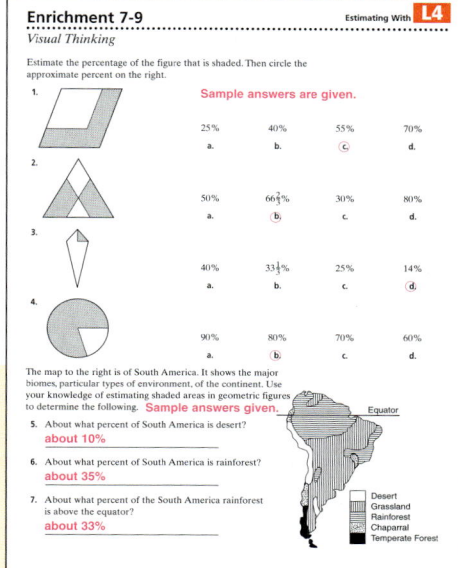

351

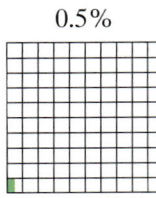

Percents Under 1% or Over 100%

This Extension of Lesson 7–9 introduces percents that are less than 1% or greater than 100%.

Guided Instruction

Begin by describing this situation: If the price of an item doubles, it costs 200% of its original price. So, percents can be greater than 100%. Ask: *How can you represent 200% using a 10-by-10 grid model?* **Completely shade two grid models.**

Percents can also be less than 1%. Such percents can be expressed as fractions less than $\frac{1}{100}$, such as $\frac{1}{200}$, or as decimal percents such as 0.5%. Ask: *How can you represent 0.5% using a 10-by-10 grid model?* **Shade half of one small square.**

Review converting percents to decimals and decimals to percents. To help students who confuse which way to move the decimal point, have them think of the percent sign as ÷ 100. When they remove the %, the decimal point moves left. When they insert the %, the decimal point moves right.

Error Prevention!

Encourage students to check their answers for reasonableness. Ask: *Is 150% of 60 going to be greater than or less than 60?* **greater than**

Resources

• Classroom Aid 10

352

Percents Under 1% or Over 100%

Percents can be less than 1% or greater than 100%.

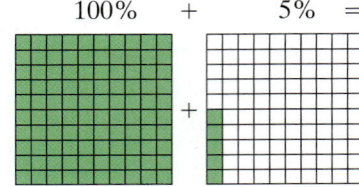

0.5%   100%   +   5%   =   105%

Less than 1%   Greater than 100%

EXAMPLES

1   Write 0.4% as a decimal.

$$0.4\% = \frac{0.4}{100} \quad \leftarrow \text{Write the percent as a fraction.}$$

$$= 0.004 \quad \leftarrow \text{Write the fraction as a decimal.}$$

As a decimal, 0.4% is 0.004. As a fraction, 0.4% is $\frac{4}{1,000}$.

2   **Nutrition** A vitamin supplement provides 150% of the Recommended Daily Allowance (RDA) of vitamin C. The RDA is 60 milligrams. How many milligrams of vitamin C are in the vitamin supplement?

$$150\% \text{ of } 60 = 1.50 \times 60 \quad \leftarrow \text{Write the percent as a decimal.}$$

$$= 90 \quad \leftarrow \text{Multiply.}$$

The vitamin supplement contains 90 milligrams of vitamin C.

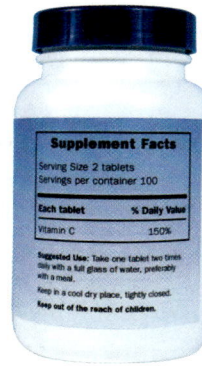

Exercises

Write each percent as a decimal.

1. 0.2% **0.002**   **2.** 0.75% **0.0075**   **3.** 110% **1.1**   **4.** 250% **2.5**

Find each answer.

                                                                        0.03

5. 400% of 5 **20**   **6.** 150% of 18 **27**   **7.** 0.5% of 300 **1.5**   **8.** 0.25% of 12

Working Backward

The problem-solving strategy *Work Backward* is useful when taking multiple-choice tests. Work backward by testing each choice in the original problem. You will eliminate incorrect answers. Eventually you will find the correct answer.

EXAMPLE

A fruit stand is selling 8 bananas for $1.00. At this rate, how much will 20 bananas cost?

A $1.50   B $2.00   C $2.50   D $3.00

Use mental math to test the choices that are easy to use.

$2.00 is twice $1.00. Twice 8 is only 16, so choice B is not the answer.

$3.00 is three times $1.00. Three times 8 is 24, so choice D is not the correct answer.

Since 20 is between 16 and 24, the cost must be between $2.00 and $3.00. The correct answer is choice C.

Exercises

1. Omar made an overseas phone call. The rate was $2.40 for the first minute and $.55 for each additional minute. His bill was $6.80. How can Omar find the total amount charged for additional minutes?   **A**
   A Subtract 2.40 from 6.80.
   B Add 0.55 and 6.80.
   C Subtract 0.55 from 6.80.
   D Add 2.40 and 6.80.

2. At a copy center, 100 copies cost $4.00. At this rate, how much will 450 copies cost?   **G**
   F $16.00   G $18.00   H $20.00   J $22.00

3. What method should NOT be used to find 88% of 40?   **D**
   A 0.88×40
   B $\frac{88}{100} \times 40$
   C $\frac{n}{40} = \frac{88}{100}$
   D $\frac{40}{n} = \frac{88}{100}$

Resources

Student Edition
Extra Skills and Word Problems
Practice, Ch. 7, pp. 624–625
English/Spanish Glossary, p. 654
Formulas and Properties, p. 652
Tables, p. 648

All in One Teaching Resources
• Vocabulary and Study
Skills 7F   **L3**

Differentiated Instruction
Spanish Vocabulary Workbook
with Study Skills   **ELL**
Interactive Textbook
• Audio Glossary
Online Vocabulary Quiz

Success Tracker™
Online at PHSchool.com

Vocabulary Review

 circle graph (p. 341)
cross products (p. 317)
equivalent ratios (p. 307)
percent (p. 331)

proportion (p. 316)
rate (p. 312)
ratio (p. 306)

scale (p. 326)
unit cost (p. 313)
unit rate (p. 312)

Go Online
PHSchool.com

For: Vocabulary quiz
Web Code: aqj-0751

Choose the vocabulary term from the column on the right that best completes the sentence.

1. Two equivalent ratios can be written as a ? . **B**

2. You can use a ? to compare a part to a part. **D**

3. An example of a ? is 25 miles per hour. **C**

4. You can use a ? to compare a number to 100. **A**

A. percent
B. proportion
C. rate
D. ratio

Skills and Concepts

Lesson 7-1
• To write ratios to compare real-world quantities

A **ratio** compares two quantities by division. To write a ratio in simplest form, divide both numbers by their GCF. **Equivalent ratios** name the same number.

A jar contains 8 tacks, 15 bolts, and 23 nails. Write each ratio in three ways. 6–8. See left.

5. bolts to nails   6. bolts to tacks   7. nails to tacks   8. bolts to total
   15 to 23, 15 : 23, $\frac{15}{23}$

6. 15 to 8, 15 : 8, $\frac{15}{8}$

7. 23 to 8, 23 : 8, $\frac{23}{8}$

8. 15 to 46, 15 : 46, $\frac{15}{46}$

Write each ratio in simplest form.   9–12. See margin.

9. 8 to 32   10. $\frac{18}{30}$ 11. 24 ft : 8 yd   12. $\frac{45 \text{ boys}}{54 \text{ girls}}$

Lesson 7-2
• To find and use unit rates and unit costs

A **rate** is a ratio that compares quantities measured in different units. To find a **unit rate,** divide the numerator by the denominator. A **unit price** gives the cost per unit.

13. You run 1 mile in 8 minutes. How long do you take to run 5 miles? **40 min**

14. You earn $400 in 32 hours. How much do you earn in 1 hour? **$12.50**

15. 15. $.10 per oz,
    $.06 per oz,
    A 24-oz loaf is the
    better buy.
    Bread One loaf of bread costs $3.09 for 32 ounces, and another costs $1.40 for 24 ounces. Which is the better buy?

9. 1 to 4

10. $\frac{3}{5}$

11. 3 ft : 1 yd

12. $\frac{5 \text{ boys}}{6 \text{ girls}}$

Spanish Vocabulary/Study Skills **ELL**

Vocabulary/Study Skills **L3**

7F: Vocabulary Review Puzzle   For use with the Chapter Review

Study Skill Turn off the television and the radio while studying or doing homework.

Read the definition, determine the word, and then find the hidden words in the puzzle. Once you have found a word, draw a circle around it and cross out the word definition. Words can be displayed forwards, backwards, up, down, or diagonally.

```
K F L R A T I O K G N A Q H E J Z V O G
P O L K O C X E M A H Z U R S D N F J E
D N L C R R F Q I R S H U U E E F S Z
P O S E E F A D G V E T H V S N P I O L
I I N D C J M S N N C K I B C O R V L V
E T D G I J R U S E R T T S A M O F U A
I A J Q P K A E J O U X D I L I P Q T D
K U O V R N F N W B C I T N E N O N I N
E Q H J O Y O B I Y T I V X G A R C O R
E E H U C C H R I M N L A I B T T J N E
V K O O A I T V G N E N W T M O I I N P B
I E S G L S K V S O C U H W I B O O U M
T S K K I X V P H B R M R I I V N I I N U
A R C D S O L O O B E E S S D G E T Q N
T E C O A Q S E Y L P R O E Z S Z C X D
U V N K Z T I E B P Y A G X E H C A W E
M N L D W W S V X P A T V L H N N R U X
M I N H I J G F F B E Q O B S P W F W I
O Y K A U X Z J M U R R X D A E J U C M
C U V X X E T A R K A X K O W N F P R V
```

• comparison of two numbers by division
• 4(8 + 6) = 4(8) + 4(6) is an example of this property.
• ratio that compares a number to 100
• predicts how a pattern may continue
• The variable *b* in the fraction $\frac{a}{b}$ is known as this.
• ratio that compares two quantities measured in different units
• one of two numbers whose product is 1
• an equation that states that two ratios are equal
• a number that describes a part of a set of a part of a whole that is divided into equal parts

• 12 + (3 + 6) = (12 + 3) + 6 is an example of this property.
• The number 4 in the fraction $\frac{3}{4}$ is referred to as this.
• the number of square units a figure encloses
• 7 + 8 = 8 + 7 is an example of this property.
• a number that makes an equation true
• mathematical statement that contains an equal sign
• operations that undo one another
• ratio that compares a length on a model to the actual length of a real object
• shows the sum of a whole number and a fraction

Lessons 7-3 and 7-4

- To understand proportions and to determine whether two ratios are proportional
- To solve proportions using number sense and cross products

A **proportion** is an equation stating that two ratios are equal.

Does each pair of ratios form a proportion?

16. $\frac{2}{5}$, $\frac{1}{3}$ **no** **17.** $\frac{6}{16}$, $\frac{21}{56}$ **yes** **18.** $\frac{15}{9}$, $\frac{5}{3}$ **yes** **19.** $\frac{3}{8}$, $\frac{9}{16}$ **no**

20. There are 944 marbles in a bag. If 3 out of 8 marbles are yellow, how many marbles are yellow? **354 marbles**

Lesson 7-5

- To find the scale of a drawing and to use scales to find actual dimensions

A **scale** is a ratio that compares a length on a drawing or a model to an actual length.

Ships The *S.S. United States,* a passenger ship, is 990 feet long. Find the length of a model with each given scale.

21. 1 foot : 10 feet **99 ft**

22. 3 inches : 20 feet **148.5 in.**

23. 2 inches : 15 feet **132 in.**

Lessons 7-6 and 7-7

- To find equivalent forms of fractions, decimals, and percents
- To use percents to find part of a whole

A **percent** is a ratio that compares a number to 100.

Write each percent as a fraction in simplest form and as a decimal.

24. 30% $\frac{3}{10}$, **0.3** **25.** 25% $\frac{1}{4}$, **0.25** **26.** 56% $\frac{14}{25}$, **0.56** **27.** 12% $\frac{3}{25}$, **0.12**

28. There are 200 students in your class, and 30% of them joined the school band. How many students in your class joined the band? **60 students**

29. Three out of 5 children enjoy swimming. What percent like to swim? **60%**

Lesson 7-8

- To read and make circle graphs to represent real-world data

30. Books Use the data in the table below to make a circle graph.

Favorite Types of Books

Mysteries	Biographies	Fiction	Humor
22%	13%	55%	10%

See margin.

Lesson 7-9

- To use mental math and estimation with percents

You can use mental math to estimate percents.

Estimate each amount.

31. 20% of 48 **10** **32.** 6% of $19.99 **$1.20** **33.** 15% of $38.56 **$6.00**

Chapter 7 Chapter Review **355**

30. See back of book.

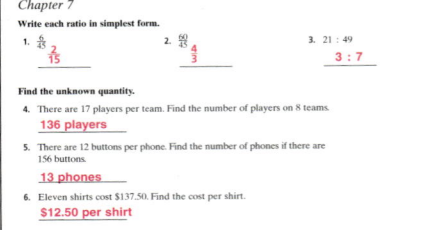

You have 3 nickels, 11 dimes, and 5 quarters in your pocket. Write each ratio in three ways. **1–4. See margin.**

1. nickels to quarters
2. dimes to nickels
3. dimes to all coins
4. quarters to dimes

5. Use the figure below. Find the ratio of the shaded region to the unshaded region in simplest form. **2 : 3**

Write three ratios equivalent to each ratio.

6. 3 to 2   7. $\frac{3}{18}$ 8. 6 : 8
6–8. See margin.

9. A car can travel 28 miles per gallon of gas. How far can the car travel on 8 gallons of gas? **224 mi**

10. A 6-ounce bottle of juice costs $.96. An 8-ounce bottle costs $1.12. Which is the better buy? **8-ounce juice bottle**

Does each pair of ratios form a proportion?

11. $\frac{5}{3}, \frac{15}{9}$ 12. $\frac{3}{4}, \frac{4}{5}$ 13. $\frac{8}{12}, \frac{12}{8}$
yes   **no**   **no**

Solve each proportion.

14. $\frac{4}{5} = \frac{x}{25}$ 15. $\frac{6}{4} = \frac{9}{m}$ 16. $\frac{a}{25} = \frac{3}{10}$
20   **6**   **7.5**

17. A grocery store sells 6 pounds of apples for $4. How much will 8 pounds of apples cost? Round your answer to the nearest cent. **$5.33**

18. **Writing in Math** The ratio of girls to boys in a science class is 5 to 6. Can there be 15 boys in the class? Explain why or why not. **No; 15 is not a multiple of 6.**

Use a map scale of 1 inch : 30 miles to find each actual distance.

19. 3 inches   20. 6 inches   21. 0.5 inches
90 mi   **180 mi**   **15 mi**

22. A scale model of a tiger measures 1.5 feet long. The tiger's actual length is 9 feet. What is the scale of the model? **1 ft : 6 ft**

Write each percent as a decimal and as a fraction.

23. 25%   24. 6%   25. 98%
0.25, $\frac{1}{4}$ **0.06, $\frac{3}{50}$**   **0.98, $\frac{49}{50}$**

Write each decimal or fraction as a percent. If necessary, round to the nearest percent.

26. 0.48 **48%**   27. 0.02 **2%**   28. $\frac{1}{10}$ **10%**

29. $\frac{3}{15}$ **20%**   30. $\frac{5}{6}$ **83%**   31. $0.\overline{9}$ **100%**

Find each percent.

32. 5% of 200   33. 80% of 8   34. 2% of 50
10   **6.4**   **1**

35. Suppose 86% of 50 people at a law firm like their jobs. How many people like their jobs? **43 people**

36. Use the circle graph.
   a. How do *most* students get to school? **bus**
   b. What method do students use *least*? **bicycle**

How Students Get to School
Walk, Bicycle, Car Pool, Bus

Estimate a 15% tip for each bill amount.

37. $32.04   38. $48.76   39. $12.83
$4.80   **$7.35**   **$1.95**

40. Suppose you buy a DVD for $12.98. The sales tax is 7%. Estimate the total cost. **$13.91**

1. 3 to 5, 3 : 5, $\frac{3}{5}$

2. 11 to 3, 11 : 3, $\frac{11}{3}$

3. 11 to 19, 11 : 19, $\frac{11}{19}$

4. 5 to 11, 5 : 11, $\frac{5}{11}$

6–8. Answers may vary. Samples are given.

6. 6 to 4, 9 to 6, 12 to 8

7. $\frac{1}{6}, \frac{2}{12}, \frac{4}{24}$

8. 3 : 4, 9 : 12, 30 : 40

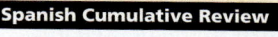
Multiple Choice
Choose the correct letter.

1. Find the product of $\frac{2}{9}$ and $\frac{5}{7}$. **A**

   Ⓐ $\frac{10}{63}$ Ⓒ $\frac{14}{45}$

   Ⓑ $\frac{5}{31}$ Ⓓ $3\frac{3}{14}$

2. Which could you use to describe how to find $1\frac{3}{4}$ divided by $\frac{1}{2}$? **J**

   Ⓕ Multiply $\frac{1}{2}$ and $\frac{7}{4}$.

   Ⓖ Multiply $\frac{1}{2}$ and $\frac{4}{7}$.

   Ⓗ Multiply $\frac{4}{7}$ and 2.

   Ⓙ Multiply $\frac{7}{4}$ and 2.

3. You bought a 12-bag variety pack of dried fruit. Each bag of dried fruit contains c ounces. How many ounces of dried fruit did you buy? **D**

   Ⓐ $c \div 12$ Ⓒ $c + 12$

   Ⓑ $12 \div c$ Ⓓ $12c$

4. Which statement is false? **J**

   Ⓕ $\frac{8}{10} = \frac{32}{40}$ Ⓗ $\frac{24}{42} = \frac{28}{49}$

   Ⓖ $\frac{1}{3} = \frac{12}{36}$ Ⓙ $\frac{13}{14} = \frac{169}{196}$

5. Which decimal represents the portion of the model that is NOT shaded? **D**

   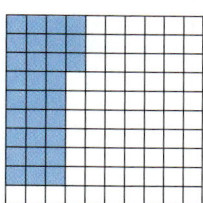

   Ⓐ 0.3   Ⓑ 0.33   Ⓒ 0.67   Ⓓ 0.7

6. Which of the following numbers is divisible by 2, 3, 5, 9 and 10? **F**

   Ⓕ 1,350   Ⓗ 945

   Ⓖ 1,010   Ⓙ 120

7. Choose an appropriate unit for measuring the length of a driveway. **B**

   Ⓐ inches Ⓑ feet   Ⓒ miles   Ⓓ tons

8. Solve $x - \frac{1}{10} = \frac{1}{2}$. **J**

   Ⓕ $\frac{1}{10}$ Ⓖ $\frac{1}{6}$ Ⓗ $\frac{2}{5}$ Ⓙ $\frac{3}{5}$

9. At a car dealer, $\frac{2}{5}$ of the vehicles sold during the year were minivans. What percent of the vehicles sold were minivans? **D**

   Ⓐ 2.5%   Ⓑ 20%   Ⓒ 25%   Ⓓ 40%

Gridded Response

10. A bank teller spends about 8 minutes helping each customer. How long does the teller spend with 7 customers? **56**

11. Solve $\frac{k}{9} = \frac{2}{5}$ for k. Write your answer as an improper fraction. **$\frac{18}{5}$**

12. Find the product of $7\frac{5}{6}$ and $2\frac{1}{2}$. Write your answer as a decimal rounded to the nearest hundredth. **19.58**

Short Response

13. Summer vacation is 68 days long and $\frac{3}{4}$ of the vacation has gone by. How many days are left? Explain. **See margin.**

Extended Response

14. Your dinner bill comes to $19.68. Estimate your total cost for dinner with a 5% tax and a 20% tip on the original bill. Justify your reasoning. **See margin.**

15. A customer service agent gets a phone call about every 12 minutes in a 7-hour work day. How many calls does she get in a 5-day work week? Explain how you found your answer. **See margin.**

Resources

Test Prep Workbook

All in One Teaching Resources
- Cumulative Review **L3**

ExamView Assessment Suite CD-ROM
- Standardized Test Practice

Differentiated Instruction

Spanish Assessment Resources
- Spanish Cumulative Review **ELL**

ExamView Assessment Suite CD-ROM
- Special Needs Practice Bank **L1**

15. **[4] About 175 calls; 5 days × 7 hours × 60 min = how many minutes in a work week. Divide the answer by 12 to find the number of calls OR other method.**

   [3] appropriate methods, one error

   [2] appropriate methods, more than one computational error

   [1] correct answer, no steps

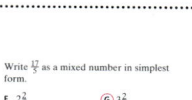
Spanish Cumulative Review   **ELL**

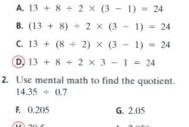
Cumulative Review   **L3**

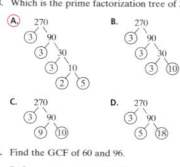

357

Item	1	2	3	4	5	6	7	8	9	10	11	12	13	14	15
Lesson	6-1	6-4	3-3	7-3	1-5	4-1	6-6	5-6	7-6	7-2	7-4	6-2	6-1	7-7	7-4

13. **[2] 17 days; multiply 68 by $\frac{1}{4}$ OR equivalent method**

   [1] correct answer, no reason

14. **[4] About $25; use $20 for the cost, find the tax. Calculate the 20% tip by multiplying the tax by 4 OR equivalent method.**

   [3] minor error, correct reasoning

   [2] correct answer, but computational error

   [1] correct answer with no reason

Applying Proportions

Students will use data from these two pages to answer the questions posed in Put It All Together.

Some students may know a great deal about dinosaurs. Invite them to share knowledge they have about dinosaurs' extraordinary characteristics. Ask questions such as:

- *How fast did they move?*
- *What colors might they have been?*
- *How much and what did they eat?*
- *Where have fossilized dinosaur remains been discovered?*

Focusing on differences in movement, appearance, and diet, discuss the wide variety of dinosaurs that once lived.

Materials
- Images of different types of dinosaurs, including a variety of different sizes

Activating Prior Knowledge

Have students read the data and look at the pictures on these pages. Draw students' attention to the different sizes of the dinosaurs (and dinosaur fossils) pictured. Point out how they compare in size to the people in some of the photos and images. Invite students to share examples of other dinosaurs they are familiar with, including those featured in films and on television shows. Ask them to describe the sizes of those dinosaurs compared with the size of a person. You may want to draw a figure of a person on the board and then make marks to indicate the relative sizes of the dinosaurs discussed.

Guided Instruction

To introduce the activity, ask:
- *About how many people tall is the dinosaur?* **8 people**

Applying Proportions

Prehistoric Giants Dinosaurs first appeared on Earth about 230 million years ago and died out about 65 million years ago. Today, scientists study dinosaur remains to learn more about them. For example, scientists can calculate the size of a dinosaur by measuring bones they have found. Then they use proportions to estimate the dimensions of other bones.

Fossilized Bones
Skeletons of animals that die in soft earth or mud can become fossils. Over time, the skeleton sinks and mud covers it. The mud turns to stone, preserving the skeleton.

Put It All Together

Data File Use the information on these two pages and on page 651 to answer these questions.

Materials centimeter ruler, poster board

1. Copy the table.
   a. Measure the dinosaur in the center of the page. Complete the first column of the table.
   b. Measure the height of one of the eight schoolgirls. Then measure your own height (in centimeters). Use the measurements to estimate the scale of the dinosaur.
   c. Use your scale to estimate the actual dimensions of the dinosaur. Complete the second column of the table.

Dinosaur Measurements (centimeters)

Body Part	Math Book Length	Actual Length	Poster Length
Height	■	■	■
Tail	■	■	■
Thigh	■	■	■
Foot	■	■	■
Neck	■	■	■

2. a. **Open-Ended** Choose a large object such as your family's car, your bicycle, your bed, or a desk in your classroom. Measure at least four different parts of the object in centimeters.
   b. Choose a scale that will allow a drawing of both the dinosaur and your object to fit on (and cover as much as possible of) the poster board. Write the scale in a corner of the poster board.
   c. Calculate the poster dimensions for the dinosaur and the object. Complete the third column of your table.
   d. Use the dimensions from part (c) to draw the dinosaur and the object on the poster board.

3. **Research** Choose an animal from the table on page 651. Find out what the animal looks like. Calculate its size using the scale for your poster. If possible, add a drawing of it to your poster.

1a. **Answers may vary.**
   Sample: 22.2 cm, 5.7 cm, 2.2 cm, 15.1 cm

b. **Answers may vary.**
   Sample: 2.8 cm; 145.6 cm; scale 1:52.

c. **Answers may vary.**
   Sample: 1,154.4 cm, 296.4 cm, 114.4 cm, 785.2 cm

2a. **Check students' work.**

b. **Answers may vary.**

c–d. **Check students' work.**

3. **Check students' work.**

Sue and Sue

In 1990, fossil hunter Sue Hendrickson discovered Sue, a *Tyrannosaurus rex* fossil that is nearly 90% complete. Here she poses with a reconstructed back foot.

How Tall Is That?

A *Brachiosaurus* was about the height of eight middle school students.

Compsognathus

Compsognathus was one of the smallest dinosaurs, about the size of a turkey.

Digging Up Dinosaurs

A paleontologist carefully chisels fossils from rock.

Go Online
PHSchool.com

For: Information about dinosaurs
Web Code: aqe-0753

359

8 Tools of Geometry

Chapter at a Glance

Lesson Titles, Objectives, and Features	Assessment	NCTM Standards	Local Standards
8-1 Points, Lines, Segments, and Rays • To identify and work with points, lines, segments, and rays	Lesson Quiz	3, 6, 7, 8, 9, 10	
8-2a Activity Lab, Hands On: Using Angle Benchmarks **8-2 Angles** • To measure and classify angles **Extension:** Basic Constructions	Lesson Quiz	3, 4, 6, 7, 8, 9, 10	
8-3 Special Pairs of Angles • To use the relationship between special pairs of angles **8-3b Activity Lab, Hands On:** Exploring Parallel Lines	Lesson Quiz Checkpoint Quiz 1	1, 3, 4, 6, 7, 8, 9, 10	
8-4a Activity Lab, Technology: Investigating Angles in a Triangle **8-4 Classifying Triangles** • To classify triangles by their angles and by their sides **Vocabulary Builder:** High-Use Academic Words	Lesson Quiz	1, 3, 4, 6, 7, 8, 9, 10	
8-5a Activity Lab, Hands On: Angles in a Quadrilateral **8-5 Exploring and Classifying Polygons** • To identify regular and non-regular polygons and to classify quadrilaterals	Lesson Quiz Checkpoint Quiz 2	1, 2, 3, 4, 6, 7, 8, 9, 10	
8-6 Congruent and Similar Figures • To identify congruent and similar figures **Guided Problem Solving:** Practice Solving Problems	Lesson Quiz	1, 3, 4, 6, 7, 8, 9, 10	
8-7 Line Symmetry • To find lines of symmetry	Lesson Quiz	3, 6, 7, 8, 9, 10	
8-8 Transformations • To identify and draw translations, reflections, and rotations **8-8b Activity Lab, Hands On:** Tessellations	Lesson Quiz	3, 4, 5, 6, 7, 8, 9, 10	
Problem Solving Application: Applying Geometry			

NCTM Standards 2000
1 Number and Operations
2 Algebra
3 Geometry
4 Measurement
5 Data Analysis and Probability
6 Problem Solving
7 Reasoning and Proof
8 Communication
9 Connections
10 Representation

Correlations to Standardized Tests

All content for these tests is contained in *Prentice Hall Math*, Course 1. This chart reflects coverage in this chapter only.

	8-1	8-2	8-3	8-4	8-5	8-6	8-7	8-8
Terra Nova CAT6 (Level 16)								
Number and Number Relations								
Computation and Numerical Estimation								
Operation Concepts								
Measurement								
Geometry and Spatial Sense	✔	✔	✔	✔	✔	✔	✔	✔
Data Analysis, Statistics, and Probability								
Patterns, Functions, Algebra								
Problem Solving and Reasoning	✔	✔	✔	✔	✔	✔	✔	✔
Communication	✔	✔	✔	✔	✔	✔	✔	✔
Decimals, Fractions, Integers, and Percent								
Order of Operations								
Terra Nova CTBS (Level 16)								
Whole Numbers, Decimals, Fractions								
Numeration, Number Theory								
Data Interpretation								
Pre-algebra					✔			
Measurement		✔	✔	✔		✔		
Geometry	✔	✔	✔	✔	✔	✔	✔	✔
ITBS (Level 12)								
Number Properties and Operations	✔	✔	✔	✔	✔	✔	✔	✔
Algebra								
Geometry	✔	✔	✔	✔	✔	✔	✔	✔
Measurement		✔	✔	✔		✔		
Probability and Statistics								
Estimation								
SAT10 (Int 2 Level)								
Number Sense and Operations								
Patterns, Relationships, and Algebra	✔	✔	✔	✔	✔	✔	✔	✔
Data, Statistics, and Probability								
Geometry and Measurement	✔	✔	✔	✔	✔	✔	✔	✔
NAEP								
Number Sense, Properties, and Operations								
Measurement								
Geometry and Spatial Sense	✔			✔	✔	✔	✔	✔
Data Analysis, Statistics, and Probability								
Algebra and Functions								

CAT6 California Achievement Test, 6th Ed. **CTBS** Comprehensive Test of Basic Skills **ITBS** Iowa Test of Basic Skills, Form M
SAT10 Stanford Achievement Test, 10th Ed. **NAEP** National Assessment of Educational Progress 2005 Mathematics Objectives

Math Background

Skills Trace

BEFORE Chapter 8
Grade 5 presented the basic geometric figures such as triangles, squares, and circles.

DURING Chapter 8
Course 1 reviews and extends geometry with special angles, congruent and similar figures, line of symmetry, and transformations.

AFTER Chapter 8
Throughout this course, students apply geometric skills, concepts, and vocabulary.

8-1 Points, Lines, Segments, and Rays

Math Understandings
- Points, lines, and planes are ideas that do not physically exist.

A **point** is a location in space, named with a capital letter. A **line** is a series of points that extends in two opposite directions without end, named by any two points on the line. A **ray** consists of one endpoint and all the points of a line on one side of the endpoint, named first by the endpoint, and then by any other point on the ray. A **segment** is part of a line with two endpoints, named by its endpoints. Points on the same line are **collinear**.

Example: *A, B,* and *C* are points. $\overleftrightarrow{CA}$ is a line. $\overrightarrow{AC}$ is a ray. $\overline{AB}$ is a segment.

A **plane** is a flat surface that extends indefinitely in all directions. **Intersecting lines** have exactly one point in common. **Parallel lines** have no points in common. **Skew lines** are lines that lie in different planes, and they are not parallel and do not intersect.

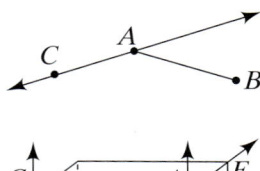

$\overleftrightarrow{AB}$ is parallel to $\overleftrightarrow{DC}$.
$\overleftrightarrow{AE}$ and $\overleftrightarrow{CD}$ are skew.

8-2 Angles

Math Understandings
- The measure of an angle describes the opening between the two sides, or rays, that form the angle. It does not depend on the lengths of the sides.

Every **angle** has two sides and a vertex. The vertex is their common endpoint. Angles are measured in units called **degrees**. Lines that intersect to form right angles are called **perpendicular lines**. You can use measures to classify angles.

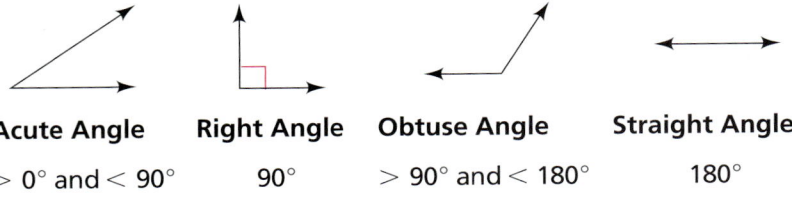

Acute Angle	**Right Angle**	**Obtuse Angle**	**Straight Angle**
$> 0°$ and $< 90°$	$90°$	$> 90°$ and $< 180°$	$180°$

8-3 Special Pairs of Angles

Math Understandings
- Pairs of angles with certain relationships have special names.
- A pair of angles need not be adjacent to be either complementary or supplementary.

If the sum of the measures of two angles is 90°, the angles are **complementary angles**. If the sum of the measures of two angles is 180°, the angles are **supplementary angles. Vertical angles** are formed by two intersecting lines. Vertical angles have equal measures. Angles with equal measures are **congruent angles**. A **transversal** crosses two or more lines at different points. **Interior angles** are on either side of a transversal between a pair of lines. **Exterior angles** are on either side of a transversal outside of a pair of lines.

8-4 Classifying Triangles
8-5 Exploring and Classifying Polygons

Math Understandings
- You can name a polygon by the number of its sides.
- You can classify polygons by the relationships among the sides and angles.

Triangles can be classified by their angle measures and the number of congruent sides as summarized below.

Name	Angles	Name	Congruent Sides
acute	3 acute	scalene	0
obtuse	1 obtuse	isosceles	2 or 3
right	1 right	equilateral	3

A **polygon** is a closed figure that has three or more line segments that do not cross. Any polygon with four sides is called a **quadrilateral**. A **trapezoid** has one pair of parallel lines. A **parallelogram** has two pairs of parallel lines. There are three special types of parallelograms: a **rectangle** (four right angles), a **rhombus** (four congruent sides), a **square** (four right angles and four congruent sides).

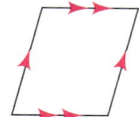 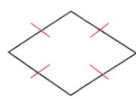 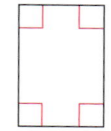 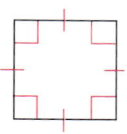

Parallelogram   **Rhombus**   **Rectangle**   **Square**

8-6   Congruent and Similar Figures

Math Understandings
- Congruent figures have congruent corresponding sides and congruent corresponding angles.
- When two figures are congruent, you can fit one exactly on top of the other, although one may have to be turned or flipped.

Congruent figures have the same size and shape. **Similar figures** have the same shape, but not necessarily the same size. Corresponding angles of similar figures are congruent and the corresponding sides of similar figures are proportional.

8-7   Line Symmetry

Math Understandings
- A figure may have no line of symmetry, one line of symmetry, or more than one line of symmetry.
- If you fold a figure on its line of symmetry, the two parts match.

A figure has **line symmetry** if a line can be drawn through the figure so that each part is a mirror image of the other. This line is a **line of symmetry**.

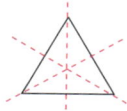

8-8   Transformations

Math Understandings
- To translate a figure, you need to know the distance and the direction of the translation.
- To reflect a figure, you need to know the line of reflection.
- To rotate a figure, you need to know the center of rotation and the angle of rotation.

Translating, rotating, and reflecting change only the position of a figure, and not its shape or size. The new figure is the **image** of the original. A **translation**, or *slide*, moves every point of a figure the same distance and in the same direction. A **reflection**, or flip, flips a figure over a line. This line is called the **line of reflection**. A **rotation**, or turn, turns a figure about a point. This point stays fixed and is called the **center of rotation**.

Additional Professional Development Opportunities

Math Background Notes for Chapter 8: Every lesson has a Math Background in the PLAN section.

Research Overview, Mathematics Strands
Additional support for these topics and more is in the front of the Teacher's Edition.

LessonLab
LessonLab, a Pearson Education company, offers comprehensive, facilitated professional development designed to help teachers to improve student achievement. To learn more, please visit lessonlab.com.

Chapter 8 Resources

Print Resources	8-1	8-2	8-3	8-4	8-5	8-6	8-7	8-8	For the Chapter
L3 Practice	●	●	●	●	●	●	●	●	
L1 Adapted Practice	●	●	●	●	●	●	●	●	
L3 Guided Problem Solving	●	●	●	●	●	●	●	●	
L2 Reteaching	●	●	●	●	●	●	●	●	
L4 Enrichment	●	●	●	●	●	●	●	●	
L3 Daily Notetaking Guide	●	●	●	●	●	●	●	●	
L1 Adapted Daily Notetaking Guide	●	●	●	●	●	●	●	●	
L3 Vocabulary and Study Skills Worksheets	●		●		●		●	●	●
L3 Daily Puzzles	●	●	●	●	●	●	●	●	
L3 Activity Labs	●	●	●	●	●	●	●	●	
L3 Checkpoint Quiz			●		●				
L3 Chapter Project									●
L2 Below Level Chapter Test									●
L3 Chapter Test									●
L4 Alternative Assessment									●
L3 Cumulative Review									●

Spanish Resources **ELL**	8-1	8-2	8-3	8-4	8-5	8-6	8-7	8-8	For the Chapter
L3 Practice	●	●	●	●	●	●	●	●	
L3 Vocabulary and Study Skills Worksheets	●		●		●		●	●	●
L3 Checkpoint Quiz			●		●				
L2 Below Level Chapter Test									●
L3 Chapter Test									●
L4 Alternative Assessment									●
L3 Cumulative Review									●

Transparencies	8-1	8-2	8-3	8-4	8-5	8-6	8-7	8-8	For the Chapter
Check Skills You'll Need	●	●	●	●	●	●	●	●	
Additional Examples	●	●	●	●	●	●	●	●	
Problem of the Day	●	●	●	●	●	●	●	●	
Classroom Aid									
Student Edition Answers	●	●	●	●	●	●	●	●	●
Lesson Quiz	●	●	●	●	●	●	●	●	
Test-Taking Strategies									●

Technology	8-1	8-2	8-3	8-4	8-5	8-6	8-7	8-8	For the Chapter
Interactive Textbook Online	●	●	●	●	●	●	●	●	●
StudentExpress™ CD-ROM	●	●	●	●	●	●	●	●	●
Success Tracker™ Online Intervention	●	●	●	●	●	●	●	●	●
TeacherExpress™ CD-ROM	●	●	●	●	●	●	●	●	●
PresentationExpress™ with QuickTake Presenter CD-ROM	●	●	●	●	●	●	●	●	●
ExamView® Assessment Suite CD-ROM	●	●	●	●	●	●	●	●	●
MindPoint® Quiz Show CD-ROM									●
Prentice Hall Web Site: PHSchool.com	●	●	●	●	●	●	●	●	●

Also available: **Prentice Hall Assessment System**
- Progress Monitoring Assessments
- Skills and Concepts Review
- Test Prep Workbook

Other Resources
Algebra Readiness Tests
All-in-One Student Workbook
All-in-One Student Workbook, Adapted Version
Multilingual Handbook

Solution Key
Math Notes Study Folder
Spanish Cumulative Assessment

Where You Can Use the Lesson Resources

Here is a suggestion, following the four-step teaching plan, for how you can incorporate Differentiated Instruction Resources into your teaching.

	Instructional Resources **L3**	**Differentiated Instruction Resources**
1. Plan		
Preparation Read the Math Background in the Teacher's Edition to connect this lesson with students' previous experience. **Starting Class** **Check Skills You'll Need** Assign these exercises to review prerequisite skills. **New Vocabulary** Help students pre-read the lesson by pointing out the new terms introduced in the lesson.	**Math Background** **Math Understandings** **Transparencies & PresentationExpress™ with QuickTake Presenter CD-ROM** Check Skills You'll Need Problem of the Day **Resources** Vocabulary and Study Skills	**Spanish Support** **ELL** Vocabulary and Study Skills
2. Teach		
L3 **Guided Instruction** Use the Activity Labs to build conceptual understanding. Teach each Example. Use the Teacher's Edition side column notes for specific teaching tips, including Error Prevention notes. Use the Additional Examples found in the side column (and on transparency and PowerPoint) as an alternative presentation for the content. After each Example, assign the Quick Check exercise for that Example to get an immediate assessment of student understanding. Use the Closure activity in the Teacher's Edition to help students attain mastery of lesson content.	**Student Edition** Activity Lab **Resources** Daily Notetaking Guide Activity Lab **Transparencies & PresentationExpress™ with QuickTake Presenter CD-ROM** Additional Examples Classroom Aids **ExamView® Assessment Suite CD-ROM**	**Teacher's Edition** Every lesson includes suggestions for working with students who need special attention. **L1** Special Needs **L2** Below Level **L4** Advanced Learners **ELL** English Language Learners **Resources** **L1** Adapted Daily Notetaking Guide **Multilingual Handbook**
3. Practice		

Assignment Guide
Check Your Understanding
Use these questions to check students' understanding before you assign homework.
Homework Exercises
Assign homework from these leveled exercises in the Assignment Guide.
  A Practice by Example
  B Apply Your Skills
  C Challenge
  Test Prep and Mixed Review
Homework Quick Check
Use these key exercises to quickly check students' homework.
	Transparencies & PresentationExpress™ with QuickTake Presenter CD-ROM
	Student Answers
	Resources
	Practice
	Guided Problem Solving
	Vocabulary and Study Skills
	Activity Lab
	Daily Puzzles
	ExamView® Assessment Suite CD-ROM
		Spanish Support
		ELL Practice
		ELL Vocabulary and Study Skills
		Resources
		L1 Adapted Practice
		L4 Enrichment

4. Assess & Reteach		
Lesson Quiz Assign the Lesson Quiz to assess students' mastery of the lesson content. **Checkpoint Quiz** Use the Checkpoint Quiz to assess student progress over several lessons.	**Transparencies & PresentationExpress™ with QuickTake Presenter CD-ROM** Lesson Quiz **Resources** Checkpoint Quiz	**Resources** **L2** Reteaching **ELL** Checkpoint Quiz Success Tracker™ Online Intervention **ExamView® Assessment Suite CD-ROM**

KEY   **L1** Special Needs   **L2** Below Level   **L3** For All Students   **L4** Advanced, Gifted   **ELL** English Language Learners

Tools of Geometry

Check Your Readiness

Answers are in the back of the textbook.

For intervention, direct students to:

Using Number Sense to Solve Equations
Lesson 3-4
Extra Skills and Word
Problems Practice, Ch. 3

Solving Equations by Adding
Lesson 3-5
Extra Skills and Word
Problems Practice, Ch. 3

Solving Equations by Subtracting
Lesson 3-6
Extra Skills and Word
Problems Practice, Ch. 3

Recognizing Proportions
Lesson 7-3
Extra Skills and Word
Problems Practice, Ch. 7

What You've Learned

- In Chapter 3, you solved one-step equations by using number sense and inverse operations.
- In Chapter 7, you used ratios to describe proportional situations.
- You used proportions to solve problems.

Check Your Readiness

For Exercises	See Lesson
1–4	3-4
5–7	3-5
8–10	3-6
11–16	7-3

GO for Help

Using Number Sense to Solve Equations

Use mental math to solve each equation.

1. $a + 9 = 18$ **9**　　**2.** $y \div 3 = 3$ **9**

3. $11k = 44$ **4**　　**4.** $c - 5 = 5$ **10**

Solving Equations

Solve each equation. Then check the solution.

5. $0.23 + x = 1.5$ **1.27**　**6.** $p + 120.5 = 180$ **59.5**　**7.** $62.9 + b = 90$ **27.1**

8. $d - 13 = 4.5$ **17.5**　**9.** $g - 22 = 11.3$ **33.3**　**10.** $c - 0.45 = 11.62$ **12.07**

Recognizing Proportions

Do the ratios in each pair form a proportion?

11. $\frac{3}{4}, \frac{18}{24}$ **yes**　　**12.** $\frac{11}{12}, \frac{121}{144}$ **no**

13. $\frac{16}{20}, \frac{64}{100}$ **no**　　**14.** $\frac{12}{15}, \frac{24}{30}$ **yes**

15. $\frac{5}{8}, \frac{15}{20}$ **no**　　**16.** $\frac{4}{9}, \frac{16}{36}$ **yes**

Chapter 8 Overview

In this chapter, students study geometric concepts and terms to get the tools they need to classify geometric figures. First, they examine the difference between lines, line segments, and rays. Next, they learn about angles and special kinds of angles. They then explore and classify different kinds of polygons. Finally, they investigate congruence, similarity, symmetry, and transformations.

Activating Prior Knowledge

In this chapter, students build on and extend their knowledge of geometry concepts. They also draw upon their understanding of ratio and proportion as they work with congruent and similar figures. Ask questions such as:
- *What is n in $\frac{n}{12} = \frac{1}{6}$?* **n = 2**
- *What is the perimeter of a rectangle with length of 4 ft and width of 2.5 ft?* **13 ft**
- *The length of a rectangle is 6 in. Its perimeter is 21 in. What is the width of the rectangle?* **4.5 in.**

What You'll Learn Next

- In this chapter, you will identify points, lines, and planes.
- You will measure angles and classify them as acute, obtuse, or right.
- You will identify and classify geometric figures.
- You will use proportions to test congruency and similarity in geometric figures.

◀)) Key Vocabulary

- angle (p. 367)
- line (p. 362)
- line symmetry (p. 398)
- parallel lines (p. 363)
- point (p. 362)
- polygon (p. 386)
- quadrilateral (p. 387)
- ray (p. 362)
- reflection (p. 403)
- rotation (p. 403)
- segment (p. 362)
- similar figures (p. 393)
- translation (p. 402)

 Problem Solving Application On pages 412 and 413, you will work an extended activity on building a house.

Chapter 8   **361**

Objective
To identify and work with points, lines, segments, and rays

Examples
1 Naming Lines, Segments, and Rays
2 Application: Maps

Math Understandings: p. 360C

Math Background

A *point* is an exact location in space that has no size. A *line* is a series of points that extends in opposite directions without end. A line has no thickness. A *ray* is part of a line with one endpoint and extends forever in one direction. A *line segment* is a part of a line with two endpoints.

More Math Background: p. 360C

Lesson Planning and Resources

See p. 360E for a list of the resources that support this lesson.

Bell Ringer Practice

✓ **Check Skills You'll Need**
Use student page, transparency, or PowerPoint. For intervention, direct students to:
Comparing and Ordering Decimals
Lesson 1-6
Extra Skills and Word Problems Practice, Ch. 1

362

✓ **Check Skills You'll Need**

1. Vocabulary Review
How can you use a *number line* to order numbers?
1–4. See below.
Use a number line to order each set of decimals.

2. 1.6, 1.3, 1.03, 1.06

3. 0.4, 0.2, 0.6, 0.9

4. 1.4, 1.04, 1.5, 1.3

GO for Help
Lesson 1-6

Check Skills You'll Need

1. **Answers may vary. Sample: Numbers are ordered from smallest to largest as you move from left to right on a number line.**

2. **1.03, 1.06, 1.3, 1.6**

3. **0.2, 0.4, 0.6, 0.9**

4. **1.04, 1.3, 1.4, 1.5**

Vocabulary Tip

A ray of sunlight begins at the sun and travels in one direction.

What You'll Learn

To identify and work with points, lines, segments, and rays
🔊 **New Vocabulary** point, line, segment, ray, plane, intersecting lines, parallel lines, skew lines

Why Learn This?

The stars in constellations are like points that can be connected to form an image. To find the constellation Orion, the Hunter, look for the three stars in a row that form the belt.

A **point** is a location in space. It has no size. You name a point with a capital letter.

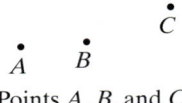

Points *A*, *B*, and *C*

A **line** is a series of points that extends in two opposite directions without end. It has no thickness. To name a line, use any two points. Read $\overleftrightarrow{DE}$ as "line *DE*."

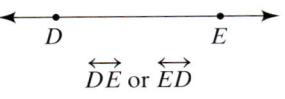

A **segment** consists of two endpoints and all the points of the line between the endpoints. You name a segment by its endpoints. Read $\overline{DE}$ as "segment *DE*."

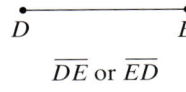

A **ray** consists of one endpoint and all the points of the line on one side of the endpoint. To name a ray, use its endpoint first and then any other point on the ray. Read $\overrightarrow{DE}$ as "ray *DE*."

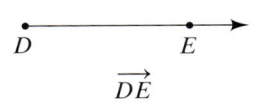

Differentiated Instruction Solutions for All Learners

Special Needs L1
Students are often confused by the idea that any two points on a line can be used to name a line. Draw a couple of rays and lines on the board, with three or four points labeled. Have students come up with several possible ways to name each ray and line.

learning style: visual

Below Level L2
Have students model the intersecting and parallel lines using two straws for the lines. Remind students that two lines in the same plane must be parallel or intersecting.

learning style: tactile

1a. Answers may vary.
Samples are given.
$\overleftrightarrow{VP}$, $\overleftrightarrow{MV}$

b. $\overline{VM}$, $\overline{VP}$, $\overline{MP}$

1 Name a line, a segment, and a ray.

line: $\overleftrightarrow{XW}$ or $\overleftrightarrow{WX}$

segment: $\overline{WX}$ or $\overline{XW}$

ray: $\overrightarrow{WX}$ or $\overrightarrow{XW}$

✓ Quick Check

1. Use the figure at the right.
  a. Give two names for the line.
  b. Name three segments.
  1a–b. See left.

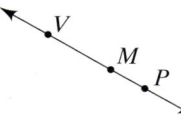

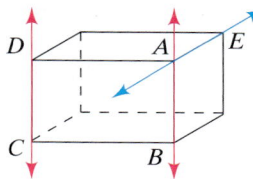

Plane *ABCD*
$\overleftrightarrow{AB}$ is parallel to $\overleftrightarrow{DC}$.
$\overleftrightarrow{AD}$ intersects $\overleftrightarrow{AB}$.
$\overleftrightarrow{AE}$ and $\overleftrightarrow{DC}$ are skew.

A **plane** is a flat surface with no thickness that extends in all directions on the surface. Plane *ABCD* is shown at the left.

Two lines that lie in the same plane are either intersecting or parallel. **Intersecting lines** are lines that have exactly one point in common. **Parallel lines** are lines that have no points in common. Parallel segments lie in parallel lines.

Skew lines are lines that are not parallel and do not intersect. Skew lines lie in different planes.

EXAMPLE Application: Maps

2. Answers may vary.
Samples are given.

a. NE 4th St. and
NE 2nd St.

b. N. Miami Ave. and
NE 2nd St.

2 Are the lines indicated on the map below parallel or intersecting?

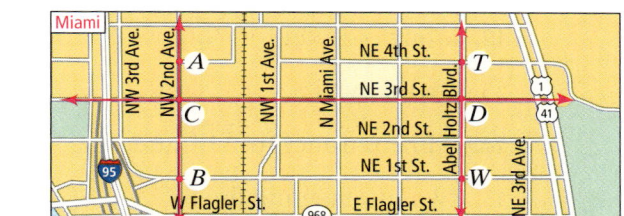

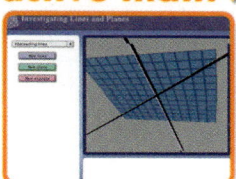

For: Lines and Rays
Activity
Use: Interactive
Textbook, 8-1

a. $\overleftrightarrow{AB}$ and $\overleftrightarrow{CD}$

$\overleftrightarrow{AB}$ and $\overleftrightarrow{CD}$ intersect at point *C*.

b. $\overleftrightarrow{AB}$ and $\overleftrightarrow{TW}$

$\overleftrightarrow{AB}$ and $\overleftrightarrow{TW}$ are parallel.

✓ Quick Check

2a–b. See left.
2. a. Name two streets on the map that are parallel.
  b. Name two streets on the map that intersect.

---

2. Teach

Activity Lab

Use before the lesson.

All in One Teaching Resources

Activity Lab 8-1: Geometry in Your Classroom

Guided Instruction

Example 2
Point out that the term *line* is often used in daily life to describe a line segment. Clarify that in mathematics the term *line* is used more precisely for a series of points that extends without end.

PowerPoint

Additional Examples

1 Name each segment, ray, or line.

a. B A **$\overline{BA}$ or $\overline{AB}$**

b. R S **$\overleftrightarrow{RS}$ or $\overleftrightarrow{SR}$**

c. O P **$\overrightarrow{OP}$**

2 Name each of the following.

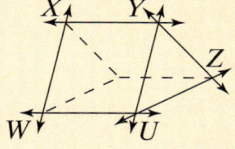

a. two parallel lines **See back of book.**

b. two intersecting lines **See back of book.**

c. two skew lines **See back of book.**

All in One Teaching Resources
- Daily Notetaking Guide 8-1 **L3**
- Adapted Notetaking 8-1 **L1**

Closure

- *What is a point, a line, a line segment, and a ray?* **A point is a location in space. A line is a series of points that extends in two opposite directions without end. A line segment is part of a line with two endpoints. A ray is part of a line with one endpoint.**

Advanced Learners **L4**
Ask: *If two line segments are in the same plane and do not intersect, are the segments parallel? Explain.* **Not necessarily; the segments might intersect if they extended into lines.**

learning style: visual

English Language Learners **ELL**
Ask students to point to pairs of "lines" within the classroom that represent the terms *parallel*, *perpendicular*, *intersecting*, and *skew*. When they point to a pair of lines, ask: *How do you know those are (intersecting, parallel, skew)?* **Answers will vary.**

learning style: visual

3. Practice

Assignment Guide

Check Your Understanding
Go over Exercises 1–5 in class before assigning the Homework Exercises.

Homework Exercises
- **A** Practice by Example   6–15
- **B** Apply Your Skills   16–24
- **C** Challenge   25
- Test Prep and Mixed Review   26–30

Homework Quick Check
To check students' understanding of key skills and concepts, go over Exercises 9, 13, 18, 19, and 24.

Differentiated Instruction **Resources**

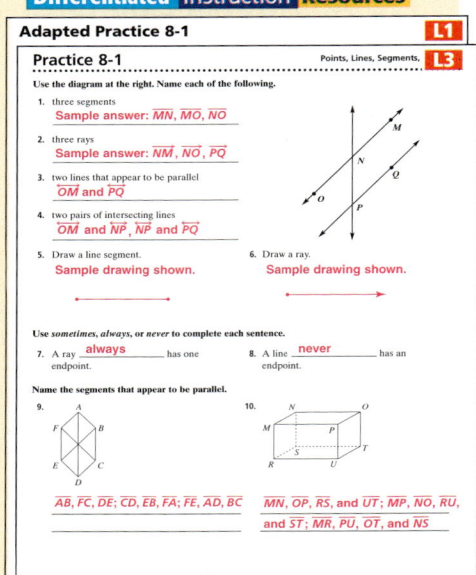

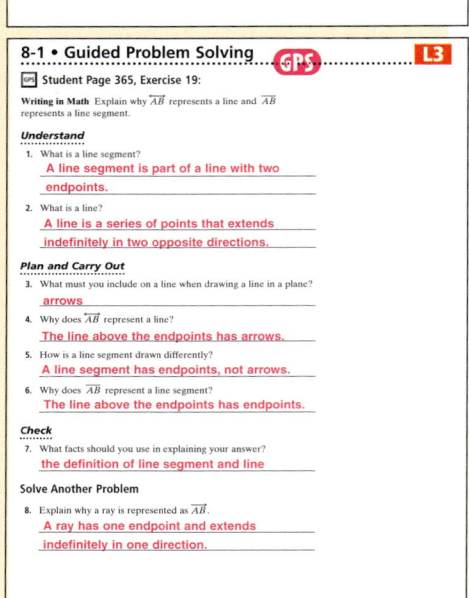

Check Your Understanding

1. **Vocabulary** Which figure can be represented by a log? **c**
   - Ⓐ point
   - Ⓑ line
   - Ⓒ segment
   - Ⓓ ray

Match each figure with its name.

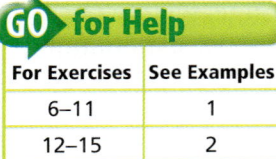

2. **B**
3. **A**
4. **D**
5. **C**

A. $\overleftrightarrow{EF}$
B. $\overline{EF}$
C. $\overrightarrow{EF}$
D. $\overrightarrow{FE}$

Homework Exercises

For more exercises, see Extra Skills and Word Problems.

Ⓐ **Name each line, segment, or ray.**

For Exercises	See Examples
6–11	1
12–15	2

6. **FG** (F ⎯ G)
7. **KJ** (J, K)
8. **HJ** (H ⎯ J)
9. **QP** (Q, P)
10. **XY** (X, Y)
11. **DW** (D, W)

12–15. Answers may vary. Samples are given.

Use the diagram at the right. Name each of the following figures.

12. a line parallel to $\overleftrightarrow{PQ}$ **SR**
13. two skew lines **RV and PQ**
14. a line parallel to $\overleftrightarrow{SW}$ and $\overleftrightarrow{RV}$ **QU**
15. two intersecting lines **SR and RQ**

Ⓑ **GPS** 16. **Guided Problem Solving** Use the picture of the cereal box. Describe how $\overleftrightarrow{AB}$ is related to $\overleftrightarrow{DC}$, $\overleftrightarrow{GH}$, and $\overleftrightarrow{BC}$.

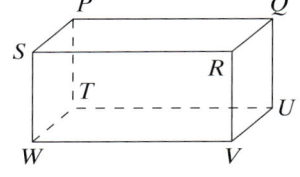

- **Understand the Problem** Are any of the lines parallel, skew, or intersecting?
- **Carry Out the Plan** $\overleftrightarrow{AB}$ is parallel to ▪. $\overleftrightarrow{AB}$ is skew to ▪. $\overleftrightarrow{AB}$ intersects ▪.

16. $\overleftrightarrow{AB}$ is parallel to $\overleftrightarrow{DC}$.

$\overleftrightarrow{AB}$ is skew to $\overleftrightarrow{GH}$.

$\overleftrightarrow{AB}$ intersects $\overleftrightarrow{BC}$.

364   **Chapter 8** Tools of Geometry

24a. all the points on line segment $\overline{AB}$

b. between A and B

Use *sometimes*, *always*, or *never* to complete each sentence.

17. A ray __?__ has one endpoint. **always**

18. Skew lines __?__ intersect. **never**

19. **Writing in Math** Explain why $\overleftrightarrow{AB}$ represents a line and $\overline{AB}$
GPS represents a line segment. **See left.**

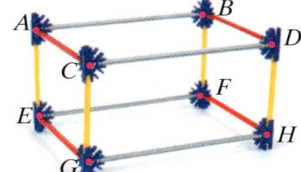

19. The arrows in the symbol for a line indicate that the line continues infinitely in both directions. The lack of arrows in the symbol for a line segment indicates that a segment has two endpoints.

Use the diagram at the left. Name each of the following.

20. the segments intersecting $\overline{GH}$ $\overline{GC}$, $\overline{GE}$, $\overline{DH}$, and $\overline{HF}$

21. a line parallel to $\overleftrightarrow{AB}$ **Answers may vary. Sample:** $\overleftrightarrow{GH}$

22. the intersection of $\overleftrightarrow{EF}$ and $\overleftrightarrow{AE}$ **E**

23. a segment skew to $\overline{AC}$ **Answers may vary. Sample:** $\overline{DH}$

24. **a.** Given two points on a line, A and B, describe the points that $\overrightarrow{AB}$ and $\overrightarrow{BA}$ have in common.
    b. Reasoning If $\overrightarrow{AB}$ contains C, but $\overrightarrow{CA}$ does not contain B, then where on the line must point C be located?
    24a–b. See margin.

C 25. Challenge On a road map, where would you find an example to illustrate a pair of skew lines? Explain. **Check students' work.**

Test Prep and Mixed Review **Practice**

Multiple Choice

26. Sung-Pil made two batches of cookies. He needed $2\frac{3}{4}$ cups of flour for each batch. How much flour did Sung-Pil use? **C**
    Ⓐ $4\frac{1}{2}$ c   Ⓑ $4\frac{3}{4}$ c   Ⓒ $5\frac{1}{2}$ c   Ⓓ $5\frac{3}{4}$ c

27. Mrs. Ortiz is making two dozen gift baskets. She wants eight ounces of cheese in each basket. How many pounds of cheese does she need? **H**
    Ⓕ 10 lb   Ⓖ 11 lb   Ⓗ 12 lb   Ⓙ 16 lb

28. A chorus has 125 members. There are 40 sopranos. What percent of the singers in the chorus are sopranos? **C**
    Ⓐ 22%   Ⓑ 30%   Ⓒ 32%   Ⓓ 35%

GO for Help

For Exercises	See Lesson
29–30	2-2

Find the median of each data set.

29. 5, 6, 8, 9, 10, 4, 7 **7**

30. 600, 550, 475, 520, 500 **520**

4. Assess & Reteach

Lesson Quiz

Name each figure.

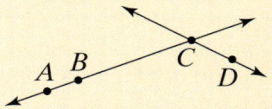

1. ray $\overrightarrow{AB}$, $\overrightarrow{BA}$, $\overrightarrow{AC}$, $\overrightarrow{CA}$, $\overrightarrow{BC}$, $\overrightarrow{CB}$, $\overrightarrow{CD}$, or $\overrightarrow{DC}$

2. line **Sample:** $\overleftrightarrow{AB}$, $\overleftrightarrow{AC}$, $\overleftrightarrow{BC}$, $\overleftrightarrow{CD}$

True or false.

3. Intersecting lines may lie in different planes. **false**

4. Parallel lines have exactly one point in common. **false**

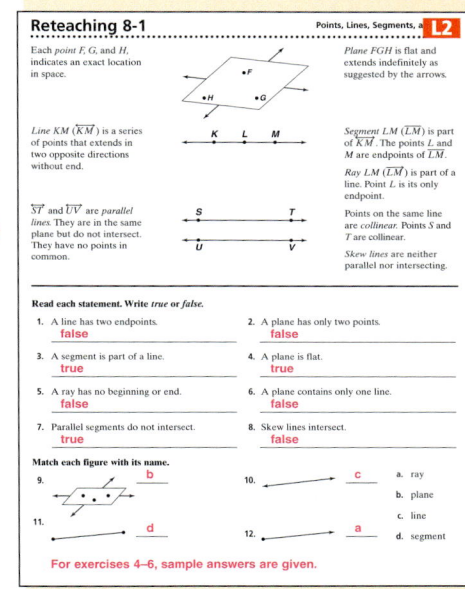

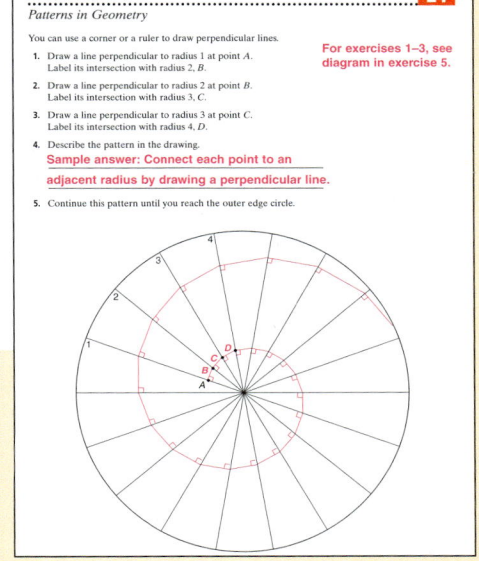

Alternative Assessment

Each student in a pair takes a turn naming a figure discussed in the lesson while the partner draws and labels the figure.

Test Prep

Resources
For additional practice with a variety of test item formats:
• Test-Taking Strategies, p. 407
• Test Prep, p. 411
• Test-Taking Strategies with Transparencies

365

Using Angle Benchmarks

Guided Instruction

Before beginning the Activity, explain to students that, just as they can use benchmarks on a ruler to estimate length, they can use benchmarks for angles. Ask questions such as:

- *How could you describe the size of wedge A?* **about half the size of wedge B, about one quarter the size of wedge C**
- *If you know the measures of wedges B and C, how could you find the measure of the angle in step 2a?* **Estimate; The angle is between wedges B and C so its measure must be between the measures of B and C.**

Exercises

Have students work independently on the Exercises. When they have finished, discuss the answers as a class and let students adjust their answers.

Alternative Method

Students may prefer to use "angles" that they can handle. Make the angles shown in the Activity and the Exercises by taping two straws together.

Resources

- Activity Lab 8-2: Critical Thinking
- scissors
- straws
- tape

Using Angle Benchmarks

You can think of an angle as a wedge or section of a circle. You can use wedges of different sizes to describe the size of angles.

ACTIVITY

1. Trace each of the wedges below. Then cut out each wedge.

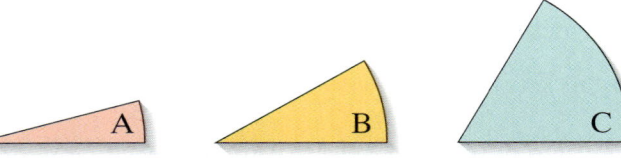

2. Use wedges A, B, and C as benchmarks to describe angles.

   a.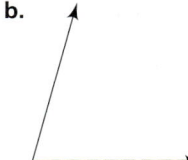

   The size of this angle is between the size of wedges B and C.

   b.

   This angle is the same size as wedge C and wedge A combined.

Exercises

1. Compare each angle to wedges A, B, and C.

   a.
   between wedge A and B

   b.
   smaller than wedge A

   c.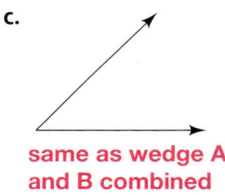
   same as wedge A and B combined

2. The measure of wedge A is 15°. Wedge B measures 30°, and wedge C measures 60°. Use the measures of angles A, B, and C to estimate the measures of the angles in Exercise 1.
   Answers may vary. Samples are given. 20°; 10°; 45°

3. **Reasoning** Use one corner of a rectangle to serve as a benchmark angle for 90°. Estimate the size of the angle.
   about 150°

8-2 Angles

✓ Check Skills You'll Need

1. **Vocabulary Review**
How is a *ray* different from a *line*?
1–3. See below.
Use the diagram.

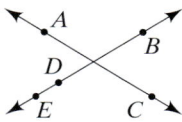

2. Name a line, a segment, and a ray.

3. Name $\overleftrightarrow{DE}$ in two other ways.

GO for Help
Lesson 8-1

Check Skills You'll Need

1. A line continues in opposite directions without end. A ray has one endpoint and continues in one direction without end.

2. Answers may vary. Samples are given.
$\overleftrightarrow{AC}$, $\overline{BE}$, $\overrightarrow{DB}$

3. Answers may vary. Sample: $\overleftrightarrow{EB}$, $\overleftrightarrow{BD}$

What You'll Learn

To measure and classify angles

🔊 **New Vocabulary** angle, vertex, degrees, acute angle, right angle, obtuse angle, straight angle, perpendicular lines

Why Learn This?

You can describe a hockey stick using geometry vocabulary. An **angle** is a figure formed by two rays with a common endpoint. The angle at the right can be called $\angle Y$, $\angle XYZ$, or $\angle ZYX$. The **vertex** is the point of intersection of two sides of an angle or figure.

You measure angles in units called **degrees.** Use the symbol (°) for degrees. Use a *protractor* to measure angles.

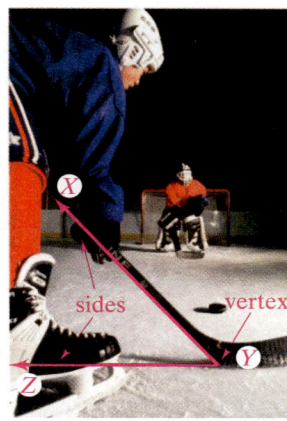
sides   vertex

EXAMPLE **Application: Ice Hockey**

① Measure the angle between the hockey stick and the ground.

③ Read the scale where it intersects the second side of the angle.

② Make sure that one side of the angle passes through zero on the scale. Start measuring from zero.

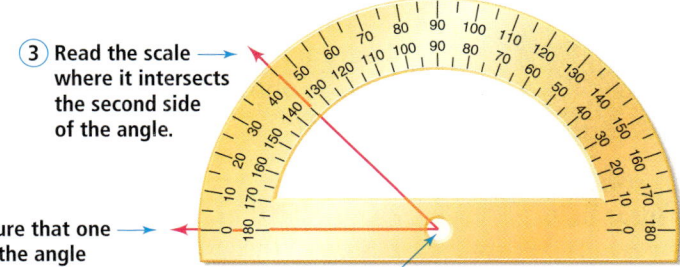

① Place the point of the protractor on the vertex of the angle.

The angle measure is 45°.

✓ Quick Check

1. Use a protractor to measure the angle at the left. **125°**

Objective
To measure and classify angles

Examples
1 Application: Ice Hockey
2 Classifying Angles
3 Application: Construction

Math Understandings: p. 360C

Professional Development

Math Background

An *angle* has two sides and a vertex. The sides are rays that share a common endpoint, called the *vertex*. The angle formed by two rays can be named in a variety of ways. For example, the angle formed by $\overrightarrow{XY}$ and $\overrightarrow{XZ}$ can be named $\angle YXZ$, $\angle ZXY$, or $\angle X$ for short. Notice that X must be the middle letter in both three-letter names because it is the vertex.

More Math Background: p. 360C

Lesson Planning and Resources

See p. 360E for a list of the resources that support this lesson.

PowerPoint

Bell Ringer Practice

✓ **Check Skills You'll Need**
Use student page, transparency, or PowerPoint. For intervention, direct students to:
Points, Lines, Segments, and Rays
Lesson 8-1
Extra Skills and Word Problems Practice, Ch. 8

Differentiated Instruction Solutions for All Learners

Special Needs L1
Some students may have difficulty measuring angles with a protractor. If so, have students work in pairs. One partner can hold the protractor, while another reads the angle measure.

learning style: tactile

Below Level L2
Have students use magazines and newspapers to find pictures that illustrate acute, obtuse, right, and straight angles.

learning style: visual

Activity Lab

Use before the lesson.
Student Edition Activity Lab, Hands On 8-2a, Using Angle Benchmarks, p. 366

All in One Teaching Resources
Activity Lab 8-2: Critical Thinking

Guided Instruction

Error Prevention!

For Quick Check 1, some students may read the wrong scale because the angle measure is greater than 90°. Have students trace the angle on their own paper. Students must extend each ray to intersect the protractor's scale. Emphasize that extending the sides of an angle does not change the angle's measure. Then help students use the correct scale by counting ten degree increments, starting at 0° and passing through 90°.

Example 3

Have students find examples of each type of angle in the classroom. **Sample: right angle: corners of the chalk board; straight angle: lines on the floor; acute: tip of a pencil; obtuse: a partially open door**

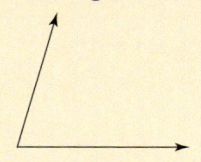
Additional Examples

❶ Use a protractor to measure the angle. **75°**

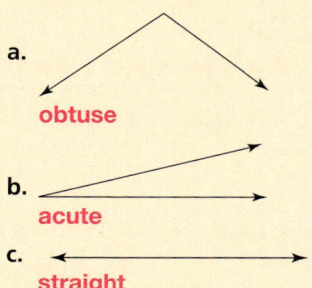

❷ Classify each angle as *acute, right, obtuse,* or *straight.*

a.

obtuse

b.

acute

c.

straight

You can classify angles by their measures.

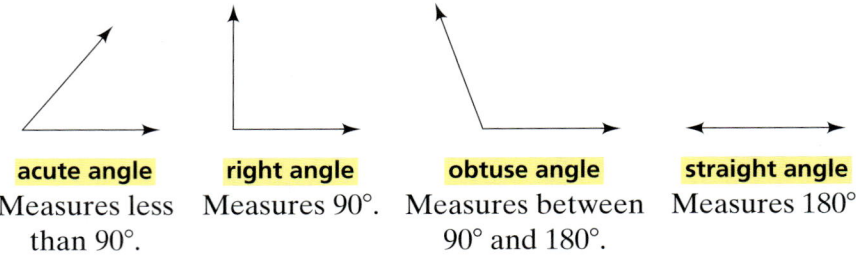

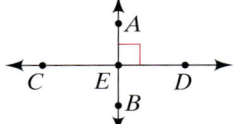

acute angle	**right angle**	**obtuse angle**	**straight angle**
Measures less than 90°.	Measures 90°.	Measures between 90° and 180°.	Measures 180°.

Test Prep Tip
The right angle symbol, ⌐, indicates that the angle measures 90°.

Lines that intersect to form right angles are called **perpendicular lines.** The symbol ⌐ in the diagram shows that $\angle AED$ is a right angle and that $\overleftrightarrow{AB}$ is perpendicular to $\overleftrightarrow{CD}$.

EXAMPLE **Classifying Angles**

② Classify each angle as *acute, right, obtuse,* or *straight.*

a.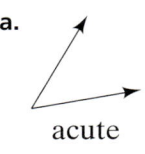

acute

b.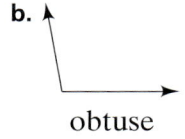

obtuse

c.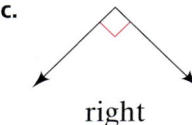

right

✓ Quick Check

2. Estimate the measure of the angle. Classify the angle as *acute, right, obtuse,* or *straight.* **about 60°; acute**

EXAMPLE **Application: Construction**

③ **Multiple Choice** The deck shown in the diagram has different types of angles. Which angle is obtuse?

Ⓐ $\angle M$ Ⓒ $\angle O$
Ⓑ $\angle N$ Ⓓ $\angle P$

$\angle O$ and $\angle P$ are right angles. $\angle N$ is less than 90°. $\angle M$ is obtuse, since it is between 90° and 180°.

The correct answer is choice A.

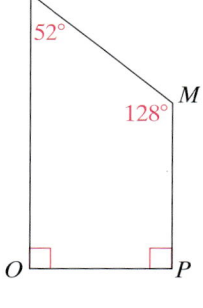

✓ Quick Check

3. Classify the angles in Example 3 as *acute, right, obtuse,* or *straight.*
   a. $\angle N$ **acute**   b. $\angle O$ **right**   c. $\angle P$ **right**

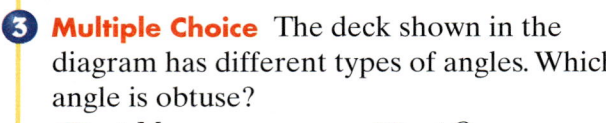
GO Online
Video Tutor Help
Visit: PHSchool.com
Web Code: aqe-0775

Advanced Learners **L4**
What angle measure do two right angles make? **180°**
What angle measure is half of a right angle? **45°**
What angle measure is a right angle plus a straight angle? **270°**

learning style: visual

English Language Learners **ELL**
Have students write some of the key terms, such as *vertex* or *degrees,* used in this lesson on note or index cards. Next to each term or word, have them draw a symbol or picture.

learning style: visual

More Than One Way

Use a protractor to measure the angle.

Elena's Method

I place the center point of the protractor on the vertex of the angle. Then I turn the protractor so that 0° lines up with the inner scale for one side of the angle. The second side crosses the inner scale at 50°.

The angle measures 50°.

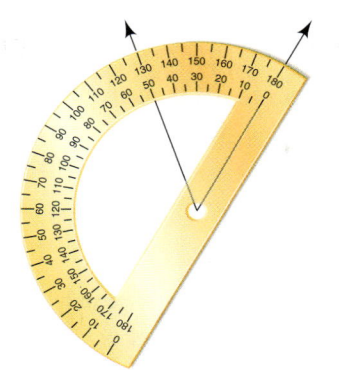

Zack's Method

I place the center point of the protractor on the vertex of the angle. I read the outer scale where each side intersects the protractor. Then I find the difference between the two scale readings.

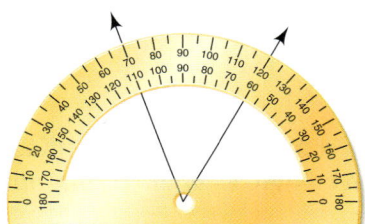

Since 120 − 70 = 50, the angle measures 50°.

Choose a Method

Measure the angle. Describe the method you chose.

70°; check students' work.

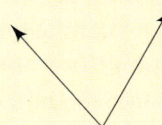

Additional Examples

③ Which angle is acute? ∠E

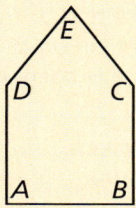

All in One Teaching Resources
- Daily Notetaking Guide 8-2 **L3**
- Adapted Notetaking 8-2 **L1**

Closure

- *How do you measure an angle with a protractor?* **Sample: Place the point of the protractor on the vertex. Make sure one side of the angle passes through 0°. Read the intersection of the second side of the angle and the scale.**
- *What are acute, obtuse, right, and straight angles?* **Sample: Acute angles are between 0° and 90°; obtuse angles are between 90° and 180°; right angles are equal to 90°; and straight angles are equal to 180° or a straight line.**

3. Practice

Assignment Guide

Check Your Understanding
Go over Exercises 1–5 in class before assigning the Homework Exercises.

Homework Exercises
A Practice by Example   6–15
B Apply Your Skills   16–28
C Challenge   29
Test Prep and
    Mixed Review   30–32

Homework Quick Check
To check students' understanding of key skills and concepts, go over Exercises 7, 14, 25, 26, and 27.

Differentiated Instruction Resources

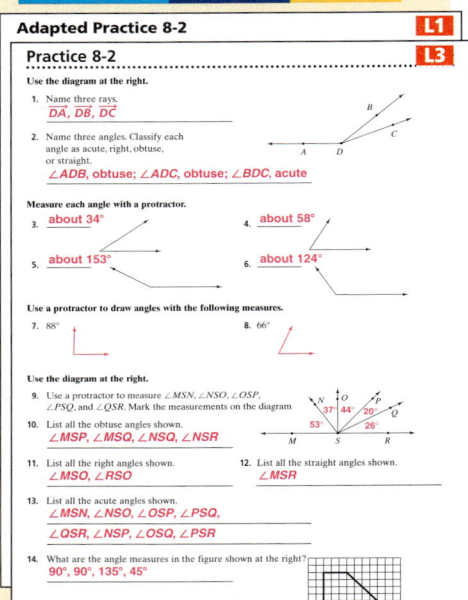

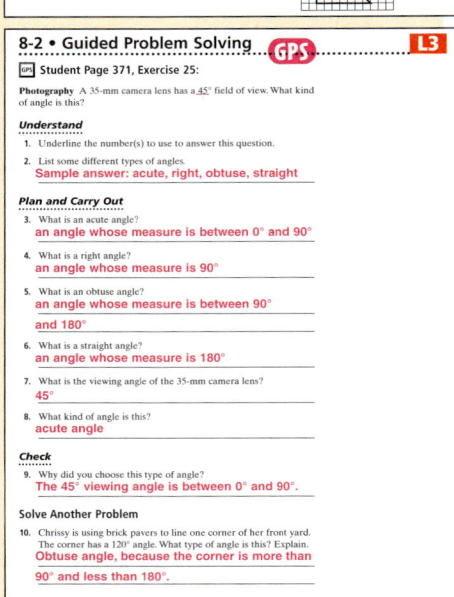

Check Your Understanding

1. A right angle measures 90°; an obtuse angle measures between 90° and 180°.

2. No; the measure of an angle is not related to the length of the sides that form the angle.

1. **Vocabulary** How are a right angle and an obtuse angle different?

2. **Reasoning** Does increasing the lengths of the sides of an angle change the measurement of the angle? Explain.

Without using your protractor, sketch angles with the following measures. Then use your protractor to see how close you are.

3. 30°   4. 60°   5. 120°
3–5. See margin.

Homework Exercises

For more exercises, see Extra Skills and Word Problems.

GO for Help

For Exercises	See Examples
6–8	1
9–11	2
12–15	3

A Measurement Use a protractor to measure each angle.

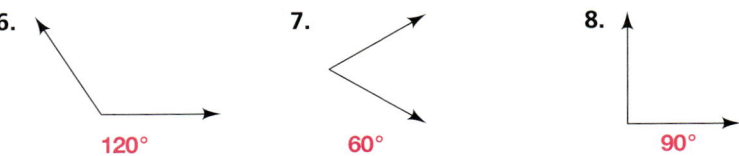

6.   120°   7.   60°   8.   90°

Classify each angle as *acute*, *right*, *obtuse*, or *straight*.

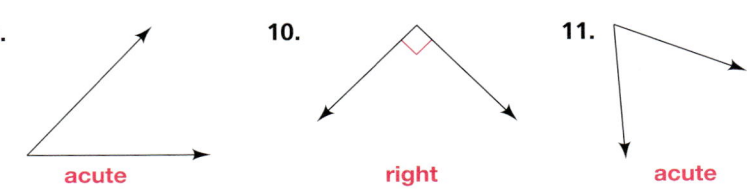

9.   acute   10.   right   11.   acute

You build a ramp as shown in the diagram. Classify each angle as *acute*, *right*, *obtuse*, or *straight*.

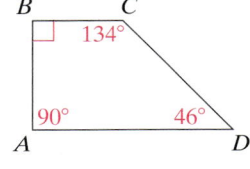

12. $\angle A$ right   13. $\angle C$ obtuse

14. $\angle B$ right   15. $\angle D$ acute

B GPS 16. **Guided Problem Solving** You are facing north. You turn 270° counterclockwise. Which direction are you now facing? **east**
- **Make a Plan** Make a sketch showing the four basic compass directions. Recall that 270 = 90 × 3. Then act out the problem by turning 90° to the left three times.
- **Carry Out the Plan** Which direction will you face after each counterclockwise turn?

3–5. **Check students' sketches. Samples are given.**

3.

4.

5.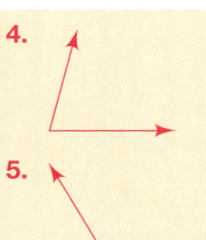

GO Online
Homework Video Tutor
Visit: PHSchool.com
Web Code: aqe-0802

21. 20°
22. 70°
23. 160°
24. 120°

Careers Photographers use different lenses to achieve various effects.

Use a protractor to draw angles with the following measures.

17. 30°   **18.** 135°   **19.** 90°   **20.** 75°
17–20. See margin.

Use the figure for Exercises 21–24.
Estimate the measure of each angle.
Then measure each angle.

21. ∠AGB   **22.** ∠BGD

23. ∠BGF   **24.** ∠EGB
21–24. See left.

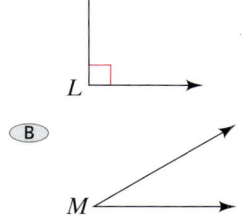

25. **Photography** A 35-mm camera lens has a 45° field of view.
GPS What kind of angle is this? acute

26. **Open-Ended** Give three examples of perpendicular lines in your classroom. Check students' work.

27. **Writing in Math** Explain how to fold a piece of paper so that the fold lines form four right angles. See margin.

28. A surveyor draws two boundary lines. One line points east. Another line points northeast. Sketch the 45° angle. See margin.

C **29.** **Challenge** Find the measure of the angle formed by the hour hand and the minute hand of a clock at 12:30 A.M. 165°

Test Prep and Mixed Review   **Practice**

Multiple Choice

30. Which angle is obtuse? **C**

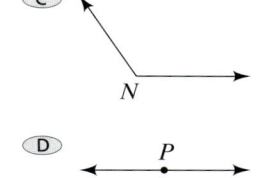

31. A bus has 25 riders at the start of its route. At each stop, 5 riders get off the bus and 1 rider gets on. How many stops will the bus make before only one rider is left on the bus? **H**
    F 4   **H** 6
    G 5   **J** 10

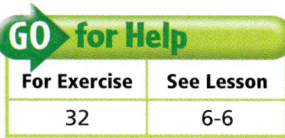

GO for Help

For Exercise	See Lesson
32	6-6

32. Choose an appropriate unit of length to measure a soccer field. Explain your choice. Yards or meters; explanations may vary.

Online lesson quiz, PHSchool.com, Web Code: aqa-0802   8-2 Angles   **371**

Alternative Assessment

Each student in a pair draws three or four angles. Partners exchange papers and measure each other's angles. Partners then challenge each other to draw angles of given measures.

17–20. See back of book.
27–28. See back of book.

Test Prep

Resources
For additional practice with a variety of test item formats:
• Test-Taking Strategies, p. 407
• Test Prep, p. 411
• Test-Taking Strategies with Transparencies

---

4. Assess & Reteach

Lesson Quiz

Classify each angle as *acute, right, obtuse,* or *straight.*

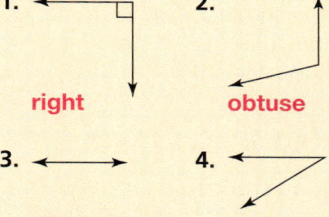

1. right
2. obtuse
3. straight
4. acute

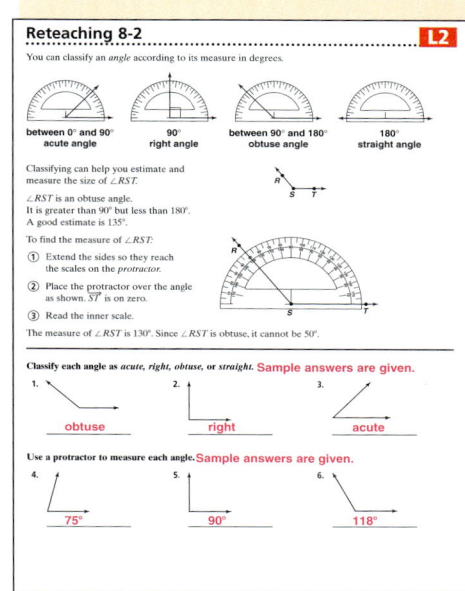

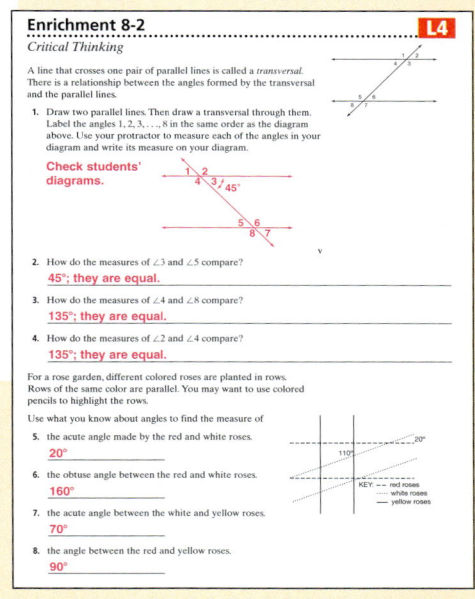

371

Extension

Basic Constructions

Guided Instruction

Error Prevention!

Basic Constructions

A *perpendicular bisector* is a line that is perpendicular to a segment and passes through that segment's *midpoint*. You can use a compass and straightedge to construct a perpendicular bisector.

EXAMPLE

1 Use a compass and a straightedge to construct the perpendicular bisector of $\overline{AB}$.

Step 1 Open the compass to more than half the length of $\overline{AB}$. Put the tip of the compass point at A. Draw a part of a circle, or *arc*, that intersects $\overline{AB}$.

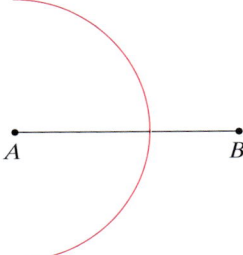

Step 2 Keep the compass open to the same width. Put the tip of the compass at B. Draw another arc that intersects $\overline{AB}$. Label the points of intersection of the two arcs C and D.

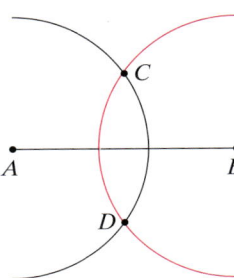

Step 3 Draw $\overleftrightarrow{CD}$. Label the intersection of $\overleftrightarrow{CD}$ and $\overline{AB}$ point M.

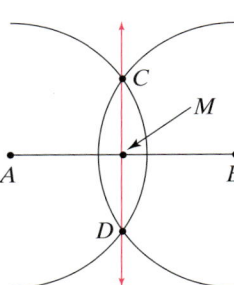

$\overleftrightarrow{CD}$ intersects $\overline{AB}$ at its midpoint M.

● $\overleftrightarrow{CD}$ is the perpendicular bisector of $\overline{AB}$.

An *angle bisector* is a ray that divides an angle into two angles with equal measures.

EXAMPLE

2 Use a compass and a straightedge to construct the angle bisector of ∠E.

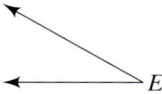

Step 1 Put the tip of the compass at *E*. Draw an arc that intersects both sides of ∠*E*. Label the points of intersection *F* and *G*.

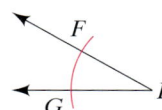

Step 2 Place the tip of the compass at *F*. Draw a large arc.

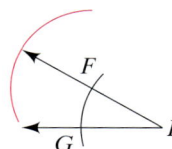

Step 3 Keep the compass open to the same width and place the tip at *G*. Draw another large arc. Label the point of intersection of the two large arcs *H*.

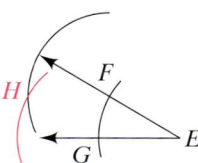

Step 4 Draw $\overrightarrow{EH}$.

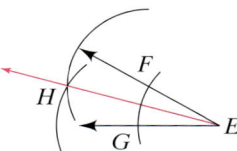

$\overrightarrow{EH}$ divides ∠*FEG* into two angles with equal measures, ∠*FEH* and ∠*HEG*.

● $\overrightarrow{EH}$ is the angle bisector of ∠*FEG*.

Exercises

1. Draw $\overline{JK}$ two inches long. Then construct its perpendicular bisector. **1–2. See margin.**

2. Draw an obtuse angle and construct its bisector.

3. **Writing in Math** Explain how you can use perpendicular bisectors and angle bisectors to construct a 45° angle.

3. Four right angles are formed at the intersection of a segment and its perpendicular bisector. The bisector of a 90° angle divides it into two 45° angles.

Extension   Basic Constructions   **373**

1–2. Check students' work.   **1.**

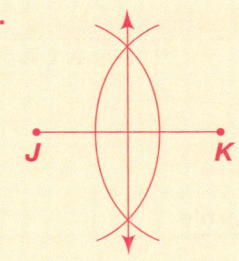

J   *K*

2.

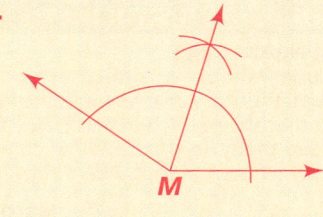

M

Objective
To use the relationship between special pairs of angles

Examples
1 Finding the Complement of an Angle
2 Using Supplementary Angles
3 Vertical Angles

Math Understandings: p. 360C

Math Background

Two angles are *complementary angles* if their sum is 90°. Two angles are *supplementary angles* if their sum is 180°. When two lines intersect, four angles are formed giving two pairs of *vertical angles*. Vertical angles are opposite from one another and congruent.

More Math Background: p. 360C

Lesson Planning and Resources

See p. 360E for a list of the resources that support this lesson.

Bell Ringer Practice

☑ **Check Skills You'll Need**
Use student page, transparency, or PowerPoint. For intervention, direct students to:
Angles
Lesson 8-2
Extra Skills and Word Problems Practice, Ch. 8

374

☑ Check Skills You'll Need

1. **Vocabulary Review** Give an example of an object with an *acute angle* in your classroom.
1–5. See below.
Use a protractor to draw each angle.

2. 30°   3. 60°

4. 45°   5. 120°

GO for Help
Lesson 8-2

Check Skills You'll Need

1. Check students' work.

2–5. See back of book.

Vocabulary Tip

The *complement* of an angle is the angle complementary to it.

What You'll Learn

To use the relationship between special pairs of angles

🔊 **New Vocabulary** complementary angles, supplementary angles, vertical angles, congruent angles

Why Learn This?

Landscapers use special angle pairs to cut stones and bricks for tiles and pathways.

If the sum of the measures of two angles is 90°, the angles are **complementary angles.** If the sum of the measures of two angles is 180°, the angles are **supplementary angles.**

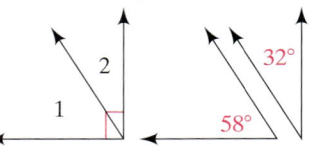
Complementary angles

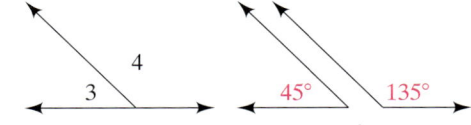
Supplementary angles

Two angles, the sum of whose measures is 90°

Two angles, the sum of whose measures is 180°

EXAMPLE   Finding the Complement of an Angle

1 (**Algebra**) Find the value of x at the right.

Let x = the measure of the angle's complement.

$x + 60° = 90°$ ← The angles are complementary.

$x + 60° - 60° = 90° - 60°$ ← Subtract 60° from each side.

$x = 30°$ ← Simplify.

☑ Quick Check

1. Find the value of x.

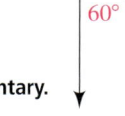

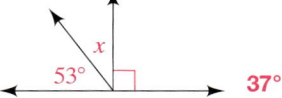

Differentiated **Instruction** **Solutions for All Learners**

Special Needs **L1**
Have students show with their arms or hands what two supplementary angles look like when they are placed adjacent to each other. (They form a straight line.) Have them do the same for complementary angles, which would look like a right angle, or a corner.

learning style: tactile

Below Level **L2**
What is the angle measure of a right angle? **90°** *What is the angle measure of a straight angle?* **180°** Then explain that complementary angles form a right angle and supplementary angles form a straight angle.

learning style: verbal

EXAMPLE Using Supplementary Angles

2 (Algebra) Find the value of x at the left.

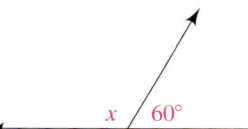

$$x + 60° = 180° \quad \leftarrow \text{The angles are supplementary.}$$
$$x + 60° - 60° = 180° - 60° \quad \leftarrow \text{Subtract 60° from each side.}$$
$$x = 120° \quad \leftarrow \text{Simplify.}$$

The value of x is 120°.

✔ Quick Check

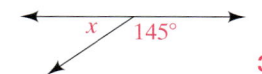

2. Find the value of x.   **35°**

Two intersecting lines form **vertical angles**. Angles 1 and 2 are vertical angles. Angles 3 and 4 are also vertical angles. Vertical angles have equal measures. Angles with equal measures are **congruent angles.**

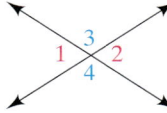

EXAMPLE Vertical Angles

3 Two boards intersect at the corner of the barn door shown below. The measure of $\angle 2$ is 38°. Find the measures of $\angle 1$ and $\angle 4$.

$$m\angle 1 + 38° = 180° \quad \leftarrow \text{∠1 and ∠2 are supplementary.}$$
$$m\angle 1 + 38° - 38° = 180° - 38° \quad \leftarrow \text{Subtract 38° from each side.}$$
$$m\angle 1 = 142° \quad \leftarrow \text{Simplify.}$$

$$m\angle 4 = 38° \quad \leftarrow \text{∠2 and ∠4 are vertical angles.}$$

The measure of $\angle 1$ is 142°. The measure of $\angle 4$ is 38°.

✔ Quick Check

3. The measure of $\angle 5$ in the photo above is 142°. Find the measures of $\angle 6$ and $\angle 7$. **38°; 142°**

Activity Lab
Use before the lesson.

All in One Teaching Resources
Activity Lab 8-3: Special Pairs of Angles

Guided Instruction

Example 3
Elicit from students that the two horizontal lines are parallel. Ask:
- *How many angles are acute?* **4** *obtuse?* **4**
- *How many pairs of angles are vertical?* **4**

PowerPoint

Additional Examples

1 Find the complement and supplement of a 66° angle.
complement: 24°; supplement: 114°

2 Find the value of x.
a. **55°**   b. **50°**

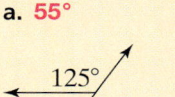
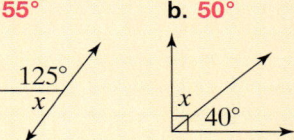

3 Identify the following.

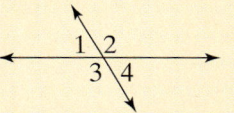

a. a pair of obtuse vertical angles **∠2 and ∠3**

b. two supplementary angles **∠1 and ∠2, ∠1 and ∠3, ∠2 and ∠4, ∠3 and ∠4**

All in One Teaching Resources
- Daily Notetaking Guide 8-3 **L3**
- Adapted Notetaking 8-3 **L1**

Closure
- *What are vertical angles?* **Sample: Vertical angles are opposite each other and congruent. Two pairs are formed when two lines intersect.**

Advanced Learners L4
If two lines are cut by a transversal, what is the sum of the measures of the interior angles? **360°** *What is the sum of the measures of the exterior angles?* **360°**

learning style: visual

English Language Learners ELL
Have students explain the difference between *vertical* angles, and a line that is drawn in a *vertical*, or up and down, orientation. Explain the difference between a compliment in every day language, and a complement in mathematics, both in spelling and meaning.

learning style: verbal

Assignment Guide

Check Your Understanding
Go over Exercises 1–5 in class before assigning the Homework Exercises.

Homework Exercises

A Practice by Example   6–18
B Apply Your Skills   19–25
C Challenge   26
Test Prep and
   Mixed Review   27–31

Homework Quick Check
To check students' understanding of key skills and concepts, go over Exercises 8, 12, 22, 24, and 25.

Differentiated Instruction Resources

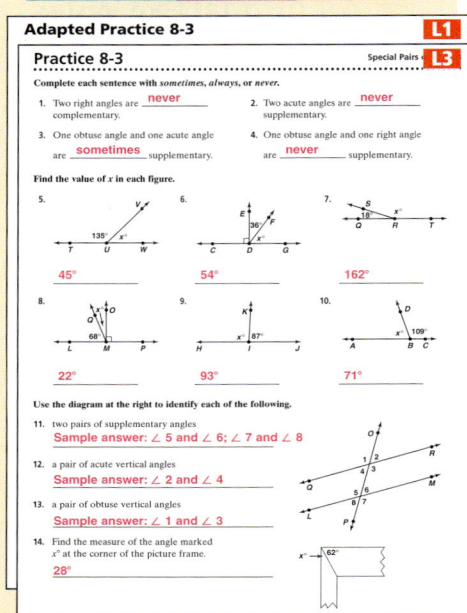

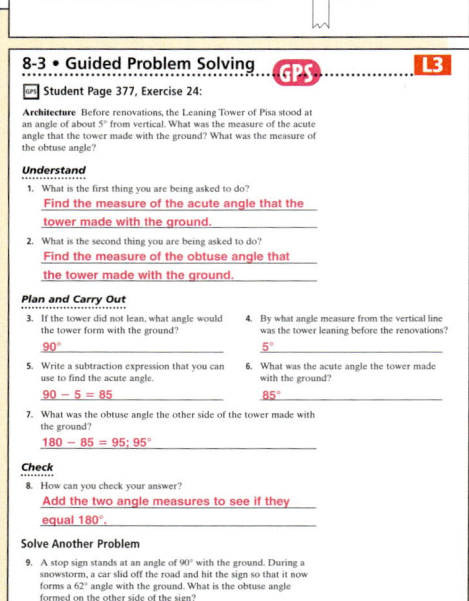

✓ Check Your Understanding

1. Complementary angles have a sum of 90°; supplementary angles add to 180°.

2. Draw a straight line and a ray with its endpoint on the line. The two angles created are supplementary.

1. **Vocabulary** Two angles are complementary. Explain why they are not supplementary angles.

2. **Writing in Math** Describe how to draw a pair of supplementary angles without using a protractor.

Match each pair of angle measurements with the correct term.

3. 47° and 47° **C**

4. 9° and 81° **A**

5. 89° and 91° **B**

A. complementary angles
B. supplementary angles
C. congruent angles

Homework Exercises

For more exercises, see Extra Skills and Word Problems.

GO for Help

For Exercises	See Examples
6–10	1
11–17	2
18	3

A **Find the complement of each angle measure.**

6. 12° **78°**   7. 45° **45°**   8. 33° **57°**   9. 68° **22°**   10. 4° **86°**

Find the supplement of each angle measure.

11. 90° **90°**   12. 176° **4°**   13. 110° **70°**   14. 144° **36°**

Find the value of x in each figure.

15. **62°**

16.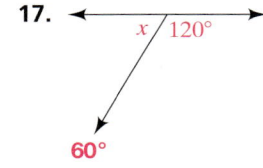
64°

17. x / 120°
60°

18. $m\angle2 = 40°$
$m\angle3 = 140°$
$m\angle4 = 140°$

18. The measure of ∠1 at the left is 40°. What are the measures of ∠2, ∠3, and ∠4? Explain your reasoning. **See above left.**

B GPS 19. **Guided Problem Solving** An angle formed at the intersection at the right has a measure of 46°. Find the measures of ∠1, ∠2, ∠3, and ∠4. **See left.**
• Which angles are vertical angles?
• How can you use what you know about special angle pairs to find the measure of each angle?

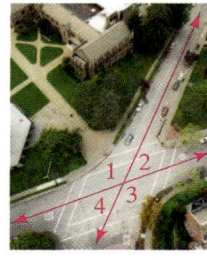

19. $m\angle1 = 134°$
$m\angle2 = 46°$
$m\angle3 = 134°$
$m\angle4 = 46°$

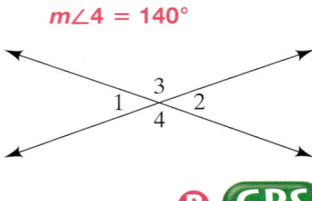

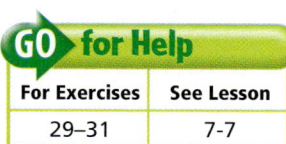

25. An obtuse angle does not have a complement.

Complete each sentence with *sometimes*, *always*, or *never*.

20. Two acute angles are __?__ complementary. **sometimes**

21. Two obtuse angles are __?__ supplementary. **never**

(Algebra) **Find the value of *x* in each figure.**

22. 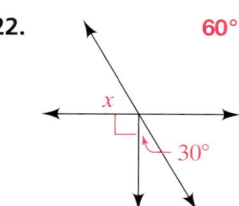 60°
  30°

23. 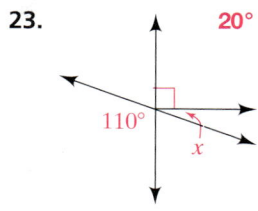 20°
  110°

24. **Architecture** Before renovations, the Leaning Tower of Pisa
GPS stood at an angle of about 5° from vertical. What was the measure of the acute angle that the tower made with the ground? What was the measure of the obtuse angle? **85°; 95°**

25. **Reasoning** An angle measures 115°. Explain why you cannot find both a complement and a supplement of the angle.
See above left.

26. **Challenge** The circle is cut into unequal
C sections. One section forms an angle whose measure is 65°. Find the measures of the angles formed by the other two sections.
115° and 180°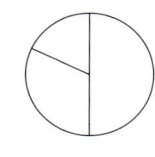

Test Prep and Mixed Review **Practice**

Multiple Choice

27. Find the measure of ∠QTR to the nearest degree. **C**

  Ⓐ 180°
  Ⓑ 110°
  Ⓒ 70°
  Ⓓ 40°

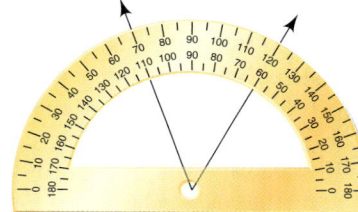

28. Alejandra types about 65 words per minute. Which proportion can she use to find the number of words that she can type in 30 minutes? **F**

  Ⓕ $\frac{65}{1} = \frac{w}{30}$ Ⓖ $\frac{1}{65} = \frac{w}{30}$ Ⓗ $\frac{65}{60} = \frac{w}{30}$ Ⓙ $\frac{60}{65} = \frac{w}{30}$

GO for Help

For Exercises	See Lesson
29–31	7-7

Find each answer.

29. 5% of 100 **5**   30. 30% of 50 **15**   31. 75% of 42 **31.5**

---

4. Assess & Reteach

Lesson Quiz

1. Find the complement and supplement of 32°. **58°; 148°**

2. Use the diagram to identify the vertical angles.
∠1 and ∠4, ∠2 and ∠3

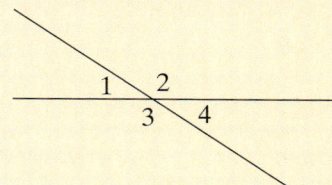

Reteaching 8-3 Special Pairs o **L2**

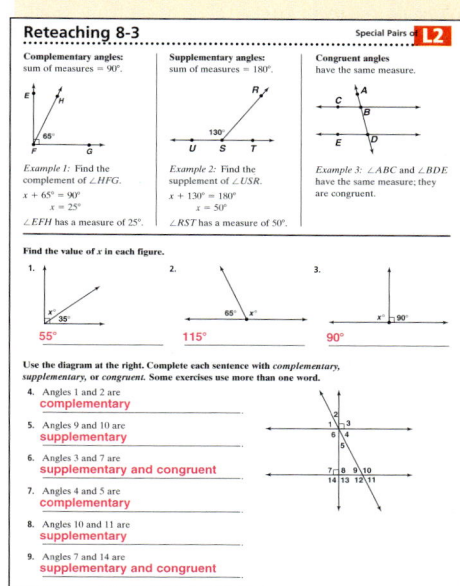

Enrichment 8-3 Special Pairs o **L4**

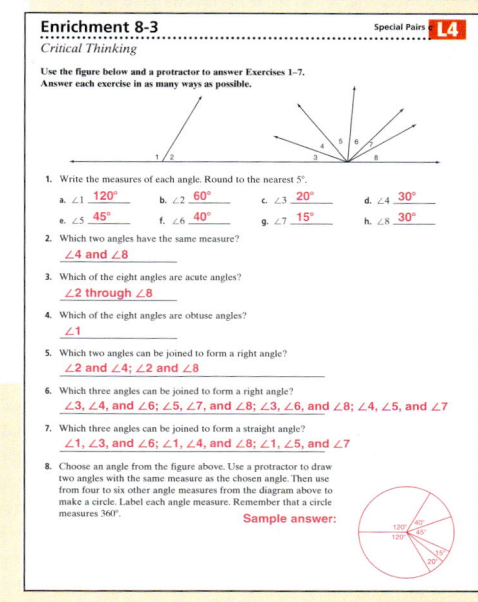

Alternative Assessment

Using a protractor, each student in a pair draws and labels angles. Have one angle measure less than 90° and one angle measure more than 90°. Partners exchange papers and identify the value of the angles' complement and supplement, respectively.

Test Prep

Resources
For additional practice with a variety of test item formats:
• Test-Taking Strategies, p. 407
• Test Prep, p. 411
• Test-Taking Strategies with Transparencies

377

Exploring Parallel Lines

Exploring Parallel Lines

Students learn about the related angles formed when a transversal crosses two parallel lines. This will extend what they learned about complementary and supplementary angles in Lesson 8-3.

Exploring Parallel Lines

A line that intersects two or more lines is a **transversal.** When a transversal crosses two parallel lines, the eight angles formed are related.

ACTIVITY

1. On a piece of notebook paper, draw two lines using the lines of the paper. What kind of lines did you draw? **parallel**

2. Draw a slanted line, or transversal, through the lines. Label the angles formed as shown in the diagram below. **Check students' work.**

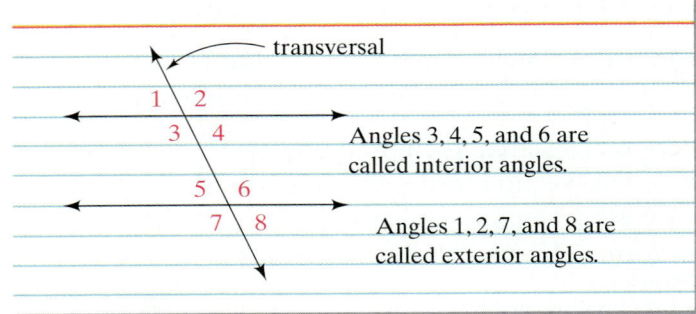

transversal

Angles 3, 4, 5, and 6 are called interior angles.

Angles 1, 2, 7, and 8 are called exterior angles.

4. interior angles with the same measure: ∠3 and ∠6, and ∠4 and ∠5; exterior angles with the same measure: ∠1 and ∠8 and ∠2 and ∠7.

3. Use your protractor to measure each of the eight angles. Record your measurements. **Check students' work.**

4. Find two pairs of interior angles that have the same measure. Next, find two pairs of exterior angles that have the same measure. **See above right.**

5. Find two interior angles that have the same measure as ∠8. Then find two pairs of interior angles that are supplementary. **∠5, ∠4; Answers may vary. Sample: ∠3 and ∠4, ∠5 and ∠6**

6. Obtain a picture that shows parallel lines intersected by a transversal. Following the guitar example at the right, highlight the lines. Then label angles that have the same measure with the same number.
6–7. Check students' work.

7. **Reasoning** Draw two parallel lines. Draw two parallel transversals that form 40° angles with your parallel lines. Label all of the congruent angles in your drawing.

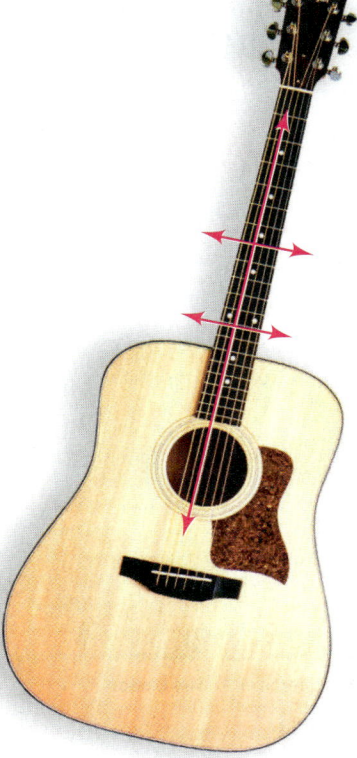

Guided Instruction

Before beginning the Activity, ask volunteers to define *complementary angle* and *supplementary angle*. Draw two parallel lines and a transversal on the board or on a transparency. Ask questions such as:

• *How do you know the two lines crossed by the transversal are parallel?* **They do not intersect each other.**

• *How are any two angles that are next to or adjacent to each other related?* **Together they form a straight angle, so they are supplementary.**

Activity

Conduct the Activity as a class. Ask volunteers to answer the questions within the Activity.

Differentiated Instruction

English Language Learners **ELL**
To help students remember the meaning of the term *transversal,* remind them that the Latin prefix *trans* means "across." Ask for other words they know containing this prefix. **Sample: transportation, transfer, translate, transaction**

Resources

• protractor
• straightedge

1–10. Answers may vary. Samples are given.

Use the diagram to name the figures.

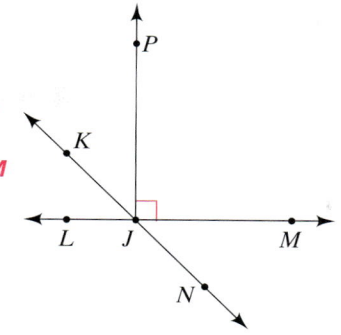

1. two lines $\overleftrightarrow{LM}$ and $\overleftrightarrow{KN}$

2. two rays $\overrightarrow{JP}$ and $\overrightarrow{NK}$

3. a right angle $\angle PJM$

4. an acute angle $\angle PJK$

5. an obtuse angle $\angle PJN$

6. a straight angle $\angle LJM$

7. a pair of vertical angles $\angle KJL$ and $\angle MJN$

8. an angle congruent to $\angle MJN$ $\angle KJL$

9. a pair of complementary angles $\angle PJK$ and $\angle KJL$

10. a pair of supplementary angles $\angle LJN$ and $\angle NJM$

8-4a Activity Lab

Technology

Investigating Angles in a Triangle

Geometry software is a fun way to investigate relationships among angles of a triangle.

ACTIVITY 1–4. Check students' work.

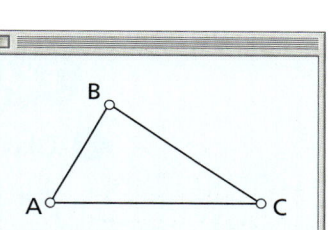

1. Draw a triangle. Label the vertices *A*, *B*, and *C*.

2. Measure the three interior angles.

3. Make a table to show the angles, their measures, and the sum of the measures.

4. Change the shape of the triangle by dragging *A*, *B*, or *C*. Make a new column in your table to find the sum of the angle measures.

5. Make a conjecture about the sum of the measures of the angles of a triangle. Compare your results with those of other students. **See margin.**

6. **Reasoning** Can a triangle have two obtuse angles? Justify your answer. **See margin.**

379

 Checkpoint Quiz

Use this Checkpoint Quiz to check students' understanding of the skills and concepts of Lessons 8-1 through 8-3.

Resources

- All-in-One Teaching Resources Checkpoint Quiz 1
- ExamView CD-ROM
- Success Tracker™ Online Intervention

Activity Lab

Investigating Angles in a Triangle

This Activity presents ways to explore relationships among the angles of triangles. By manipulating the vertices of a triangle, students learn more about the sum of the angle measures of triangles and other polygons.

Guided Instruction

Teaching Tip
As students manipulate the vertices of their triangles, ask:
- *When you drag a vertex, do only one or two angle measures change?* **Sample: All three angles change.**
- *If you drag a side of the triangle, would the angle measures change?* **Sample: Yes, all three angles would change.**

Resources

- Activity Lab 8-4: Classifying Triangles
- geometry software

5. The sum of the measures of the angles of a triangle is 180°.

6. No. Since one obtuse angle is larger than 90°, two obtuse angles together are larger than 180°.

8-4   Classifying Triangles

Objective
To classify triangles by their angles and their sides

Examples
1 Classifying Triangles by Angles
2 Finding an Angle's Measure
3 Classifying Triangles by Sides

Math Understandings: p. 360C

Math Background

A *triangle* is a closed figure with three sides that form three angles. The sum of the measures of the angles of a triangle is 180°. Triangles can be classified by their angle measures. Triangles can also be classified by the number of congruent sides.

More Math Background: p. 360C

Lesson Planning and Resources

See p. 360E for a list of the resources that support this lesson.

PowerPoint

Bell Ringer Practice

Check Skills You'll Need
Use student page, transparency, or PowerPoint. For intervention, direct students to:
Angles
Lesson 8-2
Extra Skills and Word Problems Practice, Ch. 8

380

✓ Check Skills You'll Need

1. Vocabulary Review
Can an *obtuse angle* have a *complementary angle*? Explain.
1–5. See below.
Classify each angle as *acute, right, obtuse,* or *straight*.

2. 45°   3. 105°

4. 90°   5. 180°

GO for Help
Lesson 8-2

Check Skills You'll Need

1. No; an obtuse angle itself is already larger than 90°.

2. acute

3. obtuse

4. right

5. straight

Classifying Triangles

What You'll Learn
To classify triangles by their angles and their sides

🔊 **New Vocabulary** triangle, acute triangle, obtuse triangle, right triangle, congruent segments, equilateral triangle, isosceles triangle, scalene triangle

Why Learn This?
Different types of shapes are frequently used in construction. For example, engineers use triangles to make bridges strong.

A **triangle** is a closed figure made of three line segments that meet only at their endpoints. The sum of the angle measures is 180°. You can classify triangles by their angle measures.

Classifying by Angles

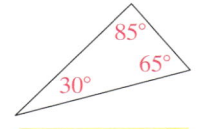

acute triangle
Three acute angles

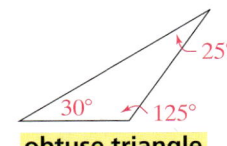

obtuse triangle
One obtuse angle

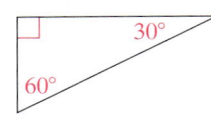

right triangle
One right angle

EXAMPLE   Classifying Triangles by Angles

1 Classify each triangle by its angles.

a.   b.   c.

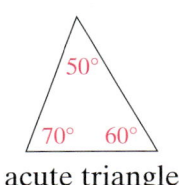

right triangle   obtuse triangle   acute triangle

✓ Quick Check

● 1. Classify the triangle by its angles.
right triangle

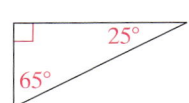

380   Chapter 8   Tools of Geometry

Differentiated Instruction Solutions for All Learners

Special Needs L1
Have students draw and cut out triangles on graph paper. Then have them sort the triangles by their angles, deciding first which ones have angles that are less than or more than 90 degrees.

learning style: tactile

Below Level L2
Have students create their own triangles using cardstock. Students trade their triangles with a partner. They measure and classify their partner's triangle by its angles and its sides.

learning style: tactile

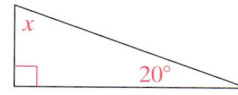

EXAMPLE **Finding an Angle's Measure**

2 **Gridded Response** Find the value of *x* in degrees.

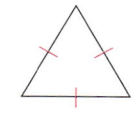

Solve an equation to find the value of *x*.

$$x + 20° + 90° = 180°$$ ← **The sum of the angle measures is 180°.**

$$x + 110° = 180°$$ ← **Add 20° and 90°.**

$$x + 110° - 110° = 180° - 110°$$ ← **Subtract 110° from each side.**

$$x = 70°$$ ← **Simplify.**

✓ Quick Check

2. The angles of a triangle measure 58°, 72°, and *x*. Find *x*. **50°**

You can use tick marks to show which sides of a figure are congruent.

Segments that are the same length are **congruent segments.** You can classify triangles by the number of congruent segments or sides.

Classifying by Sides

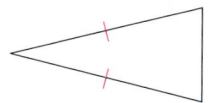

equilateral triangle
Three congruent sides

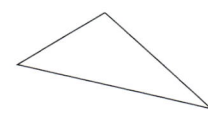

isosceles triangle
At least two
congruent sides

scalene triangle
No congruent sides

Video Tutor Help
Visit: PHSchool.com
Web Code: aqe-0775

EXAMPLE **Classifying Triangles by Sides**

3 Classify each triangle by its sides.

a.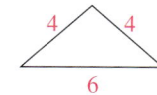
isosceles triangle

b.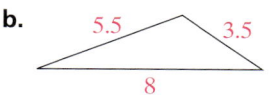
scalene triangle

c.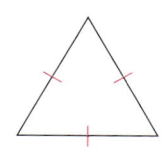
equilateral triangle

✓ Quick Check

3. Classify the triangle at the right by its sides. Explain your reasoning.
isosceles triangle; two sides are congruent

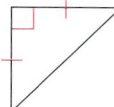

8-4 Classifying Triangles **381**

Advanced Learners **L4**
If you reduce the side lengths in a triangle proportionally, such as by $\frac{1}{3}$, how does its classification by its sides and its angles change? **No change occurs.**

learning style: visual

English Language Learners **ELL**
Have students draw a variety of triangles on graph or dot paper. Have them measure the angles, labeling each triangle using the angles for classification. Then have them measure each triangle side and label the triangles using the sides for classification.

learning style: visual

---

2. Teach

Activity Lab

Use before the lesson.
Student Edition Activity Lab Technology 8-4a, Investigating Angles in a Triangle, p. 379

All in One Teaching Resources
Activity Lab 8-4: Classifying Triangles

Guided Instruction

Example 1
Have students examine the three triangles above Example 1. Ask:
• *Why can't a triangle have more than one obtuse angle?* **Sample: because the sum of two obtuse angles is greater than 180°**
• *Why can't an acute triangle have only one or two acute angles?* **Sample: The third angle could be either 90° or obtuse and the triangle is named by its largest angle.**

PowerPoint
Additional Examples

1 Classify each triangle by its angles.

a.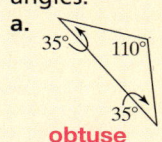
obtuse

b.
acute

2 Two angles of a triangle are 48° and 90°. What is the measure of the third? **42°**

3 Classify each triangle by its sides.

a.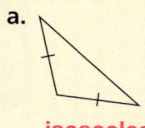
isosceles

b.
scalene

All in One Teaching Resources
• Daily Notetaking Guide 8-4 **L3**
• Adapted Notetaking 8-4 **L1**

Closure

• *How are triangles classified by their angles?* **Sample: Acute triangles have three acute angles. Obtuse triangles have one obtuse angle. Right triangles have one right angle.**

381

3. Practice

Assignment Guide

Check Your Understanding
Go over Exercises 1–4 in class before assigning the Homework Exercises.

Homework Exercises
A Practice by Example   5–16
B Apply Your Skills   17–26
C Challenge   27
Test Prep and
   Mixed Review   28–32

Homework Quick Check
To check students' understanding of key skills and concepts, go over Exercises 6, 12, 23, 24, and 25.

Differentiated Instruction **Resources**

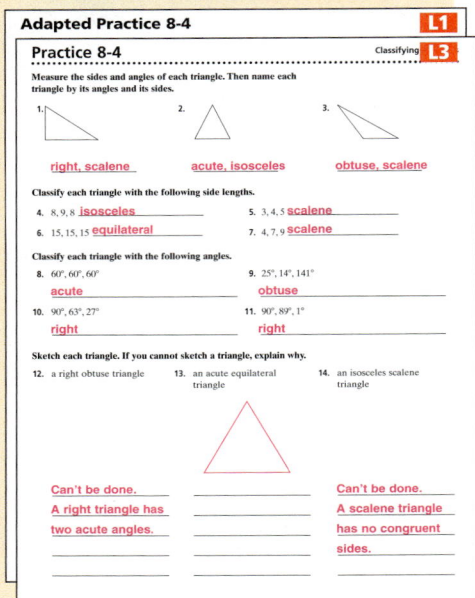

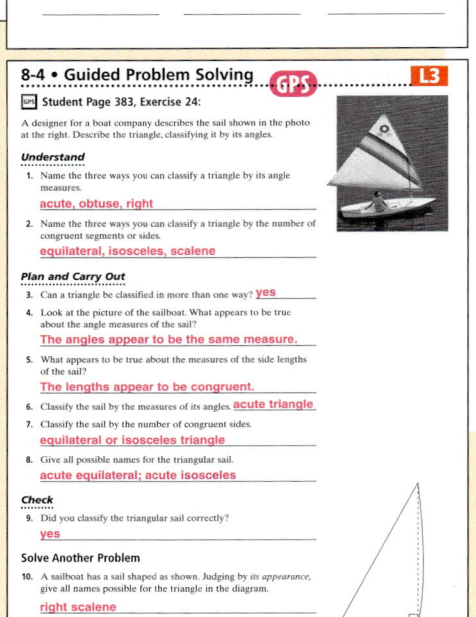

Check Your Understanding

Vocabulary Classify each triangle by its angles and sides.

1.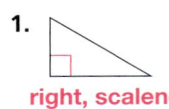
right, scalene

2.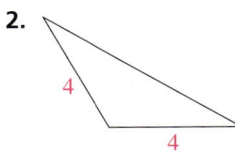

2. obtuse, isosceles

3.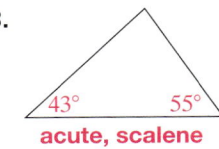
acute, scalene

4. The sides of a triangle measure 5 in., 12 in., and 13 in. The triangle has a 90° angle. Classify the triangle.
right, scalene

Homework Exercises

For more exercises, see **Extra Skills and Word Problems**.

GO for Help

For Exercises	See Examples
5–7	1
8–10	2
11–16	3

A Classify each triangle by its angles.

5.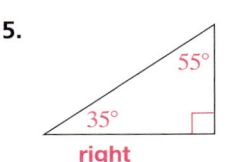
right

6.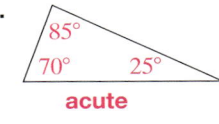
acute

7.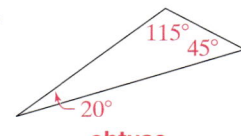
obtuse

Algebra Find the value of *x*, the measure of the third angle.

8.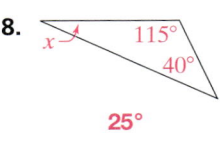
25°

9.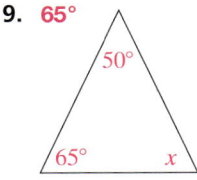
65°

10.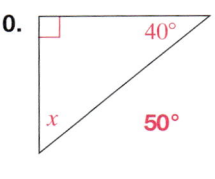
50°

Classify each triangle by its sides.

11.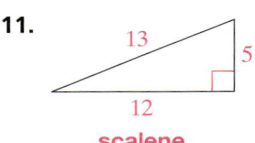
scalene

12. isosceles

13. isosceles

14. sides: 3, 3, 5
isosceles

15. sides: 6, 9, 4
scalene

16. sides: 11, 11, 11
equilateral

17. acute equilateral

B **GPS** **17. Guided Problem Solving** The triominoes shown are pieces from a game. Classify the shape of a triomino by its sides and angles.
- What is the measure of the largest angle?
- How many sides are congruent?

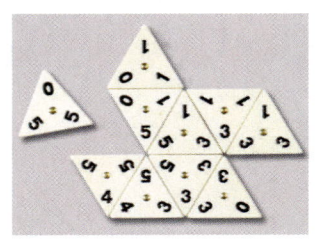

26. **Answers may vary. Sample:**

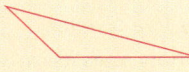

Classify each triangle by its angles.

18. 15°, 60°, x
obtuse

19. 14°, x, 76°
right

20. x, 60°, 61°
acute

Use the diagram below of the drafting triangles.

21. Classify each triangle by its angles.
right; right

22. Classify each triangle by its sides.
scalene; isosceles

23. *If you know two angles, you can subtract them from 180° to find the third. This allows you to classify the triangle.*

23. **Writing in Math** Explain why you only need to know the measure of two angles of a triangle in order to classify it by its angles.

24. A designer for a boat company describes the sail shown in the photo at the left. Describe the triangle, classifying it by its angles and sides. **Answers may vary. Sample: acute, isosceles**

25. **Algebra** The angles in an equilateral triangle are congruent. Write an equation for the sum of angles in an equilateral triangle. **3x = 180 or x + x + x = 180**

26. Sketch an obtuse scalene triangle. **See margin.**

C 27. **Challenge** An isosceles triangle has two congruent angles. Write an expression to represent the measure of the third angle of the triangle. **180° − 2x**

Test Prep and Mixed Review　　**Practice**

Gridded Response

28. A triangle has angles that measure 37° and 52°. What is the measure of the triangle's third angle in degrees? **91**

29. What is the value of the fifth term in the number sequence?
10, 20, 40, 80　　**160**

30. There are 24 nonswimmers and 20 swimmers in a swimming program. What is the ratio of nonswimmers to swimmers? Write your answer as a decimal. **1.2**

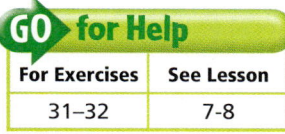
For Help

For Exercises	See Lesson
31–32	7-8

Use the graph at the right. A market researcher asked 200 people to choose their favorite dessert.

31. How many people prefer pie? **50 people**

32. How many more people prefer ice cream than prefer cake? **40 people**

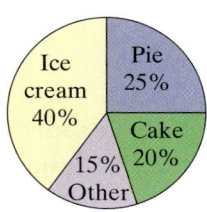

Alternative Assessment

Each student in a pair draws five different triangles. Partners exchange drawings and classify each other's triangles in as many ways as possible.

Test Prep

Resources
For additional practice with a variety of test item formats:
- Test-Taking Strategies, p. 407
- Test Prep, p. 411
- Test-Taking Strategies with Transparencies

Lesson Quiz

Name each triangle by its angles and its sides.

1.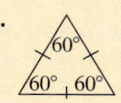
right, scalene

2.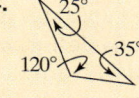
acute, equilateral, isosceles

3.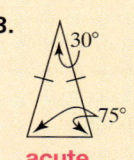
acute, isosceles

4.
obtuse, scalene

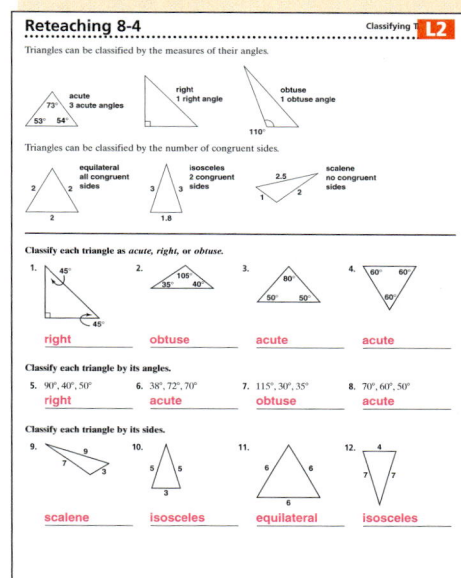
Reteaching 8-4　　　Classifying T　**L2**

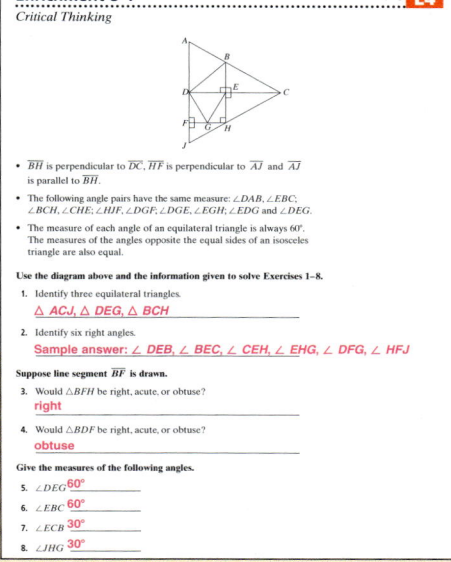
Enrichment 8-4　　　Classifying　**L4**

383

Vocabulary Builder

High-Use Academic Words

Vocabulary Builder

High-Use
Academic
Words

Students become familiar with vocabulary that is not strictly mathematical terms, but will occur frequently in their texts.

Guided Instruction

Have volunteers read each word and its definition aloud. Be sure English learners do not confuse *state* with its geographical meaning. Ask questions such as:

- *What is another way to say "Tell how many sides a triangle has?"* **State how many sides a triangle has.**
- *How can you use* measure *in a math problem?* **Sample: Measure the angles of a triangle to classify it.**
- *How does* draw *help you solve problems?* **Drawing a diagram for a problem can help you visualize it.**

Exercises

Have students work independently on the Exercises. When they have finished, have volunteers share their answers with the class to make sure students understand the meanings of the vocabulary words.

Differentiated Instruction

Below Level **L2**

Provide students with a thesaurus and have them create lists of synonyms for the vocabulary words.

High-Use Academic Words

High-use academic words are words that you will see often in textbooks and on tests. These words are not math vocabulary terms, but knowing them will help you to succeed in mathematics.

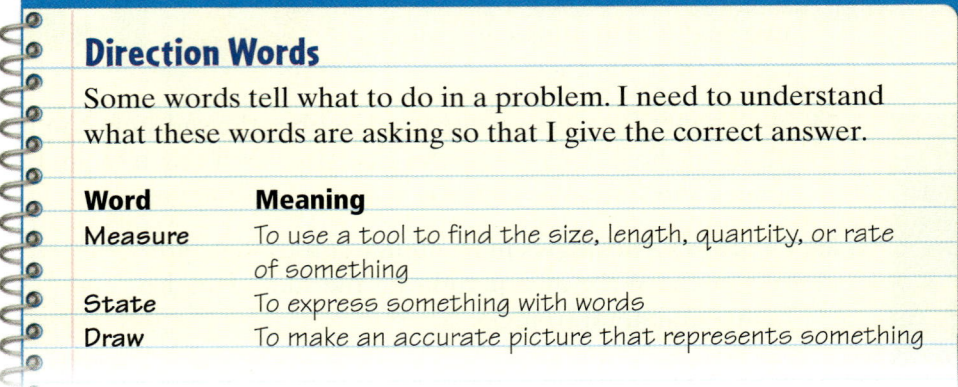

Direction Words

Some words tell what to do in a problem. I need to understand what these words are asking so that I give the correct answer.

Word	Meaning
Measure	To use a tool to find the size, length, quantity, or rate of something
State	To express something with words
Draw	To make an accurate picture that represents something

Exercises

1. Measure the length of your classroom by using your textbook. How many textbooks long is your classroom?

2. State the features of your classroom.   **1–3. Check students' work.**

3. Draw a picture of your classroom.

4. Measure the perimeter of the rectangle.
   9 cm

5. State the features of the rectangle.
   See right.

6. Draw the rectangle on your paper.
   Check students' work.

5. All angles are right angles, and all opposite sides are parallel and congruent.

7. **Word Knowledge** Think about the word *trace*.
   a. Choose the letter for how well you know the word.
      A. I know its meaning.
      B. I've seen it, but I don't know its meaning.
      C. I don't know it.
   b. **Research** Look up and write the definition of *trace*.
   c. Use the word in a sentence involving mathematics.
   7a–c. Check students' work.

Hands On

Angles in a Quadrilateral

This activity explores the four corners of a four-sided figure.

ACTIVITY

1. Trace the four-sided figure at the right.
   1–2. Check students' work.

2. Tear off the four corners of the figure. Place them together around a common point as shown below.

3. What is the sum of angles 1, 2, 3, and 4?
   360°

4. Draw another four-sided figure. Repeat Steps 2 and 3. Do you get the same result?
   Yes; check students' work.

5. Draw another four-sided figure. Label it *PQRS*. Draw a segment that connects two opposite vertices. **Check students' work.**

6. **Reasoning** How many triangles did you form? What is the relationship between the sum of the angles of figure *PQRS* and the sum of the angles of the triangles? Explain.

   6. They are the same; the two triangles have 2 × 180° or 360°. This is the same as the sum of the four angles in a quadrilateral.

7. Make a conjecture about the sum of the angles of a four-sided figure. **360°**

Exercises

1. A ferry leaves port *W*. As shown in the diagram at the right, it stops at points *X*, *Y*, and *Z*. What is the measure of ∠*W*? **81°**

Find the value of *x*.

2.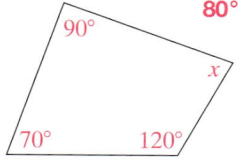
   80°

3.
   90°

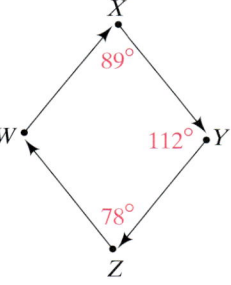

Activity Lab

Angles in a Quadrilateral

Students learn about the four corners of a four-sided figure. This will prepare them to study polygons in Lesson 8-5.

Guided Instruction

Before beginning the Activity, ask students what they think a quadrilateral is. Elicit a definition. After you have completed steps 1–4, ask:
- *What is a rule about the angles in a quadrilateral?* **The angles in a quadrilateral always have a sum of 360°.**

After you have completed steps 5–6, ask:
- *How could you test the rule using triangles?* **Draw a diagonal. Measure the angles of both resulting triangles.**

Exercises

Have students work independently on the Exercises. When they have finished, allow them to compare answers with a partner and share what they have learned.

Alternative Method

Provide students with frames of quadrilaterals, made by taping straws together. Have them use these frames to study the angles.

Resources

- Activity Lab 8-5: Classifying Polygons
- protractor
- straightedge
- straws
- tape

1. Plan

Objective
To identify regular polygons and to classify quadrilaterals

Examples
1 Identifying Polygons
2 Identifying Regular Polygons
3 Classifying Quadrilaterals
4 Finding an Angle Measure

Math Understandings: p. 360C

Math Background

Polygons are closed figures formed by three or more line segments that intersect only at their vertices. Polygons are named by the number of sides.

Quadrilaterals are four-sided polygons that can be further classified by parallel sides as a *parallelogram*, which includes a *rectangle*, a *rhombus*, and a *square*.

More Math Background: p. 360C

Lesson Planning and Resources

See p. 360E for a list of the resources that support this lesson.

Bell Ringer Practice

Check Skills You'll Need
Use student page, transparency, or PowerPoint. For intervention, direct students to:
Points, Lines, Segments, and Rays
Lesson 8-1
Extra Skills and Word Problems Practice, Ch. 8

386

✓ **Check Skills You'll Need**

1. **Vocabulary Review**
Can *parallel lines* also be *skew lines*? Explain.

2. Name 2 segments skew to $\overline{DE}$ below.

1–2 See back of book.

GO for Help
Lesson 8-1

What You'll Learn

To identify regular polygons and to classify quadrilaterals

🔊 **New Vocabulary** polygon, regular polygon, irregular polygon, quadrilateral, parallelogram, rectangle, rhombus, square, trapezoid

Why Learn This?

Signs have shapes to help you recognize them from a distance.

A **polygon** is a closed figure that has three or more line segments that do not cross.

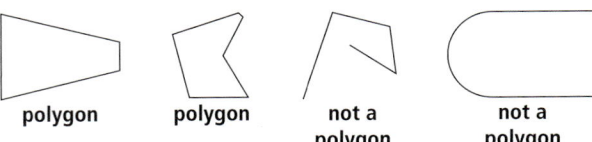

| polygon | polygon | not a polygon | not a polygon |

To name a polygon, just count the number of sides. Then refer to the table below.

EXAMPLE **Identifying Polygons**

1 Identify each polygon according to the number of sides it has.

Polygon	Number of Sides
Triangle	3
Quadrilateral	4
Pentagon	5
Hexagon	6
Octagon	8
Decagon	10

a.

pentagon

b.
STOP
octagon

c.

quadrilateral

✓ **Quick Check**

1. Identify each polygon according to the number of sides it has.

a.
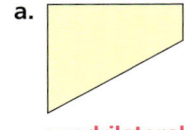
quadrilateral

b.
hexagon

c.
octagon

386 **Chapter 8** Tools of Geometry

Differentiated Instruction **Solutions for All Learners**

Special Needs **L1**
Have students work with a partner and talk about the five kinds of quadrilaterals in this lesson. As they look at the pictures and definitions, have them take turns identifying one unique feature of each quadrilateral, without including the number of sides.

learning style: visual

Below Level **L2**
Have students create a table for the five special quadrilaterals. Students should draw two examples and two non-examples for each quadrilateral.

learning style: visual

A **regular polygon** is a polygon with all sides congruent and all angles congruent. An **irregular polygon** is a polygon with sides that are not all congruent or angles that are not all congruent.

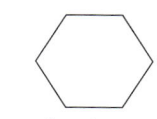
EXAMPLE **Identifying Regular Polygons**

2 Determine whether each polygon is regular or irregular.

a.

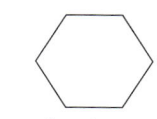

regular hexagon

b.

irregular quadrilateral

✓ **Quick Check**

2. Determine whether each polygon is regular or irregular.

a.

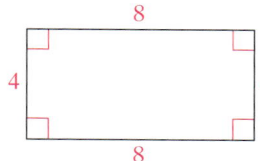

irregular

b.

irregular

A polygon with four sides is called a **quadrilateral.** Some quadrilaterals have special names.

Parallelogram
Has two pairs of parallel sides

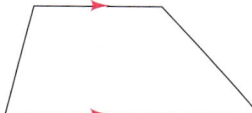

Trapezoid
Has exactly one pair of parallel sides

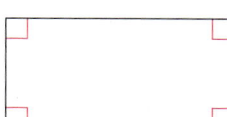

Rectangle
Parallelogram with four right angles

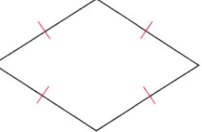

Rhombus
Parallelogram with four congruent sides

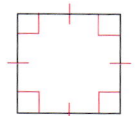

Square
Parallelogram with four right angles and four congruent sides

8-5 Exploring and Classifying Polygons **387**

2. Teach

Activity Lab

Use before the lesson.
Student Edition Activity Lab, Hands On 8-5a, Angles in a Quadrilateral, p. 385

All in One Teaching Resources
Activity Lab 8-5: Classifying Polygons

Guided Instruction

Example 1
Students can compare the names of polygons with the names of numbers in their native language. For instance, triangle, quadrilateral, octagon, and decagon come from the same roots as the numbers 3, 4, 8, and 10 in French and Spanish.

PowerPoint
Additional Examples

1 Identify each polygon according to the number of sides.

a.
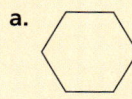

b.
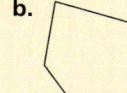

hexagon   pentagon

2 Determine whether each polygon is regular or irregular.

a.
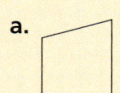

b.

irregular   regular

3 Write all the possible names for the quadrilateral. Then give the best name.
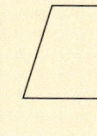
trapezoid

Advanced Learners L4
Have students create a Venn diagram that shows the relationship of the five special quadrilaterals discussed in the lesson.

learning style: visual

English Language Learners ELL
Have students create a chart of polygon names. Next to each polygon name, they should write the prefix, such as *penta* or *quad*. Next to each prefix, have them write the number of sides associated with it.

learning style: visual

387

Closure

- *How can you classify polygons?*
  by their number of sides
- *What are the five special quadrilaterals that have parallel sides?* **trapezoid, parallelogram, rectangle, rhombus, square**

3. Parallelogram, rectangle; rectangle; answers may vary. Sample: a rectangle has four right angles and two pairs of parallel lines.

GO for Help

For help with quadrilateral angle measures, go to Activity Lab 8-5a.

EXAMPLE Classifying Quadrilaterals

3 A baseball diamond is a quadrilateral. Write all of its names. Which is the best name? Explain.

Parallelogram: Both pairs of opposite sides are parallel.

Rectangle: The four angles are right angles.

Rhombus: The four sides are congruent.

Square: This is the best description of a baseball diamond. A square has four right angles and four congruent sides.

✓ Quick Check

3. Write all of the names for the quadrilateral. Which is the best name? Explain. **See below left.**

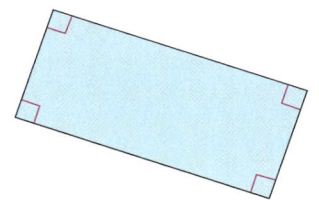

The sum of the angle measures of a quadrilateral is 360°.

EXAMPLE Finding an Angle Measure

4 **Multiple Choice** A family buys the lot of land shown. What is the measure of angle x, where Oak Street and Elm Street intersect?

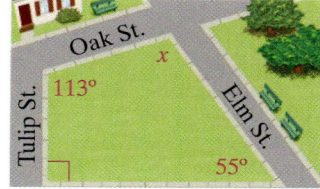

Ⓐ 35° 　　　Ⓒ 78°
Ⓑ 67° 　　　Ⓓ 102°

The four property lines form a quadrilateral. Write an equation.

$x + 55° + 90° + 113° = 360°$ ← The sum of the angle measures is 360°.

$x + 258° = 360°$ ← Add.

$x + 258° - 258° = 360° - 258°$ ← Subtract 258° from each side.

$x = 102°$ ← Simplify.

The correct answer is choice D.

✓ Quick Check

4. You landscape a yard using the design at the right. Find the measure of $\angle a$.
56°

Check Your Understanding

3. A polygon is a closed figure with 3 or more sides. A figure that is not closed or has less than 3 sides is not a polygon.

1. **Vocabulary** How can you tell whether a rectangle is a square? **All four sides will be congruent.**

2. What is the name of a five-sided polygon? **pentagon**

3. **Writing in Math** Describe how a figure that is *not* a polygon is different from one that is a polygon. **See left.**

Homework Exercises

For more exercises, see Extra Skills and Word Problems.

A **Identify each polygon according to the number of sides it has.**

GO for Help

For Exercises	See Examples
4–6	1
7–9	2
10–12	3
13–15	4

4.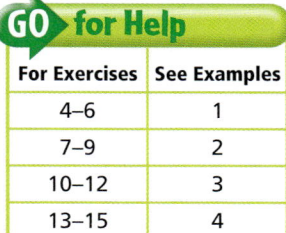
pentagon

5.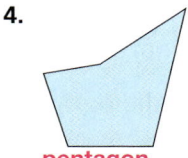
decagon

6.
quadrilateral

Determine whether each polygon is regular or irregular.

7.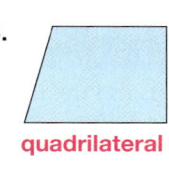
irregular

8.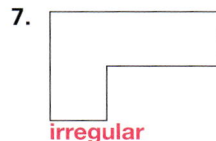
3 3
3
regular

9.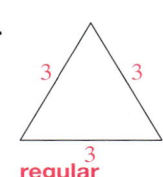
irregular

Write all of the names for each quadrilateral.

10.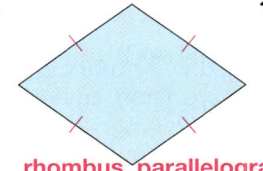
rhombus, parallelogram

11.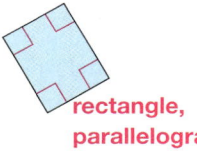
rectangle, parallelogram

12.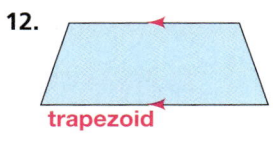
trapezoid

Find the value of each variable.

13.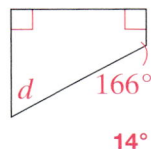
d 166°
14°

14.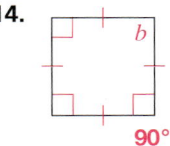
b
90°

15.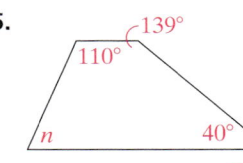
139°
110°
n 40°
71°

B **GPS** 16. **Guided Problem Solving** You need to draw a quadrilateral with two pairs of parallel sides. All of the sides are congruent. There are no right angles. Draw and label the quadrilateral.
  • Use 4 pencils of equal length as a model. **See left.**

16.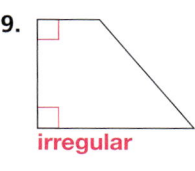

Exercises
In Exercise 16, remind students that using pencils to model the problem is a problem solving strategy called Act It Out.

3. Practice

Assignment Guide

Check Your Understanding
Go over Exercises 1–3 in class before assigning the Homework Exercises.

Homework Exercises
A Practice by Example   4–15
B Apply Your Skills   16–27
C Challenge   28
Test Prep and
  Mixed Review   29–32

Homework Quick Check
To check students' understanding of key skills and concepts, go over Exercises 5, 11, 22, 23, and 26.

Differentiated Instruction **Resources**

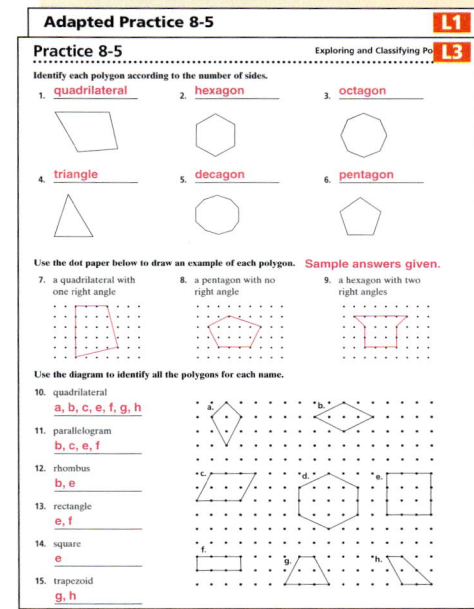

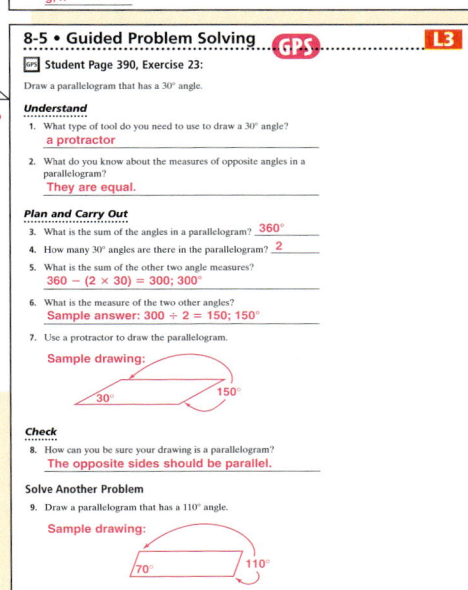

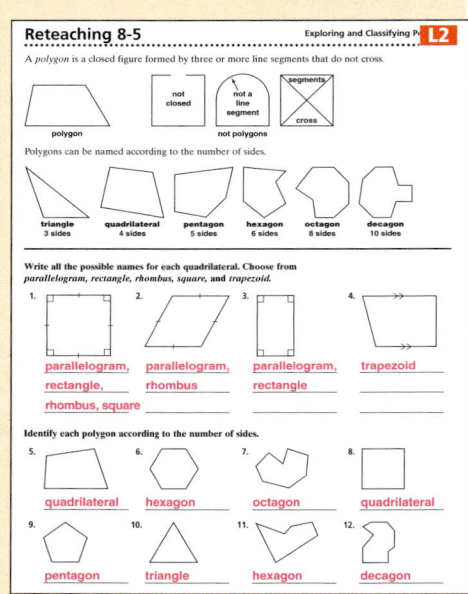

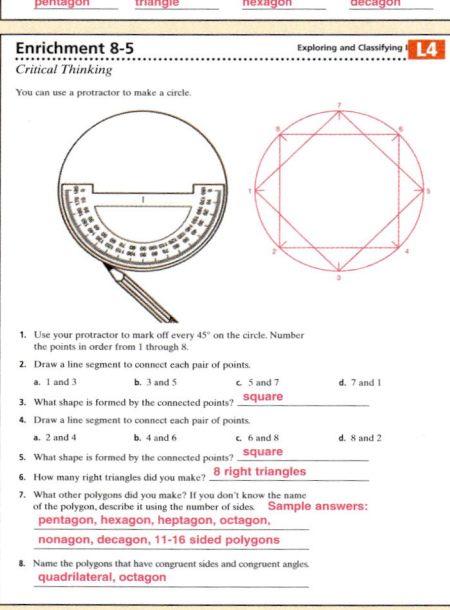

PowerPoint
Lesson Quiz

Identify each polygon. Write all the possible names. Determine if each polygon is regular or irregular.

1.
octagon; regular

2.
hexagon; regular

3.
quadrilateral, parallelogram, rhombus; irregular

4.
quadrilateral, trapezoid; irregular

Reteaching 8-5 Exploring and Classifying P... **L2**

A *polygon* is a closed figure formed by three or more line segments that do not cross.

not closed not a line segment segments

polygon not polygons cross

Polygons can be named according to the number of sides.

triangle 3 sides quadrilateral 4 sides pentagon 5 sides hexagon 6 sides octagon 8 sides decagon 10 sides

Write all the possible names for each quadrilateral. Choose from *parallelogram, rectangle, rhombus, square,* and *trapezoid.*

1. parallelogram, rectangle, rhombus, square
2. parallelogram, rhombus
3. parallelogram, rectangle
4. trapezoid

Identify each polygon according to the number of sides.

5. quadrilateral 6. hexagon 7. octagon 8. quadrilateral
9. pentagon 10. triangle 11. hexagon 12. decagon

Enrichment 8-5 Exploring and Classifying ... **L4**
Critical Thinking

You can use a protractor to make a circle.

1. Use your protractor to mark off every 45° on the circle. Number the points in order from 1 through 8.
2. Draw a line segment to connect each pair of points.
   a. 1 and 3   b. 3 and 5   c. 5 and 7   d. 7 and 1
3. What shape is formed by the connected points? square
4. Draw a line segment to connect each pair of points.
   a. 2 and 4   b. 4 and 6   c. 6 and 8   d. 8 and 2
5. What shape is formed by the connected points? square
6. How many right triangles did you make? 8 right triangles
7. What other polygons did you make? If you don't know the name of the polygon, describe it using the number of sides. Sample answers:
pentagon, hexagon, heptagon, octagon, nonagon, decagon, 11-16 sided polygons
8. Name the polygons that have congruent sides and congruent angles.
quadrilateral, octagon

390

GO Online
Homework Video Tutor

Visit: PHSchool.com
Web Code: aqe-0805

Scientists use the Raft of Treetops to work and sleep atop rain forests.

23.
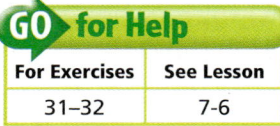
30°

Use graph paper to draw an example of each quadrilateral.

17. trapezoid **18.** rectangle

19. rhombus **20.** parallelogram

21. quadrilateral with only one right angle
17–21. See margin.

22. Science What shape is the Raft of Treetops platform at the left? Draw the polygon. Add two lines to divide it into a quadrilateral and two triangles. See margin.

23. Draw a parallelogram that has a 30° angle. **See left.**

GPS

Complete each sentence with *All, Some,* or *No.*

24. ? quadrilaterals are squares. **Some**

25. ? rhombuses are quadrilaterals. **All**

26. ? trapezoids are parallelograms. **No**

27. ? squares are rectangles. **All**

C 28. Challenge A diagonal of a polygon is a segment that connects two vertices that are not next to each other. Draw the diagonals for a quadrilateral, a pentagon, and a hexagon. Predict the number of diagonals in an octagon. **20**

Test Prep and Mixed Review
Practice

Multiple Choice

29. Jordan's backyard is a quadrilateral. The angles measure 120°, 90°, 95°, and b. What is b? **C**

b 95° 120°

Ⓐ 35°   Ⓒ 55°
Ⓑ 45°   Ⓓ 135°

30. Which number is NOT a multiple of 15? **F**
Ⓕ 5   Ⓖ 15   Ⓗ 75   Ⓙ 90

GO for Help

For Exercises	See Lesson
31–32	7-6

What percent of each grid is shaded?

31. 36%

32. 20%

Test Prep

Resources
For additional practice with a variety of test item formats:
• Test-Taking Strategies, p. 407
• Test Prep, p. 411
• Test-Taking Strategies with Transparencies

Alternative Assessment

Each student in a pair draws several polygons, including quadrilaterals. Partners exchange papers and name each polygon using as many names as they can.

17–22. See back of book.

Classify each triangle by its angles.

1. 20°, 60°, 100°
obtuse

2. 40°, 50°, 90°
right

3. 60°, 60°, 60°
acute

Classify each triangle by its sides.

4. 8, 9, and 8 units
isosceles

5. 3, 4, and 5 units
scalene

6. 10, 10, and 10 units
equilateral

7. The perimeter of an equilateral triangle is 12 m. Find the length of a side. **4 m**

Identify each polygon according to the number of sides it has.

8.
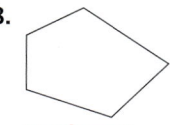
pentagon

9.

octagon

10.
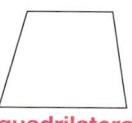
quadrilateral

Write the names for each quadrilateral. Then give the best name.

11.

trapezoid; trapezoid

12.
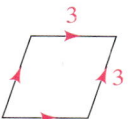

13.
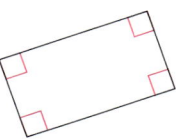

12–13. See margin.

✓ Checkpoint Quiz

Use this Checkpoint Quiz to check students' understanding of the skills and concepts of Lessons 8-4 through 8-5.

Resources

- All-in-One Teaching Resources Checkpoint Quiz 2
- ExamView CD-ROM
- Success Tracker™ Online Intervention

MATH AT WORK

Cartoonist

Students may not be aware of how studying geometry will be helpful to them in a career. This feature should generate enthusiasm about learning math skills.

Guided Instruction

Discuss favorite cartoon characters with students. Ask questions, such as:
- *What angles or shapes are used to draw your favorite cartoon character?*
- *Why is it important for a cartoonist to be able to draw lines and angles?*

MATH AT WORK   Cartoonist

A career as a cartoonist could be just right for you if you enjoy reading and can draw well. Some cartoonists produce comic strips meant for amusement. Others illustrate articles, books, or advertisements.

Cartoonists use lines, angles, measures, and perspective to draw cartoons.

Go Online
PHSchool.com
For: Information on cartoonists,
Web Code: aqb-2031

391

---

12. parallelogram, rhombus; rhombus

13. parallelogram, rectangle; rectangle

1. Plan

Objective
To identify congruent and similar figures

Examples
1 Identifying Congruent Figures
2 Identifying Similar Figures
3 Application: Architecture

Math Understandings: p. 360D

Math Background

Congruent figures have the same size and shape. Congruent figures may not appear congruent because they can be rotated and flipped. However, if you place congruent figures on top of one another—matching corresponding sides and corresponding angles—the figures exactly match.

Similar figures have the same shape but not necessarily the same size. So, corresponding angles are congruent but corresponding sides are proportional.

More Math Background: p. 360D

Lesson Planning and Resources

See p. 360E for a list of the resources that support this lesson.

Bell Ringer Practice

✓ **Check Skills You'll Need**
Use student page, transparency, or PowerPoint. For intervention, direct students to:
Special Pairs of Angles
Lesson 8-3
Extra Skills and Word Problems
Practice, Ch. 8

392

✓ **Check Skills You'll Need**

1. Vocabulary Review
How can you tell that two angles are *congruent*?
1–3. See below.
Classify each triangle by its sides.

2.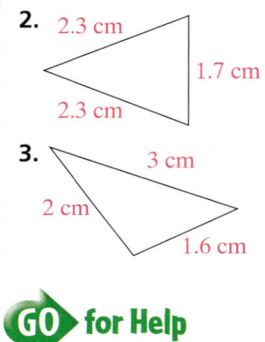
   2.3 cm
   1.7 cm
   2.3 cm

3. 3 cm
   2 cm
   1.6 cm

GO for Help
Lesson 8-3

Check Skills You'll Need

1–3. See back of book.

GO for Help

Figures are congruent even if you must flip or turn a figure to fit over another figure.

1a. no
 b. yes

What You'll Learn

To identify congruent and similar figures

🔊 **New Vocabulary** congruent figures, similar figures

Why Learn This?

Designers use congruent figures in art and architecture. You can fit some congruent figures together without gaps or spaces.

Congruent figures are figures that have exactly the same size and shape. Congruent figures have congruent *corresponding sides* and congruent *corresponding angles*. The matching sides and angles are corresponding parts.

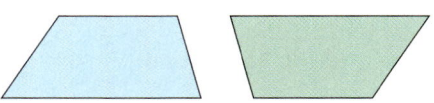

Suppose you rotate the blue trapezoid. It will fit exactly over the green trapezoid.

EXAMPLE **Identifying Congruent Figures**

1 Tell whether each triangle is congruent to triangle *PQR*.

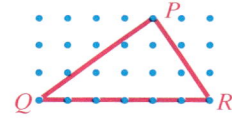

a.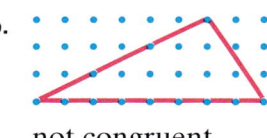
congruent

b. not congruent

✓ **Quick Check**

1. Tell whether each trapezoid is congruent to the first trapezoid.

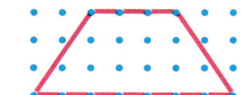

a.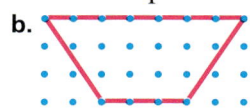

b.

Differentiated Instruction Solutions for All Learners

Special Needs L1
Have students draw two 2 × 2 squares on graph paper. Then have them draw a 3 × 3 square next to a 4 × 4 square. Label all the angles *90 degrees*. Ask, *Which squares are congruent?* **the first two** Ask, *Which two are similar?* **the last two**

learning style: visual

Below Level L2
Have students trace pattern blocks with irregular-shaped figures. Students should trace rotated figures as well a flipped figures.

learning style: tactile

Similar figures have the same shape, but not necessarily the same size. Corresponding angles of similar figures are congruent. Lengths of corresponding sides of similar figures are proportional.

EXAMPLE — Identifying Similar Figures

2 Show that the triangles are similar.

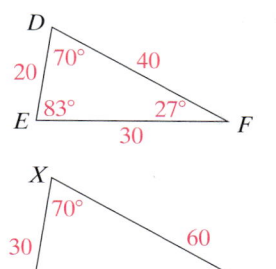

The measures of $\angle D$ and $\angle X$ are 70°.
The measures of $\angle E$ and $\angle Y$ are 83°.
The measures of $\angle F$ and $\angle Z$ are 27°.

$\frac{20}{30} = \frac{2}{3}$, $\frac{40}{60} = \frac{2}{3}$, and $\frac{30}{45} = \frac{2}{3}$

The measures of corresponding angles are equal. The lengths of corresponding sides form equal ratios. The triangles are similar.

GO for Help

For help with checking proportions, go to Lesson 7-3, Example 1.

✓ Quick Check

2. Is the triangle at the right similar to triangle DEF in Example 2? Explain your reasoning.

yes; $\frac{17}{20} = \frac{34}{40}$

If the angles of two triangles are congruent, then the triangles are similar. The sides must also be congruent for the triangles to be congruent.

EXAMPLE — Application: Architecture

3 Triangles ABC and CDE are similar. The measure of $\angle A$ is 70°. The measure of $\angle B$ is 55°. What is the measure of $\angle E$? Explain.

The measure of $\angle ACB$ is 55°, since the sum of the angles in a triangle equals 180°. $\angle ACB$ and $\angle E$ are corresponding angles. So the measure of $\angle E$ is 55°.

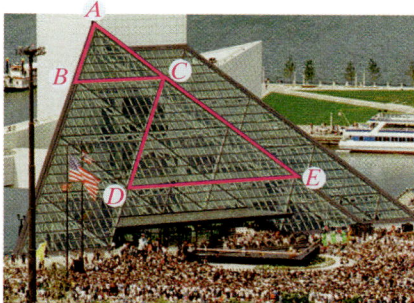

Online active math

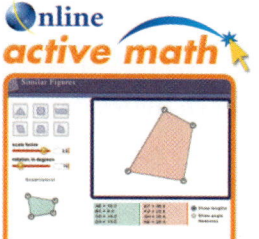

For: Congruence Activity
Use: Interactive Textbook, 8-6

✓ Quick Check

3. The measure of $\overline{AB}$ is 4 units, the measure of $\overline{BC}$ is 5 units, and the measure of $\overline{CD}$ is 12 units. Find the measure of $\overline{DE}$. **15**

Advanced Learners L4
Have students find the values of x and y if $\triangle A$ is similar to $\triangle B$. **x = 15, y = 8**

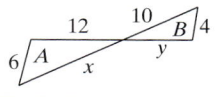

learning style: visual

English Language Learners   ELL
Have students work in small groups. Ask the groups to explain, in writing, what the words *corresponding,* *proportional,* and *congruent* mean. If needed, they should use symbols and pictures in their explanations.

learning style: verbal

---

2. Teach

Activity Lab

Use before the lesson.

All in One Teaching Resources
Activity Lab 8-6: Similar Polygons

Guided Instruction

Error Prevention!

In similar figures, proportions are formed using corresponding sides. Students can write proportions as long as the corresponding parts of the figures are corresponding terms in their proportions.

PowerPoint
Additional Examples

1 Are the pentagons congruent?

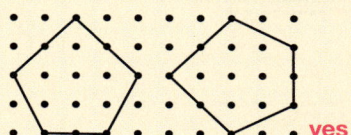

yes

2 Which triangle appears similar to $\triangle HJK$? Find if the corresponding sides are proportional. **See back of book.**

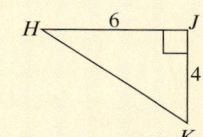

a. **b.**

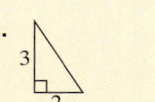 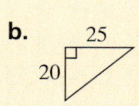

3 Are the figures *congruent* or *similar*? Explain. **See back of book.**

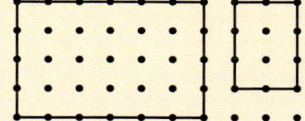

All in One Teaching Resources
• Daily Notetaking Guide 8-6 **L3**
• Adapted Notetaking 8-6 **L1**

Closure

• *How do you identify similar figures?* **See back of book.**

393

Assignment Guide

Check Your Understanding
Go over Exercises 1–5 in class before assigning the Homework Exercises.

Homework Exercises
A Practice by Example   6–14
B Apply Your Skills   15–20
C Challenge   21
Test Prep and
   Mixed Review   22–24

Homework Quick Check
To check students' understanding of key skills and concepts, go over Exercises 7, 10, 16, 17, and 18.

Differentiated Instruction **Resources**

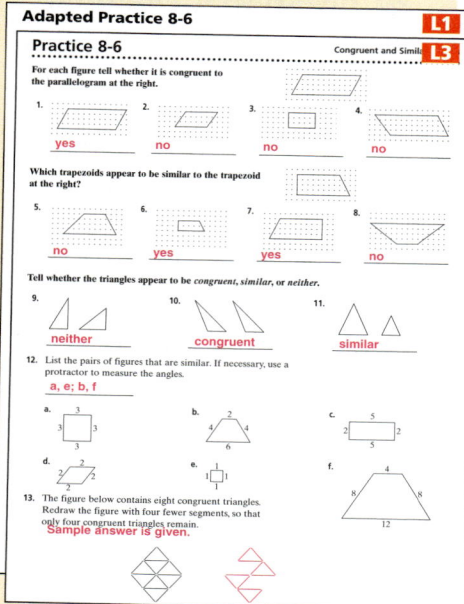

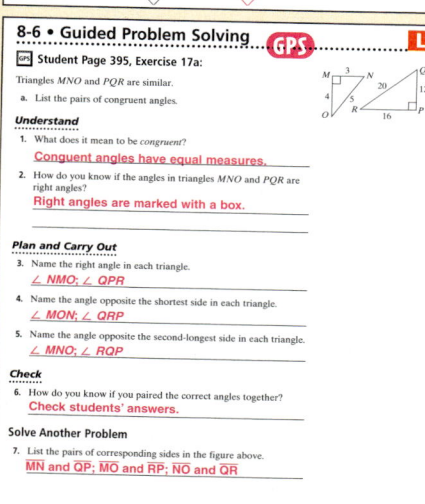

✔ Check Your Understanding

1. **Vocabulary** Congruent and similar figures have __?__ angles.
   congruent

2. **Reasoning** Are all right triangles similar? Explain your answer using words and a sketch. **See margin.**

Match the congruent triangles.

3. **A**   4. **C**   5. **B**

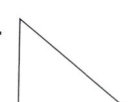

A.   B.   C.

Homework Exercises

For more exercises, see Extra Skills and Word Problems.

GO for Help

For Exercises	See Examples
6–7	1
8–11	2
12–14	3

Ⓐ **Tell whether each figure is congruent to trapezoid ABDC.**

6.   7.

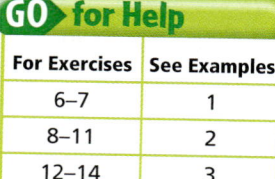 yes   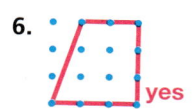 no   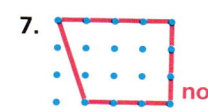

Which rectangles are similar to rectangle MNOP at the left?

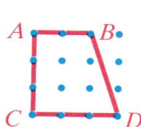

8.   9.   10.   11.

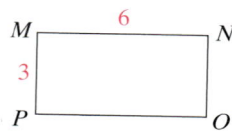   no   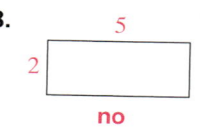 no   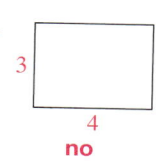 yes   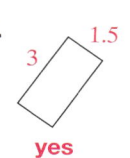 yes   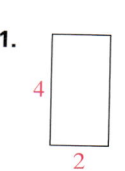

Each figure is similar to triangle PQR. Find x in each figure.

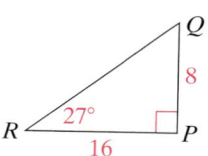

12.   13.   14.

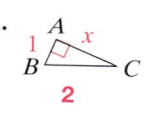   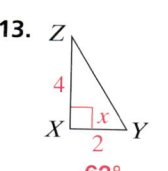 63°   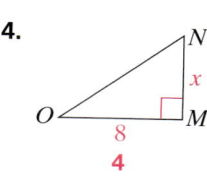

Ⓑ **GPS** 15. **Guided Problem Solving** You need to replace a broken window. Should the new window glass be congruent to the original window glass? Explain. **See left.**
   - How are congruent and similar rectangles different?
   - Can two rectangles be both similar and congruent?

15. yes; the new window pane must be exactly the same size as the original.

2. No; the acute angles are not always the same, and the side lengths are not always proportional.

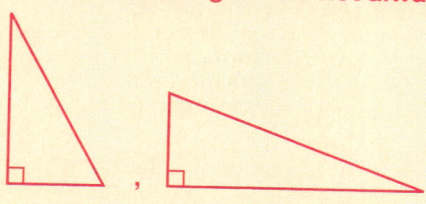

16. List the pairs of figures that are similar. If necessary, use a protractor to measure the angles. **A and E, H and J**

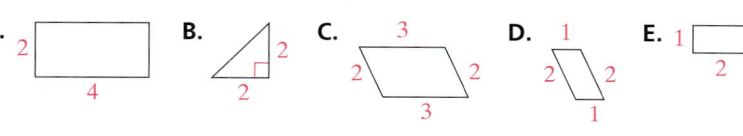

17a. ∠*MNO* and ∠*PQR*,
∠*MON* and ∠*PRQ*,
∠*OMN* and ∠*RPQ*
b. 3 : 4 : 5 = 12 : 16 : 20

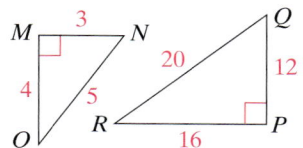

17. Triangles *MNO* and *PQR* at the left are similar.
a. List the pairs of congruent angles. **17a–b. See left.**
b. Write the proportions for the corresponding sides.

18. **Writing in Math** Are congruent figures always similar? Explain.

18. Yes; their angles are always congruent and their sides are always proportional.

Algebra Each pair of figures is congruent. Find *x*.

19.

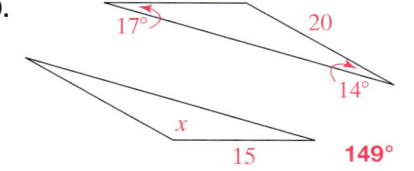

20.

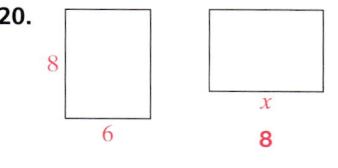

C **21. Challenge** How many congruent triangles are in the figure at the left? How many similar triangles? **4, 5**

Test Prep and Mixed Review **Practice**

Multiple Choice

22. The angle at each vertex of a regular pentagon is 108°. What type of angle is at each vertex of a regular pentagon?
  Ⓐ Acute   Ⓒ Right
  Ⓑ Obtuse   Ⓓ Straight   **B**

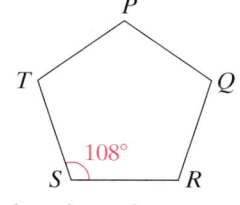

23. Eighteen classes are on a field trip. Each class has about 25 students. About how many students are on the trip? **J**
  Ⓕ 43   Ⓖ 45   Ⓗ 430   Ⓙ 450

GO for Help

For Exercise	See Lesson
24	2-4

24. Make a line graph from the data in the table below. **See margin.**

Net Profit per Week

Week	1	2	3	4	5
Store A	$1,500	$800	$700	$950	$1,000

Alternative Assessment

Each student in a pair draws two triangles on dot paper. Partners exchange drawings and draw one figure that is congruent and one figure that is similar but not congruent for each of their partners' triangles.

24. See back of book.

Test Prep

Resources

For additional practice with a variety of test item formats:
• Test-Taking Strategies, p. 407
• Test Prep, p. 411
• Test-Taking Strategies with Transparencies

---

4. Assess & Reteach

Lesson Quiz

Tell whether the figures are *congruent* or *similar.*

1.

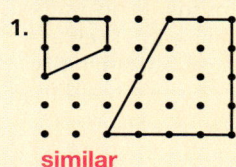

similar

2.

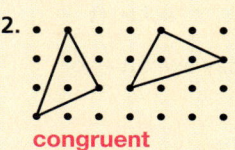

congruent

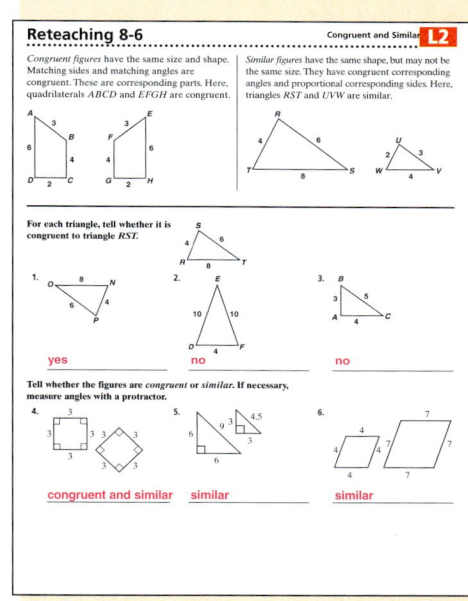

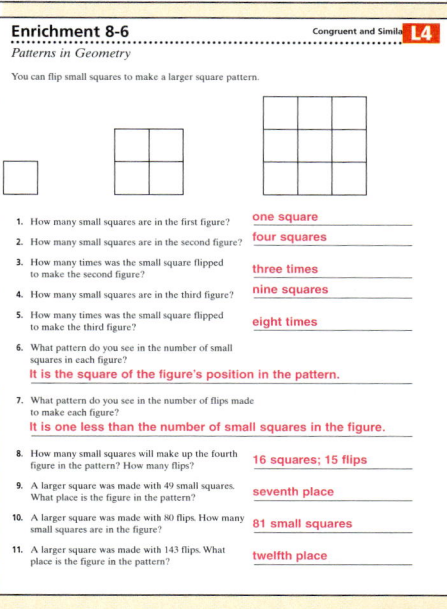

395

 **Guided Problem Solving**

Practice Solving Problems

In this feature, students practice solving problems involving polygons and similarity. They use what they know about similarity and proportion to solve real-life problems involving measures.

Guided Instruction

Discuss everyday examples of similarity with students. Explain that a scale drawing is similar to the actual object.
Ask:
- *What information is important to solving the problem?* **scale, distance from home plate to the pitcher's mound in the drawing**
- *If the scale is the same and distance in the drawing between home plate and first base is 0.45 in., how far is it from home plate to first base?* **90 ft**
- *If all sides and angles of the baseball field are congruent, what shape is the field?* **square**

Exercises

Have students work independently on the Exercises. When they have finished, they may adjust their answers based on discussion.

Practice Solving Problems

In the Ball Park   The distance from home plate to the center of the pitcher's mound in the scale drawing is about 0.3 inch. About how far is the actual distance from home plate to the center of the pitcher's mound?

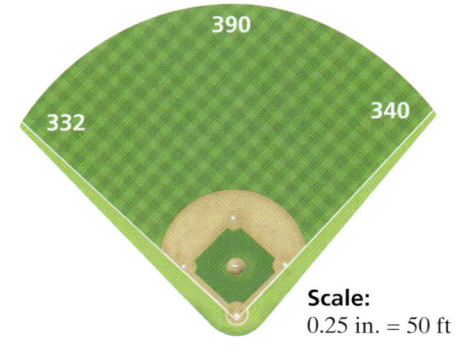

Scale:
0.25 in. = 50 ft

What You Might Think

What do I know?

What am I trying to find?

How can I write and solve a proportion to find the answer?

What is the answer?

What You Might Write

- A scale drawing is similar to the actual object, so the distances are proportional.
- scale: 0.25 in. = 50 ft
- scale distance is about 0.3 in.

the actual distance from home plate to the center of the pitcher's mound

Let $d =$ the actual distance from home plate to the center of the pitcher's mound.

$$\frac{0.25}{50} = \frac{0.3}{d}$$

$$0.25d = 15$$

$$d = 60$$

The actual distance from home plate to the center of the pitcher's mound is 60 feet.

Differentiated Instruction

Advanced Learners   **L4**
Have students draw their own polygons, then have them trade with their partners and draw similar figures to their partners' polygons.

Think It Through

1. Why is a proportion used to find the answer? **The scale gives a ratio of the distance in the picture to the actual distance.**
2. **Check for Reasonableness** How do you know the answer is reasonable? (*Hint:* Notice that 0.25 inch is close to 0.3 inch.) **See margin.**

Exercises

3. The actual distance from home plate to the center-field wall in another ballpark is 400 feet. How long should you draw that distance in a drawing with a scale of 0.25 inch = 50 feet? **2 in.**
   a. How can you use the scale 0.25 inch = 50 feet to write a proportion?
   b. **Check for Reasonableness** How can you decide if the answer is reasonable?

4. The dimensions of your science book are $8\frac{3}{4}$ inches by 11 inches. Is the photo of the book at the right similar to the shape of your science book? Explain. **No; the ratios of the sides do not form a proportion.**

5. Draw a right triangle similar to the one below. Make the lengths of the sides in your drawing $a = 4$ inches and $b = 3$ inches. What are the lengths of all of the sides for both triangles?
   3 : 4 : 5; 0.75 : 1 : 1.25

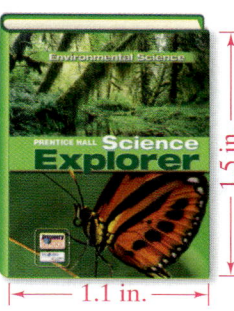

1.5 in.

|← 1.1 in. →|

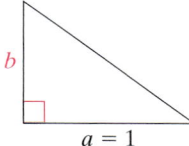

b

$a = 1$

6. Draw a figure similar to the one below but larger. Tell how you know the figures are similar. **The ratios of the sides are equal.**

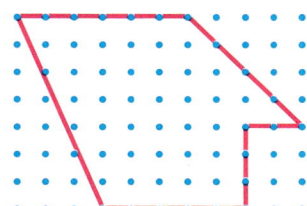

7. A box in a drawing is 2 in. wide, $5\frac{1}{2}$ in. long, and $3\frac{1}{4}$ in. high. The scale is $\frac{3}{4}$ in. = 2 ft. What are the dimensions of the actual box? **$5\frac{1}{3}$ ft; $14\frac{2}{3}$ ft; $8\frac{2}{3}$ ft**

2. **Since 0.3 is a little bigger than 0.25, it makes sense that 60 ft, which is a little bigger than 50 ft, is the answer.**

Objective
To find lines of symmetry

Examples
1   Testing for Line Symmetry
2   Application: Nature

Math Understandings: p. 360D

Math Background

Both the natural world and the human-built world are full of symmetry. A figure has *line symmetry* if a *line of symmetry* can be drawn that divides the figure into two mirror images. You can test a figure for line symmetry by folding it along the line of symmetry and seeing if the two halves match.

More Math Background: p. 360D

Lesson Planning and Resources

See p. 360E for a list of the resources that support this lesson.

Bell Ringer Practice

✓ **Check Skills You'll Need**
Use student page, transparency, or PowerPoint. For intervention, direct students to:
Congruent and Similar Figures
Lesson 8-6
Extra Skills and Word Problems
  Practice, Ch. 8

8-7 Line Symmetry

✓ **Check Skills You'll Need**

1. **Vocabulary Review**
Draw two *congruent* rectangles.
1–3. See below.
Are the two figures congruent?

2.

3.

GO for Help
Lesson 8-6

Check Skills You'll Need

1. **Answers may vary. Sample:**

2. yes

3. yes

What You'll Learn

To find lines of symmetry

🔊 **New Vocabulary** line symmetry, line of symmetry

Why Learn This?

You often see symmetry in nature, as in the butterfly at the right. You can also find symmetrical designs in fabrics, flags, architecture, and art.

A figure has ==line symmetry== if a line can divide the figure so that each half is a mirror image of the other. This dividing line is called a ==line of symmetry.== If you fold a drawing on its line of symmetry, the two sides match.

EXAMPLE   **Testing for Line Symmetry**

1 For each figure, is the dashed line a line of symmetry? Explain.

a.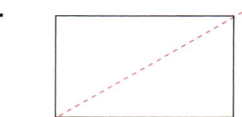

b.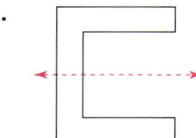

No, if you fold the figure along the line, the two parts do not match.

Yes, if you fold the figure along the line, the two parts match.

✓ **Quick Check**

1. Is the red dashed line in the figure a line of symmetry? Explain.

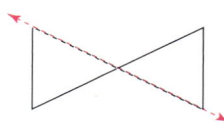

No; if you fold the figure along the line, the two parts do not match.

Differentiated Instruction   Solutions for All Learners

Special Needs L1
Some students may have a difficult time drawing. Give them precut regular and irregular shapes, such as rectangles, octagons, and triangles. Have students fold the shapes and identify lines of symmetry.

learning style: tactile

Below Level L2
Introduce the lesson by having students list as many real-world objects as they can that exhibit symmetry. Point out that the long list shows mathematics is all around us.

learning style: verbal

Some figures have more than one line of symmetry.

EXAMPLE **Application: Nature**

2 How many lines of symmetry does each figure have? Draw them.

a.

The leaf has one line of symmetry.

b.

The snowflake has 6 lines of symmetry.

2b.

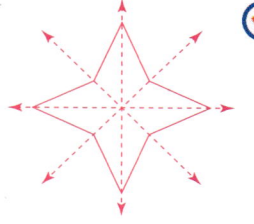

✓ Quick Check

2. How many lines of symmetry does each figure have? Trace the figure and draw the lines of symmetry.

a.

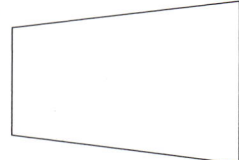

See margin.

b.

See left.

✓ Check Your Understanding

1. **Vocabulary** Is the dashed line in the square at the right a line of symmetry? **yes**

2. 4;

2. **Reasoning** How many lines of symmetry does a square have? Draw a diagram to support your answer. **See left.**

3. **Open-Ended** The word CODE has a horizontal line of symmetry. Find another word that has a horizontal line of symmetry. **Check students' work.**

◄─ **CODE** ─►

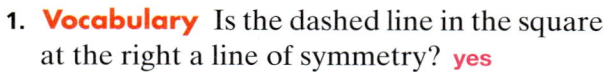
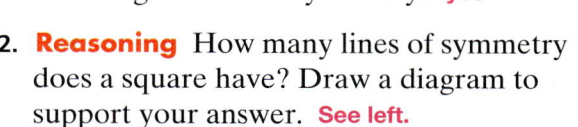
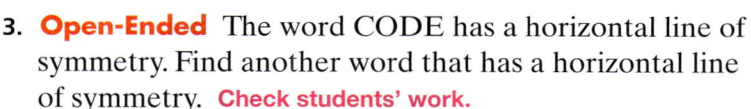

8-7 Line Symmetry   **399**

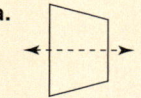
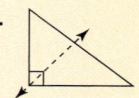

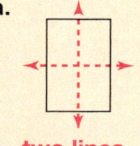

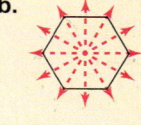
B C D E H I K O X

2a. See back of book.   **399**

3. Practice

Assignment Guide

Check Your Understanding
Go over Exercises 1–3 in class before assigning the Homework Exercises.

Homework Exercises
A Practice by Example   4–9
B Apply Your Skills   10–18
C Challenge   19
Test Prep and
   Mixed Review   20–23

Homework Quick Check
To check students' understanding of key skills and concepts, go over Exercises 5, 7, 14, 16, and 17.

Differentiated Instruction Resources

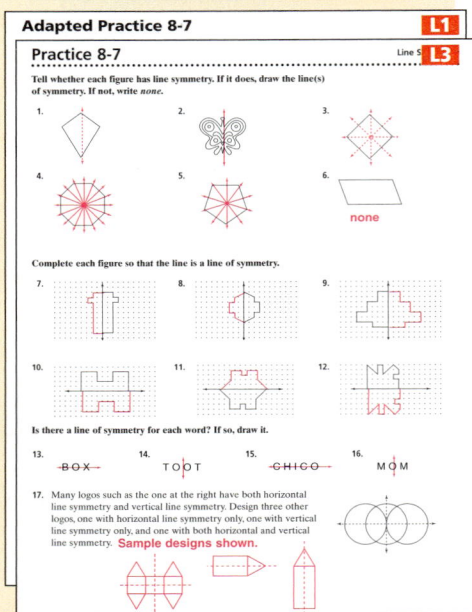

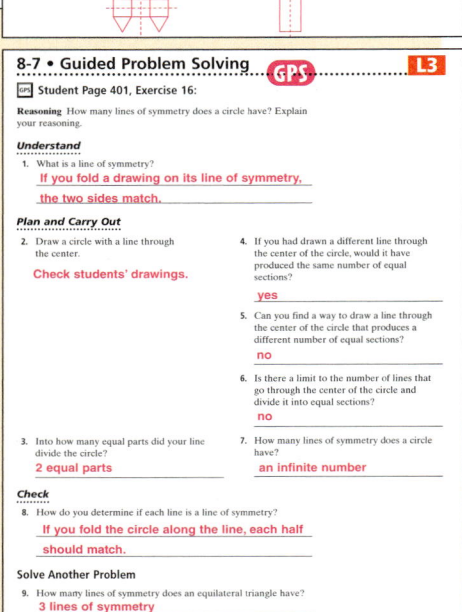

Homework Exercises

For more exercises, see Extra Skills and Word Problems.

GO for Help

For Exercises	See Examples
4–6	1
7–9	2

A Is the dashed line in each figure a line of symmetry? Explain.

4.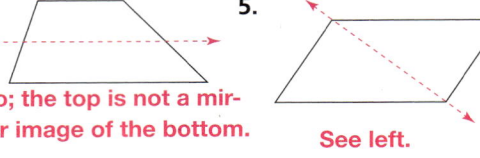
No; the top is not a mirror image of the bottom.

5.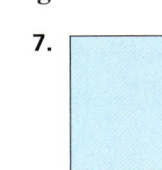
See left.

6.
Yes; the two sides match.

5. **No; the two sides do not match.**

How many lines of symmetry does each figure have? Trace the figure and draw the lines of symmetry. **7–9. See left.**

7. **2**
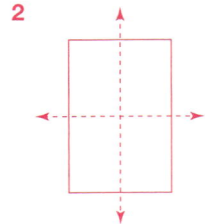

7.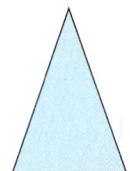

8.

9.

B GPS 10. **Guided Problem Solving** An artist designs the logo in the sketch at the right. How many lines of symmetry does the logo have? **5**
- **Make a Plan** Look for vertical, horizontal, and other lines of symmetry.
- **Check the Answer** Trace the logo and fold it along its lines of symmetry.

8. **1**

9. **1**

Tell whether each design has line symmetry.

11.  **no**

12.  **yes**

13.  **yes**

Nature Tell how many lines of symmetry each object has.

14.  **5**

15.  **3**

16. Infinitely many; every diameter is a line of symmetry.

16. Reasoning How many lines of symmetry does a circle have? **GPS** Explain your reasoning. **See left.**

17. Writing in Math Sketch a scalene, an equilateral, and an isosceles triangle. Use dashed lines to show the lines of symmetry. Describe the lines of symmetry. **See margin.**

18. Flags How many lines of symmetry does each flag have?

1

2

0

C 19. Challenge Research a Native American design with lines of symmetry. Trace the design. Draw all the lines of symmetry.
Check students' work.

Test Prep and Mixed Review
Practice

Multiple Choice

20. Which set of angle measures can you use to draw a triangle?
- Ⓐ 82°, 55°, 47°
- Ⓒ 25°, 30°, 35° **B**
- Ⓑ 90°, 30°, 60°
- Ⓓ 50°, 20°, 30°

21. In a survey, 35% of teenagers said they would keep their computer if they could keep only one electronic device. Another 30% chose a television, 20% chose a telephone, and 15% chose a radio. Which graph accurately displays the results of the survey? **F**

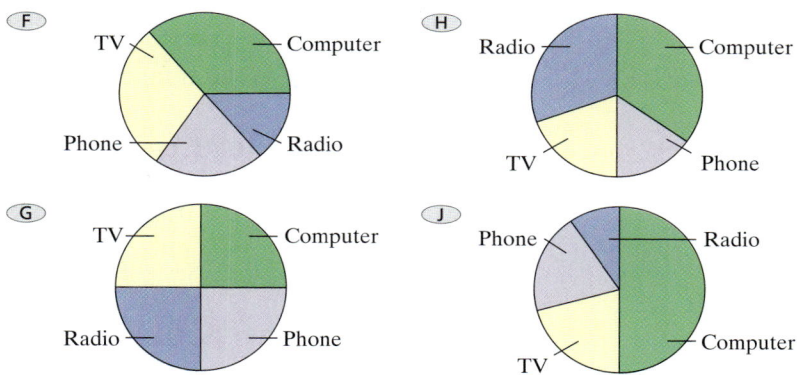

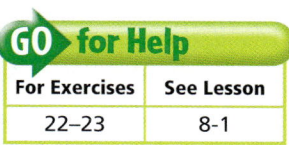

For Exercises	See Lesson
22–23	8-1

Use the diagram to name the figures.

22. three points not on the same line
Answers may vary. Sample: A, C, and D

23. three rays
Answers may vary. Sample: $\overrightarrow{AC}, \overrightarrow{BC}, \overrightarrow{AD}$

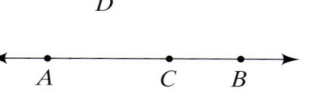

Alternative Assessment

Each student in a pair draws four figures on dot paper. Partners exchange figures and find and draw all the lines of symmetry.

17. See back of book.

Test Prep

Resources
For additional practice with a variety of test item formats:
- Test-Taking Strategies, p. 407
- Test Prep, p. 411
- Test-Taking Strategies with Transparencies

---

4. Assess & Reteach

Lesson Quiz

Is the dashed line shown in each figure a line of symmetry?

1. 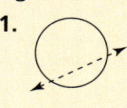   **2.**

no   **yes**

3. How many lines of symmetry does an equilateral triangle have? **3**

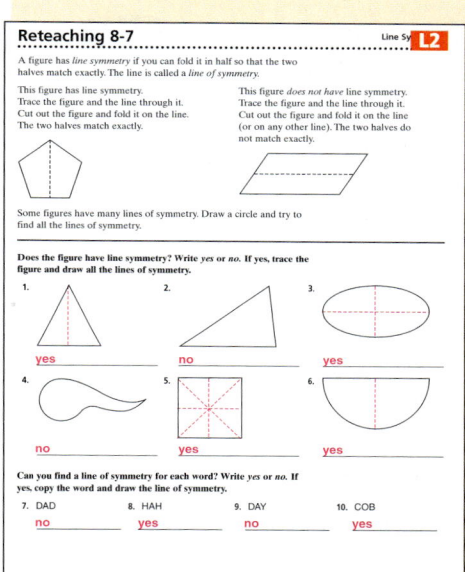

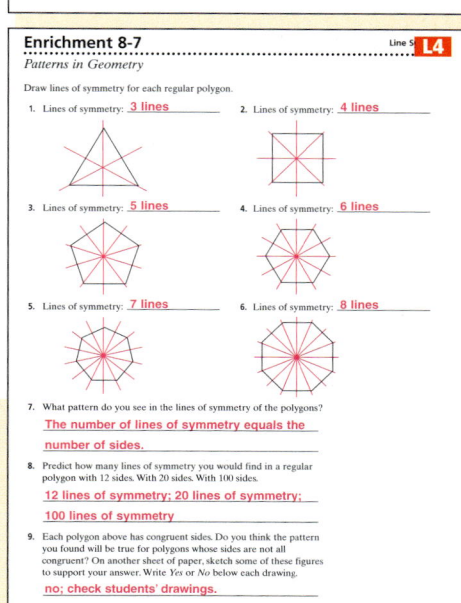

Objective
To identify and draw translations, reflections, and rotations

Examples
1 Identifying Translations
2 Drawing Reflections
3 Application: Nature

Math Understandings: p. 360D

Math Background

A *transformation* of a figure is a change in its position, shape, or size. The resulting figure is called an *image*. There are three rigid-motion transformations that change only the position of the figure: translations, reflections, and rotations.

More Math Background: p. 360D

Lesson Planning and Resources

See p. 360E for a list of the resources that support this lesson.

PowerPoint

Bell Ringer Practice

✓ **Check Skills You'll Need**
Use student page, transparency, or PowerPoint. For intervention, direct students to:
Line Symmetry
Lesson 8-7
Extra Skills and Word Problems
Practice, Ch. 8

402

✓ Check Skills You'll Need

1. **Vocabulary Review**
How can you fold paper to determine if a figure has *line symmetry*?
1–3. See below.
Trace each figure and draw the lines of symmetry.

2.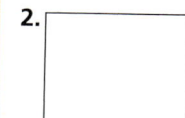

3.

GO for Help
Lesson 8-7

Check Skills You'll Need

1. See if the two sides match when the paper is folded.

2.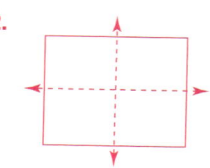

3.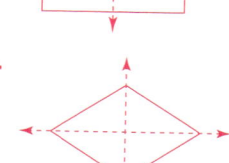

What You'll Learn

To identify and draw translations, reflections, and rotations

◄» **New Vocabulary** transformation, image, translation, reflection, line of reflection, rotation, center of rotation

Why Learn This?

Quilters make interesting patterns by transforming shapes to different positions.

A **transformation** of a figure is a change in its position, shape, or size. The new figure is the **image** of the original. Three types of transformations change only the position of the figure. They are translations, reflections, and rotations.

A **translation,** or slide, is a transformation that moves every point of a figure the same distance and in the same direction.

The blue figure is the image of the black figure after a translation.

EXAMPLE Identifying Translations

1 Is the second figure a translation of the first figure?

a.

no

b.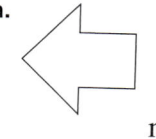

yes

✓ Quick Check

1. Is the second figure a translation of the first figure? **no**

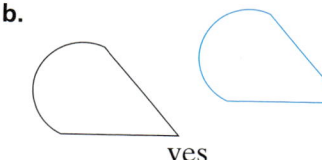

Differentiated Instruction Solutions for All Learners

Special Needs **L1**
Drawing the figures and their transformations may be too difficult for some students. If so, pair them up with students who can help with drawing or tracing the figures.

learning style: visual

Below Level **L2**
Provide students with pattern blocks to trace and manipulate when drawing the three types of transformations. Emphasize the terms slides, flips, and turns instead of translations, reflections, and rotations.

learning style: tactile

A **reflection,** or flip, is a transformation that flips a figure over a line called the **line of reflection.**

2.

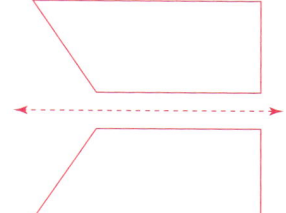

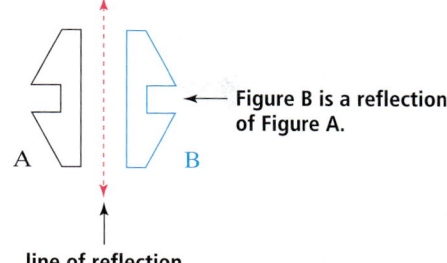

← Figure B is a reflection of Figure A.

A   B

line of reflection

EXAMPLE **Drawing Reflections**

② Draw the reflection of Figure A over the red line of reflection.

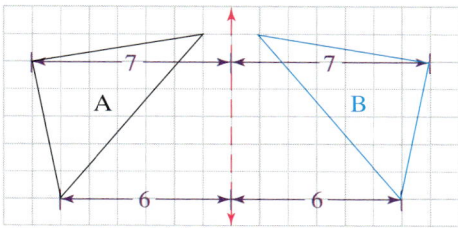

Use the grid to locate the vertices equidistant from the line of reflection.

Then connect the vertices.

✓ Quick Check

2. Copy the figure on graph paper. Draw its reflection over the given line.
   See above left.

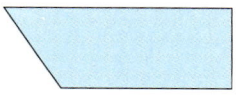

A **rotation,** or turn, is a transformation that turns a figure about a point. This point stays fixed and is called the **center of rotation.** You can describe a rotation using degrees.

EXAMPLE **Application: Nature**

③ Through how many degrees can you rotate the flower at the left so that the image and the original flower match?

The image matches the original flower after rotations of 120°, 240°, and 360°.

360°   120°

240°

✓ Quick Check

3. Tell whether each figure below is a rotation of the first shape.

 a. no    b. 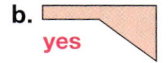 yes   c. 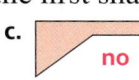 no

8-8 Transformations   **403**

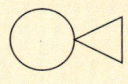 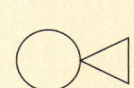
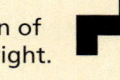 

3. Practice

Assignment Guide

Check Your Understanding
Go over Exercises 1–4 in class before assigning the Homework Exercises.

Homework Exercises
A Practice by Example   5–14
B Apply Your Skills   15–23
C Challenge   24
Test Prep and
  Mixed Review   25–30

Homework Quick Check
To check students' understanding of key skills and concepts, go over Exercises 9, 12, 18, 21, and 22.

Differentiated Instruction Resources

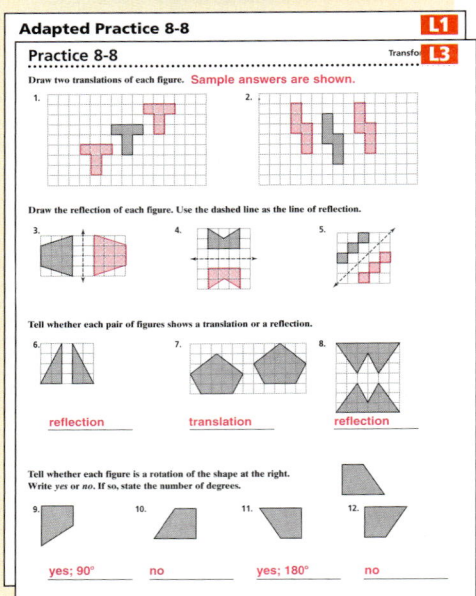

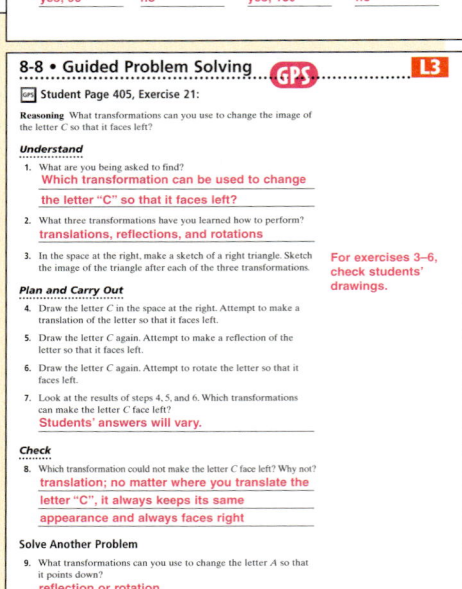

404

✓ Check Your Understanding

Vocabulary Match each type of transformation to its name.

1.  C

2.  A

3.  B

A. reflection   B. translation   C. rotation

4. What clockwise rotation of a figure will produce the same image as a counterclockwise rotation of 180°? **180°**

Homework Exercises

For more exercises, see Extra Skills and Word Problems.

GO for Help

For Exercises	See Examples
5–7	1
8–10	2
11–14	3

A Is the second figure a translation of the first figure?

5.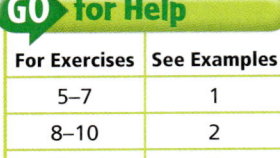
no

6.
yes

7.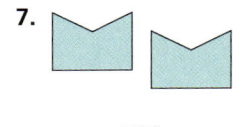
yes

Copy each diagram. Draw its reflection over the given line.

8.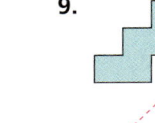

9.

10.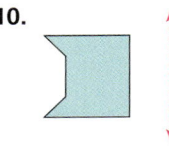

8–10. See margin.

Tell whether each shape is a rotation of the shape at the left.

R

11.
no

12.
no

13.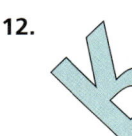
yes

14.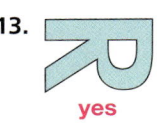
yes

15. 90°, 180°, 270°

B **GPS** **15. Guided Problem Solving** How many degrees can you rotate the figure so that the image matches the original? List all possibilities less than 360°.
- **Understand the Problem** Turn the figure so that it looks exactly the same.
- **Check the Answer** Trace and color the figure. Rotate to check the answer.

8.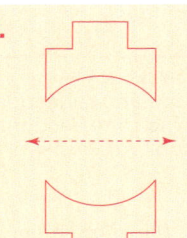

9.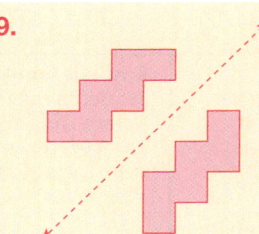

10.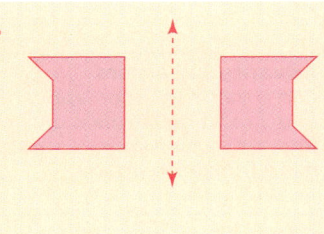

Make three copies of the figure below for Exercises 16–18.
16–18. See margin.

16. Draw a 90° clockwise rotation of the figure.

17. Draw a translation of the figure.

18. Draw a line of reflection below the figure. Then draw the reflection of the figure over the line.

19. Answers may vary. Sample: directly left, directly right and up, and directly to the right

19. Describe a translation of the figure in the fabric.
    See left.

20. Describe the transformation the blades of a windmill make.
    rotation

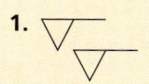

GPS 21. **Reasoning** What transformations can you use to change the image of the letter C so that it faces left? reflection or 180° rotation

22. **Writing in Math** Describe how translations and reflections are alike and how they are different. Include examples. See margin.

23. **Open-Ended** Design a pattern that consists of translations, reflections, and rotations of one basic figure. Explain in words how to find each transformation in your design.
    Check students' work.

C 24. **Challenge** State the least number of degrees you must rotate an equilateral triangle for the image to fit exactly over the original triangle. 120°

Test Prep and Mixed Review　　　**Practice**

Multiple Choice

25. The ratio of adults to children at a skating rink is about 1 to 3. If a manager counts 42 children at the rink, about how many adults would the manager expect to be at the rink? **B**
    Ⓐ 13　　Ⓑ 14　　Ⓒ 15　　Ⓓ 16

26. The stem-and-leaf plot shows the length, in minutes, of 20 movies. What is the mode of the data? **J**
    Ⓕ 86　　Ⓗ 88
    Ⓖ 87　　Ⓙ 90

Length of Movies	
6	0 5
7	4 5 9
8	1 2 4 5 6 8 8
9	0 0 0 2 5
10	6
11	5
12	2

Key: 7 | 8 means 78 minutes

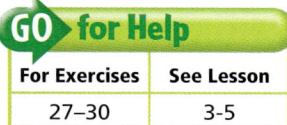
GO for Help

For Exercises	See Lesson
27–30	3-5

Solve each equation.

$21\frac{3}{4}$

27. $x + 5\frac{2}{9} = 14\frac{1}{3}$　$9\frac{1}{9}$　28. $27\frac{1}{2} = x + 5\frac{3}{4}$

29. $25 - 17\frac{2}{3} = x$　$7\frac{1}{3}$　30. $x + 6\frac{2}{3} = 18$

$11\frac{1}{3}$

Online lesson quiz, PHSchool.com, Web Code: aqa-0808　　　8-8　Transformations　**405**

Alternative Assessment

Each student in a pair draws a right triangle and its image when the triangle is rotated three different ways, reflected three different ways, and translated three different ways. Partners exchange papers and identify each image as a translation, reflection, or rotation.

Test Prep

Resources
For additional practice with a variety of test item formats:
• Test-Taking Strategies, p. 407
• Test Prep, p. 411
• Test-Taking Strategies with Transparencies

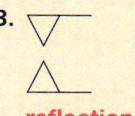
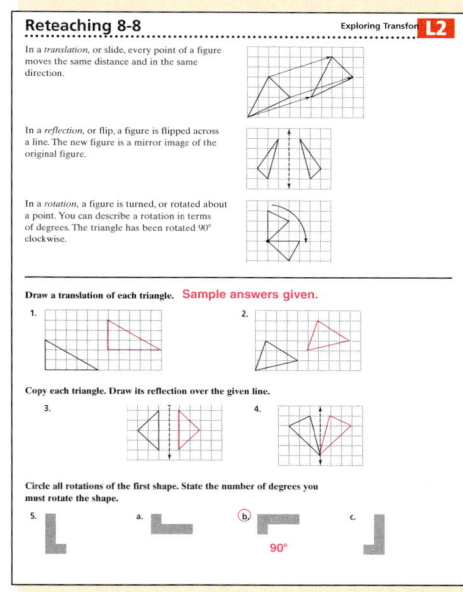
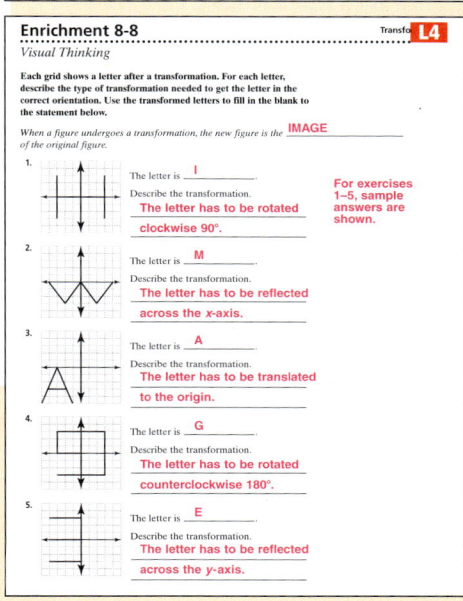
405

Activity Lab

Tessellations

In this Activity, students examine and make arrangements called tessellations.

Guided Instruction

After discussing what a tessellation is, ask students to describe where they have seen them. **Sample: mosaic work, floor tiles, jigsaw puzzles, honeycombs, M.C. Escher artworks, etc.**

To prepare students to work with tessellations, draw six congruent right triangles on the board. Ask students to name the shapes they can make by combining them. **Sample: rectangles, parallelograms, trapezoids**

Exercises

Have students work independently on the Exercises. Then discuss the answers as a class.

Remind students that figures tessellate only if they are congruent and cover a section completely without any gaps or overlaps.

Differentiated Instruction

English Language Learners   **ELL**
Point out to students that tessellate comes from the Latin *tessallare*, which means to pave with *tesserae*, or tiles.

Resources

- rulers
- scissors
- crayons or color markers
- pattern blocks

Tessellations

A **tessellation** is a pattern of repeated, congruent shapes. It covers a surface without gaps or overlaps. You can use a trapezoid to make a tessellation.

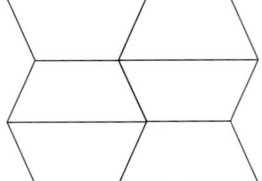

ACTIVITY

1. Draw a $1\frac{1}{2}$-inch square and cut it out. Inside the square, draw a trapezoid and a triangle with one side of each shape on a side of the square.

2. Cut out the figures and move each to the opposite side of the square. Tape them in place.

3. Trace the figure repeatedly to make a tessellation. Compare your tessellation to the figure below.

4. Repeat the activity using two other shapes inside a square.

Exercises

1–4. Check students' work.

Does each figure tessellate? Use a drawing to support your answer.

1. **yes**

2. **yes**

3. **no**
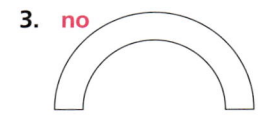

4.
    yes

406   Activity Lab   Tessellations

Drawing a Picture

Often, you can find a solution to a problem more easily if you draw a picture to show the information in the problem.

EXAMPLE

Rectangle A and rectangle B share an edge of 16 inches. The shorter side of rectangle A is 8 inches. If rectangle A is similar to rectangle B, which proportion can you use to find s, the longer side of rectangle B?

Ⓐ $\dfrac{8}{16} = \dfrac{s}{16}$ Ⓑ $\dfrac{8}{16} = \dfrac{16}{s}$ Ⓒ $\dfrac{8}{16} = \dfrac{s}{8}$ Ⓓ $\dfrac{8}{16} = \dfrac{8}{s}$

Step 1 Draw a picture of the two rectangles to visualize the information.

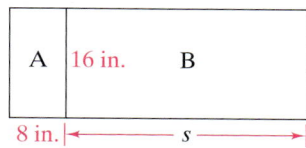

Step 2 Use the side lengths to set up a proportion.

$$\begin{array}{l}\text{shorter side of A} \rightarrow \\ \text{longer side of A} \rightarrow\end{array} \quad \dfrac{8}{16} = \dfrac{16}{s} \quad \begin{array}{l}\leftarrow \text{shorter side of B} \\ \leftarrow \text{longer side of B}\end{array}$$

● The correct answer is choice B.

Exercises

1. Triangle ABC is similar to triangle XYZ. Angle B and angle Y are right angles. If $\overline{AB}$ is 4 inches, $\overline{AC}$ is 8 inches, and $\overline{XZ}$ is 16 inches, which proportion can you use to find s, the length of $\overline{XY}$? **C**

Ⓐ $\dfrac{4}{16} = \dfrac{s}{8}$ Ⓒ $\dfrac{4}{8} = \dfrac{s}{16}$

Ⓑ $\dfrac{4}{16} = \dfrac{8}{s}$ Ⓓ $\dfrac{4}{8} = \dfrac{16}{s}$

2. $\overleftrightarrow{MN}$ and $\overleftrightarrow{RS}$ intersect at point W. If $m\angle MWR = 130°$ and $m\angle MRW = 20°$, what is the measure of $\angle WMR$? **G**

Ⓕ 20°   Ⓗ 50°

Ⓖ 30°   Ⓙ 70°

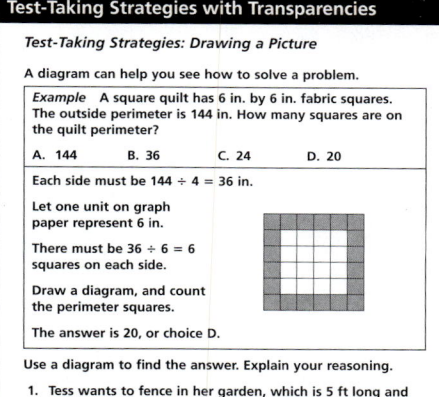

Chapter 8 Review

Chapter 8 Review

Resources

Student Edition

Extra Skills and Word Problems
  Practice, Ch. 8, p. 626
English/Spanish Glossary, p. 654
Formulas and Properties, p. 652
Tables, p. 648

All in One Teaching Resources

- Vocabulary and Study
  Skills 8F **L3**

Differentiated Instruction

Spanish Vocabulary Workbook
  with Study Skills **ELL**
Interactive Textbook
- Audio Glossary
Online Vocabulary Quiz

Success  Tracker™
Online at PHSchool.com

Vocabulary Review

 acute angle (p. 368)
acute triangle (p. 380)
angle (p. 367)
center of rotation (p. 403)
complementary angles
   (p. 374)
congruent angles (p. 375)
congruent figures (p. 392)
congruent segments (p. 381)
degrees (p. 367)
equilateral triangle (p. 381)
image (p. 402)
intersecting lines (p. 363)
irregular polygon (p. 387)
isosceles triangle (p. 381)
line (p. 362)
line of reflection (p. 403)

line of symmetry (p. 398)
line symmetry (p. 398)
obtuse angle (p. 368)
obtuse triangle (p. 380)
parallel lines (p. 363)
parallelogram (p. 387)
perpendicular lines (p. 368)
plane (p. 363)
point (p. 362)
polygon (p. 386)
quadrilateral (p. 387)
ray (p. 362)
rectangle (p. 387)
reflection (p. 403)
regular polygon (p. 387)
rhombus (p. 387)
right angle (p. 368)

right triangle (p. 380)
rotation (p. 403)
scalene triangle (p. 381)
segment (p. 362)
similar figures (p. 393)
skew lines (p. 363)
square (p. 387)
straight angle (p. 368)
supplementary angles
   (p. 374)
transformation (p. 402)
translation (p. 402)
transversal (p. 378)
trapezoid (p. 387)
triangle (p. 380)
vertex (p. 367)
vertical angles (p. 375)

Choose the correct term to complete each sentence.

1. The measure of an (acute, obtuse) angle is between 90° and 180°.
   obtuse

2. An (isosceles, equilateral) triangle has three congruent sides.
   equilateral

3. Lines that intersect to form right angles are (skew,
   perpendicular). **perpendicular**

4. A (rectangle, rhombus) always has four right angles. **rectangle**

5. A (ray, line) extends in two opposite directions without end.
   line

Go Online
PHSchool.com

For: Vocabulary quiz
Web Code: aqj-0851

Skills and Concepts

Lesson 8-1

- To identify and work with points, lines, segments, and rays

A **point** has no size, only location. A **line** continues without end in opposite directions. A **segment** is part of a line and has two endpoints. A **ray** is part of a line and has one endpoint.

Parallel lines are lines in the same plane that do not intersect. **Skew lines** lie in different planes.

6. **Answers may vary.**
   Sample: $\overleftrightarrow{EF}$ and $\overleftrightarrow{AB}$

7. **Answers may vary.**
   Sample: $\overrightarrow{BC}$, $\overrightarrow{BA}$

6. Name two parallel lines.

7. Name two rays with endpoint B.

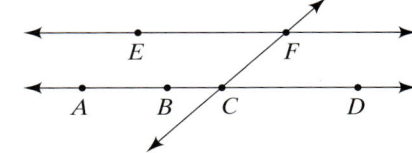

Spanish Vocabulary/Study Skills **ELL**

Vocabulary/Study Skills **L3**

8F: Vocabulary Review Puzzle For use with the Chapter Review

Study Skill Puzzles are a fun way to learn and review vocabulary.

Complete the crossword puzzle. For help, use the glossary in your textbook.

ACROSS

1. lines that intersect to form right angles
5. figures that have the same shape, but not necessarily the same size
8. angle that measures 90°
9. lines that lie in different planes
10. part of a line
12. angle that measures less than 90°
13. a triangle with no congruent sides

DOWN

2. parallelogram with four right angles
3. a triangle with at least two sides congruent
4. lines that are in the same plane and do not intersect
6. parallelogram with four congruent sides
7. an angle that measures 180°
11. a triangle with three congruent sides

Lessons 8-2 and 8-3

- To measure and classify angles
- To use relationships between special pairs of angles

Angles are classified as **acute, right, obtuse,** or **straight.** Two intersecting lines form two pairs of **vertical angles.** The sum of the measures of two **complementary angles** is 90°. The sum of the measures of two **supplementary angles** is 180°.

8–11. Answers may vary. Samples are given.

Name each of the following.

8. a pair of vertical angles
   ∠DEG and ∠BEF
9. an obtuse angle
   ∠FEG
10. two congruent angles
    ∠ABE and ∠EBC
11. an acute angle **∠DEG**

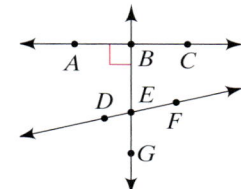

Lessons 8-4 and 8-5

- To classify triangles by their angles and their sides
- To identify regular polygons and to classify quadrilaterals

You can classify a triangle as **acute, obtuse,** or **right.** You can also classify a triangle as **scalene, isosceles,** or **equilateral.**

Polygons with four sides are called **quadrilaterals.** Three special types of **parallelograms** are the **rhombus,** the **rectangle,** and the **square.**

Give the best name for each polygon.

12. rectangle

12.

13. hexagon

14. pentagon

Lessons 8-6, 8-7, and 8-8

- To identify congruent and similar figures
- To find lines of symmetry
- To identify and draw translations, reflections, and rotations

Congruent figures have the same size and shape. **Similar** figures have the same shape, but not necessarily the same size. **Translations, reflections,** and **rotations** are transformations that change the position of a figure.

Do the triangles appear to be congruent or similar?

15. similar

16. congruent

17. Draw a translation and a reflection of the figure shown. **See margin.**

17. See back of book.

Chapter 8 Test

Go Online PHSchool.com **For:** Online chapter test **Web Code:** aqa-0852

Resources

- ExamView Assessment Suite CD-ROM
  - Ch. 8 Ready-Made Test
  - Make your own Ch. 8 test
- MindPoint Quiz Show CD-ROM
  - Chapter 8 Review

Differentiated Instruction

All in One Teaching Resources
- Below Level Chapter 8 Test **L2**
- Chapter 8 Test **L3**
- Chapter 8 Alternative Assessment **L4**

Spanish Assessment Resources **ELL**
- Below Level Chapter 8 Test **L2**
- Chapter 8 Test **L3**
- Chapter 8 Alternative Assessment **L4**

ExamView Assessment Suite CD-ROM
- Special Needs Test **L1**
- Special Needs Practice Bank **L1**

Online Chapter 8 Test at www.PHSchool.com **L3**

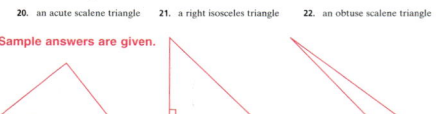

410

---

1. Draw three points that do not lie on the same line. Label them *X*, *Y*, and *Z*. Draw $\overleftrightarrow{XY}$ and $\overrightarrow{YZ}$. **See margin.**

Measure each angle. Then classify it as *acute, right, obtuse,* or *straight*.

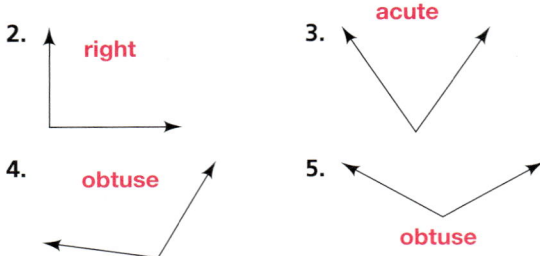

2. **right**

3. **acute**

4. **obtuse**

5. **obtuse**

Find the complement and the supplement of each angle measure.

6. 72° **18°, 108°**

7. 42° **48°, 138°**

Classify each triangle as *acute, right,* or *obtuse*.

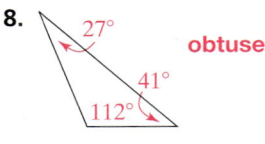

8. 27° 41° 112° **obtuse**

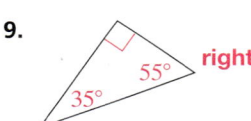

9. 55° 35° **right**

Classify each triangle as *scalene, isosceles,* or *equilateral*.

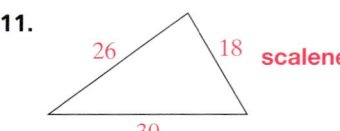

10. 15 15 15 **equilateral**

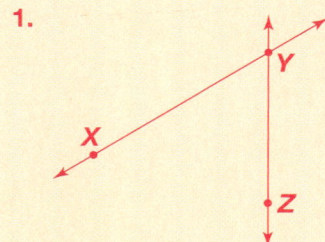

11. 26 18 30 **scalene**

---

12. Draw a quadrilateral with the given number of lines of symmetry.
    a. 0 **b.** 1 **c.** 2 **d.** 4
    12a–d. Check students' work.

Write the best name for each figure.

13. **pentagon**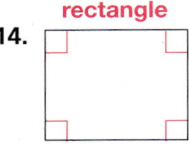

14. **rectangle**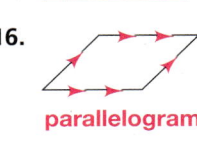

15. **octagon**

16. **parallelogram**

17. **Writing in Math** Describe how congruent figures and similar figures are alike and how they are different. **See margin.**

How many lines of symmetry does each quadrilateral have?

18. **1**

19. **2**

Use the shape below for Exercises 20–22.

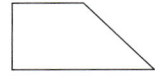

20. Draw a translation of the shape.
    20–22. See margin.

21. Draw a reflection of the shape. Show the line of reflection.

22. Draw a 180° clockwise rotation of the shape. Show the point you chose as the center of rotation.

1.

17. Congruent and similar figures both have the same shape. Congruent figures are also the same size.

20–22. See back of book.

Multiple Choice

Choose the best answer.

1. What information does the circle graph below NOT tell you about Jen? **C**

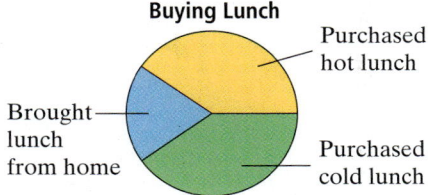

Buying Lunch

Purchased hot lunch

Brought lunch from home

Purchased cold lunch

- Ⓐ Jen purchased lunch more often than she brought it from home.
- Ⓑ Jen purchased hot lunches about as often as cold lunches.
- Ⓒ Jen brought lunch from home more often than she purchased cold lunch.
- Ⓓ Jen purchased hot lunch more often than she brought lunch from home.

2. A hot air balloon is 2,250 feet in the air. It is scheduled to land at 3:30 P.M. It descends 90 feet every minute. When should the balloonist start descending? **G**
- Ⓕ 3:55 P.M.
- Ⓗ 2:55 P.M.
- Ⓖ 3:05 P.M.
- Ⓙ 2:45 P.M.

3. In order to conclude that *MNOP* is a rhombus, what do you need to know? **D**
- Ⓐ $\overline{MO}$ has length 8.
- Ⓑ $\overline{MO}$ is perpendicular to $\overline{NP}$.
- Ⓒ $\overline{NP}$ and $\overline{MO}$ are congruent.
- Ⓓ $\overline{MP}$ and $\overline{PO}$ both have length 8.

4. Which set of decimals is ordered from least to greatest? **G**
- Ⓕ 0.2, 0.02, 0.22
- Ⓖ 0.15, 0.51, 1.05
- Ⓗ 0.24, 0.3, 0.05
- Ⓙ 0.49, 0.4, 0.05

5. The Amazon River in South America carries one sixth of Earth's water that flows into oceans. About what percent is this? **A**
- Ⓐ 17%
- Ⓑ 12.5%
- Ⓒ 10%
- Ⓓ 6%

6. Which is ordered from least to greatest? **H**
- Ⓕ $\frac{3}{7}, \frac{5}{7}, \frac{7}{11}$
- Ⓗ $\frac{1}{3}, \frac{2}{3}, \frac{4}{5}$
- Ⓖ $\frac{1}{4}, \frac{1}{2}, \frac{2}{5}$
- Ⓙ $\frac{1}{8}, \frac{2}{5}, \frac{3}{10}$

Gridded Response

7. $31.2 \times \blacksquare = 0.0312$. What is $\blacksquare$? **0.001**

8. What is the value of $3 + 4 \times 2^3$? **35**

9. What is the degree measurement of a supplement of a 32° angle? **148**

10. The greatest angle in a right triangle measures ___?___ degrees. **90**

Short Response

11. Which of the mean, median, mode, or range is the greatest for these data? Explain. **See margin.**
81, 70, 95, 73, 74, 91, 86, 74

12. a. Bagels cost $6 per dozen. Find the cost of 5 bagels. Use a proportion.
    b. Find the unit cost for a bagel.
    a–b. See margin.

Extended Response

13. Can you conclude that the two triangles below are NOT similar? Explain. **See margin.**

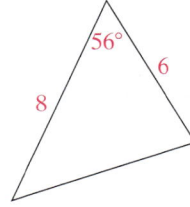 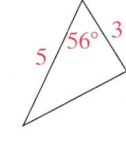

Resources

Test Prep Workbook

All in One Teaching Resources
- Cumulative Review **L3**

ExamView Assessment Suite CD-ROM
- Standardized Test Practice

Differentiated Instruction

Progress Monitoring Assessments
- Benchmark Test 4 **L3**

Spanish Assessment Resources
- Spanish Cumulative Review **ELL**

ExamView Assessment Suite CD-ROM
- Special Needs Practice Bank **L1**

[1] Correct answer with one minor error.

13. **[4]** $\frac{8}{6} \neq \frac{5}{3}$

    $24 \neq 30$

    No

    [3] correct answer without using a proportion
    [2] correct answer with incorrect work OR correct work with no answer or an incorrect answer
    [1] correct answer with no work OR some correct work

Spanish Cumulative Review ELL

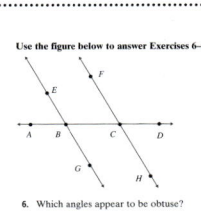

Item	1	2	3	4	5	6	7	8	9	10	11	12	13
Lesson	7-8	3-1	8-5	1-6	7-6	4-8	3-7	4-2	8-3	8-4	2-2	7-4	8-6

11. **[2] Mean.** Mean: 80.5, Median: 77.5, Mode: 74, Range: 25 OR a correct explanation including mean, median, mode, and range

[1] the answer OR correct values for 3 of the 4 terms OR a correct explanation

12. **[2]** $\frac{2.00}{12} = \frac{x}{5}$

$12x = 10.00$

$x = \frac{10}{12} = 0.83333$

5 bagels cost $0.84.

Students will use data from these two pages to answer the questions posed in Put It All Together.

Invite students to share any experiences they have had with construction or from seeing buildings being built around town. Ask questions such as:

- *What shape are most wall frames and roof frames?* **Sample: Wall frames are usually rectangles and roof frames are often triangles.**
- *How do builders know what size to make walls, windows, and doors?* **Sample: They refer to blueprints that detail the design for the building.**

Discuss the different roles of architects and builders.

Materials
- Photos or diagrams of buildings under construction
- A blueprint

Activating Prior Knowledge

Guide students to understand that a blueprint is a scale drawing and is essential to architects and builders. Ask students to share any experiences they have had examining blueprints.

Guided Instruction

Have volunteers read aloud the information about blueprints. If possible, provide students with copies of floor plans from the real estate section of the newspaper or from brochures. Ask:

- *What things a floor plan show?* **Sample: The location and footprint of walls, doors, windows, stairways, and perhaps appliances and furniture.**
- *What things do floor plans not show?* **Sample: What walls, doors, windows, stairways, appliances, and furniture actually look like.**

412

Applying Geometry

Building Outside the Box Before your home was built, it was probably drawn as a two-dimensional plan, or blueprint. A blueprint lets an architect experiment on paper with different ideas. The architect can discuss these ideas with the owner before construction begins. A blueprint also gives clear directions to a contractor on what to build. Most houses and apartments are rectangles with rectangular rooms, but they can be any shape.

Using a Blueprint
Builders read blueprints and translate the two-dimensional notes into three-dimensional buildings. A builder refers to a blueprint many times a day during the building process.

Reading a Blueprint
A blueprint shows the layout of individual floors of your home in $\frac{1}{4}$ inch–to–1 foot scale. It includes the dimensions of each room and closet and provides a key so you know what various symbols mean.

412

1a. trapezoid

b. kitchen - hexagon
bedroom - trapezoid
computer & games
room - parallelogram
bathroom - triangle
family room - pentagon

2. Answers may vary.
Sample: bedrooms,
bathrooms, kitchen,
TV room, living room,
computer room, porch

3. See margin, p. 413.

4. Check students' work.

5. Rooms with angles less or greater than 90° make it difficult to create wide spaces; the rectangular shape is very efficient.

Put It All Together

Materials ruler

1. The blueprint shows a home where no room is rectangular.
   a. What shape is the home?
   b. Identify the shape of each room.

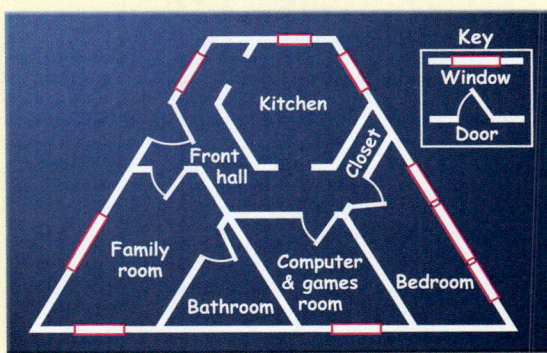

2. **Open-Ended** Suppose you are designing your own home. Make a list of the rooms you would like to include. Feel free to include rooms for hobbies or other special interests.

3. Make a rough sketch of the home, showing the shape and location of each room.
   • Use at least five different shapes from this chapter.
   • Include at least two rooms that are congruent to each other. Make one a translation or rotation of the other.
   • Remember to include hallways and doorways so that people can get into the rooms!

4. Use a ruler to make a final drawing of your design. Show windows and doors using the key in the blueprint. Label the rooms. Add furniture to your drawing if you wish.

5. **Writing in Math**  Why do you think homes usually have rectangular rooms?

Go Online
PHSchool.com
For: Information about architecture
Web Code: aqe-0853

413

Building a Landscape
Landscape architects use flowers, bushes, and trees to make a pleasing environment around a building.

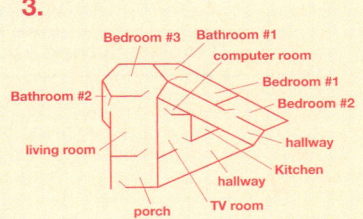

9 Geometry and Measurement

Chapter at a Glance

Lesson Titles, Objectives, and Features	Assessment	NCTM Standards	Local Standards
9-1 Metric Units of Length, Mass, and Capacity • To use metric units of measure and to choose appropriate units of length, mass, and capacity **9-1b Activity Lab:** Metric Units	Lesson Quiz	1, 4, 6, 7, 8, 9, 10	
9-2 Converting Units in the Metric System • To convert between metric measurements **Vocabulary Builder:** Using Concept Maps	Lesson Quiz	1, 4, 6, 7, 8, 9, 10	
9-3 Perimeters and Areas of Rectangles • To solve problems involving perimeters and areas of rectangles	Lesson Quiz	1, 2, 3, 4, 6, 7, 8, 9, 10	
9-4a Activity Lab, Hands On: Comparing Areas **9-4 Areas of Parallelograms and Triangles** • To solve problems involving areas of parallelograms, triangles, and complex figures	Lesson Quiz Checkpoint Quiz 1	1, 2, 3, 4, 6, 7, 8, 9, 10	
9-5a Activity Lab, Data Collection: Exploring Circles **9-5 Circles and Circumference** • To identify the parts of a circle and find radius, diameter, and circumference **Guided Problem Solving:** Practice Solving Problems	Lesson Quiz	1, 2, 3, 4, 6, 7, 8, 9, 10	
9-6 Area of a Circle • To find the area of a circle	Lesson Quiz	1, 2, 3, 4, 6, 7, 8, 9, 10	
9-7a Activity Lab, Hands On: Three-Dimensional Views **9-7 Three-Dimensional Figures and Spatial Reasoning** • To identify three-dimensional figures	Lesson Quiz	1, 3, 6, 7, 8, 9, 10	
9-8 Surface Areas of Prisms • To find the surface area of a prism	Lesson Quiz	1, 2, 3, 4, 6, 7, 8, 9, 10	
9-9a Activity Lab, Hands On: Exploring Volume **9-9 Volumes of Rectangular Prisms** • To find the volume of rectangular prisms	Lesson Quiz Checkpoint Quiz 2	1, 2, 3, 4, 6, 7, 8, 9, 10	
9-10a Activity Lab, Hands On: Exploring Cylinders **9-10 Surface Areas and Volumes of Cylinders** • To find the surface area and volume of cylinders	Lesson Quiz	1, 2, 3, 4, 6, 7, 8, 9, 10	
Problem Solving Application: Applying Measurement			

NCTM Standards 2000

1 Number and Operations	**2** Algebra	**3** Geometry
6 Problem Solving	**7** Reasoning and Proof	**8** Communication

4 Measurement   **5** Data Analysis and Probability
9 Connections   **10** Representation

Correlations to Standardized Tests

All content for these tests is contained in *Prentice Hall Math,* Course 1. This chart reflects coverage in this chapter only.

	9-1	9-2	9-3	9-4	9-5	9-6	9-7	9-8	9-9	9-10
Terra Nova CAT6 (Level 16)										
Number and Number Relations	✔	✔	✔	✔	✔	✔	✔	✔	✔	✔
Computation and Numerical Estimation	✔	✔	✔	✔	✔	✔	✔	✔	✔	✔
Operation Concepts	✔	✔	✔	✔	✔	✔	✔	✔	✔	✔
Measurement	✔	✔	✔	✔	✔	✔	✔	✔	✔	✔
Geometry and Spatial Sense			✔	✔	✔	✔	✔	✔	✔	✔
Data Analysis, Statistics, and Probability										
Patterns, Functions, Algebra	✔	✔	✔	✔	✔	✔	✔	✔	✔	✔
Problem Solving and Reasoning	✔	✔	✔	✔	✔	✔	✔	✔	✔	✔
Communication	✔	✔	✔	✔	✔	✔	✔	✔	✔	✔
Decimals, Fractions, Integers, and Percent	✔	✔	✔	✔	✔	✔	✔	✔	✔	✔
Order of Operations										
Terra Nova CTBS (Level 16)										
Whole Numbers, Decimals, Fractions	✔	✔	✔	✔	✔	✔	✔	✔	✔	✔
Numeration, Number Theory	✔	✔	✔	✔	✔	✔	✔	✔	✔	✔
Data Interpretation										
Pre-algebra			✔	✔	✔	✔		✔	✔	✔
Measurement	✔	✔	✔	✔	✔	✔	✔	✔	✔	✔
Geometry			✔	✔	✔	✔	✔	✔	✔	✔
ITBS (Level 12)										
Number Properties and Operations	✔	✔	✔	✔	✔	✔	✔	✔	✔	✔
Algebra	✔	✔	✔	✔	✔	✔	✔	✔	✔	✔
Geometry			✔	✔	✔	✔	✔	✔	✔	✔
Measurement	✔	✔	✔	✔	✔	✔	✔	✔	✔	✔
Probability and Statistics										
Estimation										
SAT10 (Int 2 Level)										
Number Sense and Operations	✔	✔	✔	✔	✔	✔	✔	✔	✔	✔
Patterns, Relationships, and Algebra	✔	✔	✔	✔	✔	✔	✔	✔	✔	✔
Data, Statistics, and Probability										
Geometry and Measurement	✔	✔	✔	✔	✔	✔	✔	✔	✔	✔
NAEP										
Number Sense, Properties, and Operations										
Measurement	✔	✔	✔	✔	✔	✔		✔	✔	✔
Geometry and Spatial Sense							✔			
Data Analysis, Statistics, and Probability										
Algebra and Functions										

CAT6 California Achievement Test, 6th Ed.   **CTBS** Comprehensive Test of Basic Skills   **ITBS** Iowa Test of Basic Skills, Form M
SAT10 Stanford Achievement Test, 10th Ed.   **NAEP** National Assessment of Educational Progress 2005 Mathematics Objectives

Math Background

Skills Trace

> ### BEFORE Chapter 9
> Grade 5 presented metric units of measure and basic perimeter and area calculations.
>
> ### DURING Chapter 9
> Course 1 reviews measurement and extends it to finding the surface area and volume of three-dimensional figures.
>
> ### AFTER Chapter 9
> Throughout this course, students apply geometric reasoning and measurement skills to solve real-world problems.

9-2 Converting Units in the Metric System

Math Understandings
- You can rewrite one metric unit as another metric unit within a measurement type (length, capacity, mass) by multiplying or dividing by a power of 10.
- To convert to smaller units, you multiply. To convert to larger units, you divide.

Length	Mass	Capacity
1,000 m = 1 km	1,000 g = 1 kg	1,000 L = 1 kL
100 cm = 1 m		
1,000 mm = 1 m	1,000 mg = 1 g	1,000 mL = 1 L
10 mm = 1 cm		

Example: Convert 236 grams to kilograms.
236 g ÷ 1,000 = 0.236 kg

9-1 Metric Units of Length, Mass, and Capacity

Math Understandings
- The metric system uses prefixes to relate the sizes of units to standard units.
- Mass (metric system) refers to the amount of matter in an object and does not vary from place to place. Weight (customary system) refers to the gravitational force exerted by the given amount of substance, and it differs, for example, on Earth and on the moon.

The **metric system** of measurement is a decimal system. The standard unit of length in the metric system is the **meter (m)**. **Mass** is a measure of the amount of matter in an object. The standard unit of mass is the **gram (g)**. **Capacity** is a measure of the amount of liquid an object holds. The standard unit of capacity is the **liter (L)**.

Common Metric Units With Examples

Unit	Relationship	Example
kilogram (kg)	1,000 g	mass of 4 videos
gram (g)	1 g	mass of paper clip
milligram (mg)	0.001 g	mass of grain of salt
kiloliter (kL)	1,000 L	water for 2 bathtubs
liter (L)	1 L	a bottle of juice
milliliter (mL)	0.001 L	2 dewdrops

9-3 Perimeters and Areas of Rectangles
9-4 Areas of Parallelograms and Triangles

Math Understandings
- You can estimate the area of any figure by using a grid and counting the number of squares it covers.
- Perimeters and other linear measures use linear units such as feet and meters. You measure area in square units.
- You can find the area of an irregular figure by separating it into familiar figures, finding the area of each smaller figure, and adding the areas together.

Any side can be considered the **base of a parallelogram.** The **height of a parallelogram** is the perpendicular distance from one base to another. Any side can be the **base of a triangle.** The **height of a triangle** is the length of the perpendicular segment from a vertex to the base opposite that vertex.

Area of a Parallelogram	Area of a Triangle
$A = bh$	$A = \frac{1}{2}bh$

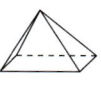   

Prism　　**Pyramid**　　**Cylinder**　　**Cone**　　**Sphere**

9-5 Circles and Circumference
9-6 Area of a Circle

Math Understandings

- For every circle, the ratio of the circumference, C, to the diameter, d, is the same.
- Although the ratio $\frac{C}{d}$, or π, is not exactly equal to $\frac{22}{7}$ or to 3.14, you can use these numbers as a good approximation of the value of π when you solve problems.

A **circle** is a set of points in a plane, each of which is the same distance from a given point called the *center*. The distance around a circle is its **circumference**.

Circumference of a Circle	Area of a Circle
$C = \pi d = 2\pi r$	$A = \pi r^2$

9-7 Three-Dimensional Figures and Spatial Reasoning

Math Understandings

- A three-dimensional figure has the three dimensions of length, width, and height.
- You name a prism by the shape of its bases. You name a pyramid by the type of base it has.

A *three-dimensional figure* is a figure that does not lie in a plane. A **prism** is a three-dimensional figure with two parallel and congruent faces that are polygons. The prism that has six congruent faces that are squares is a **cube**. A **pyramid** is a three-dimensional figure with one polygon for a base. All of the other faces are triangles. The cylinder, cone, and sphere do not use polygons for bases.

9-8 Surface Areas of Prisms
9-9 Volumes of Rectangular Prisms
9-10 Surface Areas and Volumes of Cylinders

Math Understandings

- You can use a net, or pattern that you can fold to form a three-dimensional figure, to find the surface area of a prism.

The **surface area** of a three-dimensional figure is the sum of the areas of its surfaces. The surface area of a rectangular prism is the sum of the areas of the six rectangles in its net. The surface area of a cylinder is the sum of the area of the rectangle and two circles in its net.

The **volume** of a three-decimal figure is the number of cubic units needed to fill the space inside the figure. The **cubic unit** is the amount of space in a cube that measures 1 unit long by 1 unit wide by 1 unit high.

Volume of a Prism
Volume = Area of Base × height $V = Bh$　　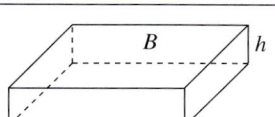

Additional Professional Development Opportunities

Math Background Notes for Chapter 9: Every lesson has a Math Background in the PLAN section.

Research Overview, Mathematics Strands
Additional support for these topics and more is in the front of the Teacher's Edition.

LessonLab
LessonLab, a Pearson Education company, offers comprehensive, facilitated professional development designed to help teachers to improve student achievement. To learn more, please visit lessonlab.com.

Chapter 9 Resources

	9-1	9-2	9-3	9-4	9-5	9-6	9-7	9-8	9-9	9-10	For the Chapter
Print Resources											
L3 Practice	●	●	●	●	●	●	●	●	●	●	
L1 Adapted Practice	●	●	●	●	●	●	●	●	●	●	
L3 Guided Problem Solving	●	●	●	●	●	●	●	●	●	●	
L2 Reteaching	●	●	●	●	●	●	●	●	●	●	
L4 Enrichment	●	●	●	●	●	●	●	●	●	●	
L3 Daily Notetaking Guide	●	●	●	●	●	●	●	●	●	●	
L1 Adapted Daily Notetaking Guide	●	●	●	●	●	●	●	●	●	●	
L3 Vocabulary and Study Skills Worksheets	●		●		●		●		●		●
L3 Daily Puzzles	●	●	●	●	●	●	●	●	●	●	
L3 Activity Labs	●	●	●	●	●	●	●	●	●	●	
L3 Checkpoint Quiz				●					●		
L3 Chapter Project											●
L2 Below Level Chapter Test											●
L3 Chapter Test											●
L4 Alternative Assessment											●
L3 Cumulative Review											●
Spanish Resources ELL											
L3 Practice	●	●	●	●	●	●	●	●	●	●	
L3 Vocabulary and Study Skills Worksheets	●		●		●		●		●		●
L3 Checkpoint Quiz				●					●		
L2 Below Level Chapter Test											●
L3 Chapter Test											●
L4 Alternative Assessment											●
L3 Cumulative Review											●
Transparencies											
Check Skills You'll Need	●	●	●	●	●	●	●	●	●		
Additional Examples	●	●	●	●	●	●	●	●	●	●	
Problem of the Day	●	●	●	●	●	●	●	●	●		
Classroom Aid				●							
Student Edition Answers	●	●	●	●	●	●	●	●	●	●	●
Lesson Quiz	●	●	●	●	●	●	●	●	●	●	
Test-Taking Strategies											●
Technology											
Interactive Textbook Online	●	●	●	●	●	●	●	●	●	●	●
StudentExpress™ CD-ROM	●	●	●	●	●	●	●	●	●	●	●
Success Tracker™ Online Intervention	●	●	●	●	●	●	●	●	●	●	●
TeacherExpress™ CD-ROM	●	●	●	●	●	●	●	●	●	●	●
PresentationExpress™ with QuickTake Presenter CD-ROM	●	●	●	●	●	●	●	●	●	●	●
ExamView® Assessment Suite CD-ROM	●	●	●	●	●	●	●	●	●	●	●
MindPoint® Quiz Show CD-ROM											●
Prentice Hall Web Site: PHSchool.com	●	●	●	●	●	●	●	●	●	●	●

Also available: **Prentice Hall Assessment System**
- Progress Monitoring Assessments
- Skills and Concepts Review
- Test Prep Workbook

Other Resources
Algebra Readiness Tests
All-in-One Student Workbook
All-in-One Student Workbook, Adapted Version
Multilingual Handbook

Solution Key
Math Notes Study Folder
Spanish Cumulative Assessment

Where You Can Use the Lesson Resources

Here is a suggestion, following the four-step teaching plan, for how you can incorporate Differentiated Instruction Resources into your teaching.

	Instructional Resources **L3**	**Differentiated** Instruction **Resources**
1. Plan		
Preparation Read the Math Background in the Teacher's Edition to connect this lesson with students' previous experience. **Starting Class** **Check Skills You'll Need** Assign these exercises to review prerequisite skills. **New Vocabulary** Help students pre-read the lesson by pointing out the new terms introduced in the lesson.	**Math Background** **Math Understandings** **Transparencies & PresentationExpress™ with QuickTake Presenter CD-ROM** Check Skills You'll Need Problem of the Day **Resources** Vocabulary and Study Skills	**Spanish Support** **ELL** Vocabulary and Study Skills
2. Teach		
L3 Guided Instruction Use the Activity Labs to build conceptual understanding. Teach each Example. Use the Teacher's Edition side column notes for specific teaching tips, including Error Prevention notes. Use the Additional Examples found in the side column (and on transparency and PowerPoint) as an alternative presentation for the content. After each Example, assign the Quick Check exercise for that Example to get an immediate assessment of student understanding. Use the Closure activity in the Teacher's Edition to help students attain mastery of lesson content.	**Student Edition** Activity Lab **Resources** Daily Notetaking Guide Activity Lab **Transparencies & PresentationExpress™ with QuickTake Presenter CD-ROM** Additional Examples Classroom Aids **ExamView® Assessment Suite CD-ROM**	**Teacher's Edition** Every lesson includes suggestions for working with students who need special attention. **L1** Special Needs **L2** Below Level **L4** Advanced Learners **ELL** English Language Learners **Resources** **L1** Adapted Daily Notetaking Guide **Multilingual Handbook**
3. Practice		

Assignment Guide
Check Your Understanding
Use these questions to check students' understanding before you assign homework.
Homework Exercises
Assign homework from these leveled exercises in the Assignment Guide.
  A Practice by Example
  B Apply Your Skills
  C Challenge
  Test Prep and Mixed Review
Homework Quick Check
Use these key exercises to quickly check students' homework.
	Transparencies & PresentationExpress™ CD-ROM
	Student Answers
	Resources
	Practice
	Guided Problem Solving
	Vocabulary and Study Skills
	Activity Lab
	Daily Puzzles
	ExamView® Assessment Suite CD-ROM
		Spanish Support
		ELL Practice
		ELL Vocabulary and Study Skills
		Resources
		L1 Adapted Practice
		L4 Enrichment

4. Assess & Reteach		
Lesson Quiz Assign the Lesson Quiz to assess students' mastery of the lesson content. **Checkpoint Quiz** Use the Checkpoint Quiz to assess student progress over several lessons.	**Transparencies & PresentationExpress™ with QuickTake Presenter CD-ROM** Lesson Quiz **Resources** Checkpoint Quiz	**Resources** **L2** Reteaching **ELL** Checkpoint Quiz Success Tracker™ Online Intervention **ExamView® Assessment Suite CD-ROM**

KEY **L1** Special Needs **L2** Below Level **L3** For All Students **L4** Advanced, Gifted **ELL** English Language Learners

Measurement

Check Your Readiness

Answers are in the back of the textbook.

For intervention, direct students to:

Choosing Units of Measurement
Lesson 6-6
Extra Skills and Word
Problems Practice, Ch. 6

Changing Units
Lesson 6-7
Extra Skills and Word
Problems Practice, Ch. 6

Classifying Polygons
Lesson 8-4, 8-5
Extra Skills and Word
Problems Practice, Ch. 8

What You've Learned

- In Chapter 6, you estimated measurements in the customary system.
- You also converted units of measure within the customary system.
- In Chapter 8, you identified and classified angles and two-dimensional figures.

Check Your Readiness

GO for Help	
For Exercises	**See Lessons**
1–2	6-6
3–8	6-7
9–11	8-4, 8-5

Choosing Units of Measurement

Choose an appropriate unit for each measurement.

1. weight of a newborn baby **pounds**

2. distance to the sun **miles**

Changing Units

Complete each statement.

3. ■ oz = 9 lb **144**   4. 46 in. = ■ ft $3\frac{5}{6}$ 5. $7\frac{1}{4}$ c = ■ pt $3\frac{5}{8}$

Use <, =, or > to complete each statement.

6. 14 ft ■ 4 yd   7. $2\frac{1}{2}$ gal ■ 11 qt   8. 5 c ■ 37 fl oz
   >   **<**   **>**

Classifying Polygons

Classify each figure. Classify the triangle by its sides.

9. **rhombus**   10. **isosceles triangle**   11. **trapezoid**

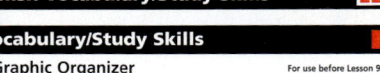

Chapter 9 Overview

In this chapter, students begin by working with metric measurements. Then they apply their geometric understandings as they learn to find perimeters, areas, volumes, and surface areas of geometric figures.

Activating Prior Knowledge

In this chapter, on measurement and geometry, students build on and extend their knowledge of customary measurement to work with metric measures. They also draw upon their understanding of geometric concepts to find perimeter, area, and volume. Ask questions such as:
- *What do you call a triangle with a right angle and two sides that have the same measure?* **right isosceles triangle**
- *What do you call a polygon with four congruent sides?* **rhombus**
- *What do you call a polygon with four congruent sides and four congruent angles?* **square**

What You'll Learn Next

- In this chapter, you will use the metric system of measurement and convert units of measure within the metric system.

- You will use formulas to find the circumference and area of a circle.

- You will find the perimeters and areas of parallelograms and triangles.

- You will identify three-dimensional figures and find their surface areas and volumes.

 Problem Solving Application On pages 472 and 473, you will work an extended activity on measurement.

🔊 Key Vocabulary

- area (p. 426)
- chord (p. 438)
- circle (p. 438)
- circumference (p. 439)
- diameter (p. 438)
- metric system (p. 416)
- perimeter (p. 426)
- prism (p. 449)
- radius (p. 438)
- surface area (p. 454)
- volume (p. 458)

Chapter 9   **415**

Metric Units of Length, Mass, and Capacity

Objective
To use metric units of measure and to choose appropriate units of length, mass, and capacity

Examples
1 Choosing a Unit of Length
2 Choosing a Unit of Mass
3 Choosing a Unit of Capacity

Math Understandings: p. 414C

Math Background

Three basic units of measure in the metric system are the *meter* for measuring length, the *gram* for measuring mass, and the *liter* for measuring liquid capacity.

The metric system is the most widely used measurement system in the world. It is also known as *SI*, from the first two words of the French name for the system, *Système International d'Unités.*

More Math Background: p. 414C

Lesson Planning and Resources

See p. 414E for a list of the resources that support this lesson.

416

✓ Check Skills You'll Need

1. **Vocabulary Review**
Name a *customary unit of measure* for length, weight, and capacity.

Name an appropriate unit for each measurement.

2. the length of a gymnasium

3. the capacity of a juice box
1–3. See back of book.

 **for Help**
Lesson 6-6

What You'll Learn

To use metric units of measure and to choose appropriate units of length, mass, and capacity

■) **New Vocabulary** metric system, meter (m), mass, gram (g), capacity, liter (L)

Why Learn This?

The metric system of measurement is a decimal system. Computing with decimals is easier than other systems. The metric system uses prefixes to indicate the size of metric units. The table at the right shows the most common prefixes.

The standard unit of length in the metric system is the meter (m). A meter is a little longer than a yard.

Metric Prefixes

Prefix	Meaning
kilo-	1,000
centi-	$\frac{1}{100}$ or 0.01
milli-	$\frac{1}{1,000}$ or 0.001

Metric Units of Length

Unit	Relationship to a Meter	Example
kilometer (km)	1 km = 1,000 meters	2.5 times around an indoor track
meter (m)	1 meter	height of a doorknob from the floor
centimeter (cm)	1 cm = 0.01 meter	thickness of a CD case
millimeter (mm)	1 mm = 0.001 meter	thickness of a CD

EXAMPLE **Choosing a Unit of Length**

1 Choose an appropriate metric unit of length for a pencil.

A pencil is much shorter than a meter but much longer than a millimeter. The most appropriate unit of measure is centimeters.

✓ Quick Check

1. Choose an appropriate metric unit of length for a city block.   *meters*

 **Differentiated** Instruction **Solutions for All Learners**

Special Needs **L1**
When possible, let students see and touch yard sticks, meter sticks, a kilogram weight, and a gram weight. Let them see and lift a liter or 2-liter bottle, and show them a dropper marked off in milliliters.

learning style: tactile

Below Level **L2**
Have students draw segments with lengths 14 cm, 14 mm, 1.4 cm, and 140 mm. Ask them to identify which pairs of measures name equal lengths. **14 cm and 140 mm; 14 mm and 1.4 cm**

learning style: visual

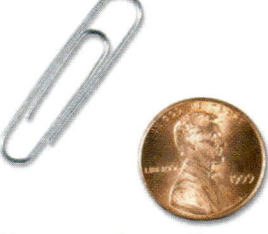

The mass of a small paper clip is 1 gram. The mass of a penny is about 2.5 grams.

Solids are sometimes measured in units of mass. **Mass** is a measure of the amount of matter in an object. The standard unit of mass is the **gram (g).**

Unit of Mass	Relationship to a Gram	Example
kilogram (kg)	1 kg = 1,000 grams	mass of 4 videocassettes
gram (g)	1 gram	mass of a small paper clip
milligram (mg)	1 mg = 0.001 gram	mass of an eyelash

EXAMPLE Choosing a Unit of Mass

❷ Choose an appropriate metric unit of mass for your math book.

The mass of a math book is much greater than the mass of a paper clip. The appropriate unit of measure is kilograms.

✓ Quick Check

2. Choose an appropriate metric unit of mass.
   a. a car **kilograms**
   b. a desk **kilograms**
   c. a robin's feather **milligrams**

Containers are measured in units of capacity. **Capacity** is a measure of the amount of space an object contains. The standard unit of capacity is the **liter (L).** A liter is a little more than a quart.

Unit of Capacity	Relationship to a Liter	Example
kiloliter (kL)	1 kL = 1,000 liters	2 or 3 bathtubs
liter (L)	1 liter	juice bottle
milliliter (mL)	1 mL = 0.001 liter	eye dropper

EXAMPLE Choosing a Unit of Capacity

❸ Choose an appropriate metric unit of capacity for a bottle cap.

A bottle cap holds about 10 to 20 drops of water. The appropriate unit of measure is milliliters.

✓ Quick Check

3. Choose an appropriate metric unit of capacity.
   a. a car's fuel tank **liters**
   b. a pond **kiloliters**
   c. a test tube **milliliters**

9-1 Metric Units of Length, Mass, and Capacity **417**

---

2. Teach

Activity Lab
Use before the lesson.

All in One Teaching Resources
Activity Lab 9-1: Metric Measures

Guided Instruction

Example 2
Students might confuse the difference between mass and weight. Tell them *mass* is a measure of the amount of material that makes up an object. *Weight* is a measure of the force an object experiences due to the pull of gravity. To illustrate, an astronaut who weighs 180 lb on Earth would weigh 30 lb on the moon, because the pull of gravity on the moon is not as great as on Earth. However, the *mass* of the astronaut on the moon is the same as his or her mass on Earth.

PowerPoint
Additional Examples

❶ Choose an appropriate metric unit of length for a classroom. **meters**

❷ Choose an appropriate metric unit of mass.
   a. a sewing needle **milligrams**
   b. a compact disc **grams**

❸ Choose an appropriate metric unit of capacity.
   a. a kitchen sink **liters**
   b. a shampoo bottle **milliliters**

All in One Teaching Resources
- Daily Notetaking Guide 9-1 **L3**
- Adapted Notetaking 9-1 **L1**

Closure

- Have students name the metric units of length, mass, and capacity in this lesson and give an example of an object they would measure using each unit. **units of length: meter, kilometer, centimeter, millimeter; units of mass: gram, kilogram, milligram; units of capacity: liter, kiloliter, milliliter; Accept reasonable examples.**

3. Practice

Assignment Guide

Check Your Understanding
Go over Exercises 1–8 in class before assigning the Homework Exercises.

Homework Exercises
A Practice by Example   9–26
B Apply Your Skills   27–37
C Challenge   38
Test Prep and
  Mixed Review   39–44

Homework Quick Check
To check students' understanding of key skills and concepts, go over Exercises 14, 22, 31, 32, and 37.

Differentiated Instruction **Resources**

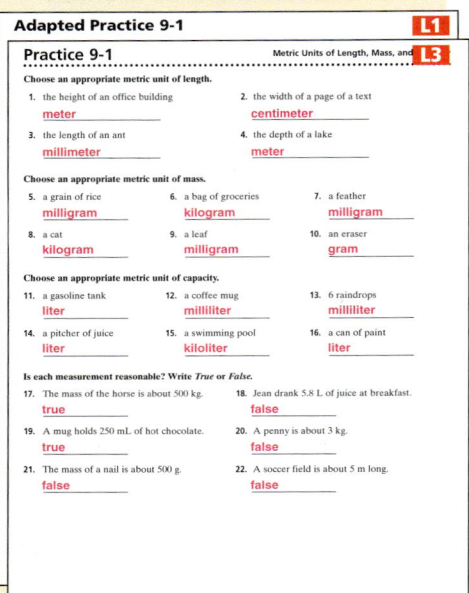

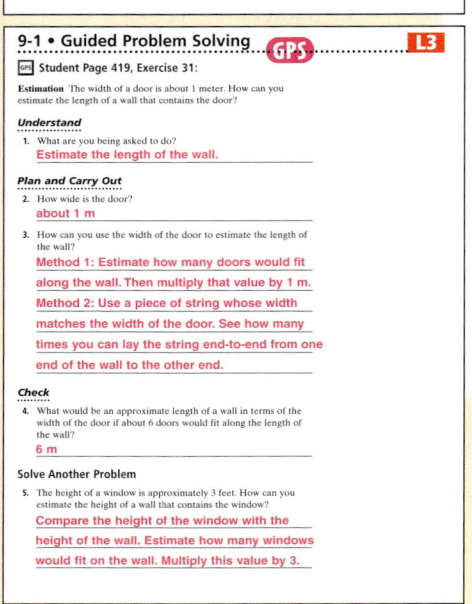

Check Your Understanding

1. **Vocabulary** Tell whether each measurement is a unit of length, mass, or capacity.

   a. 13 mg **mass**   b. 13 m **length**   c. 13 kL **capacity**

   Open-Ended For each unit, name two items that you would measure using the unit. **2–4. Answers may vary. Samples are given.**

   2. milligram **paper, staples**   3. centimeter **pencil, finger**   4. kilogram **body weight, fruit**

   Is each statement true or false? If it is false, explain why.

   5. 1,000 mg = 1 g **true**   6. 100 kg = 100,000 g **true**

   7. 10 L = 1,000 mL   8. 1 mm = 10 cm
      false; 1 L = 1,000 mL   **false; 1 cm = 10 mm**

Homework Exercises

For more exercises, see Extra Skills and Word Problems.

GO for Help

For Exercises	See Examples
9–14	1
15–20	2
21–26	3

A **Choose an appropriate metric unit of length.**

   9. width of a highway **meters**   10. length of an eyelash **millimeters**
   11. height of your desk **centimeters** 12. width of your finger **millimeters**
   13. width of your classroom door **centimeters**
   14. distance across the state of Ohio **kilometers**

   Choose an appropriate metric unit of mass.

   15. a pencil **grams**   16. a pin **milligrams**   17. a chair **kilograms**
   18. a pea **milligrams** 19. a potato **grams**   20. a shirt button **milligrams**

   Choose an appropriate metric unit of capacity.

   21. a watering can **liters**   22. a juice box **milliliters**   23. a large lake **kiloliters**
   24. a bucket of paint **liters** 25. an oil truck **kiloliters** 26. a glass of milk **milliliters**

B **GPS** 27. **Guided Problem Solving** You have two 650-milliliter bottles of sunscreen lotion. Is a 1-liter container large enough to hold all of the lotion from the two bottles? **no**

   • What is the total volume of lotion you have?
   • Is the total volume of lotion *greater than* or *less than* 1 liter?

31. **Answers may vary. Sample: Use a piece of string whose length matches the width of the door. Count how many times you can lay off end-to-end lengths from one end of the wall to the other end.**

37. **Answers may vary. Sample: Mass is a measure of the amount of matter in an object; capacity is a measure of the amount of liquid an object holds. A plastic bottle might have a mass of 10 g, but a capacity of 1 L.**

36. Mass; fruit is usually priced according to weight, which is proportional to mass.

Complete each statement.

28. 1 g = ■ kg
    0.001

29. 1 mL = ■ L
    0.001

30. ■ cm = 1 m
    100

31. **Estimation** The width of a door is about 1 meter. How can you
     estimate the length of a wall that contains the door?
    See margin.

Is each measurement reasonable? Explain.

32. A giraffe is 550 centimeters tall. **Yes; giraffes are very tall.**

33. A ladybug has a mass of 4 kilograms. **No; a ladybug would be measured in grams or milligrams.**

34. A sidewalk is 30 kilometers wide.
    No; a sidewalk would be measured in meters.

35. You place eight 12-centimeter pencils end to end. Is the total length *greater than* or *less than* 1 meter? Justify your answer.
    Less; 8 × 12 = 96, so 96 cm < 1 m.

36. **Groceries** You buy a bag of oranges. Should the price be calculated using length, mass, or capacity? Explain.
    See above left.

37. **Writing in Math** Explain the difference between mass and capacity. Give an example of each using one container.
    See margin.

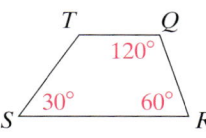

C 38. **Challenge** The deciliter (dL) is sometimes used in medical laboratory testing. The prefix *deci-* means one tenth, or 0.1. Complete each statement.
    a. 15 L = ■ dL **150**   **b.** 273 dL = ■ L **27.3**

Test Prep and Mixed Review **Practice**

Multiple Choice

39. Which measurement is NOT reasonable? **D**
    Ⓐ A teenager's height is 180 centimeters.
    Ⓑ A container holds 2 liters of juice.
    Ⓒ A pebble has a mass of 3 grams.
    Ⓓ A truck has a mass of 80 kilograms.

40. A trapezoid is shown. Find the measure of ∠T. **J**
    Ⓕ 60°
    Ⓖ 70°
    Ⓗ 130°
    Ⓙ 150°

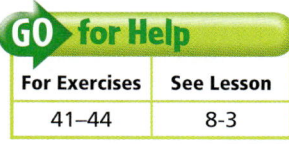

For Exercises	See Lesson
41–44	8-3

Find the complement and the supplement of each angle.

27.5°; 117.5°
41. 44° **46°; 136°** 42. 16° **74°; 164°** 43. 81° **9°; 99°** 44. 62.5°

PowerPoint

Lesson Quiz

Choose an appropriate metric unit of measure for each.

1. mass of a toothbrush **gram**

2. width of a soccer field **meter**

3. capacity of a baby's milk bottle **milliliter**

4. mass of an elephant **kilogram**

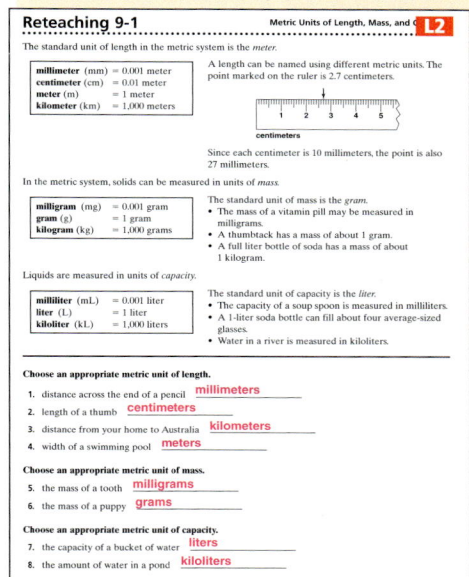

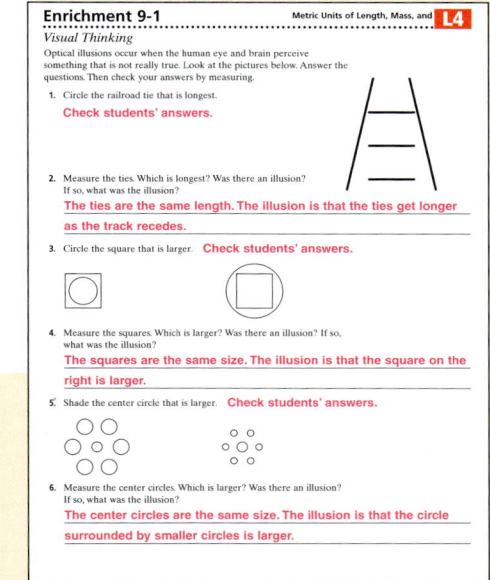

Alternative Assessment

Students work together in pairs to estimate and record the length and mass of several classroom objects. Partners then use metric rulers and a balance scale to find and record the actual measurements. Ask partners to share their estimates and measurements with the class.

Test Prep

Resources

For additional practice with a variety of test item formats:
• Test-Taking Strategies, p. 467
• Test Prep, p. 471
• Test-Taking Strategies with Transparencies

Metric Units

These activities provide practice working with metric units of volume and length.

ACTIVITY

1. What is the measure of the volume of liquid in the container at the right?

   The liquid reaches a height of 28 units. The units on this container are milliliters. So the amount in the container is 28 milliliters, or 28 mL.

2. What is the measure of the segment below in millimeters and in centimeters?

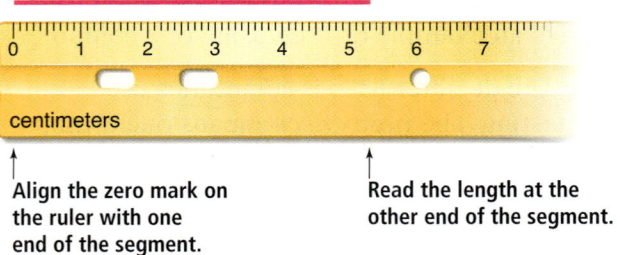

Align the zero mark on the ruler with one end of the segment.

Read the length at the other end of the segment.

The length is 53 millimeters, or 5.3 centimeters.

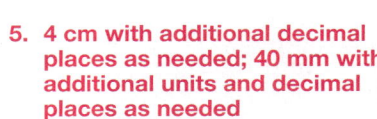
30 mL
20 mL
10 mL

5. 4 cm with additional decimal places as needed; 40 mm with additional units and decimal places as needed

Exercises

1. What is the measure of the volume of liquid in the container at the right?　**21 mL**

Measure each segment in millimeters and in centimeters.

2. 　**37 mm; 3.7 cm**

3. ——　**12 mm; 1.2 cm**

4. ————————　**79 mm; 7.9 cm**

5. **Writing in Math**　The width of a leaf measures between 4 and 5 centimeters. Explain how you can write your answer in centimeters and in millimeters.　**See above right.**

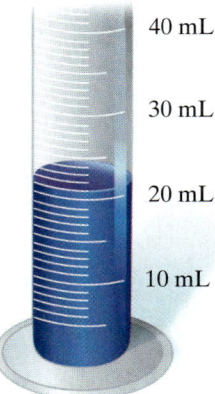
40 mL
30 mL
20 mL
10 mL

Converting Units in the Metric System

Check Skills You'll Need

1. Vocabulary Review
What operation can you use to *convert* a larger unit to a smaller unit? **multiplication**

Complete each statement.

2. 9 lb = ■ oz **144**

3. 8 qt = ■ pt **16**

4. 32 c = ■ gal **2**

for Help
Lesson 6–7

What You'll Learn

To convert between metric measurements

Why Learn This?

Most countries around the world use the metric system to describe distance, volume, and mass.

You can rewrite one metric unit as another metric unit by multiplying or dividing by a power of 10.

Next 96 km

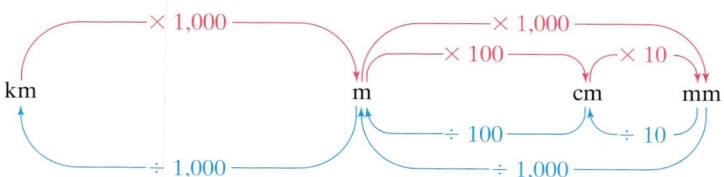

You can think of converting larger units to smaller units as creating many small units from a larger unit. To do this, you multiply.

EXAMPLE Converting to Smaller Units

1 A door is 3.2 meters tall. What is 3.2 meters in centimeters?

The meter is a larger unit than the centimeter. To convert meters to centimeters, multiply by 100.

$$3.2 \times 100 = 320. \quad \leftarrow$$ **To multiply by 100, move the decimal point 2 places to the right.**

3.2 m = 320 cm

Quick Check

1. Convert each measurement
  a. 15 cm to millimeters
      150 mm
  b. 837 km to meters
      837,000 m

Objective
To convert between metric measurements

Examples
1 Converting to Smaller Units
2 Converting to Larger Units
3 Converting Units of Mass or Capacity

Math Understandings: p. 414C

Math Background

The metric system of measurement is a decimal system. This means that all metric units for a given type of measure are related to each other by powers of ten. So conversions between units can be accomplished by multiplying or dividing by 10, 100, 1,000, and so on. Many people consider the relative ease of these calculations to be a major advantage of the metric system over the customary system of measurement.

More Math Background: p. 414C

Lesson Planning and Resources

See p. 414E for a list of the resources that support this lesson.

Bell Ringer Practice

Check Skills You'll Need
Use student page, transparency, or PowerPoint. For intervention, direct students to:
Changing Units in the Customary System
Lesson 6-7
Extra Skills and Word Problems Practice, Ch. 6

Differentiated Instruction **Solutions for All Learners**

Special Needs **L1**
Show students a meter stick. Have them identify the centimeters marked on the meter stick. Then, have them tell you whether a centimeter is larger or smaller than a meter. Ask whether it would take more or fewer centimeters or meters to measure the length of the floor.
learning style: visual

Below Level **L2**
Give students several pairs of exercises like these.

8 cm = ■ mm **80**   3 mL = ■ L **0.003**
8 mm = ■ cm **0.8**   3 L = ■ mL **3,000**
learning style: verbal

421

Guided Instruction

Example 1
Before discussing the Examples,
give students metric rulers and
have them perform several
conversions by sight. For instance,
have them locate the mark for
4 cm and count the number of
millimeters. **40 mm** Similarly, have
them count 60 mm and identify
the number of centimeters. **6 cm**

PowerPoint

Additional Examples

1 Convert 41 centimeters to
millimeters. **410 mm**

2 Convert each measurement.

a. 4,201 meters to kilometers
4.201 km

b. 195 centimeters to meters
1.95 m

3 Complete each statement.

a. 125 g = ■ kg **0.125**

b. 8.4 L = ■ mL **8,400**

 **Teaching Resources**

• Daily Notetaking Guide 9-2 **L3**
• Adapted Notetaking 9-2 **L1**

Closure

• *How do you convert a metric
measurement from one unit to
another?* **Multiply or divide by
the appropriate power of 10.**
• *How do you decide whether to
multiply or divide?* **Multiply to
convert from a larger unit to a
smaller unit. Divide to convert
from a smaller unit to a larger
unit.**

You can think of converting smaller units to larger units as
combining many smaller units. To do this, you divide. You will end
up with fewer larger units than smaller units.

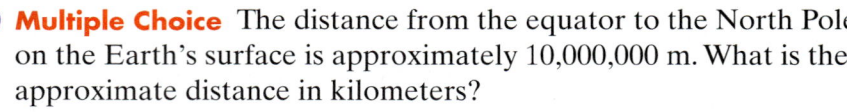 **Converting to Larger Units**

2 **Multiple Choice** The distance from the equator to the North Pole
on the Earth's surface is approximately 10,000,000 m. What is the
approximate distance in kilometers?

(A) 1,000 km
(C) 100,000 km
(B) 10,000 km
(D) 100,000,000 km

The meter is a smaller unit than the kilometer. So to convert
meters to kilometers, divide by 1,000.

$$10,000,000 \div 1,000 = 10,000.000 \leftarrow$$ **To divide by 1,000, move the decimal
point 3 places to the left.**

The equator is about 10,000 km from the North Pole. The correct
answer is choice B.

✓ Quick Check

2. A sprinter runs 60,000 m each week. How many kilometers does
the sprinter run each week? **60 km**

You can also convert grams or liters to related units.

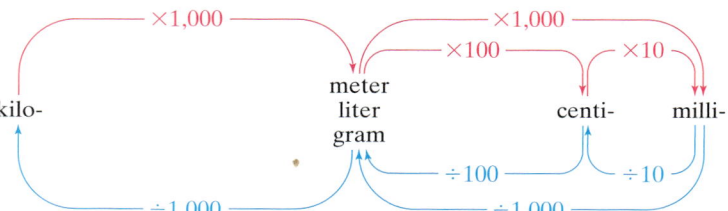

Test Prep Tip
The prefix *kilo-* means
"thousand". Knowing
what each metric prefix
means can help you
convert units.

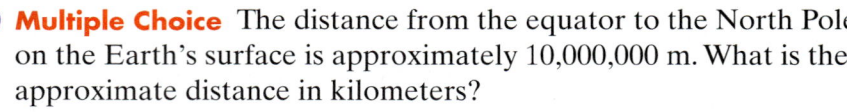 **Converting Units of Mass or Capacity**

3 Complete the statement 325 cL = ■ L.

To convert centiliters to liters, divide by 100.

$$325 \div 100 = 3.25 \rightarrow 3.25 \text{ liters} \leftarrow$$ **To divide by 100, move the decimal
point 2 places to the left.**

✓ Quick Check

3a. **0.015**
b. **0.386**
c. **0.082**

3. Complete each statement.
a. 15 mg = ■ g   **b.** 386 L = ■ kL   **c.** 8.2 cg = ■ g

Advanced Learners **L4**
One megameter (1 Mm) is one million meters. Write a
number to make each statement true.

5.2 Mm = ■ m **5,200,000**
7.6 m = ■ Mm **0.0000076**

learning style: visual

English Language Learners **ELL**
Ask questions, such as: *How many millimeters fit on a
meter stick?* **1,000** *Do you get to this number by
multiplying or dividing by 1,000?* **multiplying** *Ask
similar questions with other units of measure.*

learning style: verbal

Check Your Understanding

1. **Number Sense** Which measurement is greater, 500 millimeters or 5 meters? Explain.
5 m; 5 m = 5,000 mm

State whether you multiply or divide to change units.

2. meters to kilometers
divide
3. liters to kiloliters
divide
4. centigrams to milligrams
multiply
5. centimeters to meters
divide

For more exercises, see Extra Skills and Word Problems.

Homework Exercises

For Exercises	See Examples
6–9	1
10–14	2
15–23	3

A Convert each measurement.

6. 1.3 km to meters **1,300 m**
7. 6,000 m to centimeters **600,000 cm**
8. 59 cm to millimeters **590 mm**
9. 200 km to centimeters **20,000,000 cm**
10. 206 cm to meters **2.06 m**
11. 142 cm to kilometers **0.00142 km**
12. 7.5 mm to centimeters **0.75 cm**
13. 6,900 m to kilometers **6.9 km**

14. **Animals** One of the world's longest dogs measured 240 cm. How many meters long was this dog? **2.4 m**

Complete each statement.

15. $3,070 \text{ mm} = \blacksquare \text{ m}$ **3.07**
16. $586 \text{ cg} = \blacksquare \text{ g}$ **5.86**
17. $0.61 \text{ km} = \blacksquare \text{ m}$ **610**
18. $0.04 \text{ m} = \blacksquare \text{ cm}$ **4**
19. $4,500 \text{ g} = \blacksquare \text{ mg}$ **4,500,000**
20. $6.4 \text{ kL} = \blacksquare \text{ L}$ **6,400**
21. $150 \text{ cL} = \blacksquare \text{ L}$ **1.5**
22. $120 \text{ mg} = \blacksquare \text{ g}$ **0.12**
23. $3,000 \text{ L} = \blacksquare \text{ mL}$ **3,000,000**

B 24. **Guided Problem Solving** A carpenter is installing a pocket door in a wall. The opening for the door needs to be 2.5 cm greater than two times the width of the door. How many centimeters wide should you make the opening for a door that is 0.8 m wide? **162.5 cm**
• How many centimeters wide is the door?
• How wide is the opening for the door?

25. **Science** Light travels at approximately 299,792,458 meters per second. Approximately how many kilometers does light travel in one second? **about 299,792.458 km (or about 300,000 km)**

Assignment Guide

Check Your Understanding
Go over Exercises 1–5 in class before assigning the Homework Exercises.

Homework Exercises
A Practice by Example 6–23
B Apply Your Skills 24–37
C Challenge 38
Test Prep and Mixed Review 39–43

Homework Quick Check
To check students' understanding of key skills and concepts, go over Exercises 9, 18, 25, 35, and 37.

Differentiated Instruction Resources

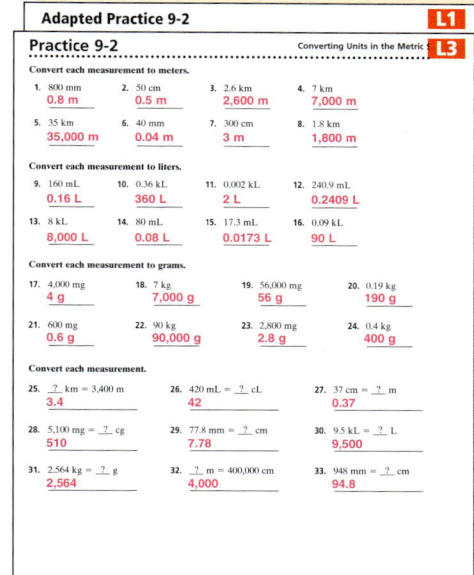

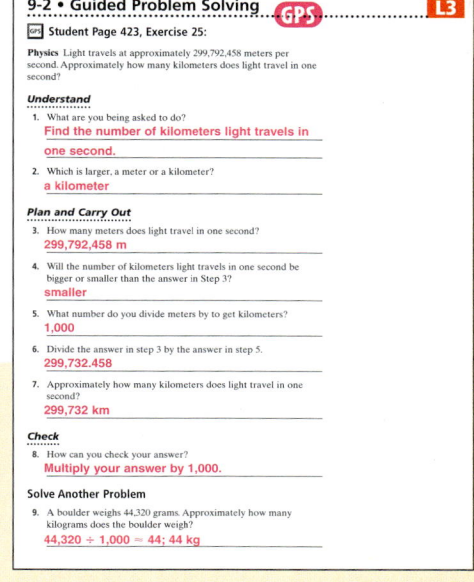

PowerPoint
Lesson Quiz

Complete each statement.

1. 678 cm = ■ m **6.78**

2. 85 kg = ■ g **85,000**

3. 7,000 mL = ■ L **7**

4. 0.95 km = ■ m **950**

Alternative Assessment

Each student in a pair writes five number statements similar to those in Exercises 15–23. Partners exchange statements and complete the statements.

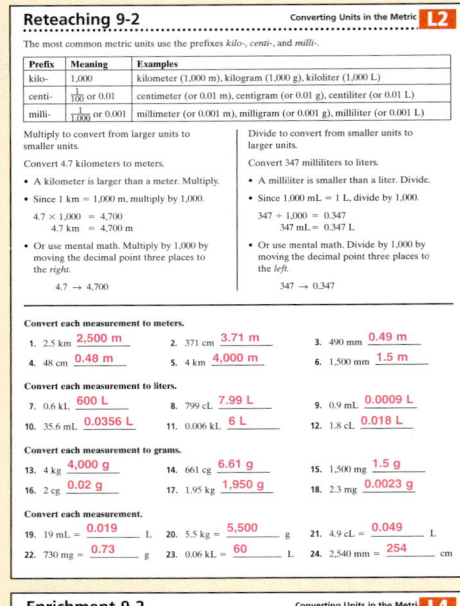

Reteaching 9-2 — Converting Units in the Metric **L2**

The most common metric units use the prefixes *kilo-, centi-,* and *milli-*.

Prefix	Meaning	Examples
kilo-	1,000	kilometer (1,000 m), kilogram (1,000 g), kiloliter (1,000 L)
centi-	$\frac{1}{100}$ or 0.01	centimeter (or 0.01 m), centigram (or 0.01 g), centiliter (or 0.01 L)
milli-	$\frac{1}{1,000}$ or 0.001	millimeter (or 0.001 m), milligram (or 0.001 g), milliliter (or 0.001 L)

Multiply to convert from larger units to smaller units.

Convert 4.7 kilometers to meters.

- A kilometer is larger than a meter. Multiply.
- Since 1 km = 1,000 m, multiply by 1,000.
  - 4.7 × 1,000 = 4,700
  - 4.7 km = 4,700 m
- Or use mental math. Multiply by 1,000 by moving the decimal point three places to the *right*.
  - 4.7 → 4,700

Divide to convert from smaller units to larger units.

Convert 347 milliliters to liters.

- A milliliter is smaller than a liter. Divide.
- Since 1,000 mL = 1 L, divide by 1,000.
  - 347 ÷ 1,000 = 0.347
  - 347 mL = 0.347 L
- Or use mental math. Divide by 1,000 by moving the decimal point three places to the *left*.
  - 347 → 0.347

Convert each measurement to meters.

1. 2.5 km **2,500 m** 2. 371 cm **3.71 m** 3. 490 mm **0.49 m**
4. 48 cm **0.48 m** 5. 4 km **4,000 m** 6. 1,500 mm **1.5 m**

Convert each measurement to liters.

7. 0.6 kL **600 L** 8. 799 cL **7.99 L** 9. 0.9 mL **0.0009 L**
10. 35.6 mL **0.0356 L** 11. 0.006 kL **6 L** 12. 1.8 cL **0.018 L**

Convert each measurement to grams.

13. 4 kg **4,000 g** 14. 661 cg **6.61 g** 15. 1,500 mg **1.5 g**
16. 2 cg **0.02 g** 17. 1.95 kg **1,950 g** 18. 2.3 mg **0.0023 g**

Convert each measurement.

19. 19 mL = **0.019** L 20. 5.5 kg = **5,500** g 21. 4.9 cL = **0.049** L
22. 730 mg = **0.73** g 23. 0.06 kL = **60** L 24. 2,540 mm = **254** cm

---

Enrichment 9-2 — Converting Units in the Metri **L4**
Critical Thinking

Newspapers make up the largest part of trash in landfills. A 30.48 cm stack of newspapers weighs about 15.87 kg. How many grams does a one-meter stack of newspapers weigh?

1. When you convert from 30.48 centimeters to meters, will the value be larger or smaller than 30.48? Explain.
   The value will be smaller since you divide centimeters by 100 to get meters.

2. How many meters are in 30.48 centimeters?
   0.3048 meters

3. When you convert from 15.87 kilograms to grams, will the value be larger or smaller than 15.87? Explain.
   The value will be larger since you multiply kilograms by 1,000 to get grams.

4. How many grams are in 15.87 kilograms?
   15,870 grams

5. How many grams does a one-meter stack of newspapers weigh? Show your work. Round your answer to the nearest gram.
   15,870 grams ÷ 0.3048 meters = 52,067 grams per meter;
   A one-meter stack of newspapers weighs 52,067 grams.

6. If newspapers in the landfill are stacked 35 meters high, how many grams does the stack weigh? How many kilograms? Round your answers to the nearest whole unit.
   1,822,345 grams; 1,822 kilograms

7. Every week you throw a stack of newspapers away. The stack measures about 22 centimeters. There are 52 weeks in one year. Find the weight of newspaper, in kilograms, that you contribute to the landfill annually. Show your work. Round your answer to the nearest kilogram.
   22 cm × 52 weeks per year = 1,144 centimeters per year;
   1,144 cm = 11.44 meters; 11.44 meters × 52,067 grams
   per meter = 595,644.48 grams ≈ 596 kilograms

GO Online
Homework Video Tutor

Visit: PHSchool.com
Web Code: aqe-0902

37. **Answers may vary. Sample: If you are converting to a smaller unit, then you multiply. If you are converting to a larger unit, then you divide.**

Convert each measurement to meters, liters, or grams.

26. 8 kL **8,000 L**
27. 7,000 mg **7 g**
28. 0.24 km **240 m**
29. 34,000 cm **340 m**
30. 0.07 cL **0.0007 L**
31. 52 kg **52,000 g**
32. 8.6 mm **0.0086 m**
33. 41.5 cg **0.415 g**

34. **Algebra** Write an expression that can be used to find the number of milligrams in *n* grams. **1,000n**

Number of Grams	1	3	5	6	n
Number of Milligrams	1,000	3,000	5,000	6,000	■

35. **Waves** The world's largest wave was about 0.524 km tall. The height of the wave shown at the left is about 5 m. How many meters greater was the height of the largest wave than the height of this wave? **519 m**

36. A bottle contains 1 liter of juice. Which measurement at the right is closest to 1 liter? **100.1 cL**

Test #	Measurement
1	1,002.3 mL
2	100.1 cL
3	0.000997 kL

37. **Writing in Math** When you convert metric measurements, how do you decide whether to multiply or divide?
   See above left.

C 38. **Challenge** A cup of whole milk contains 8.5 grams of fat. Two cups of skim milk contain 800 milligrams of fat. Find the difference in fat content per cup of milk.
   A cup of whole milk has 8.1 g more fat per cup.

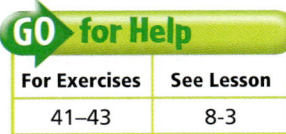

Test Prep and Mixed Review — Practice

Multiple Choice

39. The diameter of Pluto is about 3,000,000 m. What is the approximate diameter of Pluto in kilometers? **B**
   - Ⓐ 300 km
   - Ⓒ 30,000 km
   - Ⓑ 3,000 km
   - Ⓓ 3,000,000 km

40. Which unit should Lisa use to measure the length of a baseball bat? **G**
   - Ⓕ millimeter
   - Ⓗ liter
   - Ⓖ centimeter
   - Ⓙ kilometer

GO for Help

For Exercises	See Lesson
41–43	8-3

Classify each triangle by its angles and its sides.
41–43. See margin.

41.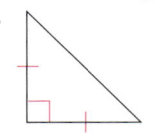
42.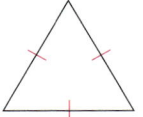
43.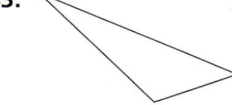

Test Prep

Resources
For additional practice with a variety of test item formats:
- Test-Taking Strategies, p. 467
- Test Prep, p. 471
- Test-Taking Strategies with Transparencies

41. **right isosceles triangle**

42. **acute equilateral triangle**

43. **obtuse scalene triangle**

Vocabulary Builder

Using Concept Maps

One way to show connections among ideas is to draw a diagram called a concept map. The lines in a concept map connect related ideas.

EXAMPLE

Make a concept map with the terms related to transformations from Chapter 8.

- center of rotation
- reflection
- rotation
- translation
- transformation
- line of reflection

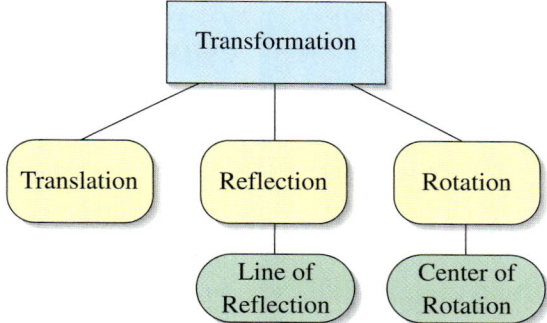

Exercises

1. Use the list below to make a concept map for the metric system. **See margin.**

metric system	millimeter	mass	kiloliter
length	gram	milliliter	centimeter
meter	kilometer	liter	milligram
kilogram	capacity		

2. Compete the concept map below as you study the next few lessons. Fill in the ovals using the appropriate terms listed below. Include area formulas on your concept map. **See margin.**

- area
- parallelogram
- square
- height
- width
- triangle
- rectangle
- base
- length
- side

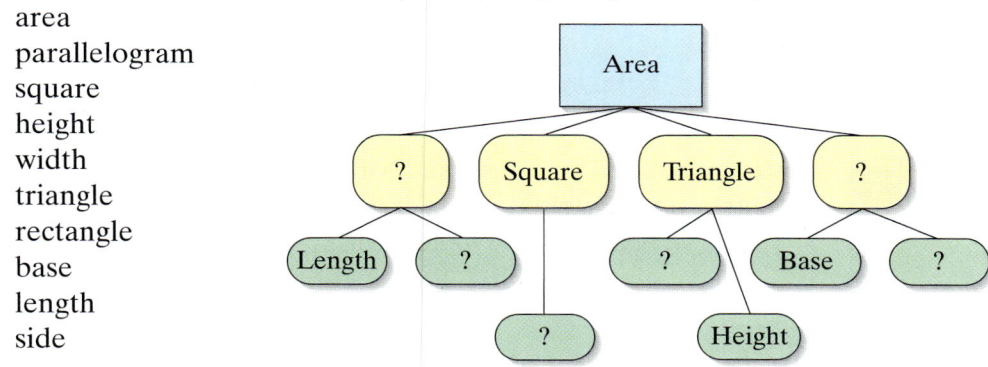

Vocabulary Builder

Using Concept Maps

A concept map is a graphic organizer that shows the relationship between a main concept and supporting details. It is useful for math vocabulary.

Guided Instruction

Discuss the importance of learning and using precise math vocabulary. Then explain what a concept map is and how it can help them focus on, understand, and remember new terms.

Discuss the sample concept map. Point out the links between the "image position" oval and the specific types of transformations that are connected to it with line segments.

Exercises

Check students' maps. Have them display and explain the choices they made. Invite students to suggest other kinds of graphic organizers they could use.

Differentiated Instruction

Below Level L2
Provide students with a list of everyday items to make a concept map such as apple, carrot, vegetable, potato, and lettuce.

English Language Learners ELL
Have small groups of students use the concept map and create their own. Help them organize the information. Modify the map to meet language needs of students.

Objective
To solve problems involving perimeters and areas of rectangles

Examples
1 Finding Perimeter and Area
2 Finding the Area of a Square

Math Understandings: p. 414C

Math Background

The *perimeter* of a plane figure is the distance around it. Perimeter is measured in *linear units*, such as inches, centimeters, and feet. The *area* of a plane figure is the amount of space it encloses. Area is measured in *square units,* such as square inches, square centimeters, and square feet.

More Math Background: p. 414C

Lesson Planning and Resources

See p. 414E for a list of the resources that support this lesson.

PowerPoint

Bell Ringer Practice

☑ **Check Skills You'll Need**
Use student page, transparency, or PowerPoint. For intervention, direct students to:

Exponents
Lesson 4-2
Extra Skills and Word Problems
Practice, Ch. 4

☑ Check Skills You'll Need

1. Vocabulary Review
Name the *base* and the *exponent* in 3^2.
base: 3; exponent: 2

Simplify each expression.

2. 4^2 **16**

3. 6^2 **36**

4. 5.4^2 **29.16**

5. 1.6^2 **2.56**

GO for Help
Lesson 4-2

What You'll Learn

To solve problems involving perimeters and areas of rectangles

◀») **New Vocabulary** perimeter, area

Why Learn This?

The length of a fence around a figure is a different measure from the area enclosed by the fence. You need to know how to find both measurements.

The **perimeter** of a figure is the distance around the figure. You can find the perimeter P of a rectangle by adding the lengths and widths of the rectangle.

$$P = \ell + w + \ell + w$$

So the perimeter is twice ℓ plus twice w, or twice the sum of ℓ and w.

$$P = 2\ell + 2w \qquad \text{or} \qquad P = 2(\ell + w)$$

The **area** of a figure is the number of square units the figure contains. You can find the area A of a rectangle by multiplying the length ℓ times the width w.

> **KEY CONCEPTS** **Perimeter and Area of a Rectangle**
>
> $P = 2(\ell + w)$
>
> $A = \ell + w$
>
>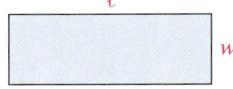

Vocabulary Tip

Read the symbol ft^2 as "square feet."

Common units for length and width are feet (ft), yards (yd), and meters (m). Common units for area are square feet (ft^2), square yards (yd^2), and square meters (m^2).

Differentiated Instruction Solutions for All Learners

Special Needs **L1**
In the More Than One Way, have students rotate square cutouts 45° from the customary horizontal/vertical orientation. Show that the squares resemble the shape of baseball diamonds.

learning style: visual

Below Level **L2**
Give students a sheet of several rectangles and squares drawn on square grids. Have them find the area and perimeter of each figure by counting grid units.

learning style: visual

EXAMPLE **Finding Perimeter and Area**

1 A landscaper plants grass and installs a fence around a rectangular backyard. Find the perimeter and area of the backyard.

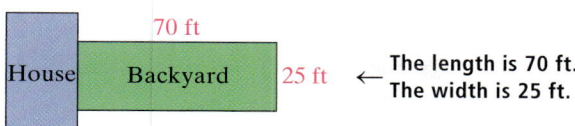

70 ft

House | Backyard | 25 ft ← The length is 70 ft.
The width is 25 ft.

$$P = 2(\ell + w) \quad \leftarrow \text{Use the formula for perimeter.}$$
$$= 2(70 + 25) \quad \leftarrow \text{Substitute 70 for } \ell \text{ and 25 for } w.$$
$$= 2 \times 95 \quad \leftarrow \text{Add.}$$
$$= 190 \quad \leftarrow \text{Multiply.}$$

$$A = \ell \times w \quad \leftarrow \text{Use the formula for area.}$$
$$= 70 \times 25 \quad \leftarrow \text{Substitute 70 for } \ell \text{ and 25 for } w.$$
$$= 1{,}750 \quad \leftarrow \text{Multiply.}$$

The perimeter is 190 feet. The area is 1,750 square feet.

Test Prep Tip

Some formulas are provided for you to use during the test.

✓ Quick Check

1. Find the perimeter and area of a rectangle with a length of 8 ft and a width of 5 ft. $P = 26$ ft, $A = 40$ ft^2

EXAMPLE **Finding the Area of a Square**

2 **Multiple Choice** The table at the left shows the area of a square with different side lengths. Which expression can be used to find the area of a square with a side s units in length?

Ⓐ $2s$ Ⓑ $4s$ Ⓒ s^2 Ⓓ s^4

Look for a relationship between the side length and the area.

$$2 \times 2 = 2^2$$
$$4 \times 4 = 4^2 \quad \leftarrow \text{Square each side length to find the area.}$$
$$s \times s = s^2$$

The expression s^2 can be used to find the area of a square with a side that is s units in length. The correct answer is choice C.

Area of Squares

Side Length (in.)	Area (in.^{2})
2	4
4	16
6	36
8	64
s	■

✓ Quick Check

2. Find the area of a square given side $s = 7$ in. 49 in.^{2}

9-3 Perimeters and Areas of Rectangles **427**

Activity Lab

Use before the lesson.

All in One Teaching Resources

Activity Lab 9-3: Patterns in Geometry

Guided Instruction

Example 2
Students have learned that the algebraic expression s^n generally is read as "s to the nth power." Here they see that the specific expression s^2, or "s to the 2nd power," can be used to represent the area of a square with sides of length s. Point out that, for this reason, s^2 is most commonly read as "s squared."

PowerPoint

Additional Examples

1 To renovate their bedroom, the Novaks are carpeting the floor and pasting a wallpaper border along the top of each wall. Find the perimeter and area of their bedroom.

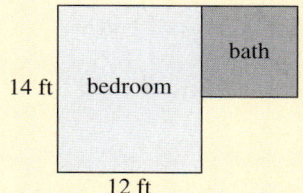

bath

14 ft | bedroom

12 ft

perimeter: 52 ft; area: 168 ft^2

2 The perimeter of a square is 28 meters. Find its area. 49 m^2

Advanced Learners **L4**
Find all possible whole-number widths and lengths for a rectangle with area 36. **1, 36; 2, 18; 3, 12; 4, 9; 6, 6**
Which combination of length/width gives the smallest perimeter? **6, 6**

learning style: visual

English Language Learners **ELL**
So that students do not get confused between the formulas for areas and perimeters, point out that the formula for the perimeter of a rectangle includes an addition sign. The formula for area does not include an addition sign.

learning style: visual

Closure

- *What is the difference between the area of a figure and the perimeter of a figure?* **The area of a figure is the number of square units it contains. The perimeter of a figure is the distance around it.**
- *How do you find the area and the perimeter of a rectangle?* **area: Use the formula $A = \ell \times w$ (Area = length × width) perimeter: Use the formula $P = 2(\ell + w)$ (Perimeter = 2 × [length + width])**

● More Than One Way

Leon and Lauren will run laps around the school playground. The playground is 310 feet long and 215 feet wide. How many laps will they run if they run about 1 mile?

Leon's Method

I can draw a model of the playground and label each side. Then I'll add the four sides to find the length of one lap.

$$310 + 215 + 310 + 215 = 1{,}050$$

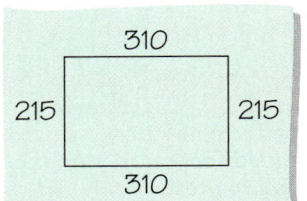

Each lap is 1,050 feet. Since 1 mile equals 5,280 feet, I will divide.

$$5{,}280 \div 1{,}050 \approx 5$$

I will run 5 laps around the playground to run about 1 mile.

Lauren's Method

I can use the formula for perimeter. I'll substitute 310 feet for the length and 215 feet for the width.

$$\begin{aligned}
P &= 2(\ell + w) \\
&= 2(310 + 215) \\
&= 2 \times 525 \\
&= 1{,}050
\end{aligned}$$

The perimeter of the playground is 1,050 feet. There are 5,280 feet in a mile, so I'll divide.

$$5{,}280 \div 1{,}050 \approx 5$$

I will run 5 laps around the playground to run about 1 mile.

30 yds.

Choose a Method

Baseball diamonds are in the shape of a square. Major league diamonds are 90 feet on each side. Little League diamonds are 60 feet on each side. What is the difference between the perimeters of the diamonds in the two leagues? Describe your method.
120 ft; check students' work.

Check Your Understanding

1. Perimeter is the distance around a figure. Area is the two-dimensional space the figure takes up.

1. **Vocabulary** Explain the difference between the perimeter and area of a figure.

Find the perimeter and area of each rectangle.

2.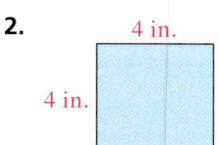
4 in.
4 in.
P = 16 in., A = 16 in.²

3.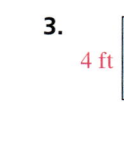
4 ft
9 ft
P = 26 ft, A = 36 ft²

4.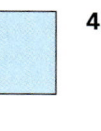
16 m
8 m
P = 48 m, A = 128 m²

Homework Exercises

For more exercises, see Extra Skills and Word Problems.

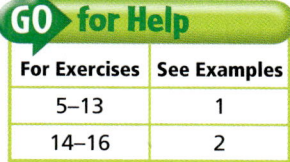

For Exercises	See Examples
5–13	1
14–16	2

Ⓐ **Find the perimeter and area of each rectangle.**

5. $\ell = 12$ in., $w = 7$ in.
   P = 38 in., A = 84 in.²

6. $\ell = 8$ ft, $w = 5$ ft
   P = 26 ft, A = 40 ft²

7. $\ell = 13$ in., $w = 9.5$ in.
   P = 45 in., A = 123.5 in.²

8. $\ell = 1.5$ m, $w = 0.25$ m
   P = 3.5 m, A = 0.375 m²

9. $\ell = 4.4$ m, $w = 3$ m   **P = 14.8 m**
   A = 13.2 m²

10. $\ell = 8.7$ ft, $w = 5.6$ ft
    P = 28.6 ft, A = 48.72 ft²

11. $\ell = \frac{4}{5}$ in., $w = \frac{3}{4}$ in.
    P = $\frac{31}{10}$ in., A = $\frac{3}{5}$ in.²

12. $\ell = 4\frac{1}{6}$ in., $w = 2\frac{1}{3}$ in.
    P = 13 in., A = $9\frac{13}{18}$ in.²

13. You want to frame a picture and hang it on your wall. The picture is 18 inches wide and 30 inches tall. Find the perimeter and area of the picture. **P = 96 in., A = 540 in.²**

Find the area of each square.

14. $s = 8$ ft   **64 ft²**

15. $s = 5$ m   **25 m²**

16. $s = 1.4$ in.
    1.96 in.²

19. There are 3 ft × 3 ft, or 9 ft², in 1 yd².

Ⓑ **GPS** 17. **Guided Problem Solving** A family is planting grass and a garden in the backyard. The rectangular backyard measures 131 ft by 52 ft. The garden measures 13 ft by 9 ft. What is the area of the backyard that will be grass? **6,695 ft²**
   • You can draw a picture to help visualize the situation.
   • Subtract the area of the garden from the area of the backyard to find the area that will be grass.

18. **Stamps** The world's smallest stamp, shown at the left,
   GPS measures 0.31 inch by 0.37 inch. Find the area of the stamp.
   0.1147 in.²

19. **Reasoning** How many square feet are in a square yard? Draw a picture and explain your answer. **See above left.**

3. Practice

Assignment Guide

Check Your Understanding
Go over Exercises 1–4 in class before assigning the Homework Exercises.

Homework Exercises
A Practice by Example   5–16
B Apply Your Skills   17–26
C Challenge   27
Test Prep and
   Mixed Review   28–30

Homework Quick Check
To check students' understanding of key skills and concepts, go over Exercises 9, 14, 18, 19, and 26.

Differentiated Instruction **Resources**

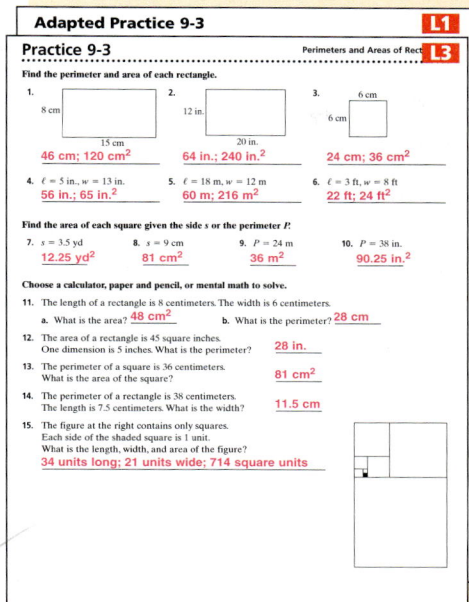

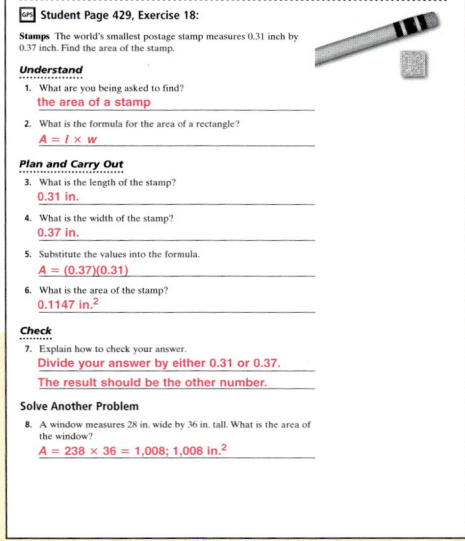

PowerPoint

Lesson Quiz

Find the perimeter and area of each.

1. a square with sides that measure 25 mm **100 mm; 625 mm²**

2. a rectangle with a length of 11 in. and a width of 8 in. **38 in.; 88 in.²**

3. a rectangle with a width of 9 cm and a length of 27 cm **72 cm; 243 cm²**

4. a square with a side of 13 ft **52 ft; 169 ft²**

Exercises

For Exercises 20–22, ask students if the results of their measurements are reasonable. Have them explain their answers.

GO Online

Homework Video Tutor

Visit: PHSchool.com
Web Code: aqe-0903

Careers Interior decorators coordinate colors of paint in schools and offices.

24. The area increases from 13.5 in.² to 54 in.², which is 4 times the area of the original rectangle. The area quadruples because you are doubling both dimensions.

Use a ruler to measure the length and width of each rectangle to the nearest millimeter. Then find the perimeter and area.

20. *P* = 98 mm; *A* = 570 mm²

21. *P* = 70 mm; *A* = 294 mm²

22. *P* = 84 mm; *A* = 425 mm²

23. **Decorating** You are going to paint a wall in your room. The wall is 12 feet long and 8 feet high. A window in the wall is 3 feet wide and 4 feet high. Find the area that you paint. **84 ft²**

24. **Number Sense** A rectangle has a length of 4.5 inches and a width of 3 inches. How would the area change if you doubled both dimensions? Explain your reasoning. **See left.**

25. **a.** Draw and label all the rectangles with a perimeter of 24 units. Use only whole units. **Check students' work.**

b. Find the area of each rectangle. Record your data in a table as shown below. **See margin.**

Length	Width	Perimeter	Area
11 units	1 unit	24 units	11 square units

c. What is true about the rectangle with the greatest area? **It is a square.**

26. **Writing in Math** You know the area of a rectangle. Can you find its perimeter? Use examples to explain why or why not. **See margin.**

C 27. **Challenge** How many square inches are in a square yard? Justify your answer. **See margin.**

Test Prep and Mixed Review
Practice

Multiple Choice

28. A rectangle has length ℓ and width *w*. Which equation can you NOT use to find the perimeter *P* of the rectangle? **A**
   Ⓐ $P = \ell \cdot w$
   Ⓒ $P = 2(\ell + w)$
   Ⓑ $P = 2\ell + 2w$
   Ⓓ $P = \ell + \ell + w + w$

29. Which container could hold 80,000 milliliters? **F**
   Ⓕ 0.5-kiloliter drum
   Ⓗ 500-milliliter beaker
   Ⓖ 28-liter fuel tank
   Ⓙ 2-liter bottle

GO for Help

For Exercise	See Lesson
30	7-5

30. The scale on a map is 1 cm : 10 km. How many centimeters on the map represent an actual distance of 25 kilometers? **2.5 cm**

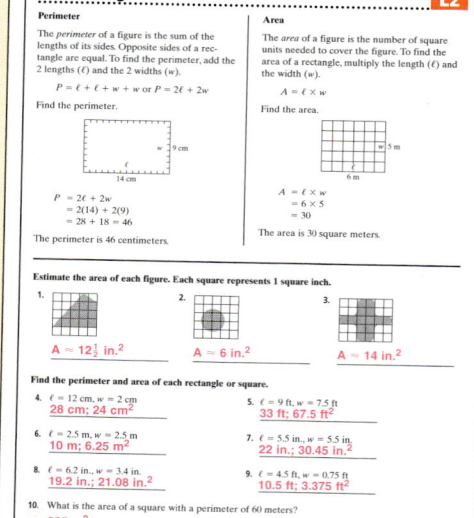

Enrichment 9-3 **L4**

Reteaching 9-3 Perimeters and Areas of Re **L2**

Perimeter

The *perimeter* of a figure is the sum of the lengths of its sides. Opposite sides of a rectangle are equal. To find the perimeter, add the 2 lengths (ℓ) and the 2 widths (*w*).

$P = \ell + \ell + w + w$ or $P = 2\ell + 2w$

Find the perimeter.

≈ 9 cm
14 cm

$P = 2\ell + 2w$
$= 2(14) + 2(9)$
$= 28 + 18 = 46$

The perimeter is 46 centimeters.

Area

The *area* of a figure is the number of square units needed to cover the figure. To find the area of a rectangle, multiply the length (ℓ) and the width (*w*).

$A = \ell \times w$

Find the area.

w 5 m
6 m

$A = \ell \times w$
$= 6 \times 5$
$= 30$

The area is 30 square meters.

Estimate the area of each figure. Each square represents 1 square inch.

1. $A \approx 12\frac{1}{2}$ in.²
2. $A \approx 6$ in.²
3. $A \approx 14$ in.²

Find the perimeter and area of each rectangle or square.

4. ℓ = 12 cm, *w* = 2 cm
28 cm; 24 cm²

5. ℓ = 9 ft, *w* = 7.5 ft
33 ft; 67.5 ft²

6. ℓ = 2.5 m, *w* = 2.5 m
10 m; 6.25 m²

7. ℓ = 5.5 in., *w* = 5.5 in.
22 in.; 30.25 in.²

8. ℓ = 6.2 in., *w* = 3.4 in.
19.2 in.; 21.08 in.²

9. ℓ = 4.5 ft, *w* = 0.75 ft
10.5 ft; 3.375 ft²

10. What is the area of a square with a perimeter of 60 meters?
225 m²

Test Prep

Resources

For additional practice with a variety of test item formats:
• Test-Taking Strategies, p. 467
• Test Prep, p. 471
• Test-Taking Strategies with Transparencies

Alternative Assessment

Students write several sets of measurements for the length and width similar to those in Exercises 5–12. They trade papers with a partner and calculate the perimeter and area of each rectangle.

25b. See back of book.

26–27. See back of book.

Comparing Areas

In this activity, you will investigate how to find the areas of parallelograms and triangles.

ACTIVITY   **1–5. Check students' work.**

1. On graph paper, draw a parallelogram that does not have a right angle. Cut out your parallelogram.

2. Draw a segment from one vertex that is perpendicular to the opposite base. Cut along that segment.

3. Arrange both pieces of the parallelogram to form a rectangle.

4. **Number Sense** Find the area of your rectangle. Is this area the same as the area of your parallelogram? Explain.

5. Repeat Steps 1–4 using a different parallelogram that does not have a right angle.

6. Write a formula that you can use to find the area of a parallelogram in the diagram on the right. Explain why the formula works. Then find the area of the parallelogram. **364 ft²; explanations may vary. Sample: A parallelogram can be cut into a triangle and trapezoid; both pieces form a rectangle, so $A = bh$.**

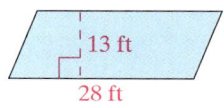
13 ft
28 ft

ACTIVITY   **7–9. Check students' work.**

7. Draw two identical triangles on graph paper. Cut out both triangles.

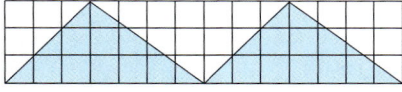

8. Arrange and tape both triangles to form a parallelogram. Then repeat Steps 2–4.

9. Repeat Steps 7 and 8 using a different triangle.

10. **Writing in Math** Write a formula that you can use to find the area of the triangle on the right. Explain why the formula works. Then find the area of the triangle. **See margin.**

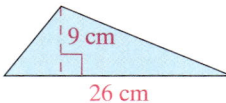
9 cm
26 cm

10. **117 cm²; answers may vary. Sample: Two identical triangles form a parallelogram, so $\frac{1}{2}bh$ equals the area of a triangle.**

Comparing Areas

Students investigate the areas of triangles and parallelograms. This will prepare them to find areas of parallelograms and triangles in Lesson 9-4.

Guided Instruction

Explain to students that it is possible to use what they know about the area of rectangles to help find the area of other polygons that do not have right angles. As you conduct the Activity, ask:
- *Why does it make sense that the area of the rectangle and the area of the parallelogram are the same?* **Sample: When you rearrange the pieces, they take up the same space.**
- *How would you write the formula for the area of a triangle, based on the Activity?* **$A = \frac{1}{2}bh$**
- *For which other figures could you use this method of rearranging pieces to find the area?* **irregular figures**

Exercises

Have students work on the Exercises. Circulate and check students' work, as each student's drawings will vary.

Alternative Method

Some students may prefer to use manipulatives of triangle, parallelogram, and trapezoid shapes and measure them with rulers. Provide these materials for them to use as an alternative.

Resources

- Activity Lab 9-4: Critical Thinking
- graph paper   •tape
- scissors
- Student Manipulatives Kit

Objective
To solve problems involving areas of parallelograms, triangles, and complex figures

Examples
1. Finding the Area of a Parallelogram
2. Finding the Area of a Triangle
3. Finding the Area of a Complex Figure

Math Understandings: p. 414C

Math Background

The area formula for a rectangle, $A = \ell \times w$, is so easily derived from a visual image. That is, given a rectangle with a whole-number length ℓ and width w, it is not difficult to imagine it enclosing $\ell \times w$ squares on a grid. This lesson provides students with visual images that can help them to derive the area formulas for a parallelogram and a triangle from the rectangle area formula.

More Math Background: p. 414C

Lesson Planning and Resources

See p. 414E for a list of the resources that support this lesson.

PowerPoint

Bell Ringer Practice

✓ **Check Skills You'll Need**
Use student page, transparency, or PowerPoint. For intervention, direct students to:
Perimeters and Areas of Rectangles
Lesson 9-3
Extra Skills and Word Problems Practice, Ch. 9

✓ Check Skills You'll Need

1. Vocabulary Review
The *area* of a rectangle is measured using __?__ units. **square**

Find the perimeter and area of each rectangle.

2. $\ell = 6$ in.; $w = 4$ in.

3. $\ell = 12$ m; $w = 5$ m
2–3. See below.

GO for Help
Lesson 9-3

Check Skills You'll Need

2. $P = 20$ in.; $A = 24$ in.^{2}

3. $P = 34$ m; $A = 60$ m^2

What You'll Learn

To solve problems involving areas of parallelograms, triangles, and complex figures

🔊 **New Vocabulary** base of a parallelogram, height of a parallelogram, base of a triangle, height of a triangle

Why Learn This?

Conservation groups purchase land to protect wildlife. The value of the land depends in part on its area.

The area of a parallelogram is the product of the base and the height. Any side can be considered the **base of a parallelogram.** The **height of a parallelogram** is the perpendicular distance between opposite bases.

KEY CONCEPTS **Area of a Parallelogram**

$A = b \times h$

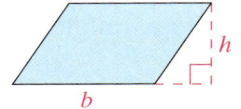

EXAMPLE **Finding the Area of a Parallelogram**

1. Find the area of the parallelogram.

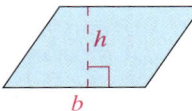

$A = b \times h$ ← Use the formula for the area of a parallelogram.

$\quad = 5 \times 3$ ← Substitute 5 for b and 3 for h.

$\quad = 15$ ← Simplify.

The area of the parallelogram is 15 m^2.

✓ Quick Check

70 m^2

1. Find the area of a parallelogram with $b = 14$ m and $h = 5$ m.

Differentiated Instruction **Solutions for All Learners**

Special Needs **L1**
Have students form a rectangle with straws or clay. Then, keeping the height the same, have them tilt parallel sides so that it looks like a more traditional parallelogram. Show them that the area is the same.

learning style: tactile

Below Level **L2**
On graph paper, have students draw a parallelogram and a triangle, each of which has area 12 square units. **Samples: $b = 4$, $h = 3$ (parallelogram), $b = 4$, $h = 6$ (triangle)** Repeat the activity for other areas.

learning style: visual

Any side of a triangle can be the **base of a triangle.** The **height of a triangle** is the length of the perpendicular segment from a vertex to the base opposite that vertex.

The diagram at the right shows that the area of a triangle is half of the area of a parallelogram with the same base length and height, or $A = \frac{1}{2}b \times h$.

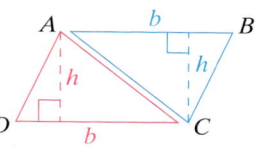

EXAMPLE Finding the Area of a Triangle

2 Conservation A conservation group plans to buy a triangular plot of land shown at the left. What is the area of the plot?

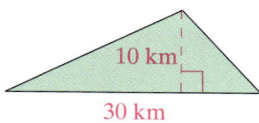

$A = \frac{1}{2}b \times h$ ← Use the formula for the area of a triangle.

$= \frac{1}{2} \times 30 \times 10$ ← Substitute 30 for b and 10 for h.

$= 150$ ← Simplify.

The area of the plot is 150 km².

✔ Quick Check

2. A triangle has a base of 30 m and a height of 17.3 m. Find the triangle's area. **259.5 m²**

Sometimes you can split a complex figure into smaller polygons.

EXAMPLE Finding the Area of a Complex Figure

3 Find the area of the figure.

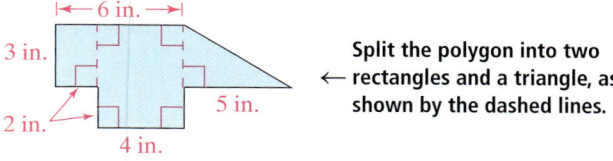

Split the polygon into two ← rectangles and a triangle, as shown by the dashed lines.

Area of smaller rectangle: $3 \times 2 = 6$, or 6 in.² ⎫
Area of larger rectangle: $5 \times 4 = 20$, or 20 in.² ⎬ Find the area of each polygon.
Area of triangle: $\frac{1}{2}(5 \times 3) = \frac{1}{2} \times 15$, or 7.5 in.² ⎭

The total area is $6 + 20 + 7.5$, or 33.5 in.².

✔ Quick Check

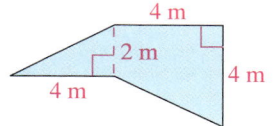

3. Find the area of the figure at the left. **16 m²**

2. Teach

Activity Lab
Use before the lesson.
Student Edition Activity Lab, Hands On 9-4a, Comparing Areas, p. 431

All in One Teaching Resources
Activity Lab 9-4: Critical Thinking

Guided Instruction

Example 3
The area of this figure can also be found as follows.

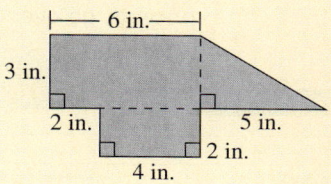

large rectangle: $A = 6 \times 3 = 18$ in.²
small rectangle: $A = 4 \times 2 = 8$ in.²
triangle: $A = \frac{1}{2}(5 \times 3) = 7.5$ in.²
total area: $18 + 8 + 7.5 = 33.5$ in.²

PowerPoint
Additional Examples

1 Find the area. **26.4 in.²**

2 A park is on a triangular plot. The plot has a base of 214 m and height of 70 m. What is the area of the plot? **7,490 m²**

3 Find the area. **56 m²**

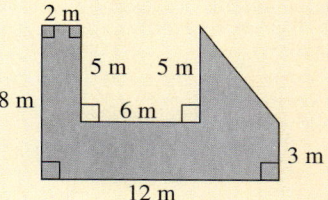

All in One Teaching Resources
• Daily Notetaking Guide 9-4 L3
• Adapted Notetaking 9-4 L1

Closure

• *How do you find the area of a complex figure?* Split the figure into smaller polygons. Find the area of each polygon and add.

433

3. Practice

Assignment Guide

Check Your Understanding
Go over Exercises 1–3 in class before assigning the Homework Exercises.

Homework Exercises
A Practice by Example   4–12
B Apply Your Skills   13–20
C Challenge   21
Test Prep and
   Mixed Review   22–27

Homework Quick Check
To check students' understanding of key skills and concepts, go over Exercises 5, 12, 14, 19, and 20.

Differentiated Instruction **Resources**

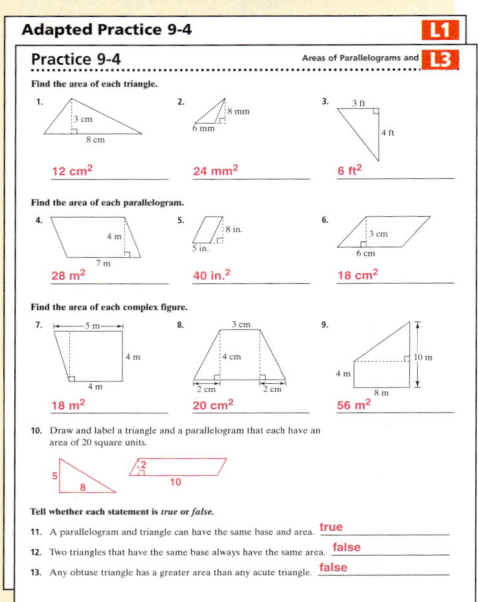

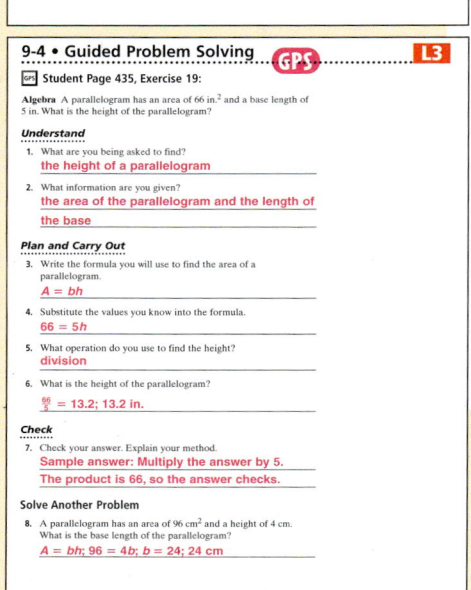

Check Your Understanding

1. The height of a triangle is the length of the perpendicular segment from a vertex to the base opposite that vertex.

1. **Vocabulary** Explain why the height of a triangle depends on which side you select for the base.

2. If you double the length of the base of a triangle, how does the area of the triangle change? **The area would double.**

3. **Reasoning** Draw a triangle and a rectangle that have the same base and the same height. How are the areas of the two figures related? **The triangle's area is half of the rectangle's area.**

Homework Exercises

For more exercises, see Extra Skills and Word Problems.

GO for Help

For Exercises	See Examples
4–6	1
7–10	2
11–12	3

A Find the area of each parallelogram or triangle.

4.
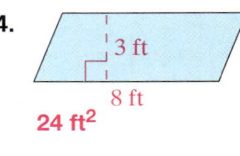
3 ft
8 ft
24 ft²

5.
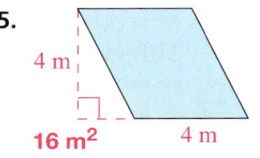
4 m
4 m
16 m²

6.
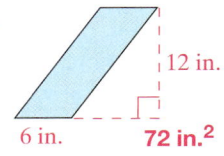
12 in.
6 in.
72 in.²

7.
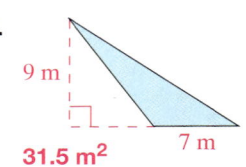
9 m
7 m
31.5 m²

8.
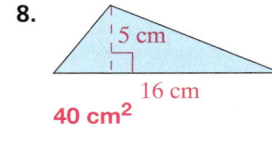
5 cm
16 cm
40 cm²

9.
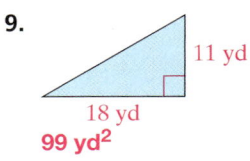
11 yd
18 yd
99 yd²

10. **Art** You sprinkle glitter on a triangular area of a card. The triangle has a base of 5 cm and a height of 10 cm. What is the area of the triangle? **25 cm²**

Find the area of each complex figure.

11.
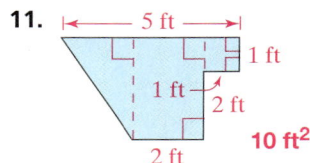
5 ft
1 ft
1 ft
2 ft
2 ft
10 ft²

12.
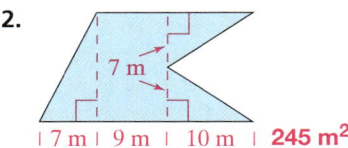
7 m
7 m   9 m   10 m   **245 m²**

B **GPS** 13. **Guided Problem Solving** Find the area of the trapezoid at the right. **15 cm²**
- How can you split the trapezoid into two triangles?
- Find the area of the two triangles.

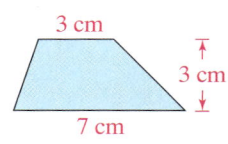
3 cm
3 cm
7 cm

Error Prevention!

Ask students to name appropriate units for area and perimeter. Remind the students to always make sure they are using the appropriate units.

Parking spaces are sometimes shaped like parallelograms.

Find the area of each figure.

14.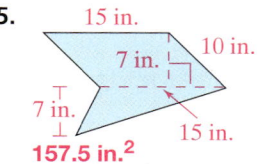
4.2 in. 5 in. 6 in.
25.2 in.²

15.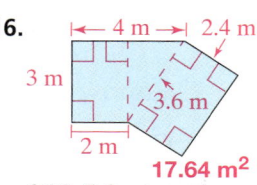
15 in. 10 in. 7 in. 7 in. 15 in.
157.5 in.²

16. 4 m 2.4 m 3 m 3.6 m 2 m
17.64 m²

17. **Parking** Each space at the left has a width of 10.5 feet and a length of 21 feet. Find the area of a parking space. **220.5 ft²**

18. **Number Sense** Two parallelograms have the same base length. The height of the first is half the height of the second. What is the ratio of the area of the smaller parallelogram to the area of the larger one? **1 : 2**

19. **(Algebra)** A parallelogram has an area of 66 in.² and a base **GPS** length of 5 inches. What is the height of the parallelogram? **13.2 in.**

20. **Writing in Math** Suppose you know the perimeter and the height of an equilateral triangle. Explain how you would find the area of the triangle.

20. Answers may vary. Sample: Divide the perimeter by 3 to get the base b. Then use $A = \frac{1}{2}bh$.

C 21. **Challenge** A parallelogram has an area of 4 ft² and a base length of 8 in. What is the height of the parallelogram? **6 ft**

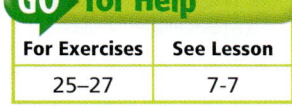
Test Prep and Mixed Review **Practice**

Multiple Choice

22. Hue cut out the triangle at the right for a craft project. What is the area of the triangle?
    (A) 12 ft²   (C) 54 ft²   **D**
    (B) 24 ft²   (D) 10 ft²
    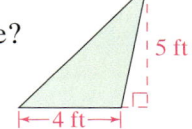
    5 ft   4 ft

23. Isaac makes 3 out of 5 free throws. If he attempts 100 free throws, how many would you expect him to make? **H**
    (F) 15   (G) 30   (H) 60   (J) 75

24. Lorenzo started doing homework at 4:15 P.M. He finished at 6:00 P.M. How long did Lorenzo spend doing homework? **B**
    (A) 1 hour 15 minutes
    (B) 1 hour 45 minutes
    (C) 2 hours 15 minutes
    (D) 2 hours 45 minutes

GO for Help

For Exercises	See Lesson
25–27	7-7

Find each answer.

25. 50% of 492 **246**   26. 35% of 84 **29.4**   27. 15% of 120 **18**

Alternative Assessment

Each student in a pair draws and labels a parallelogram, a triangle, and a complex figure similar to those in the Examples. Partners exchange drawings and find the area of each figure.

Test Prep

Resources
For additional practice with a variety of test item formats:
• Test-Taking Strategies, p. 467
• Test Prep, p. 471
• Test-Taking Strategies with Transparencies

PowerPoint
Lesson Quiz

Find the area of each.

1. parallelogram:
   $b = 6$ in., $h = 17$ in. **102 in.²**

2. triangle: $b = 8$ cm, $h = 19$ cm
   76 cm²

3. complex figure consisting of a rectangle: $A = 2$ cm $\times$ 4 cm and a triangle: $b = 4$ cm, $h = 6$ cm **20 cm**

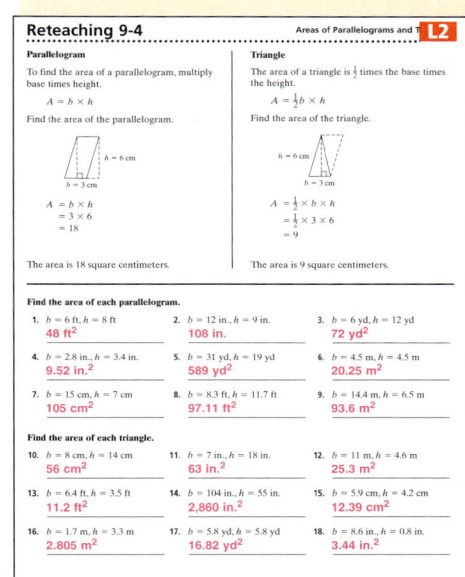

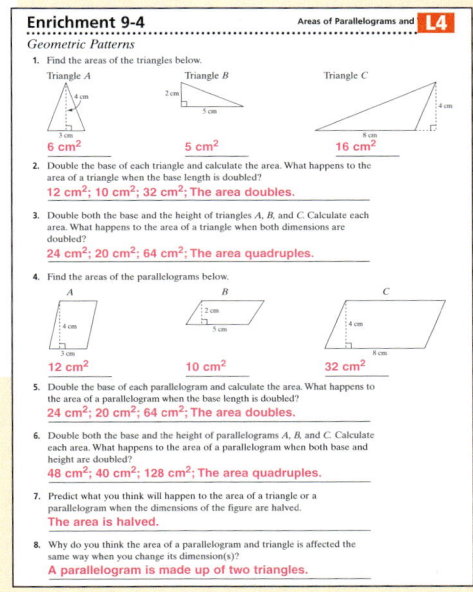

Checkpoint Quiz 1

Lessons 9-1 through 9-4

1. Choose an appropriate metric unit of length for a baseball bat. **cm**

2. Choose an appropriate metric unit of mass for a backpack. **kg**

Convert each measurement to meters, liters, or grams.

3. 62 milliliters **0.062 L**

4. 4.3 kilograms **4,300 g**

5. 178 centimeters **1.78 m**

6. 0.31 centigrams **0.0031 g**

7. 0.5 kiloliters **500 L**

8. 83 milligrams **0.083 g**

Find the perimeter and area of a figure with the given dimensions.

9. square: $s = 8.5$ cm
$P = 34$ cm, $A = 72.25$ cm^2

10. rectangle: $\ell = 9$ mi, $w = 4$ mi
$P = 26$ mi, $A = 36$ mi^2

Find the area of each figure.

11.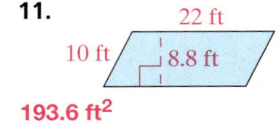
22 ft
10 ft 8.8 ft
193.6 ft^2

12.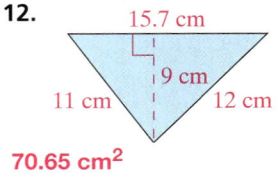
15.7 cm
9 cm
11 cm   12 cm
70.65 cm^2

13.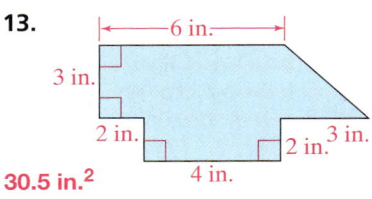
6 in.
3 in.
2 in.   2 in. 3 in.
4 in.
30.5 in.^{2}

Event Planner

Event planners organize and arrange all the details for parties, business meetings, and other group activities. Their responsibilities include finding the meeting place, choosing the menu, and arranging the decorations for an event.

Geometry is useful to event planners as they determine dimensions for room sizes, arrange rectangular or circular tables, and plan serving areas.

Go Online
PHSchool.com
For: Information on event planners
Web Code: aqb-2031

436

Exploring Circles

Recall that the perimeter of a figure is the distance around the figure. In this activity, you will explore the distance around a circle.

ACTIVITY

Materials: several circular objects, metric tape measure

1. Find several objects with circular bases, such as a can or a wastebasket. **1–4. Check students' work.**

2. Copy the table shown below.

Object	Distance around the circle	Distance across the circle	Distance around the circle / Distance across the circle

3. Measure the longest distance across each circle to the nearest tenth of a centimeter. Record the results in your table.

4. Measure the distance around each circle by wrapping the tape measure around the outside of each circle. Measure to the nearest tenth of a centimeter. Record the results in your table.

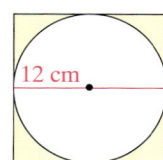

5. **Calculator** Find the ratio $\frac{\text{distance around the circle}}{\text{distance across the circle}}$ for each circle, to the nearest tenth. Record the results in your table. **The numbers are all a little greater than 3.**

6. **Patterns** What do you notice about the relationship between the distance around a circle and the distance across the circle?
See margin.

7. (**Algebra**) Suppose the distance across a circle is x. Write an expression to approximate the distance around the circle. **3.1x**

8. **a.** Estimate the distance around the circle in the diagram.
   b. Find the perimeter of the square. **48 cm**
   c. What is the difference between your estimate of the distance around the circle and the perimeter of the square? **12 cm**

36 cm
12 cm

6. **The distance around the circle is about 3 times the distance across the circle.**

Activity Lab

Exploring Circles

In this Activity Lab, students measure to investigate the relationship between the circumference and diameter of any circle. In Lesson 9-5, students formally learn the terms *radius*, *diameter*, *circumference*, and the meaning of *pi*.

Guided Instruction

For any circle, the ratio of the circumference to its diameter is *pi*, which is about 3.14. Expect student measurements of that ratio to approximate this number.

Guide students to understand that the *distance across the circle* refers to the line segment that passes through the center of the circle. It is the largest measure possible across the circle.

Error Prevention!

Review and demonstrate how to measure something to the nearest tenth of a centimeter (nearest mm). Ask students to evaluate whether their measurements are reasonable.

Activity

Have students work in pairs on the Activity. They can take turns taking and recording measurements and work together to answer the questions.

Alternative Method

Students may prefer to trace around the circular objects and measure the tracing. Provide materials for them to do so.

Resources

- Activity Lab 9-5: Circle Measurements
- metric tape measure
- calculator
- several circular objects

Objective
To identify the parts of a circle and to find the radius, diameter, and circumference

Examples
1 Identifying Parts of a Circle
2 Finding the Radius and Diameter
3 Finding Circumference
4 Calculating Circumference of a Circle

Math Understandings: p. 414D

Math Background

The perimeter of a polygon can be found by adding the lengths of its sides. However, this method does not work for a circle, since a circle does not have sides. The perimeter of a circle, called its *circumference*, must either be measured directly or calculated using one of the formulas taught in this lesson.

More Math Background: p. 414D

Lesson Planning and Resources

See p. 414E for a list of the resources that support this lesson.

PowerPoint

Bell Ringer Practice

✓ **Check Skills You'll Need**
Use student page, transparency, or PowerPoint. For intervention, direct students to:
Multiplying Decimals
Lesson 1-8
Extra Skills and Word Problems
  Practice, Ch. 1

✓ Check Skills You'll Need

1. Vocabulary Review
When you multiply two or more numbers, you are finding a __?__.
product
Find each product.

2. 2×3.14 **6.28**

3. 3.14×8 **25.12**

4. $2 \times 3.14 \times 35$ **219.8**

5. $2 \times 3.14 \times 10$ **62.8**

GO **for Help**
Lesson 1-8

What You'll Learn

To identify the parts of a circle and to find the radius, diameter, and circumference

🔊 **New Vocabulary** circle, radius, chord, diameter, circumference

Why Learn This?

To build a circular structure, such as a Ferris wheel, engineers must understand the relationships between the parts of a circle.

A **circle** is the set of points in a plane that are the same distance from a given point called the center.

A **radius** is a segment that connects the center to the circle.

A **diameter** is a chord that passes through the center of a circle.

A **chord** is a segment that has both endpoints on the circle.

Center

Vocabulary Tip

Radii (RAY dee eye) is the plural of radius.

EXAMPLE   **Identifying Parts of a Circle**

1 **a.** List the radii shown in circle *P*.
    The radii are $\overline{PA}$, $\overline{PB}$, $\overline{PC}$, and $\overline{PD}$.

b. List the chords shown in circle *P*.
    The chords are $\overline{AB}$, $\overline{BC}$, $\overline{CD}$, $\overline{DA}$, $\overline{AC}$, and $\overline{BD}$.

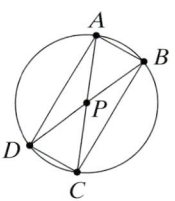

✓ Quick Check

1. List the diameters shown in circle *P*.   **$\overline{AC}$, $\overline{BD}$**

In Example 1, the diameter $\overline{AC}$ consists of two radii $\overline{PA}$ and $\overline{PC}$. The length of a diameter of a circle is twice the length of a radius.

438   Chapter 9   Geometry and Measurement

Differentiated **Instruction** **Solutions for All Learners**

Special Needs **L1**
Give students paper cutouts of circles. Have them show you what circumference means by tracing the outside of the circle with their fingers. Repeat with diameter, radius, and center.

learning style: tactile

Below Level **L2**
Have students measure the diameter of a circular object and find its circumference using $C = \pi d$. Have them check the result by wrapping string around the circumference and measuring the string.

learning style: tactile

EXAMPLE Finding the Radius and Diameter

2 **Amusement Parks** The diameter of a Ferris wheel is 250 feet. What is its radius?

$r = \frac{1}{2} \times 250$ ← The radius is half the diameter, or $r = \frac{1}{2}d$.

$= 125$ ← Simplify.

The radius of the Ferris wheel is 125 feet.

✔ Quick Check

2. Find the radius when $d = 8$ cm. **4 cm**

 **for Help**

For help with the ratio of circumference to diameter, see Activity Lab 9-5a.

The distance around a circle is its <mark>circumference.</mark> The ratio of the circumference C of a circle to its diameter d is the same for *every* circle. The symbol π (read "pi") represents this ratio. So $\pi = \frac{C}{d}$.

You can rewrite the relationship $\pi = \frac{C}{d}$ as $C = \pi \times d$, or πd.

KEY CONCEPTS Circumference of a Circle

$C = \pi d$

$C = 2\pi r$

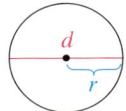

EXAMPLE Finding Circumference

3 **Multiple Choice** A regulation archery target is a circle with a 24-inch radius. Which equation can be used to find the circumference of the archery target?

(A) $C = 2 \cdot 12$ (C) $C = \pi \cdot 24$
(B) $C = \pi \cdot 12$ (D) $C = 2\pi \cdot 24$

$C = 2\pi r$ ← Use the formula for the circumference of a circle.

$= 2 \times \pi \times 24$ ← Substitute 24 for r.

$= 48\pi$ ← Multiply.

The correct answer is choice D.

✔ Quick Check

3. A circle has a radius of 11 m. What expression describes the circumference of the circle in meters? **22π**

Advanced Learners **L4**
This figure is formed by a square and a semicircle (half of a circle). Find the perimeter of the figure to the nearest meter. **37 m**

|← 8 m →|

learning style: visual

English Language Learners **ELL**
Have students draw or trace a circle on an index card. Have them draw and label a chord, a radius, the diameter, and a circumference. Have them also label the center. Next to the drawing, have them write the formula for finding circumference.

learning style: visual

---

2. Teach

Activity Lab
Use before the lesson.
Student Edition Activity Lab, Data Collection 9-5a, Exploring Circles, p. 437

All in One Teaching Resources
Activity Lab 9-5: Circle Measurements

Guided Instruction

Example 1
Some students might be confused by the pronunciation of the word *chord*. The initial sound is the same as the sound of *ch* in the word *chorus*.

PowerPoint
Additional Examples

1

a. List the radii shown in circle R. **$\overline{RB}$, $\overline{RD}$, $\overline{RE}$**

b. List the chords shown in circle R. **$\overline{AB}$, $\overline{CD}$, $\overline{BD}$**

2 On July 22, 2002, the world's largest wooden nickel was unveiled in Texas. The radius is 80 inches. What is its diameter? **160 inches**

3 The surface of one type of trampoline is bounded by a circular frame with a 7-foot radius. Find the circumference to the nearest foot. **44 feet**

All in One Teaching Resources
• Daily Notetaking Guide 9-5 **L3**
• Adapted Notetaking 9-5 **L1**

Closure

• *What is a chord and diameter?*
A chord is any segment with endpoints on the circle. A diameter is a chord that passes through the center of the circle.
• *How do you find the circumference of a circle?*
Multiply the diameter by π, or double the radius and then multiply by π.

Assignment Guide

Check Your Understanding
Go over Exercises 1–2 in class before assigning the Homework Exercises.

Homework Exercises
A Practice by Example   3–17
B Apply Your Skills   18–24
C Challenge   25
Test Prep and
   Mixed Review   26–29

Homework Quick Check
To check students' understanding of key skills and concepts, go over Exercises 8, 13, 20, 23, and 24.

Differentiated Instruction **Resources**

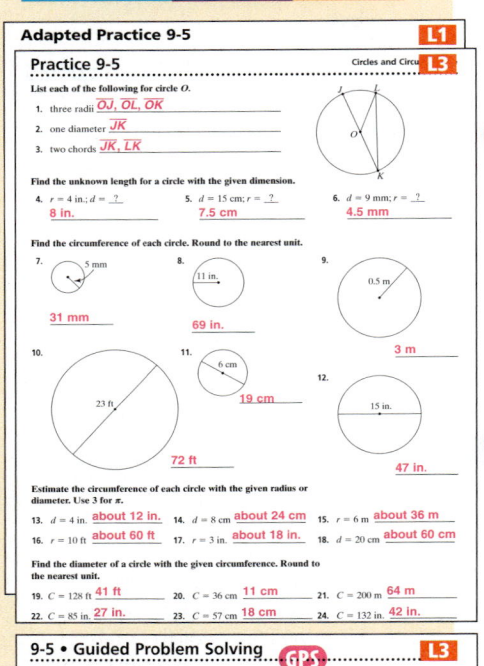

Pi is a nonrepeating, nonterminating decimal. Two approximations for π are 3.14 and $\frac{22}{7}$. Use $\frac{22}{7}$ when measurements are a multiple of 7 or involve fractions. You can also use the π key on a calculator.

EXAMPLE   Calculating Circumference of a Circle

④ Find the circumference of a circle with a 48-inch diameter. Round to the nearest inch.

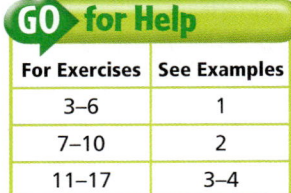

$C = \pi d$ ← Use the formula for the circumference of a circle.

$\approx 3.14 \times 48$ ← Substitute 48 for *d* and 3.14 for π.

$= 150.72$ ← Multiply.

The circumference is 151 inches.

Test Prep Tip
Be careful to use the correct formula to find circumference.

✓ **Quick Check**

4. Find the circumference of a circle with a diameter of 5.8 centimeters. Round to the nearest centimeter. **18 cm**

✓ **Check Your Understanding**

1. Yes; a chord that does not pass through the center is not a diameter.

1. **Vocabulary** Is it possible for a chord of a circle not to be a diameter of the circle? Explain.

2. **Reasoning** Draw a circle with a radius greater than 2 in. and a circumference less than 15 in. **Check students' work.**

Homework Exercises

For more exercises, see Extra Skills and Word Problems.

GO for Help

For Exercises	See Examples
3–6	1
7–10	2
11–17	3–4

A Identify each of the following for circle *Q*.

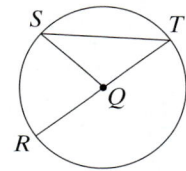

3. three radii
   $\overline{QR}, \overline{QS}, \overline{QT}$

4. one diameter
   $\overline{RT}$

5. two chords
   $\overline{RT}, \overline{ST}$

6. center
   point Q

Find the unknown length for each circle.

7. $r = 35$ mi, $d = \blacksquare$ **70 mi**
     8. $d = 6.8$ yd, $r = \blacksquare$ **3.4 yd**

9. $r = 18$ ft, $d = \blacksquare$ **36 ft**
     10. $d = 0.25$ km, $r = \blacksquare$ **0.125 km**

11. A circular water tank has a radius of 4 m. What expression describes the circumference of the tank in meters? **8π**

24. **Answers may vary. Sample: The pebble makes a mark along the circumference during every rotation. So the circumference is 69 inches.**

Find the circumference of each circle.

12. 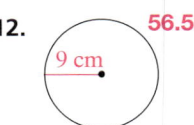 **56.52 cm**
9 cm

13. **15.7 in.**
5 in.

14. **72.22 ft**
23 ft

15. $d = 28$ mi
87.92 mi

16. $r = 7$ ft
43.96 ft

17. $d = 10$ m
31.4 m

B **GPS** 18. **Guided Problem Solving** You need to cut a circular piece of wood with a circumference of 20.5 cm. What radius should you use to draw the circle? **3.26 cm**

- Which formula should you use to find the radius, $C = \pi d$ or $C = 2\pi r$?
- How can you use the formula to find the radius?

Estimate the radius of a circle with the given circumference.

19. 192 ft
30.6 ft

20. 1,273 m
202.7 m

21. 3.75 in.
0.60 in.

22. 12.4 mi
1.97 mi

23. A dog trainer uses hoops with diameters of 24 and 30 inches.
GPS What is the difference between the circumferences? Use 3 for π. **18 in.**

24. **Writing in Math** A pebble is stuck in a bicycle's tire. As the tire turns, the pebble leaves a mark every 69 inches. Explain how you would find the circumference of the tire. **See margin.**

C 25. **Challenge** The diameter of a bicycle wheel is 2 feet. How far will the bicycle travel when the wheel makes one full turn?
about 6.3 ft

Test Prep and Mixed Review   **Practice**

Multiple Choice 26. Which statement about the parts of a circle is NOT true? **B**
- Ⓐ The radius is half as long as the diameter.
- Ⓑ The diameter is four times as long as the radius.
- Ⓒ The circumference is about 6 times the radius.
- Ⓓ The circumference is about 3 times the diameter.

27. Which type of angle measures 180°? **J**
- Ⓕ Acute
- Ⓗ Right
- Ⓖ Obtuse
- Ⓙ Straight

GO for Help

For Exercises	See Lesson
28–29	2-2

Find the median of each data set.

28. 50, 20, 42, 45, 48, 50 **46.5**

29. 8.0, 7.5, 6.6, 7.8, 7.5 **7.5**

PowerPoint
Lesson Quiz

Find the unknown length of each circle.

1. $r = 5.4$ m, $d = $ ▰ **10.8 m**

2. $d = 68$ cm, $r = $ ▰ **34 cm**

Find the circumference of each circle to the nearest unit.

3. $d = 20$ in. **63 in.**

4. $r = 35$ mm **220 mm**

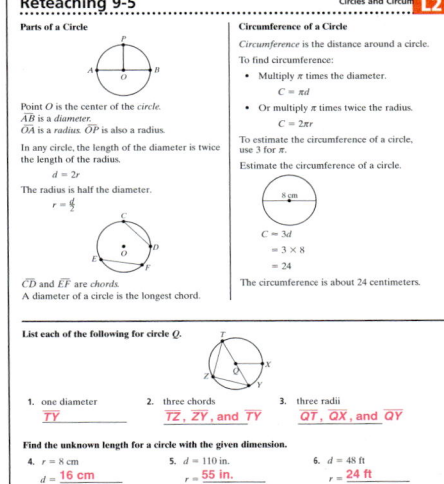

Reteaching 9-5   Circles and Circum   **L2**

Parts of a Circle
Point O is the center of the circle.
$\overline{AB}$ is a diameter.
$\overline{OA}$ is a radius. $\overline{OP}$ is also a radius.
In any circle, the length of the diameter is twice the length of the radius.
$$d = 2r$$
The radius is half the diameter.
$$r = \frac{d}{2}$$
$\overline{CD}$ and $\overline{EF}$ are chords.
A diameter of a circle is the longest chord.

Circumference of a Circle
Circumference is the distance around a circle.
To find circumference:
- Multiply π times the diameter.
$$C = \pi d$$
- Or multiply π times twice the radius.
$$C = 2\pi r$$
To estimate the circumference of a circle, use 3 for π.
Estimate the circumference of a circle.
$$C = 3d$$
$$= 3 \times 8$$
$$= 24$$
The circumference is about 24 centimeters.

List each of the following for circle Q.

1. one diameter
$\overline{TY}$

2. three chords
$\overline{TZ}$, $\overline{ZY}$, and $\overline{TY}$

3. three radii
$\overline{QT}$, $\overline{QX}$, and $\overline{QY}$

Find the unknown length for a circle with the given dimension.
4. $r = 8$ cm
$d = $ **16 cm**

5. $d = 110$ in.
$r = $ **55 in.**

6. $d = 48$ ft
$r = $ **24 ft**

Use 3 for π to estimate the circumference of a circle with the given radius or diameter.
7. $r = 12$ in. **72 in.**
8. $d = 15$ yd **45 yd**
9. $d = 7$ m **21 m**
10. $d = 13$ ft **39 ft**
11. $r = 21$ yd **126 yd**
12. $r = 19$ cm **114 cm**

Enrichment 9-5   Circles and Circu   **L4**
Geometric Relationships

A sand dollar is an animal that lives slightly buried in the sand of shallow coastal waters. Its thin, circular body is about 2 to 4 inches wide.

a. What are the smallest and largest circumferences of sand dollars? What is the range of circumferences?
b. What are the smallest and largest areas of sand dollars? What is the range of areas?

1. What mathematical term describes the "width" of a circle?
diameter

2. What radius will you use to find the measures of the smaller sand dollar? **1 inch**

3. What radius will you use to find the measures of the larger sand dollar? **2 inches**

4. Find the circumference of each sand dollar, in terms of π. Then calculate the approximate measure using 3.14 for π.
smaller sand dollar: 2π or 6.28 inches;
larger sand dollar: 4π or 12.56 inches

5. What does it mean to find the *range* of the values?
Find the difference between the greatest value
and the least value.

6. Write an equation to find the range of the sand dollar circumferences, R, in terms of π. Then calculate the approximate range.
$R = 4\pi - 2\pi$; $R = 2\pi$; The approximate range of
circumferences for sand dollars is 6.28 inches.

7. Find the area of each sand dollar, in terms of π. Then calculate the approximate measure using 3.14 for π.
smaller sand dollar: π or 3.14 in.^{2};
larger sand dollar: 4π or 12.56 in.^{2}

8. Write an equation to find the range of the sand dollar areas, in terms of π. Then calculate the approximate range.
$R = 4\pi - \pi$; $R = 3\pi$; The approximate range of areas
for sand dollars is 9.42 in.^{2}

Alternative Assessment

Each student in a pair draws several circles and labels the length of their radii or diameters. Partners exchange drawings and find the circumference of each other's circles.

Test Prep

Resources
For additional practice with a variety of test item formats:
- Test-Taking Strategies, p. 467
- Test Prep, p. 471
- Test-Taking Strategies with Transparencies

Practice Solving Problems

Students practice solving problems involving perimeter and area. They find perimeters and areas of figures and solve problems relating the two measurements to each other.

Guided Instruction

Discuss with students how perimeter and area relate to each other. Elicit everyday examples when one might need to find the perimeter or area of a space or object. Have a volunteer read the problem. Ask:

- *What is the perimeter of the new wall? Is it double the perimeter of the first wall?* **128 ft, yes**

- *Before you calculate whether 2 gallons of paint will cover the new wall, do you think it will be enough? Why?* **Answers will vary.**

- *What fraction of the new wall is the first wall?* $\frac{1}{4}$

Practice Solving Problems

Suppose you used 1 gallon of paint to paint a wall that is 20 ft long and 12 ft high. Each dimension of another wall is twice the dimension of the wall you painted. Will 2 gallons be enough paint for the larger wall? Explain.

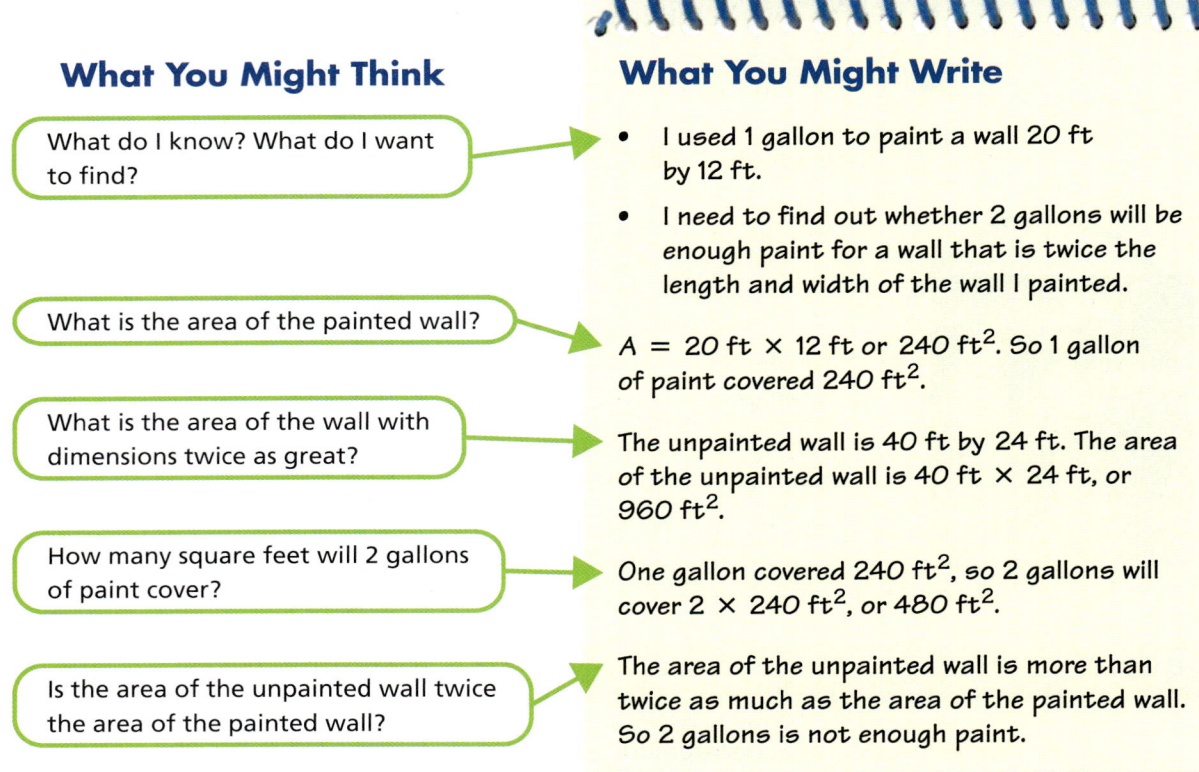

What You Might Think

What do I know? What do I want to find?

What is the area of the painted wall?

What is the area of the wall with dimensions twice as great?

How many square feet will 2 gallons of paint cover?

Is the area of the unpainted wall twice the area of the painted wall?

What You Might Write

- I used 1 gallon to paint a wall 20 ft by 12 ft.

- I need to find out whether 2 gallons will be enough paint for a wall that is twice the length and width of the wall I painted.

$A = 20$ ft $\times 12$ ft or 240 ft^2. So 1 gallon of paint covered 240 ft^2.

The unpainted wall is 40 ft by 24 ft. The area of the unpainted wall is 40 ft $\times$ 24 ft, or 960 ft^2.

One gallon covered 240 ft^2, so 2 gallons will cover 2 $\times$ 240 ft^2, or 480 ft^2.

The area of the unpainted wall is more than twice as much as the area of the painted wall. So 2 gallons is not enough paint.

Think It Through

1. Suppose you want to paint 720 ft^2. How many gallons of paint do you need? **3 gal**

2. Find the number of square feet painted per gallon. Write your answer as a unit rate. **240 ft^2/gal**

3. **Check for Reasonableness** How many gallons of paint are needed to paint the unpainted wall? How did you decide?
   4 gallons; divide 960 by 240.

Exercises

4. You have 34 feet of fence to enclose a rectangular garden. You want the length of each side to be a whole number. What dimensions of the garden enclose the greatest area? **8 ft by 9 ft**
   a. What do you know?
   b. What do you want to find?
   c. Find the enclosed area.

   $$A = b \times h$$
   $$= \blacksquare \times \blacksquare$$
   $$= \blacksquare \ ft^2$$

5. What will it cost to tile the floor shown below with 1-foot square tiles costing $3.75 each? Assume that you can buy the exact number of tiles you need.   **$581.25**

6. A rectangular figure is 9 times the area of the figure shown below. Draw the larger figure showing its dimensions. Explain how you decided on the dimensions.

Answers may vary. Sample: The new figure is 24 in. by 30 in. because the area is nine times greater; each side will be three times greater.

7. In one season, the total payroll for the Cleveland Browns was $87.7 million. The total payroll for the San Francisco 49ers was $63.0 million. About how many times greater was the payroll for the Browns? **about 1.4 times**

Objective
To find the area of a circle

Examples
1 Finding the Area of a Circle
2 Application: Mirrors

Math Understandings: p. 414D

Math Background

In a geometry course, the formula for the area of a circle is usually derived by considering a circle as a regular polygon of infinitely many sides. The derivation presented in this lesson—imagining a circle cut apart and rearranged to look like a parallelogram—provides an alternative that is within the grasp of younger children.

More Math Background: p. 414D

Lesson Planning and Resources

See p. 414E for a list of the resources that support this lesson.

Bell Ringer Practice

✓ **Check Skills You'll Need**
Use student page, transparency, or PowerPoint. For intervention, direct students to:
Exponents
Lesson 4-2
Extra Skills and Word Problems
  Practice, Ch. 4

444

✓ Check Skills You'll Need

1. Vocabulary Review
Use exponents to write
$2 \cdot 2 \cdot 2 \cdot 3 \cdot 3$.

Simplify each expression. $2^3 \cdot 3^2$

2. 12^2 **144**

3. $(7 - 3)^2$ **16**

4. $(6 + 4)^2$ **100**

5. $9 + 3^2$ **18**

 **for Help**
Lesson 4-2

 **for Help**
For help finding the area of a parallelogram, go to Lesson 9-4, Example 1.

What You'll Learn

To find the area of a circle

Why Learn This?

To plant crops on a farm using a center-pivot irrigation system, farmers must calculate the area of a circle.

Suppose you cut a circle into equal-sized wedges. You can rearrange the wedges into a figure that resembles a parallelogram.

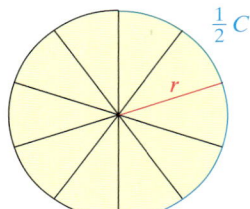   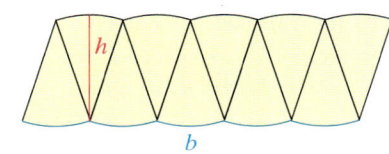

The base of the parallelogram is one half of the circumference of the circle, or πr. The height of the parallelogram is the same length as the circle's radius.

$A = b \times h$ ← Use the formula for the area of a parallelogram.

$\quad = \pi r \times r$ ← Substitute πr for b and r for h.

$\quad = \pi r^2$ ← Simplify.

The calculations suggest a formula for the area of a circle.

KEY CONCEPTS **Area of a Circle**

$A = \pi r^2$

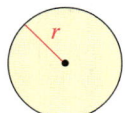

---

444   Chapter 9   Geometry and Measurement

Differentiated Instruction   Solutions for All Learners

Special Needs **L1**
Provide students with a paper circle, with 10 wedges drawn on it. Ask them to cut it and form a parallelogram as shown in the book.

learning style: tactile

Below Level **L2**
Identify the radius and diameter of a circle whose area is $\pi \times 8^2$ square units. **radius = 8 units, diameter = 16 units** *Calculate the area using 3.14 for π.* **about 201 square units**

learning style: visual

For: Area of Circles
     Activity
Use: Interactive
     Textbook, 9-6

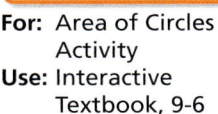

EXAMPLE **Finding the Area of a Circle**

① Find the area of the circle at the right.

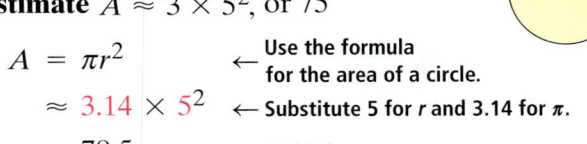

Estimate $A \approx 3 \times 5^2$, or 75

$A = \pi r^2$ ← Use the formula for the area of a circle.

$\approx 3.14 \times 5^2$ ← Substitute 5 for r and 3.14 for π.

$= 78.5$ ← Multiply.

The area is about 78.5 square feet.

Check for Reasonableness The estimate, 75 square feet, is close to 78.5 square feet. So the answer is reasonable.

✓ **Quick Check**

1. Find the area of each circle. Use 3.14 for π.

   a.
      12 km
      about 452.16 km²

   b.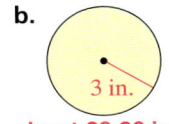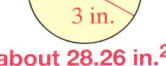
      3 in.
      about 28.26 in.²

   c.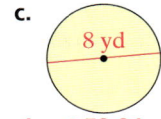
      8 yd
      about 50.24 yd²

When the radius or diameter of a circle is a multiple of 7 or a fraction, you may find it easier to use $\frac{22}{7}$ for π.

EXAMPLE **Application: Mirrors**

② Find the area of the circular mirror at the left with a diameter of 14 inches. Use $\frac{22}{7}$ for π.

The radius is one half of the diameter, or 7 inches.

$A = \pi r^2$ ← Use the formula for the area of a circle.

$\approx \frac{22}{7} \times 7^2$ ← Use $\frac{22}{7}$ for π and 7 for r.

$= \frac{22}{7} \times 49$ ← Divide 7 and 49 by their GCF, 7.

$= 154$ ← Multiply.

The area of the mirror is about 154 square inches.

Circular mirrors are used in telescopes.

✓ **Quick Check**

2. Find the area of a large pizza with a 14-inch diameter. Use $\frac{22}{7}$ for π. **154 in.²**

---

2. Teach

Activity Lab

Use before the lesson.

All in One Teaching Resources

Activity Lab 9-6: More Patterns in Geometry

Guided Instruction

Example 2
Before discussing Example 2, give each student a circle with a diameter of 14 units drawn on a grid, as shown below. Have them estimate the area of the circle using the method taught in Activity Lab 9-4a. After discussing Example 2, have them compare their estimates to 154 in.², the area found by using the formula.

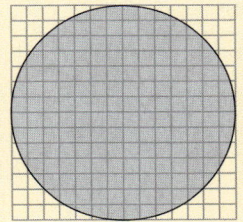

Error Prevention!

In Quick Check 2, watch for students who square the diameter.

PowerPoint
Additional Examples

① Find the area of a circle with diameter 18 inches. Round to the nearest tenth. **about 254 square inches**

② Find the area of a circular flower bed with radius 7 feet. Use $\frac{22}{7}$ for π. **about 154 square feet**

All in One Teaching Resources
• Daily Notetaking Guide 9-6 **L3**
• Adapted Notetaking 9-6 **L1**

Closure

• Explain how to find the area of a circle. **Square the radius and multiply by pi.**

Advanced Learners **L4**
Find the radius, diameter, and circumference of a circle that has an area of 314 ft². Use 3.14 for for π. **radius ≈ 10 ft; diameter ≈ 20 ft; circumference ≈ 62.8 ft**

learning style: visual

English Language Learners **ELL**
Have students prove that $\frac{22}{7}$ is close to 3.14 by using a calculator or paper and pencil. Have them decide which version of pi is an easier one to use in calculations.

learning style: visual

445

Check Your Understanding
Go over Exercises 1–6 in class before assigning the Homework Exercises.

Homework Exercises
A Practice by Example	7–16
B Apply Your Skills	17–28
C Challenge	29
Test Prep and Mixed Review	30–34

Homework Quick Check
To check students' understanding of key skills and concepts, go over Exercises 10, 14, 22, 24, and 26.

Differentiated Instruction Resources

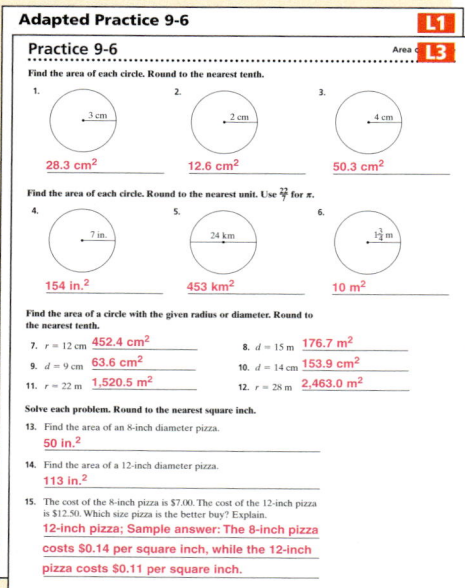

Check Your Understanding

Test Prep Tip
You can use 3 for the value of π when you are estimating to check for reasonableness.

1. Find the area of a pie with a radius of 14 cm. Use $\frac{22}{7}$ for π. **616 cm²**

2. **Patterns** Find the area of each circle. Use 3.14 for π.
   a. $r = 2$ in.   b. $r = 4$ in.   c. $r = 8$ in.
   d. What happens to the area of a circle when you double the radius? **2a–d. See left.**

   2a. 12.56 in.²
   b. 50.24 in.²
   c. 200.96 in.²
   d. It quadruples.

Mental Math Estimate the area of each circle. Use 3 for π.

3. $r = 2$ in.
12 in.²

4. $d = 6$ mm
27 mm²

5. $r = 20$ cm
1,200 cm²

6. $d = 16$ ft
192 ft²

Homework Exercises

For more exercises, see Extra Skills and Word Problems.

GO for Help

For Exercises	See Examples
7–12	1
13–16	2

A Find the area of each circle. Use 3.14 for π.

7.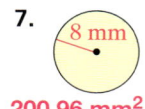
8 mm
200.96 mm²

8.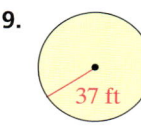
26 km
530.66 km²

9.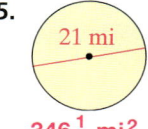
37 ft
4,298.66 ft²

10. $d = 32$ in.
803.84 in.²

11. $r = 11$ yd
379.94 yd²

12. $d = 12$ cm
113.04 cm²

Find the area of each circle. Use $\frac{22}{7}$ for π.

13.
$2\frac{1}{3}$ mm
$17\frac{1}{9}$ mm²

14.
$4\frac{1}{2}$ in.
$63\frac{9}{14}$ in.²

15.
21 mi
$346\frac{1}{2}$ mi²

16. **Camping** Campers arrange stones in a circle around their campfire site. The circle has a diameter of 14 feet. Find the area of the site. **154 ft²**

B GPS 17. **Guided Problem Solving** The Aztecs used their knowledge of astronomy and mathematics to make a calendar. They carved the calendar, called the Sun Stone, on a circular stone 3.6 meters in diameter. Find the area of the Sun Stone. Use 3.14 for π. **10.17 m²**
   • What is the radius of the stone?
   • What unit of measure will your answer include?

Find the area of each circle. Use 3.14 for π. Round your answer to the nearest tenth.

18. $r = 1.1$ mi   **19.** $d = 2.4$ cm   **20.** $r = 0.5$ m   **21.** $d = 13.7$ ft
3.8 mi²   4.5 cm²   0.8 m²   147.3 ft²

22. Writing in Math Does a circular pan with a diameter of 20 in. have a greater area than a square pan 18 inches long? Explain.
See left.

22. No; the area of the circular pan is about 314 in.², and the area of the square pan is 324 in.².

23. Games The hopscotch figure at the right is composed of squares and a semicircle. Suppose the side lengths of each square are 2 feet. Find the area of the hopscotch figure. **38.28 ft²**

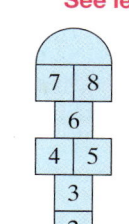

24. You can pick up the signal of one radio station within 45 miles of the station. Find the approximate area of the broadcast region.
6,358.5 mi²

Find the area of each yellow region. Use 3.14 for π.

25.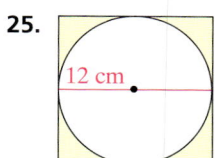
12 cm
30.96 cm²

26.
5 m
4 m
65.94 m²

27.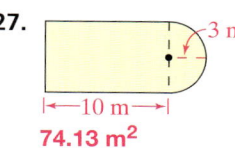
3 m
10 m
74.13 m²

28. Find the area of a circle with a circumference of 31.4 units.
78.5 square units

C 29. Challenge The diameter of a circle is tripled. How does this affect the area of the circle? **When the diameter is tripled, the area becomes 9 times greater.**

Test Prep and Mixed Review   **Practice**

Multiple Choice

30. Which expression can Jack use to find the area of a circle with diameter d and radius r? **A**

Ⓐ πr^2 Ⓑ $2\pi r$ Ⓒ πd^2 Ⓓ πd

31. The circumference of a circle is about 18.84 meters. Estimate the approximate length of the radius of the circle. **F**

Ⓕ 3 m   Ⓖ 6 m   Ⓗ 9 m   Ⓙ 12 m

for Help

For Exercises	See Lesson
32–34	8-7

Trace each figure and draw the lines of symmetry.
32–34. See margin.

32. 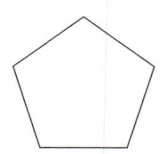   **33.**    **34.**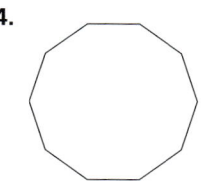

32–34. See back of book.

---

4. Assess & Reteach

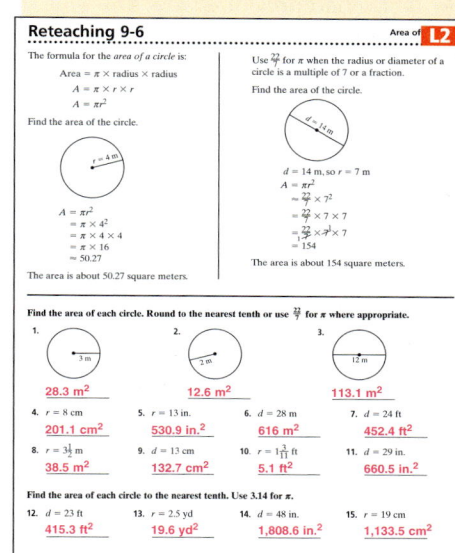

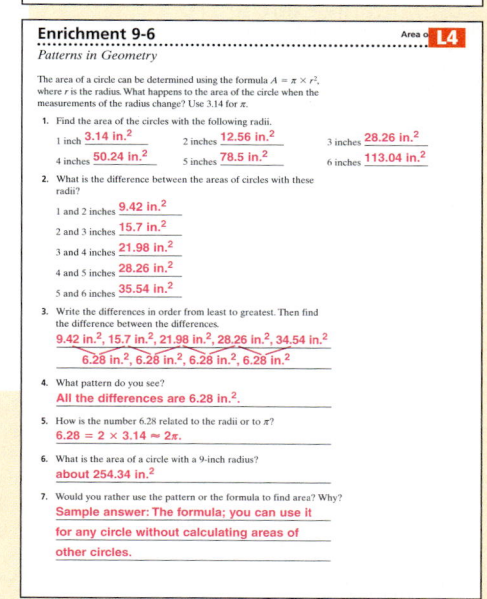

Test Prep

Resources

For additional practice with a variety of test item formats:
• Test-Taking Strategies, p. 467
• Test Prep, p. 471
• Test-Taking Strategies with Transparencies

In this feature, students draw front, right side, and top views of stacks of blocks. This Activity serves as an introduction to two-dimensional views of three-dimensional figures that is presented in Lesson 9-7.

Guided Instruction

Each of the three views—front, right, and top—show only what is visible from that point of view. Ask:
• *If you had only one view of a stack of blocks, can you know how many blocks are in the stack?* **no**
• *If you had only two views of a stack of blocks, can you know how many blocks are in the stack?* **Sample: Maybe, but not necessarily.**

Exercises

Have students work independently on the Exercises. When they have finished, have them compare their drawings with a partner's. If they are different, figure out whether or not both drawings could be accurate.

Alternative Method

Provide cubes for students to use with the Exercises. For Exercises 1–3, they can build models of the figures shown to help them draw different views. For Exercises 4–5, they can use the blocks to build the figures that the drawings represent.

Resources

• Activity Lab 9-7: Spatial Reasoning
• cube-shaped blocks
• graph paper
• Classroom Aids 2, 6
• Student Manipulates Kit

9-7a Activity Lab — Hands On

Three-Dimensional Views

You can draw three-dimensional objects so that they appear to have length, width, and height. You can also draw different views of the blocks.

ACTIVITY

1. Stack 6 blocks as shown at the right.

2. Make three different drawings. Draw a view from the:
   a. top   b. front   c. right side

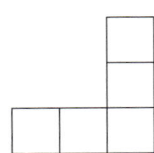
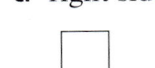

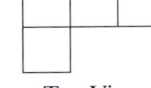

Top View   Front View   Right Side View

Exercises

1–5. See margin.

Use blocks or centimeter cubes to build the figures below. Then draw the top, front, and right side views of each figure.

1.

2.

3.

Reasoning Use the drawings below. Make a figure of blocks for each set of views.

4.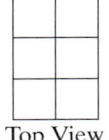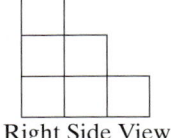

Top View   Front View   Right Side View

5.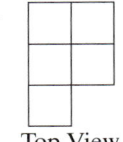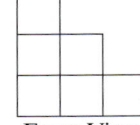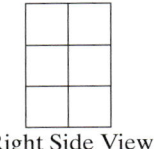

Top View   Front View   Right Side View

448 Activity Lab Three-Dimensional Views

---

1. **Top   Front   Right**

2. **Top   Front   Right**

3–5. See back of book.

Three-Dimensional Figures and Spatial Reasoning

Check Skills You'll Need

1. **Vocabulary Review** Describe a *rectangle* that is not a *square*.
See below.
Identify each polygon by the numbers of sides.

2. 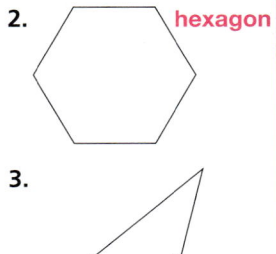 **hexagon**

3.  **triangle**

GO for Help
Lesson 8-5

What You'll Learn

To identify three-dimensional figures

🔊 **New Vocabulary** three-dimensional figure, faces, edge, vertex, prism, cube, pyramid, cylinder, cone, sphere

Why Learn This?

Architects use shapes to design buildings. To identify these figures, you need to understand how they differ.

A **three-dimensional figure** is a figure that does not lie in a plane. It has three dimensions: length, width, and height.

The flat surfaces of a three-dimensional figure are called **faces**.

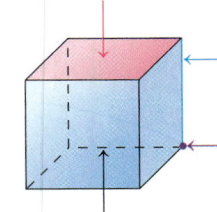

An **edge** is a segment where two faces meet.

A **vertex** is a point where two or more edges meet.

When you draw three-dimensional figures, use dashed lines to indicate "hidden" edges.

A **prism** is a three-dimensional figure with two parallel and congruent faces that are polygons. These faces are called bases. The prism above is a **cube**. All of its faces are congruent.

Base Shape	Name of Prism	
Triangle	Triangular Prism	
Rectangle	Rectangular Prism	
Pentagon	Pentagonal Prism	You name a prism by the shape of its bases.
Hexagon	Hexagonal Prism	
Heptagon	Heptagonal Prism	
Octagon	Octagonal Prism	

Vocabulary Tip

Three-dimensional is often abbreviated as 3-D.

Check Skills You'll Need

1. A rectangle that is not a square is a 4-sided polygon with 4 right angles and with the length different from the width.

9-7 Three-Dimensional Figures and Spatial Reasoning **449**

Objective
To identify three-dimensional figures

Examples
1 Naming Prisms
2 Identifying Three-Dimensional Figures

Math Understandings: p. 414D

Math Background

Plane figures such as polygons and circles lie entirely within a plane. They generally can be described by two measurements, length and width, and so they are called *two-dimensional figures*. In this lesson, students examine figures that extend beyond a plane into space. These *space figures* have an added dimension, often referred to as *depth*. For this reason, they are called *three-dimensional figures*.

More Math Background: p. 414D

Lesson Planning and Resources

See p. 414E for a list of the resources that support this lesson.

PowerPoint

Bell Ringer Practice

✓ **Check Skills You'll Need**
Use student page, transparency, or PowerPoint. For intervention, direct students to:
Exploring and Classifying Polygons
Lesson 8-5
Extra Skills and Word Problems Practice, Ch. 8

Differentiated Instruction | **Solutions for All Learners**

Special Needs **L1**
If possible, provide students with wooden or paper solid shapes. Have them trace the shapes of the faces, including the bases. Make sure students know which ones are bases so that they can use that knowledge to name the solids.

learning style: tactile

Below Level **L2**
Distribute index cards. Have students list the names of as many different polygons as they can on the card. Next to the name of each polygon, have them write its number of sides. Allow them to refer to this list when naming prisms and pyramids.

learning style: visual

449

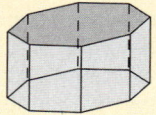
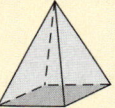
EXAMPLE **Naming Prisms**

1 Name the prism shown.

Each base is a hexagon. So the figure is a hexagonal prism.

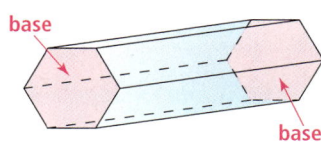

✓ Quick Check

1. Name each prism.

a.

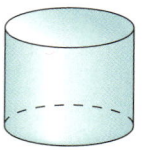

pentagonal prism

b.

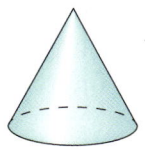

rectangular prism

c.

triangular prism

A **pyramid** is a three-dimensional figure with one polygon for a base. All of the other faces are triangles. The faces all meet at one vertex. You name a pyramid by its base.

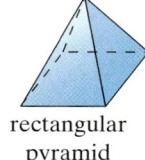

rectangular pyramid

Some three-dimensional figures do not have polygons for bases.

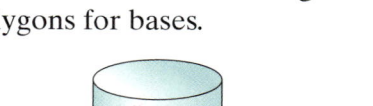

A **cylinder** has two congruent parallel bases that are circles.

A **cone** has one circular base and one vertex.

A **sphere** has no base.

EXAMPLE **Identifying Three-Dimensional Figures**

2 **Museum** The American Museum of Natural History in New York City is shown at the right. Name a three-dimensional figure in the photo.

The sphere in the photo is a three-dimensional figure without a base.

✓ Quick Check

2. Name another three-dimensional figure in the photo. **rectangular prism**

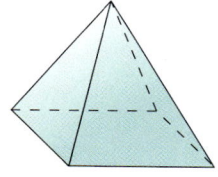

1. **Vocabulary** How are a prism and a pyramid alike? How are they different? **See left.**

2. **Writing in Math** Describe the shape of the square pyramid at the left. **See margin.**

1. Answers may vary. Sample: They are both three-dimensional shapes. A prism has two parallel and congruent bases, but a pyramid has only one base.

Label each figure as a *cylinder,* *cone,* **or** *sphere.*

3.

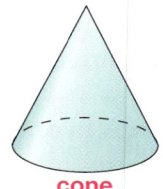

cone

4.

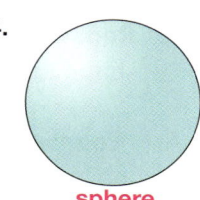

sphere

5.

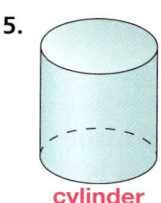

cylinder

Homework Exercises

For more exercises, see Extra Skills and Word Problems.

Assignment Guide

Check Your Understanding
Go over Exercises 1–5 in class before assigning the Homework Exercises.

Homework Exercises
A Practice by Example   6–15
B Apply Your Skills   16–20
C Challenge   21
Test Prep and
Mixed Review   22–24

Homework Quick Check
To check students' understanding of key skills and concepts, go over Exercises 6, 15, 17, 18, and 20.

Differentiated Instruction Resources

A Name each prism.

GO for Help	
For Exercises	See Examples
6–11	1
12–15	2

6.

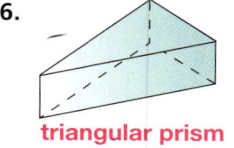

triangular prism

7.

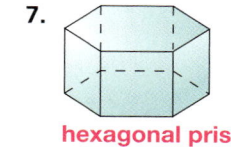

hexagonal prism

8.

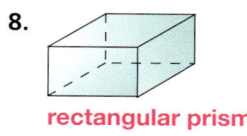

rectangular prism

9.

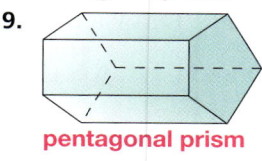

pentagonal prism

10.

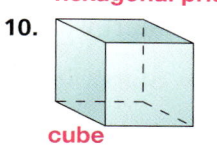

cube

11.

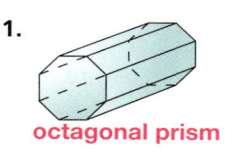

octagonal prism

Structures Name a three-dimensional figure in each photo.

12. sphere

13. pyramid

14. rectangular prism

15. cone

⬤**nline** lesson quiz, PHSchool.com, Web Code: aqa-0907

9-7 Three-Dimensional Figures and Spatial Reasoning **451**

2. Answers may vary. Sample: One face of the figure is a square. The other four faces are triangles that have a common vertex.

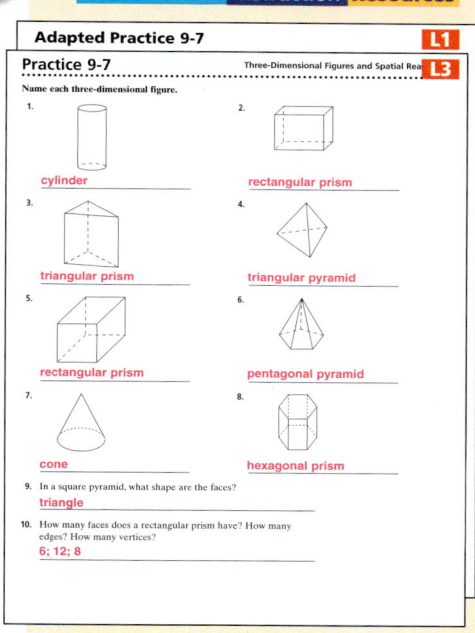

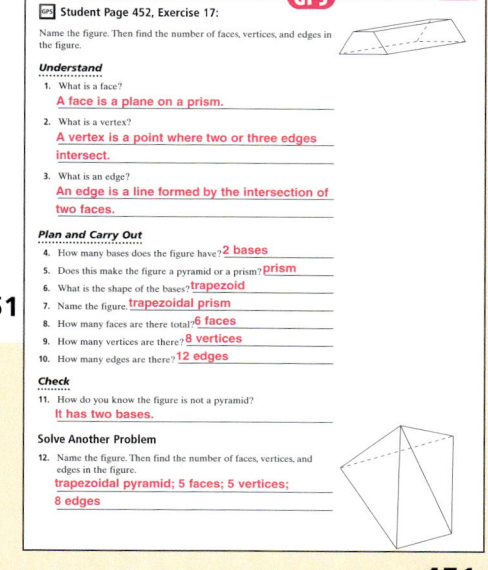

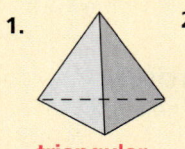

PowerPoint
Lesson Quiz

Name each figure.

1.

2.

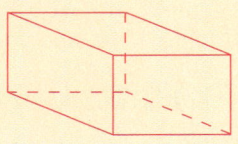

triangular
pyramid

rectangular
prism

21. Answers may vary.
Sample:

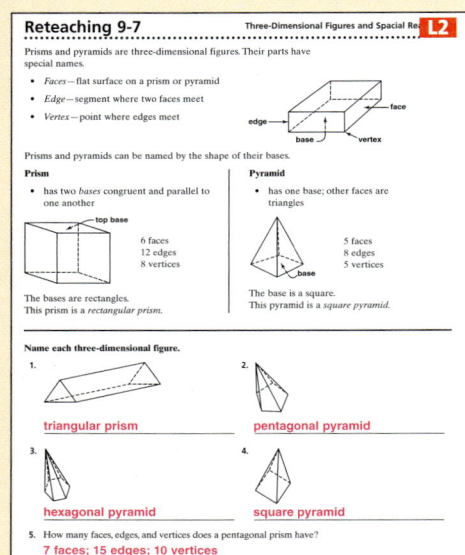

16. triangular pyramid;
4 faces, 4 vertices,
6 edges

17. trapezoidal prism;
6 faces, 8 vertices,
12 edges

19. Answers may vary.
Sample:

20. Answers may vary.
Sample:

B 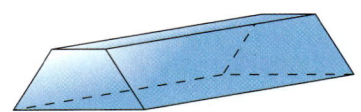 **16. Guided Problem Solving** Name the figure at the right. Find the number of faces, vertices, and edges in the figure.
- What is the shape of the base in the figure?
- How many faces does the figure have?

17. Name the figure. Then find the
GPS number of faces, vertices, and
edges in the figure.

18. Reasoning In a prism, what
shape are the faces that are not the base? **parallelograms**

Art **You can use translations to draw three-dimensional figures.**

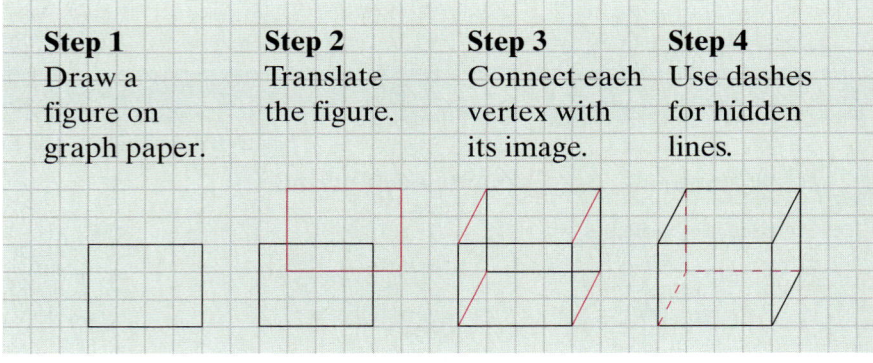

Step 1	Step 2	Step 3	Step 4
Draw a figure on graph paper.	Translate the figure.	Connect each vertex with its image.	Use dashes for hidden lines.

19. Start with a triangle. Draw a three-dimensional figure.

20. Start with a pentagon. Draw a three-dimensional figure.

C **21. Challenge** Describe the translation used in Steps 1–4. Redraw the rectangle. Use a different translation to draw the figure.
See margin.

Test Prep and Mixed Review   Practice

Multiple Choice

22. A meteorologist listed the high temperatures for one week as 74°F, 70°F, 72°F, 75°F, 79°F, 80°F, and 82°F. What was the range of high temperatures? **C**
- (A) 82°F
- (B) 70°F
- (C) 12°F
- (D) 8°F

23. Brittany drank one gallon of water in one weekend. Which measurement could NOT be expressed as one gallon? **J**
- (F) 4 quarts
- (G) 8 pints
- (H) 16 cups
- (J) 32 ounces

24. A shirt that originally costs $20 is marked 30% off. Find the sale price. **$14**

Test Prep

Resources
For additional practice with a variety of test item formats:
- Test-Taking Strategies, p. 467
- Test Prep, p. 471
- Test-Taking Strategies with Transparencies

Alternative Assessment

Each student in a pair names a prism for their partner to draw. Partners draw the prisms on graph paper by following the guidelines provided in Exercises 19–20.

Surface Areas of Prisms

Check Skills You'll Need

1. **Vocabulary Review** Describe the *area* of a piece of paper.
1–3. See below.
Find the area of each rectangle.

2. $\ell = 7$ m, $w = 3$ m

3. $\ell = 10$ m, $w = 6$ m

GO for Help
Lesson 9-3

Check Skills You'll Need

1. The area of a piece of paper is the two-dimensional space a rectangle of the same dimensions as the paper encloses.

2. 21 m²

3. 60 m²

What You'll Learn

To use nets and to find the surface areas of rectangular prisms

🔊 **New Vocabulary** net, surface area

Why Learn This?

Package designers make creative labels. The surface area of an object is the space designers have to work with.

A **net** is a pattern you can fold to form a three-dimensional figure.

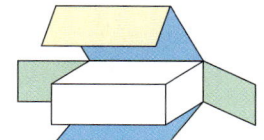

	Front	
	Top	
Side	Back	Side
	Bottom	

EXAMPLE — Drawing a Net

1 Draw a net for the triangular prism at the left.

Step 1 Draw one base.

Step 2 Draw one face that connects the two bases.

Step 3 Draw the other base.

Step 4 Draw the remaining faces.

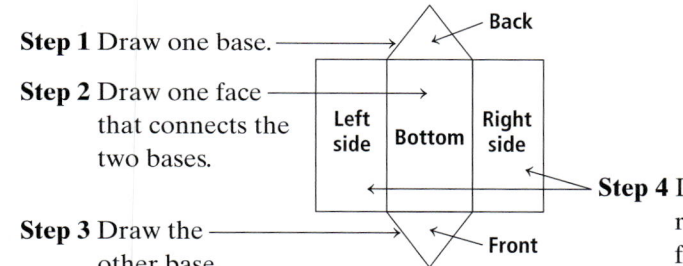

Back

Left side | Bottom | Right side

Front

1. Answers may vary. Sample:

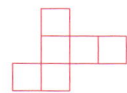

✓ Quick Check

● 1. Draw a net for a cube.

Objective

To use nets and to find the surface areas of rectangular prisms

Examples

1 Drawing a Net
2 Finding the Surface Area of a Prism

Math Understandings: p. 414D

Math Background

Prisms are three-dimensional figures. However, an important measure associated with them is two-dimensional—*surface area*. In later courses, students will be expected to learn formulas for calculating surface areas. In this lesson, however, students determine surface areas primarily by relating the length, width, and height of the three-dimensional figure to its two-dimensional net.

More Math Background: p. 414D

Lesson Planning and Resources

See p. 414E for a list of the resources that support this lesson.

PowerPoint
Bell Ringer Practice

✓ **Check Skills You'll Need**
Use student page, transparency, or PowerPoint. For intervention, direct students to:
Perimeters and Areas of Rectangles
Lesson 9-3
Extra Skills and Word Problems Practice, Ch. 9

Differentiated Instruction — Solutions for All Learners

Special Needs **L1**
Some students might have difficulty drawing nets. Provide various physical or visual assists. For example, hand out graph paper to help them with the lines. Or pair them up with a student who can draw while they direct.

learning style: visual

Below Level **L2**
Give students this net for a rectangular prism. Have them use the net to find the surface area. **216 square units**

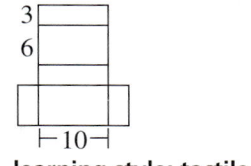

learning style: tactile

453

Activity Lab

Use before the lesson.

All in One Teaching Resources

Activity Lab 9-8: Critical Thinking

Guided Instruction

Example 2

Some students might have difficulty visualizing the three pairs of congruent faces. Give them empty cereal boxes to cut apart and match the congruent faces.

Error Prevention!

In Quick Check 2, some students may confuse the dimensions of different pairs of faces. Suggest that they list the dimensions of each face, as shown in Example 2, and to check that each dimension is correct before multiplying.

PowerPoint

Additional Examples

1 Draw a net for the triangular prism shown.

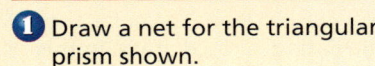
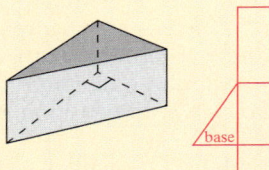
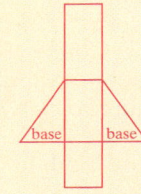

2 Find the surface area of the pizza box. **792 in.²**

$\ell = 18$ in. $w = 18$ in.

$h = 2$ in.

All in One Teaching Resources

• Daily Notetaking Guide 9-8 **L3**
• Daily Notetaking 9-8 **L1**

Closure

• *What is the surface area of a three-dimensional figure?* **the sum of the areas of all its surfaces**
• *How do you find the surface area of a prism?* **Find the area of its net.**

The **surface area** of a three-dimensional figure is the sum of the areas of its surfaces.

EXAMPLE **Finding the Surface Area of a Prism**

2 **Package Design** Find the surface area of the juice box at the left.

Step 1 Draw and label a net for the prism.

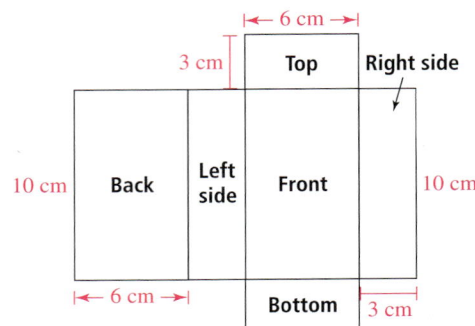

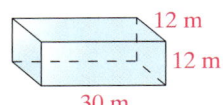

Step 2 Find and add the areas of all the rectangles.

Top	Back	Left	Front	Right	Bottom

$$3 \times 6 + 10 \times 6 + 10 \times 3 + 10 \times 6 + 10 \times 3 + 3 \times 6$$
$$= 18 + 60 + 30 + 60 + 30 + 18$$
$$= 216$$

The surface area of the juice box is 216 square centimeters.

✓ Quick Check

2. Find the surface area of the prism.
1,728 m²

12 m
12 m
30 m

✓ Check Your Understanding

1. A net lets you see a 3-dimensional object in 2 dimensions.

1. **Vocabulary** Describe how a net can help you find the surface area of an object.

Find the surface area. A small cube measures 1 cm on a side.

2.
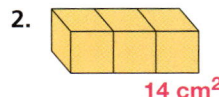
14 cm²

3.
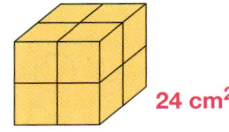
24 cm²

Advanced Learners **L4**
This figure is a box without its lid. Find its surface area.
76 in.²

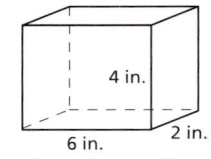

4 in.
6 in.
2 in.

learning style: visual

English Language Learners **ELL**
Have students identify the surfaces of different objects, for example, the surface of the desk, the surfaces of any cabinets, the surfaces of a box. Ensure that they understand surface area is the sum of the areas of all the surfaces on a solid.

learning style: verbal

Homework Exercises

For more exercises, see Extra Skills and Word Problems.

GO for Help

For Exercises	See Examples
4–6	1
7–13	2

A Draw a net for each three-dimensional figure.

4.

5.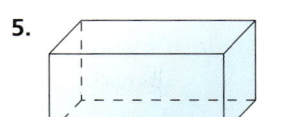

6.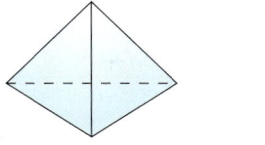

5–6. See margin.

4.
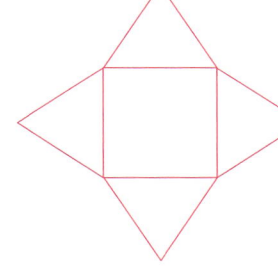

Find the surface area of each prism.

7.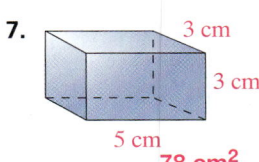
3 cm
3 cm
5 cm
78 cm²

8.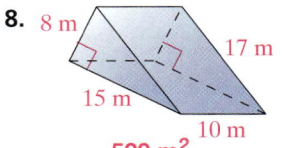
8 m
17 m
15 m
10 m
520 m²

9.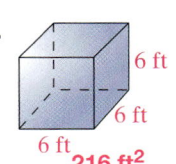
6 ft
6 ft
6 ft
216 ft²

10.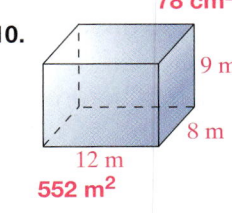
9 m
8 m
12 m
552 m²

11.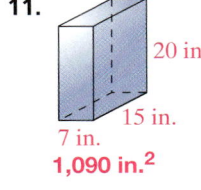
20 in.
15 in.
7 in.
1,090 in.²

12.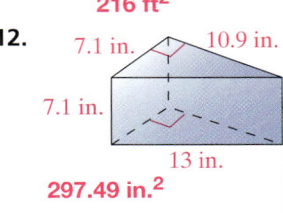
7.1 in.   10.9 in.
7.1 in.
13 in.
297.49 in.²

13. The platform of the Taj Mahal in India is a rectangular prism. It is 95 m long, 95 m wide, and 7 m high. Find the surface area of the platform. **20,710 m²**

B **GPS** **14.** **Guided Problem Solving**
Find the surface area of the spaghetti box. **582 cm²**
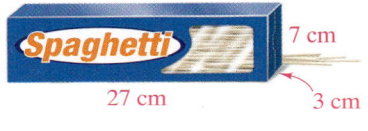
7 cm
27 cm
3 cm
- **Understand the Problem**
Draw a net of the figure, and label all sides.
- **Make a Plan** Find the area of each surface of the box. Then add the areas to find the total surface area.

15. The surface area of the prism with doubled dimensions is four times the surface area of the original prism.

15. **Writing in Math** **GPS** Suppose each dimension of a rectangular prism is doubled. How is the surface area affected?

16. Which of the following cannot be the dimensions of the piece of wrapping paper used to wrap the box? **C**
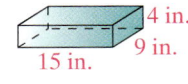
4 in.
9 in.
15 in.
  (A) 20 in. by 28 in.
  (C) 40 in. by 10 in.
  (B) 36 in. by 18 in.
  (D) 24 in. by 24 in.

GO Online
Homework Video Tutor
Visit: PHSchool.com
Web Code: aqe-0908

17. **Reasoning** The surface area of a cube is 54 square inches. What is the length of each edge? **3 in.**

5.

6.

Assignment Guide

Check Your Understanding
Go over Exercises 1–3 in class before assigning the Homework Exercises.

Homework Exercises
A Practice by Example   4–13
B Apply Your Skills   14–20
C Challenge   21
Test Prep and
  Mixed Review   22–29

Homework Quick Check
To check students' understanding of key skills and concepts, go over Exercises 5, 11, 15, 17, and 20.

Differentiated Instruction Resources

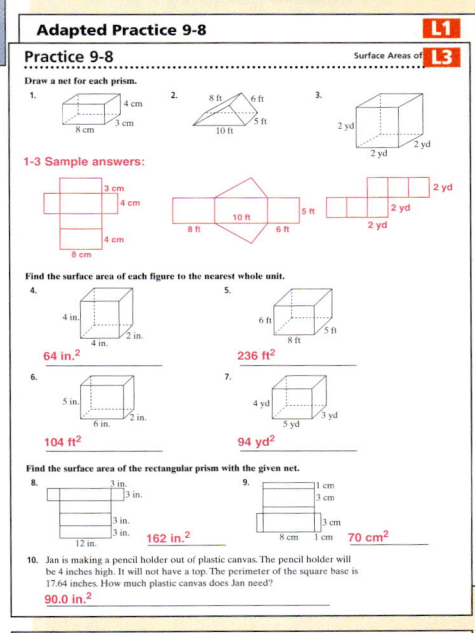

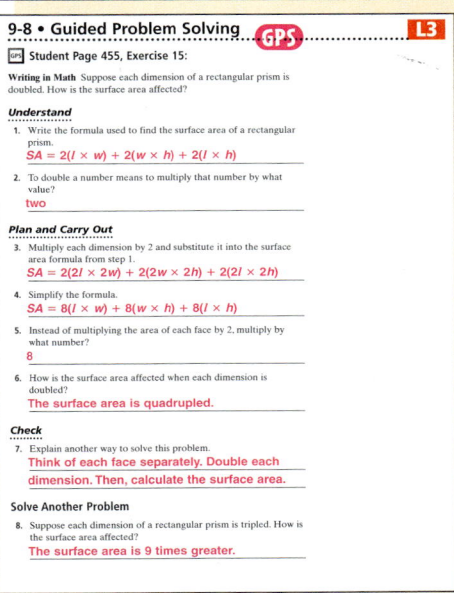

PowerPoint

Lesson Quiz

Find the surface area of each.

1.

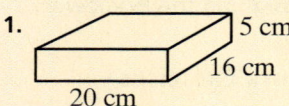

5 cm
16 cm
20 cm

1,000 cm²

2.

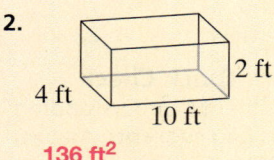

2 ft
4 ft
10 ft

136 ft²

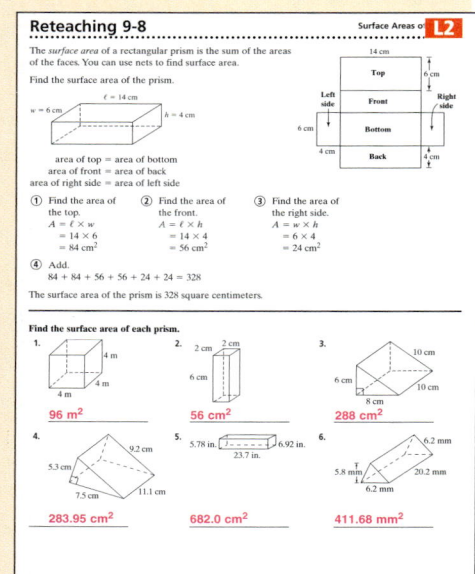
456

Find the surface area of each rectangular prism.

18. ℓ = 3 m, w = 2.2 m, h = 11 m   **127.6 m²**

19. ℓ = 6.3 in., w = 5 in., h = 8 in.   **243.8 in.²**

20. (**Algebra**) What is the surface area of a cube whose edges are s units long? **6s²**

C 21. **Challenge** Suppose each dimension of a cube is increased. What happens to the surface area when each dimension is doubled? Tripled? Quadrupled? **4 times larger; 9 times larger; 16 times larger**

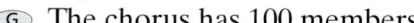

Test Prep and Mixed Review   **Practice**

Multiple Choice

22. Oscar pays $6 to enter the county fair. Then his mother gives him $10. He buys 20 ride tickets for $12 and a cold drink for $3. Oscar has $4 left. Which expression can Oscar use to find the amount of money he had before entering the fair? **B**
  Ⓐ 4 − 3 − 12 + 10 − 6   Ⓒ 6 + 10 − 12 − 3 + 4
  Ⓑ 4 + 3 + 12 − 10 + 6   Ⓓ 6 − 10 + 12 + 3 − 4

23. Find the area of the circle at the right. **H**
  Ⓕ 5π ft²
  Ⓖ 10π ft²
  Ⓗ 25π ft²
  Ⓙ 100π ft²

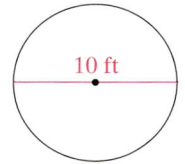

10 ft

24. Which of the following is the measure of an obtuse angle? **C**
  Ⓐ 5°   Ⓑ 90°   Ⓒ 135°   Ⓓ 180°

25. The circle graph shows the percents of chorus members who sing soprano, alto, tenor, and bass. Which statement is NOT supported by the circle graph? **G**
  Ⓕ The chorus has the same number of sopranos and altos.
  Ⓖ The chorus has 100 members.
  Ⓗ One fourth of the members sing bass.
  Ⓙ The fewest members sing tenor.

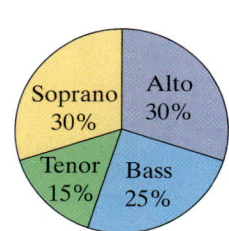

Soprano 30% Alto 30% Tenor 15% Bass 25%

GO for Help

Choose an appropriate metric unit of measure.

For Exercises	See Lesson
26–29	9-1

26. capacity of a pond
  kiloliters

27. capacity of a thimble
  milliliters

28. mass of a pencil
  grams

29. mass of a brick
  kilograms

Test Prep

Resources
For additional practice with a variety of test item formats:
• Test-Taking Strategies, p. 467
• Test Prep, p. 471
• Test-Taking Strategies with Transparencies

Alternative Assessment

Each student in a pair draws and labels the dimensions of a rectangular prism and a triangular prism. Partners exchange drawings and find the surface area of each figure. Have students save their drawings for the next lesson.

Exploring Volume

You can use centimeter cubes to find how much space is inside a rectangular prism.

ACTIVITY

1. Use centimeter cubes to build each rectangular prism. Use your models to find the missing values in the table. **See margin.**

Rectangular Prism	Length	Width	Height	Total Number of Cubes
height width length	2	4	3	■
height width length	■	■	■	■
height width length	■	■	■	■

2. Use 60 cubes to build a rectangular prism with a width of 3 cubes and a height of 4 cubes. **Check students' work.**

3. Find the length of your rectangular prism. **length of 5 cubes**

4. (**Algebra**) Use the words *base* and *height* to write a formula to calculate the volume of a rectangular prism. **V = area of base × height**

5. **Reasoning** Use your formula to find the volume of a rectangular prism that is 10 cm long, 5 cm wide, and 4 cm high. **200 cm³**

6. Use centimeter cubes to find eleven rectangular prisms that have a volume of 24 cubic centimeters. Record in a table the width, length, and height of each prism. **6–7. See margin.**

7. **Writing in Math** Add a column to your table and record the surface areas. Explain why rectangular prisms with the same volume can have different surface areas.

1.

Length	Width	Height	Total Cubes
2	4	3	24
4	3	4	48
4	5	3	60

6–7. See back of book.

Objective
To find the volume of rectangular prisms

Examples
1 Counting Cubes to Find Volume
2 Finding the Volume of a Prism

Math Understandings: p. 414D

Math Background

See p. 414D for content support.

Lesson Planning and Resources

See p. 414E for a list of the resources that support this lesson.

Bell Ringer Practice

✓ **Check Skills You'll Need**
For intervention, direct students to:
Areas of Parallelograms and Triangles
Lesson 9-4

Activity Lab

Use before the lesson.
Student Edition Activity Lab, Hands On 9-9a, Exploring Volume, p. 457

 **Teaching Resources**

Activity Lab 9-9: Exploring Rectangular Prisms

Guided Instruction

Example 1
Find the volume of each layer. The volume of 1 layer is $1 \times 3 \times 5$ or 15 cubic units. 4 layers is 4 times that volume or 60 cubic units.

458

9-9 Volumes of Rectangular Prisms

✓ **Check Skills You'll Need**

1. **Vocabulary Review**
Any side can be considered the __?__ of a parallelogram. **base**

Find the area of a triangle with the given dimensions.

2. $b = 17$, $h = 13$ **110.5**

3. $b = 1.2$, $h = 4.5$ **2.7**

 for Help
Lesson 9-4

What You'll Learn

To find the volume of rectangular prisms

🔊 **New Vocabulary** volume, cubic unit

Why Learn This?

The volume of a fish tank tells you how much water the tank can hold. You can use volume to find the amount of space that is inside an object.

A **cubic unit** is the amount of space in a cube that measures 1 unit long by 1 unit wide by 1 unit high. The **volume** of a three-dimensional figure is the number of cubic units needed to fill the space inside the figure.

EXAMPLE **Counting Cubes to Find Volume**

1 Find the volume of the rectangular prism.

Each layer of the prism is 5 cubes by 3 cubes. This equals 5×3, or 15 cubes. The prism is 4 layers high. So the prism has a total of 4×15, or 60 cubes.

The volume of the prism is 60 cubic units.

✓ **Quick Check**

1. Find the volume of the rectangular prism at the left. **36 units³**

KEY CONCEPTS **Volume of a Prism**

volume = area of base × height
$$V = B \times h$$

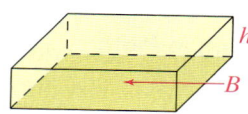

458 Chapter 9 Geometry and Measurement

Differentiated Instruction Solutions for All Learners

Special Needs L1
If available, provide nets of solids on graph paper for students to fold up. They can use this to count the cubic units, and get an understanding of what volume is.

learning style: tactile

Below Level L2
Have students build as many different prisms as they can using 48 small cubes. **possible dimensions:**
$1 \times 1 \times 48$, $1 \times 2 \times 24$, $1 \times 3 \times 16$,
$1 \times 4 \times 12$, $1 \times 6 \times 8$, $2 \times 2 \times 12$,
$2 \times 3 \times 8$, $2 \times 4 \times 6$, $3 \times 4 \times 4$

learning style: tactile

For a rectangular prism, the area of a base is $\ell \times w$, since the base is a rectangle. So the volume formula is $V = \ell \times w \times h$. Common cubic units used in measuring volume are cubic centimeters (cm³), cubic inches, (in.³), and cubic feet (ft³).

EXAMPLE Finding the Volume of a Prism

10 in.
12 in.
20 in.

② **Fish Tanks** Find the volume of the fish tank shown at the left.

$V = \ell \times w \times h$ ← Use the formula for the volume of a rectangular prism.

$= 20 \times 10 \times 12$ ← Substitute 20 for ℓ, 10 for w, and 12 for h.

$= 2,400$ ← Multiply.

The volume is 2,400 cubic inches, or 2,400 in.³.

✓ Quick Check

2. Find the volume of a rectangular prism with a length of 8 meters, a width of 7 meters, and a height of 10 meters. **560 m³**

✓ Check Your Understanding

1. Volume is the measure of an object's capacity. Area is the measure of the number of square units on the surface of the figure.

1. **Vocabulary** How are volume and area different?

2. **Number Sense** How does the volume of a cube change if its dimensions are doubled? **The volume would be 8 times greater.**

Find the volume of each rectangular prism.

3. $\ell = 6$ m, $w = 4$ m, $h = 11$ m
264 m³

4. $\ell = 3$ ft, $w = 2$ ft, $h = 9$ ft
54 ft³

Homework Exercises

For more exercises, see Extra Skills and Word Problems.

Ⓐ Find the volume of each rectangular prism.

GO for Help

For Exercises	See Examples
5–7	1
8–10	2

5.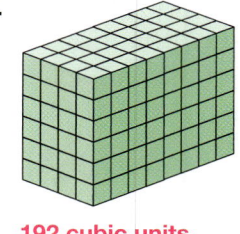
192 cubic units

6.
12 cubic units

7.
40 cubic units

A

① Find the v

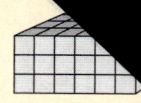

② Find the volume. **80 ft³**

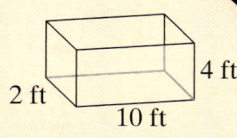
2 ft
4 ft
10 ft

All in One Teaching Resources
• Daily Notetaking Guide 9-9 **L3**
• Adapted Notetaking 9-9 **L1**

Closure

• *How do you find the volume of a rectangular prism?* **Use the formula $V = \ell \times w \times h$.**

3. Practice

Assignment Guide

Check Your Understanding
Go over Exercises 1–4 in class before assigning the Homework Exercises.

Homework Exercises
A Practice by Example 5–10
B Apply Your Skills 11–14
C Challenge 15
Test Prep and
Mixed Review 16–21

Homework Quick Check
To check student's understanding of key skills and concepts, go over Exercises 7, 9, 12, 13, and 14.

4. Assess & Reteach

PowerPoint Lesson Quiz

1. Find the volume of the figure.

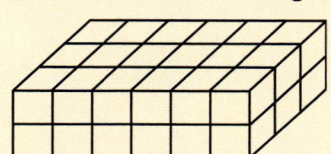

36 cubic units

2. Find the volume of a rectangular prism with $\ell = 15$ in., $w = 13$ in., and $h = 8$ in. **1,560 in.³**

459

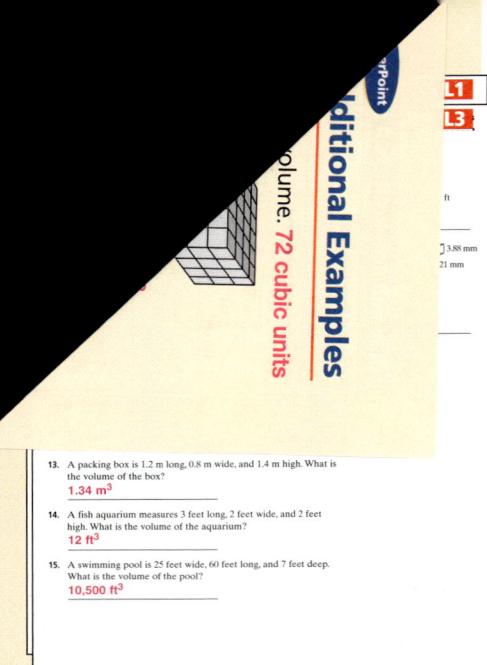
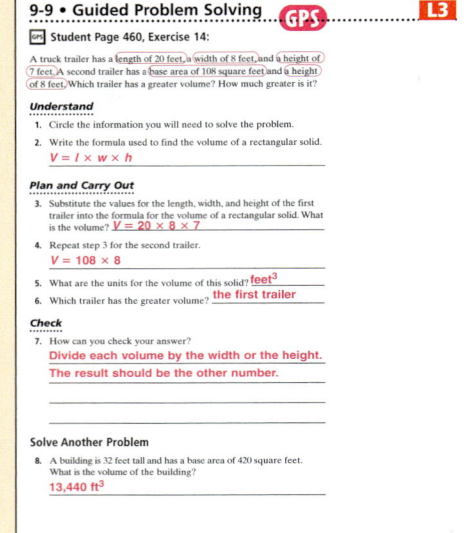
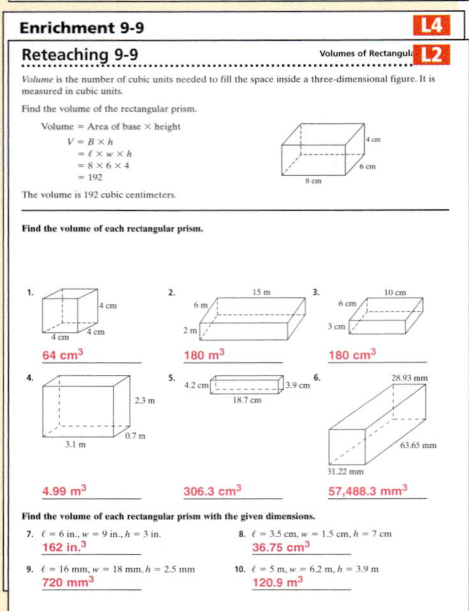
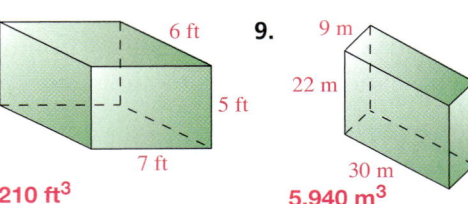
Find the volume of each rectangular prism.

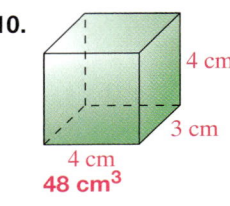

8. 6 ft, 5 ft, 7 ft
210 ft³

9. 9 m, 22 m, 30 m
5,940 m³

10. 4 cm, 3 cm, 4 cm
48 cm³

B **GPS** 11. **Guided Problem Solving** The shape of a monument is a hexagonal prism. The area of the base is 5.4 square feet and the height is 13 feet. Find the volume. **70.2 ft³**
  • Which formula should you use, $V = B \times h$ or $V = \ell \times w \times h$?

12. **The second prism's volume is twice the first prism's volume. Height is doubled and area remains the same, so volume must be doubled.**

12. **Writing in Math** Two rectangular prisms have the same base area. The height of the second prism is twice the height of the first prism. How do their volumes compare? Explain.

13. **Reasoning** One ton of coal fills a bin that is 5 ft by 4 ft by 2 ft. Find the dimensions of a bin that holds 2 tons of coal.
Answers may vary. Sample: 5 feet by 4 feet by 4 feet

14. A truck trailer has a length of 20 feet, a width of 8 feet, and a
GPS height of 7 feet. A second trailer has a base area of 108 square feet and a height of 8 feet. Which trailer has a greater volume? How much greater is it? **the trailer with a length of 20 ft, width of 8 ft, and height of 7 ft; 256 ft³**

C 15. **Challenge** A swimming pool is 24 meters long and 16 meters wide. The average depth of the water is 2.5 meters. How many 2-liter bottles of water do you need to fill the pool?
(*Hint:* 1 m³ = 1,000 L) **480,000 bottles**

Test Prep and Mixed Review **Practice**

Multiple Choice

16. A rectangular prism measures 2 meters long, 50 centimeters wide, and 1 meter high. Find the volume of the prism. **A**
  Ⓐ 1 cubic meter   Ⓒ 100 cubic centimeters
  Ⓑ 100 cubic meters   Ⓓ 10,000 cubic centimeters

17. What missing piece of information is needed to find the area of the parallelogram? **H**
  Ⓕ Side length   Ⓗ Height
  Ⓖ Base length   Ⓙ Perimeter

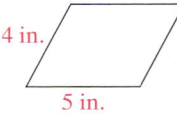
4 in.
5 in.

GO for Help

For Exercises	See Lesson
18–21	9-3

Find the area of each square with the given perimeter.
18. 12 m **9 m²**   19. 24 ft **36 ft²**   20. 34 cm **72.25 cm²**   21. 25 in. **39.0625 in.²**

Test Prep

Resources
For additional practice with a variety of test item formats:
• Test-Taking Strategies, p. 467
• Test Prep, p. 471
• Test-Taking Strategies with Transparencies

Alternative Assessment

Each student uses the drawings of prisms that they made in the Alternative Assessment for Lesson 9-8. Students then find the volume of each of the figures.

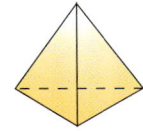

1. The circumference of a circular cover is 66 ft. What is the area of the cover? **346.8 ft²**

Name each figure.

2.

triangular pyramid

3.

cone

4.

pentagonal pyramid

5.

hexagonal prism

Use the rectangular prism at the right for Exercises 6 and 7.

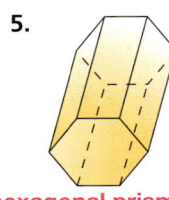

3 cm   2 cm

5 cm

6. Find the surface area. **62 cm²**

7. Find the volume. **30 cm³**

9-10a   Activity Lab

Hands On

Exploring Cylinders

A solid with a circular base is called a *cylinder*. You can find the surface area and volume of a cylinder.

ACTIVITY   **1–3. Check students' work.**

1. On a sheet of paper, draw two circles, each with a diameter of 3.5 inches. Cut out each circle.

2. Find the area of each circle. Label each circle with its area. Label a second sheet of $8\frac{1}{2}'' \times 11''$ paper with its area.

3. Tape the $8\frac{1}{2}$-inch edges of the second sheet of paper to form a tube. Tape a circle to each open end to form a cylinder.

4. **Writing in Math** Explain how you can use the areas of the circles and rectangle to find the surface area of the cylinder.
See margin.

5. Find the surface area of the cylinder. **112.7 in.²**

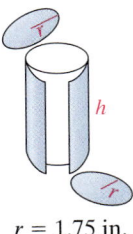

r

h

r

$r = 1.75$ in.
$h = 8.5$ in.

461

4. **Add the areas of the circles and the rectangle to find the surface area of a cylinder.**

Resources

- Activity Lab 9-10: Volumes of Cylinders
- cylindrical objects
- scissors
- tape
- paper

 Checkpoint Quiz

Use this Checkpoint Quiz to check students' understanding of the skills and concepts of Lessons 9-5 through 9-9.

Resources

- All-in-One Teaching Resources Checkpoint Quiz 2
- ExamView CD-ROM
- Success Tracker™ Online Intervention

Activity Lab

Using Measurement

Students construct a cylinder to better understand surface area and volume. This will prepare them to calculate the surface area and volume of cylinders in Lesson 9-10.

Guided Instruction

Students can find the surface area of a cylinder by looking at its parts. Review the formula for the area of the circle. Ask:
- *What three pieces make up a cylinder?* **2 circles, 1 rectangle**
- *How can you find the surface area of a cylinder?* **Find the area of one circle. Multiply by two. Add the area of the rectangle.**

Activity

Have students work independently. Then compare results as a class. Have students describe what they have learned about the surface area of cylinders.

Differentiated Instruction

Below Level   **L2**

Some students may have difficulty constructing their cylinders. Provide cylindrical objects to help them wrap their paper around.

Objective

1 To find the surface area and volume of a cylinder

Examples

1 Finding the Surface Area of a Cylinder
2 Finding the Volume of a Cylinder

Math Understandings: p. 414D

Math Background

The surface area of a cylinder can be found by measuring the area of the circles that form the bases and the rectangle that wraps around to become the rest of the cylinder. Since the length of the rectangle equals the circumference of the circle, the formula for a cylinder's surface area is $A = 2(\pi r^2) + (\pi d \times h)$. The volume of a cylinder can be found by finding the area of the base of the cylinder and multiplying this base by the height.

More Math Background: p. 414D

Lesson Planning and Resources

See p. 414E for a list of the resources that support this lesson.

✔ Check Skills You'll Need

Use student page, transparency, or PowerPoint. For intervention, direct students to:

Area of a Circle
Lesson 9-6
Extra Skills and Word Problems Practice, Ch. 9

462

✔ Check Skills You'll Need

1. **Vocabulary Review**
   Define the *radius* of a circle.
   See below.
   Find the area of each circle. Use 3.14 for π.

2.
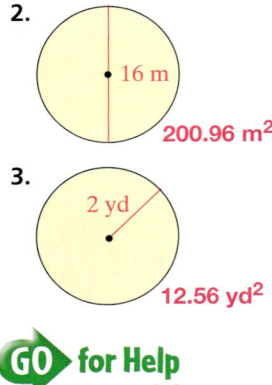
16 m

200.96 m²

3.
2 yd

12.56 yd²

GO for Help
Lesson 9-6

Check Skills You'll Need

1. The radius of a circle is the distance from the center to the edge of the circle.

What You'll Learn

To find the surface area and volume of cylinders

Why Learn This?

Food cans are usually in the shape of a cylinder. Knowing how to find the volume of a cylinder can help you find the amount of food in one can.

If you carefully peel the label from a can as shown, you will see that the label is a rectangle.

The height of the rectangle is the height of the can.

The base length of the rectangle is the circumference of the can.

Suppose you draw a net of the cylinder that is the actual vegetable can. You will see that the can is made up of a rectangle and two circles.

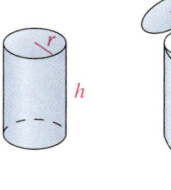 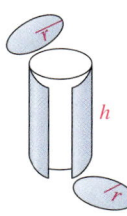 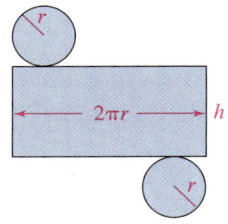

You can find the surface area of a cylinder by finding the area of its net.

Differentiated Instruction **Solutions for All Learners**

Special Needs L1
Have students find the volume of two different cylindrical shapes, such as a can and a jar. Compare which has the greatest volume. Then have them prove it by filling each container with popcorn kernels or beans to see which holds more.

learning style: tactile

Below Level L2
Have students find cylinders in the classroom or at home. Have them identify the bases as circles and the rectangle. Ask what surfaces they need to find to measure the surface area. **both bases and rectangle**

learning style: visual

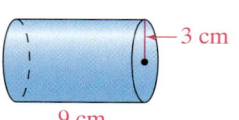

EXAMPLE   Finding the Surface Area of a Cylinder

1 Find the surface area of the cylinder at the left. Use 3.14 for π.

Step 1 Draw and label a net for the cylinder.

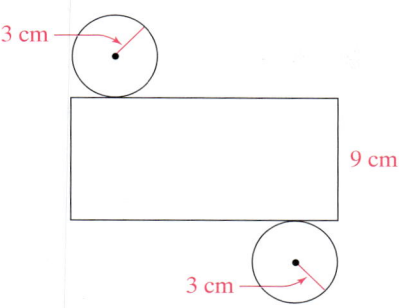

Step 2 Find the area of one circle.

$A = \pi r^2$ ← Use the formula.

$\approx 3.14 \times 3^2$ ← Substitute 3 for r and 3.14 for π.

$= 28.26$ ← Multiply.

≈ 28.3 ← Round to the nearest tenth.

Step 3 Find the area of the rectangle.

$A = \ell \times w$ ← Use the formula.

$= \pi d \times h$ ← The length of the rectangle is the circumference of the circle. The width of the rectangle is the height of the cylinder.

$\approx 3.14(6) \times 9$ ← Substitute 6 for d, 9 for h, and 3.14 for π.

$= 169.56$ ← Multiply.

≈ 169.6 ← Round to the nearest tenth.

Step 4 Add the areas of the two circles and the rectangle.

$28.3 + 28.3 + 169.6 = 226.2$

The surface area of the cylinder is about 226.2 square centimeters.

✓ Quick Check

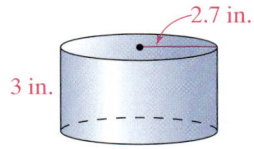

1. Find the surface area of the cylinder at the left. Use 3.14 for π. Round to the nearest tenth. **96.6 in.²**

The formula $V = B \times h$ applies to cylinders as well as prisms. For cylinders, use $A = \pi r^2$ to find the area of the base. Then multiply the area of the base by the height to find the volume of the cylinder.

Advanced Learners **L4**
The figure is half of a cylinder. Find its surface area.
about 668 in.²

18 in.

12 in.

English Language Learners **ELL**
Provide cans of vegetables and soup. Have students measure the height and circumference, and use those measurements to draw a net of the cans.

learning style: visual

learning style: tactile

2.1

Activit

Use before
Student Edit
Hands On 9-1
Cylinders, p. 46

All in One **Teaching**

Activity Lab 9-10:
Cylinders

Guided Instruct

Error Prevention!

When finding the surface a
a cylinder, students might
calculate the correct area for
circular base, but forget that th
must account for two of these
bases in determining the total
surface area.

Example 2

When $\pi \times r^2$ is substituted into
the general volume formula
$V = B \times h$, you arrive at a special
formula for the volume of a
cylinder, namely $V = \pi \times r^2 \times h$.
Some students might find it easier
to find volumes of cylinders using
this formula.

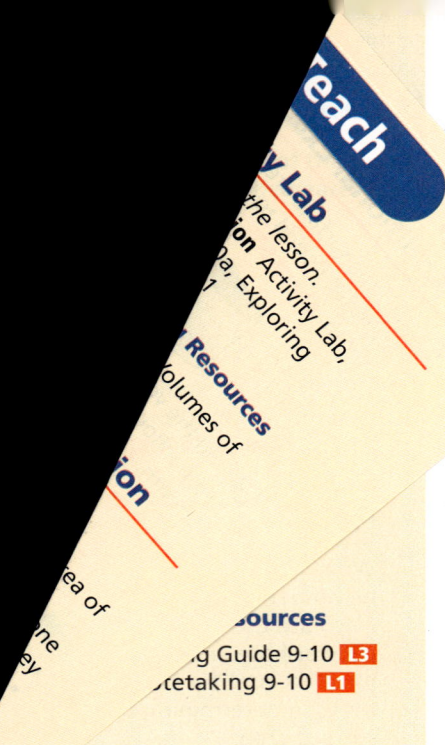
Teach
Lab
the lesson.
on Activity Lab,
a, Exploring
1
Resources
olumes of
on
ea of
ne
ey
ources
g Guide 9-10 **L3**
ctetaking 9-10 **L1**
osure

- *How do you find the surface area of a cylinder?* **Find the area of its net.**
- *How do you find the volume of a cylinder?* **Find the area of the circular base using** $A = \pi \times r^2$; **multiply the result by the height.**

EXAMPLE **Finding the Volume of a Cylinder**

2 **Food** Find the volume of the can of cheese at the left. Round to the nearest tenth. Use 3.14 for π.

Step 1 Find the area of the base.

$$B = \pi \times r^2 \qquad \leftarrow \text{Use } A = \pi r^2 \text{ to find the area of the base.}$$
$$\approx 3.14 \times 1.4^2 \qquad \leftarrow \text{Substitute 1.4 for } r \text{ and 3.14 for } \pi.$$
$$= 6.1544 \qquad \leftarrow \text{Multiply.}$$

Step 2 Find the volume.

$$V = B \times h$$
$$\approx 6.1544 \times 6 \qquad \leftarrow \text{Substitute 6.1544 for } B \text{ and 6 for } h.$$
$$= 36.9264 \qquad \leftarrow \text{Multiply.}$$

The volume is about 36.9 cubic inches, or 36.9 in.^{3}.

✓ **Quick Check**

2. Find the volume of a cylinder with a radius of 4 inches and a height of 9 inches. Round to the nearest cubic inch. **452 in.^{3}**

✓ **Check Your Understanding**

1. $2\pi r^2$ represents the area of the two circular bases and $C \times h$ represents the area of the rectangle; their sum represents the total surface area.

2. Doubling the height doubles the volume because the area of the base circle stays the same.

1. **Reasoning** Explain how the expression $2\pi r^2 + C \times h$ can be used to find the surface area of a cylinder. **See left.**

2. **Writing in Math** Explain how doubling the height of a cylinder affects the volume of the cylinder. **See left.**

Use the net of each cylinder to find each surface area. Use 3.14 for π.

3.
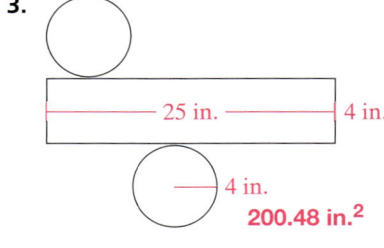
200.48 in.^{2}

4.
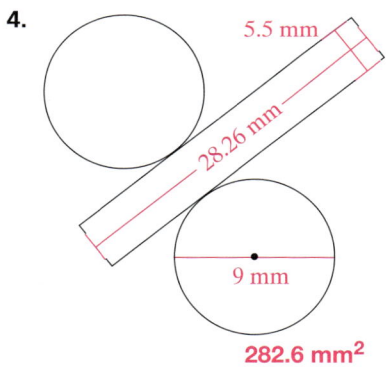
282.6 mm^2

For more exercises, see Extra Skills and Word Problems.

GO for Help

For Exercises	See Examples
5–7	1
8–13	2

A Find the surface area of each cylinder. Use 3.14 for π. Round to the nearest tenth.

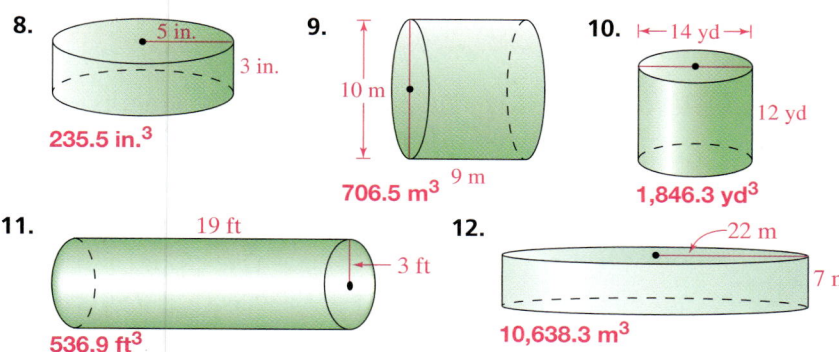

5. 4 cm · 10 cm
351.68 cm²

6. 6 m / 5 m
414.48 m²

7. 24 ft / 16 ft
1,607.68 ft²

Find the volume of each cylinder. Use 3.14 for π. Round to the nearest tenth.

8. 5 in. / 3 in.
235.5 in.³

9. 10 m / 9 m
706.5 m³

10. 14 yd / 12 yd
1,846.3 yd³

11. 19 ft / 3 ft
536.9 ft³

12. 22 m / 7 m
10,638.3 m³

13. A drinking straw has the shape of a cylinder. Find the volume of a straw with a radius of 3 mm and a height of 200 mm. **5,652 mm³**

B **GPS** 14. **Guided Problem Solving** A tennis ball container is a cylinder with a height of 8.3 inches and a diameter of $2\frac{7}{8}$ inches. The container is open at the top. Find the surface area and volume of the tennis ball container. Use 3.14 for π. **81.42 in.²; 53.85 in.³**
- What is the radius of the container?
- Use the radius to find the area of the base.
- Draw a net to help you find the surface area.

15. Find the surface area and volume of the battery below.

BATTERY — 3.2 cm / 5.5 cm
71.3 cm²; 44.2 cm³

GO Online
Homework Video Tutor
Visit: PHSchool.com
Web Code: aqe-0910

16. **Packaging** A cardboard mailing tube is 3 inches in diameter **GPS** and 20 inches long. The tube is open at both ends. Find the surface area and volume of the mailing tube. **188.4 in.²; 141.3 in.³**

Assignment Guide

Check Your Understanding
Go over Exercises 1–4 in class before assigning the Homework Exercises.

Homework Exercises
A Practice by Example   5–13
B Apply Your Skills   14–21
C Challenge   22
Test Prep and
    Mixed Review   23–26

Homework Quick Check
To check students' understanding of key skills and concepts, go over Exercises 6, 11, 16, 19, and 21.

Differentiated Instruction **Resources**

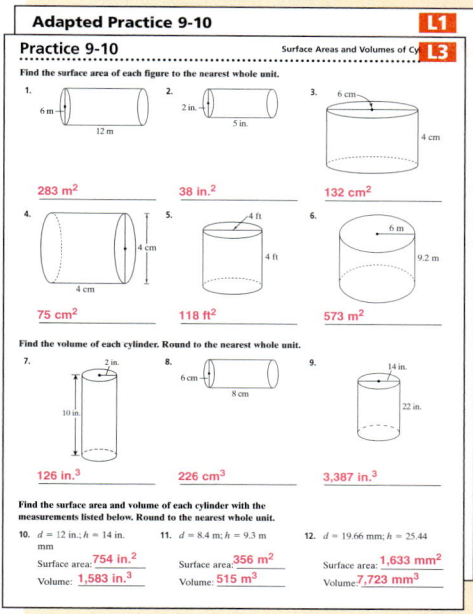

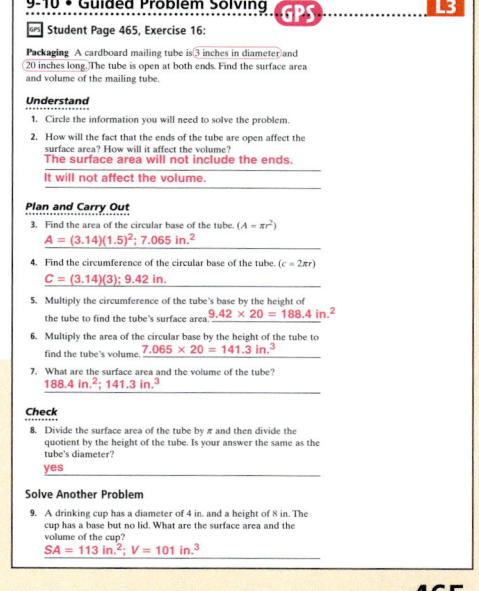

PowerPoint

📋 Lesson Quiz

Find the surface area.

1.

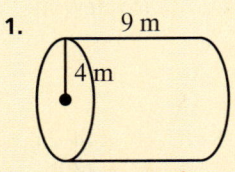

9 m

4 m

about 327 m²

2. Find the volume of a cylinder with dimensions $r = 6$ mm, and $h = 21$ mm. Use 3.14 for π. Round to the nearest tenth.

about 2,373.8 mm³

Reteaching 9-10   Surface Areas and Volumes of C   **L2**

The *surface area* of a cylinder is the sum of the areas of the faces. A cylinder has two circular faces and a rectangular face.

In a cylinder, the width of the rectangular face is equal to the circumference of the circular base, or $2\pi r$. The length is the height of the cylinder, or h. Substitute these variables into the formula:

You can find the surface area of a cylinder using the following formulas:

$$SA = 2(\pi r^2) + (2\pi rh)$$

πr^2 = area of circle
$l \times w$ = area of a rectangle
$2(\pi r^2) + (l \times w)$ = surface area of a cylinder

The *volume* of a cylinder is calculated by multiplying the area of one of the circular bases by the height of the cylinder.

$$V = \pi r^2 \times h$$

Find the surface area and volume of each of the following cylinders. Round to the nearest whole unit.

1. 12 m, 12 m
Surface area: **679 m²**
Volume: **1,357 m³**

3. 9.3 cm, 5.8 cm
Surface area: **222 cm²**
Volume: **246 cm³**

2. 6 in., 16 in.
Surface area: **358 in.²**
Volume: **452 in.³**

4. 2.66 ft, 4.82 ft
Surface area: **51 ft²**
Volume: **27 ft³**

Enrichment 9-10   Surface Areas and Volumes of (**L4**

Critical Thinking

A farmer is considering several designs for a grain silo that he is planning to build. The farmer wants to build a silo that holds the most grain compared to the amount of materials needed to build it. Each cubic meter in the silo can hold 750 kilograms of grain, and each square meter of building material costs $24.50. The four designs the farmer is considering are shown below. Calculate the cost of building each design and the amount of grain that each can hold. Then calculate how many kilograms of grain each design will hold per dollar of building cost.

1. Capacity: **459,000** kg of grain
Cost to build: **$11,025** dollars
Capacity/cost: **42.63** kg/dollar

2. Capacity: **216,000** kg of grain
Cost to build: **$8,232** dollars
Capacity/cost: **26.24** kg/dollar

3. Capacity: **452,389** kg of grain
Cost to build: **$9,852** dollars
Capacity/cost: **45.92** kg/dollar

4. Capacity: **678,584** kg of grain
Cost to build: **$12,931** dollars
Capacity/cost: **52.48** kg/dollar

5. Based on the measurements above, which design is the best choice? Explain.
Silo 4; Silo 4 has the highest capacity per dollar.

Find the volume of each cylinder with the given dimensions. Round your answer to the nearest hundredth.

17. $r = 8.1$ cm, $h = 4$ cm
824.06 cm³

18. $r = 2.4$ in., $h = 5.4$ in.
97.67 in.³

19. $r = 9$ m, $h = 23.5$ m
5,976.99 m³

20. $r = 8.2$ ft, $h = 3.2$ ft
675.63 ft³

21. **Algebra** The Great Pyramid of Khufu has a length of 230 meters, a width of 230 meters, and a height of 146 meters. Use the formula $V = \frac{1}{3} \times \ell \times w \times h$ to find the volume.
2,574,466.7 m³

C 22. **Challenge** Find the height of a cylinder with a volume of 85 cubic feet and a radius of 2.6 feet. **4 ft**

Test Prep and Mixed Review   **Practice**

Multiple Choice

23. The table shows edge lengths and volumes of rectangular prisms with a width of 2 inches and a height of 3 inches.

Volumes of Prisms

Length	Width	Height	Volume
1 in.	2 in.	3 in.	6 in.³
2 in.	2 in.	3 in.	12 in.³
3 in.	2 in.	3 in.	18 in.³
n in.	2 in.	3 in.	■

Which expression can be used to find the volume, in cubic units, of a prism with a width of 2 in., a height of 3 in., and a length of n in.? **D**

Ⓐ $n + 5$ Ⓑ $n + 6$ Ⓒ $5n$ Ⓓ $6n$

24. Which process can Wyatt use to find the circumference of a circle? **J**
Ⓕ Multiply the diameter by 2.
Ⓖ Multiply the radius by 2.
Ⓗ Multiply the diameter by 2π.
Ⓙ Multiply the radius by 2π.

25. Which unit should Timmy use to measure the length of a folder? **A**
Ⓐ Inch   Ⓑ Foot   Ⓒ Yard   Ⓓ Mile

GO for Help

For Exercise	See Lesson
26	9-5

26. A dog is tied to a post with a 10-foot rope. The dog can run in a circle without wrapping the rope around the post. What is the circumference of the circle the dog makes? Round your answer to the nearest tenth. **62.8 ft**

Test Prep

Resources
For additional practice with a variety of test item formats:
- Test-Taking Strategies, p. 467
- Test Prep, p. 471
- Test-Taking Strategies with Transparencies

Alternative Assessment

Each student in a pair draws two cylinders. They trade papers with a partner and find surface areas and volumes for both of the figures.

Test-Taking Strategies

Measuring to Solve

Some test questions ask you to measure with a protractor or ruler to solve a problem.

EXAMPLE

Emilio's yard is shaped like the quadrilateral below.

Find the measure of ∠N to the nearest degree.

Ⓐ 45°   Ⓑ 55°   Ⓒ 135°   Ⓓ 145°

∠N is an acute angle, so its measure must be less than 90°. Since the side of the angle is between the 40° and 50° marks on the protractor, ∠N has a measure of about 45°.

The angle measure is 45°. The correct answer is choice A.

Exercises

1. A hexagon is shown. Use a protractor to find the measure of ∠R to the nearest degree. **D**
   Ⓐ 25°
   Ⓑ 35°
   Ⓒ 155°
   Ⓓ 162°

2. A pentagon is shown. Use a protractor to find the measure of ∠V to the nearest degree. **F**
   Ⓕ 48°   Ⓗ 125°
   Ⓖ 62°
   Ⓙ 135°

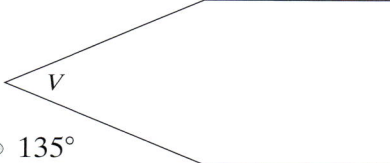

Sidebar

Measuring to Solve

Sometimes students are required to measure angles in order to answer questions on a test. This feature instructs students on the proper use of a protractor for measuring angles.

Guided Instruction

Review angle types and their meanings with students. Explain that sometimes they will need to measure angles to answer test questions. Display the Example and ask:
- *How can you use number sense to eliminate choices?* **Eliminate choices C and D as they are much too large.**
- *Which scale on the protractor should you read?* **the outer scale**

Error Prevention!

Make sure students align the center of the protractor with the vertex of the angle.

Resources

Test-Taking Strategies with Transparencies
- Transparency 12
- Practice Sheet, p. 9

Test-Taking Strategies with Transparencies

Test-Taking Strategies: Measuring to Solve

Some questions ask you to measure with a protractor or ruler to solve a problem.

Example What is the area of the circle below, to the nearest square centimeter?

A. 9 cm²   B. 19 cm²
C. 28 cm²   D. 113 cm²

Use a centimeter ruler to measure the radius of the circle. To find the area of the circle, use the formula for the area of a circle.

$A = \pi r^2$

$A = \pi(3)^2 = \pi \times 9 \approx 28.27$

The area of the circle is about 28 cm². The answer is choice C.

Example Find the measure of angle *S* in the polygon below.

F. 83°   G. 87°   H. 93°   J. 97°

The side of the angle falls between the 85° and 90° marks on the same scale that side SW crosses at its zero point. The measure of the angle is about 87°. The answer is choice G.

Transparency 12

Vocabulary Review

- **area** (p. 426)
- **base of a parallelogram** (p. 432)
- **base of a triangle** (p. 433)
- **capacity** (p. 417)
- **chord** (p. 438)
- **circle** (p. 438)
- **circumference** (p. 439)
- **cone** (p. 450)
- **cube** (p. 449)
- **cubic unit** (p. 458)
- **cylinder** (p. 450)
- **diameter** (p. 438)
- **edge** (p. 449)
- **faces** (p. 449)
- **gram (g)** (p. 417)
- **height of a parallelogram** (p. 432)
- **height of a triangle** (p. 433)
- **liter (L)** (p. 417)
- **mass** (p. 417)
- **meter (m)** (p. 416)
- **metric system** (p. 416)
- **net** (p. 453)
- **perimeter** (p. 426)
- **prism** (p. 449)
- **pyramid** (p. 450)
- **radius** (p. 438)
- **sphere** (p. 450)
- **surface area** (p. 454)
- **three-dimensional figure** (p. 449)
- **vertex** (p. 449)
- **volume** (p. 458)

Go Online
PHSchool.com
For: Vocabulary Quiz
Web Code: aqj-0951

Choose the vocabulary term that best completes each sentence.

1. A rectangular prism has three pairs of congruent and parallel   ? .   **faces**

2. A   ?   is a three-dimensional figure with one base.   **pyramid or cone**

3. A   ?   is a segment that connects a circle to its center.   **radius**

Skills and Concepts

Lessons 9-1 and 9-2
- To use metric units of measure and to choose appropriate units of length, mass, and capacity
- To convert between metric measurements

The standard units of measurement in the **metric system** are the **meter (m),** the **gram (g),** and the **liter (L).** You can convert one metric unit to another by multiplying or dividing by a power of 10.

Complete each statement.

4. $0.3 \text{ kg} = \blacksquare \text{ g}$ **300**   **5.** $150 \text{ cm} = \blacksquare \text{ m}$ **1.5**   **6.** $5,700 \text{ mL} = \blacksquare \text{ L}$ **5.7**

Lessons 9-3 and 9-4
- To solve problems involving perimeters and areas of rectangles
- To solve problems involving areas of parallelograms, triangles, and complex figures

The **area** of a figure is the number of square units inside the figure. The formula for the area of a parallelogram is $A = b \times h$. The formula for the area of a triangle is $A = \frac{1}{2}b \times h$.

Find the perimeter and the area of each figure.

7. **30 ft; 48 ft²**
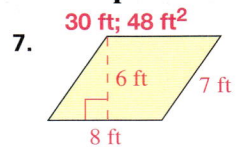
6 ft · 7 ft · 8 ft

8. **68.9 m; 187.72 m²**
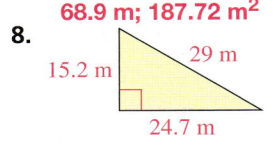
15.2 m · 29 m · 24.7 m

9. **64 in.; 240 in.²**

20 in. · 12 in.

Lessons 9-5 and 9-6

- To identify the parts of a circle and to find the radius, diameter, and circumference
- To find the area of a circle

A **circle** has three kinds of segments: a **radius, chord,** and **diameter.** The distance around a circle is the **circumference.** The symbol π represents the ratio $\frac{\text{circumference}}{\text{diameter}}$.

Circumference: $C = \pi d$, or $C = 2\pi r$ Area: $A = \pi r^2$

Use circle O for Exercises 10–14. Use 3.14 for π.

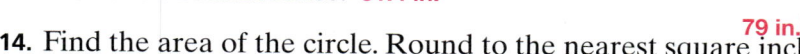

10. Name three chords. **$\overline{XV}, \overline{YW}, \overline{VW}$**

11. Name a diameter. **$\overline{XV}$**

12. Name the radii. **$\overline{OV}, \overline{OX}, \overline{OY}$**

13. Find the circumference. **31.4 in.**

14. Find the area of the circle. Round to the nearest square inch. **79 in.^{2}**

Lesson 9-7

- To identify three-dimensional figures

A **prism** is a **three-dimensional figure** with two parallel and congruent **faces** that are polygons. A **pyramid** has triangular faces and one base that is a polygon. You name a prism or a pyramid by the shape of its bases or base.

Name each figure.

15.
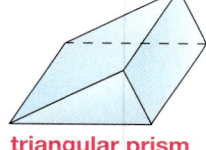
triangular prism

16.
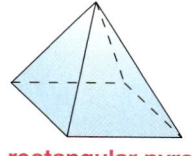
rectangular pyramid

17.
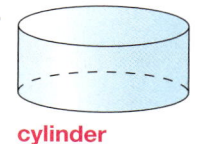
cylinder

Lessons 9-8, 9-9, and 9-10

- To use nets and to find the surface areas of rectangular prisms
- To find the volume of rectangular prisms
- To find the surface area and volume of cylinders

The **surface area** of a three-dimensional figure is the sum of the areas of all its faces.

The **volume** of a three-dimensional figure is the number of cubic units needed to fill the space inside the figure. The formula for the volume of a prism or a cylinder is $V = B \times h$, where B is the area of the base.

Find the surface area and volume of each figure. Use 3.14 for π.

18. **40 in.^{2}; 16 in.^{3}**
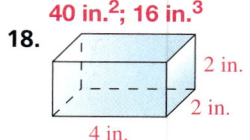

19. **122 m^2; 84 m^3**
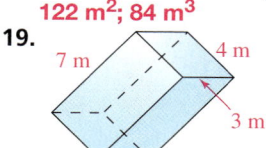

20. **715.92 ft^2; 1,469.52 ft^3**
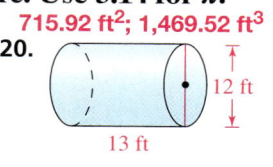

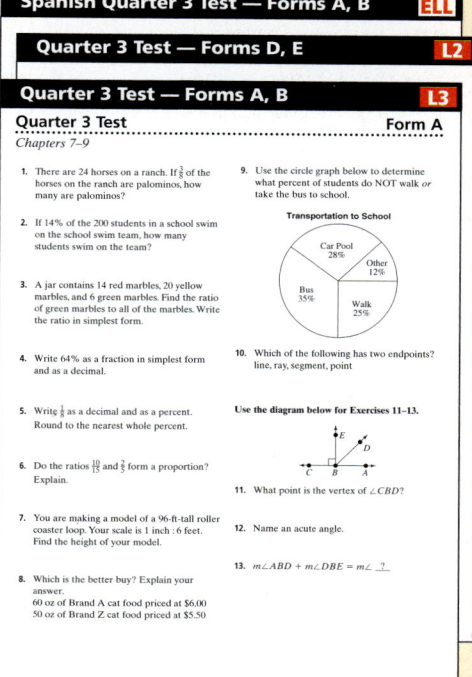

Chapter 9 Test

Go Online
PHSchool.com
For: Online chapter test
Web Code: aqa-0952

Resources

- ExamView Assessment Suite CD-ROM
  - Ch. 9 Ready-Made Test
  - Make your own Ch. 9 test
- MindPoint Quiz Show CD-ROM
  - Chapter 9 Review

Differentiated Instruction

All in One Teaching Resources
- Below Level Chapter 9 Test **L2**
- Chapter 9 Test **L3**
- Chapter 9 Alternative Assessment **L4**

Spanish Assessment Resources **ELL**
- Below Level Chapter 9 Test **L2**
- Chapter 9 Test **L3**
- Chapter 9 Alternative Assessment **L4**

ExamView Assessment Suite CD-ROM
- Special Needs Test **L1**
- Special Needs Practice Bank **L1**

Online Chapter 9 Test at www.PHSchool.com **L3**

Below Level Chapter Test **L2**

Chapter Test **L3**

Chapter Test   Form A

Chapter 9

Choose an appropriate metric unit of length.
1. distance across Texas **kilometers**   2. length of a pencil **centimeters**
3. width of a football field **meters**   4. height of a house **meters**

Choose an appropriate metric unit of mass or capacity.
5. a telephone **grams**   6. Lake Erie **kiloliter**
7. a single piece of paper **milligrams**   8. a bucket of water **liters**

Convert each measurement.
9. 8,500 cm = **85** m   10. 0.04 kL = **40** L   11. 280 mg = **0.28** g
12. 340 g = **0.34** kg   13. 4.5 L = **450** cL   14. 8.3 cg = **83** mg

Find the perimeter and area of each rectangle.
15. 12 m, 8 m   16. 6 ft   17. 14 yd, 9 yd
perimeter **40 m**   perimeter **46 ft**   perimeter **46 yd**
area **96 m²**   area **102 ft²**   area **126 yd²**

Find the perimeter and area of each rectangle.
18. ℓ = 3 m, w = 4 m   19. ℓ = 2.4 ft, w = 6 ft   20. ℓ = 2.5 cm, w = 0.6 cm
14 m; 12 m²   **16.8 ft; 14.4 ft²**   **6.2 cm; 1.5 cm²**

Find the area of each parallelogram.
21. 3.2 cm, 12 cm   22. 7.5 ft, 19 ft   23. 5 in., 7 in.
38.4 cm²   **142.5 ft²**   **35 in.²**

Find the area of each triangle.
24. b = 6 in., h = 4 in.   25. b = 12 cm, h = 5 cm   26. b = 7.9 yd, h = 8 yd
12 in.²   **30 cm²**   **31.6 yd²**

Choose an appropriate metric unit for each measurement.

1. length of a car **meters**

2. capacity of a cup **milliliters**

3. length of a skateboard **centimeters**

4. mass of a boat **kilograms**

5. capacity of a bucket **liters**

Convert each measurement.

6. 672 millimeters to centimeters **67.2 cm**

7. 25,040 milliliters to liters **25.04 L**

8. 35.1 kilograms to grams **35,100 g**

9. 125 liters to kiloliters **0.125 kL**

10. 42.9 meters to centimeters **4,290 cm**

Find the area of each figure.

11.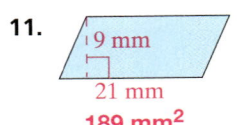
9 mm, 21 mm
189 mm²

12.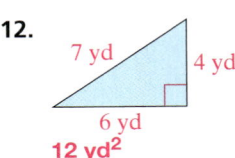
7 yd, 4 yd, 6 yd
12 yd²

13.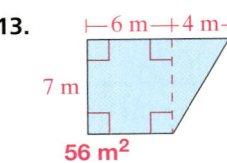
6 m, 4 m, 7 m
56 m²

14.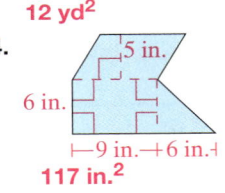
5 in., 6 in., 9 in., 6 in.
117 in.²

15. A garden is in the shape of a right triangle. The base of the triangle measures 8 feet. The height measures 4 feet. What is the area of the garden? **16 ft²**

16. **Writing in Math** Which is larger, a pie plate with a radius of 5 inches, or a pie plate with a diameter of 9 inches? Explain. **See margin.**

Find the circumference and area of each circle. Round to the nearest tenth.

17.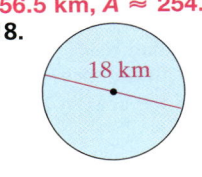
15 ft
C ≈ 94.2 ft, A ≈ 706.5 ft²

18. 18 km
C ≈ 56.5 km, A ≈ 254.3 km²

19. **Food** A rectangular cracker has a length of 5 centimeters and an area of 20 square centimeters. Find the perimeter of the cracker. **18 cm**

20. **Manufacturing** A factory fills cans with tomato juice. Each can has a radius of 2 inches and a height of 8 inches. Find the volume of a can. **about 100.5 cm³**

Find the surface area of each figure.

21.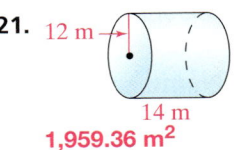
12 m, 14 m
1,959.36 m²

22.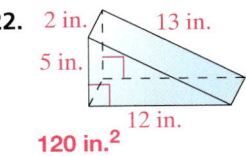
2 in., 13 in., 5 in., 12 in.
120 in.²

Find the volume of each figure.

23. 7 yd, 6 yd, 8 yd
336 yd³

24.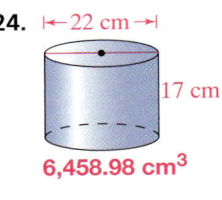
22 cm, 17 cm
6,458.98 cm³

25. The volume of a rectangular prism is 504 square centimeters. The area of the base is 72 square centimeters. Find the height of the prism. **7 cm**

26. A company makes compost bins in the shape of a cylinder. The height and diameter of each bin is 36 inches. What is the volume of each bin? **36,624.96 in.³**

16. a pie plate with a radius of 5 inches, since the diameter of the plate is 2 × 5, or 10 inches

Reading Comprehension

Read each passage and answer the questions that follow.

> **Clock Face** The Clock Tower of the Palace of Westminster in London—
> what people often call "Big Ben"—is about 316 feet tall. The tower has
> four sides, each with a large clock. Each clock face is a circle about 22 feet
> in diameter. The minute hands are about 12 feet long, measuring from the
> center of the clock face to the tip of the hand. The Clock Tower can be seen
> from many parts of the city.

1. Which expression represents the
   circumference of the circle that the tip
   of one of the minute hands traces out in
   an hour? **D**
   - Ⓐ 6π Ⓑ 10π Ⓒ 12π Ⓓ 24π

2. If the minute hand were twice as long, how
   much farther would it travel every hour? **H**
   - Ⓕ half as far   Ⓗ twice as far
   - Ⓖ the same distance   Ⓙ four times as far

3. Which expression represents the area of
   one of the clock faces? **B**
   - Ⓐ $10 \cdot 10 \cdot \pi$ Ⓒ $20 \cdot 20 \cdot \pi$
   - Ⓑ $11 \cdot 11 \cdot \pi$ Ⓓ $22 \cdot 22 \cdot \pi$

4. If the radius of the clock face were twice
   as long, how many times greater would
   the area of the face be? **H**
   - Ⓕ the same   Ⓗ four times
   - Ⓖ two times   Ⓙ eight times

> **Mountain Math** It takes about $1\frac{1}{2}$ hours to get from Al's house to Mount
> Monadnock. First you go west 40 miles on a state highway. Then you turn
> right and go north another 30 miles, and you're there. On a clear day you can
> see the tallest buildings in Al's hometown from the top of the mountain.

5. Which choice does NOT
   correctly identify a point
   in this diagram? **A**
   - Ⓐ Q is Al's house.
   - Ⓑ R is Al's house.
   - Ⓒ P is at the right turn.
   - Ⓓ Q is the mountain.

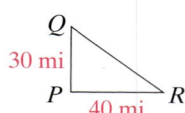

6. How long will it take Al to drive to
   Mount Monadnock if he averages a rate
   of 56 miles per hour for the whole trip?
   - Ⓕ 1 h   Ⓗ 1.5 h   **G**
   - Ⓖ 1.25 h   Ⓙ 1.8 h

7. How many miles is the trip from Al's
   house to Mount Monadnock? **D**
   - Ⓐ 30 miles   Ⓒ 50 miles
   - Ⓑ 40 miles   Ⓓ 70 miles

8. The odometer on Al's car shows how
   many miles the car travels. If the
   odometer shows 12,350 miles as Al
   leaves home, what will it show after a
   round trip to the mountain? **G**
   - Ⓕ 12,000 miles   Ⓗ 12,520 miles
   - Ⓖ 12,490 miles   Ⓙ 12,900 miles

Chapter 9   Test Prep   **471**

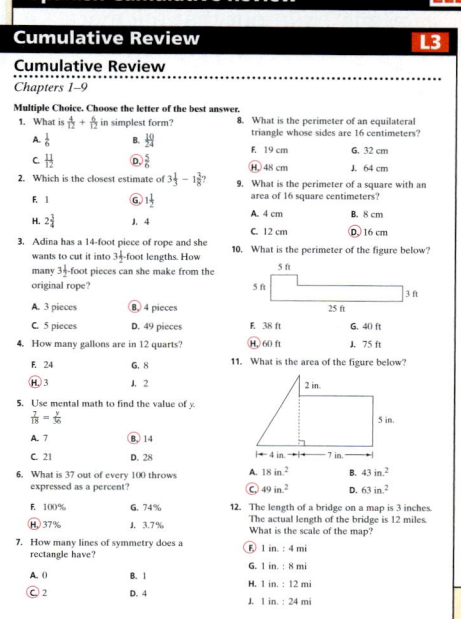

Applying Measurement

Applying Measurement

The Shape of Buildings to Come When architects design office or apartment buildings, they know that people will want as many windows as possible. The footprint, or area that a building covers, has to do with the arrangement of the windows. For example, a large square building may have inside rooms with no windows. Architects can change the shape of the footprint to make more outside walls.

Let the Sun in
This modern glass building connects two Victorian-era office buildings.

Straw-Bale Construction
College students in Wisconsin designed and built this straw-bale house. Wheat, oats, barley, rice, rye, and flax are all desirable straws for bale walls.

Straw bale   Frame

Biosphere 2
Originally constructed as a miniature Earth, Biosphere 2 is now a research facility. It covers 3.15 acres and includes five different environments: a coastal desert, a marsh, a grassy plain, a rain forest, and an ocean.

Rain forest   Grassy plain   Ocean   Kitchen

472

1.

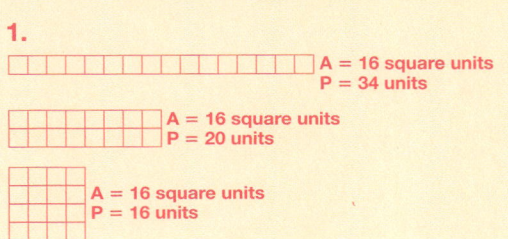

A = 16 square units
P = 34 units

A = 16 square units
P = 20 units

A = 16 square units
P = 16 units

Put It All Together

Materials graph paper

1. Draw three rectangular footprints that you can make using 16 squares. Find each area and perimeter.

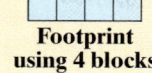

Footprint using 4 blocks

2. **Open-Ended** Draw several non-rectangular footprints that use 16 squares. Be creative! Find each perimeter.

3. **a.** Use 16 squares. Draw a square footprint with an open area in the center.
   b. Find the outside perimeter. Find the inside perimeter. Then find the total perimeter.
   c. **Reasoning** Why might an architect use a design like this for a building? Explain.

4. Consider all the footprints you have drawn. What arrangement of 16 squares gives the greatest total perimeter? The least total perimeter?

5. Buildings A, B, and C at the right are rectangular.
   a. Copy and complete the table. Calculate the volume and total exposed area of each building. (Include the top and four faces, but not the base.) How does the shape affect the surface area?
   b. Which shape gives the most space for windows? Which gives the least? Explain.

Building Entry

These binoculars are four stories tall and made from steel tubing and concrete. Each barrel is a conference room with a circular skylight at the top.

Building Data

Building	ℓ	w	h	Volume	Exposed Surface Area
A	3	2	4	■	■
B	6	2	2	■	■
C	1	3	8	■	■

A h ℓ w

B h ℓ w

C h ℓ w

Go Online
PHSchool.com
For: Information about architecture
Web Code: aqe-0953

Marsh
Library
Living quarters
Tree research buildings
Air supply
Control room

473

2. **Answers may vary. Samples:**

P = 24 units
P = 22
P = 34 units

5a. A: volume = 24 cubic units; exposed surface area = 46 square units
B: volume = 24 cubic units; exposed surface area = 44 square units
C: volume = 24 cubic units; exposed surface area = 67 square units

b. C, B. The tall shape with fewer interior cubes gives the most window options.

 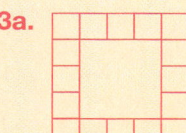

10 Exploring Probability

Chapter at a Glance

Lesson Titles, Objectives, and Features	Assessment	NCTM Standards	Local Standards
10-1 Tree Diagrams and the Counting Principle • To construct sample spaces for events and to use the counting principle **Extension:** Permutations	Lesson Quiz	1, 2, 5, 6, 7, 8, 9, 10	
10-2 Probability • To find the probability of an event and its complement	Lesson Quiz Checkpoint Quiz 1	1, 2, 5, 6, 7, 8, 9, 10	
10-3 Experimental Probability • To find experimental probability **10-3b Activity Lab, Data Collection:** Experimental and Theoretical Probabilities **Vocabulary Builder:** High-Use Academic Words	Lesson Quiz	1, 2, 5, 6, 7, 8, 9, 10	
10-4 Making Predictions from Data • To make predictions using probabilities and samples **10-4b Activity Lab, Technology:** Simulations	Lesson Quiz Checkpoint Quiz 2	1, 2, 5, 6, 7, 8, 9, 10	
10-5 Independent Events • To find probabilities of independent events **Extension:** Dependent Events **Guided Problem Solving:** Practice Solving Problems	Lesson Quiz	1, 2, 5, 6, 7, 8, 9, 10	
Problem Solving Application: Applying Probability			

NCTM Standards 2000

1 Number and Operations	**2** Algebra	**3** Geometry	**4** Measurement	**5** Data Analysis and Probability
6 Problem Solving	**7** Reasoning and Proof	**8** Communication	**9** Connections	**10** Representation

Correlations to Standardized Tests

All content for these tests is contained in *Prentice Hall Math*, Course 1. This chart reflects coverage in this chapter only.

	10-1	10-2	10-3	10-4	10-5
Terra Nova CAT6 (Level 16)					
Number and Number Relations	✔	✔	✔	✔	✔
Computation and Numerical Estimation	✔	✔	✔	✔	✔
Operation Concepts	✔	✔	✔	✔	✔
Measurement					
Geometry and Spatial Sense					
Data Analysis, Statistics, and Probability	✔	✔	✔	✔	✔
Patterns, Functions, Algebra	✔	✔	✔	✔	✔
Problem Solving and Reasoning	✔	✔	✔		✔
Communication	✔	✔	✔	✔	✔
Decimals, Fractions, Integers, and Percent	✔	✔	✔	✔	✔
Order of Operations					
Terra Nova CTBS (Level 16)					
Whole Numbers, Decimals, Fractions	✔	✔	✔	✔	✔
Numeration, Number Theory	✔	✔	✔	✔	✔
Data Interpretation	✔	✔	✔	✔	✔
Pre-algebra	✔	✔	✔	✔	✔
Measurement					
Geometry					
ITBS (Level 12)					
Number Properties and Operations	✔	✔	✔	✔	✔
Algebra	✔	✔	✔	✔	✔
Geometry					
Measurement					
Probability and Statistics	✔	✔	✔	✔	✔
Estimation					
SAT10 (Int 2 Level)					
Number Sense and Operations	✔	✔	✔	✔	✔
Patterns, Relationships, and Algebra	✔	✔	✔	✔	✔
Data, Statistics, and Probability	✔	✔	✔	✔	✔
Geometry and Measurement					
NAEP					
Number Sense, Properties, and Operations					
Measurement					
Geometry and Spatial Sense					
Data Analysis, Statistics, and Probability		✔	✔	✔	
Algebra and Functions					

CAT6 California Achievement Test, 6th Ed.   **CTBS** Comprehensive Test of Basic Skills   **ITBS** Iowa Test of Basic Skills, Form M
SAT10 Stanford Achievement Test, 10th Ed.   **NAEP** National Assessment of Educational Progress 2005 Mathematics Objectives

Math Background

Skills Trace

> ### BEFORE Chapter 10
> **Grade 5 presented basic probability concepts.**
>
> ### DURING Chapter 10
> **Course 1 extends probability to simulations, tree diagrams, the counting principle, permutations, and independent events.**
>
> ### AFTER Chapter 10
> **Throughout this course, students build a foundation for probability.**

10-1 Tree Diagrams and the Counting Principle

> #### Math Understandings
> • You can use the Counting Principle to find the number of ways to make one choice followed by a second choice.

You can use a **tree diagram** to find the probability of two or more events.

Example: This tree diagram shows the possible outcomes from rolling a number cube and then tossing a coin. What is the probability that you will get an even number and tails? The diagram shows there are 3 outcomes for these two events.

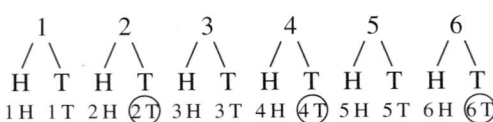

$\frac{3}{12} = \frac{1}{4}$

You can use the **counting principle** to find a large number of outcomes.

> #### Counting Principle
> Suppose there are m ways of making one choice and n ways of making a second choice. Then there are $m \times n$ ways to make the first choice followed by the second choice.

$\frac{3}{6} \cdot \frac{1}{2} = \frac{3}{12}$

10-2 Probability

> #### Math Understandings
> • In mathematics, probability is expressed as a number from 0 to 1 that estimates how often an event will occur.
> • You can write probabilities as fractions, decimals, or percents.

When you toss a fair coin once, each outcome, heads and tails, is just as likely to occur as the other. Outcomes that have the same chance of occurring are called **equally likely outcomes**. An **event** is a collection of possible outcomes. The **probability of an event**, written P(event), is a number that describes how likely it is that the event will occur.

> #### Probability of an Event
> $$P(\text{event}) = \frac{\text{number of favorable outcomes}}{\text{total number of possible outcomes}}$$

When the probability of an event is 0, the event is impossible. When the probability of an event is 1, the event is certain to happen.

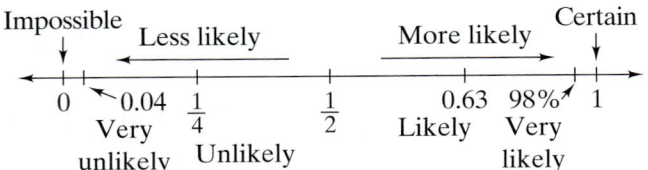

10-3 Experimental Probability

> #### Math Understandings
> • Experimental probability is based on the results of an actual experiment; theoretical probability is based on the assumption that certain outcomes are equally likely.

When you find a probability based on data you collect, you are finding experimental probability.

> #### Experimental Probability
> $$P(\text{event}) = \frac{\text{number of times an event occurs}}{\text{total number of trials}}$$

A *fair* coin or number cube generates equally likely outcomes. If coins, cubes, or spinners are unevenly made, they may *not* be fair.

Math Understandings

- **Probabilities** can help you make predictions about the outcome of an experiment. However, they do not guarantee what will actually occur.
- The probability of an event may not be a good predictor of what will happen in a small number of cases. The laws of probability predict only what will happen when you survey a very large number of events.

To predict the number of times an event will occur, multiply the probability of the event by the total number of trials.

$$P(\text{event}) \times \frac{\text{total number}}{\text{of trials}} = \frac{\text{number of predicted}}{\text{successes}}$$

A **population** is a group about which you want information. A **sample** is a part of the population. To make predictions, a sample can *represent* the population.

Math Understandings

- Two events are independent if one event does not affect the probability of the other event.
- It is a fallacy that, when tossing a fair coin, you are more likely to get heads after tossing a series of tails. The probability remains one out of two.

When the occurrence of one event does not affect the probability of another event, the two are **independent events**. A **compound event** consists of two or more separate events.

Probability of Independent Events

If A and B are independent events, then
$P(A, \text{then } B) = P(A) \times P(B)$.

Example: If you roll a six-sided number cube two times, the probability of rolling a 2 followed by a 2 is $\frac{1}{6} \times \frac{1}{6}$, or $\frac{1}{36}$.

Additional Professional Development Opportunities

Math Background Notes for Chapter 10: Every lesson has a Math Background in the PLAN section.

Research Overview, Mathematics Strands Additional support for these topics and more is in the front of the Teacher's Edition.

LessonLab LessonLab, a Pearson Education company, offers comprehensive, facilitated professional development designed to help teachers to improve student achievement. To learn more, please visit lessonlab.com.

Chapter 10 Resources

Print Resources	10-1	10-2	10-3	10-4	10-5	For the Chapter
L3 Practice	●	●	●	●	●	
L1 Adapted Practice	●	●	●	●	●	
L3 Guided Problem Solving	●	●	●	●	●	
L2 Reteaching	●	●	●	●	●	
L4 Enrichment	●	●	●	●	●	
L3 Daily Notetaking Guide	●	●	●	●	●	
L1 Adapted Daily Notetaking Guide	●	●	●	●	●	
L3 Vocabulary and Study Skills Worksheets	●	●	●	●	●	●
L3 Daily Puzzles	●	●	●	●	●	
L3 Activity Labs	●	●	●	●	●	
L3 Checkpoint Quiz		●		●		
L3 Chapter Project						●
L2 Below Level Chapter Test						●
L3 Chapter Test						●
L4 Alternative Assessment						●
L3 Cumulative Review						●

Spanish Resources ELL	10-1	10-2	10-3	10-4	10-5	For the Chapter
L3 Practice	●	●	●	●	●	
L3 Vocabulary and Study Skills Worksheets	●	●	●	●	●	●
L3 Checkpoint Quiz		●		●		
L2 Below Level Chapter Test						●
L3 Chapter Test						●
L4 Alternative Assessment						●
L3 Cumulative Review						●

Transparencies	10-1	10-2	10-3	10-4	10-5	For the Chapter
Check Skills You'll Need	●	●	●	●	●	
Additional Examples	●	●	●	●	●	
Problem of the Day	●	●	●	●	●	
Classroom Aid			●			
Student Edition Answers	●	●	●	●	●	●
Lesson Quiz	●	●	●	●	●	
Test-Taking Strategies						●

Technology	10-1	10-2	10-3	10-4	10-5	For the Chapter
Interactive Textbook Online	●	●	●	●	●	●
StudentExpress™ CD-ROM	●	●	●	●	●	●
Success Tracker™ Online Intervention	●	●	●	●	●	●
TeacherExpress™ CD-ROM	●	●	●	●	●	●
PresentationExpress™ with QuickTake Presenter CD-ROM	●	●	●	●	●	●
ExamView® Assessment Suite CD-ROM	●	●	●	●	●	●
MindPoint® Quiz Show CD-ROM						●
Prentice Hall Web Site: PHSchool.com	●	●	●	●	●	●

Also available: **Prentice Hall Assessment System**
- Progress Monitoring Assessments
- Skills and Concepts Review
- Test Prep Workbook

Other Resources
Algebra Readiness Tests
All-in-One Student Workbook
All-in-One Student Workbook, Adapted Version
Multilingual Handbook

Solution Key
Math Notes Study Folder
Spanish Cumulative Assessment

Where You Can Use the Lesson Resources

Here is a suggestion, following the four-step teaching plan, for how you can incorporate Differentiated Instruction Resources into your teaching.

	Instructional Resources L3	Differentiated Instruction Resources
1. Plan		
Preparation Read the Math Background in the Teacher's Edition to connect this lesson with students' previous experience. **Starting Class** **Check Skills You'll Need** Assign these exercises to review prerequisite skills. **New Vocabulary** Help students pre-read the lesson by pointing out the new terms introduced in the lesson.	**Math Background** **Math Understandings** **Transparencies & PresentationExpress™ with QuickTake Presenter CD-ROM** Check Skills You'll Need Problem of the Day **Resources** Vocabulary and Study Skills	**Spanish Support** ELL Vocabulary and Study Skills
2. Teach		
L3 Guided Instruction Use the Activity Labs to build conceptual understanding. Teach each Example. Use the Teacher's Edition side column notes for specific teaching tips, including Error Prevention notes. Use the Additional Examples found in the side column (and on transparency and PowerPoint) as an alternative presentation for the content. After each Example, assign the Quick Check exercise for that Example to get an immediate assessment of student understanding. Use the Closure activity in the Teacher's Edition to help students attain mastery of lesson content.	**Student Edition** Activity Lab **Resources** Daily Notetaking Guide Activity Lab **Transparencies & PresentationExpress™ with QuickTake Presenter CD-ROM** Additional Examples Classroom Aids **ExamView® Assessment Suite CD-ROM**	**Teacher's Edition** Every lesson includes suggestions for working with students who need special attention. L1 Special Needs L2 Below Level L4 Advanced Learners ELL English Language Learners **Resources** L1 Adapted Daily Notetaking Guide **Multilingual Handbook**
3. Practice		

Assignment Guide
Check Your Understanding
Use these questions to check students' understanding before you assign homework.
Homework Exercises
Assign homework from these leveled exercises in the Assignment Guide.
  A Practice by Example
  B Apply Your Skills
  C Challenge
  Test Prep and Mixed Review
Homework Quick Check
Use these key exercises to quickly check students' homework.
	Transparencies & PresentationExpress™ with QuickTake Presenter CD-ROM
	Student Answers
	Resources
	Practice
	Guided Problem Solving
	Vocabulary and Study Skills
	Activity Lab
	Daily Puzzles
	ExamView® Assessment Suite CD-ROM
		Spanish Support
		ELL Practice
		ELL Vocabulary and Study Skills
		Resources
		L1 Adapted Practice
		L4 Enrichment

4. Assess & Reteach		
Lesson Quiz Assign the Lesson Quiz to assess students' mastery of the lesson content. **Checkpoint Quiz** Use the Checkpoint Quiz to assess student progress over several lessons.	**Transparencies & PresentationExpress™ with QuickTake Presenter CD-ROM** Lesson Quiz **Resources** Checkpoint Quiz	**Resources** L2 Reteaching ELL Checkpoint Quiz Success Tracker™ Online Intervention **ExamView® Assessment Suite CD-ROM**

KEY   L1 Special Needs   L2 Below Level   L3 For All Students   L4 Advanced, Gifted   ELL English Language Learners

Exploring Probability

CHAPTER 10 Exploring Probability

 **Check Your Readiness**

Answers are in the back of the textbook.

For intervention, direct students to:

Subtracting Decimals
Lesson 1-7
Extra Skills and Word
  Problems Practice, Ch. 1

Adding Fractions With Like Denominators
Lesson 5-2
Extra Skills and Word
  Problems Practice, Ch. 5

Multiplying Fractions
Lesson 6-1
Extra Skills and Word
  Problems Practice, Ch. 6

Writing Equivalent Numerical Expressions
Lesson 7-6
Extra Skills and Word
  Problems Practice, Ch. 7

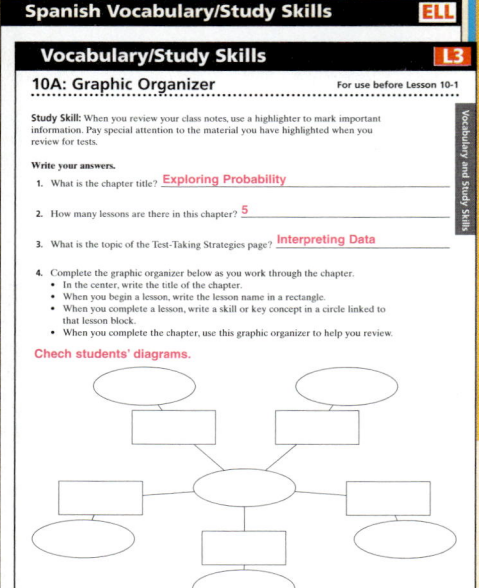
What You've Learned

- In Chapters 5 and 6, you learned to write equivalent fractions and to add, subtract, and multiply fractions.
- In Chapter 7, you used ratios to describe proportional relationships, and you solved problems.
- You also converted between decimals, fractions, and percents.

 **Check Your Readiness**

GO for Help	
For Exercises	**See Lesson**
1–4	1-7
5–8	5-2
9–12	6-1
13–16	7-6

Subtracting Decimals
Find each difference.

1. $1 - 0.32$ **0.68**   **2.** $1 - 0.08$ **0.92**

3. $1 - 0.6$ **0.4**   **4.** $1 - 0.234$ **0.766**

Adding Fractions With Like Denominators
Find each sum.

5. $\frac{2}{5} + \frac{1}{5}$ **$\frac{3}{5}$**   **6.** $\frac{3}{6} + \frac{1}{6}$ **$\frac{2}{3}$**   **7.** $\frac{2}{8} + \frac{5}{8}$ **$\frac{7}{8}$**   **8.** $\frac{3}{10} + \frac{3}{10}$ **$\frac{3}{5}$**

Multiplying Fractions
Find each product.

9. $\frac{1}{2} \times \frac{5}{6}$ **$\frac{5}{12}$**   **10.** $\frac{3}{4} \times \frac{8}{9}$ **$\frac{2}{3}$**   **11.** $\frac{7}{10} \times \frac{5}{14}$ **$\frac{1}{4}$**   **12.** $\frac{2}{3} \times \frac{8}{9}$ **$\frac{16}{27}$**

Writing Equivalent Numerical Expressions
Write each fraction as a decimal and then as a percent.

13. $\frac{2}{8}$ **0.25; 25%**   **14.** $\frac{3}{9}$ **$0.\bar{3}$; ≈ 33%**   **15.** $\frac{4}{5}$ **0.8; 80%**   **16.** $\frac{7}{10}$ **0.7; 70%**

Chapter 10 Overview

In this chapter, students explore theoretical and experimental probability, work with tree diagrams and the counting principle, and use permutations. They conclude the chapter by learning how to compute the probability of independent events.

Activating Prior Knowledge

In this chapter, students build on and extend their knowledge of fractions, decimals, and percents to understand the concept of probability and to express probabilities. Also, they use their understanding of solving proportions to find probabilities. Ask questions such as:

- *What is x in $\frac{5}{x} = \frac{15}{24}$?* **x = 8**
- *What is 80% of 80?* **64**
- *What is $\frac{88}{100}$ when simplified?* **$\frac{22}{25}$**

What You'll Learn Next

- In this chapter, you will construct sample spaces using lists and tree diagrams.

- You will find the probabilities of a simple event and of its complement.

- You will also find experimental probabilities.

- You will use probabilities and proportions to make predictions about populations.

 Problem Solving Application On pages 512 and 513, you will work an extended activity on games.

🔊 Key Vocabulary

- complement of an event (p. 483)
- compound event (p. 501)
- counting principle (p. 477)
- dependent event (p. 504)
- equally likely outcomes (p. 482)
- event (p. 476)
- experimental probability (p. 488)
- independent events (p. 500)
- outcome (p. 476)
- permutation (p. 481)
- population (p. 495)
- probability of an event (p. 482)
- sample (p. 495)
- sample space (p. 476)
- simulation (p. 498)
- tree diagram (p. 477)

Objective
To construct sample spaces for events and to use the counting principle

Examples
1 Finding a Sample Space
2 Using a Tree Diagram
3 Using the Counting Principle

Math Understandings: p. 474C

Math Background

A *tree diagram* uses branches for each choice or stage to name all the possible outcomes in an organized fashion. The structure of a tree diagram illustrates the *counting principle* because each decision or stage requires a branch. The counting principle states that the total number of outcomes is the product of the number of outcomes at each stage. Another name for the total collection of outcomes is *sample space*.

More Math Background: p. 474C

Lesson Planning and Resources

See p. 474E for a list of the resources that support this lesson.

Bell Ringer Practice

✓ **Check Skills You'll Need**
Use student page, transparency, or PowerPoint. For intervention, direct students to:
Multiplying Decimals
Lesson 1-8
Extra Skills and Word Problems
Practice, Ch. 1

10-1 Tree Diagrams and the Counting Principle

GO for Help
Lesson 1-8

✓ Check Skills You'll Need

1. **Vocabulary Review**
When you multiply, you can group numbers together using the _?_ Property.
Associative
Find each product.

2. $5 \times 0.52 \times 2$ **5.2**

3. $25 \times 1.8 \times 40$ **1,800**

4. $3 \times 0.4 \times 1000$ **1,200**

Quick Check

1. **9 outcomes;**
   model 1, color 1
   model 1, color 2
   model 1, color 3
   model 2, color 1
   model 2, color 2
   model 2, color 3
   model 3, color 1
   model 3, color 2
   model 3, color 3

Test Prep Tip
"What is the size of the sample space?" can also be worded, "How many ways are there?", or "How many possible outcomes are there?"

What You'll Learn

To construct sample spaces for events and to use the counting principle

🔊 **New Vocabulary** outcome, event, sample space, tree diagram, counting principle

Why Learn This?

A coin toss is used in sporting events to decide which team starts with the ball. If you toss a coin once, there are two possible outcomes—heads or tails. An **outcome** is the result of an action.

An **event** is an outcome or group of outcomes. The set of all possible outcomes is the **sample space**.

EXAMPLE Finding a Sample Space

1 Use the menu. Construct the sample space for selecting a main dish and a side dish. How many possible outcomes are there?

List all of the possible outcomes.

Lunch Menu

Main Dish	Grilled Chicken
	Baked Chicken
Side Dish	Salad
	Vegetable
	Rice

Grilled chicken	Salad	Baked chicken	Salad
Grilled chicken	Vegetable	Baked chicken	Vegetable
Grilled chicken	Rice	Baked chicken	Rice

The number of possible outcomes is six.

✓ Quick Check

1. A bicycle comes in three models and three colors. Construct the sample space to find how many bicycle choices you have. How many possible outcomes are there? **See left.**

Differentiated Instruction Solutions for All Learners

Special Needs L1
When constructing tree diagrams to find possible outcomes, some students have difficulty keeping track of, or drawing, the branches. Have these students work with a partner who can assist with the drawing, while he or she counts the branches.

learning style: visual

Below Level L2
Students can make a table in Example 2 to see that the same outcomes can be generated with a familiar listing method. They can then transition to a tree diagram.

learning style: visual

A **tree diagram** is an organized list of all possible outcomes.

EXAMPLE **Using a Tree Diagram**

2 You roll a standard number cube and then toss a coin. List the possible outcomes. How many are there?

Draw the tree diagram at the left to list the possible outcomes.

The diagram shows 12 possible outcomes.

Number Cube	Coin	Outcome
1	H	1H
	T	1T
2	H	2H
	T	2T
3	H	3H
	T	3T
4	H	4H
	T	4T
5	H	5H
	T	5T
6	H	6H
	T	6T

✓ **Quick Check**

2. You can choose blue or khaki pants and a red, yellow, or green shirt. Construct the sample space using a tree diagram. How many outfits are possible? **See left.**

The **counting principle** is a way to find the number of possible outcomes.

2. Pants   Shirts

Pants	Shirts
B	R
	Y
	G
K	R
	Y
	G

6 outcomes

KEY CONCEPTS **Counting Principle**

There are m ways of making one choice and n ways of making a second choice. There are $m \times n$ ways to make the first choice followed by the second choice.

EXAMPLE **Using the Counting Principle**

3 **Multiple Choice** You choose one item from each category in the menu. How many different desserts can you order?

- (A) 20
- (B) 25
- (C) 30
- (D) 35

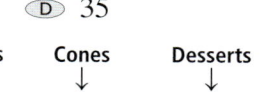

Flavors	Toppings	Cones		Desserts
↓	↓	↓		↓
5	× 3	× 2	=	30

Ice Cream Menu

Flavors	Toppings
Vanilla	Nuts
Chocolate	Sprinkles
Strawberry	Cherries
Banana	**Cones**
Peach	Waffle
	Sugar

You can order 30 different desserts. The correct answer is choice C.

✓ **Quick Check**

3. In the menu above, cherry ripple ice cream as a flavor and fudge as a topping are added. Find the new number of different desserts. **48 desserts**

10-1 Tree Diagrams and the Counting Principle   **477**

2. Teach

Activity Lab

Use before the lesson.

All in One **Teaching Resources**
Activity Lab 10-1: Tree Diagrams

Guided Instruction

Error Prevention!

In Quick Check 3, students may add $6 + 4 + 2$ instead of multiplying $6 \times 4 \times 2$. Have students make a tree diagram to see the relationship of each of the three stages.

PowerPoint
Additional Examples

1 A snack food company makes bags of potato chips in two different sizes and four different flavors. Construct a sample space to find out how many choices there are. **8**

2 Suppose you spin a spinner with 5 equal-sized sections numbered 1 through 5. You then toss a coin. What is the probability that you will get an even number and heads? Make a tree diagram to find all possible outcomes. $\frac{1}{5}$

1	2	3	4	5
H T	H T	H T	H T	H T
1H 1T	2H 2T	3H 3T	4H 4T	5H 5T

3 Flight attendants can wear one of four shirts, three pants, and two jackets. How many different combinations of uniforms are possible? **24 combinations**

Advanced Learners **L4**
Have students write an algebraic formula to represent the counting principle for a three-stage probability experiment. $m \cdot n \cdot o =$ **total outcomes**

learning style: visual

English Language Learners **ELL**
To help students understand Example 2, show them what a number cube is. Have them count the possible outcomes of any roll of that number cube. Then have them consider adding the coin toss to the outcomes.

learning style: visual

Closure

- *What does a tree diagram show?* **an organized list of all possible outcomes**
- *What is the countring principle?* **The number of outcomes for an event with two or more distinct stages is the product of the number of outcomes at each stage.**

Answers may vary. Sample: 16; I used the counting principle: 4 × 2 × 2 = 16 possible outcomes; this method takes less space, or I can calculate mentally.

● More Than One Way

Each lunch for a school field trip has a turkey, roast beef, or bologna sandwich, an orange or apple for a fruit, and a cookie or muffin for dessert. Amanda and Zack would like to know the number of possible lunch choices.

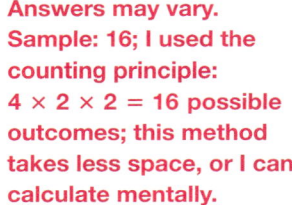

Amanda's Method

I am going to draw a tree diagram to show all possible choices.

Sandwich	Fruit	Dessert	Outcome
	O	C	TOC
		M	TOM
Turkey	A	C	TAC
		M	TAM
	O	C	ROC
		M	ROM
Roast Beef	A	C	RAC
		M	RAM
	O	C	BOC
		M	BOM
Bologna	A	C	BAC
		M	BAM

The tree diagram shows 12 choices. There are 12 lunch choices.

Zack's Method

I will use the counting principle to find the number of possible choices.

Sandwich		Fruit		Dessert		Lunches
3	×	2	×	2	=	12

There are 12 lunch choices.

Choose a Method

A fourth sandwich type, peanut butter, is added to the menu above. How many lunch choices are offered now? Describe your method. Explain why you chose it.

✓ Check Your Understanding

1. **Vocabulary** The list of all possible outcomes is called the __?__.
   sample space

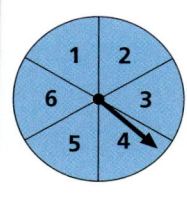

2. You spin the spinner at the left. Then you toss a coin. Use a tree diagram to find the number of possible outcomes.
   See margin.

3. **Writing in Math** You like 5 paint colors and 6 wallpaper patterns. Describe how you would find the different ways to decorate using one paint color and one wallpaper pattern.
   Answers may vary. Sample: You can use the counting principle to multiply 5 × 6 and find 30 different ways.

Homework Exercises

For more exercises, see Extra Skills and Word Problems.

GO for Help

For Exercises	See Examples
4–5	1
6–8	2
9–10	3

(A) Construct a sample space. How many possible outcomes are there?
4–5. See left.

4. A music store sells electric guitars in 3 colors and 2 sizes. How many different guitars can you buy?

5. You can choose from a model car, plane, or boat. Each model comes in 3 colors. How many choices do you have?

4. 6 outcomes;
   color 1, size 1
   color 1, size 2
   color 2, size 1
   color 2, size 2
   color 3, size 1
   color 3, size 2

5. 9 outcomes;
   car, color 1
   car, color 2
   car, color 3
   plane, color 1
   plane, color 2
   plane, color 3
   boat, color 1
   boat, color 2
   boat, color 3

Construct a sample space using a tree diagram. How many possible outcomes are there?
6–8. See margin.

6. You spin the spinner at the right twice.

7. You toss a coin twice.

8. You toss a coin. Then you roll a number cube.

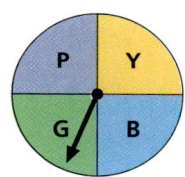

Use the counting principle. Find the number of possible outcomes.

9. You toss a coin three times. 8 outcomes

10. A theater shows 8 movies at 3 prices five times each day. How many types of tickets does the theater sell? 120 types of tickets

(B)  11. **Guided Problem Solving** You buy 2 hats, 5 shirts, and 3 pairs of pants at a store. Your friend buys 4 hats, 4 shirts, and 2 pairs of pants. Who can make the greatest number of possible outfits using one hat, one shirt, and one pair of pants? Justify your answer. your friend
   - Which method could you use to find the number of possible outcomes?
   - How many possible outfits can your friend make?

2. See back of book.

6–8. See back of book.

---

3. Practice

Assignment Guide

Check Your Understanding
Go over Exercises 1–3 in class before assigning the Homework Exercises.

Homework Exercises
- **A** Practice by Example 4–10
- **B** Apply Your Skills 11–14
- **C** Challenge 15
- Test Prep and
  Mixed Review 16–17

Homework Quick Check
To check students' understanding of key skills and concepts, go over Exercises 4, 10, 12, 13, and 14.

Differentiated Instruction Resources

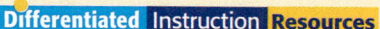

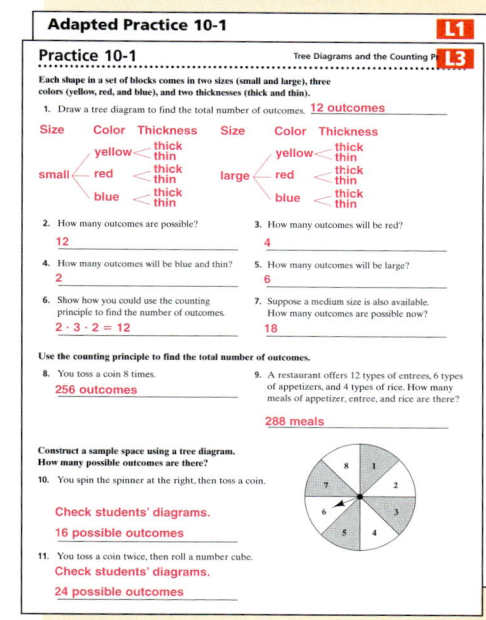

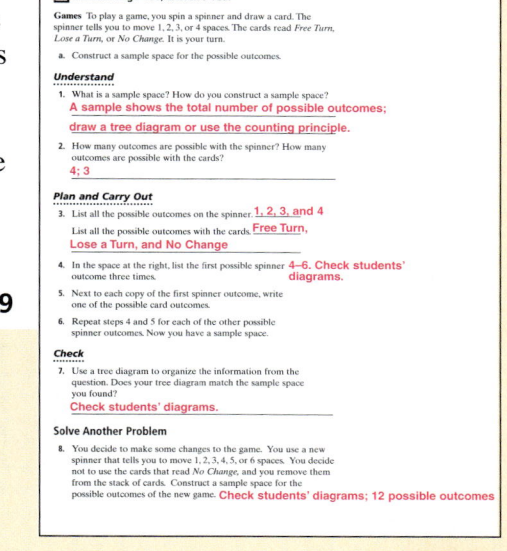

4. Assess & Reteach

Lesson Quiz

A new line of mountain bikes has two different models—Eagle and Hawk—and three possible colors—red, blue, and grey.

1. Construct a sample space. Then use a tree diagram to show all possible combinations. **Er, Eb, Eg, Hr, Hb, Hg**

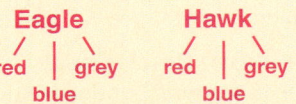

Eagle   **Hawk**
red | grey   red | grey
   blue   blue

2. Find the number of choices of bikes if wheels come in two options—aluminum or plastic. **12**

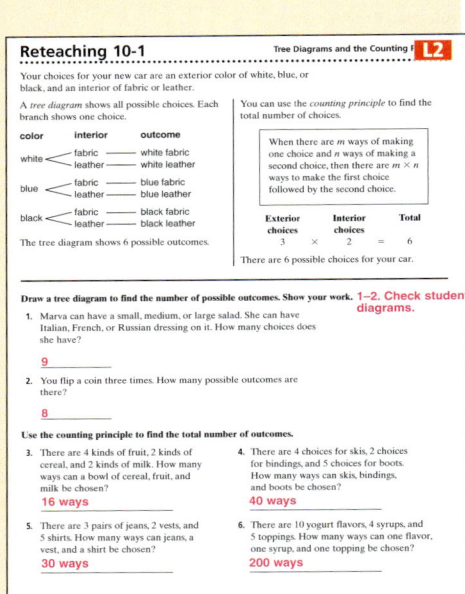

Reteaching 10-1 — Tree Diagrams and the Counting P... **L2**

Your choices for your new car are an exterior color of white, blue, or black, and an interior of fabric or leather.

A tree diagram shows all possible choices. Each branch shows one choice.

You can use the *counting principle* to find the total number of choices.

color	interior	outcome
white	fabric / leather	white fabric / white leather
blue	fabric / leather	blue fabric / blue leather
black	fabric / leather	black fabric / black leather

The tree diagram shows 6 possible outcomes.

When there are *m* ways of making one choice and *n* ways of making a second choice, then there are *m* × *n* ways to make the first choice followed by the second choice.

| Exterior choices | | Interior choices | | Total |
| 3 | × | 2 | = | 6 |

There are 6 possible choices for your car.

Draw a tree diagram to find the number of possible outcomes. Show your work. 1–2. Check student diagrams.

1. Marva can have a small, medium, or large salad. She can have Italian, French, or Russian dressing on it. How many choices does she have?
   9

2. You flip a coin three times. How many possible outcomes are there?
   8

Use the counting principle to find the total number of outcomes.

3. There are 4 kinds of fruit, 2 kinds of cereal, and 2 kinds of milk. How many ways can a bowl of cereal, fruit, and milk be chosen?
   16 ways

4. There are 4 choices for skis, 2 choices for bindings, and 5 choices for boots. How many ways can skis, bindings, and boots be chosen?
   40 ways

5. There are 3 pairs of jeans, 2 vests, and 5 shirts. How many ways can jeans, a vest, and a shirt be chosen?
   30 ways

6. There are 10 yogurt flavors, 4 syrups, and 5 toppings. How many ways can one flavor, one syrup, and one topping be chosen?
   200 ways

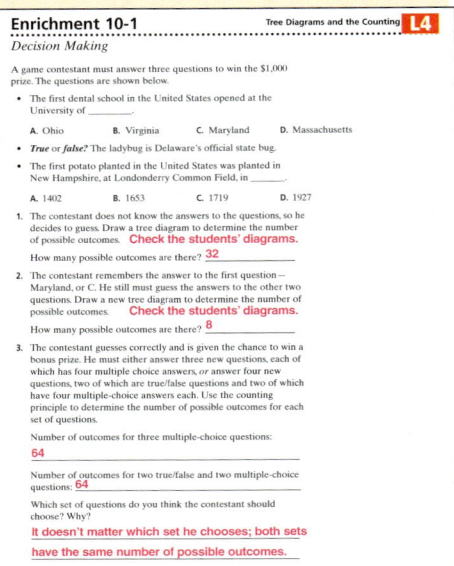

Enrichment 10-1 — Tree Diagrams and the Counting **L4**
Decision Making

A game contestant must answer three questions to win the $1,000 prize. The questions are shown below.

- The first dental school in the United States opened at the University of _____.
  A. Ohio   B. Virginia   C. Maryland   D. Massachusetts
- *True or false?* The ladybug is Delaware's official state bug.
- The first potato planted in the United States was planted in New Hampshire, at Londonderry Common Field, in _____.
  A. 1402   B. 1653   C. 1719   D. 1927

1. The contestant does not know the answers to the questions, so he decides to guess. Draw a tree diagram to determine the number of possible outcomes. **Check the students' diagrams.**
   How many possible outcomes are there? 32

2. The contestant remembers the answer to the first question— Maryland, or C. He still must guess the answers to the other two questions. Draw a new tree diagram to determine the number of possible outcomes. **Check the students' diagrams.**
   How many possible outcomes are there? 8

3. The contestant guesses correctly and is given the chance to win a bonus prize. He must either answer three new questions, each of which has four multiple choice answers, *or* answer four new questions, two of which are true/false questions and two of which have four multiple-choice answers each. Use the counting principle to determine the number of possible outcomes for each set of questions.

   Number of outcomes for three multiple-choice questions:
   64

   Number of outcomes for two true/false and two multiple-choice questions: 64

   Which set of questions do you think the contestant should choose? Why?
   It doesn't matter which set he chooses; both sets have the same number of possible outcomes.

480

GO Online
Homework Video Tutor
Visit: PHSchool.com
Web Code: aqe-1001

Careers Librarians assist people in finding information.

GPS

12. **Games** To play a game, you spin a spinner and draw a card. The spinner tells you to move 1, 2, 3, or 4 spaces. The cards read Free Turn, Lose a Turn, or No Change. It is your turn.
    a. Construct a sample space for the possible outcomes.
    b. To win the game, you need to move at least 2 spaces or draw a Free Turn card. How many of the possible outcomes will allow you to win on your next turn? **12a–b. See margin.**

13. **Reasoning** A city has 30 libraries. Each library will receive a banner. There are 5 banner styles. How many colors will you need so that each library receives a different banner? **6 colors**

14. **Choose a Method** The table below shows features for a computer. You choose one keyboard, one monitor, and one printer. How many different choices can you make? Describe your method, and explain why you chose it. **27 outcomes; answers may vary. Sample: I used the counting principle and multiplied 3 × 3 × 3, because this method was faster.**

Keyboard	Monitor	Printer
Standard	Color 15-in.	Inkjet
Extended	Color 17-in.	Color inkjet
Adjustable	Color 19-in.	Laser

C 15. **Challenge** Find the total number of four-digit numbers you can write using only digits that are even numbers. **500 four-digit numbers**

Test Prep and Mixed Review — **Practice**

Multiple Choice

16. Talia and Anthony run for class president. Josh, Matt, and Susan run for vice-president. What are the possible outcomes of the election? **B**

(A)
Anthony	Susan
Anthony	Josh
Anthony	Matt

(C)
Talia	Susan
Talia	Josh
Talia	Matt

(B)
Anthony	Susan
Anthony	Josh
Anthony	Matt
Talia	Susan
Talia	Josh
Talia	Matt

(D)
Anthony	Susan
Anthony	Susan
Anthony	Josh
Talia	Josh
Talia	Matt
Talia	Matt

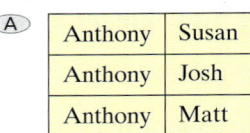
GO for Help

For Exercise	See Lesson
17	6-7

17. What is an appropriate unit of weight to describe a car? **tons**

480   Chapter 10   Exploring Probability

Test Prep

Resources
For additional practice with a variety of test item formats:
- Test-Taking Strategies, p. 507
- Test Prep, p. 511
- Test-Taking Strategies with Transparencies

Alternative Assessment

Students work in pairs to complete Exercises 6–10. One partner draws a tree diagram to find the sample space while the other uses the counting principle. Partners then compare their answers and trade tasks.

Permutations

An arrangement of objects in a particular order is called a
permutation. For the letters A and M, the permutations AM and
MA are different, because the orders of the letters are different.

EXAMPLES

1 Find the permutations of the letters in FLY.

Make an organized list. Use each letter exactly once.

FLY   LFY   YFL

FYL   LYF   YLF

2 Find the two-digit permutations you can make with the digits
1, 3, 7, and 9. How many are there?

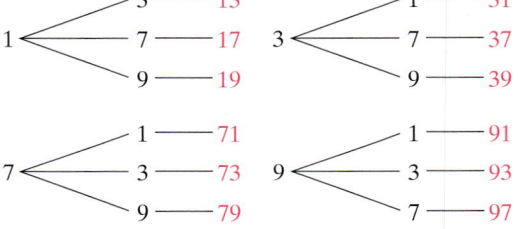

1. WORD, WODR, WROD, WRDO, WDOR,
WDRO, OWRD, OWDR, ORWD, ORDW,
ODWR, ODRW, RWOD, RWDO, ROWD,
RODW, RDWO, RDOW, DWOR, DWRO,
DOWR, DORW, DRWO, DROW

24 permutations

● There are 12 permutations.

Exercises

1. Make an organized list to find the permutations of the letters
in WORD. **See above right.**

Draw a tree diagram to find the permutations of each set. **2–4. See margin.**

2. two-digit permutations of the numbers 1, 2, 3, and 4

3. three-letter permutations of the letters in BOLT

4. In your garden you want to plant a row of carrots, a row of
peppers, a row of tomatoes, and a row of peas. Find all of the
possible arrangements of the rows.

Extension   Permutations   **481**

12a–b. See back of book.

2–4. See back of book.

Permutations

In Lesson 10-1, students identified
sample spaces using tree
diagrams. In this feature, they will
learn to use lists and tree
diagrams to create permutations,
or arrangements of elements in
which the order of elements is
important.

Guided Instruction

Call students' attention to the
organization of the list with each
letter of FLY beginning a column.
Then identify the pattern of the
second letter in each column. Ask:
Are letters repeated in any of the
permutations? **No, each letter is
used only once.**

Exercises

Have students work
independently on the Exercises.
When they have finished, have
them compare their permutation
lists with a partner to make sure
each student found all possible
permutations.

Differentiated Instruction

Advanced Learners   **L4**
Have students make permutations
of the letters in their first names.
Each letter should be used only
once, so for the name Anne the
letters used would be A, N, E.

Objective
To find the probability of an event and of its complement

Examples
1 Probability of an Event
2 Complement of an Event
3 Application: Fundraising

Math Understandings: p. 474C

Math Background

An *event* is a collection of possible outcomes or happenings. For example, tossing a coin is an experiment with two *equally likely outcomes*: heads or tails. The *probability* of an event is the likelihood the event will occur. Probability is always a number from 0 (an impossible event) to 1 (a certain event). To find probability, use $P(\text{event}) =$

$$\frac{\text{number of favorable outcomes}}{\text{total number of possible outcomes}}.$$

More Math Background: p. 474C

Lesson Planning and Resources

See p. 474E for a list of the resources that support this lesson.

Bell Ringer Practice

✓ **Check Skills You'll Need**
Use student page, transparency, or PowerPoint. For intervention, direct students to:
Percents, Fractions, and Decimals
Lesson 7-6
Extra Skills and Word Problems Practice, Ch. 7

✓ **Check Skills You'll Need**

1. **Vocabulary Review**
   What does the word *percent* mean?
   1–2. See below.
   Write each number as a percent.

2. 0.32   3. $\frac{9}{25}$ **36%**

4. $\frac{2}{5}$ **40%**   5. 0.02 **2%**

**for Help**
Lesson 7-6

Check Skills You'll Need

1. A percent is a ratio that compares a number to 100.

2. 32%

What You'll Learn
To find the probabilities of an event and of its complement

🔊 **New Vocabulary** equally likely outcomes, probability of an event, complement of an event

Why Learn This?

You can use probability to predict your chances of winning a game.

Suppose you spin the spinner below. The spinner is equally likely to land on each of the ten sections.

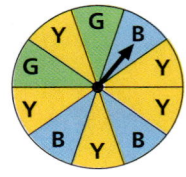

3 out of 10 possible outcomes are blue.

Outcomes that have the same chance of occurring are called <mark>equally likely outcomes.</mark> If you toss a coin once, there are two equally likely outcomes—heads or tails.

The <mark>probability of an event</mark> is a number that describes how likely it is that the event will occur.

On the spinner above, the probability of the event "blue" is 3 out of 10, or $\frac{3}{10}$. The probability of the event "not blue" is 7 out of 10, or $\frac{7}{10}$.

> **KEY CONCEPTS** **Probability of an Event**
>
> For equally likely outcomes:
>
> the probability of an event $= \dfrac{\text{number of favorable outcomes}}{\text{total number of outcomes}}$

You can write $P(\text{blue})$ for the phrase "the probability of blue." For the spinner above, $P(\text{blue}) = \frac{3}{10}$.

Differentiated **Instruction** Solutions for All Learners

Special Needs **L1**
For Example 1, have students list the even numbers on the number cube, and then list the odd numbers. Have them count the total number of even numbers and compare them to all the numbers on the cube. This way they can understand the outcome of $\frac{3}{6}$ or $\frac{1}{2}$.
learning style: visual

Below Level **L2**
Have students draw a diagram of the total number of outcomes and color the number of favorable events for both Example 1 and Quick Check 1.
learning style: visual

EXAMPLE **Probability of an Event**

1 You roll a number cube once. Find P(an even number).

There are 3 outcomes for the event "even" out of 6 equally likely outcomes.

$P(\text{even}) = \dfrac{3}{6}$ ← number of outcomes with even numbers
← total number of outcomes

$= \dfrac{1}{2}$ ← Simplify.

The probability of rolling an even number is $\dfrac{1}{2}$.

✓ **Quick Check**

1. You roll a number cube once. Find P(4 or 6). $\dfrac{1}{3}$

The collection of outcomes *not* contained in the event is the **complement of an event.** The sum of the probabilities of an event and its complement is 1.

EXAMPLE **Complement of an Event**

2 Of 20 students in a class, 18 are 12 years old. A teacher selects a student at random. What is P(12 years old)? What is P(not 12 years old)?

$P(12) = \dfrac{18}{20}$ ← number of 12-year-old students
← total number of students

$= \dfrac{9}{10}$ ← Simplify.

The event "not 12 years old" is the complement of the event "12 years old." The sum of the probabilities of an event and its complement is 1, so P(not 12 years old) $= 1 - P$(12 years old).

$P(\text{not 12 years old}) = 1 - P(\text{12 years old})$

$= 1 - \dfrac{9}{10}$ ← Substitute $\dfrac{9}{10}$ for P(12).

$= \dfrac{1}{10}$ ← Simplify.

P(12 years old) is $\dfrac{9}{10}$. P(not 12 years old) is $\dfrac{1}{10}$.

✓ **Quick Check**

2. You roll a number cube once. Find P(not 6). $\dfrac{5}{6}$

Vocabulary Tip

Random means
"equally likely."

2. Teach

Activity Lab
Use before the lesson.

All in One Teaching Resources
Activity Lab 10-2: Critical Thinking

Guided Instruction

Example 1
Provide students with number cubes to examine. Ask: *How many numbers are possible when the cube is rolled?* **6 because of the 6 sides**

PowerPoint

Additional Examples

A spinner is divided into 8 equal sections numbered 1 through 8. Find each probability for one spin of the spinner.

1 $P(6)$ $\dfrac{1}{8}$

2 If $P(2) = \dfrac{1}{6}$, find P(not 2) $\dfrac{5}{6}$

3 The 6th grade class made 73 of the 100 posters.

a. Find the probability that a randomly selected poster was made by the 6th grade class. Write your answer as a fraction, a decimal, and a percent. $\dfrac{73}{100}$, **0.73, 73%**

b. State if the event is *impossible, unlikely, likely, or certain.* **likely**

Advanced Learners **L4**
Have students express the probability in Quick Check 1 as a fraction, a decimal, and a percent. $\dfrac{1}{3}$, **0.33, 33%**

learning style: visual

English Language Learners **ELL**
Example 2 is linguistically complicated. Help students make sense of why P(not 12 years old) $= 1 - P$(12 years old), and how that is related to the sum of two complements being 1. Differentiate between the word *complement* here and the word *complement* in complementary angles.

learning style: verbal

Closure

- *How do you find the probability of an event?* **Sample: Divide the number of favorable outcomes by the total number of possible outcomes.**

Probabilities range from 0 to 1. An impossible event will never occur. Its probability is 0. If an event will definitely happen, then the event is certain. Its probability is 1.

You can write probabilities as fractions, decimals, or percents.

<table>
<tr><td>Impossible event</td><td></td><td>Event equally likely or unlikely</td><td></td><td>Certain event</td></tr>
<tr><td>0%</td><td>25%</td><td>50%</td><td>75%</td><td>100%</td></tr>
<tr><td>0</td><td>$\frac{1}{4}$ or 0.25</td><td>$\frac{1}{2}$ or 0.5</td><td>$\frac{3}{4}$ or 0.75</td><td>1</td></tr>
</table>

EXAMPLE   **Application: Fundraising**

3 **Gridded Response** You are one of 100 students who work for a fundraiser and are eligible for a prize. There are 11 prizes. Names are drawn at random. What is the probability that you will win? Write your answer as a decimal.

$$P(\text{win a prize}) = \frac{11}{100} \leftarrow \text{number of prizes} \atop \leftarrow \text{total number of students}$$

$$= 0.11$$

✓ Quick Check

3. In a bag of mixed nuts, 6 out of 10 nuts are pecans. What is the probability that a randomly selected nut is a pecan? Write your answer as a decimal. **0.6**

✓ Check Your Understanding

1. **Vocabulary** What is the relationship between the probability of an event and the probability of its complement? **The sum of the probability of an event and the probability of its complement always equals 1.**
2. **Reasoning** You roll a number cube once. Is $P(3)$ different from $P(4)$? Explain. **No; $P(3)$ and $P(4)$ are both $\frac{1}{6}$.**
3. **Open-Ended** Give an example of an impossible event. Then give an example of a certain event. **Check students' work.**

You spin the spinner once. Match each probability to a fraction.

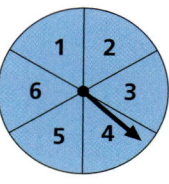

4. $P(3)$ **A**

5. $P(4 \text{ or } 5)$ **B**

6. $P(\text{not } 6)$ **C**

A. $\frac{1}{6}$

B. $\frac{1}{3}$

C. $\frac{5}{6}$

Homework Exercises

For more exercises, see Extra Skills and Word Problems.

GO for Help

For Exercises	See Examples
7–10	1
11–12	2
13–16	3

A A bag contains 4 red marbles, 3 yellow marbles, 2 black marbles, and 1 green marble. You select a marble at random. Find each probability.

7. $P(\text{red})$ $\frac{4}{10}$ or $\frac{2}{5}$

8. $P(\text{yellow})$ $\frac{3}{10}$

9. $P(\text{black})$ $\frac{2}{10}$ or $\frac{1}{5}$

10. $P(\text{green})$ $\frac{1}{10}$

11. Of 12 fish in a tank, 8 have spots. You catch a fish at random. What is $P(\text{spots})$? What is $P(\text{no spots})$? $\frac{8}{12}$ or $\frac{2}{3}$; $\frac{4}{12}$ or $\frac{1}{3}$

12. A clown has 21 balloons to sell. Seven of the balloons in the bunch are yellow. You take the string of a balloon at random. What is $P(\text{yellow})$? What is $P(\text{not yellow})$? $\frac{7}{21}$ or $\frac{1}{3}$; $\frac{14}{21}$ or $\frac{2}{3}$

Find the probability of each event. Write the probability as a decimal.

13. A spinner has equal sections of red, blue, pink, green, and yellow. You spin the spinner once and land on yellow. 0.2

14. You roll a number cube. You roll a number greater than 3. 0.5

15. You write the letters A, B, C, D, E, and F on pieces of paper. You select a piece of paper at random and pick a vowel. 0.3̄

16. Your name is selected at random from a list of 6 names. 0.16̄

Test Prep Tip

Sometimes it is easier to find the probability of an event by finding the probability of its complement.

B  **GPS** 17. **Guided Problem Solving** A package of 25 party favors contains 8 glitter balls. A package of 20 party favors contains 6 glitter balls. You randomly select a party favor from each package. In which package are you more likely to get a glitter ball as a party favor? **a package of 25 party favors**
- Find the probability of choosing a glitter ball from each package.
- Use decimals or fractions to compare the probabilities.

18. **Baseball** A baseball team has
GPS the starting and relief pitchers shown in the table. The manager selects a pitcher at random. Find the probability that the pitcher is left-handed.
$\frac{3}{8}$

Pitchers on Baseball Team

Pitchers	Number
Left-handed starters	1
Right-handed starters	4
Left-handed relievers	2
Right-handed relievers	1

---

3. Practice

Assignment Guide

Check Your Understanding
Go over Exercises 1–6 in class before assigning the Homework Exercises.

Homework Exercises
A Practice by Example 7–16
B Apply Your Skills 17–27
C Challenge 28
Test Prep and
  Mixed Review 29–35

Homework Quick Check
To check students' understanding of key skills and concepts, go over Exercises 11, 15, 18, 20, and 26.

Differentiated Instruction **Resources**

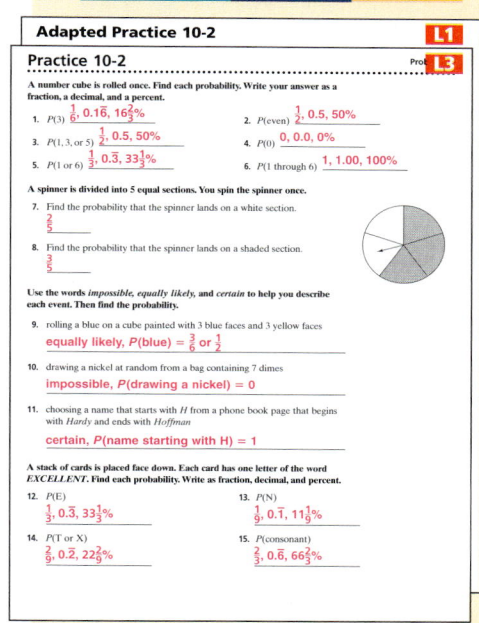

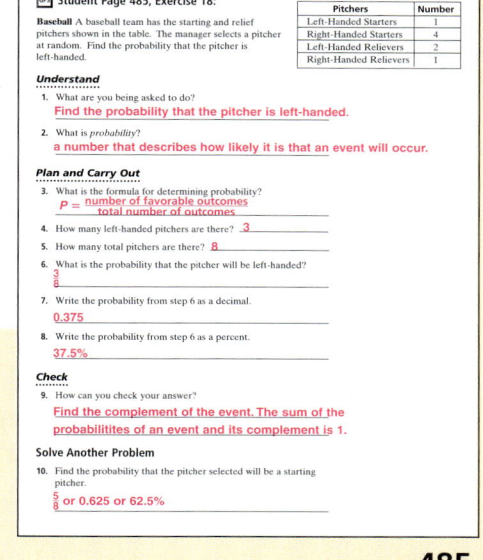

Lesson Quiz

A box contains 3 red markers, 4 green markers, 2 purple markers, 2 black markers, and 1 blue marker. You pick a marker at random. Find the probability of each event. Write each answer as a fraction, a decimal, and a percent.

1. $P(\text{green})$ $\frac{1}{3}$, 0.33, 33%

2. $P(\text{not purple or blue})$ $\frac{3}{4}$, 0.75, 75%

3. $P(\text{pink})$ 0, 0, 0%

4. $P(\text{blue})$ $\frac{1}{12}$, 0.08, 8%

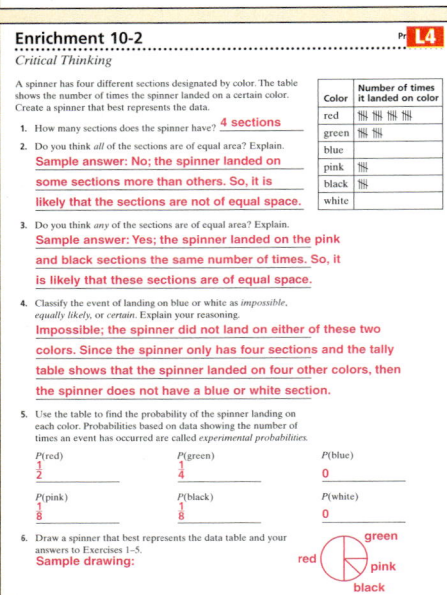

Reteaching 10-2 Pr L2

The *probability of an event* is a number that describes how likely it is that the event will occur. When the outcomes are equally likely, the probability of an event is the following ratio.

$P(\text{event}) = \frac{\text{number of favorable outcomes}}{\text{total number of outcomes}}$

Red Blue Blue Blue Blue

Find the probability of choosing the red chip if the chips are placed in a bag and mixed.

$P(\text{red}) = \frac{\text{number of favorable outcomes}}{\text{total number of outcomes}} = \frac{1}{5}$
The probability of choosing the red chip is $\frac{1}{5}$.

- If an event is impossible, its probability is 0. The probability of drawing an 11 from cards numbered 1 to 10 is impossible.
- If an event is equally likely, its probability is $\frac{1}{2}$ or 0.5. The probability that you will draw an even-number card from cards numbered 1 to 10 is equally likely.
- If an event is certain, its probability is 1. The probability that you will draw a card from 1 to 10 from a set of cards numbered 1 to 10 is certain.

Find the probability of each event.

1. You pick a vowel at random from the letters in EVENT. $\frac{2}{5}$
2. You pick a weekend day at random from days of the week. $\frac{2}{7}$
3. You pick a month at random that begins with the letter J. $\frac{1}{4}$
4. A spinner is labeled $\frac{2}{6}$ or $\frac{1}{3}$ 1–6. You spin 1 or 5.
5. You pick an odd number at random from 75 to 100. $\frac{1}{2}$
6. You pick a word at random with four letters from this sentence. $\frac{3}{5}$
7. You have a birthday on February 30. 0
8. A number cube is tossed you toss a 1, 3, or 5. $\frac{1}{2}$

Each of the 6 letters in the word EQUALS is put on a slip of paper. One slip is selected at random. Classify each event as *impossible, equally likely,* or *certain.*

9. $P(\text{consonant})$ $\frac{1}{2}$, equally likely
10. $P(D)$ 0, impossible
11. $P(\text{vowel})$ $\frac{1}{2}$, equally likely

Enrichment 10-2 Pr L4

Critical Thinking

A spinner has four different sections designated by color. The table shows the number of times the spinner landed on a certain color. Create a spinner that best represents the data.

Color	Number of times it landed on color
red	
green	
blue	
pink	
black	
white	

1. How many sections does the spinner have? 4 sections
2. Do you think *all* of the sections are of equal area? Explain.
Sample answer: No; the spinner landed on some sections more than others. So, it is likely that the sections are not of equal space.
3. Do you think *any* of the sections are of equal area? Explain.
Sample answer: Yes; the spinner landed on the pink and black sections the same number of times. So, it is likely that these sections are of equal space.
4. Classify the event of landing on blue or white as *impossible, equally likely,* or *certain.* Explain your reasoning.
Impossible; the spinner did not land on either of these two colors. Since the spinner only has four sections and the tally table shows that the spinner landed on four other colors, then the spinner does not have a blue or white section.
5. Use the table to find the probability of the spinner landing on each color. Probabilities based on data showing the number of times an event has occurred are called *experimental probabilities.*

$P(\text{red})$ $\frac{1}{2}$ $P(\text{green})$ $\frac{1}{4}$ $P(\text{blue})$ 0
$P(\text{pink})$ $\frac{1}{8}$ $P(\text{black})$ $\frac{1}{8}$ $P(\text{white})$ 0

6. Draw a spinner that best represents the data table and your answers to Exercises 1–5.
Sample drawing: red green pink black

GO Online
Homework Video Tutor
Visit: PHSchool.com
Web Code: aqe-1002

26. No; "losing" means not winning and not tying, and "not winning" could be either losing or tying.

Vocabulary Tip

Icosahedron comes from two Greek words. *Icosa–* means "twenty" and *–hedron* means "surface."

Find each probability for one roll of a number cube.

19. $P(\text{multiple of 3})$ $\frac{2}{6}$ or $\frac{1}{3}$
20. $P(\text{not a multiple of 4})$ $\frac{5}{6}$
21. $P(\text{not a factor of 8})$ $\frac{3}{6}$ or $\frac{1}{2}$
22. $P(\text{prime})$ $\frac{3}{6}$ or $\frac{1}{2}$

Estimation You spin the spinner once. Estimate each probability. Give your answer as a decimal.
Answers may vary. Samples are given.

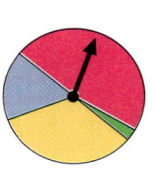

23. The spinner does *not* land on pink. 0.55
24. The spinner does *not* land on green. 0.95
25. The spinner does *not* land on yellow. 0.65

26. **Writing in Math** In a game, is the probability of "not winning" always the same as "losing"? Explain. See left.

27. **Geometry** You roll the icosahedron shown. $\frac{3}{4}$ It has 20 congruent faces and equal numbers of red, blue, yellow, and green faces. What is the probability that the top face will *not* be green?

C 28. **Challenge** A bag contains only red, green, and blue marbles. $P(\text{green}) = \frac{1}{3}$, and $P(\text{red}) = \frac{1}{2}$. There are 6 green marbles. How many blue marbles are there in the bag? 3 marbles

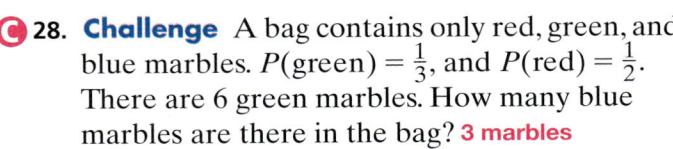
Test Prep and Mixed Review   Practice

Gridded Response

29. A spinner has equal-sized sections numbered 1 through 20. You spin the spinner once. What is the probability, written as a decimal, that you spin a multiple of 5? 0.2

30. The measurements of a wall and its window are shown in the diagram. How much wallpaper, in square feet, is needed to cover the wall? 57

3 ft   7 ft
2 ft
9 ft

31. The ratio of adults to children in a preschool classroom is 1 to 8. If there are 2 adults in the class, how many children are there? 16

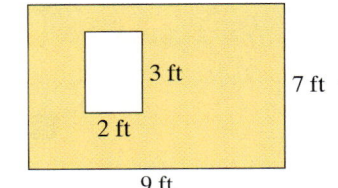
GO for Help

For Exercises	See Lesson
32–35	4-6

Write each improper fraction as a mixed number.

32. $\frac{49}{5}$ $9\frac{4}{5}$
33. $\frac{17}{3}$ $5\frac{2}{3}$
34. $\frac{49}{6}$ $8\frac{1}{6}$
35. $\frac{51}{4}$ $12\frac{3}{4}$

Test Prep

Resources

For additional practice with a variety of test item formats:
- Test-Taking Strategies, p. 507
- Test Prep, p. 511
- Test-Taking Strategies with Transparencies

Alternative Assessment

Each student in a pair draws a picture for a situation similar to that used for Exercises 7–10. Partners take turns asking each other questions about the probabilities in their drawings, including questions about events that are unlikely, likely, equally likely, impossible, and certain. Each partner records the probability as it is asked.

✔ Checkpoint Quiz 1

1. You have three shirts and two pairs of jeans. Construct a sample space of the possible outfits you can wear.

   1. shirt 1, jeans 1
   shirt 1, jeans 2
   shirt 2, jeans 1
   shirt 2, jeans 2
   shirt 3, jeans 1
   shirt 3, jeans 2

2. You roll a number cube and toss a coin. Draw a tree diagram to find the number of possible outcomes. **See margin.**

3. A store sells 8 flavors of frozen yogurt and 6 kinds of toppings. How many desserts can you order with 1 flavor of frozen yogurt and 1 topping? **48 desserts**

A number cube is rolled. Find each probability.

4. $P($less than 3$)$ $\frac{2}{6}$ or $\frac{1}{3}$
5. $P(8)$ **0**
6. $P($5 or 6$)$ $\frac{2}{6}$ or $\frac{1}{3}$

Three coins are tossed. Find each probability.

7. $P($exactly 1 tail$)$ $\frac{3}{8}$
8. $P($exactly 2 heads$)$ $\frac{3}{8}$
9. $P($3 tails$)$ $\frac{1}{8}$

10. $P($all the same$)$ $\frac{2}{8}$ or $\frac{1}{4}$
11. $P($1 or more tails$)$ $\frac{7}{8}$
12. $P($3 heads$)$ $\frac{1}{8}$

13. Alicia gets her hair braided at a salon. She has a choice of 4 styles of braid, 5 ribbon colors, and 3 barrettes. Alicia may choose one style of braid, one ribbon color, and one barrette. How many different hairdos can she get? **60 hairdos**

MATH AT WORK

Board Game Designer

Board Game Designer is a career that could be just right for you if you love games. Game design requires an eye for color and a creative mind.

Game designers also use mathematical skills. In games with spinners or number cubes, designers use probability. To evaluate marketing information about a game, they use data analysis.

Go Online
For: Information on board game designers
Web Code: aqb-2031

487

 **Checkpoint Quiz**

Use this Checkpoint Quiz to check students' understanding of the skills and concepts of Lessons 10-1 through 10-2.

Resources

- All-in-One Teaching Resources Checkpoint Quiz 1
- ExamView CD-ROM
- Success Tracker™ Online Intervention

MATH AT WORK

Board Game Designer

There are many exciting applications of mathematics in the career world. This feature highlights a career choice that should excite students about using their math skills.

Guided Instruction

Have volunteers read each paragraph. After students have finished reading the selection, discuss with the class board games they have played. Then ask questions, such as:
- *How is math used in designing games?*
- *How is it used in playing games?*
- *How does having multiple number cubes in a game affect the probability of getting a favorable roll?*

Examples
1 Experimental Probability
2 Analyzing Experimental Probability

Math Understandings: p. 474C

Math Background

The *experimental probability* of an event is the ratio of the number of times the event occurs to the total number of trials. Experimental probability is based on collected data or observations from experiments, so the results often vary from one experiment to the next. A *fair* coin or spinner has equally likely outcomes.

More Math Background: p. 474C

Lesson Planning and Resources

See p. 474E for a list of the resources that support this lesson.

Bell Ringer Practice

✓ **Check Skills You'll Need**
Use student page, transparency, or PowerPoint. For intervention, direct students to:
Ratios
Lesson 7-1
Extra Skills and Word Problems Practice, Ch. 7

488

✓ Check Skills You'll Need

1. **Vocabulary Review** Describe three ways to write a *ratio*. **See below.**
Write each ratio in simplest form.

2. $\frac{12}{20}$ $\frac{3}{5}$ 3. $\frac{18}{30}$ $\frac{3}{5}$

4. 8 to 30   5. 26 : 40
   $\frac{4}{15}$ $\frac{13}{20}$

GO for Help
Lesson 7-1

🖲 online active math

For: Experimental Probability Activity
Use: Interactive Textbook, 10-3

Check Skills You'll Need

1. You can write a ratio as a fraction, as a phrase using "to", or as an expression using a colon.

What You'll Learn

To find experimental probability

🔊 **New Vocabulary** experimental probability

Why Learn This?

The probabilities of some events are very difficult to calculate. Instead of using a formula, you can conduct an experiment.

To find the experimental probability of winning a tennis tournament, you can collect data for several tennis matches. Each match is a trial. Then you can write the **experimental probability** as a ratio of the number of times an event occurs to the total number of trials.

KEY CONCEPTS **Experimental Probability**

$$P(\text{event}) = \frac{\text{number of times an event occurs}}{\text{total number of trials}}$$

EXAMPLE **Experimental Probability**

① In 20 tennis matches against Jennie, Ai-Ling wins 9 times. What is the experimental probability that Ai-Ling wins a match?

$P(\text{Ai-Ling wins}) = \frac{9}{20}$ ← number of matches Ai-Ling wins
  ← total number of matches

The experimental probability that Ai-Ling wins a match is $\frac{9}{20}$.

✓ Quick Check

1. What is the experimental probability that Jennie wins a match?
   $\frac{11}{20}$

488 Chapter 10 Exploring Probability

Differentiated Instruction Solutions for All Learners

Special Needs L1
Relate finding the experimental probability to conducting any experiment. Provide ample opportunities for students to make predictions and spin spinners or toss coins to conduct their own "trials" and test out their ideas.

learning style: tactile

Below Level L2
Have students make sentences using the words *probability* and *experiment*. Students can compare their sentences with the definition of *experimental probability*.

learning style: verbal

A fair coin or number cube generates equally likely outcomes. If coins, cubes, or spinners are damaged or irregularly made, they may *not* be fair.

GO **Online**

Video Tutor Help
Visit: PHSchool.com
Web Code: aqe-0775

EXAMPLE **Analyzing Experimental Probability**

2 **Fair Games** You and your friend want to play a game, but your only number cube is chipped. To make a fair game, you roll the number cube 60 times. The results are shown in the table below.

Outcome	1	2	3	4	5	6
Number of Times Rolled	16	17	12	8	4	3

Which of the following games seems fair? Explain.

a. You win if the number rolled is 6. Your friend wins if the number rolled is 2.

$$P(6) = \frac{3}{60} \quad \leftarrow \textbf{There are 3 rolls of 6 in 60 trials.}$$

$$P(2) = \frac{17}{60} \quad \leftarrow \textbf{There are 17 rolls of 2 in 60 trials.}$$

You would expect $P(2)$ and $P(6)$ to be about the same with a fair number cube. Since this number cube strongly favors 2, the game seems to be unfair.

b. If the number rolled is even, you win. If it is odd, your friend wins.

$$17 + 8 + 3 = 28 \quad \leftarrow \textbf{Add to find the number of even rolls.}$$

$$16 + 12 + 4 = 32 \quad \leftarrow \textbf{Add to find the number of odd rolls.}$$

$$P(\text{even}) = \frac{28}{60} \quad \leftarrow \textbf{There are 28 even rolls in 60 trials.}$$

$$P(\text{odd}) = \frac{32}{60} \quad \leftarrow \textbf{There are 32 odd rolls in 60 trials.}$$

You would expect $P(\text{even})$ and $P(\text{odd})$ to be about the same with a fair number cube. The probabilities are about the same, so the game seems to be fair.

✓ **Quick Check**

2. Use the data in Example 2. Suppose you win with a 1, 3, or 6, and your friend wins with a 2, 4, or 5. Does this game seem fair? Explain. **Yes; the probabilities are about the same.**

Advanced Learners **L4**
Have students find the experimental probability of rolling each possible sum when rolling a pair of number cubes. Have students make a line plot of their results.

learning style: tactile

English Language Learners **ELL**
Ensure students understand the concept of *fairness* and *evenness*. For example, when they read that a fair coin or number cube generates equally likely outcomes, they may look for outcomes to be exactly the same. Make sure they understand if the outcomes are close, that is fair, too.

learning style: verbal

---

2. Teach

Activity Lab
Use before the lesson.

All in One Teaching Resources
Activity Lab 10-3: Fair or Unfair

Guided Instruction

Example 2
Lead students to the distinctions between theoretical probability and experimental probability:
• Theoretical probability represents what number students might *expect* to roll.
• Experimental probability represents the actual numbers rolled.

PowerPoint
Additional Examples

1 In 30 times at bat, Jan struck out 14 times. What is the experimental probability that Jan will strike out at her next at-bat? ***P*(strike-out)** $= \frac{7}{15}$

2 You and your friend want to play a game with a spinner. The table below shows the results of 120 spins. Which game seems fair? Explain.

Red	Yellow	Blue
58	23	39

a. You win with yellow and your friend wins with blue. **Not fair, the probabilities of** $\frac{23}{120}$ **and** $\frac{39}{120}$ **are not especially close.**

b. You win with red and your friend wins with blue or yellow. **Fair, the probabilities of** $\frac{58}{120}$ **and** $\frac{62}{120}$ **are about the same.**

All in One Teaching Resources
• Daily Notetaking Guide 10-3 **L3**
• Adapted Notetaking 10-3 **L1**

Closure
• *What is experimental probability?* **the ratio of the number of times an event occurs to the total number of trials**

489

3. Practice

Assignment Guide

Check Your Understanding
Go over Exercises 1–5 in class before assigning the Homework Exercises.

Homework Exercises
A	Practice by Example	6–13
B	Apply Your Skills	14–24
C	Challenge	25

Test Prep and
Mixed Review   26–30

Homework Quick Check
To check students' understanding of key skills and concepts, go over Exercises 8, 13, 15, 16, and 24.

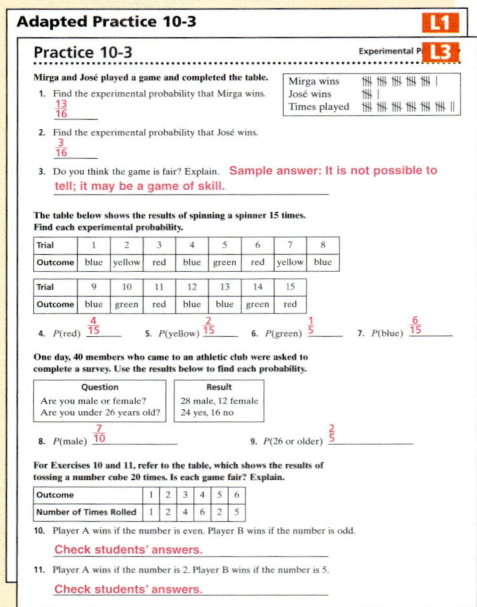
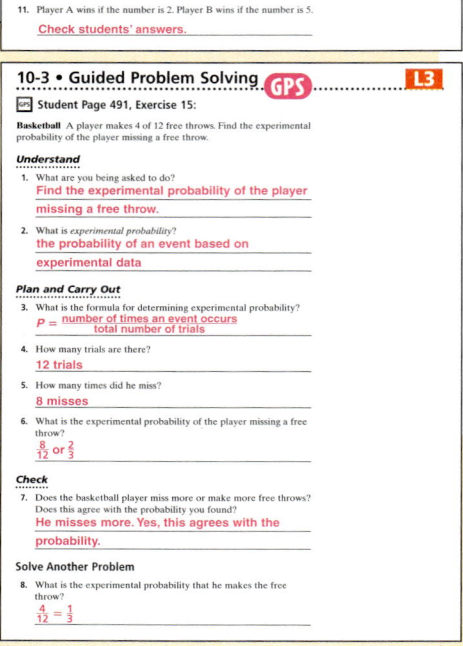
490

✔ Check Your Understanding

1. **Vocabulary** Why is experimental probability called "experimental"? **Experimental probability is found by conducting an experiment.**

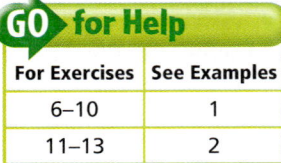
Graphing Calculator Tip
You can use a graphing calculator to simulate flips of a coin by randomly generating the numbers 1 and 2.

2. You toss a coin 20 times and record 8 tails. Find the experimental probability of the outcome tails. $\frac{8}{20}$ or $\frac{2}{5}$

A cooler contains 20 grape drinks, 13 cherry drinks, 8 lime drinks, and 9 lemon drinks. You select a drink at random.

3. Find $P(\text{grape})$.   4. Find $P(not \text{ lemon})$.   5. Find $P(\text{lime})$.

$\frac{20}{50}$ or $\frac{2}{5}$ $\frac{41}{50}$ $\frac{8}{50}$ or $\frac{4}{25}$

Homework Exercises

For more exercises, see Extra Skills and Word Problems.

GO for Help
For Exercises	See Examples
6–10	1
11–13	2

Ⓐ The table shows the results of students playing a video game. Find the experimental probability of each person winning.

Game Results

Player	Blake	Troy	Carla	Kate	Sara	Luis
Number of Wins	11	47	63	17	0	14
Number of Times Game is Played	25	80	294	17	15	30

6. Carla $\frac{3}{14}$ 7. Luis $\frac{7}{15}$ 8. Kate **1**   9. Sara **0**   10. Troy $\frac{47}{80}$

The table below shows the results of tossing a chipped number cube 80 times. Tell whether each game seems fair. Explain.

11–13. See left.

Outcome	1	2	3	4	5	6
Number of Times Rolled	9	12	19	14	25	1

11. No; the experimental probability of rolling an even number is $\frac{27}{80}$.

12. Yes; the experimental probability of rolling a 1, 2, or 3 is $\frac{1}{2}$.

13. No; the experimental probability of rolling a 5 or 6 is $\frac{13}{40}$.

11. If even, then Player A wins. Otherwise, Player B wins.

12. If 1, 2, or 3, then Player A wins. Otherwise, Player B wins.

13. If 5 or 6, then Player A wins. Otherwise, Player B wins.

Ⓑ GPS  14. **Guided Problem Solving** In your first 16 times at bat in softball, you get 6 hits. Find the experimental probability of getting a hit. Predict the number of hits you will get in 40 at-bats, if you keep hitting at the same rate. $\frac{3}{8}$, or 0.375; 15 hits
  • Find the experimental probability for the first 16 at-bats.
  • Multiply the probability by the total number of trials.

GO Online
Homework Video Tutor

Visit: PHSchool.com
Web Code: aqe-1003

24a. $\frac{1}{12}$

b. *P*(3) is the theoretical probability of getting a 3. Experimental probability tells how many times 3 was actually rolled.

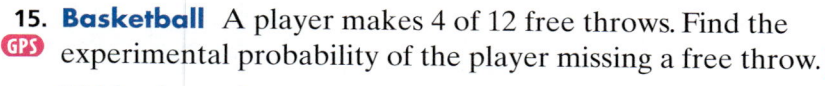

15. Basketball A player makes 4 of 12 free throws. Find the experimental probability of the player missing a free throw. $\frac{2}{3}$

16. Writing in Math You and your friend want to play a game that uses a spinner with five sections. Explain how you can use experimental probability to determine if the spinner is fair.
Spin it several times to see if it lands on each section about the same number of times.

Data Collection Roll a pair of number cubes 50 times. Record your results. Find each experimental probability.
17–22. Check students' work.

17. $P(1 \text{ and } 1)$ **18.** $P(\text{doubles})$ **19.** $P(\text{even and even})$

20. $P(\text{odd and odd})$ **21.** $P(2 \text{ and } 3)$ **22.** $P(4 \text{ and } 5)$

23. Snowboarding You and a friend go snowboarding. You make it down the mountain before your friend 13 times out of 20. What is the experimental probability that you make it down the mountain first? That your friend makes it down first? $\frac{13}{20}; \frac{7}{20}$

24. a. You roll a number cube 12 times and roll a 3 once. Find the experimental probability of rolling a 3. **a–b. See above left.**

   b. Reasoning You calculate the probability of rolling 3 on a number cube as $\frac{1}{6}$. Explain why your calculation is different from the experimental probability you found in part (a).

C 25. Challenge A dartboard has an area of 40 square inches. In the center is a triangle. In 50 random throws, you hit the triangle 30 times. Estimate the area of the triangle. **24 in.²**

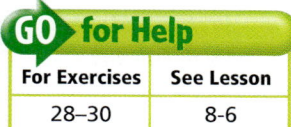
Test Prep and Mixed Review   **Practice**

Multiple Choice

26. A student rolls a number cube 40 times. The number 3 appears 8 times. What is the experimental probability of rolling a 3? **C**

   Ⓐ 8%   Ⓑ 12.5%   Ⓒ 0.20   Ⓓ $\frac{1}{4}$

27. The Yangs plan to remodel their kitchen. The kitchen is 12 feet wide. The scale of the floor plan for the kitchen is 1 inch to 8 feet. What is the width of the kitchen on the plan? **J**

   Ⓕ 1 in.   Ⓖ $1\frac{1}{4}$ in.   Ⓗ $1\frac{3}{8}$ in.   Ⓙ $1\frac{1}{2}$ in.

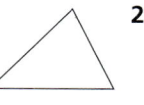
GO for Help

For Exercises	See Lesson
28–30	8-6

Tell whether the figures are congruent or similar.

28. similar   **29.**   **30.** similar
   congruent

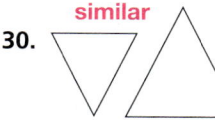

Online lesson quiz, PHSchool.com, **Web Code:** aqa-1003

Alternative Assessment

Pairs of students flip two coins twenty times and record the results. Partners find the experimental probability of two heads, two tails, and one head and one tail. Then all pairs combine their results and find the total experimental probabilities.

Test Prep

Resources
For additional practice with a variety of test item formats:
• Test-Taking Strategies, p. 507
• Test Prep, p. 511
• Test-Taking Strategies with Transparencies

---

4. Assess & Reteach

Lesson Quiz

Find the experimental probability that each person makes a foul shot in basketball.

Player	Ayala	Sanjay	Jose
Baskets	0	14	8
Attempts	12	16	12

1. Jose $\frac{2}{3}$ **2.** Ayala **0**

3. Sanjay $\frac{7}{8}$

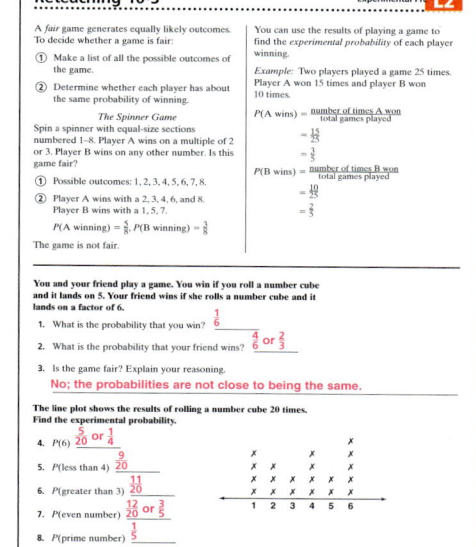

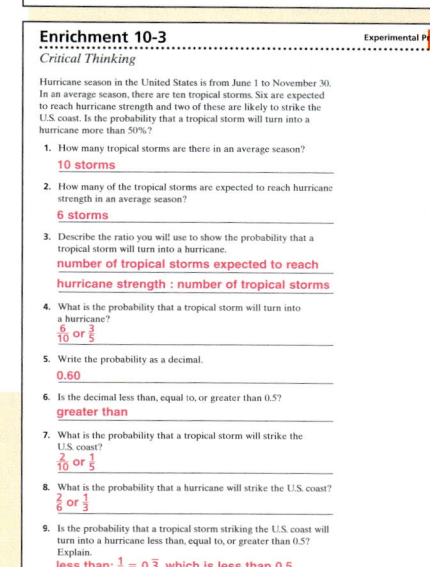

Experimental and Theoretical Probabilities

Students perform experiments to determine probability. This will extend the skills they learned in Lesson 10-3.

Guided Instruction

Before beginning the Activity, review the definition of experimental probability. Ask questions such as:

- *What is the difference between experimental probability and theoretical probability?* **Theoretical probability determines probability by using a formula while experimental probability determines probability by conducting an experiment.**

- *Why do theoretical and experimental probability differ?* **The results of an experiment may not be the same as the theoretical probability. For example, if you flip a coin five times, P(heads) = 50%, but it can't be 50% experimentally.**

Activity

Have students work in pairs to answer questions and take turns performing experiments, such as flipping the coin and surveying classmates, and recording results.

Differentiated Instruction

Advanced Learners **L4**
Have students determine the experimental probability of the second child being a girl when the first is a boy.

Resources

- 2 coins

Experimental and Theoretical Probabilities

When you calculated probability in Lesson 10-2, you found *theoretical* probability. Theoretical probability tells you what will *most likely* happen, but the actual outcome of an experiment is not always the most likely outcome.

ACTIVITY

You can calculate the theoretical probability that both children in a family with two children are girls. You can compare this prediction with the results of both an experiment and a survey.

1. List the possible outcomes for a family with exactly two children. Assume that the chance of having a boy child is equal to the chance of a girl child. Find the theoretical probability that both children are girls. Enter the probability in the first column of the table below. **BB, BG, GB, GG; $\frac{1}{4}$; 25%**

	Theoretical Probability	Experimental Probability	
		Experiment	Survey
Fraction			
Percent			

2. Toss two coins together 20 times. Record your results using a table as shown below. **2–5. Check students' work.**

Coin Toss

Coin 1	Coin 2

Let heads represent a girl.   Let tails represent a boy.

3. Find the experimental probability of having two girls. Enter the probability in the second column of the table in Step 1.

4. Survey *all* of your classmates to determine how many families have exactly two children. Of those families, how many have two girls? Enter the data in the table.

5. Calculate and compare the percents in the bottom row of the table. Explain why the values may not be exactly the same.

High-Use Academic Words

High-use academic words are words that you will see often in textbooks and on tests. These words are not math vocabulary terms, but knowing them will help you to succeed in mathematics.

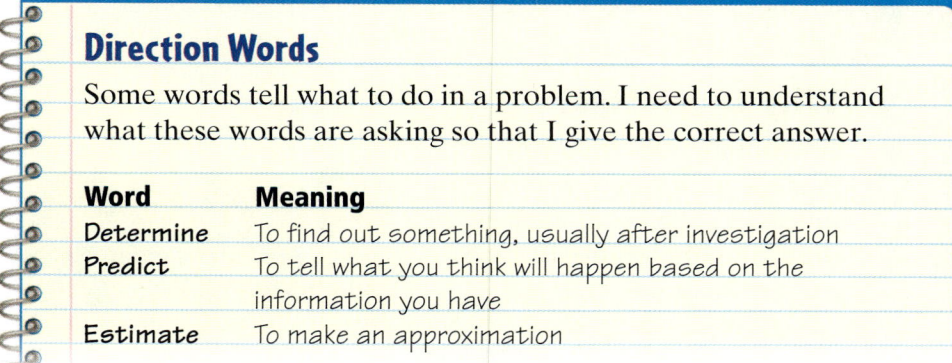

Direction Words

Some words tell what to do in a problem. I need to understand what these words are asking so that I give the correct answer.

Word	Meaning
Determine	To find out something, usually after investigation
Predict	To tell what you think will happen based on the information you have
Estimate	To make an approximation

Exercises

1–3. Check students' work.

1. Determine what you will wear to school tomorrow.

2. Predict what you will wear to school in May.

3. Estimate the number of pairs of shoes you have in your closet.

Use the table at the right for Exercises 4–6.

4. Determine the probability of eating breakfast. $\frac{3}{4}$

5. Of 75 students, predict how many students eat breakfast. **about 56 students**

6. Of 81 students, estimate how many students eat breakfast. **about 60 students**

Breakfast Survey

Do You Eat Breakfast?	Percent
Yes	75
No	25

7. **Word Knowledge** Think about the word *random*.   **7a–c. Check students' work.**
   a. Choose the letter for how well you know the word.
      A. I know its meaning.
      B. I've seen it, but I don't know its meaning.
      C. I don't know it.
   b. **Research** Look up and write the definition of *random*.
   c. Use the word in a sentence involving mathematics.

Vocabulary Builder

High-Use Academic Words

Students become familiar with words that are not strictly math related, but may occur frequently in their texts.

Guided Instruction

Explain that, although these words do not apply only to math, they are used frequently in that context. Have a volunteer read each word and its definition aloud. Then ask:
- *What is another way to say "I am going to go through problem solving steps and find the answer?"* **I am going to determine the answer.**
- *How would you use* predict *in relation to probability?* **Probability can help you predict what will happen.**
- *How could you use* estimate *in a sentence?* **Answers will vary.**

Exercises

Have students work on the Exercises. When they have completed the Exercises, allow them to check their answers with a partner and correct their answers.

Differentiated Instruction

Below Level   **L2**

Have students practice using these words in sentences in a non-mathematical context before proceeding with the Exercises. If necessary, help them look the words up in a dictionary to help them understand the meanings.

Making Predictions From Data

Objective
To make predictions using probabilities and samples

Examples
1 Making a Prediction
2 Application: Quality Control

Math Understandings: p. 474D

✓ Check Skills You'll Need

1. **Vocabulary Review**
Why is $\frac{2}{3} > \frac{4}{9}$ not a *proportion*?
See below.
Solve each proportion.

2. $\frac{2}{3} = \frac{4}{x}$ 6

3. $\frac{n}{5} = \frac{10}{25}$ 2

4. $\frac{15}{50} = \frac{z}{10}$ 3

 **for Help**
Lesson 7-4

What You'll Learn

To make predictions using probabilities and samples

◀) **New Vocabulary** population, sample

Why Learn This?

Probabilities can help you make a prediction about the outcome of an event, such as predicting the gender of each child in a family.

To predict the number of times an event will occur, multiply the probability of the event by the total number of trials.

$$P(\text{event}) \times \begin{array}{c}\text{total number} \\ \text{of trials}\end{array} = \begin{array}{c}\text{number of predicted} \\ \text{successes}\end{array}$$

A prediction cannot guarantee what will actually occur.

EXAMPLE   Making a Prediction

1 For a family with two children, suppose there is a 25% chance that both children are boys. Out of 72 families with two children, how many are likely to have two boys?

$$P(\text{two boys}) \times \begin{array}{c}\text{number of} \\ \text{families}\end{array} = \begin{array}{c}\text{number of families} \\ \text{with 2 boys}\end{array}$$

$$\frac{1}{4} \quad \times \quad 72 \quad = \quad 18 \quad \leftarrow \text{Write 25% as } \frac{1}{4}. \text{ Then multiply.}$$

About 18 of the families are likely to have two boys.

 **for Help**

For help with multiplying fractions by whole numbers, go to Lesson 6-1, Example 2.

✓ Quick Check

1. At an arcade, Juanita plays a game 20 times. She has a 30% probability of winning. How many times can she expect to win?
6 times

Math Background

A population is a group that you are interested in. Because it is generally difficult to collect information from every member in a large group, samples are investigated. Using probabilities based on the sample, predictions about the entire population can be made. However, to make accurate predictions, the sample selected must be representative of the population. This often involves randomly selecting the sample so that each member of the population is equally likely to be selected.

More Math Background: p. 474D

Lesson Planning and Resources

See p. 474E for a list of the resources that support this lesson.

 **Bell Ringer Practice**

✓ **Check Skills You'll Need**
Use student page, transparency, or PowerPoint. For intervention, direct students to:
Solving Proportions
Lesson 7-4
Extra Skills and Word Problems Practice, Ch. 7

Differentiated Instruction **Solutions for All Learners**

Special Needs **L1**
For Example 1, have students draw 72 stick figures or tallies, each one representing a family. Remind them that 25% is the same as $\frac{1}{4}$ of all the families. Have them divide their stick figures into 4 equal groups, and count the number in one group. They should have 18 in each group.
learning style: visual

Below Level **L2**
In Quick Check 1, students can estimate to check for reasonableness. Ask: *Is 30% more or less than 50%?* **less** *Did Juanita win more or less than half her games?* **less**
learning style: verbal

A **population** is a group about which you want information. A **sample** is a part of the population. You use a sample and proportions to make predictions about the population.

EXAMPLE **Application: Quality Control**

2 A company makes 15,000 toy robots. The company inspects 200 robots at random. The sample has 5 faulty robots. Predict how many of the 15,000 robots are likely to be faulty.

Words $\dfrac{\text{number faulty in sample}}{\text{total number in sample}} = \dfrac{\text{number faulty in population}}{\text{total number in population}}$

Let n = the number of faulty robots in 15,000 robots.

Proportion $\dfrac{5}{200} = \dfrac{n}{15{,}000}$

$200n = 5 \cdot 15{,}000$ ← Write the cross products.

$200n = 75{,}000$ ← Simplify.

$\dfrac{200n}{200} = \dfrac{75{,}000}{200}$ ← Divide each side by 200.

$n = 375$ ← Simplify.

It is likely that about 375 toy robots are faulty.

✓ Quick Check

2. Suppose 1,000 toy robots are selected at random from 20,000 robots, and 54 robots are found faulty. Predict how many of the 20,000 robots are likely to be faulty. **1,080 toy robots**

✓ Check Your Understanding

1. **Vocabulary** How is a sample related to a population?
   A sample is a part of a population.

2. **Writing in Math** What is the advantage of taking a random sample instead of surveying an entire population? **Answers may vary. Sample: You can save much time and money.**

3. A manufacturer finds that 50% of the light bulbs in a sample are defective. How many bulbs might be defective in 80 bulbs?
   Ⓐ 30   Ⓑ 40   Ⓒ 50   Ⓓ 60 **B**

4. You survey at random 40 people who saw a movie. Thirty-eight of them say that the movie was excellent. There were 600 people in the theater. How many of the 600 people are likely to think that the movie was excellent? **570 people**

2. Teach

Activity Lab

Use before the lesson.

All in One Teaching Resources

Activity Lab 10-4: Making Predictions from Data

Guided Instruction

Example 2

Help students understand the terms *population* and *sample*. Use plain language to explain that a sample is part of a population, much like a *part* is part of a whole.

PowerPoint
Additional Examples

1 Kiko bought 35 raffle tickets. Each ticket has a 20% probability of winning a prize. How many prizes should he expect to win? **7 prizes**

2 A random sample shows that 6 wallets out of 400 are defective. Predict how many wallets out of 15,000 will be defective. **225 wallets**

All in One Teaching Resources
- Daily Notetaking Guide 10-4 **L3**
- Adapted Notetaking 10-4 **L1**

Closure

- *How can you make predictions using the probability of an event?* **Multiply the total number of trials by the probability of the event.**
- *How does a sample relate to its population?* **The sample is a part of the population that can be used to make a prediction about the entire population.**

Advanced Learners **L4**
Is the United States census a sample of the population? Explain.
Answers may vary. Sample: No, because the entire population is polled.

learning style: verbal

English Language Learners **ELL**
Write the terms *probability, experimental probability, sample, random,* and *population* on the board. Read each definition, without using the term, and have students talk with a partner to determine what word matches the definition.

learning style: verbal

Homework Exercises

Assignment Guide

Check Your Understanding
Go over Exercises 1–4 in class before assigning the Homework Exercises.

Homework Exercises
A	Practice by Example	5–15
B	Apply Your Skills	16–22
C	Challenge	23
	Test Prep and Mixed Review	24–28

Homework Quick Check
To check students' understanding of key skills and concepts, go over Exercises 6, 14, 18, 19, and 22.

Differentiated Instruction Resources

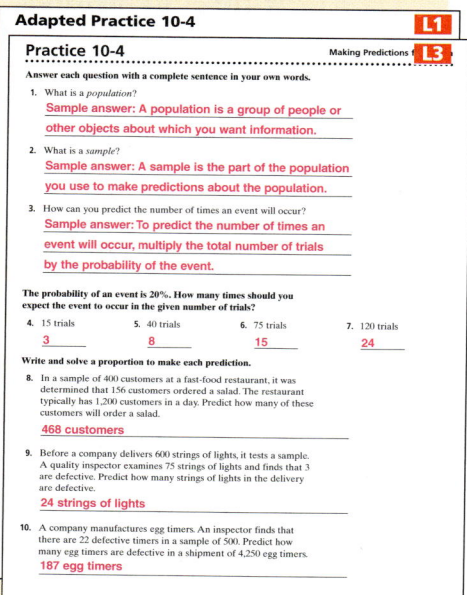

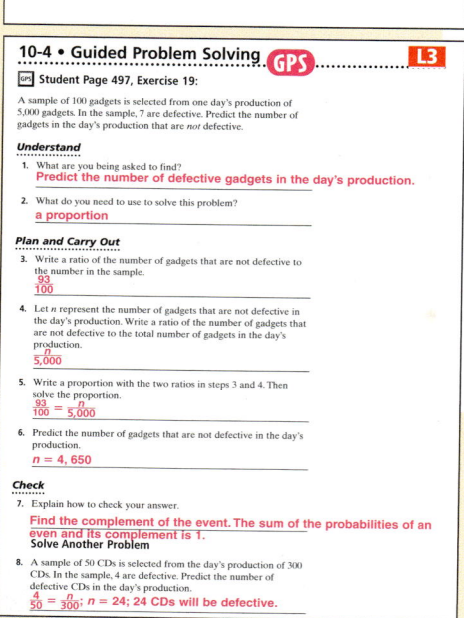

496

Homework Exercises

For more exercises, see Extra Skills and Word Problems.

GO for Help

For Exercises	See Examples
5–10	1
11–15	2

A The probability of winning a game is 40%. How many times should you expect to win if you play each number of times?

5. 5 times **2**

6. 10 times **4**

7. 15 times **6**

8. 30 times **12**

9. 85 times **34**

10. 120 times **48**

11. Art A mayor wants opinions from students about murals displayed in City Hall. He selects a random sample of 120 students from 18,000 students in the city. Twenty-two of the students surveyed like Mural A. Predict how many of the 18,000 students will like Mural A. **3,300 students**

A company makes shirts, pants, belts, and socks. It makes 24,000 of each item. For each sample, predict the number of items likely to be defective.

12. 6 defects in 500 shirts
288 shirts

13. 3 defects in 160 pairs of socks
450 pairs of socks

14. 2 defects in 250 belts
192 belts

15. 3 defects in 10 pairs of pants
7,200 pairs of pants

B GPS **16. Guided Problem Solving** Park rangers are planning programs at a national park. They conduct a survey of 200 families at the park. The results are in the table below. **camping, 6,552 families; hiking, 5,616; fishing, 3,432 families**

Reason for Visit	Number of Families
Camping	84
Hiking	72
Fishing	44

The total number of families visiting the park each summer is 15,600. Predict the number of families that will come to the park for each activity in the table.
- **Make a Plan** Write and solve a proportion for each activity.
- **Check the Answer** Since the results for all 200 families are in the table, the sum of your answers should be 15,600.

GO Online
Homework Video Tutor
Visit: PHSchool.com
Web Code: aqe-1004

17. Number Sense Suppose you take a sample of 15 pieces of colored fruit snacks and a sample of 60 pieces of colored fruit snacks from one day's production. Which sample is more likely to give you a prediction closer to the actual number of each color? Explain. **60 pieces; experimental probability is more accurate with more trials.**

18. Tour A teacher asks 70 random students, "Did you see the electricity exhibit?" Fourteen answer yes. If 1,000 students went on the trip, how many likely saw the exhibit? **200 students**

19. A sample of 100 gadgets is selected from one day's production of 5,000 gadgets. In the sample, 7 are defective. Predict the number of gadgets in the day's production that are *not* defective. **4,650 gadgets**

A computer dart game displays random points to represent darts being thrown. The areas of each section are shown.

- black: 1 in.^{2}
- blue: 3 in.^{2}
- yellow: 6 in.^{2}
- orange: 10 in.^{2}

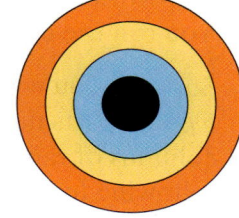

20. $\frac{6}{20}$ or $\frac{3}{10}$

20. What is the probability that a point is in the yellow section? **See left.**

21. What is the probability that a point is in the orange or yellow section? $\frac{16}{20}$ or $\frac{4}{5}$

22. What is the probability that a point is *not* in the black section? $\frac{19}{20}$

C 23. Challenge A jar holds 80 marbles that are red, green, or blue. The probability of picking a red marble at random is $\frac{1}{5}$. Find the number of red marbles you would need to add to the jar to change the probability to $\frac{1}{2}$. **48 red marbles**

Test Prep and Mixed Review **Practice**

Multiple Choice

24. The ratio of adults to children in a musical is 1 to 3. Which of the following could be the numbers of adults and children in the musical? **A**

Ⓐ 25 adults, 75 children
Ⓑ 75 adults, 25 children
Ⓒ 20 adults, 80 children
Ⓓ 80 adults, 20 children

25. You want to paint the walls of your room. A gallon of paint covers 400 square feet. Which method should you use to find how many gallons of paint you need? **F**

Ⓕ Find the area of the walls and divide by 400.
Ⓖ Find the perimeter of the walls and divide by 400.
Ⓗ Find the area of the walls and multiply by 400.
Ⓙ Find the perimeter of the walls and multiply by 400.

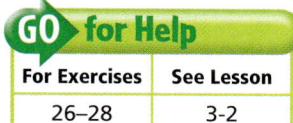

For Exercises	See Lesson
26–28	3-2

Evaluate each expression for $a = 3$, $b = 1.5$, and $c = 2$.

26. $3(a - 2)$ **3**

27. $7a \div c$ **10.5**

28. $1 + 4b$ **7**

Online lesson quiz, PHSchool.com, Web Code: aqa-1004

10-4 Making Predictions From Data **497**

Alternative Assessment

Students in pairs agree on a probability other than 40%. Partners refer to Exercises 5–10 and together find how many times they should expect to win using the new probability.

Test Prep

Resources

For additional practice with a variety of test item formats:
- Test-Taking Strategies, p. 507
- Test Prep, p. 511
- Test-Taking Strategies with Transparencies

---

4. Assess & Reteach

Lesson Quiz

The probability of Derek getting a hit when he comes to bat is 30%. How many hits should he expect to get if he comes to bat the following number of times?

1. 450 times **135**
2. 1,200 times **360**
3. 700 times **210**

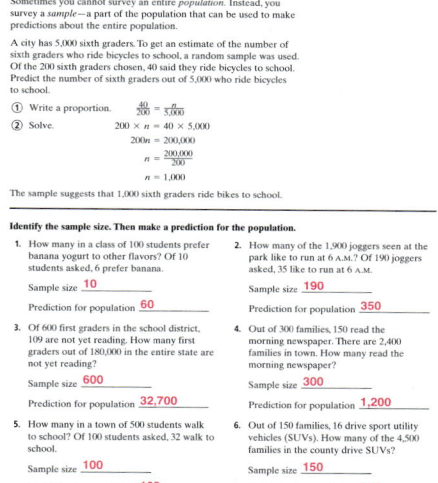

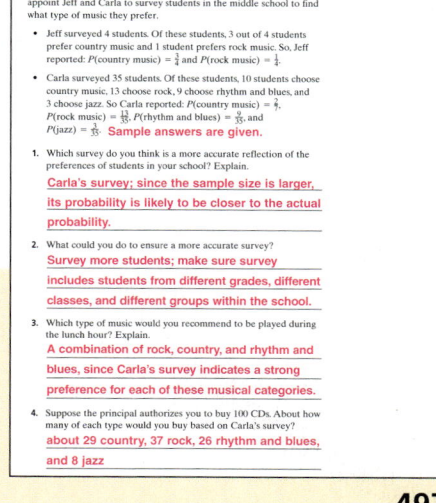

Simulations

This Activity is an extension of Lesson 10-4. It introduces students to the use of spreadsheet software, a useful and efficient tool for simulating events.

Guided Instruction

Elicit from students some of the advantages of using a computer simulation to do a probability experiment. Guide them to appreciate that spreadsheets can quickly generate a large number of trials using random numbers. Spreadsheets also can keep track of the results.

Error Prevention!

Warn students to be careful of accidentally having the computer recalculate their results before they have completed recording them.

Teaching Tip

Remind students that when using a computer to simulate a situation, the simulation is still only a model. The results generated by the spreadsheet are therefore limited to the appropriateness of the model.

Exercises

Have partners work together on the exercises. Circulate about the room as they work, checking their formulas. Have pairs share and discuss their results with classmates.

Resources

- computer
- any spreadsheet program
- Classroom Aid 4

Simulations

Sometimes it is difficult to collect data. Instead, you may be able to use a simulation. A **simulation** of a real-world situation is a model used to find probabilities. You can use computer spreadsheets to do simulations.

Suppose you want to simulate 25 spins of a spinner with 5 equal parts numbered 1 to 5. You can make rows and columns of random integers from 1 to 5 by entering the following formula in each cell.

$$=\text{RANDBETWEEN} (1, 5)$$

lowest number to choose from ↗   ↖ highest number to choose from

You can use formulas to count results automatically. To count all the 3's in the 25 squares shown, you enter

$$=\text{COUNTIF} (A1:E5, 3)$$

upper left cell location ↗ ↗ ↖ number to count

lower right cell location

According to the simulation, the experimental probability of spinning a 3 is $\frac{4}{25}$.

Random Numbers

	A	B	C	D	E	F
1	3	4	2	1	4	
2	2	4	4	2	4	
3	5	3	5	4	5	
4	4	3	1	4	2	
5	3	1	5	1	5	
6						
7						
8	Number of 3's:					
9	4					

ACTIVITY

1. **Basketball** Michelle plays basketball. She misses one free throw out of every three attempts.
   a. To simulate the probability of a successful free throw, let $1 = $ miss, $2 = $ make, and $3 = $ make. Write a spreadsheet formula to generate random numbers for this simulation.
   b. Use a spreadsheet to count the 1's in the first 6 rows.
   c. Out of 30 numbers, how many 1's would you expect?
   d. Generate 30 random numbers from 1 to 3. Find the experimental probability that Michelle misses a free throw.

   1a. $= $ **RANDBETWEEN(1,3)**

   b. $= $ **COUNTIF(A1:E6,1)**

   c. about 10 ones

   d. Check students' work.

2. a. **Writing in Math** Suppose you guess random answers to three true-or-false questions. Describe a simulation to find the probability that you answer each question correctly.
   b. Conduct the simulation in part (a). What is the probability that you answer each question correctly?

   2a–b. Check students' work.

Tristan rolls a number cube 20 times. He rolls 4 twos, 3 fours, and 5 sixes. Find the experimental probability of each event.

1. rolling a 2 $\frac{4}{20}$ or $\frac{1}{5}$

2. rolling a 4 $\frac{3}{20}$

3. rolling an even number $\frac{12}{20}$ or $\frac{3}{5}$

4. rolling an odd number $\frac{8}{20}$ or $\frac{2}{5}$

5. A pencil is dropped 20 times. It points left 8 times. Find the experimental probability that the pencil points left. $\frac{8}{20}$ or $\frac{2}{5}$

6. In a town survey, 40 out of 50 men say they eat lunch. The town has 35,000 men. Predict the number of men who eat lunch. **28,000 men**

7. In a pet store's survey, 45 of 60 customers own a cat. How many of 420 customers are likely to own a cat? **315 customers**

8. A company has 20,000 hats. In a random sample of 80 hats, 3 are defective. Overall, how many are likely to be defective? **750 hats**

MATH GAMES

Probability Race

What You'll Need

- a number cube
- a strip of paper with 12 spaces, as shown at the right
- two different coins or chips for markers

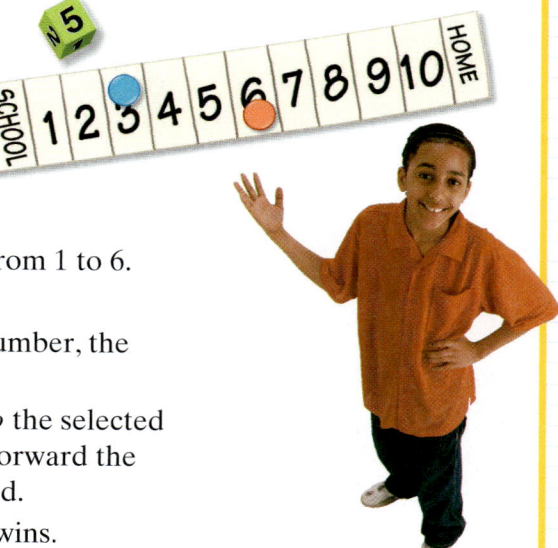

How To Play

- A player starts a turn by selecting a number from 1 to 6.
- The player rolls the number cube.
- If the number rolled is *less than* the selected number, the player does not move his or her marker.
- If the number rolled is *greater than or equal to* the selected number, the player moves his or her marker forward the number of spaces equal to the number selected.
- Players take turns. The first to land on home wins.

499

✓ Checkpoint Quiz

Use this Checkpoint Quiz to check students' understanding of the skills and concepts of Lessons 10-3 through 10-4.

Resources

- All-in-One Teaching Resources Checkpoint Quiz 2
- ExamView CD-ROM
- Success Tracker™ Online Intervention

MATH GAMES

Probability Race

This game will reinforce concepts of probability in everyday situations.

Guided Instruction

Have a volunteer read the rules. Explain that selecting lower numbers will make them more likely to move, but they will not move very far, and selecting higher numbers will make them less likely to move, but they will move further if they do move.

Resources

- number cube
- paper strip in 12 sections labeled home, school, and the numbers 1–10
- two coins or other markers

Objective
To find probabilities of independent events

Examples
1   Identifying Independent Events
2   Probability of an Independent Event
3   Application: Quiz Show

Math Understandings: p. 474D

Math Background

A *compound event* consists of two or more separate events. Two events are *independent* if the outcome of one event has no effect on the probability of the other event. The probabilities of independent events can be multiplied to find the probability of the related compound event.

More Math Background: p. 474D

Lesson Planning and Resources

See p. 474E for a list of the resources that support this lesson.

Bell Ringer Practice

✓ **Check Skills You'll Need**
Use student page, transparency, or PowerPoint. For intervention, direct students to:
Multiplying Fractions
Lesson 6-1
Extra Skills and Word Problems Practice, Ch. 6

500

10-5   Independent Events

✓ Check Skills You'll Need

1. **Vocabulary Review** When you multiply fractions, do you need to find a *common denominator*? **no**

Find the product.

2. $\frac{3}{4} \times \frac{3}{4}$ $\frac{9}{16}$ 3. $\frac{2}{3} \times \frac{1}{7}$ $\frac{2}{21}$

4. $\frac{5}{9} \times \frac{2}{5}$ $\frac{2}{9}$ 5. $\frac{5}{6} \times \frac{3}{10}$ $\frac{1}{4}$

 **for Help**
Lesson 6-1

What You'll Learn

To find probabilities of independent events

🔊 **New Vocabulary** independent events, compound event

Why Learn This?

In many games, you can plan a winning strategy by finding the probability of two or more events happening.

Suppose you draw a marble from the bag.

$$P(\text{blue}) = \frac{4}{6}, \text{ or } \frac{2}{3} \qquad P(\text{red}) = \frac{2}{6}, \text{ or } \frac{1}{3}$$

If you return or replace the marble, mix the marbles, and draw again, the probabilities do not change. If the occurrence of one event does not affect the probability of another event, then the two events are **independent events.**

EXAMPLE   Identifying Independent Events

1 Decide whether the given events are independent. Explain.

   a. You toss a coin twice. The first toss is heads. Then you make a second toss.

      Independent: The first toss has no effect on the second toss.

   b. You select a colored pen from a box of assorted colored pens. Your brother selects one after you.

      Not independent: After you select one pen, there will be one pen fewer in the box. The first selection affects the second selection.

1. Not independent; after selecting the first card, there is one card fewer from which to choose. The first selection affects the second selection.

✓ Quick Check

See left.

1. You select a card from a deck of cards. Without replacing it, you select another card. Are the events independent? Explain.

Differentiated Instruction   Solutions for All Learners

Special Needs **L1**
When possible, provide marbles or cards for students to try out what happens when you replace or do not replace a colored piece after drawing. If you do not have materials, have students cut circles from colored paper and pretend they are marbles in a bag.

learning style: visual

Below Level **L2**
Let students draw the numbers 1 to 10 from a bag, trying to draw the number 1. Try once with replacement and once without to demonstrate not independent events.

learning style: tactile

A **compound event** consists of two or more separate events. When events are independent, you can find probability with a formula.

> **KEY CONCEPTS** **Probability of Independent Events**
>
> If A and B are independent events, then
>
> $$P(A, \text{then } B) = P(A) \times P(B).$$

EXAMPLE Probability of Independent Events

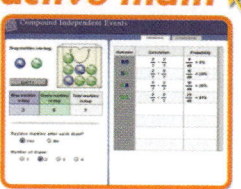

Online active math

For: Independent Events Activity
Use: Interactive Textbook, 10-5

2 You have a bag containing three red cubes and two yellow cubes. You draw a cube from the bag and replace it. Then you draw a second cube. Find the probability that both cubes are red.

The events are independent. $P(\text{red})$ is $\frac{3}{5}$.

$$P(\text{red, then red}) = \frac{3}{5} \times \frac{3}{5} \quad \leftarrow \text{Use the formula.}$$

$$= \frac{9}{25} \quad \leftarrow \text{Multiply.}$$

The probability that both cubes are red is $\frac{9}{25}$.

✓ Quick Check

2. For the situation in Example 2, find $P(\text{yellow, then yellow})$. $\frac{4}{25}$

You can multiply to find the probability of more than two events.

EXAMPLE Application: Quiz Show

3 Three questions are asked during a quiz show. Each question has choices A, B, C, and D. You guess each answer at random. What is the probability that you answer all questions correctly?

For each question, the probability of guessing the answer is $\frac{1}{4}$.

$$P(\text{three correct answers}) = \frac{1}{4} \times \frac{1}{4} \times \frac{1}{4}$$

$$= \frac{1}{64}$$

The probability that you answer all three questions correctly is $\frac{1}{64}$.

✓ Quick Check

3. You guess at random the answers of four true-or-false questions. What is the probability that all four answers are correct? $\frac{1}{16}$

Advanced Learners **L4**
Have students find the definition of *mutually exclusive*. Ask: *What is the probability that two mutually exclusive events occur simultaneously?* 0

learning style: verbal

English Language Learners **ELL**
Make sure to include the terms *with replacement* and *without replacement* when reviewing the vocabulary for this lesson. Students should know that putting something back (a marble, for example) after pulling it means that it is *with replacement*.

learning style: verbal

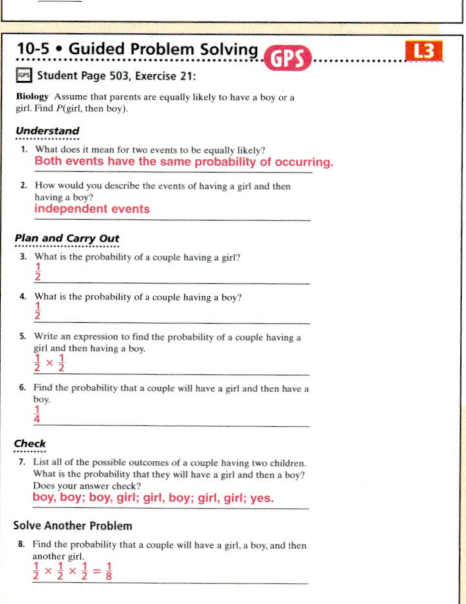

Check Your Understanding

1. **Vocabulary** Rolling a number cube and picking a number card (are, are not) independent events. **are**

2. **Mental Math** Find the probability of rolling the number 5 on a number cube and then tossing heads on a coin. $\frac{1}{12}$

3. **Writing in Math** Give examples of two events that are independent and two events that are not independent.
Check students' work.

Homework Exercises

For more exercises, see Extra Skills and Word Problems.

For Exercises	See Examples
4–6	1
7–12	2
13–16	3

GO for Help

A **Decide whether the events are independent. Explain your answer.**

4. You have nickels and dimes in your pocket. You take out a dime at random and spend it. Then you take out a second coin at random. **Not independent; the first pick affects the second, because the number of dimes will be 1 fewer.**

5. You roll five number cubes and the numbers rolled are 1, 2, 3, 4, and 5. **Independent; none of the rolls has an effect on another.**

6. A teacher selects one student and then another student. **Not independent; once the teacher selects a student, there is one student fewer from which to choose.**

A bag contains 3 red, 5 blue, and 2 green marbles. Marbles are drawn twice with replacement. Find each probability.

7. both red $\frac{9}{100}$

8. both green $\frac{4}{100}$ or $\frac{1}{25}$

9. both blue $\frac{25}{100}$ or $\frac{1}{4}$

10. red, then blue $\frac{15}{100}$ or $\frac{3}{20}$

11. blue, then red $\frac{15}{100}$ or $\frac{3}{20}$

12. red, then green $\frac{6}{100}$ or $\frac{3}{50}$

A number cube is rolled three times. What is the probability of each sequence of rolls?

13. even, even, odd $\frac{1}{8}$

14. 3, 4, 5 $\frac{1}{216}$

15. each less than 5 $\frac{64}{216}$ or $\frac{8}{27}$

16. An envelope contains two $1 bills and four $5 bills. You select three bills at random with replacement. What is the probability of choosing only $5 bills? $\frac{64}{216}$ or $\frac{8}{27}$

B **GPS**  17. **Guided Problem Solving** A new restaurant offers a choice of 4 main dishes and 3 desserts. You randomly choose a main dish and a dessert. What is the probability of choosing both the main dish and the dessert that are the chef's favorites? $\frac{1}{12}$
   - Are the two events independent?
   - What two probabilities can you use to find the answer?

One letter is drawn from the set below and then replaced. Find each probability.

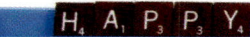

18. P(H, then U) **19.** P(Y, then S) **20.** P(A, then vowel)
$\frac{1}{144}$ $\frac{1}{48}$ $\frac{1}{48}$

21. **Biology** Assume that parents are equally likely to have a boy or **GPS** a girl. Find P(girl, then boy). $\frac{1}{4}$

22. **Bells** Each day three church bells are rung in a random order. What is the probability that the smallest bell rings first three days in a row? $\frac{1}{27}$

Suppose you spin the spinner twice.

23. Is the outcome of the second spin independent of the outcome of the first spin? Explain.
Yes; the first spin has no effect on the second spin.

24. **Choose a Method** Find the probability that both spins will be yellow. $\frac{4}{25}$

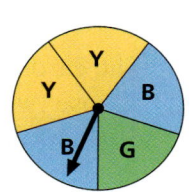

C **25.** **Challenge** A bag of five apples contains three ripe apples and two rotten apples. If a ripe apple is selected first, what is the probability that a second apple selected is rotten? $\frac{1}{2}$

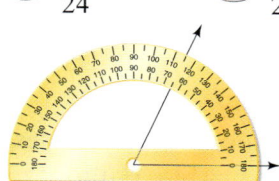
Test Prep and Mixed Review **Practice**

Multiple Choice

26. Jerry's class has 24 students. His teacher puts each student's name in a hat. One name is drawn at random from the hat. What is the probability that Jerry's name will NOT be drawn?

Ⓐ $\frac{1}{24}$ Ⓑ $\frac{1}{23}$ Ⓒ $\frac{23}{24}$ Ⓓ $\frac{24}{23}$ **C**

27. Find the measure of the angle to the nearest degree. **F**

Ⓕ 65° Ⓗ 115°
Ⓖ 75° Ⓙ 125°

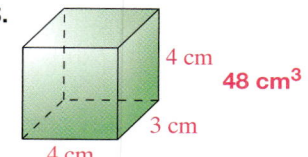

Find the volume of each rectangular prism.

28.
4 cm
3 cm
4 cm
48 cm³

29.
2 cm
3 cm
8 cm
48 cm³

GO for Help

For Exercises	See Lesson
28–29	9-9

Alternative Assessment

Each partner writes two independent events and two events that are not independent similar to those in Exercises 4–6. Partners exchange papers and identify each pair of events as independent or not independent.

Test Prep

Resources

For additional practice with a variety of test item formats:
• Test-Taking Strategies, p. 507
• Test Prep, p. 511
• Test-Taking Strategies with Transparencies

4. Assess & Reteach

Lesson Quiz

A box contains 4 red cubes, 3 blue cubes, 2 green cubes, and 1 yellow cube. You pick two cubes at random, replacing each after you pick. Find the probability of each compound event.

1. both green $\frac{1}{25}$

2. red, then yellow $\frac{1}{25}$

3. both red $\frac{4}{25}$

4. red, then blue $\frac{3}{25}$

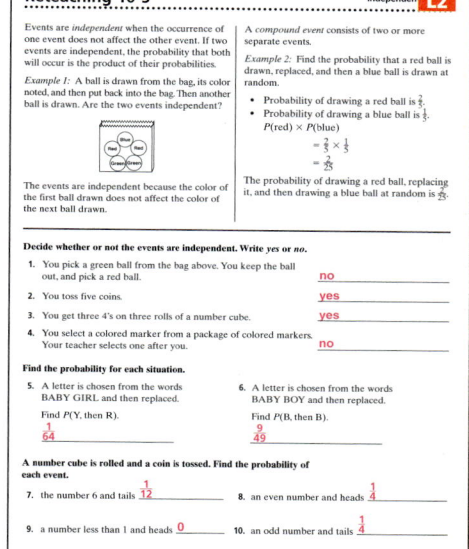

Dependent Events

In Lesson 10-5, students learned about the probability of independent events. In this feature, they will learn about the probability of events that are dependent on the outcome of another event.

Guided Instruction

Explain the formula for probability of dependent events. Then ask questions such as:
- *Is a dependent event more likely or less likely than an independent event?* less likely
- *Why?* To find probability of a dependent event, you must multiply two fractions. The product, P(A) × P(B after A), is always less than either of the probabilities.
- *Does probability of dependent events increase or decrease with each event?* decrease

Exercises

Have students work independently on the Exercises. When students have finished, allow them to discuss their work with a partner and correct their work if necessary.

Dependent Events

When the occurrence of one event affects the probability of the occurrence of another event, the two events are ==dependent events.==

The formula for the probability of dependent events states that if event B depends on event A, then
$P(A, \text{then } B) = P(A) \times P(B \text{ after } A)$.

EXAMPLE

The cards at the right are placed in a bag and shaken. You choose two cards at random. Find the probability that you draw M out first and, without replacing it, draw A next.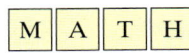

The probability of drawing M first is $\frac{1}{4}$. Then, since M is not in the bag, A is one of 3 letters in the bag. So the probability of drawing A next is $\frac{1}{3}$.

$P(M, \text{then } A) = P(M) \times P(A \text{ after } M)$ ← Use the formula for dependent events.

$\phantom{P(M, \text{then } A)} = \frac{1}{4} \times \frac{1}{3}$ ← Substitute and multiply.

$\phantom{P(M, \text{then } A)} = \frac{1}{12}$

Exercises

Twenty cards are numbered 1–20. You draw a card. Without replacing it, you draw a second card. Find each probability.

1. $P(1, \text{then } 20)$ $\frac{1}{380}$

2. $P(3, \text{then even})$ $\frac{1}{38}$

3. $P(\text{even, then } 7)$ $\frac{1}{38}$

A bag contains 3 blue marbles, 4 red marbles, and 2 white marbles. You draw a marble. Without replacing it, you draw a second marble. Find each probability.

4. $P(\text{red, then blue})$ $\frac{1}{6}$

5. $P(\text{red, then white})$ $\frac{1}{9}$

6. $P(\text{both blue})$ $\frac{1}{6}$

7. $P(\text{both white})$ $\frac{1}{36}$

8. **Writing in Math** You draw marbles at random without replacing them. Are these independent or dependent events? Explain. Dependent; after selecting one marble, there is one fewer from which to choose. The first draw affects the second.

Practice Solving Problems

You can use what you know about counting outcomes to solve problems.

A Close Vote Andres, Bonita, Chen, Debi, and Erin have the same number of votes in an election for three student council members. So a random selection is made. Letters A–E are put on cards to represent the first letter in each of their names. Three cards are then selected at random to choose the three council members. What is the probability that Erin (E) is selected?

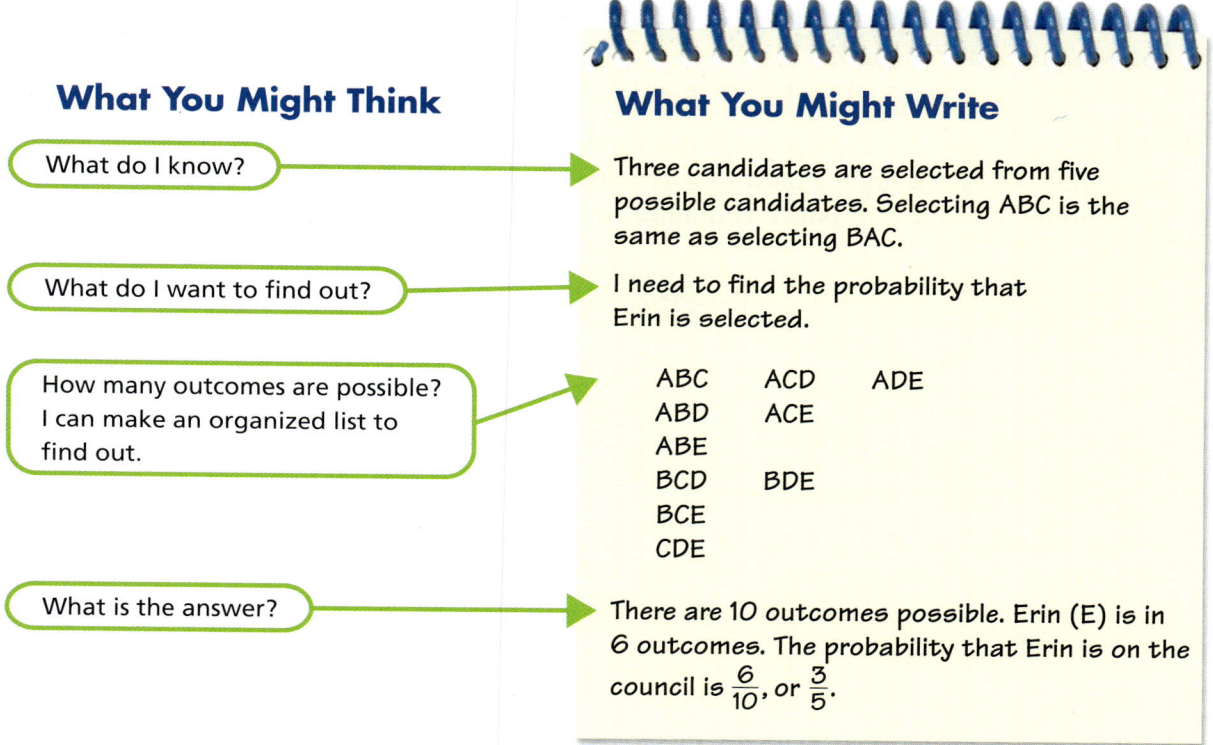

What You Might Think

What do I know?

What do I want to find out?

How many outcomes are possible? I can make an organized list to find out.

What is the answer?

What You Might Write

Three candidates are selected from five possible candidates. Selecting ABC is the same as selecting BAC.

I need to find the probability that Erin is selected.

ABC	ACD	ADE
ABD	ACE	
ABE		
BCD	BDE	
BCE		
CDE		

There are 10 outcomes possible. Erin (E) is in 6 outcomes. The probability that Erin is on the council is $\frac{6}{10}$, or $\frac{3}{5}$.

Think It Through 1–2. Answers may vary. Samples are given.

1. What does this statement mean: *Selecting ABC is the same as selecting BAC?* **Order does not matter. Selecting ABC for the three seats is the same as selecting BAC.**

2. **Check for Reasonableness** Does the probability of each of the other candidates being elected also equal $\frac{3}{5}$? Explain. **Yes; each person has the same chance to be elected.**

Practice Solving Problems

In this feature, students practice solving problems involving probability. They determine sample spaces and find the probabilities of independent and dependent events.

Guided Instruction

Discuss with students how determining probability can be useful in everyday situations. They can find the total number of outcomes in any situation and determine what the probability of any of those outcomes is. Ask:

- *Are all the outcomes equally likely? Why?* **Yes, all 5 students have an equal number of cards with the letter for their name so it is equally likely that each will be selected.**

- *What is the important information you need to solve the problem?* **number of students that could be selected, number of students that will be selected, size of group of students that will be selected**

- *If only two students are selected, do Erin's chances increase or decrease? Why?* **decrease, because there will only be four out of ten possible combinations with Erin in them and $\frac{2}{5}$ is less than $\frac{3}{5}$**

505

Error Prevention!

Students may duplicate possible outcomes. Make sure students understand the concept of *BAC* is the same as *ABC*. If necessary, have them write out all combinations and then scratch out duplicates.

Exercises

Have students work independently on the Exercises. Then have them form small groups to discuss their answers. Allow students to correct any mistakes.

Differentiated Instruction

Below Level   L2

For practice, provide students with problems that have fewer possible outcomes.

Exercises

3. The results from a survey of 1,012 adults are shown below. About how many of the people in the 2005 survey said they always wear a seat belt?

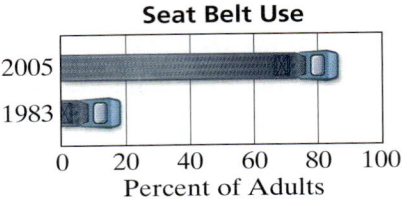

Seat Belt Use

Percent of Adults

3a. The number of people who always wear their seat belt

b. The percent of people who always wear a seat belt and the number of people who answered the survey

c. Estimate; the survey is only given to a sample of the population, so the answer is not exact.

a. What are you trying to find?

b. What data do you need?

c. Do you need an exact answer or an estimate? Explain.

4. Blindfolded, you toss a magnetic dart once. It sticks to a random spot on the game board shown below. What is the probability that the dart lands within the circle? about $\frac{1}{10}$

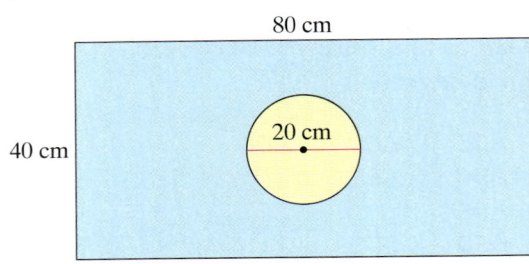

5. Without looking, you toss a magnetic dart once, and it sticks to a random spot on the game board shown at the right. What is the probability that the dart lands inside the triangle? $\frac{15}{36}$ or $\frac{5}{12}$

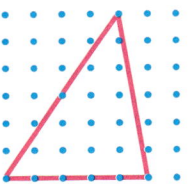

6. You put prizes for first, second, and third place in separate wrapped boxes, but the prize labels fall off. You put a label on one of the boxes at random. What is the probability that the label is correct? $\frac{1}{3}$

7. Suppose you have 6 blue socks, 8 red socks, and 4 black socks in the same drawer. Without looking, you pick one sock out of the drawer. Without returning it, you pick another. What is the probability that both socks are blue? $\frac{5}{51}$

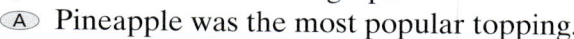

Interpreting Data

You may need to compare data displayed in a graph. You can use number sense to help you compare.

EXAMPLE

Several students were asked to name their favorite pizza topping. Their responses are displayed in the bar graph.

Favorite Pizza Topping

(bar graph: Number of Students vs. topping — Pepperoni 6, Pineapple 2, Sausage 5, Mushroom 6)

Which statement is best supported by the information in the graph?
- Ⓐ Pineapple was the most popular topping.
- Ⓑ Mushroom was the least popular topping.
- Ⓒ Pepperoni was more popular than sausage.
- Ⓓ Sausage was the most popular topping.

- More people chose mushroom than pineapple, so you can eliminate choices A and B.
- Since only 5 people chose sausage, the answer is not D.
- Six people chose pepperoni. Only 5 people chose sausage. The correct answer is choice C.

Exercises

1. Which statement is best supported by the graph? **B**
   - Ⓐ More people played 11 games than 15 games.
   - Ⓑ The same number of people played 11 games as played 14 games.
   - Ⓒ More than 50% of the people played 12 games.
   - Ⓓ Fewer than 5 people played 13 games.

Games Played at Arcade

```
x
x   x
x   x
x   x       x
x   x   x   x   x
x   x   x   x   x
11  12  13  14  15
    Games Played
```

2. What is the mode of the data represented in the graph above? **G**
   - Ⓕ 4
   - Ⓖ 12
   - Ⓗ 13
   - Ⓙ 26

Interpreting Data

Students learn to use number sense and compare data in a graph to answer questions.

Guided Instruction

Explain that sometimes it is necessary to interpret data from a graph to answer questions. Display the graph from the Example. Ask:
- *What was the least popular choice?* pineapple
- *Which statement does that disprove? Why?* A, because pineapple can't be the most popular choice if it is the least popular choice
- *Why is B untrue?* Fewer people picked sausage and pineapple than mushroom, so mushroom can't be the least popular.

Lead students to see that they don't need to calculate an answer, they can interpret the data to discover false answers and eliminate them.

Resources

Test-Taking Strategies with Transparencies
- Transparency 13
- Practice sheet, p. 10

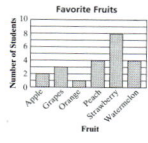

Test-Taking Strategies with Transparencies

Test-Taking Strategies: Interpreting Data

Before you answer a question that involves interpreting data from a table, graph, or plot, make sure that you understand the information displayed.

Example The bar graph below shows the favorite fruit choices of a class of students. Which statement is best supported by the graph?

(bar graph: Favorite Fruits)

A. More students chose grapes than chose apple and orange combined.

B. The fewest students chose apple.

C. The same number of students chose peach as chose watermelon.

D. More than half the students chose strawberry.

- 3 students chose grapes, 2 students chose apple, and 1 chose orange. Since 3 ≯ 2 + 1, eliminate choice A.
- 2 students chose apple. This is not the fewest, since only 1 student chose orange. Eliminate choice B.
- The total number of students choosing was 2 + 3 + 1 + 4 + 8 + 4 = 22. 8 is not more than half of 22, so eliminate choice D.
- 4 students chose peach, and 4 students chose watermelon. This is the same number, so the correct answer is choice C.

Transparency 13

507

Vocabulary Review

 complement of an event
  (p. 483)
compound events (p. 501)
counting principle (p. 477)
dependent event (p. 504)
equally likely outcomes
  (p. 482)

event (p. 476)
experimental probability
  (p. 488)
independent events (p. 500)
outcome (p. 476)
permutation (p. 481)
population (p. 495)

probability of an event
  (p. 482)
sample (p. 495)
sample space (p. 476)
simulation (p. 498)
tree diagram (p. 477)

Choose the vocabulary term from the column at the right that best completes each sentence.

1. When tossing a coin, one possible __?__ **C** is "coin shows heads."

2. __?__ have the same chance of occurring. **B**

3. The __?__ can be used to find the number of outcomes in a compound event. **A**

4. To make predictions about a population, you can use a(n) __?__ that represents that population. **D**

A. counting principle
B. equally likely outcomes
C. event
D. sample

Go Online
PHSchool.com
For: Vocabulary quiz
Web Code: aqj-1051

Skills and Concepts

Lesson 10-1
- To construct sample spaces for events and to use the counting principle

You can make an organized list, draw a tree diagram, or use the **counting principle** to find the number of arrangements of objects.

The set of all possible outcomes is the **sample space.**

5. **Flags** Suppose you want to make a flag with four stripes colored red, blue, green, and white. Use the counting principle to find the number of ways you can order the colors. **24 ways**

Lesson 10-2
- To find the probabilities of an event and of its complement

An **event** is an outcome or group of outcomes. The **probability of an event** is the ratio

$$P(\text{event}) = \frac{\text{number of favorable outcomes}}{\text{total number of outcomes}}.$$

A number cube is rolled once. Find each probability.

6. $P(5)$ $\frac{1}{6}$

7. $P(\text{even})$ $\frac{3}{6}$ or $\frac{1}{2}$

8. $P(4 \text{ or } 6)$ $\frac{2}{6}$ or $\frac{1}{3}$

Lesson 10-3
- To find experimental probability

You can find probabilities by collecting data. For a series of trials, the **experimental probability** of an event is the ratio

$$P(\text{event}) = \frac{\text{number of times event occurs}}{\text{total number of trials}}.$$

9. Noel and Kayla play a game 30 times. Noel wins 20 times. What is the experimental probability that Kayla wins? That Noel wins? **Kayla: $\frac{1}{3}$; Noel: $\frac{2}{3}$**

You spin a spinner 60 times. It stops on blue 15 times, green 25 times, and red 20 times. Find each experimental probability.

10. $P(\text{blue})$ $\frac{1}{4}$ 11. $P(\text{red})$ $\frac{1}{3}$ 12. $P(\text{not green})$ $\frac{7}{12}$

Lesson 10-4
- To make predictions from probabilties and samples

You can predict the number of times an event will occur by multiplying the probability of the event by the total number of trials. If you want to make predictions about a **population**, you can use a **sample** to gather the information you need. You can model many situations with a **simulation**.

13. **Computers** Out of 300 computers, 22 are defective. How many defective computers would you expect in a group of 30,000?
2,200 defective computers

14. The probability of rain in San Francisco on a given day is $\frac{1}{6}$. The probability of rain in Miami is $\frac{5}{6}$. Use two number cubes to find the simulated probability of rain in both cities.
Check students' work.

Lesson 10-5
- To find probabilities of independent events

A **compound event** consists of two or more separate events. If A and B are independent events, you can find the probability of the compound event "A, then B" with the formula $P(A, \text{then } B) = P(A) \times P(B)$.

Decide whether the events are independent. Explain your answers.

15. A roll of a number cube is 3. The fourth roll of the number cube is 6. **Independent; the first roll does not affect the fourth roll.**

16. You draw a pink cube from a bag containing pink and yellow cubes. Without replacing the pink cube, you draw a yellow cube.
Not independent; after drawing the first cube, there is one cube fewer in the bag.

A bag contains two red, four blue, and three green marbles. You draw marbles twice with replacement. Find each probability.

17. both green $\frac{9}{81}$ or $\frac{1}{9}$ 18. green, then red   19. red, then blue $\frac{8}{81}$

$\frac{6}{81}$ or $\frac{2}{27}$

Chapter 10 Chapter Review **509**

Chapter 10 Test

Go Online
PHSchool.com
For: Online chapter test
Web Code: aqa-1052

For Exercises 1 and 2, use the diagram below. Suppose you spin the spinner three times.

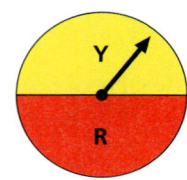

1. Make a tree diagram to show the sample space. How many possible outcomes are there? **See margin.**

2. Find P(yellow, then red, then yellow). $\frac{1}{8}$

3. Suppose you read in the newspaper that the probability of rain is 10%. Write the probability as a fraction and as a decimal. $\frac{1}{10}$, 0.1

4. The figure at the right has faces numbered from 1 through 12. All outcomes are equally likely. Find each probability for one roll.
   a. P(even number) $\frac{1}{2}$
   b. P(prime) $\frac{5}{12}$
   c. P(7 or 8) $\frac{1}{6}$
   d. P(13) 0

5. Pam and Tony play a game 18 times. Tony wins 8 times and Pam wins 10 times.
   a. Find the experimental probability that Pam wins. $\frac{10}{18}$ or $\frac{5}{9}$
   b. Find the experimental probability that Tony wins. $\frac{8}{18}$ or $\frac{4}{9}$
   c. **Writing in Math** If Pam and Tony play the game 18 more times, must the experimental probabilities remain the same? Explain. **See margin.**

6. A ranch has 132 cows. You pick 32 of them at random and find that 18 of those cows have spots. Predict the number of cows on the ranch that have spots. **about 74 cows**

7. A bag contains only blue and green chips. The probability of drawing a blue chip is $\frac{5}{12}$. Find P(green). $\frac{7}{12}$

A bag contains 4 red, 4 blue, and 3 green cubes. Cubes are drawn twice with replacement. Find each probability.

8. P(blue, then green) $\frac{12}{121}$

9. P(both red) $\frac{16}{121}$

10. P(both green) $\frac{9}{121}$

11. P(red, then blue) $\frac{16}{121}$

12. Determine whether the events are independent. Explain your answers.
    a. You roll two number cubes. One shows a 3. The other shows a 1.
    b. You draw a red marble from a bag containing red and yellow marbles. You do not put the marble back. You draw another red marble. **12a–b. See margin.**

13. Suppose you roll a number cube twice. What is the probability of getting a 2 on the first roll and a 5 on the second roll? $\frac{1}{36}$

The letters of the word *PROBABILITY* are written on 11 cards. You draw a card at random, replace it, and draw a second card. Find each probability.

14. P(B, then R) $\frac{2}{121}$

15. P(I, then vowel) $\frac{8}{121}$

510 Chapter 10 Chapter Test

1. **See back of book.**

5c. **Answers may vary. Sample: No; Tony could improve and win more often.**

12a. **Independent; one roll does not affect the other.**

b. **Not independent; after you remove the first marble, there is one marble fewer in the bag.**

Reading Comprehension

Read each passage and answer the questions that follow.

E-commerce In the future, purchasing items online is likely to become more popular than shopping at a store. During a recent year, the most popular items bought online were computer hardware goods. Online sales for the year were as follows: 24% for computer hardware, 13% for clothing and footwear, 4% for music and videos, and 3% for toys and games.

1. Suppose a website that sells all types of goods receives 200 orders. How many sales would you expect to be for computer hardware goods? **D**

   Ⓐ 4   Ⓑ 13   Ⓒ 24   Ⓓ 48

2. What is the probability, given as a fraction, that any online sale during the year will be for clothing and footwear? **H**

   Ⓕ $\frac{1}{24}$ Ⓖ $\frac{1}{13}$ Ⓗ $\frac{13}{100}$ Ⓙ $\frac{6}{25}$

3. What is the percentage of sales that will NOT be any of the items listed in the article? **A**

   Ⓐ 56%   Ⓑ 44%   Ⓒ 37%   Ⓓ 7%

4. Suppose an employee of an e-commerce company selects 20 orders at random. Of these, 4 are for clothing and footwear. In this sample, what is the experimental probability of a clothing or footwear order?

   Ⓕ 2.6%   Ⓖ $\frac{13}{100}$ Ⓗ $\frac{1}{5}$ Ⓙ $\frac{4}{5}$ **H**

Sports Trends Are "ball" sports becoming less popular? From 1993 to 2000, the number of youths who play baseball went down from 23% to 12%. In that same period, the number of youths who play basketball decreased from 58% to 46%. From 1993 to 2000, in-line skating participation increased from 17% to 30% and snowboarding participation rose by about 8%.

5. In 2000, what was the probability of a youth participating in in-line skating? **C**

   Ⓐ 0.58   Ⓑ 0.46   Ⓒ 0.30   Ⓓ 0.17

6. About which sport are you NOT given enough information to find the probability of a youth playing the sport in 1993? **J**

   Ⓕ baseball   Ⓗ in-line skating
   Ⓖ basketball   Ⓙ snowboarding

7. In 1993, suppose 300 youths were asked what sports they played. How many youths were likely to say basketball? **A**

   Ⓐ 174   Ⓑ 138   Ⓒ 58   Ⓓ 46

8. Which sport discussed in the article had the greatest decrease in percentage of participation? **G**

   Ⓕ baseball   Ⓗ in-line skating
   Ⓖ basketball   Ⓙ snowboarding

Resources

Test Prep Workbook

All in One Teaching Resources
- Cumulative Review   **L3**

ExamView Assessment Suite CD-ROM
- Standardized Test Practice

Differentiated Instruction

Progress Monitoring Assessments
- Benchmark Test 5   **L3**

Spanish Assessment Resources
- Spanish Cumulative Review **ELL**

ExamView Assessment Suite CD-ROM
- Special Needs Practice Bank **L1**

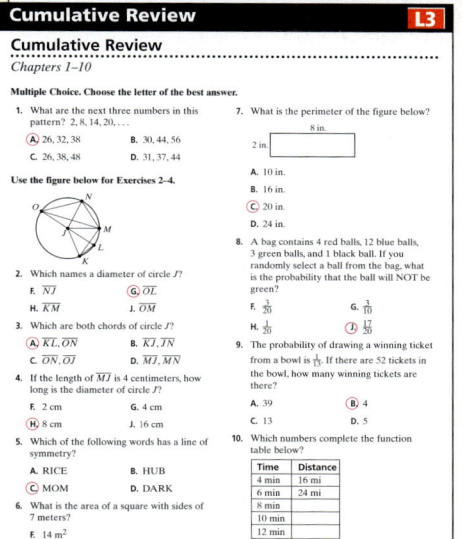

Applying Probability

Students will use data from these two pages to answer the questions posed in Put It All Together.

Invite students to describe games of chance they have played. Ask questions such as:

- *When you flip a coin, what is your probability of guessing if it lands heads or tails?* $\frac{1}{2}$
- *How would you describe that probability as a percentage?* **50%**
- *When you roll a 6-sided number cube, what is your probability of guessing the number it will land on?* $\frac{1}{6}$

Materials
- A coin
- A 6-sided number cube

Activating Prior Knowledge

Have students share any experiences they have had playing carnival games, like this one, or others in which they toss to win. Ask them to describe what about each game made it hard to win.

Guided Instruction

Have students examine the information provided. Discuss that the concept of probability is at the heart of all carnival games and games of chance. Ask:
- *What makes a game more or less fair?* **The probability of winning on any one attempt. The lower the probability, the less fair the game is.**
- *What can help a player shift the odds in his favor?* **Skill. In a game such as a ring toss, a player with good aim can improve his or her odds.**
- *Is this possible in all games?* **No. In games of pure chance such as flipping a coin or rolling a number-cube, where no skill is involved, there is no way for a player to improve the probability of winning.**

Applying Probability

Fair Chance? Toss a ring onto a post, hit a target with a baseball, or pop a balloon with a dart. The real pleasure comes from playing the game, but how likely are you to win? Sometimes you can figure it out by using geometry and probability together.

Horseshoes
The game of horseshoes uses special shoes with a maximum weight of 2 pounds 10 ounces. A shoe must fall within 6 inches of the stake to score.

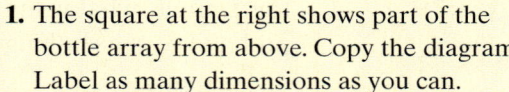

Heads or Tails?
A coin toss has two possible outcomes: heads or tails.

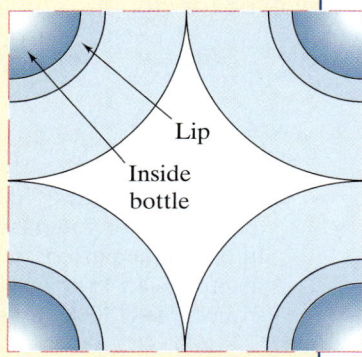

Milk-bottle array

Bottle Dimensions
2 inches — Lip
Base
5 inches

Put It All Together

At the school fair, the student council set up 100 old milk bottles in rows. The challenge is to throw a coin into one of the bottles. The game seems easy because there are so many bottles.

1. The square at the right shows part of the bottle array from above. Copy the diagram. Label as many dimensions as you can.

2. Since a coin can land anywhere within one of these square regions, the diagram shows the possible outcomes of each throw. What is the area of the square?

3. A favorable outcome is when a coin lands inside a bottle.
   a. On your copy of the square, shade the regions in which the coin must land for a favorable outcome.
   b. **Reasoning** If you made several copies of the square and put the shaded regions together, what shapes would be shaded?
   c. Find the area of the shaded parts of your square.

Top view of bottles
Lip
Inside bottle

4. a. Calculate the probability of winning the game. Write your answer as a percent.
   b. How many times would you expect to win if you played 100 times?
   c. **Number Sense** It costs $1 for one toss. The student council pays $1.75 for each prize. If 50 people play, how much money can the student council expect to raise with this game? Show your work.

---

1. Diagrams may vary. Sample:

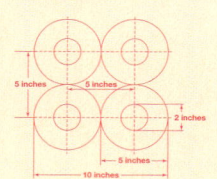

2. 25 in.^{2}

4. a. about 12.56%

   b. about 13 times

c. 50 people pay $50 to play once each. Expected wins
≈ 0.1256(50) ≈ 6;
6(1.75) = 10.50;
50 − 10.50 = 39.50;
they can expect to raise $39.50.

Carnival Games

Some schools use carnival games as fundraisers.

Go Online

PHSchool.com

For: Information about games
Web code: aqe-1053

513

Activity

Have students work in pairs to answer the questions.

Teaching Tip

Discuss ways to improve or weaken the probability of winning this game. Discuss how to make it a completely fair game. Then ask: *What appeal, if any, is there to playing games that are hard to win because the probabilities are not in the player's favor?* Accept all reasonable responses.

Exercise 4 Ask: *if you use two squares to analyze the milk bottle game, how might your answer compare with the probability you found originally?* Guide students to see that the probability of winning does not change because the area under consideration is double the original area.

Differentiated Instruction

Special Needs **L1**

As needed, review the distinction between the concepts of favorable and unfavorable outcomes. Use this situation: *You open a 300-page book, hoping to open to a page in the hundreds.*

- *What is an example of a favorable outcome?* any page from 100 through 199
- *An unfavorable outcome?* any page < 100 or > 199

3a. Diagrams may vary. Sample:

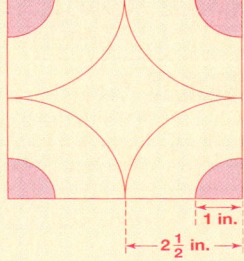

1 in.

$2\frac{1}{2}$ in.

b. circles

c. about 3.14 in.^{2}

11 Integers

Chapter at a Glance

Lesson Titles, Objectives, and Features	Assessment	NCTM Standards	Local Standards
11-1 Exploring Integers • To use integers, opposites, and absolute values to represent real-life situations	Lesson Quiz	1, 2, 6, 7, 8, 9, 10	
11-2 Comparing and Ordering Integers • To compare and order integers	Lesson Quiz	1, 2, 6, 7, 8, 9, 10	
11-3a Activity Lab, Hands On: Modeling Addition of Integers			
11-3 Adding Integers • To add integers and to solve problems by adding integers	Lesson Quiz Checkpoint Quiz 1	1, 2, 6, 7, 8, 9, 10	
11-4a Activity Lab, Hands On: Modeling Subtraction of Integers			
11-4 Subtracting Integers • To subtract integers and to solve problems by subtracting integers	Lesson Quiz	1, 2, 6, 7, 8, 9, 10	
11-5 Multiplying Integers • To multiply integers and to solve problems by multiplying integers	Lesson Quiz	1, 2, 6, 7, 8, 9, 10	
Guided Problem Solving: Practice Solving Problems			
11-6 Dividing Integers • To divide integers and to solve problems by dividing integers	Lesson Quiz	1, 2, 5, 6, 7, 8, 9, 10	
11-7 Solving Equations With Integers • To solve equations containing integers	Lesson Quiz	1, 2, 6, 7, 8, 9, 10	
11-7b Activity Lab, Algebra Thinking: Thinking About Solutions			
11-8a Activity Lab, Technology: Graphing Points			
11-8 Graphing in the Coordinate Plane • To name and graph points on a coordinate plane	Lesson Quiz Checkpoint Quiz 2	1, 2, 3, 5, 6, 7, 8, 9, 10	
Extension: Reflections in the Coordinate Plane			
11-9 Applications of Integers • To apply integers to profit and loss situations	Lesson Quiz	1, 2, 6, 7, 8, 9, 10	
11-10 Graphing Functions • To make a function table and to graph a function	Lesson Quiz	1, 2, 6, 7, 8, 9, 10	
Problem Solving Applications: Applying Integers			

NCTM Standards 2000

1 Number and Operations	**2** Algebra	**3** Geometry	**4** Measurement	**5** Data Analysis and Probability
6 Problem Solving	**7** Reasoning and Proof	**8** Communication	**9** Connections	**10** Representation

Correlations to Standardized Tests

All content for these tests is contained in *Prentice Hall Math*, Course 1. This chart reflects coverage in this chapter only.

	11-1	11-2	11-3	11-4	11-5	11-6	11-7	11-8	11-9	11-10
Terra Nova CAT6 (Level 16)										
Number and Number Relations	✔	✔	✔	✔	✔	✔	✔	✔	✔	✔
Computation and Numerical Estimation	✔	✔	✔	✔	✔	✔	✔	✔	✔	✔
Operation Concepts	✔	✔	✔	✔	✔	✔	✔	✔	✔	✔
Measurement										
Geometry and Spatial Sense								✔		
Data Analysis, Statistics, and Probability										
Patterns, Functions, Algebra	✔	✔	✔	✔	✔	✔	✔	✔	✔	✔
Problem Solving and Reasoning	✔	✔	✔	✔	✔	✔	✔	✔	✔	✔
Communication	✔	✔	✔	✔	✔	✔	✔	✔	✔	✔
Decimals, Fractions, Integers, and Percent	✔	✔	✔	✔	✔	✔	✔	✔	✔	✔
Order of Operations										
Terra Nova CTBS (Level 16)										
Whole Numbers, Decimals, Fractions	✔	✔	✔	✔	✔	✔	✔	✔	✔	✔
Numeration, Number Theory	✔	✔	✔	✔	✔	✔	✔	✔	✔	✔
Data Interpretation										
Pre-algebra	✔	✔	✔	✔	✔	✔	✔	✔	✔	✔
Measurement										
Geometry								✔		
ITBS (Level 12)										
Number Properties and Operations	✔	✔	✔	✔	✔	✔	✔	✔	✔	✔
Algebra	✔	✔	✔	✔	✔	✔	✔	✔	✔	✔
Geometry								✔		
Measurement										
Probability and Statistics										
Estimation										
SAT10 (Int 2 Level)										
Number Sense and Operations	✔	✔	✔	✔	✔	✔	✔	✔	✔	✔
Patterns, Relationships, and Algebra	✔	✔	✔	✔	✔	✔	✔	✔	✔	✔
Data, Statistics, and Probability										
Geometry and Measurement								✔		
NAEP										
Number Sense, Properties, and Operations	✔	✔	✔	✔	✔	✔	✔			
Measurement										
Geometry and Spatial Sense										
Data Analysis, Statistics, and Probability										
Algebra and Functions								✔	✔	✔

CAT6 California Achievement Test, 6th Ed. **CTBS** Comprehensive Test of Basic Skills **ITBS** Iowa Test of Basic Skills, Form M
SAT10 Stanford Achievement Test, 10th Ed. **NAEP** National Assessment of Educational Progress 2005 Mathematics Objectives

Math Background

Skills Trace

> ### BEFORE Chapter 11
> Grade 5 presented integer computations.
>
> ### DURING Chapter 11
> Course 1 extends the four operations with integers to graphing in the coordinate plane and introduces functions.
>
> ### AFTER Chapter 11
> Throughout this course, students apply number patterns to solve real-world patterns.

11-1	Exploring Integers
11-2	Comparing and Ordering Integers
11-3	Adding Integers

> ### Math Understanding
> - Integers are the set of counting numbers (positive integers), their opposites (negative integers), and zero (neither positive nor negative).
> - Two opposites have the same absolute value. The opposite of 0 is 0.
> - As you move from left to right on a horizontal number line, the integers become greater.
> - You can use a number line to model adding integers.

Two numbers are **opposites** if they are the same distance from 0 on a number line, but in opposite directions. **Integers** are the set of positive whole numbers, their opposites, and 0. The **absolute value** of a number is its distance from 0 on a number line.

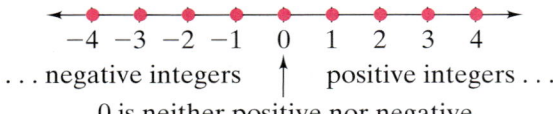

. . . negative integers   ↑   positive integers . . .

0 is neither positive nor negative.

Adding Integers With the Same Sign The sum of two positive integers is positive. The sum of two negative integers is negative.

Example: $2 + 3 = 5$ $-2 + (-3) = -5$

Adding Integers With Different Signs To add integers with different signs, first find the absolute value of each integer. Then, subtract the lesser absolute value from the greater. The sum has the sign of the integer with the greater absolute value.

Example:

$$-2 + (-3) = -5$$
Use the sign of -3.
So, $2 + (-3) = -1$.

$$-2 + 3 = \blacksquare$$
$|-2| = 2$ and $|3| = 3$
$3 - 2 = 1$
Use the sign of 3.
So, $-2 + 3 = 1$.

11-4   Subtracting Integers

> ### Math Understandings
> - Subtracting an integer gives the same result as adding its opposite.

Subtracting Integers You subtract an integer by adding its opposite.

Example: $10 - 6 = 10 + (-6) = 4$
$10 - (-6) = 10 + 6 = 16$
$-10 - 6 = -10 + (-6) = -16$
$-10 - (-6) = -10 + 6 = -4$

11-5	Multiplying Integers
11-6	Dividing Integers
11-7	Solving Equations With Integers

> ### Math Understandings
> - You can think of multiplication as repeated addition.
> - Multiplication and division are inverse operations because they undo each other.
> - The rules for finding the sign of a quotient when dividing two integers are similar to the rules for finding the sign of a product when multiplying integers.
> - You can solve addition and subtraction equations with integers using the same methods you used to solve equations with whole numbers.
> - You can solve multiplication and division equations with integers using the same methods you used to solve equations with whole numbers.

Multiplying Integers

The product of two integers with the *same* sign is positive.
The product of two integers with *different* signs is negative.

Examples:

$$4 \times 5 = 20 \qquad 4 \times (-5) = -20$$
$$-4 \times (-5) = 20 \qquad -4 \times 5 = -20$$

Dividing Integers

The quotient of two integers with the *same* sign is positive.
The quotient of two integers with *different* signs is negative.

Examples:

$$20 \div 4 = 5 \qquad 20 \div (-4) = -5$$
$$-20 \div (-4) = 5 \qquad -20 \div 4 = -5$$

11-8 Graphing in the Coordinate Plane

Math Understandings

- You can name any point on a coordinate plane by an ordered pair of numbers, and you can graph any ordered pair of real numbers as a point on the plane.
- An ordered pair (x, y) is ordered because you always name the horizontal coordinate first. If you reverse the order, you change the location of the point that the pair names.

The **coordinate plane** is formed by the intersection of two number lines. The plane is divided into four regions, called **quadrants**. The **origin** is the place where the two number lines intersect. An **ordered pair** is a pair of numbers that describes the location of a point in a coordinate plane.

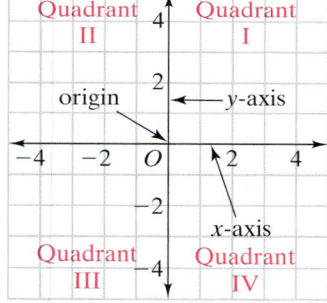

11-9 Applications of Integers

Math Understandings

- You can use line graphs to look at trends of monthly balances.

In business, money received is *income* and money spent is *expenses*. A balance is a company's *profit* or *loss*. A positive balance means that there is a profit. A negative balance means that there is a loss.

11-10 Graphing Functions

Math Understandings

- You can represent the relationship between two quantities using a table, a rule, or a graph.

A **function** is a rule that assigns exactly one output value to each input value. You can show a function relationship on a coordinate plane by graphing the input (x) on the horizontal axis and the output (y) on the vertical axis. When the points you graph for a function lie along a line, this type of function is a *linear function*.

Example: Make a table and graph the function $y = x - 1$.

Input	−2	0	2	4
Output	−3	−1	1	3

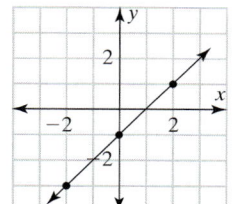

Additional Professional Development Opportunities

Math Background Notes for Chapter 11: Every lesson has a Math Background in the PLAN section.

Research Overview, Mathematics Strands
Additional support for these topics and more is in the front of the Teacher's Edition.

LessonLab
LessonLab, a Pearson Education company, offers comprehensive, facilitated professional development designed to help teachers to improve student achievement. To learn more, please visit lessonlab.com.

Chapter 11 Resources

	11-1	11-2	11-3	11-4	11-5	11-6	11-7	11-8	11-9	11-10	For the Chapter
Print Resources											
L3 Practice	●	●	●	●	●	●	●	●	●	●	
L1 Adapted Practice	●	●	●	●	●	●	●	●	●	●	
L3 Guided Problem Solving	●	●	●	●	●	●	●	●	●	●	
L2 Reteaching	●	●	●	●	●	●	●	●	●	●	
L4 Enrichment	●	●	●	●	●	●	●	●	●	●	
L3 Daily Notetaking Guide	●	●	●	●	●	●	●	●	●	●	
L1 Adapted Daily Notetaking Guide	●	●	●	●	●	●	●	●	●	●	
L3 Vocabulary and Study Skills Worksheets	●		●		●				●	●	●
L3 Daily Puzzles	●	●	●	●	●	●	●	●	●	●	
L3 Activity Labs	●	●	●	●	●	●	●	●	●	●	
L3 Checkpoint Quiz			●					●			
L3 Chapter Project											●
L2 Below Level Chapter Test											●
L3 Chapter Test											●
L4 Alternative Assessment											●
L3 Cumulative Review											●
Spanish Resources ELL											
L3 Practice	●	●	●	●	●	●	●	●	●	●	
L3 Vocabulary and Study Skills Worksheets	●		●		●				●	●	
L3 Checkpoint Quiz			●					●			
L2 Below Level Chapter Test											●
L3 Chapter Test											●
L4 Alternative Assessment											●
L3 Cumulative Review											●
Transparencies											
Check Skills You'll Need	●	●	●	●	●	●	●	●	●	●	
Additional Examples	●	●	●	●	●	●	●	●	●	●	
Problem of the Day	●	●	●	●	●	●	●	●	●	●	
Classroom Aid								●			
Student Edition Answers											●
Lesson Quiz	●	●	●	●	●	●	●	●	●	●	
Test-Taking Strategies											●
Technology											
Interactive Textbook Online	●	●	●	●	●	●	●	●	●	●	●
StudentExpress™ CD-ROM	●	●	●	●	●	●	●	●	●	●	
Success Tracker™ Online Intervention	●	●	●	●	●	●	●	●	●	●	●
TeacherExpress™ CD-ROM	●	●	●	●	●	●	●	●	●	●	●
PresentationExpress™ with QuickTake Presenter CD-ROM	●	●	●	●	●	●	●	●	●	●	●
ExamView® Assessment Suite CD-ROM	●	●	●	●	●	●	●	●	●	●	●
MindPoint® Quiz Show CD-ROM											●
Prentice Hall Web Site: PHSchool.com	●	●	●	●	●	●	●	●	●	●	●

Also available:

Prentice Hall Assessment System
- Progress Monitoring Assessments
- Skills and Concepts Review
- Test Prep Workbook

Other Resources
Algebra Readiness Tests
All-in-One Student Workbook
All-in-One Student Workbook, Adapted Version
Multilingual Handbook

Solution Key
Math Notes Study Folder
Spanish Cumulative Assessment

Where You Can Use the Lesson Resources

Here is a suggestion, following the four-step teaching plan, for how you can incorporate Differentiated Instruction Resources into your teaching.

	Instructional Resources **L3**	**Differentiated Instruction Resources**
1. Plan		
Preparation Read the Math Background in the Teacher's Edition to connect this lesson with students' previous experience. **Starting Class** **Check Skills You'll Need** Assign these exercises to review prerequisite skills. **New Vocabulary** Help students pre-read the lesson by pointing out the new terms introduced in the lesson.	**Math Background** **Math Understandings** **Transparencies & PresentationExpress™ with QuickTake Presenter CD-ROM** Check Skills You'll Need Problem of the Day **Resources** Vocabulary and Study Skills	**Spanish Support** **ELL** Vocabulary and Study Skills
2. Teach		
L3 Guided Instruction Use the Activity Labs to build conceptual understanding. Teach each Example. Use the Teacher's Edition side column notes for specific teaching tips, including Error Prevention notes. Use the Additional Examples found in the side column (and on transparency and PowerPoint) as an alternative presentation for the content. After each Example, assign the Quick Check exercise for that Example to get an immediate assessment of student understanding. Use the Closure activity in the Teacher's Edition to help students attain mastery of lesson content.	**Student Edition** Activity Lab **Resources** Daily Notetaking Guide Activity Lab **Transparencies & PresentationExpress™ with QuickTake Presenter CD-ROM** Additional Examples Classroom Aids **ExamView® Assessment Suite CD-ROM**	**Teacher's Edition** Every lesson includes suggestions for working with students who need special attention. **L1** Special Needs **L2** Below Level **L4** Advanced Learners **ELL** English Language Learners **Resources** **L1** Adapted Daily Notetaking Guide **Multilingual Handbook**
3. Practice		

Assignment Guide
Check Your Understanding
Use these questions to check students' understanding before you assign homework.
Homework Exercises
Assign homework from these leveled exercises in the Assignment Guide.
  A Practice by Example
  B Apply Your Skills
  C Challenge
  Test Prep and Mixed Review
Homework Quick Check
Use these key exercises to quickly check students' homework.
	Transparencies & PresentationExpress™ with QuickTake Presenter CD-ROM
	Student Answers
	Resources
	Practice
	Guided Problem Solving
	Vocabulary and Study Skills
	Activity Lab
	Daily Puzzles
	ExamView® Assessment Suite CD-ROM
		Spanish Support
		ELL Practice
		ELL Vocabulary and Study Skills
		Resources
		L1 Adapted Practice
		L4 Enrichment

4. Assess & Reteach		
Lesson Quiz Assign the Lesson Quiz to assess students' mastery of the lesson content. **Checkpoint Quiz** Use the Checkpoint Quiz to assess student progress over several lessons.	**Transparencies & PresentationExpress™ with QuickTake Presenter CD-ROM** Lesson Quiz **Resources** Checkpoint Quiz	**Resources** **L2** Reteaching **ELL** Checkpoint Quiz Success Tracker™ Online Intervention **ExamView® Assessment Suite CD-ROM**

KEY   **L1** Special Needs   **L2** Below Level   **L3** For All Students   **L4** Advanced, Gifted   **ELL** English Language Learners

CHAPTER 11

Integers

Integers

Check Your Readiness

Answers are in the back of the textbook.

For intervention, direct students to:

Algebra: Solving Equations
Lessons 3-5, 3-6
Extra Skills and Word
 Problems Practice, Ch. 3

Algebra: Solving Multiplication and Division Equations
Lesson 3-7
Extra Skills and Word
 Problems Practice, Ch. 3

Comparing and Ordering Fractions
Lesson 4-8
Extra Skills and Word
 Problems Practice, Ch. 4

What You've Learned

- In earlier chapters, you learned to add, subtract, multiply, and divide decimals and fractions.
- You wrote and solved equations.
- You graphed numbers on a number line and used graphs to analyze data.

Check Your Readiness

GO for Help

For Exercises	See Lessons
1–2	3-5
3–4	3-6
5–10	3-7
11–16	4-8

Algebra **Solving Equations**

Solve each equation.

1. $a + 13 = 92$ **79**
2. $b + 12 = 43$ **31**

3. $c - 31 = 8$ **39**
4. $d - 23 = 8$ **31**

Algebra **Solving Multiplication and Division Equations**

Solve each equation.

5. $7g = 4.2$ **0.6**
6. $h \div 6 = 11$ **66**
7. $8j = 328$ **41**

8. $k \div 9 = 8$ **72**
9. $16m = 240$ **15**
10. $n \div 14 = 18$ **252**

Comparing and Ordering Fractions

Compare each pair of numbers. Use $<$, $=$, or $>$.

11. $\frac{1}{3}$ ▪ $\frac{2}{5}$
 $<$

12. $\frac{3}{4}$ ▪ $\frac{2}{3}$
 $>$

13. $\frac{2}{16}$ ▪ $\frac{1}{8}$
 $=$

Order each set of numbers from least to greatest.

14. $\frac{1}{8}, \frac{1}{3}, \frac{1}{12}$ $\frac{1}{12}, \frac{1}{8}, \frac{1}{3}$
15. $\frac{4}{9}, \frac{5}{6}, \frac{7}{12}$ $\frac{4}{9}, \frac{7}{12}, \frac{5}{6}$
16. $\frac{1}{4}, \frac{6}{7}, \frac{1}{2}$ $\frac{1}{4}, \frac{1}{2}, \frac{6}{7}$

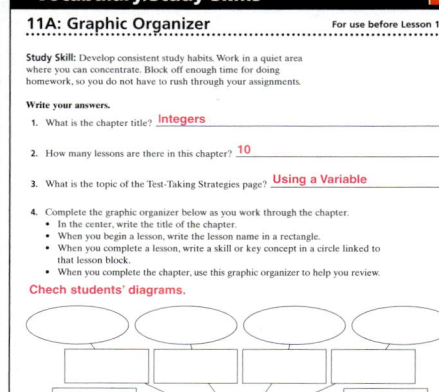

In this chapter, students study integers and explore common applications of integers. First they examine integers using a number line. Next, they add, subtract, multiply, and divide integers. Finally, they graph integers and functions containing integers on a coordinate plane.

Activating Prior Knowledge

In this chapter, students build on and extend their understanding of negative numbers (depths, temperatures below zero, golf scores) and knowledge of numbers and the number line to work with numbers less than zero. They also draw upon their understanding of graphing ordered pairs of whole numbers to plot points on a coordinate grid. Ask questions such as:

- *What is the order of these temperatures from warmest to coldest: 15°F, 0°F, and 4°F?*
  15°F, 4°F, 0°F

What You'll Learn Next

- In this chapter, you will use integers, opposites, and absolute values to represent real-world situations.

- You will locate and graph points in the coordinate plane using ordered pairs of integers.

- You will add, subtract, multiply, and divide integers.

- You will solve equations using integers.

🔊 Key Vocabulary

- absolute value (p. 517)
- coordinate plane (p. 548)
- function (p. 558)
- integers (p. 516)
- opposites (p. 516)
- ordered pair (p. 548)
- origin (p. 548)
- quadrants (p. 548)

Problem Solving Application On pages 568 and 569, you will work an extended activity on elevation.

Chapter 11   **515**

Objective
To use integers, opposites, and absolute values to represent real-world situations

Examples
1 Representing Situations with Integers
2 Identifying Opposites
3 Finding Absolute Value

Math Understandings: p. 514C

Math Background

A number line can be helpful to represent integers. A number line also exemplifies the concepts of opposites and absolute value. Numbers that are *opposites* are the same distance from 0 on a number line. So, the sum of two opposites, such as −3 and 3, is always 0. The *absolute value* of a number is its distance from 0 on a number line. This means that the absolute value of both 5 and −5 is 5; both numbers are 5 positions from 0 on a number line. Absolute value is never negative because it expresses a distance.

More Math Background: p. 514C

Lesson Planning and Resources

See p. 514E for a list of the resources that support this lesson.

Bell Ringer Practice

✓ **Check Skills You'll Need**
Use student page, transparency, or PowerPoint. For intervention, direct students to:
Properties of Numbers
Lesson 1-3
Extra Skills and Word Problems Practice, Ch. 1

516

✓ Check Skills You'll Need

1. **Vocabulary Review** Compare the *identity properties* of addition and multiplication. **See back of book.**
Find each missing number.

2. $8 + 9 = \blacksquare + 8$ **9**

3. $(10 + 1) + 6 = \blacksquare + (1 + 6)$ **10**

4. $140 + \blacksquare = 140$ **0**

GO for Help
Lesson 1-3

What You'll Learn

To use integers, opposites, and absolute values to represent real-world situations

🔊 **New Vocabulary** opposites, integers, absolute value

Why Learn This?

You can use integers to represent real-world situations. In the tug-of-war below, the team on the right has gained 2 feet. The position of the flag is positive 2, or +2. You write +2 as 2.

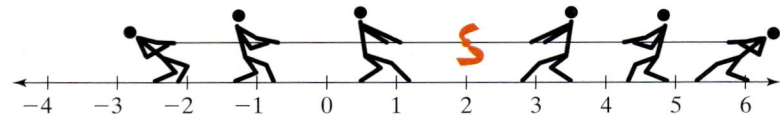

Suppose the team on the right had lost 2 feet instead. The position of the flag would have been negative 2, or −2.

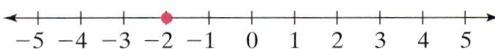

Opposites are two numbers that are the same distance from 0 on a number line but in opposite directions. **Integers** are the set of positive whole numbers, their opposites, and zero. The opposite of 0 is 0.

EXAMPLE   Representing Situations with Integers

1 **Multiple Choice** Dry ice is solid carbon dioxide, which freezes at about 109 degrees below zero Fahrenheit. Which integer represents the freezing point of dry ice?
Ⓐ −109   Ⓑ −19   Ⓒ +19   Ⓓ +109

The freezing point is 109 degrees below zero. Use a negative sign for an integer less than zero: −109. The answer is choice A.

✓ Quick Check

1. The lowest elevation in New Orleans, Louisiana, is 8 feet below sea level. Use an integer to represent this elevation.   **−8**

The "smoke" that makes a performance exciting is actually from dry ice.

Differentiated Instruction Solutions for All Learners

Special Needs L1
Have students draw a vertical number line so that they can better visualize measures of temperature above and below zero. This also works for above and below sea level.

learning style: visual

Below Level L2
To help students distinguish between positive and negative integers, have them use the word *positive* when naming positive integers. For instance, have them read 3 as "positive three."

learning style: verbal

EXAMPLE Identifying Opposites

2 Write the opposite of 3.

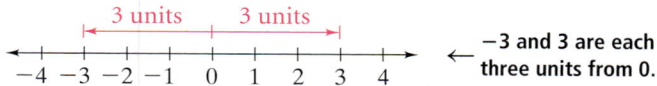

3 units   3 units

−4 −3 −2 −1 0 1 2 3 4

← −3 and 3 are each three units from 0.

The opposite of 3 is −3.

✓ Quick Check

2. Write the opposite of −5. **5**

The **absolute value** of a number is its distance from 0 on a number line. The symbol for the absolute value of a number n is $|n|$. Opposite numbers have the same absolute value.

EXAMPLE Finding Absolute Value

3 Find $|-4|$ and $|2|$.

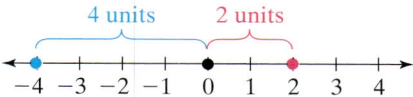

4 units   2 units

−4 −3 −2 −1 0 1 2 3 4

Since −4 is four units from 0, $|-4| = 4$. Since 2 is two units from 0, $|2| = 2$.

✓ Quick Check

3. a. Find $|-1|$. **1**   b. Find $|7|$. **7**

✓ Check Your Understanding

1. **Vocabulary** Give examples of numbers that are integers and numbers that are *not* integers.

2. **Open-Ended** Describe two different real-life situations that can be represented by the integer −9. **Answers may vary. Sample: Temperature, golf score.**

1. Answers may vary. Sample: Some integers are −1, 0, 1, 2, and 3; −5.7, 0.3, 2.92, and 10.5 are not integers.

Match each integer with a point on the number line.

     M   N   P   Q

−6 −5 −4 −3 −2 −1 0 1 2 3 4 5 6

3. −6 **M**   4. 5 **Q**   5. 1 **P**   6. −4 **N**

11-1 Exploring Integers **517**

3. Practice

Assignment Guide

Check Your Understanding
Go over Exercises 1–6 in class before assigning the Homework Exercises.

Homework Exercises
A Practice by Example   7–28
B Apply Your Skills   29–42
C Challenge   43
Test Prep and
   Mixed Review   44–48

Homework Quick Check
To check student's understanding of key skills and concepts, go over Exercises 7, 18, 30, 32, and 42.

Differentiated Instruction Resources

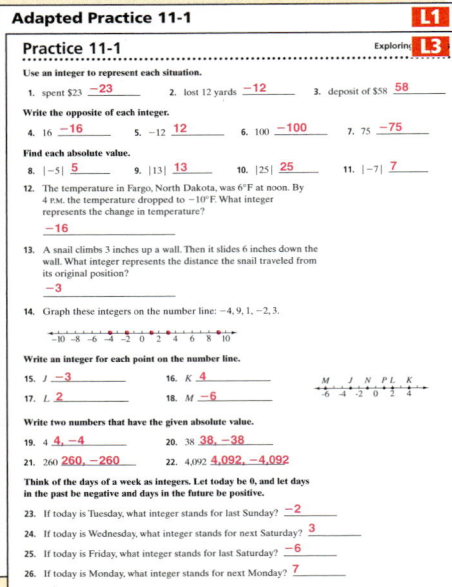

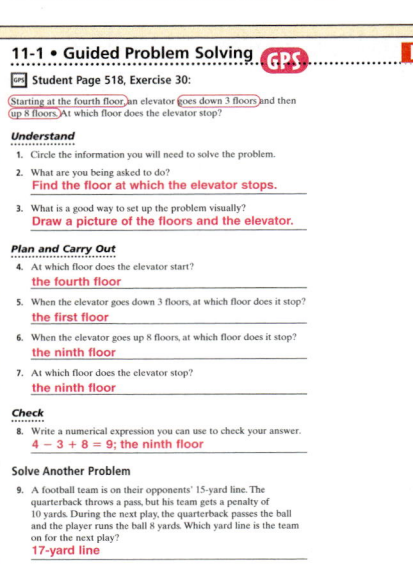

Homework Exercises

For more exercises, see Extra Skills and Word Problems.

GO for Help

For Exercises	See Examples
7–12	1
13–20	2
21–28	3

A Use an integer to represent each situation.

7. earned $100   **100**

8. 800 ft gain in elevation   **800**

9. 12° below 0°C   **–12**

10. 4° above 0°F   **4**

11. a debt of $25   **–25**

12. lost 5 pounds   **–5**

Write the opposite of each integer.

13. -10 **10**

14. -21 **21**

15. 14 **–14**

16. 0 **0**

17. 13 **–13**

18. -8 **8**

19. 150 **–150**

20. -1 **1**

Find each absolute value.

21. $|38|$ **38**

22. $|2|$ **2**

23. $|-9|$ **9**

24. $|-97|$ **97**

25. $|-4|$ **4**

26. $|17|$ **17**

27. $|-65|$ **65**

28. $|0|$ **0**

B  29. **Guided Problem Solving** The reading on a thermometer outside is 55°F when you leave for school at 8:00 A.M. At 3:00 P.M., the reading is 72°F. What integer can you use to represent the change in temperature? **17**
  • You can use a number line to help visualize the problem.

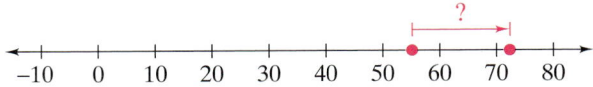

30. Starting at the fourth floor, an elevator goes down 3 floors and then up 8 floors. At which floor does the elevator stop? **9th floor**

31. **Divers** Dean dives 17 feet below the surface of Canyon Lake. Janet dives 25 feet below the lake's surface. Use absolute values to find who dives farther below the surface. **Janet**

32. **Writing in Math** Can the absolute value of a number be negative? Explain your reasoning. **Answers may vary.**
Sample: No; the absolute value of a number gives its distance from 0 on a number line, and distances are never negative.

Write an integer for each point on the number line.

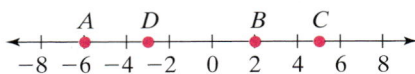

33. A **–6**

34. B **2**

35. C **5**

36. D **–3**

Homework Video Tutor

Visit: PHSchool.com
Web Code: aqe-1101

Microchips used in computers are made of silicon, a chemical element found in ordinary beach sand.

Write two numbers that have the given absolute value.

37. 3 **–3; 3**   **38.** 22 **–22; 22**   **39.** 101 **–101; 101**   **40.** 2,004
–2,004; 2,004

41. (**Algebra**) The absolute value of a certain integer *n* equals the opposite of *n*. If *n* does not equal 0, is *n* positive or negative?
negative

42. History A timeline is a number line that shows dates.

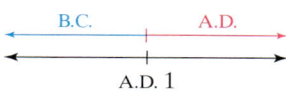

Draw a timeline from 2000 B.C. to A.D. 2000 using intervals of 500 years. Then graph the following events on the timeline.
See margin.

A.D. 1971   The first microcomputer is introduced.
776 B.C.   The first Olympic Games are held.
1600 B.C.   Stonehenge is completed.
A.D. 1492   Columbus lands in the New World.
1190 B.C.   The city of Troy falls to Greek warriors.

C **43. Challenge** Explain how to locate 225 on the number line.
See margin.

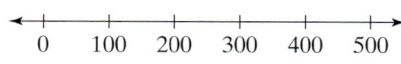

Test Prep and Mixed Review   **Practice**

Multiple Choice

44. Tara was 50 feet below the surface of the ocean. She then swam up 20 feet. Which integer represents her starting depth?
Ⓐ −50   Ⓑ −20   Ⓒ 20   Ⓓ 50 **A**

45. Kaida has 4 red marbles, 3 blue marbles, and 5 green marbles in a bag. If she randomly draws one marble from the bag, what is the probability that she does NOT draw a red marble? **J**
Ⓕ $\frac{1}{8}$ Ⓖ $\frac{1}{3}$ Ⓗ $\frac{1}{2}$ Ⓙ $\frac{2}{3}$

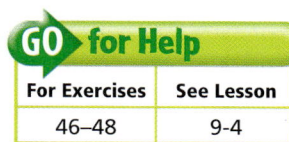

for Help

For Exercises	See Lesson
46–48	9-4

Use the data in the graph for Exercises 46–48.

46. Which waterfall has the greatest height? **Angel Falls**

47. Which waterfall has the least height? **Dudhsagar Falls**

48. Which waterfalls are between 2,000 feet and 2,500 feet?
Piemans Falls and Yosemite Falls

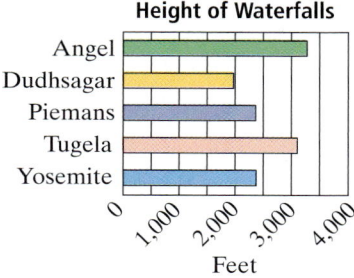

Height of Waterfalls

Angel
Dudhsagar
Piemans
Tugela
Yosemite

0 1,000 2,000 3,000 4,000

Feet

Online lesson quiz, PHSchool.com, Web Code: aqa-1101   11-1 Exploring Integers   **519**

Lesson Quiz

1. The surface of the Dead Sea is about 1,300 feet below sea level. Use an integer to represent this elevation.
−1,300

2. Write the opposite of −12. **12**

Find each value.

3. |6| **6**   **4.** |−3| **3**

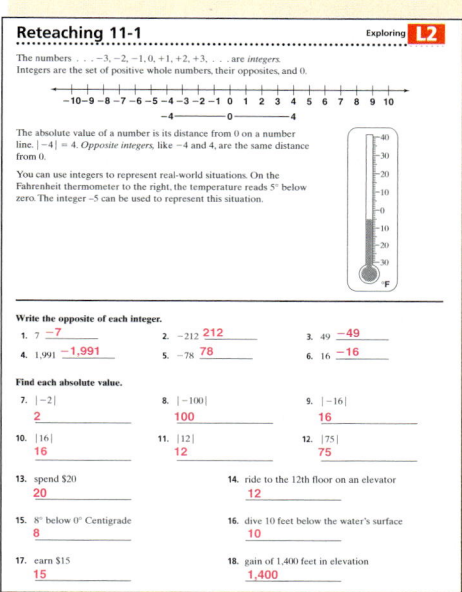

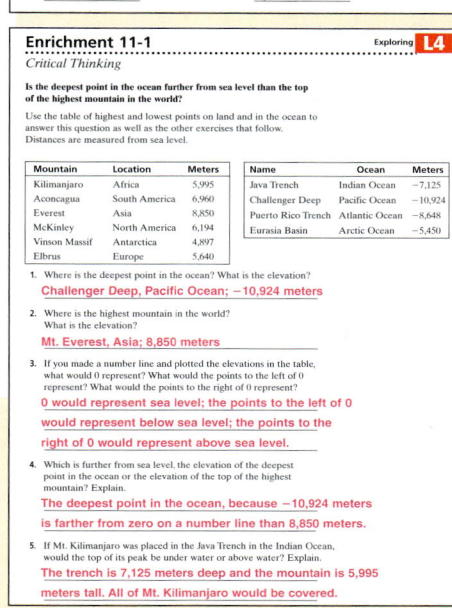

Alternative Assessment

Provide students with number lines and have them place several integers on them. Then have them trade papers with a partner and find the opposites of their partners' integers.

42. See back of book.
43. See back of book.

Test Prep

Resources

For additional practice with a variety of test item formats:
• Test-Taking Strategies, p. 563
• Test Prep, p. 567
• Test-Taking Strategies with Transparencies

519

Objective
To compare and order integers

Examples
1 Comparing Integers
2 Ordering Integers

Math Understandings: p. 514C

Math Background

Integers can be on a number line. To the right of 0 are positive integers and to the left of 0 are negative integers. Zero is neither positive nor negative.

More Math Background: p. 514C

Lesson Planning and Resources

See p. 514E for a list of the resources that support this lesson.

Bell Ringer Practice

✓ **Check Skills You'll Need**
For intervention, direct students to:
Comparing and Ordering Fractions
Lesson 4-8
Extra Skills and Word Problems Practice, Ch. 4

Activity Lab

Use before the lesson.

 **Teaching Resources**

Activity Lab 11-2: Extend Your Thinking

Guided Instruction

Example 2
Have students draw a number line. They can write the numbers in the Exercises on self-stick notes and place them in order.

520

11-2

Comparing and Ordering Integers

✓ **Check Skills You'll Need**

1. Vocabulary Review
The symbol $<$ means __?__, and the symbol $>$ means __?__. **less than; greater than**

Compare each pair of numbers. Use $<$, $=$, or $>$.

2. $\frac{2}{3}$ ■ $\frac{7}{10}$ $<$

3. $\frac{2}{3}$ ■ $\frac{8}{12}$ $=$

4. $\frac{3}{5}$ ■ $\frac{5}{11}$ $>$

GO for Help
Lesson 4-8

What You'll Learn

To compare and order integers

Why Learn This?

Negative points and scores are possible in some games. You need to compare and order integers to find who is winning.

You can use a number line to compare integers. As you move to the right on a number line, the numbers become greater.

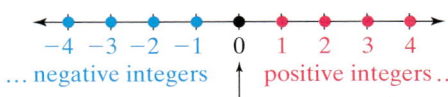

… negative integers   positive integers …

0 is neither positive nor negative.
The opposite of 0 is 0.

EXAMPLE   **Comparing Integers**

① Compare -6 and -4.

Graph -4 and -6 on the same number line.

Since -6 is to the left of -4 on the number line, $-6 < -4$, or $-4 > -6$.

✓ Quick Check

1. Compare, using $<$ or $>$.
   a. 5 ■ -3 **b.** -12 ■ 9
   $>$ $<$

You can also use a number line to order integers.

Differentiated Instruction Solutions for All Learners

Special Needs L1
Provide students with a copy of Example 2. Have them cut around the number line, and fold it with zero as the center. Point out the symmetry between the unit distances on either side of zero, such as that the relative distance from zero to 100 and -100 is equal.

learning style: tactile

Below Level L2
Create a number line for Quick Check 2. Students can place the numbers on the line. They can move their fingers from left to right. Remind them that movement to the right shows a greater integer.

learning style: tactile

online
active math

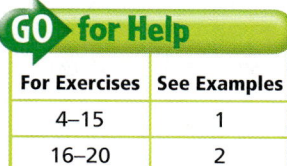

For: Comparing Integers Activity
Use: Interactive Textbook, 11-2

EXAMPLE Ordering Integers

② **Games** Order the scores on the scoreboard from least to greatest.

Tigers	−200
Bulldogs	+300
Lions	−400
Spartans	+100

Use one hundred as the number line interval.

←――+――――+――――+――――+――――+――――+――――+――――+――――→
−400 −300 −200 −100 0 100 200 300 400

−400, −200, 100, 300 ← Order the scores from least to greatest.

In order, the scores are −400, −200, 100, and 300.

✓ Quick Check

2. Order these scores from least to greatest: −25, 100, −50, 75.
   −50, −25, 75, 100

✓ Check Your Understanding

3. **Answers may vary. Sample:** On a number line, numbers increase from left to right. Since negative numbers are less than 0, they are on the left. Positive numbers are greater than 0 and on the right, so $a < b$.

1. Which statement is NOT true? **C**
   (A) $-9 < -7$ (B) $-3 < 5$ (C) $-5 > -3$ (D) $-2 < 6$

2. Order −2, 4, 0, and −6 from least to greatest. **−6, −2, 0, 4**

3. **Writing in Math** Suppose a is negative and b is positive. Use a number line to explain how you know that $a < b$. **See left.**

Homework Exercises

For more exercises, see Extra Skills and Word Problems.

GO for Help

For Exercises	See Examples
4–15	1
16–20	2

Ⓐ **Compare, using < or >.**

4. −7 ■ −8
   >
5. −3 ■ 3
   <
6. 0 ■ −9
   >
7. −7 ■ 0
   <

8. −5 ■ 0
   <
9. 6 ■ −18
   >
10. −12 ■ −2
    <
11. 0 ■ −3
    >

12. 2 ■ −12
    >
13. −9 ■ −17
    >
14. −1 ■ 10
    <
15. −23 ■ −4
    <

Order each set of integers from least to greatest.

16. −9, −12, −4, −15
    −15, −12, −9, −4

17. −2, 5, 0, −5, 2
    −5, −2, 0, 2, 5

18. 40, −30, 30, −50, −60
    −60, −50, −30, 30, 40

19. −28, −16, −33, −13
    −33, −28, −16, −13

20. **Golf** In golf, a negative score is called "under par." List the golf scores −1, +2, −3, and +4 from least to greatest. **−3, −1, +2, +4**

Online **lesson quiz,** PHSchool.com, **Web Code:** aqa-1102   11-2 Comparing and Ordering Integers **521**

Advanced Learners L4
Have students compare absolute value such as these.

$|-(-(-9))| \blacksquare 0$ **>**
$-|-65| \blacksquare -|56|$ **<**
$-|-|32|| \blacksquare -(-|-23|)$ **<**

learning style: visual

English Language Learners ELL
Provide students with more language describing the relative sizes of integers. For example, tell students that numbers at a greater distance to the left of zero are going to be of lesser value than those closer to zero, and numbers further from zero to the right are greater in value.

learning style: verbal

PowerPoint Additional Examples

① Compare −12 and −10.
   −12 < −10

② Order from least to greatest.
   a. 16, −2, −35, 68, −10
      −35, −10, −2, 16, 68
   b. −87, −14, 41, −104, 78
      −104, −87, −14, 41, 78

All in One Teaching Resources
• Daily Notetaking Guide 11-2 L3
• Adapted Notetaking 11-2 L1

Closure

• *How can you compare integers?*
  Place them on a number line. The rightmost integer is greatest.

3. Practice

Assignment Guide

Check Your Understanding
Go over Exercises 1–3 in class before assigning the Homework Exercises.

Homework Exercises
A Practice by Example   4–20
B Apply Your Skills   21–25
C Challenge   26
Test Prep and
   Mixed Review   27–31

Homework Quick Check
To check student's understanding of key skills and concepts, go over Exercises 12, 18, 22, 24, and 25.

4. Assess & Reteach

PowerPoint Lesson Quiz

Order from least to greatest.

1. −4, 0, 5, −6 **−6, −4, 0, 5**

2. −3, 3, −6, −5 **−6, −5, −3, 3**

Alternative Assessment

Provide pairs of students with number lines. Partners graph the integers in Exercises 4–15 on the number lines. Then partners compare and order the integers.

521

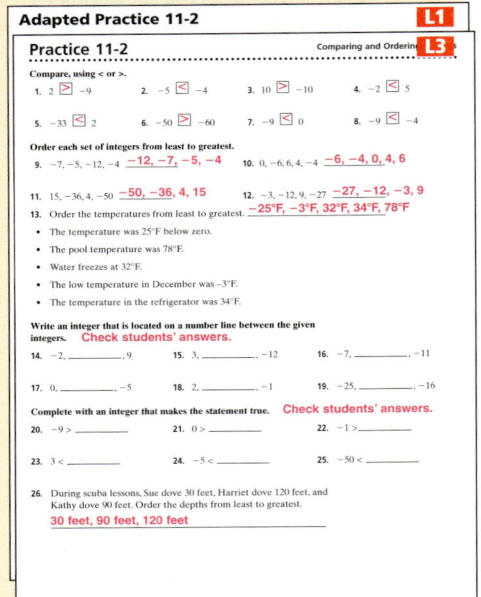
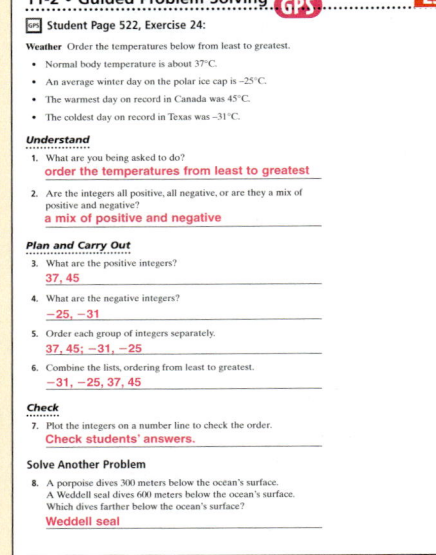
B **GPS** 21. **Guided Problem Solving** Here are the coldest and hottest temperatures on record for four Alaskan cities:
$-34°F, 85°F, -62°F, 96°F, -22°F, 90°F, -54°F, 86°F.$

Write the temperatures in order from coldest to hottest.
• Separate the list into negative and positive integers.
• Order each group of integers separately.
$-62°F, -54°F, -34°F, -22°F, 85°F, 86°F, 90°F, 96°F$

GO **Online**
Homework Video Tutor

Visit: PHSchool.com
Web Code: aqe-1102

22. **Number Sense** What is the greatest negative integer? **-1**

23. How many integers are *greater than* -5 and *less than* 5? **9**

24. **Weather** Order the temperatures below from least to greatest.
GPS • Normal body temperature is about 37°C.
• An average winter day on the polar ice cap is -25°C.
• The warmest day on record in Canada was 45°C.
• The coldest day on record in Texas was -31°C.
$-31°C, -25°C, 37°C, 45°C$

25. (**Algebra**) Compare, using < or >.
a. If $x > y$, then the opposite of x ▇ the opposite of y. **<**
b. If $x < y$, then the opposite of x ▇ the opposite of y. **>**

C 26. **Challenge** Write the numbers in order from least to greatest:
$-2, -1.3, \frac{1}{4}, 0, -4, -\frac{1}{2}, -2\frac{3}{4}, 3, -3.5, 2\frac{1}{2}.$ **$-4, -3.5, -2\frac{3}{4}, -2, -1.3,$**
$-\frac{1}{2}, 0, \frac{1}{4}, 2\frac{1}{2}, 3$

Test Prep and Mixed Review **Practice**

Multiple Choice

27. The temperature on the moon varies from $-387°F$ to $253°F$. Which integer represents the highest moon temperature? **C**
Ⓐ -387 Ⓑ -253 Ⓒ 253   Ⓓ 387

28. Two students measured the length of the shelves in a school library. The results are shown in the table. Which expression can be used to find the length, in yards, of shelf E? **J**
Ⓕ $3n$ Ⓗ $n - 3$
Ⓖ $\frac{3}{n}$ Ⓙ $\frac{n}{3}$

Library Shelves

Shelf	Length (feet)	Length (yards)
A	3	1
B	6	2
C	12	4
D	15	5
E	n	▇

GO **for Help**

For Exercises	See Lesson
29–31	9-4

Find the area of each parallelogram.

29.
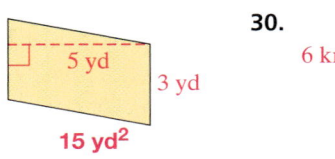
5 yd
3 yd
15 yd²

30.
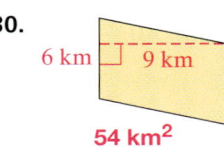
6 km   9 km
54 km²

31.
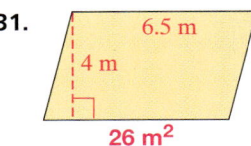
6.5 m
4 m
26 m²

EXAMPLE   Application: Sports

2 A football team loses 3 yards on one play. On the next play, the team gains 2 yards. Find $-3 + 2$.

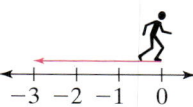

Start at 0, and face the positive direction. Move **backward 3 units** for -3.

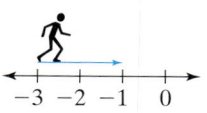

Then move **forward 2 units** for **2**. You stop at -1.

The result is a loss of 1 yard.

✓ Quick Check

2. Find $-4 + 1$. **−3**

KEY CONCEPTS   Adding Integers

Same Signs The sum of two positive integers is positive. The sum of two negative integers is negative.

Examples: $2 + 6 = 8$ $-2 + (-6) = -8$

Different Signs Find the absolute value of each integer. Then subtract the lesser absolute value from the greater. The sum has the sign of the integer with the greater absolute value.

Examples: $3 + (-7) = -4$ $-3 + 7 = 4$

EXAMPLES   Adding Integers

3 Find $-3 + (-7)$.

$-3 + (-7) = -10$ ← **The sum of two negative numbers is negative.**

4 Find $8 + (-5)$.

$|8| = 8$ and $|-5| = 5$ ← **Find the absolute value of each integer.**

$8 - 5 = 3$ ← **Subtract the absolute values.**

$8 + (-5) = 3$ ← **Since 8 has the greater absolute value, the sum is positive.**

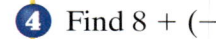
GO for Help

For help with absolute values, go to Lesson 11-1, Example 3.

✓ Quick Check

3. Find $-9 + (-12)$. **−21**   4. Find $-11 + 4$. **−7**

Activity Lab

Use before the lesson.
Student Edition Activity Lab, Hands On 11-3a, Modeling Addition of Integers, p. 523

All in One Teaching Resources
Activity Lab 11-3: Adding Integers with Technology

Guided Instruction

Error Prevention!

Point out that bars are used for absolute value.

PowerPoint
Additional Examples

1 Use a number line to find each sum.

a. $5 + 2$ **7**

b. $-3 + (-5)$ **−8**

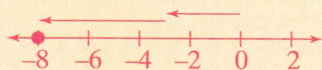

2 A painter climbs up 26 rungs of a ladder. Then she climbs down 14 rungs. What is her current position?
$26 + (-14) = 12$; She is on the 12th rung.

3 Find each sum.

a. $-8 + (-10)$ **−18**

b. $-4 + 16$ **12**

All in One Teaching Resources
• Daily Notetaking Guide 11-3 **L3**
• Adapted Notetaking 11-3 **L1**

Closure

• *How would you add integers with different signs?* **Sample: First find the absolute value of each integer. Then subtract the lesser absolute value from the greater. The sum has the sign of the integer with the greater absolute value.**

Advanced Learners **L4**
Students write two expressions whose sum is −8. They use two negative integers for one expression, and a positive and a negative integer for the other. **Sample: −2 + (−6); 4 + (−12)**

learning style: visual

English Language Learners **ELL**
Have students use words and pictures to *explain* why it makes sense that the sum of two negative integers is negative. Have them practice explaining this to a partner.

learning style: verbal

3. Practice

Assignment Guide

Check Your Understanding
Go over Exercises 1–4 in class before assigning the Homework Exercises.

Homework Exercises
A Practice by Example   5–23
B Apply Your Skills   24–31
C Challenge   32
Test Prep and
    Mixed Review   33–39

Homework Quick Check
To check students' understanding of key skills and concepts, go over Exercises 10, 16, 25, 28, and 30.

Differentiated Instruction **Resources**

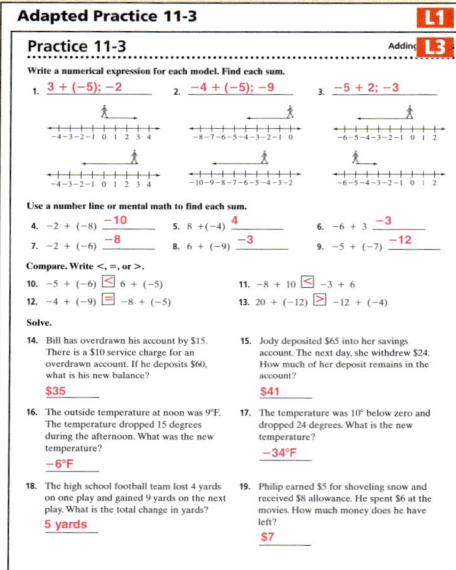

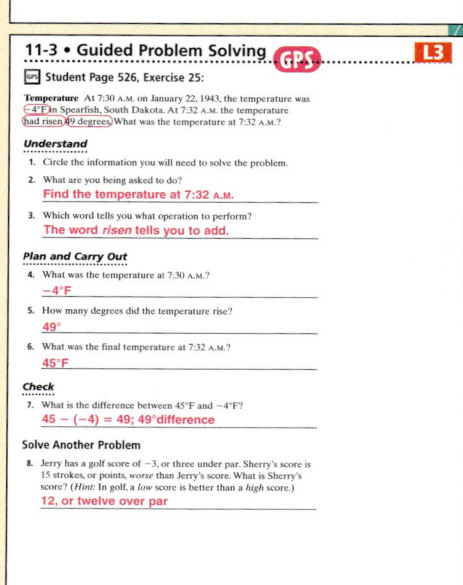

✓ Check Your Understanding

Complete each statement with *always*, *sometimes*, or *never*.

1. The sum of two negative integers is __?__ negative. **always**

2. The sum of two positive integers is __?__ negative. **never**

3. The sum of a positive integer and a negative integer is __?__ negative. **sometimes**

4. **Number Sense** Explain how you can tell whether the sum of two numbers is positive or negative before you add.
   Answers may vary. Sample: If the sign of the integer with the greater absolute value is positive, the sum will be positive.

Homework Exercises

For more exercises, see Extra Skills and Word Problems.

GO for Help

For Exercises	See Examples
5–11	1–2
12–23	3–4

A Use a number line to find each sum.

5. $-5 + (-3)$ **−8**
6. $2 + 4$ **6**
7. $-2 + (-2)$ **−4**
8. $6 + (-7)$ **−1**
9. $-1 + 4$ **3**
10. $-6 + 6$ **0**

11. **Money** Suppose you borrow $8 from a friend. You pay him back $6. How much do you still owe? **$2**

Find each sum.

12. $-2 + (-7)$ **−9**
13. $-6 + 3$ **−3**
14. $9 + (-9)$ **0**
15. $-31 + (-16)$ **−47**
16. $-12 + (-9)$ **−21**
17. $13 + 29$ **42**
18. $91 + 28$ **119**
19. $-47 + (-41)$ **−88**
20. $-51 + (-9)$ **−60**
21. $23 + (-15)$ **8**
22. $-8 + 72$ **64**
23. $18 + (-39)$ **−21**

B GPS 24. **Guided Problem Solving** A jellyfish was 64 feet below sea level. It rose 19 feet. What integer describes the new position of the jellyfish? **−45**
   • What integer represents 64 feet below sea level?
   • What operation represents a rise of 19 feet?

25. **Temperature** At 7:30 A.M. on January 22, 1943, the temperature was $-4°$F in Spearfish, South Dakota. At 7:32 A.M. the temperature had risen 49 degrees. What was the temperature at 7:32 A.M.? **45°F**

29. **Answers may vary. Samples are given.**
   a. You deposit $30 and withdraw $40. What is your balance?
   b. The balance in your account is $89. If you withdraw $45, what is the new balance?
   c. You deposit $60 and write a check for $60. What is your balance?

32. **Placement of numbers may vary. Sample:**

3	−4	1
−2	0	2
−1	4	−3

28. Answers may vary. Sample: Adding a negative number is the same as subtracting the absolute value of that negative number.

Find each sum.

26. $8 + (-1) + (-6) + 5$ **6**

27. $-2 + 6 + (-3) + (-4)$ **−3**

28. **Writing in Math** Why do you use subtraction when you add a positive integer and a negative integer? **See left.**

29. **Open-Ended** Use a positive integer and a negative integer to write a word problem about each bank account. **29a–c. See margin.**
  a. The sum of the integers is negative.
  b. The sum of the integers is positive.
  c. The sum of the integers is zero.

30. **Skyscrapers** The mail center of a building is on the fifteenth floor. A clerk delivers mail by going up 5 floors, down 3 floors, and then down another 4 floors. Where is the clerk in relation to the mail center? $15 + 5 + (-3) + (-4) = 13$; **2 floors below the mail room**

31. **Submarines** A submarine is 86 feet below sea level. The submarine then rises 16 feet and dives 58 feet. What integer describes the position of the submarine? **−128**

 **32.** **Challenge** Copy the square shown. Write the integers $-4, -3, -2, -1, 0, 1, 2, 3,$ and 4 in the boxes so that the vertical, horizontal, and diagonal sums are 0. **See margin.**

Test Prep and Mixed Review **Practice**

Multiple Choice

33. Rita ate less than half of her sandwich for lunch. Which fraction is NOT less than $\frac{1}{2}$? **C**
  Ⓐ $\frac{1}{4}$ Ⓑ $\frac{2}{5}$ Ⓒ $\frac{4}{7}$ Ⓓ $\frac{5}{11}$

34. A 5-kilometer run is about 3.1 miles long. How many meters long is a 5-kilometer run? **J**
  Ⓕ 0.005 m Ⓖ 0.05 m Ⓗ 500 m Ⓙ 5,000 m

35. You need to add three simplified fractions. The denominators are 9, 12, and 18. What is the least common denominator? **B**
  Ⓐ 18 Ⓑ 36 Ⓒ 72 Ⓓ 108

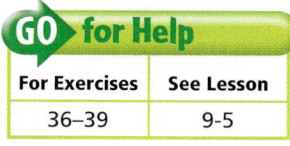
GO for Help

For Exercises	See Lesson
36–39	9-5

Name each of the following for circle J.

36. radii $\overline{JC}, \overline{JD}, \overline{JE}, \overline{JF}, \overline{JG}, \overline{JH}$

37. diameters $\overline{CF}, \overline{DG}, \overline{EH}$

38. chords $\overline{CD}, \overline{DE}, \overline{EF}, \overline{FG}, \overline{GH}, \overline{HC}, \overline{CF}, \overline{DG}, \overline{EH}$

39. the center **J**

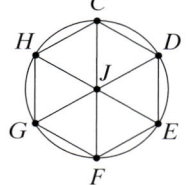

Alternative Assessment

Provide student pairs with counters or integer chips. Have partners take turns using the integer chips to model the additions in Exercises 5–23. One partner models the addition; the other partner records the sum.

Test Prep

Resources

For additional practice with a variety of test item formats:
• Test-Taking Strategies, p. 563
• Test Prep, p. 567
• Test-Taking Strategies with Transparencies

Lesson Quiz

Find each sum.

1. $-9 + (-5)$ **−14**

2. $8 + (-7)$ **1**

3. $-12 + 5$ **−7**

4. $48 + (-22)$ **26**

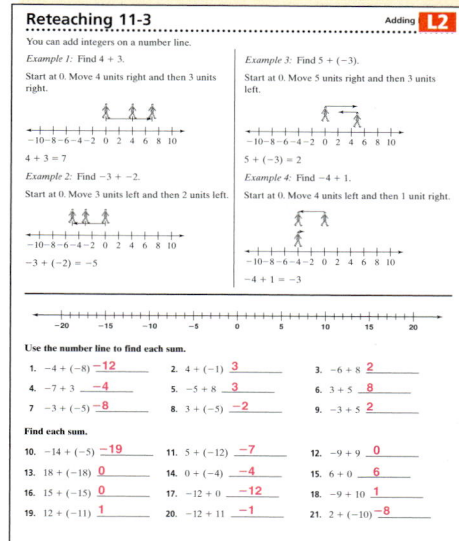

Reteaching 11-3 Adding **L2**

Enrichment 11-3 Adding **L4**

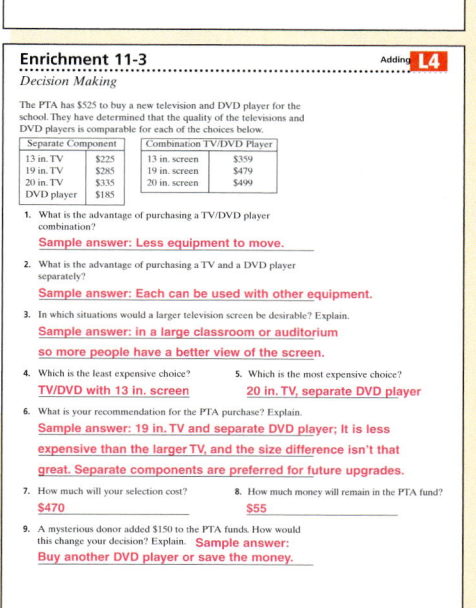

Checkpoint Quiz

Use this Checkpoint Quiz to check students' understanding of the skills and concepts of Lessons 11-1 through 11-3.

Resources

- All-in-One Teaching Resources Checkpoint Quiz 1
- ExamView Assessment Suite CD-ROM
- Success Tracker Online Intervention

A Race to the End

In this game, students practice adding integers with different signs. As players roll the number cubes and add the integers shown, they move their game piece the number of spaces and direction indicated by the sum.

Guided Instruction

Before they play the game, remind students that the greatest of two or more integers is the one that is farthest to the right on the number line. Ask:
Are all positive integers greater than any negative integer? **yes**

Have a volunteer read the rules. Then have students play the game in pairs.

Resources

- game board
- two different-colored number cubes
- two different-colored place markers

Checkpoint Quiz 1

Lessons 11-1 through 11-3

Find each absolute value.

1. $|-13|$ **13**

2. $|64|$ **64**

Find each sum.

3. $-8 + 5$ **−3**

4. $-10 + (-2)$ **−12**

5. You write a check for \$32. What integer represents the change in your checking account balance? **−32**

6. Order 16, −17, 18, −15, and −14 from least to greatest. **−17, −15, −14, 16, 18**

7. In the morning, the temperature was −7°F. The temperature rose 19 degrees by noon. What was the temperature at noon? **12°F**

MATH GAMES

A Race to the End

What You'll Need

- game board
- two different-colored number cubes
- two different-colored place markers

How To Play

- Each player places a marker on 0.
- Use one cube to represent positive integers and the other cube to represent negative integers.
- One player rolls the two number cubes.
- The player adds the integers represented by the cubes and then moves his or her marker the number of spaces in the direction indicated by the sum.
- Players take turns rolling both number cubes and moving their markers.
- The first player who reaches or goes past either end of the board wins.

528

Modeling Subtraction of Integers

ACTIVITY

1. Find $-5 - (-2)$.

Show 5 "−" chips.	Take away 2 "−" chips.	There are 3 "−" chips left. So $-5 - (-2) = -3$.

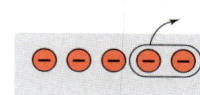

Remember that ⊕ and ⊖ are a zero pair. Sometimes you need to insert zero pairs in order to subtract.

ACTIVITY

2. Find $5 - (-2)$.

Show 5 "+" chips.	Insert two zero pairs. Then take away 2 "−" chips.	There are 7 "+" chips left. So $5 - (-2) = 7$.

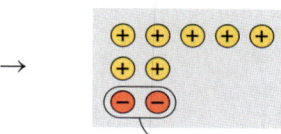

3. Find $-5 - 2$.

Show 5 "−" chips.	Insert two zero pairs. Then take away 2 "+" chips.	There are 7 "−" chips left. So $-5 - 2 = -7$.

Exercises

Use chips or mental math to help you subtract the following integers.

1. $5 - 8$ **−3**
2. $-3 - 7$ **−10**
3. $5 - (-9)$ **14**
4. $-8 - (-13)$ **5**

Activity Lab

Modeling Subtraction of Integers

Students use models to subtract integers.

Guided Instruction

Teaching Tip
Remind students about the meaning of *zero pair*. Ask: *When you subtract an integer from an integer with a different sign, what counters must you add to your model?* **Add a zero pair—the same number of positive and negative counters as the absolute value of the number subtracted.**

Exercises
Have students work on the Exercises. Circulate, helping students who are having difficulty.

Alternative Method
Students place a marker on a number line. Discuss that a move representing subtraction of a positive integer is to the left. A move representing subtraction of a negative integer is to the right. The number of spaces moved is equal to the absolute value of the integer being subtracted. Compare this subtraction method with the number-line method they used to add integers.

Differentiated Instruction **Resources**

Tactile Learners
To model the subtraction of positive and negative integers, give 5 students one sheet of colored paper each and have them stand together. Ask 2 students to sit on the floor to represent subtracting −2. Students can see $-5 - (-2)$ is −3.

Resources

- Activity Lab 11-4: Subtracting Integers with Technology
- counters in two colors
- Student Manipulatives Kit

Objective
To subtract integers and to solve problems by subtracting integers

Examples
1 Using a Number Line to Subtract
2 Subtracting Integers
3 Application: Submarines

Math Understandings: p. 514C

Math Background

The subtraction of integers can be modeled on a number line. Zero is the starting point and the ending point of the last move indicates the difference. Positive numbers are shown as moves to the right. Negative numbers are shown as moves to the left. A subtraction operation changes the direction of movement for the number that follows it. This change of direction represents how you subtract an integer by adding its opposite.

More Math Background: p. 514C

Lesson Planning and Resources

See p. 514E for a list of the resources that support this lesson.

Bell Ringer Practice

✓ **Check Skills You'll Need**
Use student page, transparency, or PowerPoint. For intervention, direct students to:
Adding Integers
Lesson 11-3
Extra Skills and Word Problems Practice, Ch. 11

530

 **Check Skills You'll Need**

1. **Vocabulary Review**
   What is the *opposite* of 6? −6

Find each sum.

2. 13 + (−3) **10**

3. −10 + 5 **−5**

4. (−7) + (−4) **−11**

5. 8 + 6 **14**

 for Help
Lesson 11-3

What You'll Learn
To subtract integers and to solve problems by subtracting integers

Why Learn This?
You can subtract integers to find changes in the depth of vehicles or creatures underwater.

You can use a model to subtract integers. On a number line, the subtraction operation tells you to turn around and face the opposite direction.

EXAMPLE **Using a Number Line to Subtract**

Vocabulary Tip

The expression 3 − (−2) is read "3 minus negative 2."

1 Use a number line to find 3 − (−2).

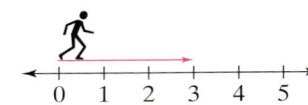
Start at 0. Face the positive direction. Move **forward 3 units** for **3**.

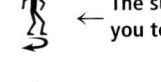
The subtraction sign tells you to turn around.

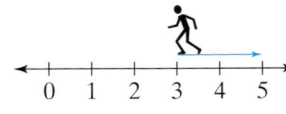
Then move **backward 2 units** for **−2**. You stop at 5.

So 3 − (−2) = 5.

✓ **Quick Check**

1. **a.** Find 5 − (−1). **6**   **b.** Find −3 − 3. **−6**

530 Chapter 11 Integers

Differentiated **Instruction** **Solutions for All Learners**

Special Needs **L1**
Help students differentiate between moving towards the left and moving backward. Point out that backwards mean that the back of the figure is turned towards the direction it is moving.

learning style: visual

Below Level **L2**
Give students practice changing subtraction problems into addition problems as shown below.

5 − 3 **5 + (−3)**   −4 − 3 **−4 + (−3)**
6 − (−6) **6 + 6**   −3 − (−4) **−3 + 4**

learning style: visual

Subtracting an integer is the same as adding its opposite.

$$3 - 2 = 1 \text{ and } 3 + (-2) = 1$$

> **KEY CONCEPTS** **Subtracting Integers**
>
> You subtract an integer by adding its opposite.
>
> **Examples:**
>
> $10 - 6 = 10 + (-6)$ $10 - (-6) = 10 + 6$
>
> $-10 - 6 = -10 + (-6)$ $-10 - (-6) = -10 + 6$

EXAMPLE **Subtracting Integers**

2

a. Find $-8 - (-3)$.

$-8 - (-3) = -8 + 3$ ← To subtract −3, add its opposite, 3.

           $= -5$ ← Simplify.

b. Find $-2 - 7$.

$-2 - 7 = -2 + (-7)$ ← To subtract 7, add its opposite, −7.

         $= -9$ ← Simplify.

GO for Help

For help adding integers, go to Lesson 11-3, Example 3.

✓ Quick Check

2. Find $-6 - (-2)$.   **−4**

EXAMPLE **Application: Submarines**

3

The submarine *Alvin* was 1,500 feet below sea level (−1,500). Then it moved to 1,872 feet below sea level (−1,872). How far did *Alvin* move?

Find $-1,872 - (-1,500)$.

$-1,872 - (-1,500) = -1,872 + 1,500$ ← To subtract −1,500, add its opposite.

                   $= -372$ ← Simplify.

Alvin moved down 372 feet.

GO Online

Video Tutor Help
Visit: PHSchool.com
Web Code: aqe-0775

✓ Quick Check

3. Suppose *Alvin* moved from 1,872 feet below sea level to a position 1,250 feet below sea level. How far did *Alvin* move? Did it finish closer to sea level or farther from sea level?
622 ft; closer

11-4   Subtracting Integers   **531**

2. Teach

Activity Lab

Use before the lesson.
Student Edition Activity Lab, Hands On 11-4a, Modeling Subtraction of Integers, p. 529

All in One Teaching Resources
Activity Lab 11-4: Subtracting Integers with Technology

Guided Instruction

Error Prevention!

Students may confuse opposites with absolute values. To subtract integers, they should add the opposite. Opposite integers can be positive or negative.

Example 2
Help students understand that they must make two changes when rewriting a subtraction as an addition.
1. Change the minus sign to a plus sign.
2. Change the second number to its opposite.

PowerPoint

Additional Examples

1 Use a number line to find $4 - (-4)$. **8**

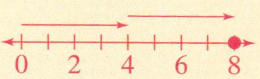

2 Find each difference.
  a. $-5 - (-7)$ **2**
  b. $-9 - 6$ **−15**

3 Juan owes his sister $14. She told him to subtract $8 of what he owes if he feeds the dog. Write an integer to show how much Juan will have if he feeds the dog. **−6**

All in One Teaching Resources
• Daily Notetaking Guide 11-4 **L3**
• Adapted Notetaking 11-4 **L1**

Closure

• *What is the rule for subtracting integers?* **To subtract an integer, add its opposite.**

531

3. Practice

Assignment Guide

Check Your Understanding
Go over Exercises 1–5 in class before assigning the Homework Exercises.

Homework Exercises
A Practice by Example   6–21
B Apply Your Skills   22–29
C Challenge   30
Test Prep and
   Mixed Review   31–36

Homework Quick Check
To check students' understanding of key skills and concepts, go over Exercises 8, 15, 23, 28, and 29.

Differentiated Instruction **Resources**

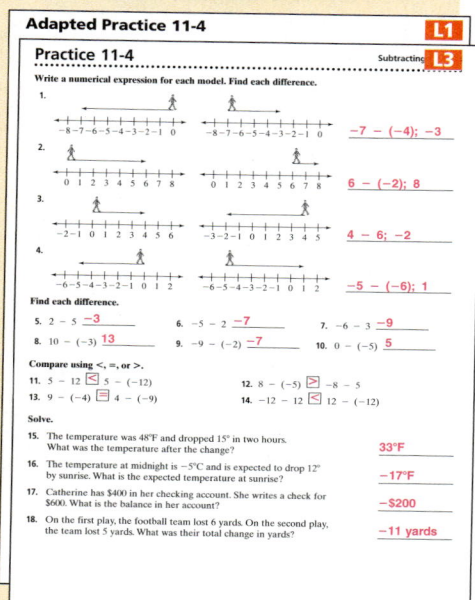

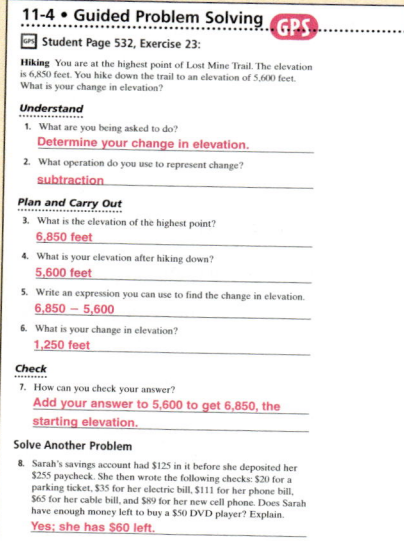

532

✓ Check Your Understanding

1. Write an expression you can model using the steps below.

$-3 - (-2)$

2. **Writing in Math** Explain why $2 - 7$ is not the same as $7 - 2$.

See left.

2. Answers may vary. Sample: When you subtract 7 from 2, you get −5, whereas 7 − 2 gives you +5.

Rewrite each difference as a sum.

3. $-10 - 3$ $-10 + (-3)$ **4.** $2 - (-8)$ $2 + 8$ **5.** $-1 - (-3)$ $-1 + 3$

Homework Exercises

For more exercises, see **Extra Skills and Word Problems.**

GO for Help

For Exercises	See Examples
6–11	1
12–21	2–3

A **Use a number line to find each difference.**

6. $7 - 4$ **3**   **7.** $4 - (-5)$ **9**   **8.** $3 - 8$ **−5**

9. $-1 - 6$ **−7**   **10.** $-2 - (-3)$ **1**   **11.** $-4 - (-1)$ **−3**

Find each difference.

12. $-1 - (-1)$ **0**   **13.** $2 - 7$ **−5**   **14.** $-4 - 3$ **−7**

15. $-9 - 7$ **−16**   **16.** $81 - 106$ **−25**   **17.** $12 - (-17)$ **29**

18. $43 - (-21)$ **64**   **19.** $-24 - (-12)$ **−12**   **20.** $-25 - (-57)$ **32**

21. **Biology** A fish was at 1,965 feet below sea level. It then swam down to 2,327 feet below sea level. How far did the fish swim?
   362 ft

B **GPS** **22.** **Guided Problem Solving** Temperatures on the surface of Mercury vary from −279°F to 801°F. What is the range of temperatures on the surface of Mercury?   **1,080°F**

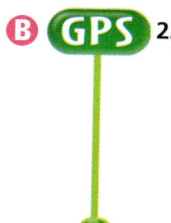

- **Make a Plan** To find the range, you subtract the lowest temperature from the highest temperature.
- **Check the Answer** Round −292 to −300 to check your answer.

GO Online
Homework Video Tutor
Visit: PHSchool.com
Web Code: aqe-1104

23. **Hiking** You are at the highest point of Lost Mine Trail. Your **GPS** elevation is 6,850 feet. You hike down the trail to an elevation of 5,600 feet. What is your change in elevation?   **−1,250 ft**

28. Cairo, 3:30 P.M.; Honolulu, 3:30 A.M.; Los Angeles, 5:30 A.M.; Paris, 2:30 P.M.; Sydney, 11:30 P.M.; Tokyo, 10:30 P.M.; Washington D.C., 8:30 A.M.

29. Answers may vary. Sample:
$3 - 7 = -4$, $7 - 3 = 4$, $-4 \neq 4$.

Find each difference.

24. $17 - 18 - (-81)$ **80** **25.** $-18 - 13 - 12$ **-43**

26. $23 - (-18) - (-54)$ **95** **27.** $16 - 28 - (-38)$ **26**

The two sides of this house are in different time zones.

28. Time Zones Standard time is computed in relation to Greenwich Mean Time (GMT). The table shows the number of hours from GMT for each city. It is 1:30 P.M. GMT. Find the time for each city.
See margin.

29. (**Algebra**) Explain why $a - b$ is not always the same as $b - a$.
See margin.

Cairo, Egypt	+2
Honolulu, Hawaii	-10
Los Angeles, Calif.	-8
Paris, France	+1
Sydney, Australia	+10
Tokyo, Japan	+9
Washington, D.C.	-5

C 30. Challenge Copy and complete the pyramid so that each number represents the sum of the two numbers directly beneath it. **See margin.**

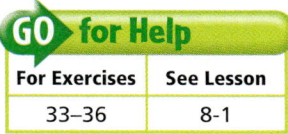

Test Prep and Mixed Review **Practice**

Multiple Choice

31. The low temperature on Monday was 6 degrees below zero. The high temperature was 10 degrees above zero. Which integer represents the low temperature? **B**

   (A) -16 (B) -6 (C) 6 (D) 16

32. Mr. Young has 20 students in his art class. He buys paint in packages of 12 jars. He wants to give the same number of jars of paint to each student. Arrange the steps below to find the least amount of paint Mr. Young needs to buy. **H**

   Step K. Find the least common multiple of 12 and 20.
   Step L. List the multiples of 12 and the multiples of 20.
   Step M. Divide the least common multiple by 12.

   (F) K, M, L   (G) K, L, M   (H) L, K, M   (J) L, M, K

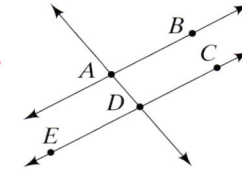

Use the figure to name the following.
33–36. Answers may vary. Samples are given.

33. three rays   **34.** three segments
  $\overrightarrow{AB}, \overrightarrow{DC}, \overrightarrow{DE}$ $\overline{AB}, \overline{AD}, \overline{DC}$

35. three points   **36.** three lines
  A, D, E $\overleftrightarrow{AB}, \overleftrightarrow{AD}, \overleftrightarrow{CE}$

GO for Help

For Exercises	See Lesson
33–36	8-1

Online lesson quiz, PHSchool.com, Web Code: aqa-1104

30.

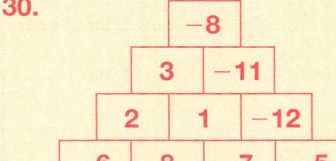

Test Prep

Resources
For additional practice with a variety of test item formats:
• Test-Taking Strategies, p. 563
• Test Prep, p. 567
• Test-Taking Strategies with Transparencies

---

4. Assess & Reteach

Lesson Quiz

Find each difference.

1. $3 - 6$ **-3**

2. $-7 - 8$ **-15**

3. $10 - (-4)$ **14**

4. $-9 - (-9)$ **0**

Alternative Assessment

Provide student pairs with integer chips. Partners use the integer chips to model the subtractions in Exercises 6–20. One student models the Exercise; the other student records the difference.

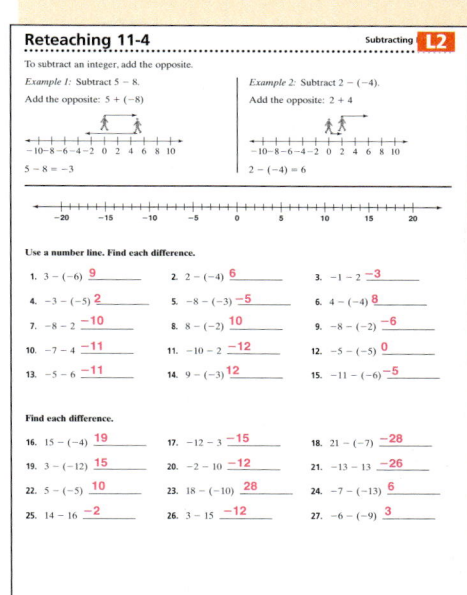

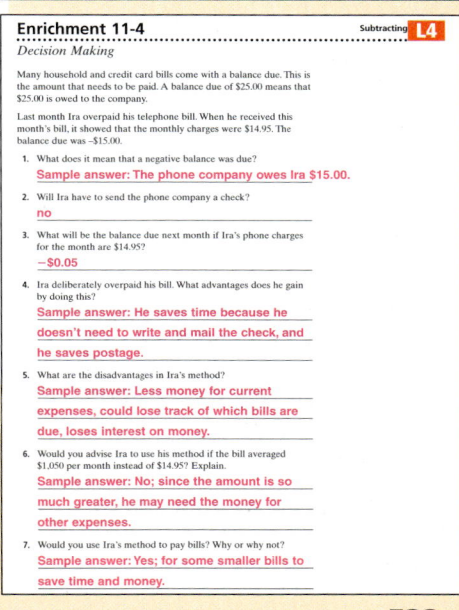

Objective
To multiply integers and to solve problems by multiplying integers

Examples
1   Using a Model to Multiply Integers
2, 3 Multiplying Integers

Math Understandings: p. 514C

Math Background

When two positive integers are multiplied, or when two negative integers are multiplied, the product is always a positive integer. The product of two integers with *different signs* is always *negative*.

More Math Background: p. 514C

Lesson Planning and Resources

See p. 514E for a list of the resources that support this lesson.

PowerPoint

Bell Ringer Practice

Check Skills You'll Need
Use student page, transparency, or PowerPoint. For intervention, direct students to:
Adding Integers
Lesson 11-3
Extra Skills and Word Problems
  Practice, Ch. 11

534

11-5 Multiplying Integers

Check Skills You'll Need

1. **Vocabulary Review**
The sum of two negative integers is always __?__.
negative
Find each sum.

2. $-4 + (-4)$ **−8**

3. $32 + 32$ **64**

4. $-14 + (-14)$ **−28**

5. $-45 + (-45)$ **−90**

GO for Help
Lesson 11-3

What You'll Learn

To multiply integers and to solve problems by multiplying integers

Why Learn This?

Computers multiply time by a negative rate to tell skydivers when to open their parachutes.

Recall that multiplication is an easy way to do repeated addition. You can use a number line to multiply integers. Always start at 0.

3×2 means three groups of 2 each: $3 \times 2 = 6$.

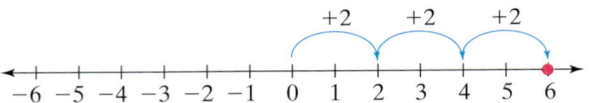

$3 \times (-2)$ means three groups of -2 each: $3 \times (-2) = -6$.

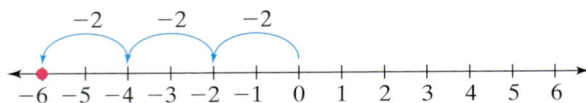

The integers 3 and -3 are opposites. You can think of -3×2 as the opposite of three groups of 2 each. So $-3 \times 2 = -6$.

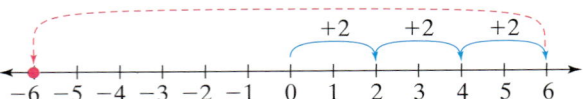

You can think of $-3 \times (-2)$ as the opposite of three groups of -2 each. Since $3 \times (-2) = -6$, $-3 \times (-2) = 6$.

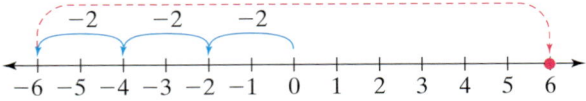

Differentiated Instruction   **Solutions for All Learners**

Special Needs **L1**
If possible, use counters to model negative and positive numbers. Have students make groups of negative or positive integers so they can see that 3 groups of -2 is equal to -6.

learning style: tactile

Below Level **L2**
Provide students with several exercises like these.

5×3 **15** -5×3 **−15**

$-5 \times (-3)$ **15** $5 \times (-3)$ **−15**

learning style: visual

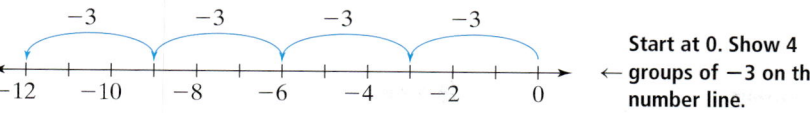

EXAMPLE **Using a Model to Multiply Integers**

1 Use a number line to find $4 \times (-3)$.

$$-3 \quad -3 \quad -3 \quad -3$$

Start at 0. Show 4
← groups of -3 on the
number line.

The sum of 4 groups of -3 is -12. So $4 \times (-3) = -12$.

✓ **Quick Check**

1. a. Find $3 \times (-4)$. **–12**

b. Find $-3 \times (-4)$. **12**

You can use the following rules to multiply integers.

KEY CONCEPTS **Multiplying Integers**

The product of two integers with the *same* signs is positive.
The product of two integers with *different* signs is negative.

Examples: $\quad 4 \times 5 = 20 \qquad 4 \times (-5) = -20$
$\quad\quad\quad\quad -4 \times (-5) = 20 \qquad -4 \times 5 = -20$

EXAMPLES **Multiplying Integers**

2 Find $-5 \times (-6)$.

$-5 \times (-6) = 30$ ← same signs, positive product

3 A skydiver falls 56 meters each second. The skydiver waits
8 seconds before opening her parachute. Use an integer to
express the change in the skydiver's elevation.

$(-56) \times 8 = -448$ ← Use a negative number to represent falling.

The integer -448 expresses the change in the skydiver's elevation.

✓ **Quick Check**

2. a. Find $-9 \times (-3)$. **27**

b. Find $5 \times (-3)$. **–15**

3. The temperature drops 5°F each hour for four hours. Use an
integer to express the total drop in temperature. **–20**

GO **nline**

Video Tutor Help
Visit: PHSchool.com
Web Code: aqe-0775

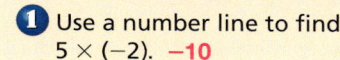

11-5 Multiplying Integers **535**

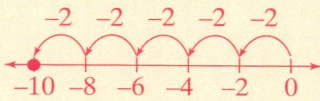

---

2. Teach

Activity Lab

Use before the lesson.

All in One Teaching Resources
Activity Lab 11-5: Patterns in
Numbers

Guided Instruction

Example 2
Have students predict what the
sign of each product will be
before they make any
calculations.

Error Prevention!

Students might confuse the rules
for multiplying integers with the
rules for adding integers.

PowerPoint
Additional Examples

1 Use a number line to find
$5 \times (-2)$. **–10**

2 Find each product.
a. $-2 \times (-6)$ **12**
b. -7×2 **–14**

3 The value on a telephone
calling card decreases 20¢ for
each minute used. Write an
integer to express the change
in the card's value for a
4-minute call. **–80**

All in One Teaching Resources
• Daily Notetaking Guide 11-5 **L3**
• Adapted Notetaking 11-5 **L1**

Closure

• *What are the rules for
multiplying two integers?* **The
product of two integers with the
same sign is positive. The
product of two integers with
different signs is negative.**

Advanced Learners **L4**
Have students place the correct operational symbols in
each equation:

$6 \boxed{+} (-2) \boxed{\times} 5 \boxed{-} 12 \boxed{\div} (-3) = 0$
$-14 \boxed{-} 2 \boxed{\times} 6 \boxed{+} 14 \boxed{\div} (-7) = -28$

learning style: visual

English Language Learners **ELL**
The idea of multiplying by a negative rate and
skydiving may seem quite foreign to students. Try to
show them pictures of skydivers and parachutes, and
explain why they multiply by a negative rate to
calculate when to open their parachutes.

learning style: verbal

535

Assignment Guide

Check Your Understanding

Go over Exercises 1–5 in class before assigning the Homework Exercises.

Homework Exercises

A	Practice by Example	6–22
B	Apply Your Skills	23–30
C	Challenge	31

Test Prep and
Mixed Review   32–35

Homework Quick Check

To check students' understanding of key skills and concepts, go over Exercises 7, 19, 28, 29, and 30.

Differentiated Instruction Resources

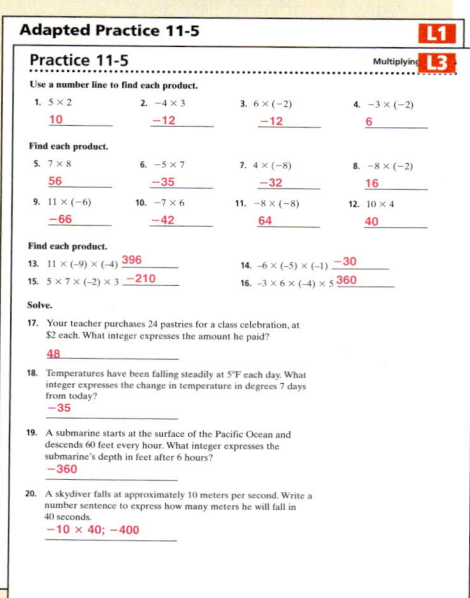

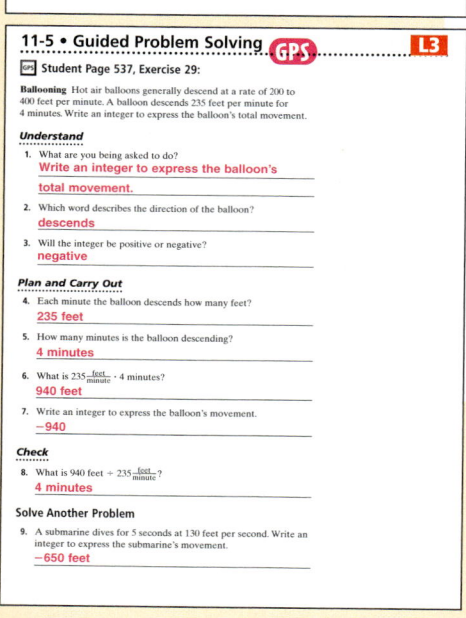

Check Your Understanding

1. **Writing in Math**   Explain how to find $5 \times (-2)$.
   Start at 0. Make 5 groups of −2 on the number line.

2. Copy and complete the table with *positive* or *negative*.
   See margin.

Multiplication of Integers

positive	×	positive	=	?
negative	×	negative	=	?
positive	×	negative	=	?
negative	×	positive	=	?

State whether each product is positive or negative.

3. -8×4 negative
4. $-3 \times (-5)$ positive
5. $7 \times (-6)$ negative

Homework Exercises

For more exercises, see Extra Skills and Word Problems.

GO for Help

For Exercises	See Examples
6–11	1
12–22	2–3

A Use a number line to find each product.

6. 6×3 18
7. $-4 \times (-2)$ 8
8. $5 \times (-2)$ −10
9. $8 \times (-1)$ −8
10. -2×7 −14
11. $-1 \times (-3)$ 3

Find each product.

12. -7×5 −35
13. $11 \times (-2)$ −22
14. 7×12 84
15. $-6 \times (-9)$ 54
16. $(-4) \times 9$ −36
17. $15 \times (-3)$ −45
18. $-25 \times (-5)$ 125
19. -16×4 −64
20. $-1 \times (-124)$ 124

21. **Money** You withdraw $10 from a bank account once a week for four weeks. What integer expresses the change in value?
    −40

22. The temperature fell three degrees per hour for four hours. What was the total change in the temperature? −12

B GPS 23. **Guided Problem Solving** A game show awards 25 points for correct answers and deducts 15 points for incorrect answers. Use the table to determine which player wins.

Game Show Results

Player	Correct Answers	Incorrect Answers
A	9	21
B	5	8

- Find the score for each player. Player B wins.
- Compare the scores. You may find a number line helpful.

536   Chapter 11   Integers

2.
Multiplication of Integers

positive	×	positive	=	positive
negative	×	negative	=	positive
positive	×	negative	=	negative
negative	×	positive	=	negative

28. when at least 1 integer is zero; when both integers are 0 or when the two integers are opposites

Find each product.

24. $-3 \times (-4) \times (-5)$ **−60**

25. $12 \times (-12) \times (-1)$ **144**

26. $-6 \times 2 \times (-2) \times 8$ **192**

27. $7 \times 3 \times (-3) \times 2$ **−126**

28. **Number Sense** When does the product of two integers equal zero? When does the sum of two integers equal zero? **See margin.**

29. **Ballooning** Hot air balloons generally descend at a rate of 200 to 400 feet per minute. A balloon descends 235 feet per minute for 4 minutes. Write an integer to express the balloon's total movement. **−940**

30. **a.** Is the product of 3 negative integers positive or negative?
b. Is the product of 4 negative integers positive or negative?
c. What happens when you multiply five negative integers?
d. **Patterns** Will the product of 101 negative integers be positive or negative? Explain. **30a–d. See margin.**

C **31.** **Challenge** Find $1 - 2 + 3 - 4 + 5 - 6$. Then change one of the operation symbols in the expression to multiplication so that the new value is eight times the original value.
−3; 1 − 2 + 3 − 4 × 5 − 6

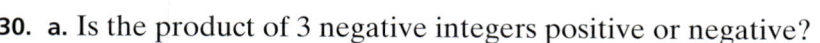
Test Prep and Mixed Review   Practice

Multiple Choice

32. Rhonda runs in a marathon. Which statement is NOT supported by the graph? **C**
Ⓐ Rhonda ran the first 20 miles in 3 hours.
Ⓑ Rhonda ran the last 6 miles in less than 1 hour.
Ⓒ Rhonda ran the first half of the race in less than 2 hours.
Ⓓ Rhonda ran the second half of the race in less than 2 hours.

33. Reed randomly chooses two marbles from a bag of yellow marbles and red marbles. Which list shows all of the possible combinations of marbles Reed could choose? **H**
Ⓕ 2 red; 2 yellow
Ⓗ 2 red; 2 yellow; 1 of each
Ⓖ 1 red and 1 yellow
Ⓙ 1 red; 1 yellow; 2 of each

GO for Help

For Exercises	See Lesson
34–35	9-8

Find the surface area of each rectangular prism.

34. $\ell = 5$ m, $w = 3$ m, $h = 4$ m
94 m²

35. $\ell = 9$ m, $w = 6$ m, $h = 7$ m
318 m²

30a. negative

b. positive

c. You get a negative number.

d. Negative; an odd number of negative factors results in a negative product.

PowerPoint
Lesson Quiz

Find each product.

1. -8×7 **−56**

2. $-7 \times (-3)$ **21**

3. $3 \times (-6)$ **−18**

4. $9 \times 5 \times (-2)$ **−90**

Alternative Assessment

Each student in a pair writes five integer multiplication problems. Students exchange papers and predict whether each product will be positive or negative. Partners then find each product.

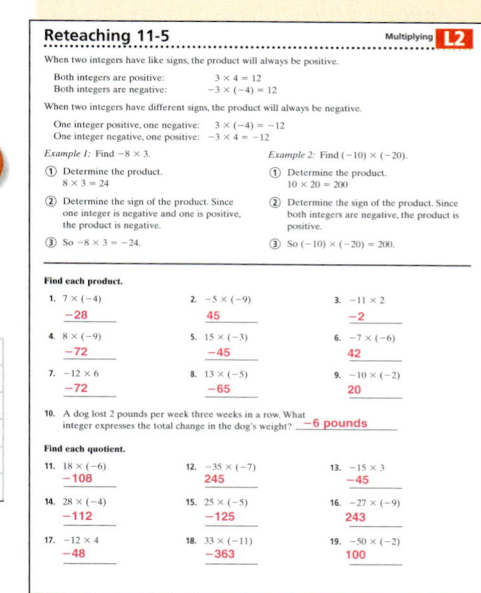

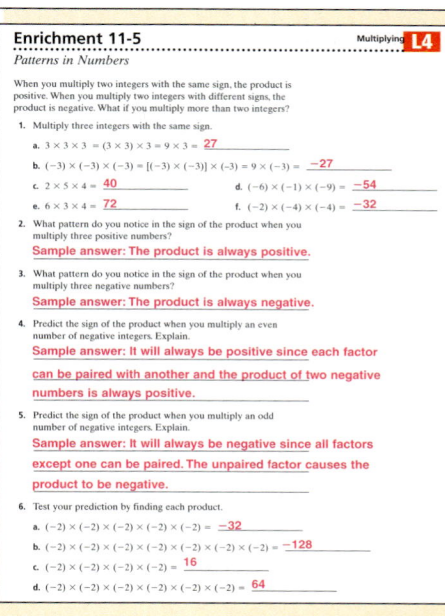

Test Prep

Resources

For additional practice with a variety of test item formats:
• Test-Taking Strategies, p. 563
• Test Prep, p. 567
• Test-Taking Strategies with Transparencies

Practice Solving Problems

In this feature, students practice solving problems involving ordering, adding, subtracting, and multiplying integers. They use diagrams and write equations.

Guided Instruction

Explain to students that they can use integers to solve problems in the real world. Ask volunteers for examples of adding, subtracting, or multiplying integers in everyday life.
Ask:
- *What is the information you need to solve this problem?* **time when the tape began, time when the tape stopped**
- *How could you solve this problem using a number line?* **draw a number line, mark $-4\!:\!15$ and $18\!:\!54$, find the distance between**
- *How can you check whether your answer is reasonable? Explain.* **estimate; 18:54 is close to 19, $|-4\!:\!15|$ is 4:15 and that is close to 4, $19 + 4 = 23$**

Practice Solving Problems

Interpreting Time You start a video tape at the beginning to record a show. The time readings on the recorder when you stop recording and when you finish rewinding are shown below. How long is the recording?

Time Stopped	18:54
Time Started	−4:15

What You Might Think

> What do I know? What do I want to find?

> What diagram can I draw to show the situation?

> What equation can I write using the diagram?

> What is the answer?

What You Might Write

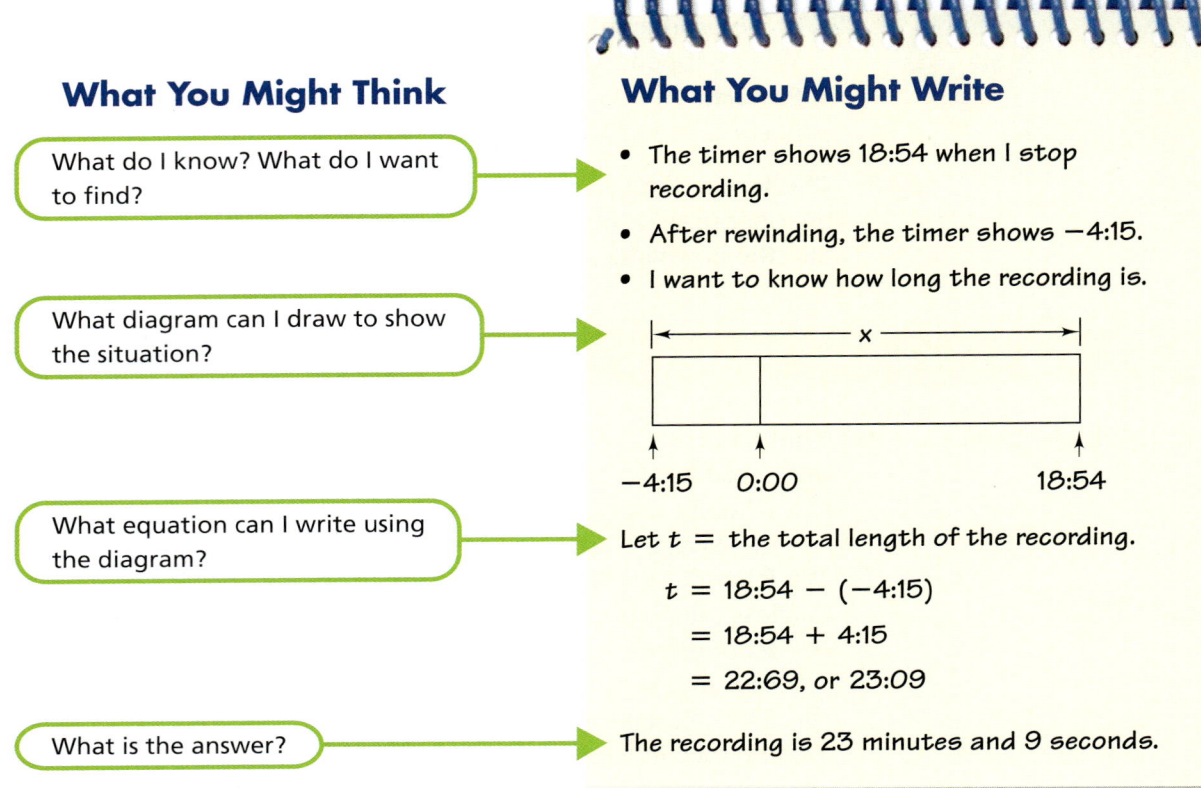

- The timer shows 18:54 when I stop recording.
- After rewinding, the timer shows −4:15.
- I want to know how long the recording is.

Let t = the total length of the recording.

$$t = 18\!:\!54 - (-4\!:\!15)$$
$$= 18\!:\!54 + 4\!:\!15$$
$$= 22\!:\!69, \text{ or } 23\!:\!09$$

The recording is 23 minutes and 9 seconds.

Think It Through   1–3. Answers may vary. Samples are given.

1. Why did you use subtraction in the equation? **Change in time is equivalent to final time minus initial time.**

2. How was 22:69 changed to 23:09? **60 s was subtracted from the total seconds and changed to 1 min, which was added to the total minutes.**

3. **Number Sense** Can you use the equation $-4\!:\!15 - 18\!:\!54 = t$ to show this situation? Explain. **No; you cannot have a negative total time.**

Exercises

4. Use the graph below. Find the increase in pay a person would expect from earning an advanced degree after a bachelor's degree. Is that amount greater than the increase expected by someone earning a bachelor's degree after a high school diploma?

4. Answers may vary. Sample: $23,396; There is a larger increase in pay from a bachelor's degree to an advanced degree than from a high school diploma to a bachelor's degree.

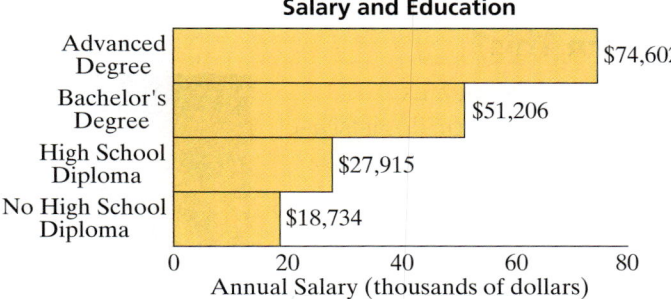

Salary and Education

Advanced Degree	$74,602
Bachelor's Degree	$51,206
High School Diploma	$27,915
No High School Diploma	$18,734

Annual Salary (thousands of dollars)

a. Use the differences in the amounts earned to decide.

b. What is your conclusion? Explain.

The expected score in golf is called the "par" score. Golfers who play well score below par (−). Use the table below for Exercises 5–7.

Golf Earnings

Player	Score	Relative to Par	Earnings
Phil Mickelson	208	−8	$900,000
Bo Van Pelt	226	+10	$9,500

5. Draw a picture and write an equation to show by how many points Phil Mickelson outscored Bo Van Pelt in this tournament.

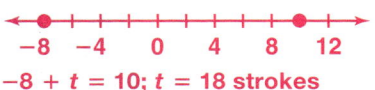

−8 + t = 10; t = 18 strokes

6. What was par for the tournament? **216**

7. How much did Phil Mickelson earn per stroke under par? **$112,500 per stroke**

8. **Reasoning** Time is sometimes given in terms of a 24-hour day. The time 0:00 represents midnight. The time 16:30 represents 16 hours and 30 minutes after midnight, or 4:30 P.M. Find both a positive and a negative number to represent 10:36 P.M. **22:36, −1:24**

Examples
1 Dividing Integers
2 Application: Weather

Math Understandings: p. 514C

Math Background

When dividing integers, the quotient of integers with the same sign is positive and with different signs is negative.

More Math Background: p. 514C

Lesson Planning and Resources

See p. 514E for a list of the resources that support this lesson.

Bell Ringer Practice

✓ **Check Skills You'll Need**
For intervention, direct students to:
Multiplying Integers
Lesson 11-5
Extra Skills and Word Problems
   Practice, Ch. 11

2. Teach

Activity Lab

Use before the lesson.

All in One Teaching Resources

Activity Lab 11-6: Operations with
   Integers

Guided Instruction

Example 1
Ask: *How do the rules for multiplying integers and dividing integers compare?* **The rules are the same: same sign, positive result; different signs, negative result.**

540

11-6 Dividing Integers

What You'll Learn

To divide integers and to solve problems by dividing integers

Why Learn This?

Many professionals, such as stockbrokers and meteorologists, use rates of change. You can find a rate of change by dividing integers.

The rules for finding the sign of a quotient when dividing integers are similar to the rules for multiplying integers.

> **KEY CONCEPTS** **Dividing Integers**
>
> The quotient of two integers with the same sign is positive.
> The quotient of two integers with different signs is negative.
>
> **Examples:** $20 \div 4 = 5$ $20 \div (-4) = -5$
> $-20 \div (-4) = 5$ $-20 \div 4 = -5$

EXAMPLE **Dividing Integers**

1 **a.** Find $-15 \div (-3)$.

   $-15 \div (-3) = 5$ ← same signs, positive quotient

   b. Find $-24 \div 8$.

   $-24 \div 8 = -3$ ← different signs, negative quotient

✓ **Quick Check**

1. Find each quotient.
   a. $-24 \div 6$ **-4**   **b.** $-36 \div (-2)$ **18**   **c.** $48 \div (-12)$ **-4**

EXAMPLE   Application: Weather

2 **Multiple Choice** The temperature changed from 0°C to −56°C in four hours. Find the average rate of change in degrees per hour.

Ⓐ −52   Ⓑ −14   Ⓒ 14   Ⓓ 52

$$-56 \div 4 = -14 \quad \leftarrow \text{different signs, negative quotient}$$

The average rate of change is −14°C per hour.

The correct answer is choice B.

✓ Quick Check

2. The value of one share of stock decreased $20 over the last five days. Find the average rate of change in dollars per day. **−$4/day**

✓ Check Your Understanding

1. Zarita; the quotient of 2 negative numbers is always positive.

1. **Error Analysis** Who found the correct quotient? Explain.

Zarita	Zurina
−6 ÷ (−2) = 3	−6 ÷ (−2) = −3

2. **Writing in Math** Explain how you know without computing that the quotient −400 ÷ 25 is less than 0.
The quotient of a negative number and a positive number is always negative.

3. Over three hours, the temperature decreased 6°. Find the average rate of change in degrees per hour. **−2°/hour**

Tell whether each quotient is *positive* or *negative*.

4. −24 ÷ (−3)   5. 30 ÷ (−10)   6. −81 ÷ 9
   positive   negative   negative

Homework Exercises

For more exercises, see Extra Skills and Word Problems.

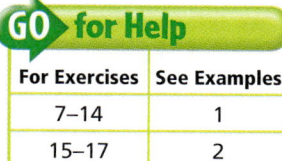

For Exercises	See Examples
7–14	1
15–17	2

Ⓐ **Find each quotient.**

7. −64 ÷ (−8)   **8**   8. −25 ÷ (−5)   **5**

9. −12 ÷ (−2)   **6**   10. −15 ÷ 3   **−5**

11. 72 ÷ (−1)   **−72**   12. −28 ÷ 4   **−7**

13. 100 ÷ (−20)   **−5**   14. −84 ÷ 7   **−12**

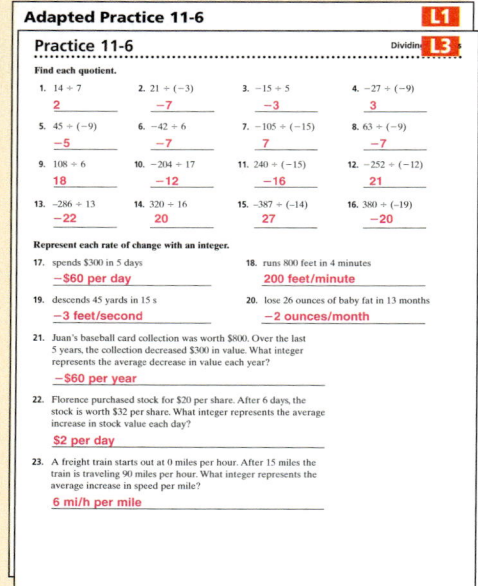
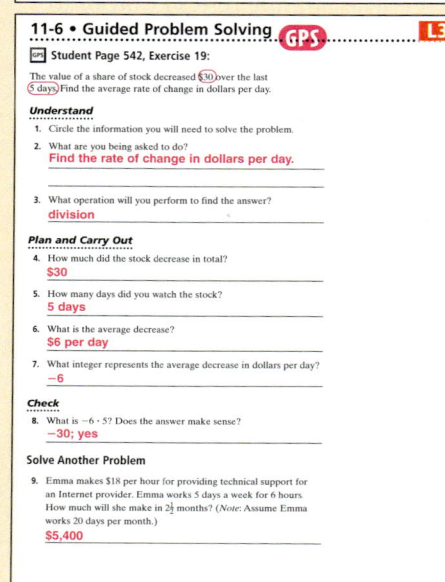
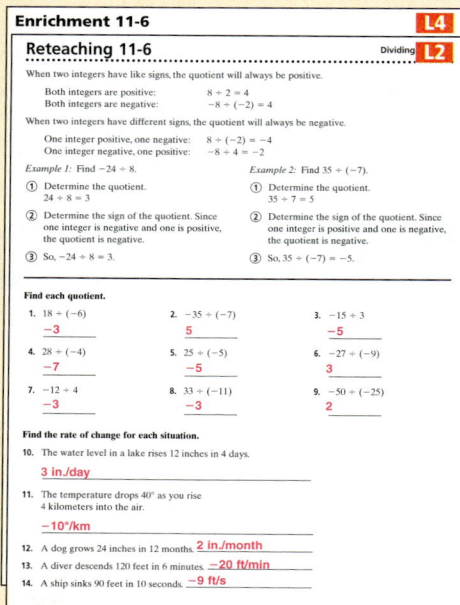
Find the average rate of change for each situation.

15. You climb 72 stairs in 4 minutes. **18 stairs/min**

16. The price of shoes decreases $21 over 7 days. **−$3/day**

17. A rock sinks 160 feet in 20 seconds. **−8 ft/sec**

B **GPS** 18. **Guided Problem Solving** Copy and complete the pyramid so that each number represents the product of the two numbers directly beneath it. **See margin.**

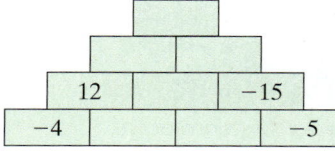

- You can *work a simpler problem* to complete the pyramid.
- Find the missing numbers below.

19. The value of a share of stock decreased $30 over the last 5 days. Find the average rate of change in dollars per day. **−$6/day**

Go Online
Homework Video Tutor

Visit: PHSchool.com
Web Code: aqe-1106

21. **Yes; fresh water evaporates at 125 mL/ day. Salt water evaporates at 120 mL/ day.**

20. **Reasoning** Is the mean of 5 negative numbers positive or negative? Explain your reasoning. **Negative; the sum of five negative numbers is negative; the sum divided by 5 will also be negative.**

21. **Science** You fill a 500-mL bowl with fresh water and a 600-mL bowl with salt water. All of the fresh water evaporates in 4 days. All of the salt water evaporates in 5 days. Does fresh water evaporate faster than salt water? Explain. **See left.**

C 22. **Challenge** Is the division of integers commutative? Give examples to support your answer. **No; $10 \div 20 = \frac{1}{2}$, and $20 \div 10 = 2$.**

Test Prep and Mixed Review **Practice**

Multiple Choice

23. Stacia's hair grows at an average rate of 6 inches each year. How many months will it take for her hair to grow 18 inches? **D**

Ⓐ 3 Ⓑ 24 Ⓒ 30 Ⓓ 36

24. What is the measure of $\angle W$? **G**

Ⓕ 30° Ⓗ 120°
Ⓖ 60° Ⓙ 150°

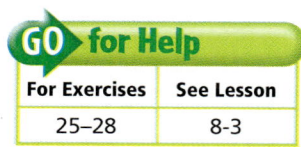

Find the complement and the supplement of each angle.

25. 50° **40°; 130°** 26. 19° **71°; 161°** 27. 67° **23°; 113°** 28. 81° **9°; 99°**

Go for Help

For Exercises	See Lesson
25–28	8-3

542 Chapter 11 Integers

11-7 Solving Equations With Integers

1. Plan

Check Skills You'll Need

1. Vocabulary Review
Name two pairs of *inverse operations.*
See below.
Solve each equation.

2. $a + 15 = 32$ **17**

3. $b - 9 = 16$ **25**

4. $2c = 28$ **14**

5. $d \div 16 = 4$ **64**

GO for Help
Lesson 3-6

Check Skills You'll Need

1. addition and subtraction, multiplication and division

What You'll Learn

To solve equations containing integers

Why Learn This?

Equations can help you find an unknown amount of money.

You can solve equations that contain integers the same way you solve other equations. Use the properties of equality and inverse operations to get the variable alone on one side of the equation.

EXAMPLE   Solving Equations with Integers

1 Solve each equation. Check the solution.

a.

$$t + 9 = 5$$
$$t + 9 - 9 = 5 - 9 \qquad \leftarrow \text{Subtract 9 from each side to undo the addition.}$$
$$t = 5 + (-9) \qquad \leftarrow \text{To subtract 9, add its opposite, } -9.$$
$$t = -4 \qquad \leftarrow \text{Simplify.}$$

Check $-4 + 9 = 5$ ✔ $\leftarrow$ Check by replacing t with -4.

b.

$$m \div 5 = -7$$
$$m \div 5 \times 5 = -7 \times 5 \qquad \leftarrow \text{Multiply each side by 5 to undo the division.}$$
$$m = -35 \qquad \leftarrow \text{Simplify.}$$

Check $-35 \div 5 = -7$ ✔ $\leftarrow$ Check by replacing m with -35.

✔ Quick Check

1. Solve each equation. Check the solution.
  a. $c - 15 = -5$ **10**   **b.** $k \div (-7) = -28$ **28**   **c.** $-6z = 36$ **-6**

Objective
To solve equations containing integers

Examples
1 Solving Equations with Integers
2 Application: Budget

Math Understandings: p. 514C

Professional Development

Math Background

The rules for adding, subtracting, multiplying, and dividing integers can be used to solve equations.

More Math Background: p. 514C

Lesson Planning and Resources

See p. 514E for a list of the resources that support this lesson.

PowerPoint

Bell Ringer Practice

✔ **Check Skills You'll Need**
For intervention, direct students to:
Solving Subtraction Equations
Lesson 3-6
Extra Skills and Word Problems Practice, Ch. 3

2. Teach

Activity Lab

Use before the lesson.

All in One  **Teaching Resources**
Activity Lab 11-7: Solving Integer Equations

Guided Instruction

Error Prevention!

Remind students that the product of same sign integers is positive and of different signs is negative.

Differentiated Instruction   Solutions for All Learners

Special Needs **L1**
For Example 2, let students make a table that shows the balance after each month of withdrawals. They can check their table against the solution to the equation.

learning style: visual

Below Level **L2**
Provide students with sets of equations such as these. Discuss each step with them.
$6 + x = -1$
$x + (-7) = -1$
$5 \times x = -15$
$x \times -3 = -15$

learning style: verbal

EXAMPLE **Application: Budget**

2 **Gridded Response** You earn $200 during the summer and deposit it into a new savings account. You withdraw $25 on the first day of each month, starting in September. For how many months can you withdraw $25?

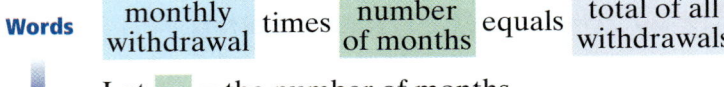

Words | monthly withdrawal | times | number of months | equals | total of all withdrawals

Let m = the number of months.

Equation | -25 | $\times$ | m | $=$ | -200

$-25m = -200$ ← Write the equation.

$-25m \div (-25) = -200 \div (-25)$ ← Divide each side by -25.

$m = 8$ ← Simplify.

You can withdraw $25 per month for 8 months.

✓ Quick Check

2. **Budget** Use Example 2. If you make 10 monthly withdrawals instead of 8, how much can you withdraw each month? **$20**

✓ Check Your Understanding

2. **Same; the first and only step is to undo the multiplication by dividing both sides by the appropriate factor in order to isolate x.**

1. **Open-Ended** Write a word problem that can be solved by using the equation $x - 10 = -50$. **Check students' work.**

2. **Reasoning** Is the first step in solving $8x = -56$ the *same as* or *different from* the first step in solving $-8x = 56$? Explain.

3. Suppose a scuba diver is 100 feet below sea level. The diver rises to the surface at a rate of 25 feet per minute. How long will it take the diver to reach the surface? **4 min**

Mental Math **Match each equation with the correct solution.**

4. $-3x = -6$ **E**

5. $x - 6 = -7$ **B**

6. $-5x = -5$ **D**

7. $x \div 2 = 0$ **C**

8. $x + 3 = 1$ **A**

A. -2
B. -1
C. 0
D. 1
E. 2

Homework Exercises

For more exercises, see Extra Skills and Word Problems.

GO for Help

For Exercises	See Examples
9–20	1
21	2

A **Solve each equation. Check the solution.**

9. $t + 12 = 9$ **–3**
10. $v - 6 = -4$ **2**
11. $-3 + c = -8$ **–5**

12. $w - 18 = -13$ **5**
13. $x - (-6) = 18$ **12**
14. $x + 20 = -20$ **–40**

15. $-6y = 42$ **–7**
16. $-4y = -64$ **16**
17. $7h = -84$ **–12**

18. $c \div (-8) = 3$ **–24**
19. $z \div (-7) = -1$ **7**
20. $p \div 2 = -2$ **–4**

21. A metro train ride costs \$4. After the ride, your card has a balance of −\$3. Find your balance before the train ride. **\$1**

B  **GPS** 22. **Guided Problem Solving** After the first round in a game show, a contestant had 250 points. At the end of the second round, the contestant had −300 points. How did the score change during the second round? **–550**
   • First define the variable. Then write an equation.

23. Four friends divided a restaurant bill evenly. Each owed \$20. **GPS** What was the total amount of the bill? **\$80**

24. **Writing in Math** Explain why $t + 4 = -6$ and $t + 6 = -4$ have the same solution. **Answers may vary. Sample: To solve both equations, −4 is added to −6.**

GO Online
Homework Video Tutor
Visit: PHSchool.com
Web Code: aqe-1107

25. **Temperature** At midnight the temperature was $0°F$. It then began to decrease about 4 degrees per hour. After about how many hours did the temperature reach $-20°F$? **5 hours**

C 26. **Challenge** Solve the equation $2x - 10 = -8$ by using two inverse operations. Check the solution. **1**

Test Prep and Mixed Review
Practice

Gridded Response

27. The Perez family drives 473.7 miles to a vacation spot. They drive the same route to get home. Find the total distance the family drives, in miles. **947.4**

28. A diner offers 3 appetizers, 4 main courses, and 2 desserts. Latoya wants to order one appetizer, one main course, and one dessert. How many choices does she have? **24**

GO for Help

For Exercises	See Lesson
29–30	3-6

Solve each equation.

29. $d - 25 = 39$ **64**
30. $n - 13 = 74$ **87**

Alternative Assessment

Each student in a pair writes several equations involving integers. Students exchange papers and solve each other's equations.

Test Prep

Resources
For additional practice with a variety of test item formats:
• Test-Taking Strategies, p. 563
• Test Prep, p. 567
• Test-Taking Strategies with Transparencies

Differentiated Instruction Resources

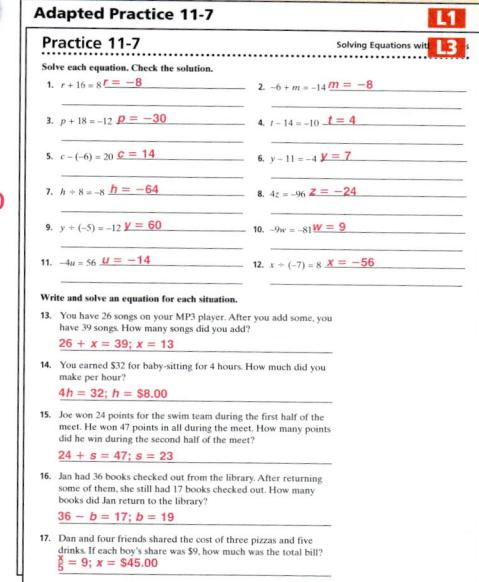

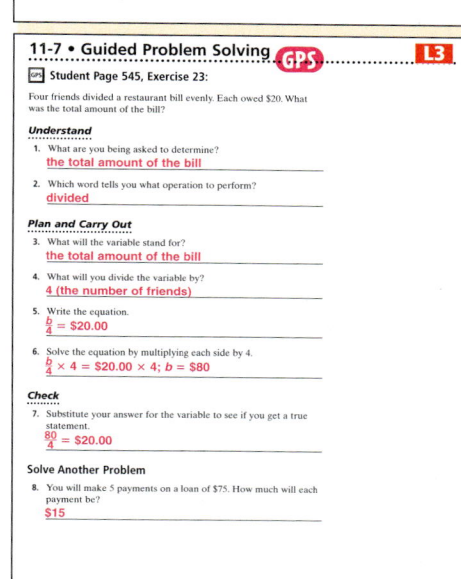

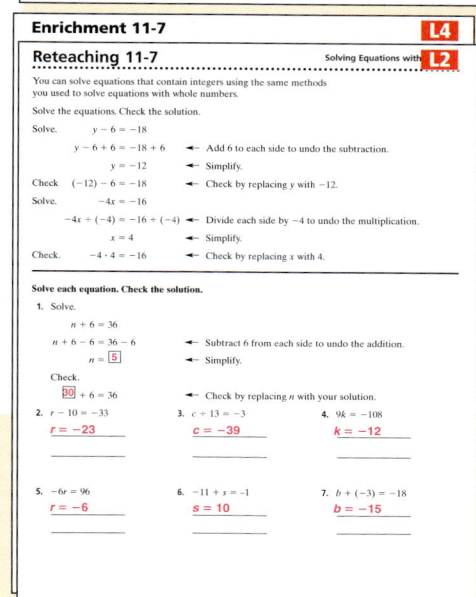

Thinking About Solutions

Thinking About Solutions

Thinking about numbers is a good first step when solving an equation. This will alert you to mistakes you might make when solving the equation.

EXAMPLE

Decide which statements are true for $x - 19\frac{1}{2} = 30$.

a. $x \approx 20$
b. x is negative.
c. $x > 30$

- "$x \approx 20$" is false. The left side of the equation would be close to 0.

- "x is negative" is false. The left side of the equation would be negative.

- "$x > 30$" is true. The left side must be large enough that when $19\frac{1}{2}$ is subtracted 30 remains.

Statements (a) and (b) are false. Statement (c) is true.

Exercises

Use number sense to decide which statements are true for the given equation. More than one choice may be true. Explain your answer.   **1–6. See margin.**

1. $x + 7 = -13$
   a. $x > 0$
   b. x is an integer.
   c. $x < -13$

2. $11x = 100$
   a. x is a whole number.
   b. x is negative.
   c. $x < 10$

3. $3x = -16$
   a. $x < 0$
   b. $x \approx -50$
   c. $x \approx 5$

4. $x + 8 = 3$
   a. $x > 0$
   b. x is an integer.
   c. $x < 0$

5. $100 - x = 49\frac{1}{2}$
   a. $x \approx 90$
   b. $x > 0$
   c. $x \approx 50$

6. Write two true statements about x for the equation $2x = -81$. Then write two false statements about the same equation.

1–6. Answers may vary. Samples are given.

1a. False; the left side would be positive.

b. True; adding an integer to an integer results in another integer.

c. True; the left side would be negative.

2a. False; 11 is not a factor of 100.

b. False; both given numbers are positive, so the unknown must be positive.

c. True; $100 \div 10 = 10$, so dividing 100 by a larger number should result in a number smaller than 10.

3–6. See back of book.

Graphing Points

You can use a graphing calculator to explore how to graph points. An ordered pair is a pair of numbers that describe the location of a point on your screen.

First, prepare your calculator for this activity. Press **2nd** [PLOT] 4: PlotsOff to turn off the plots. Press **Y=** and clear any equations. Press **ZOOM** 4: ZQuadrant1 to set the window.

ACTIVITY

1–5. Check students' work.

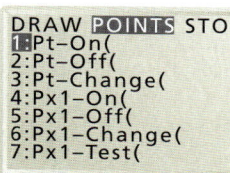

1. First press **CLEAR**.

2. Press **DRAW** to select the **Draw** menu. Press **▶** to highlight **Points.** Select 1: Pt-On. Then press **ENTER**.

3. To graph the point (6, 4), press 6 **,** 4 **)** **ENTER**.

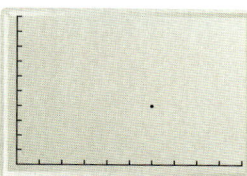

4. The ordered pair (6, 4) tells you the location of the point. How far to the right of the vertical line is the point (6, 4)? How far above the horizontal line is the point?

5. Repeat steps 1–3 to graph (4, 5). Describe the location of the point on the screen.

Exercises

Use a graphing calculator to graph each point. **6–9. Check students' work.**

6. (1, 6)   7. (9, 7)   8. (2, 3)   9. (6, 1)

10. **Reasoning** Without using a graphing calculator, describe the location of the point (4, 8). Draw a diagram to check your answer. **The point (4, 8) is 4 units right and 8 units above the origin.**

11. Graph (0, 4) on a calculator. Why does the point not appear on the screen? **The point is on the y-axis.**

12. **Writing in Math** Your classmate needs to graph (3, 14). Write directions for your classmate explaining how to graph the point on the calculator. **Check students' work.**

Graphing Points

Students use graphing calculators to graph ordered pairs for points on a coordinate plane.

Guided Instruction

Activity
Be sure students know how to prepare their graphing calculators. Go over the steps with the class before beginning the Activity. Ask questions such as:

- *Why are you zooming in on Quadrant 1?* **All the points in the Activity have non negative x- and y-coordinates and are in Quadrant 1 or on an axis.**

After beginning the Activity, ask:

- *Why do you repeat steps 1–3 for each point you want to graph?* **The process for graphing a point on the calculator is the same for each point except for the actual insertion of the coordinates.**

Differentiated Instruction

Advance Learners **L4**
Have students explore graphing points in Quadrants other than the first. Ask:

- *How would the preparation of the calculator differ?* **Students would not press ZQuadrant1.**

Resources

- Activity Lab 11-8: Exploring the Coordinate Plane

11-8

Objective
To name and graph points on a coordinate plane

Examples
1 Naming Coordinates
2 Graphing Ordered Pairs
3 Using Map Coordinates

Math Understandings: p. 514D

Math Background

A coordinate plane is formed by two number lines—one horizontal and one vertical. The *origin* describes the point where the two axes intersect. An ordered pair of numbers describes the location of a point in the coordinate plane. For instance, the point (0, 0) describes the origin.

More Math Background: p. 514D

Lesson Planning and Resources

See p. 514E for a list of the resources that support this lesson.

Bell Ringer Practice

✓ **Check Skills You'll Need**
Use student page, transparency, or PowerPoint. For intervention, direct students to:
Exploring Integers
Lesson 11-1
Extra Skills and Word Problems Practice, Ch. 11

548

11-8 Graphing in the Coordinate Plane

✓ Check Skills You'll Need

1. **Vocabulary Review** *Opposites* are the same distance from __?__ on a number line. **0**

Graph each integer on a number line.
2–5. See below.
2. −2   **3.** 3

4. 0   **5.** −6

GO for Help
Lesson 11-1

Check Skills You'll Need

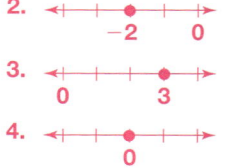

2.
   −2   0

3.
   0   3

4.
      0

5.
   −6   −2

Vocabulary Tip
The plural of *axis* is *axes*.

What You'll Learn

To name and graph points on a coordinate plane

🔊 **New Vocabulary** coordinate plane, quadrants, origin, ordered pair

Why Learn This?

You can use coordinates to find and describe locations on a map.

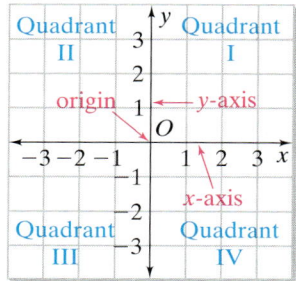

The **coordinate plane** is a surface formed by the intersection of two number lines. The plane is divided into four regions, called **quadrants**. The **origin** is the point where the two number lines intersect.

An **ordered pair** is a pair of numbers that describes the location of a point in a coordinate plane. The ordered pair (0, 0) describes the origin.

The *x*-coordinate tells how far to move right or left along the *x*-axis. The *y*-coordinate tells how far to move up or down along the *y*-axis.

EXAMPLE **Naming Coordinates**

1 Find the coordinates of point *C*.

Point *C* is 1 unit to the right of the *y*-axis. So the *x*-coordinate is 1.

Point *C* is 3 units above the *x*-axis. So the *y*-coordinate is 3.

The coordinates of point *B* are (1, 3).

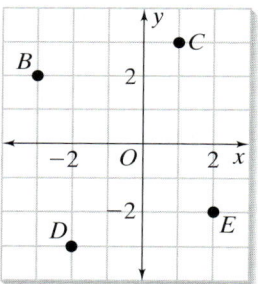

✓ Quick Check

1. Find the coordinates of each point in the coordinate plane.
   a. *B* **B(−3, 2)**   **b.** *D* **D(−2, −3)**   **c.** *E* **E(2, −2)**

Differentiated Instruction | **Solutions for All Learners**

Special Needs L1
Give students blank copies of a coordinate grid. Have them highlight the negative parts of the *x*- and *y*-axes in one color. Then, have them highlight the positive parts in a different color.

learning style: visual

Below Level L2
Have students graph these points in a coordinate plane. Have them connect the points in order. Ask: *What is the figure?*

(4, 3), (−3, 3), (4, −3), (−3, −3) **rectangle**

learning style: visual

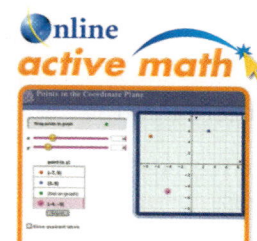

You can graph points if you know their coordinates. You move right from the *origin* to graph a positive *x*-coordinate and left from the *origin* to graph a negative *x*-coordinate. You move up from the *x*-axis to graph a positive *y*-coordinate and down from the *x*-axis to graph a negative *y*-coordinate.

EXAMPLE **Graphing Ordered Pairs**

② Graph point $P(3, 2)$ on a coordinate plane.

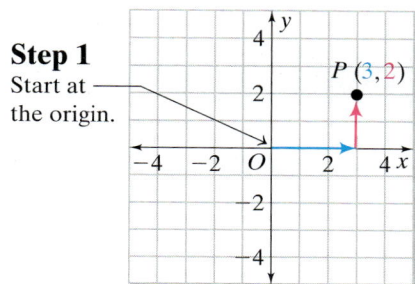

Step 1
Start at the origin.

Step 3
Move 2 units up.

Step 2
Move 3 units to the right.

✓ Quick Check

2. Graph each point on the same coordinate plane.
   a. $A(1, 3)$ **b.** $B(-3, 2)$ **c.** $C(-4, -4)$
   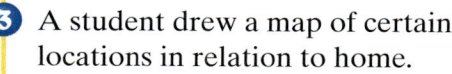
   2a–c. See back of book.

EXAMPLE **Using Map Coordinates**

③ A student drew a map of certain locations in relation to home.

   a. Identify the coordinates of the library.

   The library is located at $(-2, 1)$.

   b. You leave the library and ride your scooter 2 blocks north and then 4 blocks east. At which building do you arrive?

   You are at the grocery store.

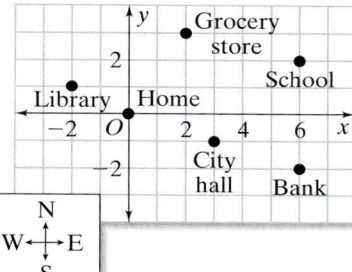

✓ Quick Check

3. **a.** Suppose you leave the library and walk 5 blocks east and then 2 blocks south. At which building do you arrive?   **City Hall**
   b. What are the coordinates of the building?   **(3, −1)**

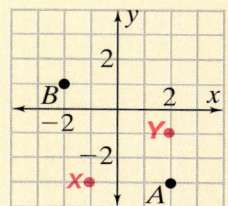

Assignment Guide

Check Your Understanding
Go over Exercises 1–3 in class before assigning the Homework Exercises.

Homework Exercises
A Practice by Example   4–20
B Apply Your Skills   21–34
C Challenge   35
Test Prep and
Mixed Review   36–38

Homework Quick Check
To check students' understanding of key skills and concepts, go over Exercises 8, 19, 22, 31, and 33.

Differentiated Instruction Resources

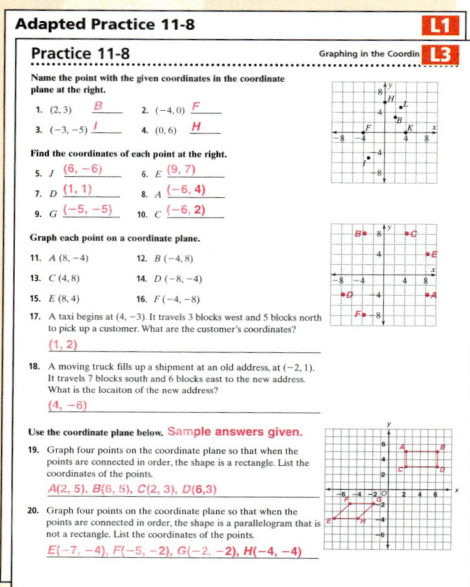

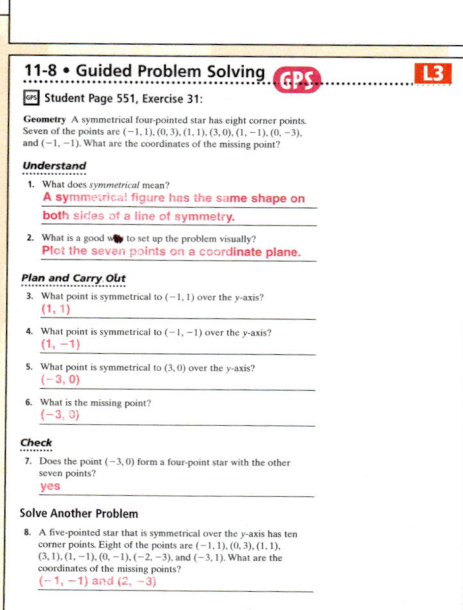

✓ Check Your Understanding

1. Answers may vary. Sample: The first coordinate tells how far to move left or right. The second coordinate tells how far to move up or down.

1. **Vocabulary** Why is order important in an ordered pair?

2. **Open-Ended** Name four points on a coordinate plane that form a square when connected by straight lines. **Answers may vary.**
   Sample: (0, 0), (1, 0), (1, 1), (0, 1)

3. Which point is NOT in the same quadrant as the other three? **B**
   Ⓐ $(8, -4)$ Ⓑ $(-5, 6)$ Ⓒ $(1, -7)$ Ⓓ $(2, -2)$

Homework Exercises

For more exercises, see Extra Skills and Word Problems.

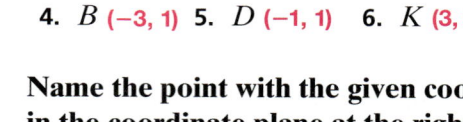

For Exercises	See Examples
4–11	1
12–17	2
18–20	3

A **Find the coordinates of each point at the right.**

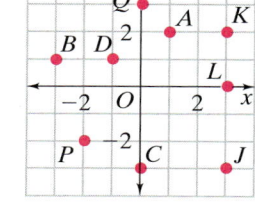

4. B **(–3, 1)** 5. D **(–1, 1)** 6. K **(3, 2)** 7. Q **(0, 3)**

Name the point with the given coordinates in the coordinate plane at the right.

8. $(1, 2)$ **A**   9. $(-2, -2)$ **P**

10. $(3, -3)$ **J**   11. $(0, -3)$ **C**

Graph each point on the same coordinate plane. **12–17. See margin.**

12. $A(1, 5)$ 13. $B(-5, -3)$ 14. $C(2, -4)$

15. $D(-2, 3)$ 16. $E(1, -4)$ 17. $F(-5, 5)$

Use the map below for Exercises 18–20.

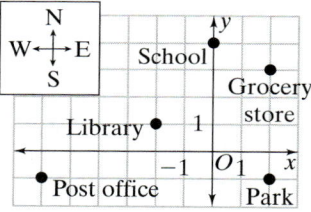

18. You travel 2 units north of the library and 4 units east. Where do you arrive? **Grocery store**

19. Find the coordinates of the park.
    (2, –1)

20. Find the coordinates of the school.
    (0, 4)

B 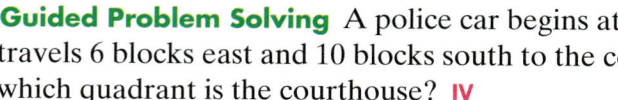 21. **Guided Problem Solving** A police car begins at $(-2, 8)$. It travels 6 blocks east and 10 blocks south to the courthouse. In which quadrant is the courthouse? **IV**
   • Which direction on the coordinate plane is east?
   • Which direction on the coordinate plane is south?

22. **Writing in Math** What do all points located on the y-axis have in common? Explain. **Their x-coordinate is 0.**

550   **Chapter 11**   Integers

12–17. See back of book.

GO Online
Homework Video Tutor

Visit: PHSchool.com
Web Code: aqe-1108

Name the quadrant or axis in which each point lies.

23. $(-2, -2)$ **III**   **24.** $(6, 4)$ **I**   **25.** $(0, 4)$ *y*-axis   **26.** $(-1, 9)$ **II**

27. $(-3, 0)$ *x*-axis   **28.** $(5, -8)$ **IV**   **29.** $(8, 0)$ *x*-axis   **30.** $(0, -10)$ *y*-axis

31. Geometry A symmetrical four-pointed star has eight corner
GPS points. Seven of the points are
$(-1, 1), (0, 3), (1, 1), (3, 0), (1, -1), (0, -3),$ and $(-1, -1)$.
What are the coordinates of the missing point? **(−3, 0)**

32. (0, 2), (1, 2), (1, 4), (0, 4),
(2, 6), (2, 5), (4, 5), (4, 6),
(6, 4), (5, 4), (5, 2), (6, 2),
(4, 0), (4, 1), (2, 1), (2, 0)

32. Quilt Making Quilt designers often
use coordinate grids to design
patterns. Find the coordinates of the
pattern shown at the right. **See left.**

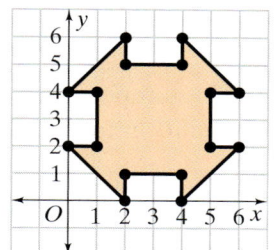

33. Geography Maps of Earth use a
coordinate system to describe
locations. The horizontal axis is the
equator, and the vertical axis is the
prime meridian.

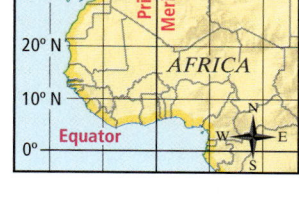

    a. On what continent is 20° N latitude, 20° E longitude? **Africa**
    b. On what continent is 48° N latitude, 5° E longitude? **Europe**

34. (**Algebra**) On which axis does the point $(n, 0)$ lie? *x*-axis

C **35. Challenge** A parallelogram has vertices at $(3, 2), (2, 5),$ and
$(6, 5)$. Find three possible points for the fourth vertex.
(−1, 2), (7, 2), (5, 8)

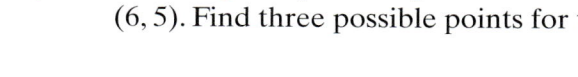

Test Prep and Mixed Review   **Practice**

Multiple Choice

36. Which ordered pair represents a
point located inside both the circle
and the rectangle at the right? **C**
    Ⓐ $(1, 2)$ Ⓒ $(3, 2)$
    Ⓑ $(2, 4)$ Ⓓ $(5, 2)$

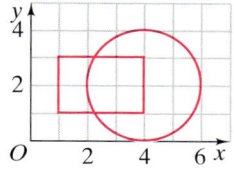

37. Belle cut a rectangle from paper for a geometry project.

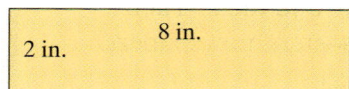

2 in.   8 in.

What is the perimeter of the rectangle in inches? **J**
    Ⓕ 6   Ⓖ 10   Ⓗ 16   Ⓙ 20

GO for Help

For Exercise	See Lesson
38	9-6

38. Find the circumference and the area of a circle with a radius of
6 millimeters. Round your answer to the nearest millimeter.
38 mm; 113 mm²

Online lesson quiz, PHSchool.com, Web Code: aqa-1108   11-8 Graphing in the Coordinate Plane   **551**

Alternative Assessment

Using all four quadrants, each student in a pair
plots six points and labels the points *A* through *F*.
Partners exchange papers and name the
coordinates of each point.

Test Prep

Resources

For additional practice with a variety of test item
formats:
- Test-Taking Strategies, p. 563
- Test Prep, p. 567
- Test-Taking Strategies with Transparencies

---

4. Assess & Reteach

PowerPoint
Lesson Quiz

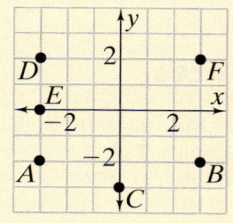

Find the coordinates of each
point.

1. A **(−3, −2)**   **2.** F **(3, 2)**

Name each point with the given
coordinates.

3. $(-3, 2)$ **D**   **4.** $(0, -3)$ **C**

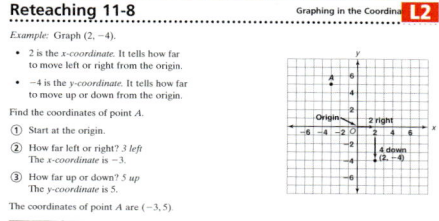

Reteaching 11-8   Graphing in the Coordin... **L2**

Example: Graph $(2, -4)$.

- 2 is the *x-coordinate*. It tells how far
  to move left or right from the origin.
- −4 is the *y-coordinate*. It tells how far
  to move up or down from the origin.

Find the coordinates of point A.

① Start at the origin.
② How far left or right? *3 left*
    The *x-coordinate* is −3.
③ How far up or down? *5 up*
    The *y-coordinate* is 5.

The coordinates of point A are $(-3, 5)$.

Graph each point in a coordinate plane.

1. $B(1, 6)$	2. $C(-4, -3)$
3. $D(0, 5)$	4. $E(-2, 2)$
5. $F(-1, -5)$	6. $G(6, -4)$
7. $H(5, 5)$	8. $J(4, 0)$
9. $K(-4, -4)$	10. $L(2, -3)$
11. $M(-2, 0)$	12. $N(5, -1)$
13. $P(0, -3)$	14. $Q(-4, 0)$

Find the coordinates of each point.

15. R **(4, −1)**	16. S **(3, 5)**	
17. T **(0, −1)**	18. U **(−3, −2)**	

Look at the coordinate grid above.

19. If you travel 7 units down from S, at which point will you be located?
    U

20. If you travel 4 units right from T and 2 units down, at which point will you be located?
    R

Enrichment 11-8   Graphing in the Coordin... **L4**
Critical Thinking

One item that Cheryl had to find on a treasure hunt was located at
the point $(3, 4)$ on the map. When Cheryl got there, she realized she
had the map upside down. How many units left, right, up, and down
on the map should Cheryl walk to find the correct location?

1. Mark $(3, 4)$ on the coordinate plane. Label it A.
2. Turn this page upside down. Imagine that
   the graph was scaled in the usual way.
   Then mark $(3, 4)$. Label it B.
3. Turn your page to original position.
   Follow the grid lines to mark the shortest
   path between the B and A.

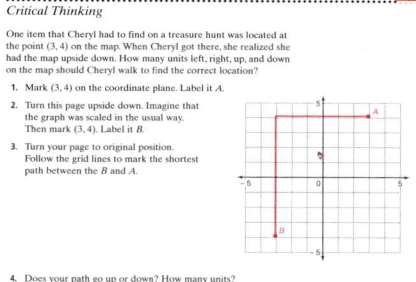

4. Does your path go up or down? How many units?
    up; 8 units
5. Does your path go left or right? How many units?
    right; 6 units
6. Are there other paths that you could choose? Explain.
    Yes; for example, one path could start out going right, then up.
7. What is the relationship between the number of units the path
    takes and the original coordinates?
    The path is two times the value of each coordinate.
8. One item that Norm had to find on a treasure hunt was located
    at the point $(-2, 5)$ on the map. When Norm got there, he realized
    he had the map upside down. How many units left, right, up, and
    down on the map should Norm walk to find the correct location?
    up 10, left 4

551

MATH AT WORK

Graphic Designer

This feature highlights the use of math in a career that may be unfamiliar to students. Many students may not think of a designer as using math. The feature should generate enthusiasm about the use of math in the real world.

Guided Instruction

Explain to students the job of a graphic designer. Have a volunteer read the paragraph. Then discuss examples of graphic design they have seen in everyday life. Ask:
- *How does a graphic designer use math?*
- *Can you think of examples of math in product or packaging design that you have seen?*
- *Do you think you would enjoy a career as a graphic designer? Why or why not?*

 **Checkpoint Quiz 2** | **Lessons 11-4 through 11-8** |

Find each answer.

1. $-4 - (-2)$ **–2**

2. $-10 - 2$ **–12**

3. $12 \times (-3)$ **–36**

4. -8×2 **–16**

5. $14 \div (-2)$ **–7**

6. $-21 \div (-3)$ **7**

Solve each equation.

7. $x + 5 = -8$ **–13**

8. $r - 10 = -2$ **8**

9. $3d = -12$ **–4**

10. The temperature decreased 15°F to −2°F. Write and solve an equation to find the starting temperature. **$t - 15 = -2$; 13°F**

11. A police car begins at $(-2, 8)$. It travels 12 blocks south and 4 blocks east to the courthouse. What are the coordinates of the courthouse? **$(2, -4)$**

Name the coordinates of each point.

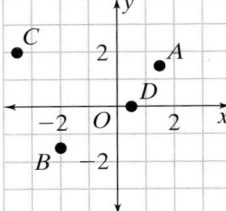

12. A **(1.5, 1.5)**

13. B **(−2, −1.5)**

14. C **(−3.5, 2)**

15. D **(0.5, 0)**

MATH AT WORK

Graphic Designer

If you are creative and like art, a career as a graphic designer could be just right for you. Graphic designers use computers to produce images for logos, packaging, or advertising for goods, services, and ideas. Their designs are seen in magazines, posters, newspapers, and television advertisements.

Designers also use mathematical skills. They use coordinates to ensure the exact placement of images.

Go Online
PHSchool.com   **For:** Information on graphic designers
Web Code: aqb-2031

Reflections in the Coordinate Plane

In Chapter 8, you studied reflections. When you use the *x*- or *y*-axis as the line of reflection, there is a relationship between the coordinates of the reflected points.

EXAMPLES

1 List the ordered pairs of the vertices of the parallelograms that are in Quadrants I and II. Find a pattern.

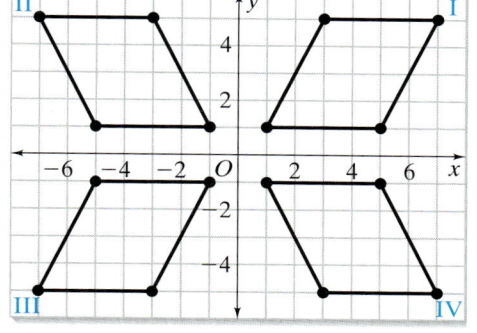

Quadrant I	
x	**y**
1	1
3	5
7	5
5	1

Quadrant II	
x	**y**
−1	1
−3	5
−7	5
−5	1

All corresponding *x*-coordinates are opposites and all corresponding *y*-coordinates are the same.

2 List the ordered pairs of the vertices of the parallelograms that are in Quadrants I and IV. Find a pattern.

Quadrant I	
x	**y**
1	1
3	5
7	5
5	1

Quadrant IV	
x	**y**
1	−1
3	−5
7	−5
5	−1

All corresponding *x*-coordinates are the same and all corresponding *y*-coordinates are opposites.

Exercises

Plot the given points and connect them in order. Reflect the figure over the *y*-axis. Then reflect the original figure over the *x*-axis. **1–3. See margin.**

1. (2, 2),(4, 6),(6, 2), (2, 2)

2. (−1, −1), (−1, −6), (−7, −6), (−1, −1)

3. (1, −1), (4, −1), (4, −3), (3, −4), (2, −4), (1, −3), (1, −1)

1–3. See back of book.

Reflections in the Coordinate Plane

Students use a coordinate plane to explore transformations, or movements, of geometric figures.

Guided Instruction

Example 1
Have students list ordered pairs of vertices of the parallelograms in Quadrants III and IV. They will find the same relationships for Quadrants I and II.

Example 2
Have students use the ordered pairs for the parallelograms in Quadrants II and III to see the relationship between *x*-coordinates and *y*-coordinates.

Exercises
Have students work on the Exercises. Then have them compare graphs with a partner and discuss any differences.

Differentiated Instruction Resources

English Language Learners   **ELL**
Review the meanings of the words *congruent, parallelogram,* and *quadrant.*

Tactile Learners
For students having difficulty visualizing the reflections, have them copy the parallelograms on a coordinate grid. Then have them fold their papers over one axis, and hold their paper up to the light. The figures should match exactly.

Resources

• graph paper
• Classroom Aid 3

Objective
To apply integers to profit and loss situations

Examples
1 Finding Profit or Loss
2 Drawing and Interpreting Graphs

Math Understandings: p. 514D

Math Background

To make a useful graph, choose appropriate *scales* and *intervals* for the data. The scale is the units used, such as time or dollar amounts. The interval is the distance between values on a scale such as $5 or $100 increments.

More Math Background: p. 514D

Lesson Planning and Resources

See p. 514E for a list of the resources that support this lesson.

PowerPoint

Bell Ringer Practice

☑ **Check Skills You'll Need**
Use student page, transparency, or PowerPoint. For intervention, direct students to:
Adding Integers
Lesson 11-3
Extra Skills and Word Problems Practice, Ch. 11

554

✓ Check Skills You'll Need

1. **Vocabulary Review** Explain how you use *absolute value* when you add integers.   **See below.**
Find each sum.
2. $12 + 26$ **38**
3. $(-9) + 18$ **9**
4. $41 + (-54)$ **−13**
5. $-19 + (-10)$ **−29**

for Help
Lesson 11-3

Check Skills You'll Need

1. Answers may vary. Sample: If the signs of both integers are the same, add their absolute values and use the same sign. If the integers' signs are different, subtract their absolute values and use the sign of the integer with the larger absolute value.

What You'll Learn

To apply integers to profit and loss situations

Why Learn This?

Businesses, such as flower shops, keep track of the money they receive and spend. Money received is called income. Money spent is called expenses.

To find a balance, add the income (positive numbers) and the expenses (negative numbers). A positive balance means that there is a *profit*. A negative balance means that there is a *loss*.

EXAMPLE Finding Profit or Loss

1 **Small Business** Find Flower Mania's profit or loss for February.

Income and Expenses for Flower Mania		
Month	Income	Expenses
Jan.	$11,917	−$14,803
Feb.	$12,739	−$9,482
Mar.	$11,775	−$10,954
Apr.	$13,620	−$15,149

$12,739 + (−$9,482) = $3,257   ← **Add income and expenses for February.**

Flower Mania had a profit of $3,257 for February.

✓ Quick Check

1. Find the profit or loss for Flower Mania for January and for March. **−$2,886; $821**

Differentiated Instruction Solutions for All Learners

Special Needs **L1**
If students have a difficult time drawing line graphs in the Homework Exercises, ask them to work those problems with a partner. One person can draw the graph, while the other decides on the labels for the axes and the titles.

learning style: visual

Below Level **L2**
Give students two numbers and have them make a reasonable scale as shown. **Answers may vary.**
−$328 and $562 **−$400 to $600**
−$4,563 and $2,091 **−$5,000 to $2,500**

learning style: visual

You can use line graphs to look at trends of monthly balances.

EXAMPLE Drawing and Interpreting Graphs

2 **Business** Draw a line graph of the monthly profits and losses for Beth's Pottery Shop. During which month was the profit greatest?

Profit/Loss for Beth's Pottery Shop					
Month	Profit/Loss	Month	Profit/Loss	Month	Profit/Loss
Jan.	−$1,917	May	−$150	Sept.	−$417
Feb.	−$682	June	$250	Oct.	−$824
Mar.	$303	July	$933	Nov.	$1,566
Apr.	$781	Aug.	$1,110	Dec.	$1,945

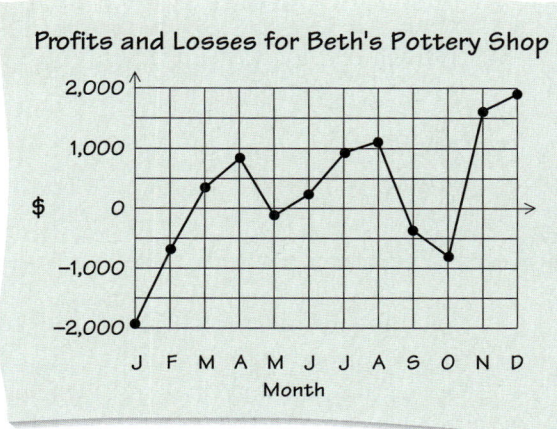

Profits and Losses for Beth's Pottery Shop

The balances vary from −$1,917 to $1,945. So make a scale from −$2,000 to $2,000. Use intervals of $500.

Beth's Pottery Shop made its greatest profit in December.

Quick Check

2. In which months did Beth's shop show a profit?
Mar., Apr., June, July, Aug., Nov., Dec.

Check Your Understanding

1. **Vocabulary** State whether you would use a positive number or a negative number to represent each of the following.
   a. loss — negative
   b. income — positive
   c. expense — negative
   d. profit — positive

2. **Number Sense** If expenses and income for a business are equal in July, how much money does the business make in July? $0

Advanced Learners L4
Mel babysits, charging $2 per hour per child. Each week she sits 2 children for 3 hours, 3 children for 1 hour, and 2 children for 4 hours. What are her weekly earnings? $34

learning style: verbal

English Language Learners ELL
For Example 2, ask students to use words to explain the line graph. Ask: *What does each point represent on the graph?* the intersection of the month and the profit or loss *What do the lines connecting the points represent?* increase or decrease

learning style: verbal

---

2. Teach

Activity Lab

Use before the lesson.

All in One Teaching Resources
Activity Lab 11-9: Exploring a Checkbook Register

Guided Instruction

Error Prevention!

Help students determine what scale and interval to use for each axis. Guide them to estimate where to plot points that lie between labeled tick marks.

PowerPoint
Additional Examples

1 Find the profit or loss for each month.

Month	Income	Expenses
Sept	$1,250	−$1,250
Oct	$3,200	−$2,550
Nov	$4,250	−$3,570
Dec	$2,530	−$2,840

   a. Sept. $0   b. Oct. $650
   c. Nov. $680   d. Dec. −$310

2 Draw a line graph based on your answers to Example 1a–d. In which month did the greatest profit occur? Nov.

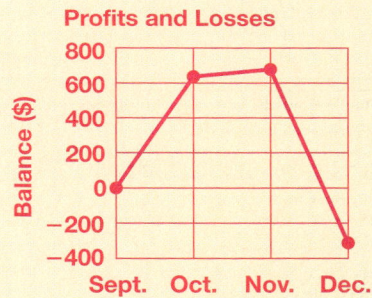

Profits and Losses

All in One Teaching Resources
- Daily Notetaking Guide 11-9 L3
- Adapted Notetaking 11-9 L1

Closure

- *How do you find a profit and a loss?* Add the income and expenses. A positive balance means a profit and a negative balance means a loss.

555

Assignment Guide

Check Your Understanding
Go over Exercises 1–2 in class before assigning the Homework Exercises.

Homework Exercises
A Practice by Example   3–10
B Apply Your Skills   11–21
C Challenge   22
Test Prep and
   Mixed Review   23–29

Homework Quick Check
To check students' understanding of key skills and concepts, go over Exercises 4, 9, 12, 13, and 19.

Differentiated Instruction **Resources**

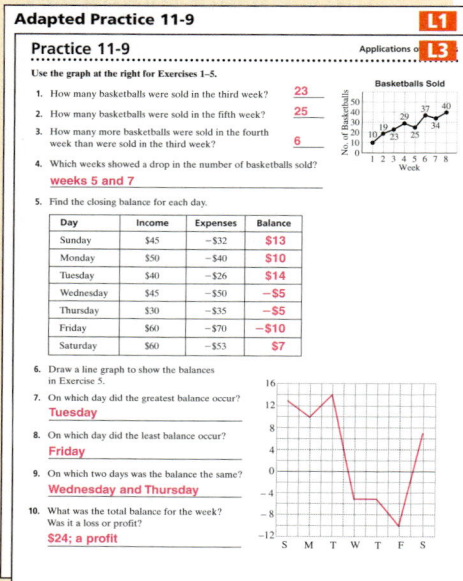

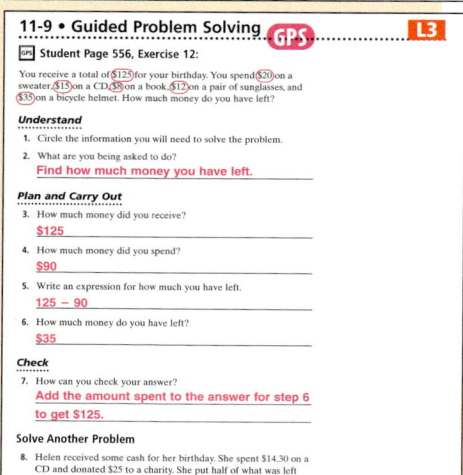

Homework Exercises

For more exercises, see Extra Skills and Word Problems.

GO for Help

For Exercises	See Examples
3–7	1
8–10	2

A Use the data for Rad's Books. Find the profit or loss.

Income and Expenses for Rad's Books

Week	Income	Expenses
Week 1	$4,257	−$6,513
Week 2	$3,840	−$2,856
Week 3	$4,109	−$3,915
Week 4	$3,725	−$4,921

3. Week 1 −$2,256
4. Week 2 $984
5. Week 3 $194
6. Week 4 −$1,196

Use the table showing income and expenses for several days.

7. Monday: $9; Tuesday: $18; Wednesday: −$9; Thursday: $17; Friday: −$12; Saturday: −$1

7. Find the profit or loss for each day. See left.

8. Draw a line graph to show the profits and losses. See margin.

9. On which day was the profit greatest? Tuesday

10. On which day was the loss greatest? Friday

Day	Income	Expenses
Mon.	$94	−$85
Tues.	$78	−$60
Wed.	$13	−$22
Thurs.	$90	−$73
Fri.	$37	−$49
Sat.	$15	−$16

B  **11. Guided Problem Solving** You sell bottled water at sports games. You pay $20 per game to rent a cooler. You pay $1 each for bottles of water and sell them for $2 each. How many bottles must you sell during a game to make a profit of $100?
• What are your expenses? 120 bottles
• How much profit do you earn from each bottle of water?

12. You receive a total of $125 for your birthday. You spend $20 on a sweater, $15 on a CD, $8 on a book, $12 on a pair of sunglasses, and $35 on a bicycle helmet. How much money do you have left? $35

13. Writing in Math Explain how you can determine whether a company has made a profit. A company has made a profit if its total expenses are less than its total income.

14. $197, $149, $124, −$11, $204; −$11

14. Accounting Find the balance after each transaction in the checking account. What was the amount of the least balance? See left.

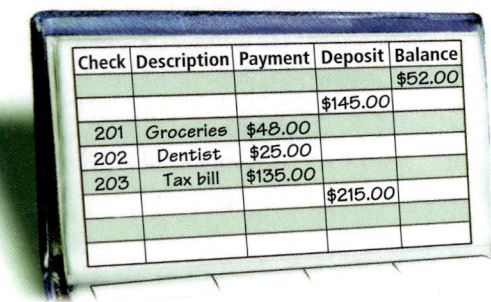

Check	Description	Payment	Deposit	Balance
				$52.00
			$145.00	
201	Groceries	$48.00		
202	Dentist	$25.00		
203	Tax bill	$135.00		
			$215.00	

8. See back of book.

Use the graph for Exercises 15–18.

15. How many CDs were sold in the fifth week? **30**

16. How many more CDs were sold in the sixth week than were sold in the second week? **23**

17. In which two weeks were the same number of CDs sold? **Weeks 1 and 3**

18. Which week showed a decrease in the number of CDs sold? **Week 2**

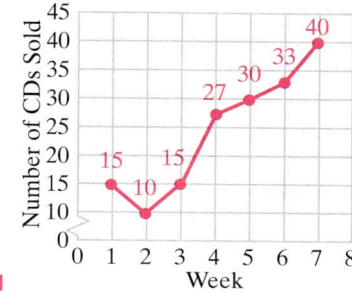

CD Sales

Population **Use the table below for Exercises 19–22.**

City	Population (thousands)					
	1950	1960	1970	1980	1990	2000
Miami, Fla.	249	292	335	347	359	362
Rochester, N.Y.	322	319	296	242	232	220

19. Display the data in a double line graph. **See margin.**

20. Use the graph you created in Exercise 19. Which city shows a positive trend in population? A negative trend in population? **Miami; Rochester**

21. In 1950, which city had a larger population? **Rochester**

C 22. **Challenge** Use your graph to predict the population of each city in 2020. **Answers may vary. Sample: Miami: 368,000; Rochester: 200,000**

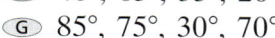

Test Prep and Mixed Review **Practice**

Multiple Choice

23. Which point on the graph corresponds to the coordinate pair $\left(2\frac{1}{2}, 3\right)$? **D**

Ⓐ *A*　　　Ⓒ *C*
Ⓑ *B*　　　Ⓓ *D*

24. Which of the following could be the measures of the angles of a quadrilateral? **J**

Ⓕ 40°, 65°, 55°, 20°　　　Ⓗ 80°, 120°, 90°, 90°
Ⓖ 85°, 75°, 30°, 70°　　　Ⓙ 115°, 75°, 45°, 125°

Classify each angle as *acute*, *obtuse*, *right*, or *straight*.

25. 123° **obtuse**　　26. 54° **acute**　　27. 90° **right**　　28. 173° **obtuse**　　29. 180° **straight**

GO for Help

For Exercises	See Lesson
25–29	8-2

PowerPoint
Lesson Quiz

Find the profit or loss for each month.

Month	Income	Expenses
May	$2,575	−$3,325
June	$3,280	−$4,850
July	$5,210	−$3,960
Aug.	$5,460	−$2,430

1. May **−$750**　　2. June **−$1,570**
3. July **$1,250**　　4. Aug. **$3,030**
5. Draw a line graph based on your answers to 1–4.

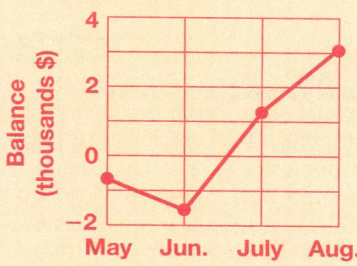

Profits and Losses

Enrichment 11-9 **L4**

Reteaching 11-9 Application of I **L2**

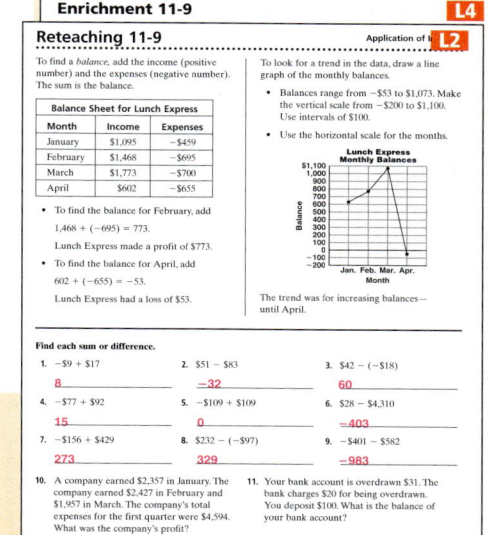

Alternative Assessment

Each student in a pair writes word problems similar to Exercises 3–10. Partners exchange problems and then solve them. Have partners discuss how they solved each other's problems.

19. See back of book.

Test Prep

Resources
For additional practice with a variety of test item formats:
• Test-Taking Strategies, p. 563
• Test Prep, p. 567
• Test-Taking Strategies with Transparencies

1. Plan

Objective
To make a function table and to graph a function

Examples
1 Completing a Function Table
2 Graphing a Function
3 Application: Salaries

Math Understandings: p. 514D

Math Background

A function table shows input and output values for a particular function. The input and output values in a table can be graphed as ordered pairs on a coordinate grid. The input is graphed on the horizontal axis and the output on the vertical axis. If the graphed points lie along a line, the function is called a *linear function*. Functions can also be expressed using algebraic equations. So functions can be expressed in tables, graphs, word rules, and algebraic rules.

More Math Background: p. 514D

Lesson Planning and Resources

See p. 514E for a list of the resources that support this lesson.

Bell Ringer Practice

✓ **Check Skills You'll Need**
Use student page, transparency, or PowerPoint. For intervention, direct students to:
Variables and Expressions
Lesson 3-2
Extra Skills and Word Problems
  Practice, Ch. 3

558

✓ Check Skills You'll Need

1. Vocabulary Review
Explain how an *expression* and an *equation* are different. **See below.**

Evaluate each expression for $x = 3$.
2. $8 + x$ **11** **3.** $18 \div x$ **6**
4. $4x$ **12** **5.** $21 - x$ **18**

 for Help
Lesson 3-2

Check Skills You'll Need

1. An expression does not have an equal sign.

What You'll Learn
To make a function table and to graph a function

🔊 **New Vocabulary** function

Why Learn This?

Pretend you have a machine. You can put any number, or input, into the machine. The machine performs an operation on the number and provides a result, or output. A **function** is a rule that assigns exactly one output value to each input value.

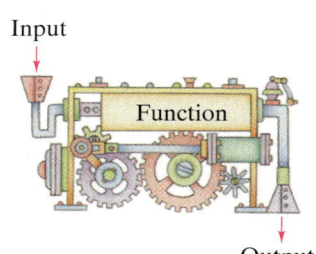

Input

Function

Output

Suppose you tell the machine to multiply by 4. A function table, such as the one at the right, shows the input and output values.

Input	Output
3	12
−7	−28

EXAMPLE   Completing a Function Table

1 Complete the function table if the rule is Output = Input · (−2).

Input	Output
−1	2
1	−2
3	−6

← Multiply −1 by −2. Place 2 in the Output column.
← Multiply 1 by −2. Place −2 in the Output column.
← Multiply 3 by −2. Place −6 in the Output column.

✓ Quick Check

1. Complete the function table for each rule.
   a. Output = Input ÷ 4   **b.** Output = Input − 8

Input	Output	
16	■	4
−24	■	−6
36	■	9

Input	Output	
−6	■	−14
−1	■	−9
4	■	−4

Differentiated Instruction   **Solutions for All Learners**

Special Needs L1
Pair students, who might have difficulty graphing functions, with students who can draw. One partner can make the table, while the other student graphs the values.

learning style: visual

Below Level L2
Have students complete function tables for the values −3, −1, 0, 2, and 5 for function rules as shown.
   Add 1 **−2, 0, 1, 3, 6**
   Divide by (−1) **3, 1, 0, −2, −5**
   Subtract 3 **−6, −4, −3, −1, 2**

learning style: visual

You can write the function rule in Example 1 using variables.

$$\text{Output} = \text{Input} \cdot (-2)$$
$$y = x \cdot (-2) \text{ or } y = -2x$$

You can graph a function on the coordinate plane. Use the horizontal axis for input (x) and the vertical axis for output (y).

EXAMPLE   Graphing a Function

② Make a table and graph some points of the function $y = x + 3$.

Input (x)	Output (y)
−2	1
−1	2
0	3
1	4
2	5

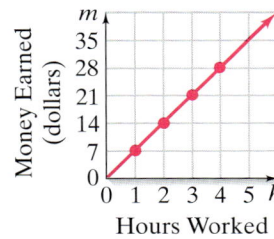

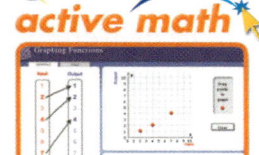

Online
active math

For: Graphing Functions
 Activity
Use: Interactive
 Textbook, 11-10

✓ Quick Check

2. Make a table and graph some points of the function $y = x - 3$.
See back of book.

In Example 2, the points lie on a line. This type of function is a linear function. You can join the points with a line.

Vocabulary Tip

The graph of a *linear* function is a *line*.

EXAMPLE   Application: Salaries

③ Workers at a grocery store make $7 an hour. The function $m = 7h$ shows how the money m they earn relates to the number of hours h they work. Make a table and graph the function.

Hours Worked	Money Earned (dollars)
1	7
2	14
3	21
4	28

✓ Quick Check

3. A car is driven at a steady rate of 45 miles per hour. The function $d = 45t$ shows how time t relates to distance d. Make a table and graph the function. **See back of book.**

11-10 Graphing Functions   **559**

---

2. Teach

Activity Lab
Use before the lesson.

All in One Teaching Resources
Activity Lab 11-10: Critical
 Thinking

Guided Instruction

Example 2
Help students understand that y depends on the value of x. Elicit the fact that students substitute values for x (input) to find the corresponding y-values (output).

Advanced Learners **L4**
The input integers for a function rule are 0, 4, and 8. The output is 2, 10, and 18. Write an equation for the function rule. **y = 2x + 2**

learning style: visual

English Language Learners **ELL**
Make sure that students understand that $2x$ in the More Than One Way example represents what the pizza delivery person receives for every single pizza he delivers, which is different than his daily rate.

learning style: verbal

559

1 Complete the function table given the rule:

Output = Input ÷ (−3).

Input	−9	−3	12	15
Output	3	1	−4	−5

2 Make a table and graph the function $y = -2x$.

Input	−2	−1	0	1	2
Output	4	2	0	−2	−4

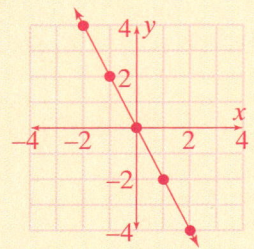

3 Henry receives $8.00 per hour for babysitting two children. The function $e = 8h$ shows how the earnings e relate to the number of hours h that Henry babysits. Make a table and graph the function.

Hours	1	2	3	4
Earnings ($)	8	16	24	32

See back of book for graph.

Closure

• *What is a function?* **a rule that assigns exactly one output value to each input value**
• *When might you not connect the points of a function graph?* **when not every point on the line represents a solution**

● More Than One Way

A pizza delivery person receives $5 each day he reports to work and $2 for each pizza he delivers. You can express this situation as the function $y = 5 + 2x$, where y = earnings and x = number of pizzas he delivers. How much will the delivery person earn in one day if he delivers 25 pizzas?

Jessica's Method

I can evaluate the equation to find the amount the delivery person earns. To do so, I replace x with the 25 pizzas he delivers.

$y = 5 + 2x$ ← Write the equation.

$y = 5 + 2(25)$ ← Substitute 25 for x.

$y = 55$

The delivery person will earn $55 for delivering 25 pizzas.

Leon's Method

If I make a table and a graph, I can tell how much the delivery person earns for delivering different numbers of pizzas.

x	y
0	5
5	15
10	25
15	35

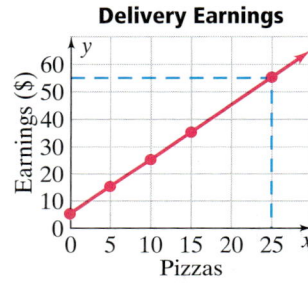

Delivery Earnings

All the points lie on a line, so I can use the graph to find the amount earned for 25 pizzas delivered. When $x = 25$, the y-value is 55. So the delivery person earned $55.

$90; answers may vary. Sample: I substituted 15 for x in the equation and solved for y; I chose this method because it was easier than making a table or graph.

Choose a Method

Tracy is a member of a discount CD club. She pays an annual fee of $30 and $4 for each CD. The function $y = 30 + 4x$ models this situation. If Tracy buys 15 CDs during the year, what will be her total cost? Describe your method and explain why you chose it.

See left.

Use the function $y = 3x$.

1. **Vocabulary** Which variable represents the input? **x**

2. Explain how to find the value of y when $x = 4$.
   Substitute the value 4 into the equation for x.

3. Describe the function: For each value of x, __?__ by 3 to find the value of y. **multiply**

4. Make a table of values and graph the function. **See margin.**

Homework Exercises

For more exercises, see Extra Skills and Word Problems.

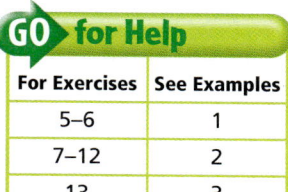

For Exercises	See Examples
5–6	1
7–12	2
13	3

Ⓐ **Complete the function table using the rule.**

5. Output = Input + 4

Input	Output	
−5	▦	**−1**
8	▦	**12**
31	▦	**35**

6. Output = Input − 4

Input	Output	
−2	▦	**−6**
5	▦	**1**
14	▦	**10**

Make a table and graph some points for each function. Use −2, −1, 0, 1, and 2 for x. **7–12. See margin.**

7. $y = x + 2$

8. $y = x - 2$

9. $y = 2x$

10. $y = \frac{x}{2}$

11. $y = \frac{x}{2} + 1$

12. $y = -\frac{x}{2}$

15. $11, $14, $17, $20; answers may vary. Sample: I evaluated $3t + 5$ for each number of tees because it is easier than making a table or graph.

13. **Library** Suppose a library charges a fine of $0.25 for each day a book is overdue. The function $f = 0.25d$ shows how the number of days d relates to the fine f. Make a table and graph the function. **See margin.**

Ⓑ  14. **Guided Problem Solving** You buy shirts for $9 each. You have a coupon for $2 off your total purchase. Find the final price of seven shirts. **$61**
   • What function models this situation?
   • What number will you substitute for t, the price of a shirt?

GO **Online**
Homework Video Tutor
Visit: PHSchool.com
Web Code: aqe-1110

15. **Choose a Method** A store sells kicking tees by mail for $3 each. The shipping charge is $5. Find the total prices for 2, 3, 4, or 5 tees. Describe your method and explain why you chose it. **See above left.**

🌐nline lesson quiz, PHSchool.com, Web Code: aqa-1110

11-10 Graphing Functions **561**

4. See back of book.

7–13. See back of book.

Assignment Guide

Check Your Understanding
Go over Exercises 1–4 in class before assigning the Homework Exercises.

Homework Exercises
A Practice by Example   5–13
B Apply Your Skills   14–21
C Challenge   22
Test Prep and
  Mixed Review   23–25

Homework Quick Check
To check students' understanding of key skills and concepts, go over Exercises 6, 11, 15, 18, and 20.

Differentiated Instruction Resources

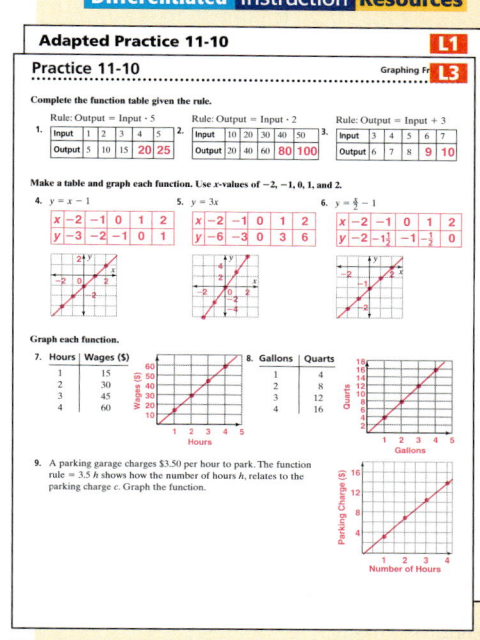

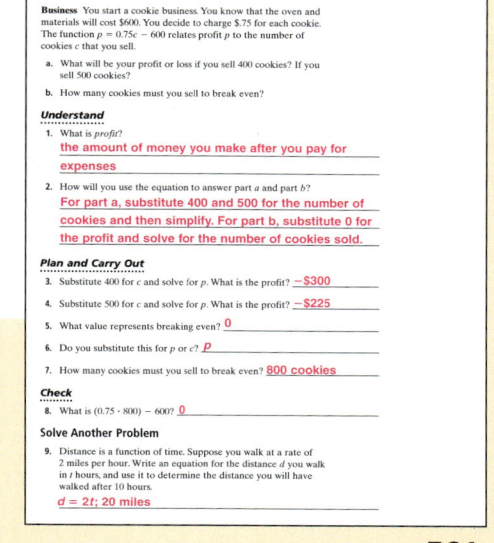

PowerPoint
Lesson Quiz

1. Complete the function table given the rule:
Output = Input · (−4).

Input	−3	0	6
Output	12	0	−24

2. Make a table and graph the function $y = \dfrac{x}{2} - 1$.

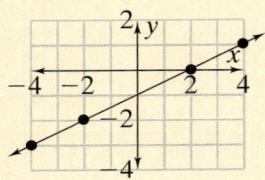

Input	−2	0	2	4
Output	−2	−1	0	1

Enrichment 11-10 — L4

Reteaching 11-10 — Graphing Fu... L2

A table or a graph can show how the input and output of a *function* are related.

Make a table to show how number of feet is a function of number of yards.

Use the values in the table to draw a graph of the function.

Input (yards)	Output (feet)
1	3
2	6
3	9
4	12
5	15

① Locate the points from the table: (1, 3), (2, 6), (3, 9), (4, 12), (5, 15)
② Draw a line through the points.

The table shows that for every yard, there are 3 feet. You multiply the number of yards by 3 to find the number of feet.

Complete the table.

1.
Input	Output
1	4
2	5
3	6
4	7
5	8

2.
Input	Output
4	2
6	4
8	6
10	8
12	10

3.
Input	Output
2	10
3	15
4	20
5	25
6	30

Complete each table given the rule. Then graph some points for the function.
Sample answers given.

4. cups as a function of quarts
Quarts	Cups
1	4
2	8
3	12
4	16

5. days as a function of weeks
Weeks	Days
1	7
2	14
3	21
4	28

Complete each function table. Then write a rule for the function.

16.

Input	Output
3	5
4	6
5	7
6	8
7	9

add 2

17.

Input	Output
10	2
15	3
20	4
25	5
30	6

divide by 5

18. Business You start a cookie business. You know that the oven **GPS** and materials will cost $600. You decide to charge $.75 for each cookie. The function $p = 0.75c - 600$ relates profit p to the number of cookies c that you sell.

    a. What will be your profit or loss if you sell 400 cookies? If you sell 500 cookies? **−$300; −$225**

    b. How many cookies must you sell to break even? **800 cookies**

Writing in Math **Classify each function as *linear* or *not linear*. Explain your answer.** **19–21. See left.**

19. $y = x$

20. $y = x^2$

21. $y = \dfrac{1}{x}$

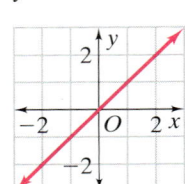
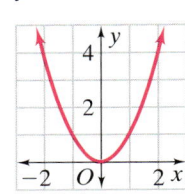
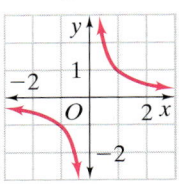

19. Linear; the graph is a line.

20. Not linear; the graph is not a line.

21. Not linear; the graph is not a line.

C **22. Challenge** Graph $y = -2x$ and $y = -x^2$. What points do the graphs have in common? How are the graphs different?
See margin.

Test Prep and Mixed Review
Practice

Multiple Choice

23. Which ordered pair shows the coordinates of point P? **A**

  Ⓐ $\left(1\frac{1}{2}, 2\right)$ Ⓒ $\left(2, 1\frac{1}{2}\right)$

  Ⓑ $\left(1, 2\frac{1}{2}\right)$ Ⓓ $\left(2\frac{1}{2}, 1\right)$

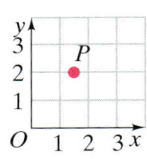

24. Tim drives his car 240 miles in 4 hours. If he travels at this rate, how far will Tim drive in the next 7 hours? **H**

  Ⓕ 1,680 miles   Ⓖ 600 miles   Ⓗ 420 miles   Ⓙ 60 miles

GO for Help

For Exercise	See Lesson
25	5-7

25. You will drive for 5 hours and make three $\frac{1}{2}$-hour stops. You want to arrive at 3:30 P.M. What time should you leave? **9:00 A.M.**

Test Prep

Resources

For additional practice with a variety of test item formats:
- Test-Taking Strategies, p. 563
- Test Prep, p. 567
- Test-Taking Strategies with Transparencies

Alternative Assessment

Each student in a pair writes a linear function such as $y = 2x - 3$. Partners exchange papers and make a table and graph of their partner's function rule.

22. See back of book.

Using a Variable

Use a variable to represent the unknown quantity. You can choose a letter that reminds you of what the variable represents. Then write an equation.

EXAMPLE

Admission to a county fair is $4.50 per person. The Rodriguez family pays $22.50 for admission to the fair. Which equation can you use to find p, the number of people in the Rodriguez family?

Ⓐ $p = 22.50 + 4.50$ Ⓒ $p = 22.50 \times 4.50$
Ⓑ $p = 22.50 - 4.50$ Ⓓ $p = 22.50 \div 4.50$

Words | number of people | equals | total cost | divided by | cost of one person

Let p = the number of people.

Equation p =   22.50   ÷   4.50

$p = 22.50 \div 4.50$ ← Write the equation.

● The correct answer is choice D.

Exercises

1. Stephanie scored 17 points in the first half of a game. In all, she scored 25 points. Which equation can you use to find p, the number of points Stephanie scored in the second half? **B**
   Ⓐ $p = 25 + 17$ Ⓒ $p = 25 \times 17$
   Ⓑ $p = 25 - 17$ Ⓓ $p = 25 \div 17$

2. You want to make 18 double-decker sandwiches. You need 3 slices of bread for each sandwich. Which equation can you use to find s, the number of slices of bread that you need? **H**
   Ⓕ $s = 18 + 3$ Ⓗ $s = 18 \times 3$
   Ⓖ $s = 18 - 3$ Ⓙ $s = 18 \div 3$

3. Russell volunteers 36 hours at a hospital. He volunteers over a period of 15 weekends. Which equation can you use to find h, the average number of hours he works each weekend? **D**
   Ⓐ $h = 36 + 15$ Ⓒ $h = 36 \times 15$
   Ⓑ $h = 36 - 15$ Ⓓ $h = 36 \div 15$

Test-Taking Strategies   Using a Variable   **563**

Chapter 11 Review

Vocabulary Review

 absolute value (p. 517)
coordinate plane (p. 548)
function (p. 558)

integers (p. 516)
opposites (p. 516)
ordered pair (p. 548)

origin (p. 548)
quadrants (p. 548)

Go Online
PHSchool.com
For: Vocabulary quiz
Web Code: aqj-1151

Choose the vocabulary term that correctly completes each sentence.

1. A(n) __?__ assigns one output value to each input value. **function**

2. The numbers −4, −2, −1, 0, and 3 are __?__. **integers**

3. __?__ are the regions of the coordinate plane. **quadrants**

4. −3 and 3 are __?__. **opposites**

Skills and Concepts

Lessons 11-1, 11-2
• To use integers, opposites, and absolute values to represent real-world situations
• To compare and order integers

Integers are the set of positive whole numbers, their opposites, and 0. The **absolute value** of a number is its distance from 0 on a number line.

5. Write an integer to represent 14 degrees below zero. **−14**

Compare, using < or >.

6. $|-5|$ ■ $|4|$ **>**
7. -8 ■ 12 **<**
8. 4 ■ $|-9|$ **<**
9. -12 ■ -14 **>**

Order from least to greatest.

10. $-1, 1, 2, -2$ **−2, −1, 1, 2**
11. $0, -4, 5, -6$ **−6, −4, 0, 5**
12. $-3, 5, -7, 9$ **−7, −3, 5, 9**

Lessons 11-3, 11-4
• To add integers and to solve problems by adding integers
• To subtract integers and to solve problems by subtracting integers

The sum of two positive integers is positive. The sum of two negative integers is negative. The sum of integers with different signs has the sign of the number with the greater absolute value.

You subtract an integer by adding its opposite.

Find each sum or difference.

13. $3 + 8$ **11**
14. $5 + (-9)$ **−4**
15. $-4 + 2$ **−2**
16. $-7 + (-6)$ **−13**

17. $11 - 3$ **8**
18. $2 - (-6)$ **8**
19. $-7 - 4$ **−11**
20. $-10 - (-2)$ **−8**

Lessons 11-5, 11-6

- To multiply integers and to solve problems by multiplying integers
- To divide integers and to solve problems by dividing integers

The product or quotient of two integers with the same sign is positive. The product or quotient of two integers with different signs is negative.

Find each product or quotient.

21. 4×9 **36**   **22.** $7 \times (-3)$ **−21** **23.** -5×2 **−10**   **24.** $-6 \times (-8)$
                                                                                                48

25. $16 \div 4$ **4**   **26.** $25 \div (-5)$ **−5** **27.** $-49 \div (-7)$ **7** **28.** $-32 \div 8$
                                                                                              −4

Lesson 11-7

- To solve equations containing integers

You use properties of equality and inverse operations to solve equations.

Solve each equation.

29. $x + 3 = -12$ **−15**   **30.** $x - 3 = -12$ **−9**

31. $-3x = 12$ **−4**   **32.** $\frac{x}{3} = -12$ **−36**

Lesson 11-8

- To name and graph points on a coordinate plane

A **coordinate plane** is formed by the intersection of an x-axis and a y-axis at the **origin**. An **ordered pair** identifies the location of a point.

Graph each point on the same coordinate plane. **33–36. See margin.**

33. $A(0, 6)$ **34.** $B(5, -4)$ **35.** $C(-6, 1)$ **36.** $D(-2, -3)$

Lesson 11-9

- To apply integers to profit and loss situations

The sum of a business's income and expenses is called a balance. A positive balance is a profit. A negative balance is a loss.

Use the table at the right.

37. Find the total balance for the four months. **$26,286**

38. Did Pie in the Sky Balloons have a profit or a loss during that time? **profit**

Pie in the Sky Balloons	
Month	**Profit/Loss**
January	−$985
February	$10,241
March	−$209
April	$17,239

Lesson 11-10

- To make a function table and to graph a function

A **function** assigns exactly one output value to each input value.

Make a table and graph each function. Use x-values −2, −1, 0, 1, and 2. **39–41. See margin.**

39. $y = x + 3$ **40.** $y = 2x - 3$ **41.** $y = \frac{x}{4}$

33–36. See back of book.

39–41. See back of book.

Chapter 11 Test

Go Online
PHSchool.com
For: Online chapter test
Web Code: aqa-1152

1. What integer represents 7°F below 0°F? **−7**

2. Name the opposite of each integer.
a. 89 **−89**   b. −100 **100**

Compare, using <, =, or >.

3. 18 ▉ −24 **>**

4. −15 ▉ −9 **<**

5. 27 ▉ −27 **>**

6. Order the integers from least to greatest. 3, −1, −13, 5, 0 **−13, −1, 0, 3, 5**

7. **Writing in Math** Define *absolute value* and illustrate with a number line. **See margin.**

Find each answer.

8. $9 + (−4)$ **5**

9. $−13 + 6$ **−7**

10. $−7 + (−5)$ **−12**

11. $−2 − 8$ **−10**

12. $−3 − (−3)$ **0**

13. $3 − 9$ **−6**

14. $5 × (−4)$ **−20**

15. $−3 × (−6)$ **18**

16. $−2 × 7$ **−14**

17. $9 ÷ (−3)$ **−3**

18. $−5 ÷ (−5)$ **1**

19. $−12 ÷ 4$ **−3**

20. Solve $d + 6 = −3$. **−9**

21. **Temperature** The temperature is 18°F at 1:00 A.M. The temperature falls 22 degrees by 6:00 A.M. Find the temperature at 6:00 A.M. **−4°F**

22. On a math quiz worth 50 points, a student misses 2 points on the first section, 3 points on the second, 2 points on the third, and 1 point on the last. Find the student's score. **42 points**

Use the coordinate plane below for Exercises 23 and 24.

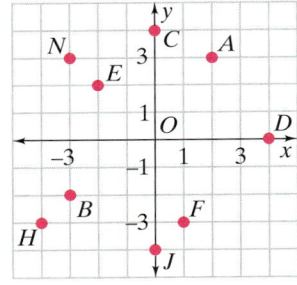

23. Name the point with the given coordinates.
a. $(0, 4)$ **C**   b. $(−3, 3)$ **N**   c. $(−4, −3)$ **H**

24. Write the coordinates of each point.
a. A b. B c. F d. J
(2, 3) **(−3, −2)** **(1, −3)** **(0, −4)**

25. Graph each point on a coordinate plane.
a. $(−2, −3)$ b. $(4, −5)$ c. $(2, 6)$
25a–c. See margin.

26. a. Use the data below to find Royale Bakery's profit or loss for each month. **26a–b. See margin.**
b. Graph the profit and loss data.

Income and Expenses for Royale Bakery		
Month	**Income**	**Expenses**
Jan.	$1,314	−$828
Feb.	$2,120	−$120
Mar.	$1,019	−$1,285
Apr.	$1,438	−$765

27. Draw a graph for the linear function $y = x − 3$. **See margin.**

28. **Estimation** A climber starts at 50 feet above sea level at 7:00 A.M. At 11:00 A.M., she is 210 feet above sea level. If she maintains a steady rate, estimate her height above sea level at 12:30 P.M. **270 ft**

7. See back of book.

25a–c. See back of book.

26a–b. See back of book.

27. See back of book.

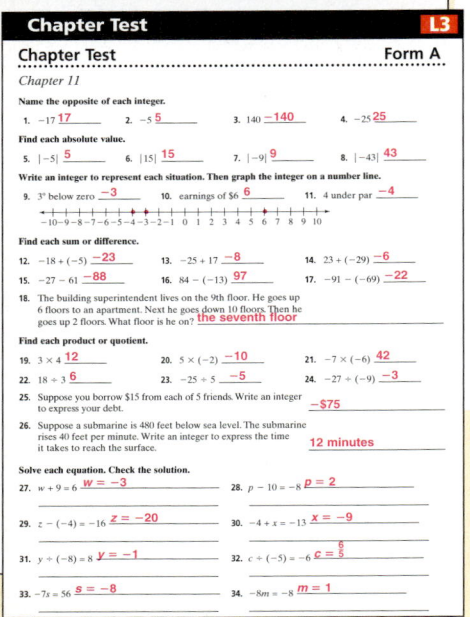

Multiple Choice
Choose the correct letter.

1. Evaluate the expression $b - a - 8$ when $a = 7$ and $b = 24$. **C**
   - (A) -25
   - (B) -9
   - (C) 9
   - (D) 11

2. Which amount is the same as $1\frac{1}{2}$ pints? **G**
   - (F) 25 fluid ounces
   - (H) $\frac{3}{5}$ quart
   - (G) 3 cups
   - (J) $\frac{1}{8}$ gallon

3. Suppose you purchase 9 peaches, 6 oranges, 12 pears, and 8 plums. What is the ratio of plums to pears? **A**
   - (A) $\frac{2}{3}$
   - (C) $12 : 8$
   - (B) 9 to 12
   - (D) $4 : 2$

4. Find the median of the following set of data: 9, 19, 9, 17, 13, 14, 11, 9, 13. **J**
   - (F) 9
   - (G) 10
   - (H) $12\frac{2}{3}$
   - (J) 13

5. Suppose you have a fresh lemonade stand. You spend \$7 on the lemons, sugar, and cups. During the day, you sell 12 cups of lemonade for \$.50 each. What is your profit or loss? **A**
   - (A) $-\$1$
   - (B) $-\$.50$
   - (C) \$0
   - (D) \$1

6. Which of the following is the area of a circle with a diameter of 9 inches? Round to the nearest square unit. **H**
   - (F) 28 in.^{2}
   - (H) 64 in.^{2}
   - (G) 57 in.^{2}
   - (J) 254 in.^{2}

7. Simplify: $-8 + 9 \div 3$. **D**
   - (A) $-\frac{1}{3}$
   - (B) $\frac{1}{3}$
   - (C) 5
   - (D) -5

8. Which statement is false? **H**
   - (F) A square is always a rectangle.
   - (G) Some rectangles are rhombuses.
   - (H) All quadrilaterals are parallelograms.
   - (J) A square is always a rhombus.

9. Which equation is NOT correct? **D**
   - (A) $\frac{3}{4} + 2\frac{1}{2} = 3\frac{1}{4}$
   - (C) $1\frac{7}{8} + 1\frac{5}{6} = 3\frac{17}{24}$
   - (B) $3\frac{4}{5} - \frac{6}{8} = 3\frac{1}{20}$
   - (D) $5\frac{2}{5} - 2\frac{1}{3} = 3\frac{1}{10}$

10. Find the volume of a rectangular prism with the dimensions $\ell = 10$ m, $w = 7$ m, and $h = 8$ m. **J**
    - (F) $V = 25$ m^3
    - (H) $V = 56$ m^3
    - (G) $V = 70$ m^3
    - (J) $V = 560$ m^3

11. The angles of 4 triangles have the following measures. Which of the triangles is obtuse? **C**
    - (A) $86°, 53°, 41°$
    - (C) $89°, 45.5°, 45.5°$
    - (B) $123°, 32°, 25°$
    - (D) $74°, 71°, 35°$

Gridded Response

12. How many kilometers are in 120 meters? **0.12**

13. Jack saves \$32.75 from his newspaper delivery job. On Saturday, he spends \$23.52 of his savings on a CD. How much does he have left? **9.23**

Short Response 14–16. See margin.

14. On a scale drawing, the scale shown is 1 in. to 10 ft. The length of a room is 2.5 in. on the drawing. Make a sketch and find the actual length of the room.

15. Write an integer to represent three degrees Fahrenheit below zero. Then graph the integer on a number line.

Extended Response

16. **a.** A parallelogram has a base of 9 in. and a height of 7 in. Find its area.
    b. The base and the height of the parallelogram are doubled. Is the area doubled? Explain.

Chapter 11   Test Prep   **567**

Resources

Test Prep Workbook

All in One **Teaching Resources**
• Cumulative Review   **L3**

ExamView Assessment Suite CD-ROM
• Standardized Test Practice

Differentiated Instruction

Spanish Assessment Resources
• Spanish Cumulative Review   **ELL**

ExamView Assessment Suite CD-ROM
• Special Needs Practice Bank   **L1**

16. **[4] a. 63 in.^{2};
    b. No; the new area, 252 in.^{2}, is 4 times the area in part (a).**
    [3] appropriate methods, computational error
    [2] did not double the base and height accordingly OR no explanation given
    [1] correct areas given without work shown

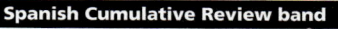
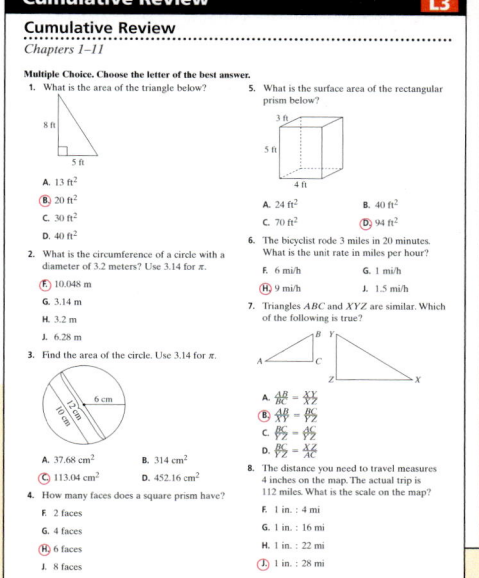

Spanish Cumulative Review band   **ELL**

Cumulative Review   **L3**

Cumulative Review
Chapters 1–11

Multiple Choice. Choose the letter of the best answer.
1. What is the area of the triangle below?
   - A. 13 ft^2
   - B. 20 ft^2
   - C. 30 ft^2
   - D. 40 ft^2
2. What is the circumference of a circle with diameter of 3.2 meters? Use 3.14 for π.
   - F. 10.048 m
   - G. 3.14 m
   - H. 3.2 m
   - J. 6.28 m
3. Find the area of the circle. Use 3.14 for π.
   - A. 37.68 cm^2
   - B. 314 cm^2
   - C. 113.04 cm^2
   - D. 452.16 cm^2
4. How many faces does a square prism have?
   - F. 2 faces
   - G. 4 faces
   - H. 6 faces
   - J. 8 faces
5. What is the surface area of the rectangular prism below?
   - A. 24 ft^2
   - B. 40 ft^2
   - C. 70 ft^2
   - D. 94 ft^2
6. The bicyclist rode 3 miles in 20 minutes. What is the unit rate in miles per hour?
   - F. 6 mi/h
   - G. 1 mi/h
   - H. 9 mi/h
   - J. 1.5 mi/h
7. Triangles ABC and XYZ are similar. Which of the following is true?
   - A. $\frac{AB}{BC} = \frac{XY}{YZ}$
   - B. $\frac{AB}{XY} = \frac{BC}{YZ}$
   - C. $\frac{BC}{YZ} = \frac{XY}{AC}$
   - D. $\frac{BC}{YZ} = \frac{XZ}{AC}$
8. The distance you need to travel measures 4 inches on the map. The actual trip is 112 miles. What is the scale on the map?
   - F. 1 in. : 4 mi
   - G. 1 in. : 16 mi
   - H. 1 in. : 22 mi
   - J. 1 in. : 28 mi

Item	1	2	3	4	5	6	7	8	9	10	11	12	13	14	15	16
Lesson	3-2	6-7	7-1	2-2	11-4	9-6	11-6	8-5	5-5	9-9	8-4	9-2	1-7	7-5	11-1	9-4

14. **[2] Check students' work; 25 ft**
    [1] correct length without sketch OR with incorrect sketch

15. **[2] −3**

    [1] incorrect integer OR incorrect number line

Applying Integers

Students will use data from these two pages to answer the questions posed in Put It All Together.

Remind students that, like temperature, common elevation measurements can include negative, as well as positive numbers. Ask:

- *Do you know of places that are below sea level?* **Sample: Death Valley, CA; New Orleans, LA; and the Dead Sea in Israel.**
- *What are the approximate elevations of those places?* **Death Valley, −282 ft; New Orleans, −8 ft; the Dead Sea, −417 ft**

Discuss how a place's elevation is a major factor in determining its average temperature.

Materials
- A chart of average monthly temperatures in Antarctica
- Photos of the Dead Sea

Activating Prior Knowledge

Have students share any experiences they have had at high (or low) altitudes and in very warm and cold temperatures. Have them describe the effects of these extremes.

Guided Instruction

Have volunteers read aloud the data about the places on these pages. Discuss the information. Ask:

- *If you stood at the base of Mt. Whitney how high would the peak be above you?* **Sample: The peak would be much less than it's actual 14,459 feet height.**
- *Why would the heigh to the peak be less than its recorded elevation?* **Sample: Because you would be standing above sea level, so the elevation between the peak and the base would be less than if at sea level.**

568

Applying Integers

Peaks and Valleys Elevations in the United States vary from tens of thousands of feet above sea level to several hundred feet below sea level. Aerial photography and relief maps show these differences clearly.

Put It All Together

Data File Use the information on these two pages and on page 651 to answer these questions.

1. Which featured location has the highest elevation? The lowest elevation?

2. **a.** How much higher is the elevation of Vostok Station, Antarctica, than the elevation of Death Valley, California?

   b. How much higher is the elevation of New Orleans, Louisiana, than the elevation of Death Valley, California?

3. Which location has an elevation 5,512 feet lower than Colorado Springs, Colorado? Show your work.
   - **A.** Colossal Cave, Arizona   **B.** Detroit, Michigan
   - **C.** Houston, Texas   **D.** New Orleans, Louisiana

4. Which location has an elevation 16 feet higher than New Orleans, Louisiana? Show your work.
   - **A.** Atlantic Ocean   **B.** Death Valley, California
   - **C.** Key West, Florida   **D.** Long Island, New York

5. **Reasoning** Which of these places do you think has the highest elevation: Boston, Massachusetts; Denver, Colorado; or Memphis, Tennessee? Explain.

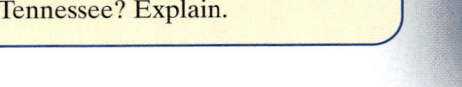
Go Online
PHSchool.com
For: Information about geography
Web Code: aqe-1153

568

Seattle, Washington

Mt. Whitney, California
Elevation: 14,495 feet
Highest point in the contiguous United States

Las Vegas, Nevada

Death Valley, California
Elevation: −282 feet
Average temperature: high 90.5°F, low 62.2°F
Lowest point in the contiguous United States.

Pacific Ocean
Elevation: Sea level (0 feet)

1. **Mt. Whitney; Death Valley**

2a. **11,502 ft**

b. **274 ft**

3. **B. Detroit, Michigan**
   $6{,}145 - 5{,}512 = x$
   $633 = x$

4. **C. Key West, Florida**
   $y - 16 = -8$
   $y = 8$

Detroit, Michigan
Elevation: 633 feet
Average temperature:
high 58.4°F, low 41°F

Boston,
Massachusetts

Minneapolis,
Minnesota

Long Island, New York
Elevation: 16 feet
Average temperature:
high 61.2°F, low 43.5°F

Denver, Colorado

Chicago,
Illinois

Washington, D.C.

Colorado Springs,
Colorado
Elevation: 6,145 feet
Average temperature:
high 61.8°F, low 33.7°F

Oklahoma City,
Oklahoma

Memphis,
Tennessee

New Orleans, Louisiana
Elevation: −8 feet
Average temperature:
high 78°F, low 59.6°F

Atlantic Ocean
Elevation: Sea level (0 feet)

Houston, Texas
Elevation: 96 feet
Average temperature:
high 79.4°F, low 58.2°F

Key West, Florida
Elevation: 8 feet
Average temperature:
high 82.9°F, low 73.2°F

Activity

Have students work in pairs to answer the questions. Begin by asking a volunteer to explain the difference between a relief map and a political map. Discuss reasons for using either kind.

Exercise 5 Suggest that students use a relief map of the United States to answer these questions or that they us a road atlas and make inferences from it based on a city's proximity to mountains or sea shores.

Geography Connection
Invite students to identify the highest and lowest points in your state, as well as the warmest and coldest places. Ask them to compare this with some of the data presented on these pages.

Differentiated Instruction

Special Needs L1
Remind students that there are 5,280 feet in a mile. You might want to convert some elevations into miles.

569

5. **Answers may vary. Sample: Denver, Colorado; Boston, Massachusetts is on the coast and therefore is at about sea level; Memphis, Tennessee is** on the Mississippi River and should be fairly low in elevation. Denver, Colorado is located near Colorado Springs, which has an elevation of over 6,000 ft.

Chapter at a Glance

Lesson Titles, Objectives, and Features	Assessment	NCTM Standards	Local Standards
12-1 Solving Two-Step Equations • To solve two-step equations and to use two-step equations to solve problems **12-1b Activity Lab, Algebra Thinking:** Using Equation Language	Lesson Quiz	1, 2, 5, 6, 7, 8, 9, 10	
12-2 Inequalities • To express and identify solutions of inequalities	Lesson Quiz	1, 2, 5, 6, 7, 8, 9, 10	
12-3 Solving One-Step Inequalities • To solve one-step inequalities by adding or subtracting **12-3b Activity Lab, Data Analysis:** Applying Inequalities	Lesson Quiz Checkpoint Quiz 1	1, 2, 5, 6, 7, 8, 9, 10	
12-4a Activity Lab, Hands On: Exploring Squares **12-4 Exploring Square Roots and Rational Numbers** • To find square roots and identify rational numbers	Lesson Quiz	1, 2, 5, 6, 7, 8, 9, 10	
12-5 Introducing the Pythagorean Theorem • To solve problems using the Pythagorean Theorem • **Guided Problem Solving:** Practice Solving Problems	Lesson Quiz	1, 2, 5, 6, 7, 8, 9, 10	
Problem Solving Application: Applying Equations			

NCTM Standards 2000

1 Number and Operations	**2** Algebra	**3** Geometry	**4** Measurement	**5** Data Analysis and Probability
6 Problem Solving	**7** Reasoning and Proof	**8** Communication	**9** Connections	**10** Representation

Correlations to Standardized Tests

All content for these tests is contained in *Prentice Hall Math,* Course 1. This chart reflects coverage in this chapter only.

	12-1	12-2	12-3	12-4	12-5
Terra Nova CAT6 (Level 16)					
Number and Number Relations	✔	✔	✔	✔	✔
Computation and Numerical Estimation	✔	✔	✔	✔	✔
Operation Concepts	✔	✔	✔	✔	✔
Measurement					✔
Geometry and Spatial Sense					✔
Data Analysis, Statistics, and Probability					
Patterns, Functions, Algebra	✔	✔	✔	✔	✔
Problem Solving and Reasoning	✔	✔	✔	✔	✔
Communication	✔	✔	✔	✔	✔
Decimals, Fractions, Integers, and Percent	✔	✔	✔	✔	✔
Order of Operations					
Terra Nova CTBS (Level 16)					
Decimals, Fractions, Integers, Percents	✔	✔	✔	✔	✔
Order of Operations, Numeration, Number Theory	✔	✔	✔	✔	✔
Data Interpretation					
Pre-algebra	✔	✔	✔	✔	✔
Measurement					✔
Geometry					✔
ITBS (Level 12)					
Number Properties and Operations	✔	✔	✔	✔	✔
Algebra	✔	✔	✔	✔	✔
Geometry					✔
Measurement					✔
Probability and Statistics					
Estimation					
SAT10 (Int 2 Level)					
Number Sense and Operations	✔	✔	✔	✔	✔
Patterns, Relationships, and Algebra	✔	✔	✔	✔	✔
Data, Statistics, and Probability					
Geometry and Measurement					✔
NAEP					
Number Sense, Properties, and Operations				✔	
Measurement					
Geometry and Spatial Sense					✔
Data Analysis, Statistics, and Probability					
Algebra and Functions	✔	✔	✔		

CAT6 California Achievement Test, 6th Ed. **CTBS** Comprehensive Test of Basic Skills **ITBS** Iowa Test of Basic Skills, Form M
SAT10 Stanford Achievement Test, 10th Ed. **NAEP** National Assessment of Educational Progress 2005 Mathematics Objectives

Math Background

Skills Trace

> ### BEFORE Chapter 12
> Grade 5 presented solving of basic equations.
>
> ### DURING Chapter 12
> Course 1 extends the solving of equations to two-step equations and inequalities.
>
> ### AFTER Chapter 12
> Throughout this course, students write and solve equations to solve real-world problems.

12-1 Solving Two-Step Equations

Math Understandings
- A two-step equation has two operations, each of which must be undone by using an inverse operation and the properties of equality.
- The usual order for solving a two-step equation is the reverse of the order of operations: first, undo addition or subtraction; then undo multiplication or division. However, it is possible to undo the multiplication or division first if you are careful to multiply or divide each term on each side of the equation.

A **two-step equation,** like $2y + 3 = 11$, is an equation containing two operations. To solve any two-step equation, begin by undoing the addition and subtraction, then undo the multiplication or division.

Example: Solve $2y + 3 = 11$.

$$2y + 3 = 11$$
$$2y + 3 - 3 = 11 - 3 \quad \leftarrow \text{Subtract 3 from each side.}$$
$$2y = 8 \quad \leftarrow \text{Simplify.}$$
$$\frac{2y}{2} = \frac{8}{2} \quad \leftarrow \text{Divide each side by 2.}$$
$$y = 4 \quad \leftarrow \text{Simplify.}$$

Check
$$2y + 3 = 11 \quad \leftarrow \text{Check using the orginal equation.}$$
$$2(4) + 3 = 11 \quad \leftarrow \text{Substitute 4 for } y.$$
$$8 + 3 = 11 \quad \leftarrow \text{Simplify.}$$
$$11 = 11 \quad \leftarrow \text{Simplify.}$$

12-2 Inequalities

Math Understandings
- The solution set for an equation in one variable is most often a single value. The solution set for an inequality in one variable is most often a set of values.
- Graphing the solution set for an inequality on a number line is often the best way to visualize all the solutions.

An **inequality** is a mathematical sentence that contains $<$, $>$, $\leq$, $\geq$, or $\neq$.

$<$ is less than	$>$ is greater than
$\leq$ is less than or equal to	$\geq$ is greater than or equal to
$\neq$ is not equal to	

The **graph of an inequality** shows all the solutions that satisfy the inequality. An open circle shows that the starting number is *not* included. A closed circle shows that the starting number is included. A **solution of an inequality** is any number that makes the inequality true.

Examples: Graph $x > -3$.

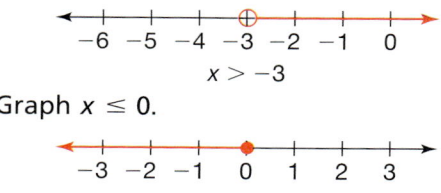

Graph $x \leq 0$.

12-3 Solving One-Step Inequalities

Math Understandings
- You can use a similar process to solve an inequality as you use to solve an equation.
- When the only operations you use to solve an inequality are addition and subtraction, the procedure is the same as it is for solving an equation.

To solve an inequality by adding or subtracting, use inverse operations to get the variable alone on one side of the inequality symbol.

Example: Solve $x - 7 > 3$.

$$x - 7 > 3$$
$$x - 7 + 7 > 3 + 7 \quad \leftarrow \text{Add 7 to each side.}$$
$$x > 10 \quad \leftarrow \text{Simplify.}$$

Math Understandings

- The inverse of squaring is finding the square root.
- Mathematicians have agreed that the symbol $\sqrt{}$ indicates the nonnegative square root of a number.
- When you find the square root of a number that is not a perfect square, you can use a calculator.
- A rational number gets the name from the fact that it is the ratio of two integers.

A **square root** of a given number is a number that, when multiplied by itself, is the given number.

Example: Since 3×3 is 9, $\sqrt{9}$ is 3.

A **perfect square** is the square of a whole number.

Example: 1, 4, 9, 16, 25, 36, 49, 64, 81, and 100 are all perfect squares.

You can also estimate square roots of numbers that are not perfect squares.

Example: Tell which two consecutive whole numbers $\sqrt{5}$ is between.

$$4 < 5 < 9 \qquad \leftarrow \text{Find the perfect squares close to 5.}$$
$$\sqrt{4} < \sqrt{5} < \sqrt{9} \qquad \leftarrow \text{Write the square roots in order.}$$
$$2 < \sqrt{5} < 3 \qquad \leftarrow \text{Simplify.}$$

A **rational number** is any number that can be written as a quotient of two integers, where the denominator is not 0.

Math Understandings

- The Pythagorean Theorem shows how the lengths of the sides in a right triangle are related.
- The labels a, b, and c are commonly used to label the unknown lengths of sides in right triangles (with c most often used for the hypotenuse).

In a right triangle, the two shorter sides are called **legs.** The longest side, which is opposite the right angle, is called the **hypotenuse.** If you know the lengths of any two sides of a right triangle, you can use the Pythagorean Theorem to find the length of the other side.

Pythagorean Theorem

In any right triangle, the sum of the squares of the lengths of the legs (a and b) is equal to the square of the length of the hypotenuse (c).

$$a^2 + b^2 = c^2$$

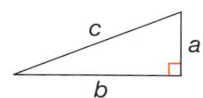

Example: Find the missing side length in a right triangle whose side lengths are 6 and 7.

$$a^2 + b^2 = c^2 \quad \leftarrow \text{Write the Pythagorean Theorem.}$$
$$6^2 + 7^2 = c^2 \quad \leftarrow \text{Substitute 6 and 7 for } a \text{ and } b.$$
$$36 + 49 = c^2 \quad \leftarrow \text{Square 6 and 7.}$$
$$85 = c^2 \quad \leftarrow \text{Add.}$$
$$\sqrt{85} = c \quad \leftarrow \text{Find the square root of each side.}$$
$$9.2 \approx c \quad \leftarrow \text{Simplify.}$$

Additional Professional Development Opportunities

Math Background Notes for Chapter 12: Every lesson has a Math Background in the PLAN section.

Research Overview, Mathematics Strands
Additional support for these topics and more is in the front of the Teacher's Edition.

LessonLab
LessonLab, a Pearson Education company, offers comprehensive, facilitated professional development designed to help teachers to improve student achievement. To learn more, please visit lessonlab.com.

Chapter 12 Resources

Print Resources	12-1	12-2	12-3	12-4	12-5	For the Chapter
L3 Practice	●	●	●	●	●	
L1 Adapted Practice	●	●	●	●	●	
L3 Guided Problem Solving	●	●	●	●	●	
L2 Reteaching	●	●	●	●	●	
L4 Enrichment	●	●	●	●	●	
L3 Daily Notetaking Guide	●	●	●	●	●	
L1 Adapted Daily Notetaking Guide	●	●	●	●	●	
L3 Vocabulary and Study Skills Worksheets	●	●	●	●	●	●
L3 Daily Puzzles	●	●	●	●	●	
L3 Activity Labs	●	●	●	●	●	●
L3 Checkpoint Quiz			●			
L3 Chapter Project						●
L2 Below Level Chapter Test						●
L3 Chapter Test						●
L4 Alternative Assessment						●
L3 Cumulative Review						●

Spanish Resources **ELL**	12-1	12-2	12-3	12-4	12-5	For the Chapter
L3 Practice	●	●	●	●	●	
L3 Vocabulary and Study Skills Worksheets	●	●	●	●	●	●
L3 Checkpoint Quiz			●			
L2 Below Level Chapter Test						●
L3 Chapter Test						●
L4 Alternative Assessment						●
L3 Cumulative Review						●

Transparencies	12-1	12-2	12-3	12-4	12-5	For the Chapter
Check Skills You'll Need	●	●	●	●	●	
Additional Examples	●	●	●	●	●	
Problem of the Day	●	●	●	●	●	
Classroom Aid				●		
Student Edition Answers	●	●	●	●	●	●
Lesson Quiz	●	●	●	●	●	
Test-Taking Strategies						●

Technology	12-1	12-2	12-3	12-4	12-5	For the Chapter
Interactive Textbook Online	●	●	●	●	●	●
StudentExpress™ CD-ROM	●	●	●	●	●	●
Success Tracker™ Online Intervention	●	●	●	●	●	●
TeacherExpress™ CD-ROM	●	●	●	●	●	●
PresentationExpress™ with QuickTake Presenter CD-ROM	●	●	●	●	●	●
ExamView® Assessment Suite CD-ROM	●	●	●	●	●	●
MindPoint® Quiz Show CD-ROM						●
Prentice Hall Web Site: PHSchool.com	●	●	●	●	●	●

Also available:

Prentice Hall Assessment System
- Progress Monitoring Assessments
- Skills and Concepts Review
- Test Prep Workbook

Other Resources
Algebra Readiness Tests
All-in-One Student Workbook
All-in-One Student Workbook, Adapted Version
Multilingual Handbook

Solution Key
Math Notes Study Folder
Spanish Cumulative Assessment

Where You Can Use the Lesson Resources

Here is a suggestion, following the four-step teaching plan, for how you can incorporate Differentiated Instruction Resources into your teaching.

	Instructional Resources **L3**	**Differentiated** Instruction **Resources**
1. Plan		
Preparation Read the Math Background in the Teacher's Edition to connect this lesson with students' previous experience. **Starting Class** **Check Skills You'll Need** Assign these exercises to review prerequisite skills. **New Vocabulary** Help students pre-read the lesson by pointing out the new terms introduced in the lesson.	**Math Background** **Math Understandings** **Transparencies & PresentationExpress™ with QuickTake Presenter CD-ROM** Check Skills You'll Need Problem of the Day **Resources** Vocabulary and Study Skills	**Spanish Support** **ELL** Vocabulary and Study Skills
2. Teach		
L3 Guided Instruction Use the Activity Labs to build conceptual understanding. Teach each Example. Use the Teacher's Edition side column notes for specific teaching tips, including Error Prevention notes. Use the Additional Examples found in the side column (and on transparency and PowerPoint) as an alternative presentation for the content. After each Example, assign the Quick Check exercise for that Example to get an immediate assessment of student understanding. Use the Closure activity in the Teacher's Edition to help students attain mastery of lesson content.	**Student Edition** Activity Lab **Resources** Daily Notetaking Guide Activity Lab **Transparencies & PresentationExpress™ with QuickTake Presenter CD-ROM** Additional Examples Classroom Aids **ExamView® Assessment Suite CD-ROM**	**Teacher's Edition** Every lesson includes suggestions for working with students who need special attention. **L1** Special Needs **L2** Below Level **L4** Advanced Learners **ELL** English Language Learners **Resources** **L1** Adapted Daily Notetaking Guide **Multilingual Handbook**
3. Practice		

Assignment Guide
Check Your Understanding
Use these questions to check students' understanding before you assign homework.
Homework Exercises
Assign homework from these leveled exercises in the Assignment Guide.
  A Practice by Example
  B Apply Your Skills
  C Challenge
  Test Prep and Mixed Review
Homework Quick Check
Use these key exercises to quickly check students' homework.
	Transparencies & PresentationExpress™ with QuickTake Presenter CD-ROM
	Student Answers
	Resources
	Practice
	Guided Problem Solving
	Vocabulary and Study Skills
	Activity Lab
	Daily Puzzles
	ExamView® Assessment Suite CD-ROM
		Spanish Support
		ELL Practice
		ELL Vocabulary and Study Skills
		Resources
		L1 Adapted Practice
		L4 Enrichment

4. Assess & Reteach		
Lesson Quiz Assign the Lesson Quiz to assess students' mastery of the lesson content. **Checkpoint Quiz** Use the Checkpoint Quiz to assess student progress over several lessons.	**Transparencies & PresentationExpress™ with QuickTake Presenter CD-ROM** Lesson Quiz **Resources** Checkpoint Quiz	**Resources** **L2** Reteaching **ELL** Checkpoint Quiz Success Tracker™ Online Intervention **ExamView® Assessment Suite CD-ROM**

KEY   **L1** Special Needs   **L2** Below Level   **L3** For All Students   **L4** Advanced, Gifted   **ELL** English Language Learners

CHAPTER 12

Equations and Inequalities

Check Your Readiness

Answers are in the back of the textbook.

For intervention, direct students to:

Solving Equations
Lessons 3-5, 3-6
Extra Skills and Word
  Problems Practice, Ch. 3

Solving Equations
Lesson 3-7
Extra Skills and Word
  Problems Practice, Ch. 3

Writing Exponents
Lesson 4-2
Extra Skills and Word
  Problems Practice, Ch. 4

Comparing Integers
Lesson 11-2
Extra Skills and Word
  Problems Practice, Ch. 11

Spanish Vocabulary/Study Skills   ELL

Vocabulary/Study Skills   L3

12A: Graphic Organizer   For use before Lesson 12-1

Study Skill As your teacher presents new material in the chapter, keep a paper and pencil handy to write down notes and questions. If you miss class, borrow a classmate's notes to catch up.

Write your answers.

1. What is the chapter title? Equations and Inequalities

2. How many lessons are there in this chapter? 5

3. What is the topic of the Test-Taking Strategies page? Estimating the Answer

4. Complete the graphic organizer below as you work through the chapter.
  • In the center, write the title of the chapter.
  • When you begin a lesson, write the lesson name in a rectangle.
  • When you complete a lesson, write a skill or key concept in a circle linked to that lesson block.
  • When you complete the chapter, use this graphic organizer to help you review.

Chech students' diagrams.

Algebra

CHAPTER 12 — Equations and Inequalities

What You've Learned

• In earlier chapters, you solved one-step equations and used equations to solve problems.

• In Chapter 8, you learned to identify right triangles.

• In Chapter 11, you learned to add, subtract, multiply, and divide integers.

Check Your Readiness

GO for Help

For Exercises	See Lessons
1–2	3-5
3–4	3-6
5–10	3-7
11–13	4-2
14–16	11-2

(Algebra) **Solving Equations**

Solve each equation.

1. $c + 9 = 34$ **25**
2. $a + 5 = -8$ **−13**
3. $y - 15 = 28$ **43**
4. $b - 21 = -11$ **10**
5. $9x = 117$ **13**
6. $5r = 35$ **7**
7. $14z = 266$ **19**
8. $m \div 4 = 16$ **64**
9. $s \div 9 = 7$ **63**
10. $y \div 25 = 5$ **125**

Writing Exponents

Write each expression using an exponent. Name the base and the exponent.

11. $4 \times 4 \times 4$
   4^3; 4; 3
12. 2×2
   2^2; 2; 2
13. $1 \times 1 \times 1 \times 1$
   1^4; 1; 4

Comparing Integers

Compare using < or >.

14. $4 \; \blacksquare \; 8$
   <
15. $-2 \; \blacksquare \; -1$
   <
16. $-100 \; \blacksquare \; -101$
   >

Chapter 12 Overview

In this chapter, students continue their work with equations and algebraic concepts by exploring inequalities and solving inequalities, by exploring square roots and rational numbers, and by working with the Pythagorean Theorem.

Activating Prior Knowledge

In this chapter, students build on and extend their knowledge of algebraic concepts, integers, and their writing and solving of equations to solve inequalities. They draw upon their understanding of integers and fractions when they work with rational numbers. They apply their knowledge of the properties of triangles when they learn about and apply the Pythagorean Theorem. Ask questions such as:

- *Write these numbers in order from greatest to least:*
  $-6, 2, 2\frac{3}{4}, -1, \frac{1}{2}$.
  $2\frac{3}{4}, 2, \frac{1}{2}, -1, -6$

- *How many right angles does a right triangle have? Explain.*
  Sample: 1; triangles have 180°, two right angles would add to 180° by themselves.

- *What is x in 4x = 30?* **x = 7.5**

What You'll Learn Next

- In this chapter, you will solve two-step equations.

- You will solve and graph inequalities.

- You will find square roots and identify rational numbers.

- You will use the Pythagorean Theorem to solve problems involving right triangles.

🔊 Key Vocabulary

- graph of an inequality (p. 579)
- hypotenuse (p. 591)
- inequality (p. 578)
- legs (p. 591)
- perfect square (p. 588)
- Pythagorean Theorem (p. 591)
- rational number (p. 588)
- solution of an inequality (p. 579)
- square root (p. 587)
- two-step equation (p. 572)

 Problem Solving Application On pages 604 and 605, you will work an extended activity on electricity costs.

Objective
To solve two-step equations and to use two-step equations to solve problems

Examples
1 Solving a Two-Step Equation
2 Application: Party Planning

Math Understandings: p. 570C

Math Background

Two-step equations involve two distinct operations—either addition or subtraction for one step and multiplication or division for the other step. The goal in solving two-step equations is the same as solving any equation: To get the variable alone on one side of the equation by using inverse operations.

More Math Background: p. 570C

Lesson Planning and Resources

See p. 570E for a list of the resources that support this lesson.

PowerPoint

Bell Ringer Practice

✓ **Check Skills You'll Need**
Use student page, transparency, or PowerPoint. For intervention, direct students to:
Solving Multiplication and Division Equations
Lesson 3-7
Extra Skills and Word Problems
 Practice, Ch. 3

✓ Check Skills You'll Need

1. **Vocabulary Review**
 Which symbol is always used in an *equation*? =

Solve each equation.

2. $\frac{c}{4} = 5$ 20   3. $\frac{n}{4} = 12$ 48

4. $\frac{1}{7}x = 3$ 21   5. $\frac{1}{8}y = 24$ 192

GO for Help
Lesson 3-7

What You'll Learn

To solve two-step equations and to use two-step equations to solve problems

🔊 **New Vocabulary** two-step equation

Why Learn This?

Suppose your dog has a litter of 3 puppies. You weigh the puppies in a basket. The empty basket weighs 2 pounds. The basket and puppies weigh a total of 14 pounds.

To find the average weight of a puppy, you can solve the equation $3x + 2 = 14$. Algebra tiles can help you understand the solution.

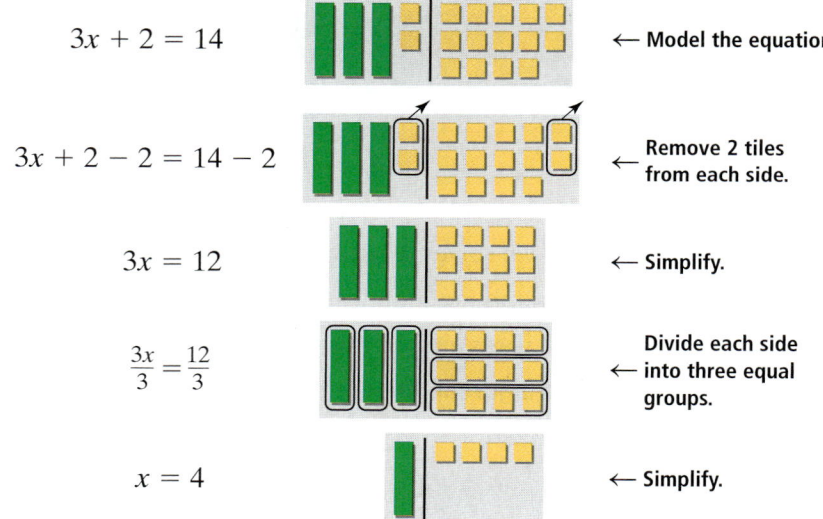

$3x + 2 = 14$ ← Model the equation.

$3x + 2 - 2 = 14 - 2$ ← Remove 2 tiles from each side.

$3x = 12$ ← Simplify.

$\frac{3x}{3} = \frac{12}{3}$ ← Divide each side into three equal groups.

$x = 4$ ← Simplify.

A **two-step equation,** such as $3x + 2 = 14$, is an equation that contains two operations. To solve a two-step equation, you use inverse operations and the properties of equality to get the variable alone. For many equations, you first undo the addition or subtraction. Then you undo the multiplication or division.

Differentiated Instruction **Solutions for All Learners**

Special Needs **L1**
Have students use algebra tiles, when available, for Example 1 and the Quick Check 1. When algebra tiles are not available, have students draw the algebra tiles for one example, and cross out the tiles not needed as each operation is undone.

learning style: tactile

Below Level **L2**
Give students two-step expressions to evaluate for $x = 6$. Have students show their work.

$3x - 4$ $3(6) - 4 = 18 - 4 = 14$
$5x + 1$ $5(6) + 1 = 30 + 1 = 31$
$\frac{x}{2} + 7$ $\frac{6}{2} + 7 = 3 + 7 = 10$

learning style: visual

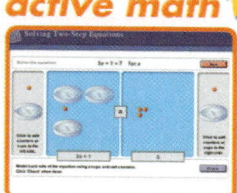

For: Two-Step Equation Activity
Use: Interactive Textbook, 12-1

EXAMPLE   Solving a Two-Step Equation

① **Multiple Choice** Solve $2y + 3 = 11$.

  Ⓐ 4   Ⓑ 7   Ⓒ 16   Ⓓ 28

$$2y + 3 = 11$$
$$2y + 3 - 3 = 11 - 3 \quad \leftarrow \text{Subtract 3 from each side to undo the addition.}$$
$$2y = 8 \quad \leftarrow \text{Simplify.}$$
$$\frac{2y}{2} = \frac{8}{2} \quad \leftarrow \text{Divide each side by 2 to undo the multiplication.}$$
$$y = 4 \quad \leftarrow \text{Simplify.}$$

The correct answer is choice A.

✓ Quick Check

1. Solve each equation. Check the solution.
  a. $5x + 3 = 18$ **3**   **b.** $3x - 4 = 23$ **9**

EXAMPLE   **Application: Party Planning**

② Three neighbors host a party. Each neighbor buys a watermelon for $8. They split the cost of paper goods, p, equally. If each neighbor spends $20, what is the total cost of the paper goods? Solve the equation $\frac{p}{3} + 8 = 20$.

$$\frac{p}{3} + 8 = 20$$
$$\frac{p}{3} + 8 - 8 = 20 - 8 \quad \leftarrow \text{Subtract 8 from each side to undo the addition.}$$
$$\frac{p}{3} = 12 \quad \leftarrow \text{Simplify.}$$
$$3 \cdot \frac{p}{3} = 12 \cdot 3 \quad \leftarrow \text{Multiply each side by 3 to undo the division.}$$
$$p = 36 \quad \leftarrow \text{Simplify.}$$

The total cost of the paper goods is $36.

✓ Quick Check

2. You and a friend split the cost of a moped rental. Your friend pays the bill. You owe your friend only $12, because your friend owed you $9 from yesterday. How much was the total bill? Let m represent the cost of the moped rental. Solve the equation $\frac{m}{2} - 9 = 12$. **$42**

2. Teach

Activity Lab

Use before the lesson.

All in One Teaching Resources

Activity Lab 12-1: Solving Two-Step Equations

Guided Instruction

Example 1
Emphasize that it is often easier to solve a two-step equation if students add or subtract before they multiply or divide. Solve Quick Check 1b by adding first and dividing second and then by dividing first and adding second to illustrate the point.

Error Prevention!

Help students rewrite $\frac{p}{3} + 8 = 20$ in Example 2 as $\frac{1}{3}p + 8 = 20$. In this form, students may better understand that they need to multiply by the reciprocal of $\frac{1}{3}$, or 3.

Additional Examples

① Solve $6x - 14 = 16$. Check the solution. **5**

② The Science Club sells birdfeeders for $8 each. The club spends $32 in building materials. The club's profit is $128. How many birdfeeders did the club sell? Use b to represent the number of birdfeeders. Use the equation $8b - 32 = 128$. **20 birdfeeders**

Advanced Learners   **L4**
Explain that $7x - 2x = 5x$ and $7y + 2y = 9y$. Then have students solve these equations:

$$7x - 4 = 2x + 6 \quad \textbf{2}$$
$$7y + 3 = 30 - 2y \quad \textbf{3}$$

learning style: visual

English Language Learners   **ELL**
To help students with the equation on page 572, write a heading on the board such as: *What We Know,* and list things like *the number of puppies, the weight of the empty basket,* and *the total weight of the puppies and the basket.* Elicit the values of each of these from the students.

learning style: verbal

Closure

- *What is a two-step equation?* **an equation that contains two operations**
- *How do you solve a two-step equation?* **Sample: Use inverse operations to get the variable alone on one side of the equation.**
- *How can you check your solution?* **Sample: Substitute the solution for the variable in the original equation and simplify. You should get the same value on both sides.**

● **More Than One Way**

Solve $2b - 18 = 34$.

Michael's Method

First I add. Then I divide.

$$2b - 18 = 34$$
$$2b - 18 + 18 = 34 + 18 \quad \leftarrow \text{Add 18 to each side.}$$
$$2b = 52 \quad \leftarrow \text{Simplify.}$$
$$\frac{2b}{2} = \frac{52}{2} \quad \leftarrow \text{Divide each side by 2.}$$
$$b = 26 \quad \leftarrow \text{Simplify.}$$

Lauren's Method

Since each number in the equation is an even number, I begin by dividing each side of the equation by 2.

$$2b - 18 = 34$$
$$(2b - 18) \div 2 = 34 \div 2 \quad \leftarrow \text{Divide each side by 2.}$$
$$b - 9 = 17 \quad \leftarrow \text{Divide } 2b, 18, \text{ and 34 by 2.}$$
$$b - 9 + 9 = 17 + 9 \quad \leftarrow \text{Add 9 to each side.}$$
$$b = 26 \quad \leftarrow \text{Simplify.}$$

34; answers may vary. Sample: First I subtracted 75 from both sides of the equation. Then I divided both sides by 5. I chose this method because I would only have to divide 5p and 170 by 5.

Choose a Method

Solve $5p + 75 = 245$. Describe your method and explain why you chose it. **See left.**

✓ Check Your Understanding

Vocabulary Identify each equation as one-step or two-step.

1. $6n + 3 = 21$
two-step

2. $b - 4 = 12$
one-step

3. $4j + 4 = 12$
two-step

4. Mental Math What is the solution of $3a - 1 = 11$? **4**

5. $2b + 4 = 12$;
$2b + 4 - 4 = 12 - 4$;
$2b \div 2 = 8 \div 2$;
$b = 4$

5. Copy the equation. Then complete the solution. **See left.**
$$2b + 4 = 12$$
$$2b + 4 - \blacksquare = 12 - \blacksquare$$

For more exercises, see Extra Skills and Word Problems.

GO for Help

For Exercises	See Examples
6–14	1
15–16	2

A **Solve each equation. Check your solution.**

6. $2y + 5 = 9$ **2**   **7.** $2p + 13 = 3$ **–5**   **8.** $5x + 7 = 22$ **3**

9. $\frac{a}{2} + 4 = 8$ **8**   **10.** $\frac{x}{3} + 2 = 5$ **9**   **11.** $\frac{n}{6} - 1 = 3$ **24**

12. $2y - 3 = -11$ **–4**   **13.** $-6 = 4b - 10$ **1**   **14.** $1 + \frac{g}{2} = -5$ **–12**

15. You need to buy a pair of pants and three shirts. You have $90 to spend on clothes. You do not pay sales tax. The pants you choose cost $24. How much can you spend on each shirt? Let s represent the cost of a shirt. Solve $3s + 24 = 90$. **$22**

16. You order a backpack for $34 and pens for $2 each. You spend $46, excluding the shipping cost and tax. How many pens do you order? Let p represent the number of pens. Solve $2p + 34 = 46$. **6 pens**

B  **GPS** **17. Guided Problem Solving** Mr. Lewis donates $200 to his favorite charities. He begins by giving $35 to an animal shelter. He also makes $15 donations to several other charities. How many other charities does he support? Let c represent the number of other charities. Solve $35 + 15c = 200$. **11 other charities**
  - Which operation do you undo first?
  - Which operation do you undo second?

18. You save $26 each week to buy a digital camera that costs $260. You have already saved $182. In how many weeks will you save $260? Let w represent the number of weeks. Solve $26w + 182 = 260$. **3 weeks**

26. Answers may vary. Sample: To solve $16e - 32 = 176$, first add 32 to each side and then divide each side by 16. To solve $16e = 176$, simply divide each side by 16.

Mental Math **Solve each equation.**

19. $2y + 1 = 11$ **5**   **20.** $5c + 15 = 30$ **3**   **21.** $4d - 12 = 8$ **5**

22. $3n - 1 = 17$ **6**   **23.** $\frac{w}{2} - 6 = 4$ **20**   **24.** $\frac{a}{5} + 7 = 12$ **25**

25. Error Analysis What error is made in the solution of the equation $4 + \frac{m}{5} = 19$ at the right? **The error is dividing by 5 instead of multiplying by 5.**

$$4 + \frac{m}{5} = 19$$
$$\frac{m}{5} = 15$$
$$m = 3 \quad ✗$$

GO Online

Homework Video Tutor

Visit: PHSchool.com
Web Code: aqe-1201

26. Writing in Math How is solving $16e - 32 = 176$ different from solving $16e = 176$? **See above left.**

Assignment Guide

Check Your Understanding
Go over Exercises 1–5 in class before assigning the Homework Exercises.

Homework Exercises
A Practice by Example   6–16
B Apply Your Skills   17–30
C Challenge   31
Test Prep and
  Mixed Review   32–37

Homework Quick Check
To check students' understanding of key skills and concepts, go over Exercises 9, 16, 26, 27, and 28.

Differentiated Instruction Resources

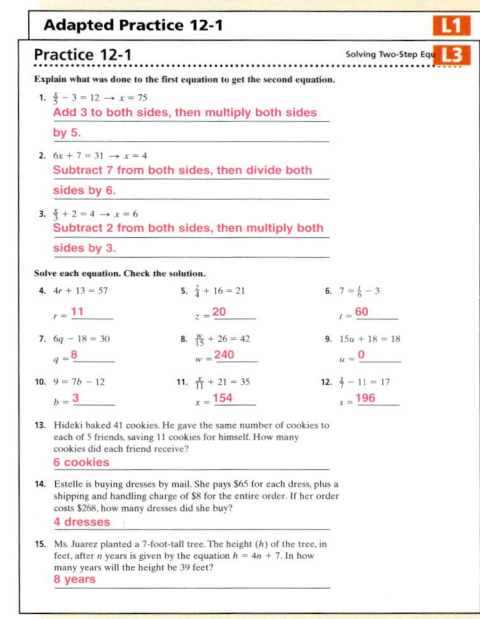

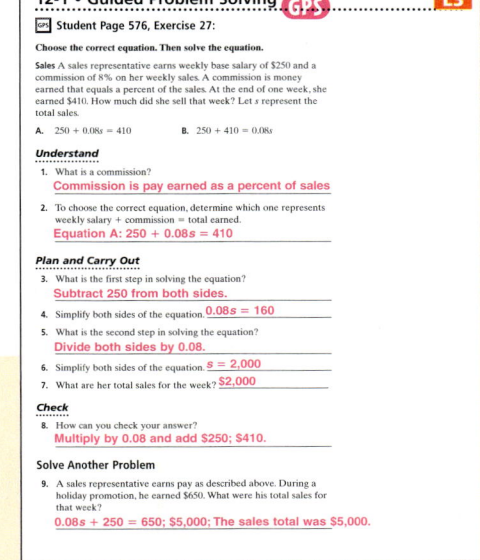

Lesson Quiz

Solve each equation.

1. $6a + 12 = 30$ **3**

2. $\frac{b}{5} + 21 = 24$ **15**

3. $4c - 40 = 28$ **17**

4. $\frac{d}{7} + 15 = 22$ **49**

Alternative Assessment

Provide algebra tiles to pairs of students. Partners use the tiles to model and solve exercises such as Exercises 6–14. Partners take turns recording each step of the solution process.

Reteaching 12-1   Solving Two-Step Eq **L2**

Some equations contain two operations. To solve them, use inverse operations to get the variable alone on one side of the equation. Begin by undoing addition or subtraction. Then undo multiplication or division.

Example: Solve $2d + 1 = 9$.

$2d + 1 = 9$

$2d + 1 - 1 = 9 - 1$ Subtract 1 from each side to undo the addition.

$\frac{2d}{2} = \frac{8}{2}$ Divide each side by 2 to undo the multiplication.

$d = 4$ Simplify.

   Check your work by substituting 4 for d in the equation and solving.

$2 \cdot 4 + 1 \stackrel{?}{=} 9$

$9 = 9$ Since $9 = 9$, the solution is correct.

1. Solve $7x - 5 = 16$.

a. What must you first do to both sides? **add 5**

b. What must you next do to both sides? **divide by 7**

c. What is the solution? **$x = 3$**

2. Solve $12 = \frac{t}{5} + 8$.

a. What must you first do to both sides? **subtract 8.**

b. What must you next do to both sides? **multiply by 5.**

c. What is the solution? **$t = 20$**

Solve each equation. Check the solution.

3. $7y - 6 = 8$ **$y = 2$**

4. $81 = 3x - 6$ **$x = 29$**

5. $\frac{c}{8} + 10 = 15$ **$c = 40$**

6. $2f - 6 = 4$ **$f = 5$**

7. $4k + 20 = 24$ **$k = 1$**

8. $\frac{e}{5} + 100 = 120$ **$e = 100$**

Enrichment 12-1   Solving Two-Step E **L4**

Problem Solving

Solve the equation $6x - 2 = 16$.

- Emma solved the equation by using inverse operations.

$6x - 2 = 16$

$6x - 2 + 2 = 16 + 2$

$6x = 18$

$\frac{6x}{6} = \frac{18}{6}$

$x = \frac{18}{6}$

$x = 3$

- Evan solved the equation by first dividing all terms by 6, the coefficient of x.

$6x - 2 = 16$

$\frac{6x}{6} - \frac{2}{6} = \frac{16}{6}$

$x - \frac{2}{6} = \frac{16}{6}$

$x - \frac{2}{6} + \frac{2}{6} = \frac{16}{6} + \frac{2}{6}$

$x = \frac{18}{6}$

$x = 3$

1. Did both students arrive at the same solution? **yes**

2. Compare the two approaches. Which one was easier? Explain.
   Sample answer: Emma's; using the inverse operations involved fewer steps.

3. Use Emma's method to solve the equation.
   $6x - 18 = 48$
   $x = 11$

4. Use Evan's method to solve the equation.
   $6x - 18 = 48$
   $x = 11$

5. Use Emma's method to solve the equation.
   $10x + 50 = 70$
   $x = 2$

6. Use Evan's method to solve the equation.
   $10x + 50 = 70$
   $x = 2$

7. When does dividing first work best?
   Sample answer: When each of the numbers in the equation is divisible by the whole number coefficient of x.

576

Careers A sales representative for a clothing company sells the latest fashions to retail stores.

Choose the correct equation. Then solve the equation.

27. **Sales** A sales representative earns a weekly base salary of $250 and a commission of 8% on her weekly sales. (A commission is money earned that equals a percent of the sales.) At the end of one week, she earned $410. How much did she sell that week? Let s represent the total sales. **A; $2,000**

   Ⓐ $0.08s + 250 = 410$ Ⓑ $250 + 410 = 0.08s$

28. **Exercise** You pay $75 to join a health club and then pay a monthly fee. The total cost for the first year is $495. What is the monthly fee? Let m represent the monthly fee. **A; $35**

   Ⓐ $12m + 75 = 495$ Ⓑ $75 + 495 = 12m$

For each table, write a rule that uses two operations. Then complete the table. (*Hint:* **Multiply or divide first.**)

29.

Input	Output	
2	7	**Rule: Multiply by 2 and then add 3.**
4	11	
7	17	
8	▦	**19**
15	▦	**33**

30.

Input	Output	
6	−6	**Rule: Divide by 3 and then subtract 8.**
9	−5	
15	−3	
30	▦	**2**
63	▦	**13**

Ⓒ 31. **Challenge** Solve $\frac{a}{2} + \frac{2}{3} = 5\frac{1}{3}$. **$9\frac{1}{3}$**

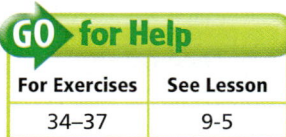
Test Prep and Mixed Review   **Practice**

Multiple Choice

32. A triangle has angles that measure 90° and 32°. What is the measure of the third angle? **A**

   Ⓐ 58°   Ⓑ 68°   Ⓒ 78°   Ⓓ 88°

33. Cameron's father tiles a floor with square tiles. Each box of tile holds 50 tiles. The floor measures 13 feet by 15 feet. What additional piece of information does Cameron's father need to find the number of boxes of tile he must buy? **F**

   Ⓕ area of a tile   Ⓗ perimeter of the room
   Ⓖ area of the floor   Ⓙ height of the tile box

GO for Help

For Exercises	See Lesson
34–37	9-5

Find the radius or diameter of each circle.

34. $r = 12$ inches, $d = $ ▦   **24 in.**

35. $d = \frac{1}{2}$ in., $r = $ ▦   **$\frac{1}{4}$ in.**

36. $d = 0.36$ meter, $r = $ ▦   **0.18 m**

37. $r = 4.7$ cm, $d = $ ▦   **9.4 cm**

576   Chapter 12   Equations and Inequalities

Test Prep

Resources

For additional practice with a variety of test item formats:

- Test-Taking Strategies, p. 597
- Test Prep, p. 601
- Test-Taking Strategies with Transparencies

Using Equation Language

Equations describe real-world situations. Solve the puzzles below using equation language.

ACTIVITY   1–4. See right.

A class makes puzzles with quarters that honor the 50 U.S. states. For each puzzle, find the number of quarters from each of three states.

1. Martin's Puzzle

Clue 1   10 quarters from Mississippi, Maryland, or Florida

Clue 2   4 fewer Mississippi quarters than Maryland quarters

Clue 3   3 times as many Maryland quarters as Florida quarters

2. Sara's Puzzle

Clue 1   6 Indiana quarters

Clue 2   2 more Kentucky quarters than Tennessee quarters

Clue 3   12 quarters from Indiana, Kentucky, or Tennessee

3. Joaquin's Puzzle

Clue 1 $\frac{1}{2}$ are Ohio quarters

Clue 2   18 quarters from Ohio, Texas, or Tennessee

Clue 3   Twice as many Tennessee quarters as Texas quarters

4. Donelle's Puzzle

Clue 1   15 quarters from Maine, Louisiana, or Idaho

Clue 2   1 fewer Maine quarter than Louisiana quarters

Clue 3   1 more Maine quarter than Idaho quarters

Answers (see right):

1. Mississippi: 2
   Maryland: 6
   Florida: 2

2. Indiana: 6
   Kentucky: 4
   Tennessee: 2

3. Ohio: 9
   Texas: 3
   Tennessee: 6

4. Maine: 5
   Louisiana: 6
   Idaho: 4

5. Make a puzzle by choosing quarters from three states. Then write clues. Include the total number of quarters as a clue. **Check students' work.**

6. Exchange puzzles with another student. Solve the puzzle. **Check students' work.**

7. **Writing in Math** How did you solve Joaquin's puzzle? Explain.
   Answers may vary. Sample: I divided 18 by 2 to get 9 Ohio quarters. Then I found that there were 6 Tennessee quarters and 3 Texas quarters by using clue 3.

Activity Lab

Using Equation Language

Students use equation language to solve puzzles in real-world applications. This will extend their work with two-step equations from Lesson 12-1.

Guided Instruction

Explain to students that they can use equation language to solve puzzles like these. Help them relate variables to each other and substitute until all the variables are the same. Ask:

- *In Martin's puzzle, what part of the equation is Clue 1?* **total**
- *How can you make the equation in Sara's puzzle simpler?* **You know there are 12 quarters and 6 of them are from Illinois, so since 12 − 6 = 6, you know that there are a total of 6 quarters from Kentucky and Tennessee.**
- *What does the equation for Joaquin's puzzle look like?* **Sample:**
  $$\frac{18}{2} + 3T = 18$$
  $$OH = \frac{18}{2}, TX = T, TN = 2T$$

Differentiated Instruction

Advanced Learners   **L4**

Have students write their own quarter puzzles and trade papers with a partner to solve. Remind them that quarters cannot be divided so each variable must represent a whole number.

1. Plan

Objective
To express and identify solutions of inequalities

Examples
1 Writing an Inequality
2 Graphing Inequalities
3 Identifying Solutions of an Inequality

Math Understandings: p. 570C

Math Background

An equation is a mathematical sentence with an equal sign, =. An *inequality* is a mathematical sentence that contains one of five symbols: $<$, $>$, $\leq$, $\geq$, or $\neq$.

The *solution of an inequality* is any number that makes the inequality true and may have many solutions. You can graph an inequality on a number line. An open circle indicates the endpoint is not included, and is used with $<$ or $>$. A closed circle indicates the endpoint is included, and is used with $\leq$ or $\geq$.

More Math Background: p. 570C

Lesson Planning and Resources

See p. 570E for a list of the resources that support this lesson.

Bell Ringer Practice

✔ **Check Skills You'll Need**
Use student page, transparency, or PowerPoint. For intervention, direct students to:
Comparing and Ordering Integers
Lesson 11-2
Extra Skills and Word Problems Practice, Ch. 11

12-2 Inequalities

✔ Check Skills You'll Need

1. **Vocabulary Review**
How can you use a number line to *compare* integers?
See below.
Compare using $<$ or $>$.

2. $4 \blacksquare -9$ $>$

3. $-2 \blacksquare -3$ $>$

4. $-94 \blacksquare -93$ $<$

5. $1,001 \blacksquare 1,010$ $<$

 **for Help**
Lesson 11-2

Check Skills You'll Need

1. **A number line shows integers from least to greatest. A number to the left of another number on a number line is less than the other number.**

What You'll Learn

To express and identify solutions of inequalities

🔊 **New Vocabulary** inequality, graph of an inequality, solution of an inequality

Why Learn This?

Inequalities can tell you time limits, the height limits for amusement-park rides, and many other things.

An **inequality** is a mathematical sentence that contains $<$, $>$, $\leq$, $\geq$, or $\neq$. Real-world situations can sometimes be represented by inequalities.

DONT CROSS THIS FIELD UNLESS YOU CAN DO IT IN 99 SECONDS. THE BULL CAN DO IT IN 10

Inequality Symbols			
$<$	less than	$>$	greater than
$\leq$	less than or equal to	$\geq$	greater than or equal to
	$\neq$	not equal to	

EXAMPLE Writing an Inequality

1 **Time** The sign above warns you to cross the field in less than 10 seconds. Write an inequality that represents the time limit.

Words | your time | is | less than | bull's time

Let t = your time.

Inequality | t | $<$ | 10

The inequality is $t < 10$.

✔ Quick Check

1. Skydivers jump from an altitude of 14,500 feet or less. Write an inequality to express the altitude from which skydivers jump.
Let a represent the altitude from which most skydivers jump. $a \leq 14,500$

Differentiated Instruction Solutions for All Learners

Special Needs L1
If students have a difficult time graphing the inequalities, have them work with a partner who can do the graphing. Provide each pair with colored pencils or markers so one partner can check the graph while the other draws.

learning style: visual

Below Level L2
Help students interpret the graph below. Ask: *Can x be 0?* **yes** *Can x be 1?* **no** *How can you tell?* **There is an open circle at 1.**

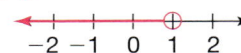

learning style: visual

The **graph of an inequality** shows all solutions of the inequality. A **solution of an inequality** is any number that makes the inequality true. An open circle on a graph shows that the number is *not* a solution. A closed circle shows that the number *is* a solution.

EXAMPLE Graphing Inequalities

2 Write the inequality. Then graph the inequality.

a. You ride your scooter more than 2 miles.

Let k = your distance.

$k > 2$

b. The temperature is 3 degrees or less.

Let t = temperature.

$t \leq 3$

✓**Quick Check**

2. You spend at least 2 hours studying. Write the inequality for the situation. Then graph the inequality. **Let t represent the number of hours you spend studying. $t \geq 2$.**

You can use an inequality to show which numbers meet a limit.

EXAMPLE Identifying Solutions of an Inequality

3 **Roller Coasters** You must be at least 48 inches tall to ride a certain roller coaster. Which of the children in the table can ride the roller coaster?

Name	Height
Sally	$48\frac{1}{2}$ in.
Dean	48 in.
Kelsey	$46\frac{3}{4}$ in.

Words child's height is at least 48 inches

Let h = the child's height.

Inequality $h \geq 48$

Decide whether the inequality is true or false for each person.

Sally $48\frac{1}{2} \geq 48$ Dean $48 \geq 48$ Kelsey $46\frac{3}{4} \geq 48$

     true   true   false

Sally and Dean may ride the roller coaster.

✓**Quick Check**

3. Ian is 3 ft 11 in. tall. Is Ian tall enough to ride the roller coaster? **no**

12-2 Inequalities   **579**

3. Practice

Assignment Guide

Check Your Understanding
Go over Exercises 1–3 in class before assigning the Homework Exercises.

Homework Exercises
A Practice by Example   4–11
B Apply Your Skills   12–19
C Challenge   20
Test Prep and
  Mixed Review   21–24

Homework Quick Check
To check students' understanding of key skills and concepts, go over Exercises 5, 9, 16, 17, and 18.

Differentiated Instruction **Resources**

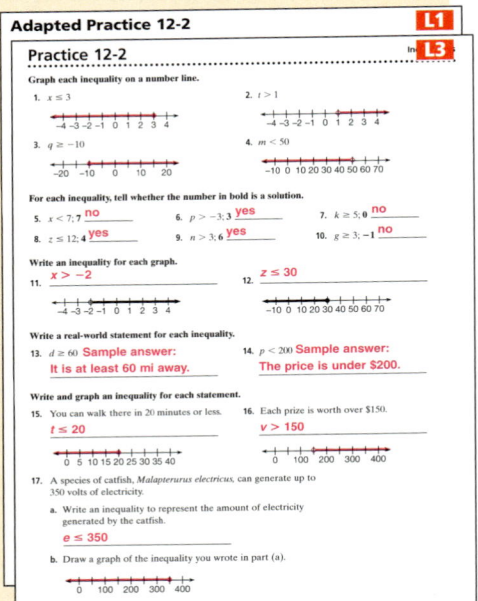

Check Your Understanding

1. **Vocabulary** A graph of an inequality shows all the __?__ of the inequality. **solutions**

2. **Reasoning** Are the solutions of $x < 3$ and $x \le 3$ the same? Explain. **No, 3 is a solution to $x \le 3$ but not to $x < 3$.**

3. Write an inequality for the graph.   (number line: −4 −3 −2 −1 0 1 2, open circle at −1)
$x < -1$

Homework Exercises

For more exercises, see **Extra Skills and Word Problems.**

GO for Help

For Exercises	See Examples
4–6	1
7–9	2
10–11	3

Ⓐ Write an inequality for each situation.

4. No more than 45 students work in the car-wash fundraiser.
   $s \le 45$

5. There are more than 15 ladybugs on the windowsill.
   $\ell > 15$

6. A sign reads, "Maximum height of vehicles is 12 feet."
   $h \le 12$

Write an inequality for each situation. Then graph the inequality.
7–9. See margin for graphs.

7. Four people or fewer are allowed on the ride at once. **$p \le 4$**

8. Kristen has less than three days to write her paper. **$k < 3$**

9. You must deposit at least $20 to open a bank account. **$d \ge \$20$**

Name	Weight
Hugh	50 pounds
Paul	45 pounds
Andrea	25 pounds
Michelle	53 pounds
Tim	49 pounds

10. Use the table at the left. A child must weigh less than 50 pounds to ride on the playground animals. Who may ride the animals?
   Paul, Andrea, Tim

11. You must be at least 13 years old to buy a certain DVD. From the following list of students, who may buy the DVD? Carl (12 years, 9 months), Cara (15 years, 4 days), Molly (13 years), Peter (8 years, 11 months) **Cara, Molly**

Ⓑ  **GPS** 12. **Guided Problem Solving** Which appliances in the table below use an average of more than 50 kilowatt-hours of energy per month? Write an inequality and graph the solution.

Average Monthly Energy Use

Appliance	VCR	Dryer	Washer	Dishwasher
Energy (kilowatt-hours)	4	100	10	50

• Which symbol can you use to represent "more than"?
• On your graph, should you use an open or closed circle?

See margin for graphs. dryer; $e > 50$

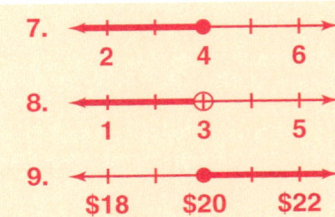

7. (number line: 2 4 6, closed circle at 4, shaded left)
8. (number line: 1 3 5, open circle at 3, shaded left)
9. (number line: $18 $20 $22, closed circle at $20, shaded right)

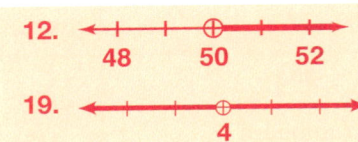

12. (number line: 48 50 52, open circle at 50, shaded right)
19. (number line: 4, open circle at 4, shaded right)

17. Answers may vary. Sample: Use an open circle at −20, and shade to the left of the open circle to show numbers less than −20.

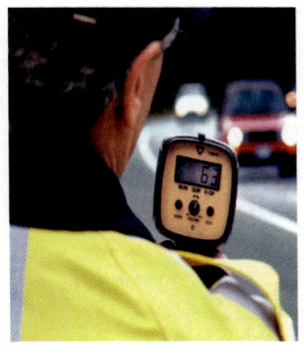

Tell whether each inequality is true or false.

13. $-2 \leq 2$ **true**

14. $|-5| < 5$ **false**

15. $-4^2 < (-4)^2$ **true**

16. **Football** You must weigh 120 pounds or less to play in a junior football league. Use the table at the right. Who qualifies to play?

Aaron, Steve, James

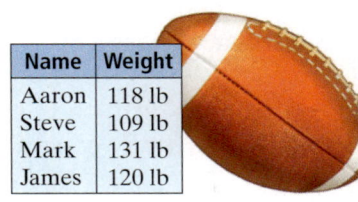

Name	Weight
Aaron	118 lb
Steve	109 lb
Mark	131 lb
James	120 lb

17. **Writing in Math** Describe how to graph $x < -20$. **See left.**

18. **Driving** The minimum speed limit on an interstate is 45 miles per hour. The maximum speed limit is 65 miles per hour.
   a. Write an inequality that describes the speed of a car going slower than the minimum limit. $s < 45$
   b. Write an inequality that describes the speed of a car going faster than the maximum limit. $s > 65$

19. **Number Sense** Graph the inequality $x \neq 4$. **See margin.**

20. **Challenge** Solve and graph $|x| < 2$.

$-2 < x < 2$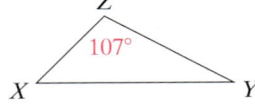

Test Prep and Mixed Review

Practice

Multiple Choice

21. Chris wrote the coordinates of 5 vertices of the hexagon at the right.

$(3, 7), (1, 4), (7, 6), (1, 3), (4, 1)$

Which ordered pair represents the vertex that is NOT listed? **A**

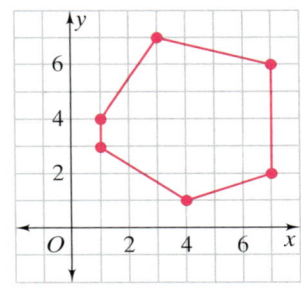

Ⓐ $(7, 2)$ Ⓒ $(2, 5)$
Ⓑ $(7, 4)$ Ⓓ $(2, 7)$

22. Abby plans to practice piano 30 minutes per day, 5 days per week, over the next 10 weeks. How can she find the total number of minutes she will practice? **H**
   Ⓕ Multiply 30 and 5.
   Ⓖ Multiply 5 and 10.
   Ⓗ Multiply 30, 5, and 10.
   Ⓙ Multiply 0.5, 5, and 10.

23. What kind of angle is $\angle Z$? **C**
   Ⓐ Acute   Ⓒ Obtuse
   Ⓑ Right   Ⓓ Straight

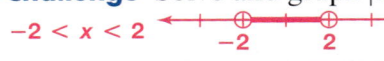

GO for Help

For Exercise	See Lesson
24	10-3

24. Tom won 84 games and lost 24 games. Find the experimental probability of Tom winning a game. $\frac{7}{9}$

PowerPoint
Lesson Quiz

Use x as the variable. Write an inequality for each graph.

1.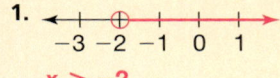
   $x > -2$

2.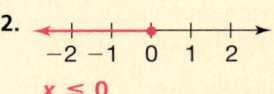
   $x \leq 0$

3. Graph the inequality $x < 2$ on a number line.

4. Tell which numbers are solutions of $x \geq -4$:
   $-6, -4, -2, 0, 2.$ **$-4, -2, 0, 2$**

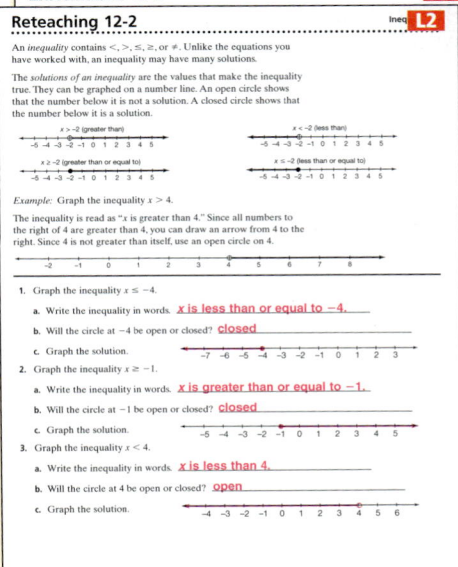

Enrichment 12-2 **L4**

Reteaching 12-2 **L2**

Alternative Assessment

Each partner writes an inequality such as $x > -8$ or $n \geq 7$. Partners exchange papers, graph the inequality, and check each other's graphs.

Test Prep

Resources

For additional practice with a variety of test item formats:
- Test-Taking Strategies, p. 597
- Test Prep, p. 601
- Test-Taking Strategies with Transparencies

581

Objective
To solve one-step inequalities by adding or subtracting

Examples
1, 2 Solving Inequalities
3 Application: Running

Math Understandings: p. 570C

Math Background

Solving an inequality involves the same basic goal as solving an equation: isolating the variable.

Lesson Planning and Resources

See p. 570E for a list of the resources that support this lesson.

PowerPoint

Bell Ringer Practice

✓ **Check Skills You'll Need**
For intervention, direct students to:
Solving Equations with Integers
Lesson 11-7

2. Teach

Activity Lab

Use before the lesson.

All in One Teaching Resources

Activity Lab 12-3: Cost Ranges

Guided Instruction

Example 1
Some students understand the process better when it is shown vertically.

$$
\begin{array}{r}
s - 7 < 3 \\
\underline{+\,7 = +\,7} \\
s < 10
\end{array}
$$

582

✓ **Check Skills You'll Need**

1. **Vocabulary Review** What is the *Subtraction Property of Equality?*
See below.
Solve each equation.

2. $y + 4 = -5$ **−9**

3. $x - 6 = 9$ **15**

 **for Help**
Lesson 11-7

Check Skills You'll Need

1. If you subtract the same value from each side of an equation, the two sides remain equal.

What You'll Learn

To solve one-step inequalities by adding or subtracting

Why Learn This?

You can solve inequalities when you need to find an unknown amount. For example, you can determine how close you are to meeting a goal in sports or in business.

To solve an inequality, use inverse operations to get the variable alone.

EXAMPLES **Solving Inequalities**

1 Solve $s - 7 < 3$.

$$
\begin{aligned}
s - 7 &< 3 \\
s - 7 + 7 &< 3 + 7 \qquad \leftarrow \text{Add 7 to each side to undo the subtraction.} \\
s &< 10 \qquad\quad \leftarrow \text{Simplify.}
\end{aligned}
$$

2 Solve $n + 12 \geq 18$.

$$
\begin{aligned}
n + 12 &\geq 18 \\
n + 12 - 12 &\geq 18 - 12 \qquad \leftarrow \text{Subtract 12 from each side to undo the addition.} \\
n &\geq 6 \qquad\qquad \leftarrow \text{Simplify.}
\end{aligned}
$$

✓ **Quick Check**

1. Solve $u - 6 \leq 3$. **$u \leq 9$**
2. Solve $z + 15 > 24$. **$z > 9$**

You can also solve inequalities in real-world situations.

Differentiated Instruction Solutions for All Learners

Special Needs **L1**
For Example 3, have students draw a number line to show the number of miles run. Then have them circle the distance from 42 to 55. Point to the words *at least* and explain that the circled distance on the number line represents the minimum number of miles left to run.

learning style: visual

Below Level **L2**
Write inequalities like the following. Have students write the inverse operation on each side.

$$
\begin{aligned}
t + 3 &< 10 \quad t + 3 - 3 < 10 - 3 \\
x - 7 &\leq 9 \quad x - 7 + 7 \leq 9 + 7
\end{aligned}
$$

learning style: visual

EXAMPLE **Application: Running**

3 A marathon runner plans to run at least 55 miles this week. He has already run 42 miles. Write and solve an inequality to find how many more miles he plans to run this week.

Words   miles run + miles left is at least 55 miles

   Let m = number of miles left.

Inequality   42   + m ≥   55

$$42 + m \geq 55$$
$$42 + m - 42 \geq 55 - 42 \qquad \leftarrow \text{Subtract 42 from each side.}$$
$$m \geq 13 \qquad \leftarrow \text{Simplify.}$$

The marathon runner plans to run at least 13 more miles this week.

✓**Quick Check**

3. A restaurant can serve a maximum of 115 people. There are now 97 people dining in the restaurant. Write and solve an inequality to find how many more people can be served. **Let p = the number of additional people the restaurant can serve; $p + 97 \leq 115$, $p \leq 18$; the restaurant can serve at most 18 more people.**

 **Check Your Understanding**

Name the operation used to solve each inequality.

1. $c - 4 \geq 8$
addition

2. $n + 2 < 13$
subtraction

3. $t + 11 \leq 11$
subtraction

4. Reasoning What number is a solution of $y + 2 \geq 10$ but is not a solution of $y + 2 > 10$? **8**

5. Mental Math Solve $c - 2 \leq 8$. **$c \leq 10$**

Homework Exercises

For more exercises, see Extra Skills and Word Problems.

 GO for Help

For Exercises	See Examples
6–11	1
12–18	2–3

A Solve each inequality. **15–17. See margin.**

6. $x - 2 \geq 5$
$x \geq 7$

7. $z - 5 < 0$
$z < 5$

8. $k - 21 > 1$
$k > 22$

9. $j - 2 > -9$
$j > -7$

10. $n - 96 < -58$
$n < 38$

11. $s - 4 \leq 8$
$s \leq 12$

12. $r + 5 \geq 7$
$r \geq 2$

13. $y + 12 \leq 11$
$y \leq -1$

14. $w + 2 > -7$
$w > -9$

15. $14 + d \leq 24$

16. $13 + f > 7$

17. $5 + g \leq 62$

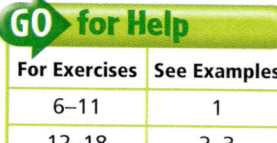 **nline lesson quiz**, PHSchool.com, Web Code: aqa-1203

12-3 Solving One-Step Inequalities   **583**

PowerPoint **Additional Examples**

1 Solve $f - 4 \geq 8$. **$f \geq 12$**

2 Missy wants to save at least $150 this month. She has saved $112 so far. Write and solve an inequality to find how much more money she would like to save this month. **$d + 112 \geq 150$; $d \geq \$38$**

All in One Teaching Resources
- Daily Notetaking Guide 12-3 **L3**
- Adapted Notetaking 12-3 **L1**

Closure

- *How do you solve a one-step inequality?* **Sample: Use inverse operations to get the variable alone on one side of the inequality.**

3. Practice

Assignment Guide

Check Your Understanding
Go over Exercises 1–5 in class before assigning the Homework Exercises.

Homework Exercises
A	Practice by Example	6–18
B	Apply Your Skills	19–22
C	Challenge	23
Test Prep and Mixed Review		24–28

Homework Quick Check
To check student's understanding of key skills and concepts, go over Exercises 11, 15, 20, 21, and 22.

4. Assess & Reteach

PowerPoint **Lesson Quiz**

Solve each inequality.

1. $q - 5 \geq 8$ **$q \geq 13$**

2. $r + 10 < 4$ **$r < -6$**

3. $6 + x \leq 21$ **$x \leq 15$**

4. $m - 9 > 7$ **$m > 16$**

15. **$d \leq 10$**

16. **$f > -6$**

17. **$g \leq 57$**

583

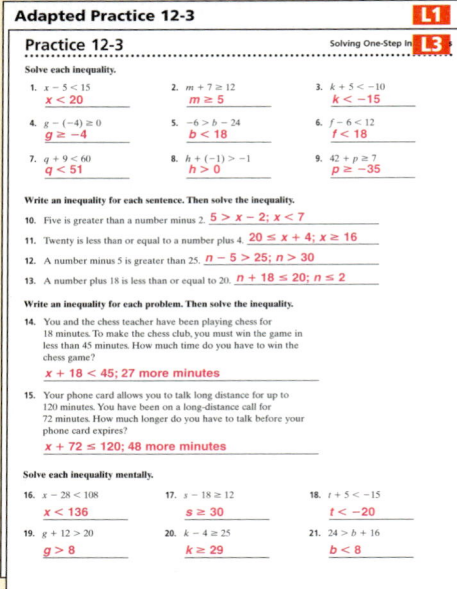
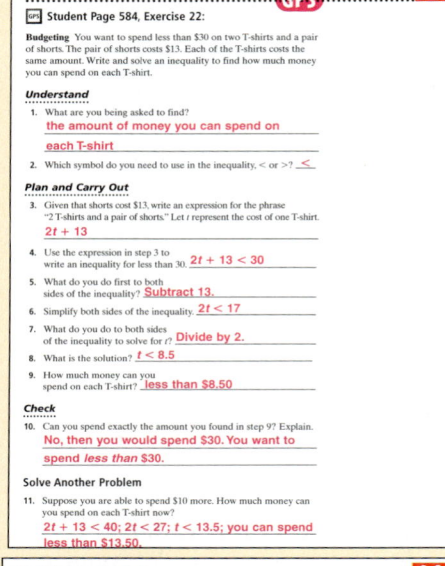
19. Let d = the money you must deposit; $d + 143 \geq 250, d \geq 107;$ you must deposit at least $107.

B GPS

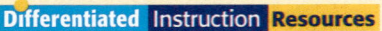

GO Online
Homework Video Tutor

Visit: PHSchool.com
Web Code: aqe-1203

22. Let t = the cost of each T-shirt; $2t + 13 < 30, t < 8.5;$ each T-shirt must cost less than $8.50.

18. You have $15 to spend on souvenirs. You buy a visor for $7.99. Write and solve an inequality to find how much more money you can spend.   Let m = the money that you have left to spend. $m + 7.99 \leq 15; m \leq \$7.01$

19. **Guided Problem Solving** Your bank requires a minimum of $250 in an account to avoid fees. You have $143 in your account. Write and solve an inequality to find how much money you must deposit to avoid fees. **See left.**
    - **Make a Plan** Decide which operation to use in the inequality. Undo the operation in the inequality.
    - **Check the Answer** Draw a graph of the inequality.

20. **Writing in Math** Explain how you know that $3n > 3n$ has no solutions. **Answers may vary. Sample: No algebraic expression can be greater than itself.**

21. To avoid a storm, a pilot of a vintage biplane flies up 2,500 feet but stays below 32,000 feet. Write an inequality to find the maximum original altitude of the plane. $a + 2,500 < 32,000; a < 29,500$ ft

22. **Budgeting** You want to spend less than $30 on two T-shirts and a pair of shorts. The pair of shorts costs $13. Each of the T-shirts costs the same amount. Write and solve an inequality to find how much money you can spend on each T-shirt. **See left.**

C 23. **Challenge** Which integers are solutions to both $x + 7 \leq 9$ and $x + 7 > 4$? $-3 < x \leq 2;$ so the integer solutions are $-2, -1, 0, 1,$ and 2.

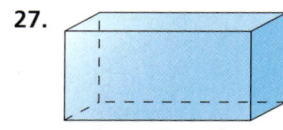
Test Prep and Mixed Review   **Practice**

Multiple Choice

24. The elevation of Death Valley in California is 282 feet below sea level. Mount McKinley in Alaska is 20,320 feet above sea level. What integer represents the elevation of Death Valley? **B**
    - (A) $-20,320$
    - (B) -282
    - (C) 282
    - (D) $20,320$

25. Which line segment is twice as long as the radius? **G**
    - (F) $\overline{DE}$
    - (G) $\overline{DF}$
    - (H) $\overline{FG}$
    - (J) $\overline{EG}$

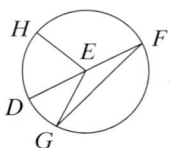

GO for Help

For Exercises	See Lesson
26–28	9-7

Name each figure.

26.

pentagonal pyramid

27.

rectangular prism

28.

hexagonal prism

Applying Inequalities

You can use floating bar graphs to represent inequalities. On the graph below, each bar represents a range of costs for an item that you might want to buy.

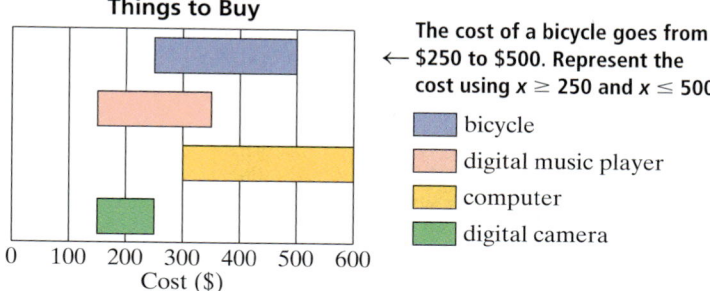

Things to Buy

The cost of a bicycle goes from ← $250 to $500. Represent the cost using $x \geq 250$ and $x \leq 500$.

- ▣ bicycle
- ▣ digital music player
- ▣ computer
- ▣ digital camera

Cost ($)

ACTIVITY

1. You have saved $120 for a computer. Use the floating bar graph above. Write and solve two inequalities to find the minimum and maximum amount of money you still need to save for the computer. $m + 120 \geq 300$; $m \geq \$180$; $m + 120 \leq 600$; $m \leq \$480$

2. You begin saving $25 per week for a digital camera. Write and solve two inequalities to find the minimum and maximum number of weeks it will take to save the money you need. $25w \geq 150$; $w \geq 6$; $25w \leq 250$; $w \leq 10$

Checkpoint Quiz 1

Lessons 12-1 through 12-3

Solve each equation.

1. $4t + 5 = 37$ **8**
2. $\frac{r}{2} - 8 = -4$ **8**
3. $5m - 8 = 57$ **13**

Solve each inequality. Graph the solution on a number line. **4–6. See margin for graphs.**

4. $p + 8 < 3$ **$p < -5$**
5. $n - 5 \geq -17$ **$n \geq -12$**
6. $d + 2 \leq 6$ **$d \leq 4$**

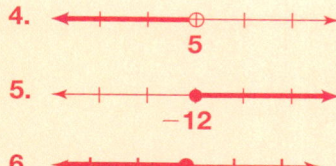

4.
5.
6.

Activity Lab

Applying Inequalities

Students use floating bar graphs that show range to write inequalities for real-life applications. This will extend the skills with writing inequalities they learned in Lesson 12-3.

Guided Instruction

Display the floating bar graph and explain that it shows a range of costs. For example, a digital music player can cost from $150 to $350 or $150 \leq cost \geq $350. Ask:

- *What inequality shows the range of the cost of a computer?*
  $300 \leq cost \leq \$600$
- *You have saved x amount towards the bicycle, and you still need y amount. Write an inequality for the minimum amount you still need to save.*
  $x + y \geq \$250$

Activity

Have students work in small groups. When they have finished, have volunteers from each group give answers.

Differentiated Instruction

Below Level **L2**
Provide students with problems that deal with smaller quantities. For example, give them the prices of four items that would all have a cost range of ten dollars or less.

Use this Checkpoint Quiz to check students' understanding of the skills and concepts of Lessons 12-1 through 12-3.

Resources

- All-in-One Teaching Resources Checkpoint Quiz 2
- ExamView CD-ROM
- Success Tracker™ Online Intervention

Exploring Squares

Students use a geoboard to model squares with different areas in order to investigate patterns involving the areas of squares and the lengths of their sides. This will prepare them to work with square roots in Lesson 12-4.

Guided Instruction

Have students examine the numbers in the first column. Ask:

- *What can you say about each of these numbers?* **Each is a square number.**
- *If you continue the pattern, what are the next three numbers?* **25, 36, 49**

Activity

Have students work in pairs to form the different squares. As needed, discuss that the squares they make may appear in a different orientation than what they customarily see in texts. Circulate as partners make the different-size squares. Invite pairs to share their results and conclusions with others.

Alternative Method

Instead of using geoboards, students can construct the squares on graph paper or dot paper. If they do, guide them to use a straightedge to make the drawings.

Resources

- Activity Lab 12-4: Exploring Square Roots
- geoboard
- rubber bands
- calculator
- Student Manipulatives Kit
- Classroom Aid 36

12-4a Activity Lab

Hands On

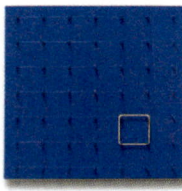

Exploring Squares

You will need a geoboard and rubber bands. Look at the geoboard at the right. Each side of the square is 1 unit long. The area is 1 square unit.

ACTIVITY

1a. Check students' work.

1. **a.** Use your geoboard to make squares with areas of 4, 9, and 16 square units.
   b. Copy the table at the right. Enter the length of a side for each square you made in part (a). **See margin.**

Area of Square (units²)	Length of Side (units)
1	
4	
9	
16	

2. **a.** Look at your table. What pattern(s) do you notice? **The length is the square root of the area.**
   b. Continue the table for squares with areas of 25, 36, and 49 square units. **See margin.**

3. Use your geoboard to make the figure shown at the right. The figure is a square with an area of 2 square units.

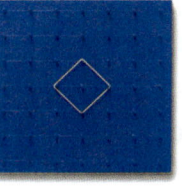

   a. Use your table to estimate the length of a side of this square. **about 1.5**
   b. Recall that the formula for the area of a square is $A = s^2$. Use a calculator and the *Systematic Guess and Check* strategy. To the nearest hundredth, find the length of a side of a square with an area of 2 square units. **1.41**

4. **a.** Use your calculator and the *Systematic Guess and Check* strategy. To the nearest hundredth, find the length of a side of a square with an area of 8 square units. **2.83**
   b. How does the side length you found in Step 3b compare with your answer to Step 4a? **It is about half as long.**

5. Use your geoboard to make a square with an area of 8 square units. **Check students' work.**

6. **Challenge** Use your geoboard to make a square with an area of 5 square units. **Check students' work.**

1b. See back of book.

2b. See back of book.

12-4 Exploring Square Roots and Rational Numbers

Check Skills You'll Need

1. **Vocabulary Review** What operation can you use to find 4 *squared*?
multiplication

Write each expression using an exponent.
2–3. See below.

2. $4 \times 4 \times 4 \times 4 \times 4$

3. $999 \times 999 \times 999$

4. 3.6×3.6 $\quad$ **3.6^2**

for Help
Lesson 4-2

Check Skills You'll Need

2. 4^5

3. 999^3

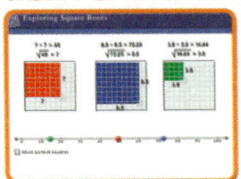

For: Square Root Activity
Use: Interactive Textbook, 12-4

What You'll Learn

To find square roots and to identify rational numbers

◄》 **New Vocabulary** square root, perfect square, rational number

Why Learn This?

Suppose you know the area of a square object or space, such as a garden. You can use square roots to find the length of the garden without measuring.

In the diagram, the area of a square with side length 3 is 3^2, or 9. The inverse of squaring is finding the square root. The square root of 9 is 3. In symbols, $\sqrt{9} = 3$.

$3 \times 3 = 9$

A **square root** of a given number is a number that, when multiplied by itself, equals the given number.

EXAMPLE Finding Square Roots

1 **a.** Find $\sqrt{64}$.
$8 \times 8 = 64$, so $\sqrt{64} = 8$.

b. Find $\sqrt{49}$.
$7 \times 7 = 49$, so $\sqrt{49} = 7$.

✔ Quick Check

1. Find $\sqrt{100}$. **10**

Objective
To find square roots and to identify rational numbers

Examples
1 Finding Square Roots
2 Using a Calculator
3 Identifying Rational Numbers

Math Understandings: p. 570D

Math Background

The *square* of a number is the number multiplied by itself. A *square root* is a number that when multiplied by itself is equal to the given number. A *perfect square* is the square of a whole number. Square roots of perfect squares are also whole numbers.

A rational number can be expressed as a terminating or a repeating decimal such as 2.5 or 2.$\bar{3}$ or 2.333333 . . . . Numbers that are not perfect squares, such as $\sqrt{15}$ are called *irrational* because they neither terminate nor repeat when written as a decimal.

More Math Background: p. 570D

Lesson Planning and Resources

See p. 570E for a list of the resources that support this lesson.

PowerPoint
Bell Ringer Practice

✔ **Check Skills You'll Need**
Use student page, transparency, or PowerPoint. For intervention, direct students to:
Exponents
Lesson 4-2
Extra Skills and Word Problems Practice, Ch. 4

Differentiated Instruction **Solutions for All Learners**

Special Needs **L1**
Using graph paper, have students draw representations of square numbers with dimensions that are 1×1, 2×2, 3×3, 4×4, 5×5 and so on. Underneath each drawing, they should write the number (for example, 16) and its square root (4).

learning style: visual

Below Level **L2**
Have students copy and continue this pattern to find the perfect squares from 1 to 100: 1, 4, 9, . . . , 100.

$1 \times 1 = 1 \;\; \sqrt{1} = 1$ $\qquad$ $2 \times 2 = 4 \;\; \sqrt{4} = 2$
$3 \times 3 = 9 \;\; \sqrt{9} = 3$ $\qquad$ $4 \times 4 = 16 \;\; \sqrt{16} = 4$

learning style: visual

Guided Instruction

Example 2
Make sure students round
correctly in Quick Check 2. To
round to the nearest tenth,
students must examine the
number in the hundredths' place.

PowerPoint
Additional Examples

1 Find $\sqrt{25}$. **5**

2 Use a calculator to find $\sqrt{20}$
to the nearest tenth. **4.5**

3 Tell whether each number is
rational.

  a. 1.5 **rational**

  b. $\frac{3}{4}$ **rational**

  c. 1.42443444 . . . **not rational**

  d. $\sqrt{8}$ **not rational**

Closure

• *What is a square root? Give an
example.* **Sample: A number
that, when multiplied by itself,
is equal to the given number.
$\sqrt{9}$ is 3.**

• *How can you tell if a number is a
rational number?* **Sample: A
rational number can be
expressed as a decimal that
terminates or has a repeating
pattern. The square root of a
number is rational if the number
is a perfect square.**

A **perfect square** is the square of a whole number. The number 64 is
a perfect square because $64 = 8^2$. You can use a calculator to
approximate the square root of a number that is not a perfect square.

EXAMPLE   Using a Calculator

2 **Gridded Response** You need 50 square feet of land to plant a square
garden. How long will the side be? Find $\sqrt{50}$ to the nearest tenth.

$$\sqrt{50} \approx 7.071067812 \quad \leftarrow \text{Press } \boxed{\text{2nd}} \; \boxed{x^2} \; 50 \; \boxed{=}.$$

$$\approx 7.1 \quad \leftarrow \textbf{Round to the nearest tenth.}$$

The side is about 7.1 feet.

✓ Quick Check

• **2.** Find $\sqrt{10}$ to the nearest tenth. **3.2**

A **rational number** is any number that can be written as a quotient
of two integers in which the denominator is not zero. You can write
any integer as a quotient with a denominator of 1, so all integers
are rational numbers. Examples of rational numbers are
$2 \left(\text{or } \frac{2}{1} \right)$, $\frac{4}{5}$, $0.38 \left(\text{or } \frac{38}{100} \right)$, and $-8 \left(\text{or } \frac{-8}{1} \right)$.

The square root of a whole number is a rational number only when
the whole number is a perfect square. Rational numbers in decimal
form are either terminating or repeating.

EXAMPLE   Identifying Rational Numbers

> **Vocabulary Tip**
>
> A repeating decimal, such
> as $2.\overline{3}$, can be written
> with a bar over the
> repeating digits. A
> decimal that does not
> repeat *cannot* be written
> with a bar.

3 Tell whether each number is rational.

  a. 6.7

    Rational: 6.7 is a terminating decimal.

  b. $\frac{1}{5}$

    Rational: $\frac{1}{5}$ is a quotient of integers.

  c. $\sqrt{26}$

    Not rational: 26 is not a perfect square.

  d. 3.22272228 . . .

    Not rational: the decimal does not repeat or terminate.

✓ Quick Check

**No; the decimal
does not terminate
or repeat.**

• **3.** Is 12.112111211112 . . . a rational number? Explain.

---

1. **Vocabulary** Is $\sqrt{4}$ a rational number? Explain. **Yes. $\sqrt{4} = 2$; 2 is an integer, and integers are rational numbers.**

2. Which number is NOT a perfect square? **C**

   A. 9   C. 32

   B. 16   D. 36

3. Find $\sqrt{7}$ to the nearest tenth. Use a calculator. **2.6**

4. **Estimate** Is $\sqrt{5}$ closer to 2 or 3? Draw a number line. Then justify your reasoning. **2;**

   $\sqrt{5}$ is closer to 2 on the number line.

Homework Exercises

For more exercises, see Extra Skills and Word Problems.

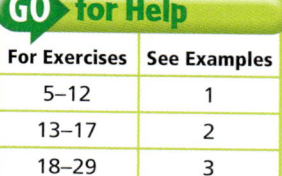

GO for Help	
For Exercises	**See Examples**
5–12	1
13–17	2
18–29	3

Ⓐ Find each square root without using a calculator.

5. $\sqrt{1}$ **1**   6. $\sqrt{25}$ **5**   7. $\sqrt{81}$ **9**   8. $\sqrt{9}$ **3**

9. $\sqrt{16}$ **4**   10. $\sqrt{36}$ **6**   11. $\sqrt{100}$ **10**   12. $\sqrt{144}$ **12**

Calculator Find each square root to the nearest tenth.

13. $\sqrt{21}$ **4.6**   14. $\sqrt{33}$ **5.7**   15. $\sqrt{51}$ **7.1**   16. $\sqrt{75}$ **8.7**

17. The area of a square quilt is 40 ft². How long is each side?

    6.3 ft

Tell whether each number is rational.

18. $6.\overline{8}$ **rational**   19. $\frac{9}{11}$ **rational**   20. $\sqrt{1}$ **rational**

21. $-2\frac{1}{2}$ **rational**   22. $\frac{7}{9}$ **rational**   23. $\sqrt{18}$ **not rational**

24. 6.2319743 **rational**   25. $3\frac{1}{3}$ **rational**   26. $\sqrt{49}$ **rational**

27. 15 **rational**   28. 0.101001 … **not rational**   29. $\sqrt{32}$ **not rational**

Ⓑ GPS 30. **Guided Problem Solving** A square patio has an area of 169 square feet. What is the perimeter of the patio? **52 ft**

  • **Make a Plan** Draw a picture. Find the side length of the square using square roots. Then find the perimeter.

  • **Check the Answer** How can you check to make sure you are using the correct side lengths for the patio?

Assignment Guide

Check Your Understanding
Go over Exercises 1–4 in class before assigning the Homework Exercises.

Homework Exercises
A Practice by Example   5–29
B Apply Your Skills   30–39
C Challenge   40
Test Prep and
   Mixed Review   41–47

Homework Quick Check
To check students' understanding of key skills and concepts, go over Exercises 14, 23, 37, 38, and 39.

Differentiated Instruction Resources

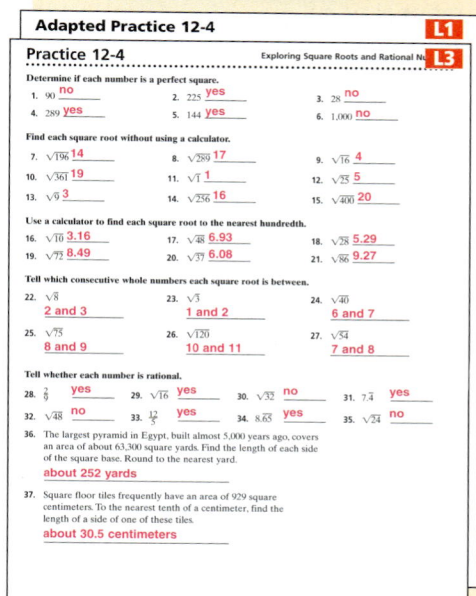

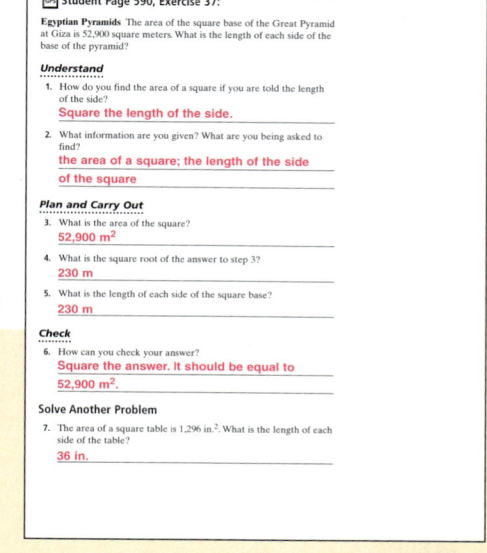

PowerPoint

Lesson Quiz

Find each square root.

1. $\sqrt{49}$ **7**   2. $\sqrt{84}$ **9.165**

Tell whether each number is rational or not.

3. $\sqrt{27}$ **not rational**

4. 3.45 **rational**

Alternative Assessment

Students list several numbers inside the square root symbol and trade papers with a partner. They must then find the square roots and tell if each square root is rational or not.

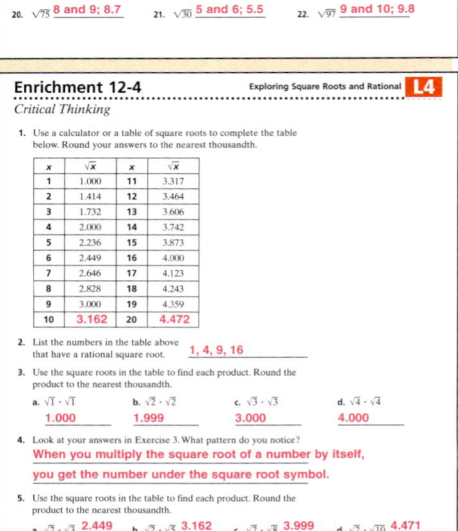

Reteaching 12-4   Exploring Square Roots and Rational N **L2**

A *perfect square* is the square of a whole number. The number 81 is a perfect square because it is the square of 9.

You can also say that 9 is the *square root* of 81, or $\sqrt{81}$ = 9. The square root of a given number is a number that, when multiplied by itself, is the given number. You can use a calculator to find square roots.

Example 1

a. Find $\sqrt{4}$.   b. Find $\sqrt{75}$.

Since 2 × 2 = 4, $\sqrt{4}$ = 2. $\sqrt{75} \approx 8.6602540$

You can estimate square roots using perfect squares.

Example 2

Tell which two consecutive whole numbers $\sqrt{52}$ is between.

49 < 52 < 64   Find perfect squares close to 52.

$\sqrt{49} < \sqrt{52} < \sqrt{64}$ Write the square roots in order.

7 < $\sqrt{52}$ < 8   Simplify.

$\sqrt{52}$ is between 7 and 8.

Determine if each number is a perfect square.

1. 24 **no**   2. 36 **yes**   3. 49 **yes**   4. 121 **yes**

Find each square root.

5. $\sqrt{9}$ **3**   6. $\sqrt{25}$ **5**   7. $\sqrt{4}$ **2**

8. $\sqrt{100}$ **10**   9. $\sqrt{400}$ **20**   10. $\sqrt{2,500}$ **50**

Use a calculator to tell whether each number is a perfect square.

11. 576 **yes**   12. 1,200 **no**   13. 2,401 **yes**

14. 900 **yes**   15. 1,521 **yes**   16. 1,875 **no**

Tell which two consecutive whole numbers the square root is between. Use a calculator to find each square root to the nearest tenth.

17. $\sqrt{42}$ **6 and 7; 6.5**   18. $\sqrt{88}$ **9 and 10; 9.4**   19. $\sqrt{63}$ **7 and 8; 7.9**

20. $\sqrt{75}$ **8 and 9; 8.7**   21. $\sqrt{30}$ **5 and 6; 5.5**   22. $\sqrt{97}$ **9 and 10; 9.8**

Enrichment 12-4   Exploring Square Roots and Rational **L4**

Critical Thinking

1. Use a calculator or a table of square roots to complete the table below. Round your answers to the nearest thousandth.

x	$\sqrt{x}$	x	$\sqrt{x}$
1	1.000	11	3.317
2	1.414	12	3.464
3	1.732	13	3.606
4	2.000	14	3.742
5	2.236	15	3.873
6	2.449	16	4.000
7	2.646	17	4.123
8	2.828	18	4.243
9	3.000	19	4.359
10	3.162	20	4.472

2. List the numbers in the table above that have a rational square root.   **1, 4, 9, 16**

3. Use the square roots in the table to find each product. Round the product to the nearest thousandth.

a. $\sqrt{1} \cdot \sqrt{1}$ b. $\sqrt{2} \cdot \sqrt{2}$ c. $\sqrt{3} \cdot \sqrt{3}$ d. $\sqrt{4} \cdot \sqrt{4}$
1.000   **1.999**   **3.000**   **4.000**

4. Look at your answers in Exercise 3. What pattern do you notice?
When you multiply the square root of a number by itself, you get the number under the square root symbol.

5. Use the square roots in the table to find each product. Round the product to the nearest thousandth.

a. $\sqrt{2} \cdot \sqrt{3}$ **2.449**   b. $\sqrt{2} \cdot \sqrt{5}$ **3.162**   c. $\sqrt{2} \cdot \sqrt{8}$ **3.999**   d. $\sqrt{2} \cdot \sqrt{10}$ **4.471**

6. Look at your answers in Exercise 5. What pattern do you notice?
The product of the square roots of two integers is equal to the square root of the product of the two integers.

7. Write the product of the following using the square root symbol.

a. $\sqrt{2} \cdot \sqrt{12}$ **$\sqrt{24}$**   b. $\sqrt{3} \cdot \sqrt{5}$ **$\sqrt{15}$**   c. $\sqrt{5} \cdot \sqrt{8}$ **$\sqrt{40}$**   d. $\sqrt{6} \cdot \sqrt{10}$ **$\sqrt{60}$**

590

GO Online

Homework Video Tutor

Visit: PHSchool.com
Web Code: aqe-1204

Estimation **Estimate to the nearest whole number.**

31. $\sqrt{6}$ **2**   32. $\sqrt{7}$ **3**   33. $\sqrt{11}$ **3**   34. $\sqrt{26}$ **5**

35. **Reasoning** Is $\sqrt{2}$ greater than 1? Is $\sqrt{2}$ greater than 2? Explain. **Yes; no; explanations may vary. Sample: Since $\sqrt{1} = 1$, $\sqrt{2}$ must be greater than 1. Since $\sqrt{4} = 2$, $\sqrt{2}$ must be less than 2.**

36. **Calculator** Use a calculator and evaluate $\sqrt{27}$, $\sqrt{9} \times \sqrt{3}$, and $3 \times \sqrt{3}$. What do you notice about the answers? **The expressions are all equal.**

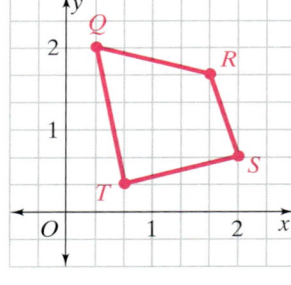

37. **Egyptian Pyramids** The area of the square base of the Great Pyramid at Giza is 52,900 square meters. What is the length of each side of the base of the pyramid? **230 m**

38. Simplify each expression.

a. $\left(\sqrt{2}\right)^2$ **2**   b. $\left(\sqrt{3}\right)^2$ **3**   c. $\left(\sqrt{16}\right)^2$ **16**

d. **Patterns** What happens when you square the square root of a number? **You get the original number.**

39. 5 and 6; explanations may vary. Sample: 25 < 29 < 36, and since $\sqrt{25}$ = 5 and $\sqrt{36}$ = 6, $\sqrt{29}$ lies between 5 and 6.

39. **Writing in Math** Find two consecutive whole numbers between which $\sqrt{29}$ is located. Explain your choice. **See left.**

C 40. **Challenge** Find two perfect squares whose sum is 100.
36 and 64

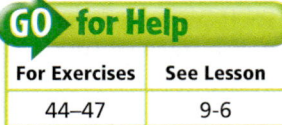

Test Prep and Mixed Review

Practice

Multiple Choice

41. Which point on the graph shows the location of the ordered pair $\left(2, \frac{2}{3}\right)$? **C**

Ⓐ Q   Ⓒ S
Ⓑ R   Ⓓ T

42. Casey withdraws $12 from his bank account. Then he deposits $27. What integer represents the withdrawal? **J**

Ⓕ 12   Ⓗ −27
Ⓖ 27   Ⓙ −12

43. Ana serves 72 customers every 4 hours at a snack bar. Which is the ratio of hours to customers served? **A**

Ⓐ 1 : 18   Ⓑ 18 : 1   Ⓒ 72 : 4   Ⓓ 36 : 2

GO for Help

For Exercises	See Lesson
44–47	9-6

Find the area of each circle to the nearest tenth. Use 3.14 for π.

44. $r = 2$ in.   45. $d = 4$ ft   46. $r = 6$ m   47. $d = 15$ km
12.6 in.²   **12.6 ft²**   **113.0 m²**   **176.6 km²**

Test Prep

Resources

For additional practice with a variety of test item formats:

• Test-Taking Strategies, p. 597
• Test Prep, p. 601
• Test-Taking Strategies with Transparencies

12-5 Introducing the Pythagorean Theorem

Check Skills You'll Need

1. **Vocabulary Review**
   List 3 numbers that
   are examples of
   perfect squares.
   See below.
   Find each
   square root.

2. $\sqrt{9}$ **3**   3. $\sqrt{64}$ **8**

4. $\sqrt{25}$ **5**   5. $\sqrt{36}$ **6**

6. $\sqrt{121}$ 7. $\sqrt{625}$
   11   **25**

GO for Help
Lesson 12-4

Check Skills You'll Need

1. Answers may vary.
   Sample: 36; 25; 16

What You'll Learn

To solve problems using the Pythagorean Theorem

🔊 **New Vocabulary** legs, hypotenuse, Pythagorean Theorem

Why Learn This?

Suppose you want to take the
shortest route from one corner
of a rectangular park to the
opposite corner. You can use the
Pythagorean Theorem to find
the shortest distance.

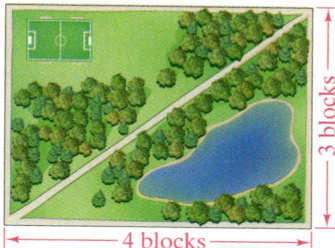

Recall that a right triangle has an angle measuring 90°. In a right
triangle, the two shorter sides are called **legs.** The longest side,
opposite the right angle, is called the **hypotenuse.**

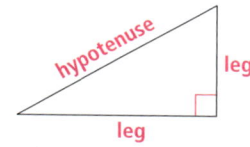

The Pythagorean Theorem shows the relationship of the side
lengths in a right triangle. You usually use the letters *a*, *b*, and *c* to
label the unknown lengths of a right triangle.

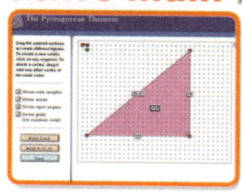

Online
active math

For: Pythagorean
     Theorem Activity
Use: Interactive
     Textbook, 12-5

KEY CONCEPTS   **Pythagorean Theorem**

In any right triangle, the sum of the squares of the lengths of
the legs (*a* and *b*) is equal to the square of the length of the
hypotenuse (*c*).

Arithmetic

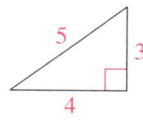

$3^2 + 4^2 = 5^2$

Algebra

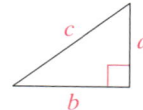

$a^2 + b^2 = c^2$

12-5 Introducing the Pythagorean Theorem **591**

Objective
To solve problems using the
Pythagorean Theorem

Examples
1 Finding the Length of a
   Hypotenuse
2 Finding the Length of a Leg

Math Understandings: p. 570D

Professional
Development

Math Background

The Pythagorean Theorem states
the relationship between the two
shorter sides of a right triangle,
called *legs,* and the longest side,
or *hypotenuse.* The sum of the
squares of the legs (*a* and *b*) in
any right triangle is equal to
the square of the hypotenuse
(*c*): $a^2 + b^2 = c^2$. So, given the
lengths of two sides of a right
triangle, you can always find the
length of the third side.

More Math Background: p. 570D

Lesson Planning and Resources

See p. 570E for a list of the
resources that support this lesson.

PowerPoint

Bell Ringer Practice

✓ **Check Skills You'll Need**
*Use student page, transparency,
or PowerPoint. For intervention,
direct students to:*

**Exploring Square Roots and
Rational Numbers**
Lesson 12-4
Extra Skills and Word Problems
   Practice, Ch. 12

Differentiated Instruction Solutions for All Learners

Special Needs **L1**
Provide copies of Examples 1 and 2 for the students.
Have them outline the triangles with the legs one
color, and the hypotenuse a different color. They
should label the legs *a* and *b*, and label each
hypotenuse *c*.

learning style: visual

Below Level **L2**
Draw several right triangles of different sizes and
orientations. Help students identify the hypotenuse as
the longest side and opposite the right angle. Have
students label the sides *a*, *b*, and *c*.

learning style: visual

Activity Lab

Use before the lesson.

All in One Teaching Resources

Activity Lab 12-5: The
Pythagorean Theorem

Guided Instruction

Example 1
In Quick Check 1, students may
forget to find the square root
of c^2.

PowerPoint

Additional Examples

1 Two legs of a right triangle
measure 20 and 21 units long.
Find the length of the
hypotenuse. **29 units**

2 On a map, the towns of Shake,
Rattle, and Roll form a right
triangle. Shake is 5 miles due
north of Rattle. Roll is directly
east of Rattle. Shake and Roll
are 15 miles apart. How far
apart are Rattle and Roll?
about 14.1 mi

All in One Teaching Resources
• Daily Notetaking Guide 12-5 **L3**
• Adapted Notetaking 12-5 **L1**

Closure

• *How can you find the length of
a missing side of a right triangle
given two other side lengths?*
**Sample: Substitute the two
given lengths for the
appropriate variables in the
Pythagorean Theorem,
$a^2 + b^2 = c^2$; solve for the
variable; take a square root of
each side of the equation to
find the missing length.**

GO Online

Video Tutor Help
Visit: PHSchool.com
Web Code: aqe-0775

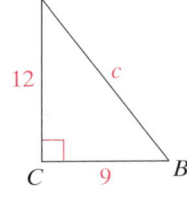

EXAMPLE **Finding the Length of a Hypotenuse**

1 **Multiple Choice** A rectangular park is 12 city blocks long and
9 city blocks wide, as shown below. Find the distance from point A
to point B in city blocks.

Ⓐ 14 　　　　Ⓑ 15 　　　　Ⓒ 16 　　　　Ⓓ 18

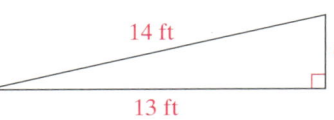

$$a^2 + b^2 = c^2 \qquad \leftarrow \text{Write the Pythagorean Theorem.}$$
$$9^2 + 12^2 = c^2 \qquad \leftarrow \text{Substitute 9 for } a \text{ and 12 for } b.$$
$$225 = c^2 \qquad \leftarrow \text{Square 9 and 12. Then add.}$$
$$\sqrt{225} = \sqrt{c^2} \qquad \leftarrow \text{Find the square root of each side.}$$
$$15 = c \qquad \leftarrow \text{Simplify.}$$

The shortest distance in city blocks is 15. The
correct answer is choice B.

✓ Quick Check

1. Find the length of the hypotenuse of a triangle with legs that
have lengths of 12 inches and 16 inches. **20 in.**

EXAMPLE **Finding the Length of a Leg**

2 A ramp forms a right triangle with the
ground. How high is the top of the
ramp? Round to the nearest tenth.

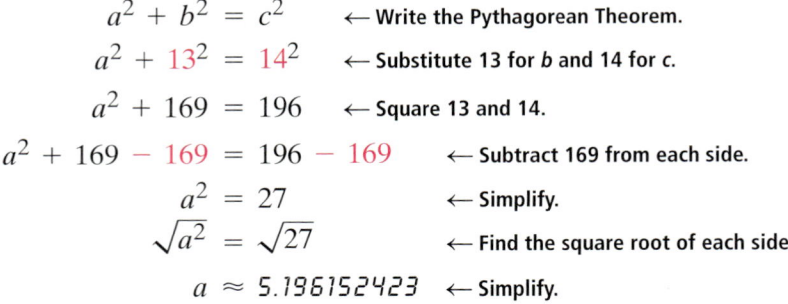

$$a^2 + b^2 = c^2 \qquad \leftarrow \text{Write the Pythagorean Theorem.}$$
$$a^2 + 13^2 = 14^2 \qquad \leftarrow \text{Substitute 13 for } b \text{ and 14 for } c.$$
$$a^2 + 169 = 196 \qquad \leftarrow \text{Square 13 and 14.}$$
$$a^2 + 169 - 169 = 196 - 169 \qquad \leftarrow \text{Subtract 169 from each side.}$$
$$a^2 = 27 \qquad \leftarrow \text{Simplify.}$$
$$\sqrt{a^2} = \sqrt{27} \qquad \leftarrow \text{Find the square root of each side.}$$
$$a \approx 5.196152423 \qquad \leftarrow \text{Simplify.}$$

The top of the ramp is about 5.2 feet high.

✓ Quick Check

2. A ramp leading into a truck forms a right triangle with the
ground. One leg is 10 feet long. The hypotenuse is 11 feet long.
How high is the top of the ramp? Round to the nearest tenth.
4.6 ft

592 **Chapter 12** Equations and Inequalities

Advanced Learners **L4**
Have students explain whether the equation
$(a + b)^2 = c^2$ is the same as $a^2 + b^2 = c^2$. **Sample:**
No; exponents cannot be distributed over addition.

learning style: verbal

English Language Learners **ELL**
The words *Pythagorean, theorem,* and *hypotenuse* are
difficult to pronounce for many English learners.
Provide opportunities for student to practice saying
them in a safe environment, with you or a partner,
before requiring them to say the words in front of the
whole class.

learning style: verbal

1. **Vocabulary** How can you identify the hypotenuse in a right triangle? **It is the longest side and opposite the right angle.**

2. Fill in the blanks to find the missing side length of the triangle.

$$a^2 + b^2 = c^2$$
$$21^2 + \blacksquare^2 = c^2$$
$$\blacksquare + \blacksquare = c^2$$
$$\sqrt{841} = c$$

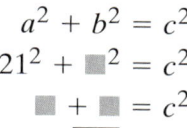

3. **Number Sense** Can you use $a = 5$, $b = 12$, and $c = 13$ to form a right triangle? Explain. **yes; $5^2 + 12^2 = 13^2$**

4. **Writing in Math** Can a leg of a right triangle ever be longer than the hypotenuse? Explain. **No; the hypotenuse is always the longest side of a right triangle.**

Homework Exercises

For more exercises, see **Extra Skills and Word Problems.**

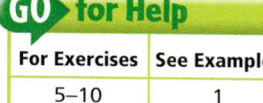

GO for Help

For Exercises	See Examples
5–10	1
11–15	2

A Find the missing side length. Round to the nearest tenth.

5.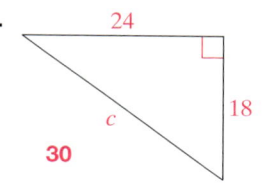

6.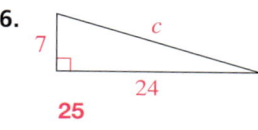

7. $a = 4$, $b = 3$, $c = \blacksquare$ **5**

8. $a = 10$, $b = 24$, $c = \blacksquare$ **26**

9. $a = 6$, $b = 8$, $c = \blacksquare$ **10**

10. $a = 12$, $b = 20$, $c = \blacksquare$ **23.3**

11.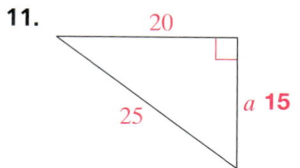

12.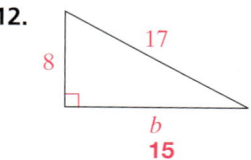

13. $a = \blacksquare$, $b = 7$, $c = 9$ **5.7**

14. $a = 2$, $b = \blacksquare$, $c = 5$ **4.6**

GO Online
Homework Video Tutor
Visit: PHSchool.com
Web Code: aqe-1205

15. A 10-foot ladder leans against a building. The base of the ladder is 6 feet from the building. How high is the point where the ladder touches the building? **8 ft**

Assignment Guide

Check Your Understanding
Go over Exercises 1–4 in class before assigning the Homework Exercises.

Homework Exercises
A	Practice by Example	5–15
B	Apply Your Skills	16–19
C	Challenge	20
	Test Prep and Mixed Review	21–26

Homework Quick Check
To check students' understanding of key skills and concepts, go over Exercises 6, 13, 15, 17, and 19.

Differentiated Instruction Resources

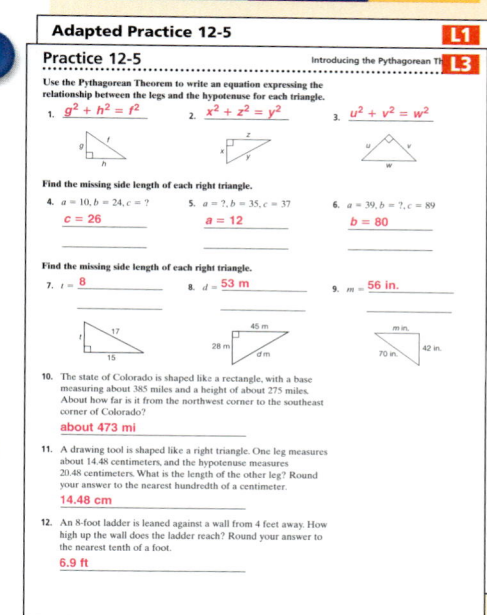

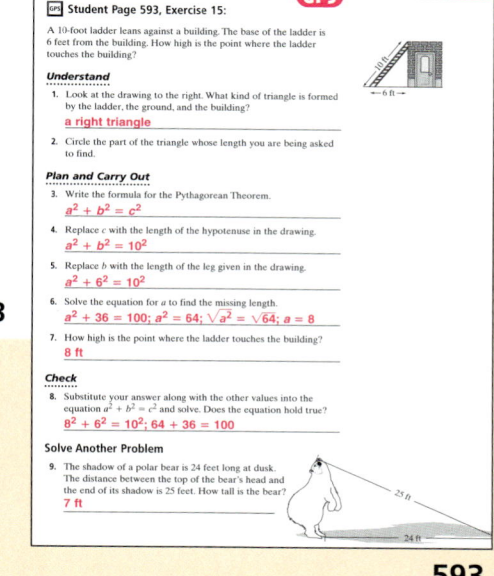

Lesson Quiz

Find the missing side length of each right triangle.

1. $a = \blacksquare$, $b = 24$, $c = 30$ **18**

2. $a = 8$, $b = \blacksquare$, $c = 10$ **6**

3. $a = 5$, $b = 3$, $c = \blacksquare$ **5.8**

Alternative Assessment

Students in pairs take turns naming two out of three lengths in a right triangle. The partner finds the missing length. Together they verify the results by showing that $a^2 + b^2 = c^2$.

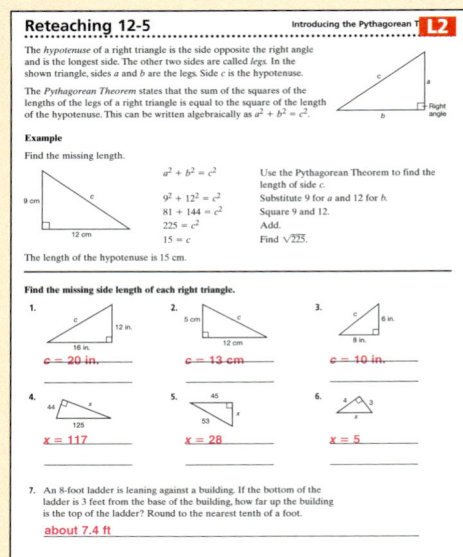

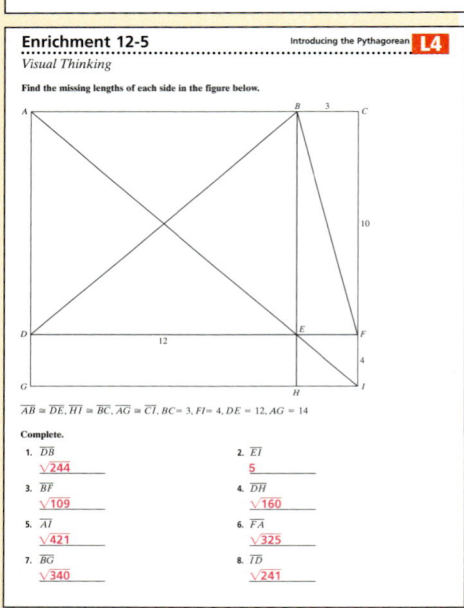

B  **16. Guided Problem Solving** A landscaper hammers a stake 9 feet from the base of a tree. A wire goes from the stake to a spot 40 feet up the trunk. How long must the wire be? **41 ft**

- **Make a Plan** Draw a sketch of the triangle. Label the legs and hypotenuse. Find the hypotenuse using $a^2 + b^2 = c^2$.
- **Carry Out the Plan** Solve for c.

In Exercises 17–18, you find the diagonal length in a rectangle. A diagonal of a rectangle connects opposite vertices.

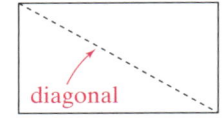
diagonal

17. Framing Corey builds a picture frame. The length of the frame is 24 inches. The width is 10 inches. Corey measures the diagonal to make sure the frame has square corners. What is the length of the diagonal? **26 in.**

18. Television The size of a television screen is based on the diagonal of the screen. You buy a 27-inch television set. The screen has a height of 15 inches. What is the width of the screen, to the nearest inch? **22 in.**

19. (**Algebra**) Use the Pythagorean Theorem. Write an equation to express the relationship between the legs and the hypotenuse of the triangle.

$$r^2 + s^2 = t^2$$

20. Challenge Draw a triangle with hypotenuse $\sqrt{2}$ inches long. **See margin.**

C

Test Prep and Mixed Review
Practice

Multiple Choice

21. The table shows a sequence of terms. Which expression can you use to find the value of a term in the sequence?

  Ⓐ $n - 1$ Ⓒ $n + 1$ **B**

  Ⓑ $n - 5$ Ⓓ $n + 5$

Position, n	Value of Term
10	5
11	6
12	7
n	$\blacksquare$

22. Jessica's cat eats about 2 cans of food every 7 days. About how many cans of food does her cat eat in 30 days? **H**

  Ⓕ 7   Ⓖ 8   Ⓗ 9   Ⓙ 10

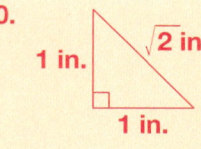

For Exercises	See Lesson
23–26	11-1

Find each value.

23. $|0|$ **0**   **24.** $|-3|$ **3**   **25.** $|85|$ **85**   **26.** $|-84|$ **84**

Test Prep

Resources

For additional practice with a variety of test item formats:

- Test-Taking Strategies, p. 597
- Test Prep, p. 601
- Test-Taking Strategies with Transparencies

20.

1 in. $\sqrt{2}$ in.

1 in.

Practice Solving Problems

You can use proportions and the Pythagorean Theorem to solve real-life problems.

Carpentry The slope, or pitch, of the roof in the diagram is $\frac{3}{12}$. The slope indicates that each time the horizontal distance changes by 12 inches, the vertical distance changes by 3 inches. Use the diagram to find the length x.

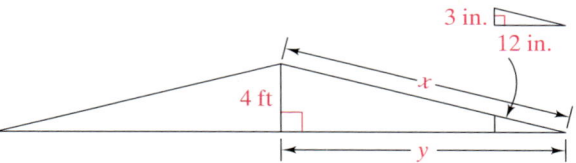

What You Might Think

> What do I know?
> What do I want to find?

> First I will use a proportion to find length y.

> Then I will use the Pythagorean Theorem to find length x.

> Is the answer reasonable?

What You Might Write

- The legs of the small right triangle are 3 in. and 12 in.
- The triangles are similar. The corresponding sides of the triangles are proportional.
- I want to find length x and length y.

I can change 4 ft to 48 in.

$$\frac{48}{3} = \frac{y}{12}$$

$$\frac{48}{3} \xrightarrow{\times 4} \frac{y}{12} \xleftarrow{\times 4}$$

$$y = 192$$

$$48^2 + y^2 = x^2$$
$$48^2 + 192^2 = x^2$$
$$2{,}304 + 36{,}864 = x^2$$
$$39{,}168 = x^2$$
$$x = \sqrt{39{,}168} \approx 198$$

The length x is about 198 inches, or $16\frac{1}{2}$ feet.

The hypotenuse must be longer than the leg.

GPS Guided Problem Solving

Practice Solving Problems

In this feature, students use proportions and the Pythagorean Theorem to solve real-life problems in carpentry, temperature change, costs for calling internationally, and angles on clocks.

Guided Instruction

Discuss with students the Pythagorean Theorem and proportions associated with it. Ask:
- *Why should you change the 4 feet given in the diagram to inches?* **The dimensions of the small triangle are given in inches.**
- *Could you change the inches to feet?* **Yes, but you would need to work with fractions.**
- *Why should you multiply 48 × 4?* **Because the denominator 3 is multiplied by 4 to get the denominator 12.**

Think It Through

1. How can you tell that the two triangles are similar? **The angles have the same measure.**

2. Explain how you can use the proportion $\frac{4}{3} = \frac{y}{12}$ to find y. **The proportion $\frac{4}{3} = \frac{y}{12}$ can be used to find y in feet.**

3. Solve the proportion $\frac{4}{3} = \frac{y}{12}$ to find the value of y in feet. Use the Pythagorean Theorem to find x. **y = 16 feet; $x \approx$ 16.5 feet**

Exercises

4. Find the length x shown in the diagram below of the roof.

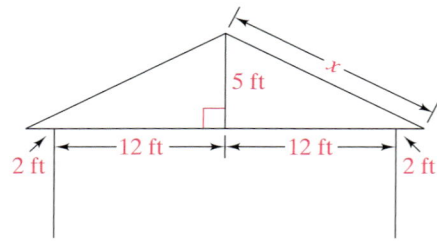

a. What is the total length of the base of the right triangle? **14.9 ft**

b. What formula can you use to find x? **$5^2 + 14^2 = x^2$**

5. As you climb a mountain, the air temperature decreases about 6.5°C for each kilometer you climb.
a. Assume the air temperature stays the same at the base of a mountain during the day. How many kilometers would you have to climb to feel the temperature decrease 10°C? **about 1.5 km**
b. How many kilometers would you have to climb to feel the temperature decrease 15°C? **about 2.3 km**

6. The first minute of an international phone call costs $0.25. Each additional minute costs $0.12. What is the greatest number of minutes you can talk without spending more than $15? **122 minutes**

7. The minute hand of a clock rotates 360° every hour. The hour hand rotates 360° every 12 hours. What angle do the hands of a clock make at exactly 7:15? **127.5°**

Test-Taking Strategies

Estimating the Answer

You can use estimation to find an answer, check an answer, or eliminate possible answers from multiple-choice questions.

EXAMPLE

You and a friend owe $4.90 for a taxi ride. The ride costs $1.90 for the first eighth of a mile. Each additional eighth of a mile costs $0.25. About how many miles did you travel?

    Ⓐ $\frac{1}{2}$ Ⓑ $1\frac{1}{2}$ Ⓒ 2   Ⓓ $2\frac{1}{2}$

You can estimate the cost by rounding $1.90 to $2.00. You can also round $4.90 to $5.00. Then you can solve a two-step equation using mental math.

$$0.25y + 2 = 5 \qquad \leftarrow \text{Write a rule for finding the taxi fare. Let } y \text{ be the number of eighths.}$$
$$0.25y + 2 - 2 = 5 - 2 \qquad \leftarrow \text{Subtract 2 from each side to undo the addition.}$$
$$0.25y = 3 \qquad \leftarrow \text{Simplify.}$$
$$\frac{0.25y}{0.25} = \frac{3}{0.25} \qquad \leftarrow \text{Divide each side by 0.25 to undo the multiplication.}$$
$$y = 12 \qquad \leftarrow \text{Simplify.}$$
$$\frac{1}{8} + \frac{12}{8} = \frac{13}{8} \qquad \leftarrow \text{Add the number of eighths traveled.}$$

● 13 eighths is about $1\frac{1}{2}$ miles. The correct answer is choice B.

Exercises

1. Students organize a community clothing drive. They pack 27 boxes of clothes. Each box weighs about 30 pounds. About how many pounds of clothing do they collect? **D**
     Ⓐ 400   Ⓒ 600
     Ⓑ 500   Ⓓ 900

2. Mr. Cortez distributes 4 worksheets to each of his students. He has 116 worksheets. Which equation can be used to find s, the number of students in his class? **F**
     Ⓕ $s = 116 \div 4$ Ⓗ $s = 116 \times 4$
     Ⓖ $s = 116 - 4$ Ⓙ $s = 116 + 4$

Test-Taking Strategies

Estimating the Answer

This feature presents the valuable test-taking strategy of using estimation to find answers, rule out answers, or check answers.

Guided Instruction

Explain to students that solving a simpler problem using estimation may save them time when taking a test. Take them through the Example step by step. Explain to them that they can also use number sense to eliminate answer choices. For example, $2\frac{1}{2}$ miles would cost roughly $7. Since $7 > 5$, they can eliminate choice D.

Have students work independently on the Exercises. Allow them to trade papers with a partner and compare answers and strategies.

Resources

Test-Taking Strategies with Transparencies
• Transparency 10
• Practice sheet, p. 12

Test-Taking Strategies with Transparencies

Test-Taking Strategies: Estimating the Answer

Sometimes you can estimate to find the answer.

Example Find the sum: $0.75 + 8.23 + 5.5$

A. 15.53	B. 14.48	C. 9.53	D. 21.23

Estimate: Round to the nearest whole number.

$$0.75 + 8.23 + 5.5$$
$$1 + 8 + 6 = 15$$

Both A and B are near 15, so round to the nearest tenth.

$0.8 + 8.2 + 5.5$ must be less than 15.

The answer is 14.48, or choice B.

Estimate to find the answer. Explain your reasoning.

1. The area of a square with side 2.7 cm is
   A. 5.4 cm².   B. 7.29 cm².   C. 54 cm².   D. 72.9 cm².

2. Reese went grocery shopping to buy spaghetti sauce, spaghetti noodles, and a loaf of french bread. These items cost $1.59, $1.79, and $1.89. About how much should Reese's grocery bill be?
   F. less than $5   G. between $5 and $6
   H. between $6 and $7   J. more than $7

Transparency 10

Chapter 12 Review

Resources

Student Edition
Extra Skills and Word Problems
  Practice, Ch. 12, p. 634
English/Spanish Glossary, p. 654
Formulas and Properties, p. 652
Tables, p. 648

All in One Teaching Resources
Vocabulary and Study Skills 12F

Differentiated Instruction

Spanish Vocabulary Workbook
  with Study Skills   **ELL**
Interactive Textbook
Audio Glossary
Online Vocabulary Quiz

Success Tracker™
Online at PHSchool.com

Vocabulary Review

🔊 **graph of an inequality**
  (p. 579)
hypotenuse (p. 591)
inequality (p. 578)
legs (p. 591)

perfect square (p. 588)
Pythagorean Theorem
  (p. 591)
rational number (p. 588)

solution of an inequality
  (p. 579)
square root (p. 587)
two-step equation (p. 572)

Go Online
PHSchool.com
For: Vocabulary quiz
Web Code: aqj-1251

Choose the vocabulary term from the column on the right that best completes each sentence. Not all choices will be used.

1. A(n) __?__ in decimal form terminates or repeats. **E**

2. A(n) __?__ is the square of a whole number. **D**

3. A(n) __?__ is a mathematical sentence using one of the symbols $<, >, \leq, \geq$, or $\neq$. **B**

4. The inverse of squaring a number is finding the __?__. **F**

5. The longest side of a right triangle is called the __?__. **A**

A. hypotenuse
B. inequality
C. leg
D. perfect square
E. rational number
F. square root

Skills and Concepts

Lesson 12-1
• To solve two-step equations and to use two-step equations to solve problems

A **two-step equation** is an equation containing two operations. To solve many two-step equations, undo the addition or subtraction and then undo the multiplication or division.

Solve each equation. Check the solution.

6. $3h + 6 = 15$ **3**   7. $2j - 4 = -2$ **1**   8. $\frac{f}{5} + 4 = 29$ **125**

Lesson 12-2
• To express and identify solutions of inequalities

An **inequality** compares expressions that are not equal. A **solution of an inequality** is any number that makes the inequality true.

State whether the given number is a solution of $x \leq -4$.

9. 4 **no**   10. -4 **yes**   11. -2 **no**   12. -6 **yes**

Graph each inequality on a number line. 13–16. See margin.

13. $p > -4$ 14. $h < 8$ 15. $k \geq -5$ 16. $g \leq 3$

Spanish Vocabulary/Study Skills **ELL**

Vocabulary/Study Skills **L3**

12F: Vocabulary Review   For use with the Chapter Review

Study Skill: When solving a crossword puzzle, read the clues first.

Complete the crossword puzzle below. For help, use the glossary in your textbook.

Crossword with answers:
ASSOCIATIVE, INDEPENDENT, POWER, CIRCUMFERENCE, SOLUTION, CONJECTURE, EQUATIVE, RATIONAL, AREA, VOLUME, EXPRESSION

ACROSS
2. The outcome of one event does not depend on the outcome of another event.
6. the distance around a circle
8. a number that can be written as a quotient of two integers, $\frac{a}{b}$, where $b \neq 0$
9. the number of square units inside a figure
10. the number of cubic units needed to fill the space inside a figure
11. a mathematical phrase containing numbers and operations

DOWN
1. $15 + (23 + 14) = (15 + 23) + 14$ is an example of this property.
3. a number expressed with an exponent
4. point where edges meet
5. a number that makes an equation true
6. predicts how a pattern may continue
7. a mathematical statement that contains an equal sign

598

13.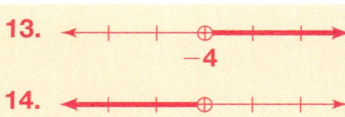
    −4

14.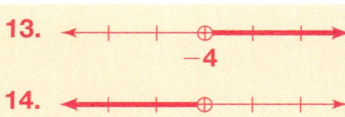
    8

15.
    −5

16.
    3

Lesson 12-3

• To solve inequalities by adding or subtracting

To solve an inequality, get the variable alone on one side of the inequality.

Solve each inequality.

17. $q + 6 < 9$ *q < 3*

18. $t - 7 < -2$ *t < 5*

19. $v - 4 > 12$ *v > 16*

20. $y + 9 \geq -11$ *y ≥ −20*

Lesson 12-4

• To find square roots and to identify rational numbers

A **square root** of a number is a number that, when multiplied by itself, equals the given number. A **perfect square** is the square of a whole number.

A **rational number** is a number that can be written as a quotient of two integers, where the divisor is not 0.

Find each square root. Round to the nearest tenth, if necessary.

21. $\sqrt{81}$ **9**

22. $\sqrt{24}$ **4.9**

23. $\sqrt{30}$ **5.5**

24. $\sqrt{144}$ **12**

25. between 2 and 3

26. between 3 and 4

27. between 4 and 5

28. between 5 and 6

Tell which two consecutive whole numbers each square root is between.   **25–28. See left.**

25. $\sqrt{6}$

26. $\sqrt{12}$

27. $\sqrt{21}$

28. $\sqrt{31}$

Tell whether each number is rational.

29. $0.\overline{3}$
rational

30. $\sqrt{18}$
not rational

31. 0.123
rational

32. $\sqrt{64}$
rational

Lesson 12-5

• To solve problems using the Pythagorean Theorem

The **Pythagorean Theorem** states that, given the triangle at the right, $a^2 + b^2 = c^2$.

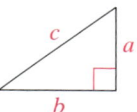

Find the missing side length of each right triangle. Round to the nearest tenth, if necessary.

33. $a = 6$, $b = 8$, $c = \blacksquare$ **10**

34. $a = 15$, $b = \blacksquare$, $c = 17$ **8**

35. $a = 1$, $b = 2$, $c = \blacksquare$ **2.2**

36. $a = \blacksquare$, $b = 6$, $c = 8$ **5.3**

37. For a quilting frame to be rectangular, the diagonals must be the same length. What should the lengths of the diagonals be for a quilting frame 86 inches by 100 inches? Round to the nearest inch.   **132 in.**

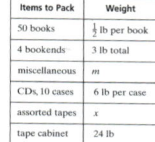

Chapter 12 Test

Go Online
For: Online chapter test
PHSchool.com **Web Code:** aqa-1252

Resources

- ExamView Assessment Suite CD-ROM
  - Ch. 12 Ready-Made Test
  - Make your own Ch. 12 Test
- MindPoint Quiz Show CD-ROM
  - Chapter 12 Review

Differentiated Instruction

All-in-One Teaching Resources
- Below Level Chapter 12 Test **L2**
- Chapter 12 Test **L3**
- Chapter 12 Alternative Assessment **L4**

Spanish Assessment Resources ELL
- Below Level Chapter 12 Test **L2**
- Chapter 12 Test **L3**
- Chapter 12 Alternative Assessment **L4**

ExamView Assessment Suite CD-ROM
- Special Needs Test **L1**
- Special Needs Practice Bank **L1**

Online Chapter 12 Test at www.PHSchool.com **L3**

Below Level Chapter Test **L2**

Chapter Test **L3**

Chapter Test — Form A
Chapter 12

Solve each equation. Check the solution.
1. $-8x + (-6) = -14$ **x = 1**
2. $2x + (-8) = 10$ **x = 9**
3. $-2x + (-7) = 11$ **x = -9**
4. $4x + (-4) = -36$ **x = -8**
5. $2x + 5 = 11$ **x = 3**
6. $6x + 5 = 29$ **x = 4**
7. Suppose you save $52 each month so that you can buy a guitar. So far, you have saved $364. The guitar costs $1,040. How many more months will you have to save? Write and solve a two-step equation to represent the situation. **52x + 364 = 1,040; x= 13**

Write an inequality for each situation.
8. There are more than 25 states in the country. **x > 25**
9. A sign on a tunnel says, "Maximum height of vehicles is 15 feet." **x ≤ 15**
10. Water boils at a temperature of at least 212°F. **x ≥ 212**
11. Your brother had, at most, 25 people at his party. **x ≤ 25**

Write an inequality for each graph.
12. **x ≥ -3**
13. **x < -1**

Solve each inequality.
14. $x - 8 < 15$ **x < 23**
15. $y + 17 ≥ 12$ **y ≥ -5**
16. $j + 5 < -12$ **j < -17**
17. $r + (-4) > 17$ **r > 21**
18. $g - (-5) ≥ 25$ **g ≥ 20**
19. $-6 > b - 31$ **b < -30**
20. Fifteen is greater than a number minus 7. **15 > x - 7; x < 22**
21. A number plus 11 is less than or equal to 9. **n + 11 ≤ 9; n ≤ -2**

Solve each equation. Check the solution.

1. $4u + 7 = 35$ **7**
2. $6r - 4 = 20$ **4**
3. $\frac{f}{3} + 5 = 20$ **45**
4. $\frac{n}{8} - 2 = -1$ **8**

5. An eraser and five pencils cost $1.20. If the eraser costs $.45, how much does each pencil cost? **$.15**

6. Write an inequality for each situation.
   a. There are fewer than six hamsters in the cage. **h < 6**
   b. Fifty or more people are at the county fair. **p ≥ 50**

7. Write an inequality for the graph below.

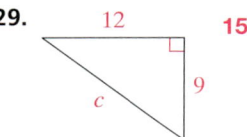

$x \le -6$

8. Tell whether each number is a solution of $c \le -8$.
   a. 8 **no**
   b. -7 **no**
   c. -8 **yes**
   d. -10 **yes**

Graph each inequality on a number line.
9–12. See margin.

9. $w > -5$
10. $x \le 4$
11. $y < 5$
12. $z \ge -12$

13. **Writing in Math** Is -9 a solution of the inequality $d \le -9$? Explain. **See margin.**

Solve each inequality.

14. $j + 4 \ge 9$ **j ≥ 5**
15. $k - 6 < 2$ **k < 8**
16. $s - 6 < 42$ **s < 48**
17. $f + 2 \ge -1$ **f ≥ -3**

18. **Bank Fees** You have $59 in a bank account. You need at least $200 to avoid bank fees. Write and solve an inequality to find how much more money you should deposit. **m + 59 ≥ 200; m ≥ $141**

---

19. To get an A on a four-part test, Dana must score a minimum of 270 points. She scored 240 points on the first three parts of the test. Write and solve an inequality to find what she needs to earn on the fourth part to receive an A.
    p + 240 ≥ 270; p ≥ 30

Find the square root. Round to the nearest tenth, if necessary.

20. $\sqrt{25}$ **5**
21. $\sqrt{49}$ **7**
22. $\sqrt{60}$ **7.7**

Tell which two consecutive whole numbers each square root is between. **See margin.**

23. $\sqrt{5}$
24. $\sqrt{14}$
25. $\sqrt{97}$

Tell whether each number is rational.

26. $\sqrt{14}$ **not rational**
27. $5.\overline{5}$ **rational**
28. $\frac{1}{13}$ **rational**

Find the missing side length.

29.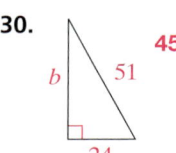

30.

31. The solution to which inequality is represented by the graph below? **C**

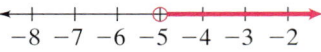

Ⓐ $25 > y + 20$
Ⓑ $y - 5 < -10$
Ⓒ $y - 15 > -20$
Ⓓ $y + 10 \ge -15$

9.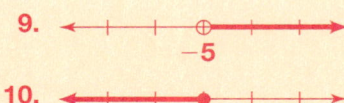
   -5

10.
   4

11.
   5

12.
   -12

13. Yes; answers may vary. Sample: The inequality includes the equal sign, so -9 is a solution.

23. between 2 and 3
24. between 3 and 4
25. between 9 and 10

Multiple Choice
Choose the correct letter.

1. What operation would you perform first in the expression
$3.9 + 4.1 \times 16 - 6 \div 4.8$? **B**
- Ⓐ Add 3.9 and 4.1.
- Ⓑ Multiply 4.1 and 16.
- Ⓒ Subtract 6 from 16.
- Ⓓ Divide 10 by 4.8.

2. Four servers at a restaurant equally share $87.44 in tips. How much does each server receive? **H**
- Ⓕ $20.68
- Ⓖ $20.86
- Ⓗ $21.86
- Ⓙ $22.86

3. Find the next two terms in the pattern: $2, 6, 12, 20, \ldots$ **C**
- Ⓐ 24, 32
- Ⓑ 28, 36
- Ⓒ 30, 42
- Ⓓ 32, 44

4. Solve the equation $0.2x = 46$. **J**
- Ⓕ 2.3
- Ⓖ 9.2
- Ⓗ 23
- Ⓙ 230

5. Find the quotient $0.317 \div 0.08$. **B**
- Ⓐ 0.039625
- Ⓑ 3.9625
- Ⓒ 39.625
- Ⓓ 396.25

6. Simplify the expression
$4 + 6 \times (-3) - (-10) \div (-2)$. **F**
- Ⓕ -19
- Ⓖ -10
- Ⓗ 10
- Ⓙ 19

7. Solve the equation $c + 3\frac{2}{3} = 7\frac{4}{5}$. **C**
- Ⓐ $3\frac{2}{15}$
- Ⓑ $3\frac{7}{15}$
- Ⓒ $4\frac{2}{15}$
- Ⓓ $4\frac{7}{15}$

8. Estimate the product $7\frac{5}{6} \times 5\frac{3}{4}$. **J**
- Ⓕ 35
- Ⓖ 40
- Ⓗ 42
- Ⓙ 48

9. Find the reciprocal of $4\frac{2}{5}$. **A**
- Ⓐ $\frac{5}{22}$
- Ⓑ $\frac{1}{4}$
- Ⓒ $\frac{5}{2}$
- Ⓓ $2\frac{4}{5}$

Go Online For: Online end-of-course test
PHSchool.com **Web Code:** aqa-1254

10. What is the ordered pair for P? **J**
- Ⓕ $(3, 2)$
- Ⓖ $(-2, -3)$
- Ⓗ $(2, -2)$
- Ⓙ $(-3, 2)$

11. Estimate the 8% sales tax for a sweater that costs $29.99. **A**
- Ⓐ $2.40
- Ⓑ $20.40
- Ⓒ $24.00
- Ⓓ $240.00

12. Which of the following is NOT equivalent to 48%? **H**
- Ⓕ $\frac{48}{100}$
- Ⓖ $\frac{24}{50}$
- Ⓗ 0.048
- Ⓙ 0.48

13. Which of the following is the most appropriate choice to display your height for each year since your birth? **C**
- Ⓐ circle graph
- Ⓑ line plot
- Ⓒ bar graph
- Ⓓ frequency table

14. What is the value of cell D3 in the spreadsheet below? **F**

	A	B	C	D
1	Test A	Test B	Test C	Mean
2	92	86	80	
3	79	82	82	
4	95	95	95	

- Ⓕ 81
- Ⓖ 86
- Ⓗ 243
- Ⓙ 285

15. Find the LCM of $20, 35,$ and 100. **D**
- Ⓐ 5
- Ⓑ 10
- Ⓒ 100
- Ⓓ 700

Chapter 12 Test Prep **601**

Item	1	2	3	4	5	6	7	8	9	10	11	12	13	14	15	16
Lesson	1-4	1-9	3-1	3-7	1-9	1-4	5-6	6-1	6-3	11-8	7-9	7-69	2-4	2-5	4-7	1-8

Item	17	18	19	20	21	22	23	24	25	26	27	28	29	30	31	32
Lesson	7-4	8-8	4-9	11-7	1-5	8-3	4-8	10-2	10-4	9-8	10-4	12-1	Deleted	4-2	1-4	3-2

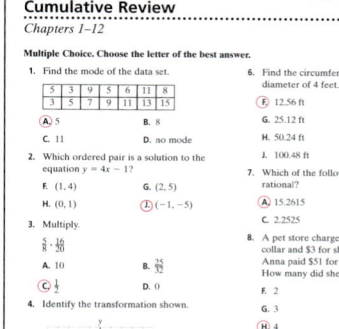
Test Prep

601

34. [2] 4.358898944...; $\sqrt{19}$ is not a rational number because 19 is not a perfect square. (OR some equivalent explanation)
[1] correct response with incorrect explanation

35. [2] $\overline{RS} \cong \overline{WU}$; $\overline{RT} \cong \overline{WV}$; $\overline{ST} \cong \overline{UV}$; $\angle SRT \cong \angle UWV$; $\angle RTS \cong \angle WVU$; $\angle RST \cong \angle WUV$
[1] one incorrect congruence

36. [2] 37.41; $x = 0.43 \times 87$, $x = 37.41$ (OR equivalent equation)
[1] appropriate method, but with one computational error OR correct answer with no work shown

37. [2] 3 h 45 min; 7 h 45 min − 3 h 15 min = 4 h 30 min, 4 h 30 min − 45 min = 3 h 90 min − 45 min = 3 h 45 min
[1] appropriate method but with one computational error OR correct answer with no work shown

38. [2] 2; $-\frac{b}{2} + 5 = 4$, $-\frac{b}{2} + 5 - 5 = 4 - 5$, $-\frac{b}{2} = -1$, $-\frac{b}{2} \times (-2) = (-1) \times (-2)$, $b = 2$
[1] appropriate method but with one computational error OR correct answer with no work shown

39. [2] $k > 28$; $\frac{k}{4} > 7$, $\frac{k}{4} \times 4 > 7 \times 4$, $k > 28$
[1] appropriate method but with one computational error OR correct answer with no work shown

40. [2] $2 \times 7 \times 7$; 98

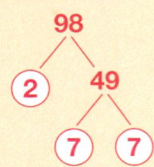

---

16. You buy tape and seven boxes for $18.55. If the tape costs $2.10, how much is each box? **G**
F $.70   G $2.35   H $2.65   J $2.95

17. Solve the proportion $\frac{2m}{21} = \frac{8}{35}$. **B**
Ⓐ $1\frac{3}{5}$ Ⓑ $2\frac{2}{5}$ Ⓒ 7   Ⓓ 12

18. Which drawing shows a rotation of the face below? **G**

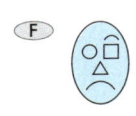

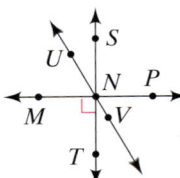

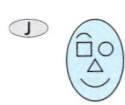

19. Which decimal is equivalent to $\frac{3}{8}$? **B**
Ⓐ 0.037   Ⓑ 0.375   Ⓒ 0.38   Ⓓ 3.75

20. Solve $-9 + w < 12$. **H**
F $w < -21$ H $w < 21$
G $w > -21$ J $w > 21$

21. What is 4.3 in words? **D**
Ⓐ four and thirteen hundredths
Ⓑ four hundred and three
Ⓒ forty-three
Ⓓ four and three tenths

22. Which of the following is NOT true about the diagram below? **H**

F $\angle TNV$ is congruent to $\angle SNU$.
G $\angle SNP$ is a right angle.
H $\angle UNS$ is congruent to $\angle PNV$.
J $\overleftrightarrow{ST}$ is perpendicular to $\overrightarrow{NP}$.

---

23. Which set of numbers is ordered from least to greatest? **B**
Ⓐ $\frac{1}{2}, \frac{3}{4}, \frac{2}{3}, \frac{4}{5}, \frac{9}{10}$ Ⓒ $\frac{1}{3}, \frac{1}{2}, \frac{2}{3}, \frac{9}{10}, \frac{4}{5}$
Ⓑ $\frac{1}{2}, \frac{2}{3}, \frac{3}{4}, \frac{4}{5}, \frac{9}{10}$ Ⓓ $\frac{1}{4}, \frac{3}{10}, \frac{8}{5}, \frac{1}{2}, \frac{2}{3}$

Gridded Response
Record your answer in a grid.

24. A bag contains 1 red marble, 1 yellow marble, and 1 green marble. Your friend chooses the yellow marble. Your turn is next. If the yellow marble is *not* replaced in the bag, find the probability that you will choose the red marble. $\frac{1}{2}$

25. Out of a sample of 125 CDs, 9 were found to have scratches. In a shipment of 5,000 CDs, how many would you predict will have scratches? **360**

26. Find the surface area in square feet of the figure. **108**

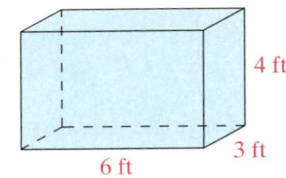

27. The probability of losing a particular game is 55%. Suppose you play this game 20 times. How many times would you expect to win the game? **9**

28. Solve the equation $4j - 8 = 12$ for j. **5**

29. Write 5.6×10^3 in standard form. **5,600**

30. Simplify the expression $(16 - 8) \times 2 + (10 \div 100)$. **16.1**

31. Evaluate the expression $j \div 10 + 8.3$ for $j = 11$. **9.4**

32. Simplify the expression $3 \times 8 - 4 + 5$. **25**

Item	33	34	35	36	37	38	39	40	41	42	43	44	45	46	47
Lesson	1-4	Deleted	12-2	12-4	Deleted	8-6	7-7	5-7	12-1	12-3	4-3	7-5	Deleted	2-2 & 2-1	9-3

Item	48	49	50
Lesson	9-8 & 9-9	7-9	10-1 & 10-2

[1] correct prime factorization but no factor tree shown

Short Response 33–41. See margin.

33. No more than 12 students volunteered to work at the local food pantry.
 a. Write an inequality for this situation.
 b. Graph the solution on a number line.

34. a. Find $\sqrt{19}$.
 b. Is $\sqrt{19}$ a rational number?

35. The triangles below are congruent. Write two congruences involving corresponding parts of the triangles.

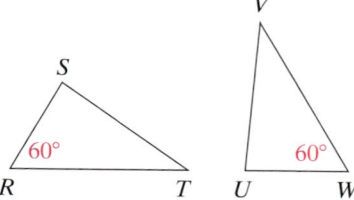

36. Write and then use an equation to find 43% of 87.

37. Sam works at a book store. When he punched in, the time clock read 3:15 P.M. When he punched out, the time clock read 7:45 P.M. He took a 15-minute break. How long did he work?

38. Solve $\frac{b}{2} + 5 = 4$.

39. Solve $n + 9 \geq 17$.

40. Find the prime factorization of 98 by using a factor tree.

41. A map with the scale 5 inches : 325 miles shows two landmarks that are 2 inches apart. How many miles apart are the landmarks?

Extended Response 42–46. See margin.

42. The sum of a number t and 7 is greater than 20.
 a. Write an inequality for this situation.
 b. Solve the inequality.
 c. Graph the solution on a number line.

43. A rectangle measures 5 inches by 7 inches.
 a. What is the area of the rectangle?
 b. A 1 inch-by-1 inch square is cut from each corner of the rectangle. What is the area of the new figure? Explain.

44. An open box is made by folding the sides of the net below.

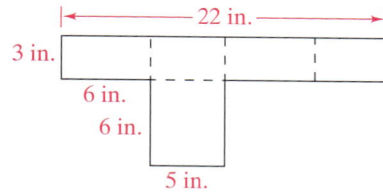

 a. Find the surface area of the open box.
 b. Now find the volume of the box.

45. The cost of your dinner is $18.64. You want to leave a 15% tip for the server.
 a. How much is the tip?
 b. What is the total cost of dinner, excluding any tax?

46. A store sells socks in two colors (gray or white), three sizes (small, medium, or large), and two fabrics (cotton or wool).
 a. Make a tree diagram to find the number of sock choices.
 b. If the store has one of every type of sock, what is the probability you will choose a wool sock at random?

41. [2] 130 mi; by an appropriate method such as cross multiplication:
$\frac{5}{325} = \frac{2}{x}$, $5x = 2 \times 325$, $5x = 650$, $x = 130$

[1] incorrect method OR incorrect solution

42. [4] $3c \geq 1.83$ (OR an equivalent inequality); $c \geq 0.61$; $3c \geq 1.83$, $3c \div 3 \geq 1.83 \div 3$, $c \geq 0.61$

 a. ← + + + ●———+——+——→
            0.61

[3] appropriate methods, one computational error
[2] incorrect solution, correct graph
[1] correct inequality OR solution OR graph, without work shown

43. [4] a. 35 in.²; $5 \times 7 = 35$
 b. 31 in.²; the area of each square is $1 \times 1 = 1$, or 1 in.². Total area is $1 + 1 + 1 + 1 = 4$, or 4 in.². $35 - 4 = 31$, or 31 in.².

[3] correct methods, one computational error
[2] incorrect rectangular area OR area of 2nd figure
[1] one correct solution no explanation

44. [4] a. 96 in.²; by an appropriate method such as: $(3 \times 22) + (6 \times 5) = 66 + 30 = 96$
 b. 90 in.³; $3 \times 6 \times 5 = 90$

[3] appropriate methods, one computational error
[2] surface area correct OR volume correct
[1] correct surface area OR volume, without work shown

45. [4] a. $2.80; $18.64 \times 0.15 = 2.796 \approx 2.80$
 c. $21.44; $18.64 + 2.80 = 21.44$

[3] correct methods, one computational error
[2] 2 out of 3 correct OR correct tax, tip and total no work shown
[1] correct tax OR tip OR total, no work shown

46. [4] a.

 b. $\frac{1}{2}$

[3] correct tree diagram, but incorrect part (b)
[2] incorrect diagram, but correct probability according to tree
[1] correct probability with no tree diagram

Applying Equations

Students will use data from these two pages to answer the questions posed in Put It All Together.

Invite students to explore how choices about what they eat affect how much money they spend for lunch. Ask questions such as:

- *If you bring your lunch and a drink from home, how much money do you spend in the cafeteria that day?* None.

- *How much does a school lunch cost?* Answers will vary.

- *If you bought a new lunch box and bring your lunch every day of a 180-day school year, how much does the lunch box cost per day?* The cost of the lunch box divided by 180.

- *If you bring your lunch in a new paper bag every day, how much do you spend on bags for the year?* The cost of a bag multiplied by 180.

Discuss how a lunch box is an expensive one-time purchase, but it can prove to be cheaper than using a new bag every day.

Materials
- A lunch box with the price tag
- A package of paper bags with the price tag on it

Activating Prior Knowledge

Have students share what they know about different kinds of lighting, including the nature of the light each emits, how long each lasts, and the costs.

Guided Instruction

Have volunteers read aloud. Ask:
- *What are some wattages for incandescent bulbs you use at home?* Sample: 25-, 60-, 75-, 100-, and 150-watt bulbs.
- *Does the higher wattage bulb use more or less energy?* More.
- *How does a fluorescent bulb compare to an incandescent bulb?* The fluorescent bulb will use less energy per hour and will last longer.

604

Applying Equations

A Bright Idea Suppose you are changing the light bulbs in your bedroom. Regular (incandescent) light bulbs provide light, but they also get warm. Fluorescent light bulbs stay cool because they convert more energy into light. They cost more than regular bulbs, but they're cheaper to run. Should you replace your regular bulbs with fluorescent bulbs?

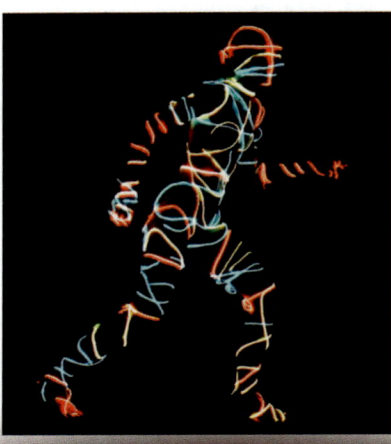

Neon Light
Colored glass tubes filled with neon gas glow when an electrical charge moves through the gas.

Fireflies
Fireflies, or lightning bugs, make light inside their bodies. The light can be any color from pale yellow to reddish green.

604

1. $14.00

2a. incandescent light bulb: 1,000 watts
    fluorescent light bulb: 320 watts

b. incandescent light bulb: 1 kilowatt-hour

fluorescent light bulb: 0.32 kilowatt-hour

c. $.15/$.05

3a. incandescent light bulb life: 1,000 hours;
    $365 \times 10 = 3,650$ hours/year
    $3,650 \div 1,000 = 3.65$.

You will use about 4 light bulbs.
fluorescent light bulb life: 10,000 hours;
$365 \times 10 = 3,650$ hours/year
$3,650 < 10,000$. You will need only one light bulb.

Go Online

PHSchool.com

For: Information about energy use
Web Code: aqe-1253

Incandescent light bulb
Cost: $1.80
Power: 100 watts per hour
Duration: 1,000 hours

Electricity costs $.15 per kilowatt-hour.

Fiber-Optic Light

Each hair-thin optical fiber has two layers of glass. Light travels from one end of the fiber to the other by bouncing along the sides of the fiber. A transparent colored disc between the light bulb and the fibers gives the fibers their color.

Fluorescent light bulb
Cost: $15.80
Power: 32 watts per hour
Duration: 10,000 hours

Put It All Together

1. How much more does a fluorescent light bulb cost than an incandescent light bulb?

2. **a.** How much power does each bulb use in 10 hours?
   b. Divide your answers to part (a) by 1,000 to find the number of kilowatt-hours each bulb uses in 10 hours.
   c. What is the cost of electricity for each bulb for 10 hours of use? Round your answer to the nearest cent.

3. Suppose the light is on for 10 hours each day.
   a. How many of each type of bulb would you use in one year? (*Hint:* 1 year = 365 days)
   b. How much would one year's supply of each type of bulb cost?
   c. What is the cost of electricity for each type of bulb for one year? Round your answer to the nearest cent.
   d. Calculate your total cost for each type of bulb for one year.

4. **Writing in Math**  Which type of light bulb would you recommend to a friend? Explain.

Activity

Help students work in pairs to answer the questions.

Exercise 1 Students may think the fluorescent bulb gives less light than the incandescent bulb based on its wattage, only 32 watts compared to 100 watts. Inform students that watts measure electrical power going into the bulb, whereas the brightness of the light produced by a lamp is measured in *lumens*. Guide students to see that although it may appear otherwise, the two lights are comparable in the amount of light they provide.

Exercise 4 Ask students to tell whether limited use of the bulb, say only 5 hours per day, would affect their recommendation. Have them explain their reasoning.

Science Connection

Many students are likely to be familiar with another kind of electric light—a halogen light. Ask students to find out how a halogen bulb differs from both fluorescent and incandescent bulbs. In addition, challenge students to find out what an "electric flowerpot" is and what we call it today. **It was a light for plants invented in the 1890s; now we call it a flashlight.**

Differentiated Instruction

Special Needs   L1
Help students distinguish between some of the terms that appear in the Activity: *fluorescent* and *incandescent; light* and *bulb; watt* and *kilowatt*.

---

b. incandescent light bulb:
4 × $1.80 = $7.20
fluorescent light bulb:
1 × $15.80 = $15.80

c. incandescent light bulb:
$.15 × 365 = $54.75;

fluorescent light bulb:
$.05 × 365 = $18.25

d. incandescent light bulb:
$7.20 + $54.75 = $61.95;
fluorescent light bulb:
$15.80 + $18.25 = $34.05

4. Check students' work.

Celebration

Students apply their number sense and common sense to plan a celebration.

Resources

All in One Teaching Resources
- Chapter 1 Project Support

Guided Instruction

Activating Prior Knowledge
Have students share experiences planning parties. Then ask:
- *What things will you consider to help you plan your celebration?*
Sample: how many guests; what foods, entertainment, and decorations to have; what these things cost; how many people will share the cost

Careers
Event planning and fundraising are careers that might interest students. Discuss what skills these careers require.

On Your Own Time

Students apply their knowledge of data collection and graphing to conduct a survey and present their results.

Resources

All in One Teaching Resources
- Chapter 2 Project Support

Guided Instruction

Activating Prior Knowledge
Discuss the different graphs and the kinds of data each displays. Then ask:
- *Which graph would be appropriate to show students' findings?* **Sample: bar graphs**

Careers
Have students list jobs in which gathering, organizing, displaying, and interpreting data play a key role. **Sample: marketing director, baseball manager**

606

Suppose your class is planning to honor someone special in the community or to congratulate a winning team. You need to decide when and where you will hold the event, how you will decorate, and what entertainment and refreshments you will provide. You may also need to decide how to raise funds for the celebration.

Chapter 1 *Whole Numbers and Decimals*

Plan a Celebration Your chapter project is to plan a celebration. You must decide how much it will cost and how much money each member of the class must raise. Your plan should include a list of supplies for the event and their costs.

Go Online PHSchool.com
For: Information to help you complete your project
Web Code: aqd-0161

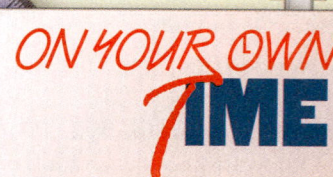

RING!!! The last bell of the day has rung. You and your classmates will soon head in different directions. Some of your classmates are on the same team or in the same club as you. Some of them are not. Do you know how much time your classmates spend on their favorite activities? You could guess the answers to the last question, but a more accurate method of finding the answers would be to collect real data.

Chapter 2 *Data and Graphs*

Conduct a Survey For this chapter project, you will survey 25 of your friends and classmates. You can choose the survey subject, such as how much time your classmates spend on sports. You will organize and graph the data. Then you will present your findings to your class.

Go Online PHSchool.com
For: Information to help you complete your project
Web Code: aqd-0261

STEPPING STONES

Think about a historic building, such as one of the ancient pyramids or the Eiffel Tower. How many pieces of stone do you think were needed for the bottom of a pyramid compared to the top? Many buildings use mathematical patterns in their designs.

Chapter 3 Patterns and Variables

Building a Fort For this project, you will build a model of a simple fort. You will record the amounts of materials needed for each course, or layer of blocks. You will look for patterns and write equations to describe the patterns.

Go Online
PHSchool.com

For: Information to help you complete your project
Web Code: aqd-0361

HOME COURT ADVANTAGE

In Malcolm's daydream, he floats in the air on his way to a slam dunk. In reality, he tosses pieces of paper into a wastebasket. He makes some shots, and he misses others.

Chapter 4 Number Theory and Fractions

Compare Basketball Statistics Your project will be to record and compare baskets attempted and baskets made by the players on your own imaginary basketball team. You can shoot baskets with a real basketball on a real court, or you can toss pieces of paper into a wastebasket.

Go Online
PHSchool.com

For: Information to help you complete your project
Web Code: aqd-0461

Chapter Projects **607**

Stepping Stones

Students apply their knowledge of geometrical patterns to construct a model of a fort.

Resources

All in One Teaching Resources
• Chapter 3 Project Support

Guided Instruction

Activating Prior Knowledge
Discuss the kinds of patterns that might emerge when students build their forts. Ask:
• *How will you record the patterns?* **Sample: using tables**

Social Studies Connection
Invite volunteers to research the architecture of the Maya and compare Mayan structures with those of the Egyptians or Greeks.

Home Court Advantage

Students apply their knowledge of comparing fractions to making a basket in basketball.

Resources

All in One Teaching Resources
• Chapter 4 Project Support

Guided Instruction

Activating Prior Knowledge
Initiate a discussion on free-throw statistics. Ask:
• *How can you tell if your "shooting" improves over time?* **Sample: Shoot in regular sets of 5 or 10; record your results as fractions and compare them.**

Physical Education Connection
Have students discuss free-throw statistics for both men and women pro players.

Seeing is Believing

Students apply their knowledge of adding fractions to prove that an adding technique works.

Resources

All in One Teaching Resources
- Chapter 5 Project Support

Guided Instruction

Activating Prior Knowledge
Discuss the idea of carefully designing an experiment and recording the results. Then ask:
- *How can you use models to add fractions with different denominators?* **Sample: use fraction models that demonstrate renaming**

Inclusion
Discuss and demonstrate that "renaming" a fraction as an equivalent fraction with a different denominator does not change the value of that fraction.

Crack It and Cook It

Students apply their knowledge of multiplying fractions and mixed numbers to adjust a recipe.

Resources

All in One Teaching Resources
- Chapter 6 Project Support

Guided Instruction

Activating Prior Knowledge
Discuss how cooks adjust the amounts of ingredients in recipes to feed different numbers of diners. Ask:
- *How would you have to adjust the amounts of the ingredients of a dish that serves 4 in order to serve 12?* **multiply the quantity of each ingredient by 3**

Careers
Discuss mathematical skills that a chef might need. For example, estimating cooking time, amounts of ingredients; working with cost amounts, percents, and so on.

608

SEEing is Believing

Chapter 5 *Adding and Subtracting Fractions*

Have you ever conducted a science experiment? Scientists perform experiments to determine whether an idea is correct or incorrect. You can determine whether something is correct or not in math class, too.

Design a Demonstration You will learn ways to add fractions and mixed numbers with unlike denominators, but can you show that these techniques really work? Your goal is to show that they do by giving several demonstrations.

Go Online
PHSchool.com
For: Information to help you complete your project
Web Code: aqd-0561

CRACK IT and Cook It!

Chapter 6 *Multiplying and Dividing Fractions*

Eating a hearty breakfast is a great way to start any day! You are probably familiar with pouring a bowl of cereal, making toast, or maybe even scrambling eggs. But have you ever made an omelet? An omelet recipe can be simple—eggs, water, and maybe some salt or pepper. However, you can add other ingredients to this basic recipe to suit your taste. A cheese omelet is delicious. So is a bacon-and-tomato omelet. You might also add mushrooms, onions, and peppers.

Create a Recipe Put on your chef's hat. In this chapter project, you will write and name your own recipe for an omelet. Your final project will be a recipe that can feed everyone in your class.

Go Online
PHSchool.com
For: Information to help you complete your project
Web Code: aqd-0661

Planet of the Stars

When you look up at the stars in the sky, you may not think about how far away they are. Stars appear a lot closer than they really are. The same is true of planets. The huge distances between planets make it impossible for books to show how vast our solar system really is.

Chapter 7 *Ratios, Proportions, and Percents*

Make a Scale Model In this chapter project, you will make scale models of two planets. You will compare their sizes and distances from the sun and calculate the ratios involved in your scale model.

Go Online
PHSchool.com

For: Information to help you complete your project
Web Code: aqd-0761

Chapter Projects

Puzzling Pictures

Chapter 8 *Tools of Geometry*

Do you remember putting together simple puzzles when you were younger? Puzzles designed for young children are often made of wood and have large pieces. Many of the pieces have corners or straight sides so that a child can put the puzzle together easily.

Create a Puzzle Think about one of your favorite pictures. How would it look as a puzzle? Your project is to make an attractive but challenging puzzle for your classmates. Include as many geometric shapes as you can.

Go Online
PHSchool.com

For: Information to help you complete your project
Web Code: aqd-0861

Chapter Projects

Planet of the Stars

Students apply their knowledge of ratios to make scale models of two planets.

Resources

All in One Teaching Resources
- Chapter 7 Project Support

Guided Instruction

Activating Prior Knowledge
Talk about models of the solar system that students have seen in planetariums or museums. Ask:
- *How do you think the builders of these models chose the scale to use?* Sample: the size of the space available or the size they want the models to be.

Puzzling Pictures

Students apply their knowledge of geometric shapes to make a puzzle.

Resources

All in One Teaching Resources
- Chapter 8 Project Support

Guided Instruction

Activating Prior Knowledge
Discuss how solving jigsaw puzzles can help make one. Ask:
- *What math concepts can help you make your puzzle?* Sample: congruent and similar figures, slides, flips, turns, tessellations

Inclusion
Have students begin by dividing their puzzle into rectangles. They can then sub-divide the rectangles into other, smaller shapes.

Go Fish

Students apply their knowledge of geometry and measurement to design a class aquarium.

Resources

All in One Teaching Resources
- Chapter 9 Project Support

Guided Instruction

Activating Prior Knowledge
Invite students to share their experiences setting up and caring for a fish tank. Ask:
- *What considerations must you keep in mind when planning your proposed aquarium?*
Sample: number of fish desired, what plants and objects you want

Science Connection
Have students visit a pet store to learn more about aquariums and differences types of fish.

Now Playing

Students apply their understanding of probability to design a fair way to choose among three movies.

Resources

All in One Teaching Resources
- Chapter 10 Project Support

Guided Instruction

Activating Prior Knowledge
Discuss the idea of equally likely outcomes with students. Ask:
- *How could you use a six-sided number cube to give each of the three movies the same chance of being chosen?* **Sample: Assign 1–2 for one movie, 3–4 for another, and 5–6 for the third.**

Physical Education Connection
Have students talk about how the idea of equal outcomes applies in the sports world.

610

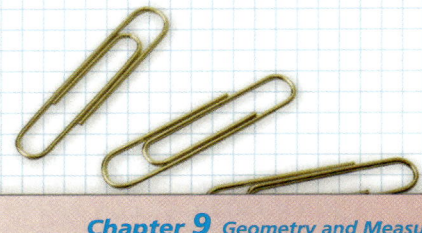

Have you ever spent time gazing into an aquarium full of fish? You can get lost in thought as you watch the fish through the glass. Many people enjoy having an aquarium because they feel peaceful while observing nature in this miniature environment.

Chapter 9 *Geometry and Measurement*

Design an Aquarium In this chapter project, you will design an aquarium for your classroom. You should consider how many fish you want in the aquarium. Also consider the size of each type of fish that you plan to place in the aquarium. As part of your final project, you will create a drawing of your proposed aquarium.

Go Online
PHSchool.com
For: Information to help you complete your project
Web Code: aqd-0961

Chapter 10 *Exploring Probability*

Suppose you and a friend have to choose among three movies, and you can't make up your minds. Should you flip a coin? You'd probably agree that assigning heads to one movie, tails to the second, and "lands on edge" to the third would not give the third movie much of a chance. What should you do?

Design a Three-Choice System Your project will be to design a device or system that is fair for three different outcomes. You will test your system to make sure each outcome can be expected one third of the time over a large number of trials.

Go Online
PHSchool.com
For: Information to help you complete your project
Web Code: aqd-1061

The TIME of your life

Chapter 11 Integers

Do you know an older person who has lived an interesting life? That person could probably tell you many stories about his or her life. You can tell stories about your life, too. You may not have lived as long, but there have been important events in your past, and there will be others in your future.

Draw a Timeline Your project will be to build a timeline of your life—past, present, and future. Think about the timelines you have seen in your social studies classes. You will have a chance to apply math concepts such as ratios, measurements, scale drawings, and integers.

Go Online
PHSchool.com

For: Information to help you complete your project
Web Code: aqd-1161

WORKING for a Cause

Chapter 12 Equations and Inequalities

Have you ever participated in a fundraiser? Schools and sports clubs often use fundraisers as a way to pay for such things as equipment, trips, and camps. You have probably purchased candy bars, magazines, or wrapping paper to help a friend or group raise money.

Plan a Fundraiser In this chapter project, you will plan a fundraiser. You will choose a cause or charity, decide how much money you would like to raise, and determine the type of event to hold or the type of product to sell. As part of your final project, you will present a fundraising plan to your class.

Go Online
PHSchool.com

For: Information to help you complete your project
Web Code: aqd-1261

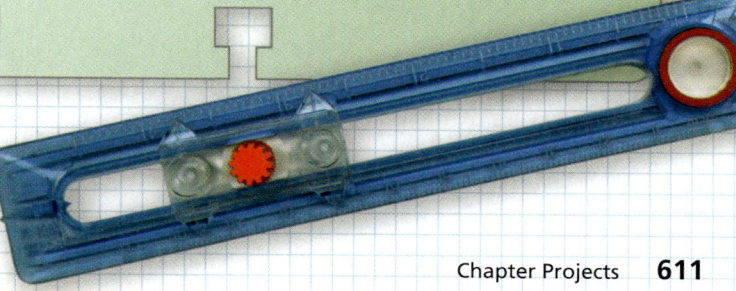

Chapter Projects **611**

The Time of Your Life

Students apply their knowledge of measurement to create time lines that show key events in their lives.

Resources

All in One Teaching Resources
• Chapter 11 Project Support

Guided Instruction

Activating Prior Knowledge
Have students discuss what kinds of events belong on a time line of their lives. Then ask:
• *What might be your first step in setting up a time line of your life?* **Sample: choose time intervals**

Diversity
Have students who are not comfortable displaying personal data make a time line for a day in a pet's life.

Working for a Cause

Students apply their knowledge of operations with money to come up with a fundraising plan.

Resources

All in One Teaching Resources
• Chapter 12 Project Support

Guided Instruction

Activating Prior Knowledge
Discuss fundraising by focusing on who does it and how they do it. Invite students to share their experiences raising money. Ask:
• *What must you consider when you plan how to raise money for a charity?* **Sample: how much money is needed, where to find interested contributors, how to motivate them to contribute, how to keep track of and safeguard the money**

CHAPTER 1 Extra Practice

Skills

● **Lesson 1-1 and Lesson 1-2**   Write each number in words.

1. 854　　　　2. 10,059　　　　3. 7,302　　　　4. 1,205,807

5. 0.26　　　　6. 0.3481　　　　7. 72.053　　　　8. 691.4

Use rounding, front-end estimation, or compatible numbers to estimate each answer.

9. 5.32×2.01　　　10. $15.348 - 7.92$　　　11. $22.961 \div 3.6$　　　12. $728.6 + 36.09$

● **Lesson 1-3**   Tell whether each equation is true or false.

13. $65 = 10 + 65$　　14. $8 \times 0 = 8$　　15. $1 \times 9.8 = 9.8$　　16. $4 + 5 + 7 = 4 + 11$

● **Lesson 1-4**   Find the value of each expression.

17. $2 + 6 \times 3 + 1$　　18. $(14 + 44) \div 2$　　19. $3 + 64 \div 4 - 10$　　20. $144 + 56 \div 4$

● **Lesson 1-5**   Write each number in standard form.

21. two hundred sixteen　　　　　　　22. two hundred twenty-two thousandths

● **Lesson 1-6**   Order each set of decimals from least to greatest.

23. 0.2, 0.4, 0.7　　　　24. 0.2, 0.02, 0.202, 0.002　　　25. 6.25, 6.05, 6.2, 6.025

● **Lesson 1-7**   First estimate and then find each sum or difference.

26. $1.14 + 9.3$　　　27. $3.541 + 1.333$　　　28. $5.45 - 2.8$　　　29. $4.11 - 2.621$

● **Lesson 1-8**   Find each product.

30. 1.8×4.302　　31. $0.29(0.43)$　　32. $7.4(930)$　　33. $0.617 \cdot 0.09$

● **Lesson 1-9**   Find each quotient.

34. $8 \div 9$　　　35. $23 \div 25$　　　36. $348 \div 60$　　　37. $11 \div 16$

34. $0.\overline{8}$

35. 0.92

36. 5.8

37. 0.6875

38. 295,734,134;
    1,080,264,580;
    1,306,313,812

39. about $3

40. 56

41. $496

42. 2.56

43. 0.23, 0.35, 0.74, 0.8, 1.5

44. $47.99

45. $50

46. 4.24 gal

Extra Skills and Word Problems

Word Problems

● Lesson 1-1

38. **Social Studies** Order the populations in the table at the right from least to greatest.

Population

India	1,080,264,588
China	1,306,313,812
United States	295,734,134

Source: U.S. Census Bureau, 2005

● Lesson 1-2

39. You spend $546 on school lunches for the school year. There are about 180 days of school in the school year. About how much do you spend on lunch each day?

● Lessons 1-3 and 1-4

40. **Music** What is the total number of instruments in the orchestra shown in the table at the right?

Orchestra

Instrument	Number
Violin	29
Viola	13
Bass	2
Cello	12

41. A group of 28 students and 3 teachers goes to the theater. Each student pays $12. The school pays an additional $4 per student and $16 per adult. Find the total cost of the trip.

● Lesson 1-5

42. **Currency** The rupee and the paisa are units of money in India. One paisa is equal to $\frac{1}{100}$ of an Indian rupee. Using decimals, write 256 paisas as a number of rupees.

● Lesson 1-6

43. **Animals** The table shows typical weights regularly reached by some adult animals. Order the animals by weight from least to greatest.

Animal	Weight (tons)
American bison	1.5
Anaconda	0.23
Gorilla	0.35
Kodiak bear	0.74
Leatherback turtle	0.8

● Lesson 1-7

44. At a bicycle store, an 18-speed bicycle costs $174.99. At another store, the same bicycle costs $222.98. What is the difference in prices?

● Lessons 1-8 and 1-9

45. **Money** There are 40 coins in a roll of nickels. Find the value of 25 rolls of nickels.

46. Regular unleaded gasoline costs $2.359 per gallon. You spend $10 on gasoline. About how many gallons do you buy?

Chapter 1 Extra Practice **613**

Left margin answers

CHAPTER 2

1. 32.25

2. 264.6

3. 9.56

4. median: 22.5
   mode: 22

5. median: 12.5
   mode: none

6. median: 43.5
   mode: 29

7.
Books Read	Tally	Frequency
1	III	3
2	III	3
3	II	2
4	IIII	4

```
                  X
                  X
X     X           X
X     X     X     X
X     X     X     X
1     2     3     4
```

8.
wpm	Tally	Frequency
35	IIII	4
40	III	3
45		0
50		0
55	II	2
60		0
65	II	2
70	I	1

```
X
X     X
X     X           X           X
X     X     X     X     X
X     X     X     X     X     X
35  40  45  50  55  60  65  70
```

9. hours of reading per year per person and type of print medium read

10. about 100 hours

11a. 39

b. The United States received 39 silver medals during the 2004 Summer Olympics.

12. E2 = B2 + C2 + D2

614

Main content

Skills

● **Lesson 2-1** Find the mean of each data set.

1. 35, 39, 27, 28
2. 253, 277, 249, 279, 265
3. 7.5, 3.8, 12.4, 11.7, 12.4

● **Lesson 2-2** Find the median and mode of each data set.

4. 23, 26, 22, 25, 22, 28, 22, 10
5. 14.2, 11.3, 12.0, 11.1, 13.0, 13.3
6. 36, 42, 58, 29, 45, 63, 57, 29

● **Lesson 2-3** Make a frequency table and a line plot for each set of data.

7. books read each month:
   3, 1, 4, 2, 4, 1, 3, 2, 4, 4, 2, 1

8. words typed per minute:
   65, 35, 40, 65, 40, 40, 55, 35, 35, 70, 35, 55

● **Lesson 2-4** Use the bar graph for Exercises 9–10.

9. What information is given on each axis?

10. What is the average yearly reading time for books?

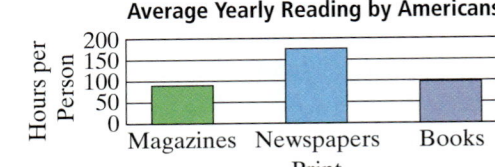

Average Yearly Reading by Americans

● **Lesson 2-5** The spreadsheet below shows the number of medals the United States won during the 2004 Summer Olympics.

11. a. What is the value in C2?
    b. What does this number mean?

12. Write the formula for cell E2.

	A	B	C	D	E
1	Country	Gold	Silver	Bronze	Total
2	United States	35	39	29	■

● **Lesson 2-6** Make a stem-and-leaf plot and a box-and whisker plot for the set of data below.

13. test scores (percents): 86, 76, 72, 85, 69, 85, 78, 91, 77

● **Lesson 2-7** Use the line graph at the right.

14. Explain why the graph is misleading.

15. Use the data to draw a graph that is not misleading.

Daily Total Sales

13.
```
6 | 9
7 | 2 6 7 8
8 | 5 5 6
9 | 1
```
Key: 6 | 9 means 69%

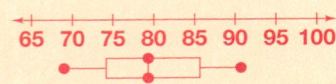

14. The vertical scale does not start at 0.

Lessons 2-1 and 2-2

16. Biology The weights, in pounds, of 5 adult coyotes are 36, 25, 28, 39, and 30. What is the mean weight of the adult coyotes?

17. Weather The daily high temperatures (°F) for one week are 86°, 78°, 92°, 79°, 87°, 77°, and 91°. Find the median and the mode of the high temperatures.

Lesson 2-3

18. The frequency table at the right shows the number of correct answers each student wrote on a 24-question quiz. What is the range of the number of correct answers?

Number	Tally	Frequency
15	I	1
17	I	1
18	I	1
19	II	2
20	IIII	4
21	II	2
22	II	2
24	I	1

Lesson 2-4

19. Language Make a bar graph showing how many different languages are spoken in each country. Use the table.

Languages

Country	Number of Languages
Bolivia	36
Brazil	188
Colombia	80
Mexico	291
Venezuela	40

SOURCE: *Ethnologue: Languages of the World*

Lesson 2-5

20. Write a formula to find the mean score in cell G4 below.

Calories

	A	B	C	D	E	F	G	
1	Day	Breakfast	Lunch	Dinner	Snacks	Total	Mean	
2	Monday	550	730	920	200			
3	Tuesday	420	660	750	600			
4	Wednesday	250	880	1200	120			

Lesson 2-6

21. Animals Make a stem-and-leaf plot for the data in the table at the right showing the speeds of animals.

Animal Speeds

Animal	Miles per hour
Coyote	43
Hyena	40
Rabbit	35
Giraffe	32
Grizzly bear	30
Elephant	25

SOURCE: *World Almanac*

Lesson 2-7

22. Track and Field In successive track meets, Andre jumps the following distances.
11 ft 5 in.   11 ft 8 in.   12 ft 1 in.   11 ft 10 in.   12 ft 1 in.
Draw a line graph that appears to show Andre's jumps varying widely. Explain why the graph is misleading.

15.

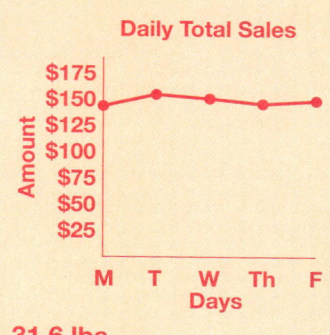

Daily Total Sales

16. 31.6 lbs

17. 86; none

18. 9

19.

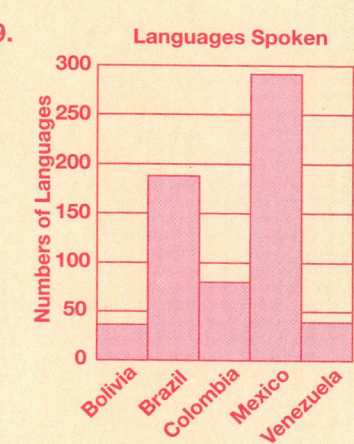

Languages Spoken

20. *F4* ÷ 4

21. **Animal Speeds (mph)**

```
2 | 5
3 | 0 2 5
4 | 0 3
```

Key: 2 | 5 means 25 mph

22. Answers may vary. Sample: The graph is misleading because the vertical scale uses unequal intervals.

1. 256; 1,024; 4,096; the first term is 1. Multiply each term by 4.

2. 162; 486; 1,458; the first term is 2. Multiply each term by 3.

3. 23, 27, 31; the first term is 7. Add 4 to each term.

4. 56, 50, 44; the first term is 80. Subtract 6 from each term.

5. 2

6. 22

7. 4

8. 6

9. $b - 1$

10. $2p$

11. $b + 4$

12. $n \div 2$

13. 2

14. 8

15. 0

16. 6.3

17. 19

18. 34

19. 9

20. 17.8

21. 3.7

22. 4

23. 9.7

24. 8.6

25. 40

26. 31

27. 12.5

28. 7

29. 546

30. 57

Extra Practice

Skills

● **Lesson 3-1**   Write the next three terms and write a rule for each pattern.

1. $1, 4, 16, 64, \ldots$
2. $2, 6, 18, 54, \ldots$
3. $7, 11, 15, 19, \ldots$
4. $80, 74, 68, 62, \ldots$

● **Lesson 3-2**   Evaluate each expression for $n = 9$.

5. $n - 7$
6. $3n - 5$
7. $22 - 2n$
8. $4n \div 6$

● **Lesson 3-3**   Write an expression for each word phrase.

9. 1 less than b
10. p times 2
11. 4 more than b
12. n divided by 2

● **Lesson 3-4**   Use mental math to solve each problem.

13. $x + 6 = 8$
14. $5x = 40$
15. $36 = 36 - x$
16. $x + 2 = 8.3$

Use mental math to solve each equation.

17. $20 = y + 1$
18. $t - 10 = 24$
19. $a \div 3 = 3$
20. $178 = 10b$

● **Lessons 3-5 and 3-6**   Solve each equation. Then check the solution.

21. $b + 4 = 7.7$
22. $c + 3.5 = 7.5$
23. $n - 1.7 = 8$
24. $8.4 = s - 0.2$

● **Lesson 3-7**   Solve each equation.

25. $15t = 600$
26. $62 = 2b$
27. $x \div 5 = 2.5$
28. $a \div 0.05 = 140$

● **Lesson 3-8**   Use the Distributive Property to simplify each expression.

29. 7×78
30. 3×19
31. 6×66
32. 4×47

Word Problems

● **Lesson 3-1**

33. **Trains** The schedule shows the departure times for the Red and Blue Trains. Predict the remaining departure times before 6 P.M. for each train.

Departures

Red Train	Blue Train
12:51 P.M.	12:17 P.M.
1:51 P.M.	1:02 P.M.
2:51 P.M.	1:47 P.M.
3:51 P.M.	2:32 P.M.

Lesson 3-2

34. A company selling T-shirts charges $45 to create a design it will print on shirts. Each T-shirt costs $3. You can use the expression $3x + 45$ to find the cost of an order, where x stands for the number of T-shirts. How much does it cost to order 350 T-shirts?

Lesson 3-3

35. Boating A paddleboat rents for $10 plus $8 per hour. How much does it cost to rent a paddleboat for h hours? Draw a model and write an expression for the situation.

Lesson 3-4

36. Sports A hockey team spends $75 on chin straps. Each strap costs $5. Solve the equation $5n = 75$ to find how many straps the team buys.

Lesson 3-5

37. Biology The height of the female giraffe in a zoo is 14.1 feet. The female is 3.2 feet shorter than the male giraffe. Write and solve an equation to find the male's height.

Lesson 3-6

38. In a class of 26 students, 15 students have birthdays in the first half of the year. Write and solve an equation to find how many students have birthdays in the last half of the year.

Lesson 3-7

39. Geography The area of the Pacific Ocean is about 64,000,000 square miles. This area is about twice the area of the Atlantic Ocean. Find the approximate area of the Atlantic Ocean.

Lesson 3-8

40. Your family buys carpeting for the two rooms shown at the right. Write an expression for the total square feet of carpet that your family buys.

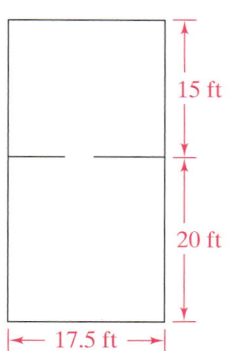

15 ft

20 ft

|← 17.5 ft →|

CHAPTER 4 Extra Practice

Skills

● **Lesson 4-1** Test each number for divisibility by 2, 3, 5, 9, or 10.

1. 324   **2.** 2,685   **3.** 540   **4.** 114   **5.** 31   **6.** 981

● **Lesson 4-2** Simplify each expression.

7. $7 + 5^2$ **8.** $(6-2)^3 \times 3$ **9.** 8^3 **10.** $9^2 + 2^2$

● **Lesson 4-3** Tell whether each number is prime or composite.

11. 24   **12.** 49   **13.** 7   **14.** 81   **15.** 37   **16.** 29

● **Lesson 4-4** Find the GCF of each set of numbers.

17. 10, 30   **18.** 15, 18   **19.** 25, 35   **20.** 28, 36   **21.** 45, 72   **22.** 8, 12, 20

● **Lesson 4-5** Write each fraction in simplest form.

23. $\frac{6}{60}$ **24.** $\frac{3}{5}$ **25.** $\frac{27}{36}$ **26.** $\frac{40}{50}$ **27.** $\frac{3}{4}$ **28.** $\frac{42}{70}$

● **Lesson 4-6** Write each mixed number as an improper fraction. Write each improper fraction as a mixed number in simplest form.

29. $1\frac{7}{8}$ **30.** $2\frac{3}{5}$ **31.** $11\frac{1}{9}$ **32.** $\frac{25}{7}$ **33.** $\frac{39}{12}$ **34.** $\frac{12}{5}$

● **Lesson 4-7** Find the LCM of each set of numbers.

35. 4, 8   **36.** 6, 14   **37.** 15, 25   **38.** 20, 36   **39.** 3, 4, 12   **40.** 8, 10, 15

● **Lesson 4-8** Order each set of numbers from least to greatest.

41. $\frac{4}{7}, \frac{4}{5}, \frac{4}{9}$ **42.** $\frac{6}{16}, \frac{7}{16}, \frac{5}{16}$ **43.** $\frac{2}{3}, \frac{5}{6}, \frac{7}{12}$ **44.** $\frac{3}{4}, \frac{4}{6}, \frac{7}{9}$ **45.** $2\frac{3}{4}, 2\frac{1}{8}, 2\frac{1}{2}$ **46.** $\frac{5}{8}, \frac{3}{5}, \frac{9}{20}$

● **Lesson 4-9** Write each decimal as a fraction or mixed number in simplest form.

47. 1.25   **48.** 0.02   **49.** 0.32   **50.** 3.45   **51.** 0.175   **52.** 2.16

Write each fraction or mixed number as a decimal. Use a bar to indicate repeating digits.

53. $\frac{2}{3}$ **54.** $\frac{2}{5}$ **55.** $\frac{1}{4}$ **56.** $7\frac{5}{12}$ **57.** $4\frac{2}{3}$ **58.** $\frac{13}{8}$

Word Problems

Lesson 4-1

59. You and three friends eat lunch at a restaurant. The bill totals $18.21. Can you and your friends split the bill evenly? Explain.

Lessons 4-2 through 4-4

60. The table shows the number of rectangles you make each time you fold a piece of paper in half. After 6 folds, how many rectangles have you made? Write your answer using an exponent.

Number of Folds	Number of Rectangles
1	2
2	4
3	8
4	16

61. A photographer arranges 126 students for a class picture. Each row has the same number of students. What numbers of rows can he make?

62. On a field day, 84 girls and 78 boys are divided into teams. Each team has the same number of girls and the same number of boys. At most, how many teams are possible?

Lessons 4-5 and 4-6

63. A framer uses an inch ruler marked in sixteenths to measure the frame at the right. What is the measure of the height of the frame to the nearest sixteenth of an inch?

$32\frac{5}{8}$ in.

$\leftarrow$ 25 in. $\rightarrow$

64. A chef uses 2 slices of bread for each of 50 sandwiches. Each loaf of bread has 12 equal slices. Write a mixed number for the number of loaves of bread he uses to make sandwiches.

Lessons 4-7 and 4-8

65. Use the table. Find the least number of folders, stickers, and pens you can buy so that you have the same number of each.

Item	Number in Pack
Folders	6
Stickers	10
Pens	12

66. What mixed number is halfway between $1\frac{1}{8}$ and $1\frac{3}{8}$? Show your answer on a number line.

Lesson 4-9

67. Arrange the side lengths of the triangle in order from least to greatest. Explain your reasoning.

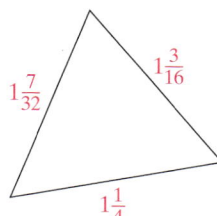

$1\frac{7}{32}$ $1\frac{3}{16}$ $1\frac{1}{4}$

39. 12

40. 120

41. $\frac{4}{9}, \frac{4}{7}, \frac{4}{5}$

42. $\frac{5}{16}, \frac{6}{16}, \frac{7}{16}$

43. $\frac{7}{12}, \frac{2}{3}, \frac{5}{6}$

44. $\frac{4}{6}, \frac{3}{4}, \frac{7}{9}$

45. $2\frac{1}{8}, 2\frac{1}{2}, 2\frac{3}{4}$

46. $\frac{9}{20}, \frac{3}{5}, \frac{5}{8}$

47. $1\frac{1}{4}$

48. $\frac{1}{50}$

49. $\frac{8}{25}$

50. $3\frac{9}{20}$

51. $\frac{7}{40}$

52. $2\frac{4}{25}$

53. $0.\overline{6}$

54. 0.4

55. 0.25

56. $7.41\overline{6}$

57. $4.\overline{6}$

58. 1.625

59. No; it is not possible to split a penny.

60. 2^6

61. 1, 2, 3, 6, 21, 42, 63, 126

62. 6

63. $32\frac{10}{16}$ in.

64. $8\frac{1}{3}$

65. 10, 6, 5

66. $1\frac{1}{4}$

67. $1\frac{3}{16}, 1\frac{7}{32}, 1\frac{1}{4}$; I used a common denominator of 32 to compare.

CHAPTER 5 Extra Practice

Skills

● **Lesson 5-1**

Estimate each sum or difference. Use the benchmarks 0, $\frac{1}{2}$, and 1.

1. $\frac{2}{3} + \frac{1}{8}$ 2. $\frac{3}{5} + \frac{4}{7}$ 3. $\frac{5}{6} - \frac{3}{8}$ 4. $\frac{3}{8} - \frac{5}{12}$

Estimate each sum or difference.

5. $12\frac{3}{4} - 7\frac{4}{9}$ 6. $5\frac{7}{9} + 9\frac{3}{5}$ 7. $2\frac{1}{3} - 1\frac{6}{7}$ 8. $6\frac{3}{10} + 4\frac{5}{8}$

● **Lessons 5-2 and 5-3**   Find each sum or difference.

9. $\frac{5}{8} + \frac{1}{8}$ 10. $\frac{4}{5} - \frac{2}{5}$ 11. $\frac{11}{12} + \frac{5}{12}$ 12. $\frac{7}{8} - \frac{3}{8}$

13. $\frac{5}{6} + \frac{2}{3}$ 14. $\frac{7}{8} - \frac{3}{4}$ 15. $\frac{3}{5} + \frac{5}{8}$ 16. $\frac{3}{8} - \frac{1}{12}$

● **Lesson 5-4**   Find each sum.

17. $6\frac{2}{3} + 1\frac{1}{2}$ 18. $5\frac{7}{8} + 1\frac{3}{4}$ 19. $8\frac{1}{4} + 3\frac{1}{3}$ 20. $7\frac{3}{10} + 3\frac{1}{4}$

● **Lesson 5-5**   Find each difference.

21. $7\frac{3}{8} - 1\frac{2}{3}$ 22. $11\frac{1}{6} - 2\frac{3}{4}$ 23. $7\frac{5}{6} - 2\frac{1}{10}$ 24. $6\frac{1}{3} - 2\frac{1}{4}$

● **Lesson 5-6**   Solve each equation.

25. $x + 6\frac{4}{9} = 8\frac{1}{9}$ 26. $y + 2\frac{3}{8} = 8\frac{1}{5}$ 27. $a + 9 = 12\frac{7}{9}$ 28. $4\frac{5}{7} = b - 3\frac{1}{2}$

29. $c - 11\frac{2}{3} = 15$ 30. $n + 4\frac{1}{2} = 5$ 31. $m - 5\frac{3}{4} = 10\frac{1}{2}$ 32. $p - 8\frac{1}{3} = 9\frac{1}{4}$

● **Lesson 5-7**   Find the elapsed time in each interval.

33. from 3:45 P.M. to 5:15 P.M.

34. from 8:10 P.M. to 11:55 P.M.

35. from 11:45 A.M. to 6:23 P.M.

36. from 4:05 A.M. to 4:10 P.M.

37. from 3:25 P.M. to 5:02 P.M.

38. from 8:10 A.M. to 11:55 P.M.

Word Problems

● Lesson 5-1

39. You need $1\frac{5}{8}$ yards of solid-colored fabric and $\frac{3}{4}$ yard of print fabric for a quilt. Given the prices in the table at the right, about how much will the fabric cost? Justify your answer.

Fabric Cost

Print	$8.25 per yard
Solid	$7.95 per yard

● Lesson 5-2

40. Two scouts explore a cove. One scout explores $\frac{1}{8}$ mile at one end of the cove. The other scout explores $\frac{3}{8}$ mile of the cove at the opposite end. Together, how much of the cove do they explore?

● Lesson 5-3

41. You buy two goldfish. One goldfish weighs $\frac{1}{6}$ ounce. The other goldfish weighs $\frac{1}{3}$ ounce. What is the combined weight of the goldfish?

● Lesson 5-4

42. Apples You have $1\frac{3}{4}$ pounds of red apples and $2\frac{1}{2}$ pounds of green apples. How many pounds of apples do you have?

● Lesson 5-5

43. Science You and a partner are growing bean plants for a science project. The table at the right shows the heights of the plants after one week of growth. Find the difference in the heights of the two plants.

Plant Growth
Height
Bean 1 $7\frac{7}{8}$ in.
Bean 2 $5\frac{15}{16}$ in.

● Lesson 5-6

44. You have a rope that is $18\frac{1}{2}$ feet long for a tug-of-war. The team captains agree to shorten the rope by cutting off $1\frac{1}{8}$ feet. How long is the rope after it is cut?

45. A piece of poster board is $2\frac{3}{4}$ feet long. You shorten the length by $\frac{1}{2}$ ft. How long is the shortened poster board?

● Lesson 5-7

46. A family reunion begins at 1 P.M. and lasts for 3 hours. It takes 45 minutes to drive from your house to the reunion. How long will you be away from home?

38. 15 h 45 min

39. about $19.00; $\frac{13}{8} + \frac{6}{8} = \frac{19}{8}$, $\frac{19}{8} \times \$8 = \$19.00$

40. $\frac{1}{2}$ mile

41. $\frac{1}{2}$ oz

42. $4\frac{1}{4}$ lb

43. $1\frac{15}{16}$ in.

44. $17\frac{3}{8}$ ft

45. $2\frac{1}{4}$ ft

46. $4\frac{1}{2}$ h

Skills

● Lesson 6-1   Find each product.

1. $\frac{1}{2}$ of $\frac{2}{3}$

2. $\frac{1}{3}$ of $\frac{1}{5}$

3. $\frac{7}{8} \times \frac{3}{4}$

4. $\frac{7}{6} \times 42$

● Lesson 6-2   Find each product.

5. $7\frac{1}{2} \times 2\frac{2}{3}$

6. $6\frac{2}{3} \times 7\frac{1}{5}$

7. $5\frac{5}{8} \times 2\frac{1}{3}$

8. $12\frac{1}{4} \times 6\frac{2}{7}$

● Lesson 6-3   Find each quotient.

9. $2 \div \frac{4}{5}$

10. $\frac{2}{3} \div \frac{2}{5}$

11. $\frac{1}{4} \div \frac{1}{5}$

12. $\frac{4}{11} \div 8$

● Lesson 6-4   Estimate each quotient.

13. $12 \div 3\frac{1}{5}$

14. $7\frac{3}{7} \div 1\frac{2}{5}$

15. $41\frac{8}{10} \div 6\frac{1}{3}$

16. $36\frac{2}{7} \div 4\frac{3}{9}$

Find each quotient.

17. $2\frac{1}{4} \div \frac{2}{3}$

18. $4\frac{1}{2} \div 3\frac{1}{3}$

19. $2\frac{2}{5} \div \frac{2}{25}$

20. $5\frac{2}{3} \div 1\frac{1}{2}$

● Lesson 6-5   Solve each equation. Check the solution.

21. $\frac{x}{4} = 8$

22. $\frac{a}{3} = 9$

23. $\frac{c}{7} = 24$

24. $\frac{m}{2} = 14$

25. $\frac{r}{4} = 3.5$

26. $\frac{t}{12} = 3$

27. $\frac{1}{3}y = 15$

28. $\frac{3}{4}w = 12$

● Lesson 6-6   Choose an appropriate unit for each measurement.

29. capacity of a bathtub

30. weight of a school bus

31. width of a computer monitor

32. weight of a pair of jeans

33. your height

34. capacity of a water pitcher

● Lesson 6-7   Complete each statement.

35. 4 ft = ▩ yd

36. 48 oz = ▩ lb

37. 32 qt = ▩ gal

38. 8,000 lb = ▩ t

39. 10 lb = ▩ oz

40. ▩ ft = 60 in.

41. 64 c = ▩ pt

42. 9 mi = ▩ ft

Word Problems

Lesson 6-1

43. To save money, you buy some clothes on sale. You buy a shirt for $\frac{4}{5}$ of the full price, a pair of jeans for $\frac{3}{4}$ of the full price, and a pair of shoes for $\frac{9}{10}$ of the full price. How much money do you save by buying these clothes on sale?

Item	Full Price
Shirt	$21.00
Jeans	$40.00
Shoes	$27.00

Lesson 6-2

44. Carpentry A carpenter needs 6 pieces of wood that are $3\frac{1}{2}$ feet long. She has two 10-foot boards. Does she have enough wood? Explain.

Lesson 6-3

45. Baking You bake an apple pie. The recipe calls for eight sliced apples. You cut the apples into eighths. How many pieces of apple do you have?

Lesson 6-4

46. Stock Market The price of one technology stock rises $71\frac{5}{8}$ points in $7\frac{1}{2}$ hours. Find the number of points gained per hour during that time.

Lesson 6-5

47. Pedro bikes $3\frac{1}{3}$ times as far as Pat, and Pat bikes $\frac{1}{5}$ as far as Jen. If Pedro rides 8 miles a day, how far does Jen ride?

Lesson 6-6

48. Games Jai alai is a game played in Cuba, Spain, Mexico, and the United States. The ball, or pelota, weighs $4\frac{1}{2}$ ounces. How many ounces do 16 pelotas weigh?

49. Teresa has 200 yards of ribbon. She needs $1\frac{1}{6}$ yards of ribbon to make a bow. How many bows can she make?

Lesson 6-7

50. Animals In parts of Alaska, moose cause traffic jams. An adult moose weighs about 1,000 pounds. How many tons does an adult moose weigh?

51. Geography The volcano Aconcagua in Argentina is 22,831 feet high. How many miles high is Aconcagua?

39. 160
40. 5
41. 32
42. 47,520
43. $16.90
44. No; She needs two $10\frac{1}{2}$ ft boards.
45. 64 pieces
46. $9\frac{11}{20}$ pts/h
47. 12 mi
48. 72 oz
49. 171 bows
50. $\frac{1}{2}$ ton
51. about 4.3 miles

1–5. Answers may vary.
Samples are given.

1. $\frac{1}{2}, \frac{4}{8}$

2. $\frac{1}{3}$, 1 : 3, $\frac{5}{15}$

3. 1 : 4, $\frac{13}{52}, \frac{1}{4}$

4. 1 to 11, 1 : 11, $\frac{1}{11}$

5. 18 : 72, 1 to 4, 1 : 4

6. $.25, $.22; 16 ounces

7. $.24, $.20; 8 ounces

8. yes

9. no

10. yes

11. no

12. no

13. 2

14. 60

15. 9

16. 3

17. 60

18. 350 km

19. 130 km

20. 70 km

21. 500 km

22. 0.42; $\frac{21}{50}$

23. 0.96; $\frac{24}{25}$

24. 0.8; $\frac{4}{5}$

25. 0.01; $\frac{1}{100}$

26. 0.87; $\frac{87}{100}$

27. 0.88; $\frac{22}{25}$

28. 16

29. 3.375

30. 43

31. 90

32. rent

33. 25%

34. $5.25

35. $1.50

36. $2.70

37. $3.75

CHAPTER 7 Extra Practice

Skills

● **Lesson 7-1** Write two different ratios equal to each ratio.

1. $\frac{30}{60}$　　　2. 5 : 15　　　3. 13 to 52　　　4. 7 : 77　　　5. 18 to 72

● **Lesson 7-2** Find each unit price. Round to the nearest cent. Then determine the better buy.

6. cereal: 12 ounces for $2.99　　　　7. rice: 8 ounces for $1.95
　　　　16 ounces for $3.59　　　　　　　　　15 ounces for $2.99

● **Lesson 7-3** Do the ratios in each pair form a proportion?

8. $\frac{6}{30}, \frac{3}{15}$　　9. $\frac{9}{12}, \frac{12}{9}$　　10. $\frac{13}{3}, \frac{26}{6}$　　11. $\frac{5}{225}, \frac{2}{95}$　　12. $\frac{64}{130}, \frac{5}{10}$

● **Lesson 7-4** Solve each proportion.

13. $\frac{a}{50} = \frac{3}{75}$　　14. $\frac{18}{b} = \frac{3}{10}$　　15. $\frac{51}{17} = \frac{c}{3}$　　16. $\frac{2}{16} = \frac{d}{24}$　　17. $\frac{3}{45} = \frac{4}{g}$

● **Lesson 7-5** Find each actual distance. Use a map scale of 1 centimeter : 100 kilometers.

18. 3.5 cm　　　19. 1.3 cm　　　20. 0.7 cm　　　21. 5 cm

● **Lesson 7-6** Write each percent as a decimal and as a fraction in simplest form.

22. 42%　　23. 96%　　24. 80%　　25. 1%　　26. 87%　　27. 88%

● **Lesson 7-7** Find each answer.

28. 20% of 80　　　29. 15% of 22.5　　　30. 50% of 86　　　31. 90% of 100

● **Lesson 7-8** Use the circle graph for Exercises 32–33.

32. What item accounts for the most money in Malinda's budget?

33. About what percent of her budget does Malinda use for rent?

Malinda's Budget

Clothes, Food, Rent, Savings, Charity, Insurance, Other

● **Lesson 7-9** Estimate a 15% tip for each bill amount.

34. $34.90　　　35. $9.54　　　36. $17.50　　　37. $24.80

Word Problems

Lessons 7-1 and 7-2

38. Seven out of 21 students at a school do not like horror movies. Write the ratio, in simplest form, of students who like horror movies to students who dislike horror movies.

39. You baby-sit for four hours and earn $22.00. How much money do you make each hour?

Lesson 7-3

40. The table at the right shows the prices a cable television company and rental store charges for movies. Do the ratios of price to number of movies form a proportion? Explain.

Business	Number of Movies	Price
Movie store	10	$22.50
Cable TV	6	$21.00

Lesson 7-4

41. Each team in the Hopkinton soccer league has 22 players and 3 coaches. How many coaches are needed for 198 players?

Lesson 7-5

42. Aaron builds a model train set. The rails of the model track are 1.5 inches apart. The actual train's rails are 57 inches apart. The actual locomotive is 76 feet long. Write and solve a proportion to find the model locomotive's length.

Lessons 7-6 and 7-7

43. You answer 29 questions correctly on a 40-question test. What percent of your answers are correct?

44. **Basketball** Hector made 80% of his free throws. He attempted 200 free throws. How many free throws did Hector make?

Lesson 7-8

45. **Market Research** A video arcade records the ages of customers over a one-hour period. The results are shown in the line plot at the right. Draw a circle graph.

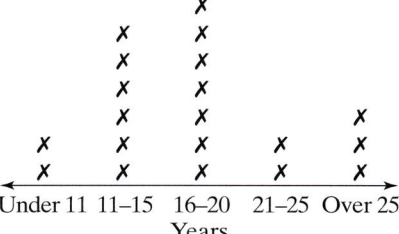

Customer Ages at Video Arcade

Lesson 7-9

46. You buy a camera for 20% off the regular price of $89.99, plus a 7% sales tax. Estimate the cost of the camera.

38. 2 to 1
39. $5.50
40. No; Cable TV costs more per movie.
41. 27
42. $\frac{1.5}{57} = \frac{x}{76}$; 2 feet
43. 72.5%
44. 160
45.

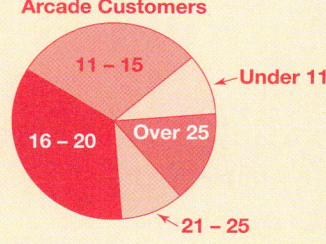

Ages of Video Arcade Customers

46. Answers may vary. Sample: $77

CHAPTER 8 Extra Practice

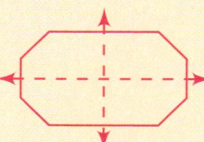

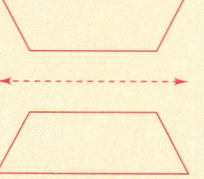

Skills

● **Lessons 8-1 and 8-2**   Use the diagram at the right for Exercises 1–8.
Name each of the following.

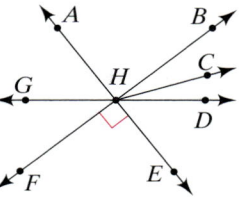

  1. three collinear points   2. six rays   3. two perpendicular lines

Use a protractor to measure each angle. Classify each angle as *acute, right,*
obtuse, or *straight.*

  4. ∠*BHF*   5. ∠*FHC*   6. ∠*FHA*   7. ∠*CHD*   8. ∠*AHC*

● **Lesson 8-3**   Find the complement and the supplement of each
angle measure.

  9. 28°   10. 13.5°   11. 56.3°   12. 79°   13. 85°

● **Lesson 8-4**   Classify each triangle with the given side lengths by its sides.

  14. 7 inches, 9 inches, 7 inches   15. 3 feet, 3 feet, 3 feet   16. 18 yards, 16 yards, 5 yards

● **Lesson 8-5**   Classify each statement as *true* or *false.*

  17. All octagons have eight sides. 18. All rhombuses are squares.   19. All squares are rectangles.

● **Lesson 8-6**   Each pair of figures appears to be *similar.* Use proportions to
determine whether each pair is similar.

  20. 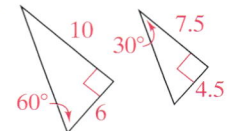   21. 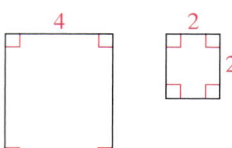   22.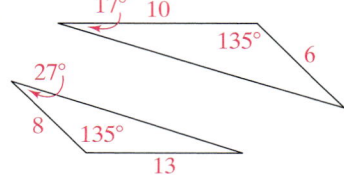

● **Lesson 8-7**   Trace the figure at the right.

  23. Draw all lines of symmetry in the figure.

● **Lesson 8-8**   Copy the figure at the right on graph paper.

  24. Draw its reflection over the given line of reflection.

Word Problems

● Lesson 8-1

25. Explain why $\overrightarrow{AB}$ represents a ray, and $\overleftrightarrow{AB}$ represents a line.

● Lessons 8-2 and 8-3

26. A telescope has a 68° viewing angle. What kind of angle is this angle?

27. Find the complement and the supplement of angle *RST* in the diagram at the right.

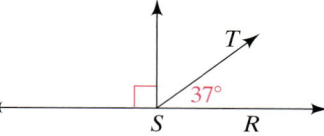

● Lesson 8-4

28. A company makes puzzles with triangular pieces. The side lengths of each piece are 2 in., 2 in. and 2 in. What is the type of triangle that the company makes?

● Lesson 8-5

29. Give four other names for the shape of a square.

30. **Signs** The shape of some traffic signs in recreation areas and national forests is a trapezoid. What is another name for the shape of a trapezoid?

● Lesson 8-6

31. Triangles *QRS* and *MNO* at the right are similar. List the pairs of corresponding sides and corresponding angles.

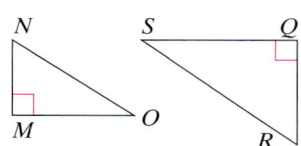

● Lesson 8-7

32. The Double Snake Nose Native American basket pattern is shown at the right. How many lines of symmetry does it have? Copy the design and draw the lines of symmetry.

33. How many lines of symmetry does a regular hexagon have? Sketch a regular hexagon and the lines of symmetry to support your answer.

Double Snake Nose

● Lesson 8-8

34. A designer makes a logo by copying the shape shown at the right and then drawing its reflection. Draw the shape and its reflection.

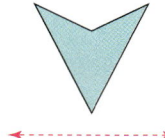

25. A one-sided arrow represents a ray and a double-sided arrow represents a line.

26. acute

27. 53°; 143°

28. equilateral

29. rectangle, parallelogram, rhombus, quadrilateral

30. quadrilateral

31.

$\overline{QR}$, $\overline{MN}$; $\overline{RS}$, $\overline{NO}$; $\overline{SQ}$, $\overline{OM}$; $\angle Q$, $\angle M$; $\angle R$, $\angle N$; $\angle S$, $\angle O$

32. 2;

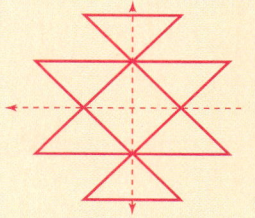

33. 6;

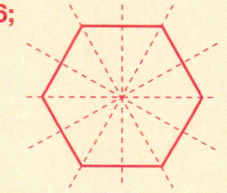

34.

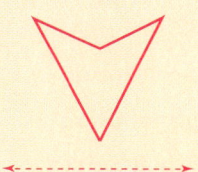

CHAPTER 9 Extra Practice

Skills

● **Lesson 9-1**   Choose an appropriate metric unit of measure.

  1. capacity of a shampoo bottle   2. mass of a television   3. length of your shoe

● **Lesson 9-2**   Complete each statement.

  4. 35 mm = ▮ cm   5. 10.8 km = ▮ m   6. ▮ L = 2,400 mL   7. 1,008 g = ▮ kg

● **Lesson 9-3**   Estimate the area of each figure. Each square represents 1 square centimeter.

  8. 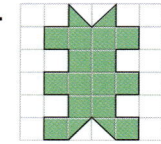   9. 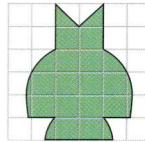   10.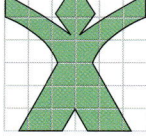

● **Lessons 9-3 and 9-4**   Find the area of each figure.

  11. 5.5 ft   9.5 ft   12. 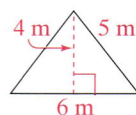 4 m 5 m 6 m   13. 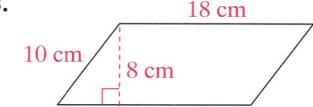 18 cm 10 cm 8 cm

● **Lessons 9-5 and 9-6**   Find the circumference and the area of a circle with the given diameter *d* or radius *r*. Use 3.14 for *π* and round to the nearest whole number.

  14. *d* = 26 yards   15. *d* = 10.6 feet   16. *r* = 30 inches   17. *r* = 11 miles   18. *d* = 8.5 meters

● **Lesson 9-7**   Name each figure.

  19. 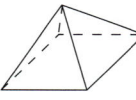   20. 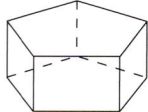   21. 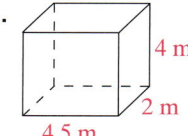 4 m 2 m 4.5 m

● **Lessons 9-8 and 9-9**   Find the surface area and the volume of each rectangular prism with the given dimensions.

  22. ℓ = 10 ft, *w* = 5 ft, *h* = 8 ft   23. ℓ = 12 m, *w* = 16 m, *h* = 12 m

Word Problems

● **Lessons 9-1 and 9-2**

24. The width of a ceiling tile is about $\frac{1}{2}$ meter. How can you estimate the length of a wall that intersects a tiled ceiling?

25. Angel Falls in Venezuela is 0.807 kilometers high. How many meters high is Angel Falls?

● **Lessons 9-3 and 9-4**

26. Construction Find the area of the sheet of plywood in the drawing at the right.

27. A parallelogram has an area of 96 square inches and a base length of 12 inches. What is the height of the parallelogram?

3 ft

6 ft

● **Lesson 9-5**

28. Two cylinders have diameters of 16 and 21 inches. What is the difference in their circumferences? Use 3 for π.

● **Lesson 9-6**

29. Weather Severe thunderstorms are forecast within a 55-mile radius of St. Louis, Missouri. What is the approximate area of the storm region? Use 3 for π.

● **Lesson 9-7**

30. Name the figure at the right. Then find the number of faces, vertices, and edges.

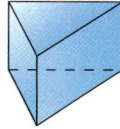

● **Lessons 9-8 and 9-9**

31. Suppose each dimension of a rectangular prism is tripled. How much larger is the surface area of the prism?

32. A packing crate has a length of 8 feet, a width of 6 feet, and a height of 4 feet. What is the volume of the packing crate?

● **Lesson 9-10**

33. A plastic pipe has a radius of 18 in. and a length of 34 in. Find the volume of the pipe. Use 3 for π.

Extra Skills and Word Problems

24. Count the number of ceiling tiles along a length of a wall. Multiply by $\frac{1}{2}$ meter.

25. 807 m

26. 18 sq. ft

27. 8 in.

28. 15 in.

29. 9,075 sq. mi

30. triangular prism; faces, 5; vertices, 6; edges, 9

31. 9 times larger

32. 192 ft^3

33. 33,048 in.^{3}

Extra Skills and Word Problems

CHAPTER 10 — Extra Practice

Skills

● **Lesson 10-1**   Draw a tree diagram to find the total number of outcomes.

1. You flip a coin three times.

2. You roll a number cube. Then you toss a coin.

● **Lesson 10-2**   A jar contains 2 red, 4 yellow, 3 green, and 5 blue marbles. You select a marble without looking. Find each probability.

3. $P(\text{yellow})$
4. $P(\text{green})$
5. $P(\text{red or blue})$
6. $P(\text{red, green, or blue})$

● **Lesson 10-3**   Find the experimental probability that each person wins.

7. Yelena won 168 of 196 games.

8. Chang played a game 43 times and did not lose a game.

● **Lesson 10-4**   The probability of winning a game is 80%. How many times should you expect to win if you play the following number of times?

9. 4
10. 10
11. 30
12. 55
13. 125
14. 520

Write and solve a proportion to make the prediction.

15. In a school of 2,037 students, 500 were asked to name their favorite fruit. Apples were named by 325 students. Predict how many of the 2,037 students would name apples as their favorite fruit.

● **Lesson 10-5**   A bag contains 2 red, 6 blue, and 2 green marbles. Marbles are drawn twice with replacement. Find the probability of each compound event.

16. blue, then red
17. both blue
18. both not green

Word Problems

● **Lesson 10-1**

19. A car dealership has 9 different models of cars in 6 different colors for you to choose from. How many choices do you have?

Lesson 10-2

20. **Games** A game has a square board divided into 4 equal sections numbered 1 through 4. You win when you toss a chip and it lands on the section numbered 4. What is the probability of winning when a toss lands on the board?

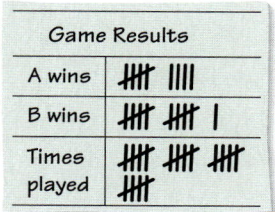

21. **Party** A package of 25 party balloons has 8 red, 6 blue, 6 green, and 5 yellow balloons. Find the probability of selecting a yellow balloon at random. Write your answer as a fraction, a decimal, and a percent.

Lesson 10-3

22. You toss a paper cup 48 times. It lands on its side 36 times. Find the experimental probability that it lands on its side.

23. **Fair Games** The Mandan people played a game in which two players toss a bone disk in a basket. Player A wins if the disk lands in the basket with the decorated side up. Otherwise, Player B wins. In 100 trials, $P(A \text{ wins}) = \frac{30}{100}$ and $P(B \text{ wins}) = \frac{70}{100}$. Does this seem to be a fair game?

24. The table below shows the number of wins for two players after many games. Find the experimental probability of each player winning.

Game Results	
A wins	卌 IIII
B wins	卌 卌 I
Times played	卌 卌 卌 卌

Lesson 10-4

25. On election day, a pollster surveys 510 people as they leave the voting booths. Two hundred eighty people say they voted for Candidate A. Predict how many votes Candidate A receives if 10,000 people vote.

Lesson 10-5

26. At a soccer game, a referee tosses a coin that comes up heads. At the next game, he tosses a coin and it comes up heads again. Are these two events independent? Explain.

20. $\frac{1}{4}$

21. $\frac{1}{5}$; 0.2; 20%

22. $\frac{3}{4}$

23. No

24. A: $\frac{9}{20}$; B: $\frac{11}{20}$

25. 5,490 votes

26. Each event is independent. The first toss has no effect on the second toss.

1. 1,000

2. −125

3. −17

4. 11

5. −2, −1, 0, 3

6. −8, −5, 2, 4

7. −8, −6, 7, 8

8. −8, −1, 0, 1

9. 14

10. −125

11. −4

12. 0

13. −40

14. 36

15. −31

16. 2.5

17. −4

18. 9

19. 17

20. −12

21. (2, 3)

22. (3, −3)

23. (−3, −1)

24. (−3, 3)

25. G

26. I

27. H

28. J

29. $5,002

30. $1,263

31. −$86

32.

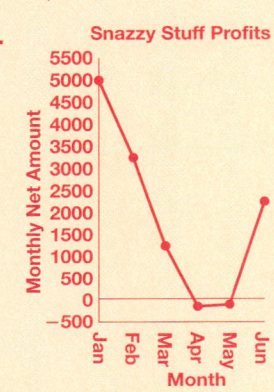

Snazzy Stuff Profits

CHAPTER 11 Extra Practice

Skills

● **Lesson 11-1** Use an integer to represent each situation.

1. 1,000 ft above   **2.** in debt $125   **3.** 17° below 0°C   **4.** gaining 11 lb

● **Lesson 11-2** Order from least to greatest.

5. 3, −1, 0, −2   **6.** 4, −8, −5, 2   **7.** −6, 8, 7, −8   **8.** −1, −8, 0, 1

● **Lessons 11-3 and 11-4** Find each sum or difference.

9. $-14 + 28$ **10.** $-72 + (-53)$ **11.** $-3 - 1$ **12.** $-27 - (-27)$

● **Lessons 11-5 and 11-6** Find each product or quotient.

13. -8×5 **14.** $-4 \times (-9)$ **15.** $93 \div (-3)$ **16.** $-5 \div (-2)$

● **Lesson 11-7** Solve each equation. Check the solution.

17. $-4 + c = -8$ **18.** $x - (-6) = 15$ **19.** $-4y = -68$ **20.** $p \div 3 = -4$

● **Lesson 11-8** Use the coordinate grid at the right for Exercises 21–28. Find the coordinates of each point.

21. A   **22.** B   **23.** C   **24.** D

Name the point with the given coordinates.

25. (4, 2)   **26.** (2, −2)   **27.** (−4, 1)   **28.** (−2, −4)

● **Lesson 11-9** Look at the data for Snazzy Stuff in table at the right. Find the profit or loss for each month.

29. January   **30.** March   **31.** May

32. Draw a line graph based on the profits and losses for Snazzy Stuff.

● **Lesson 11-10** Make a table and graph each function.

33. kilometers as a function of meters

34. yards as a function of feet

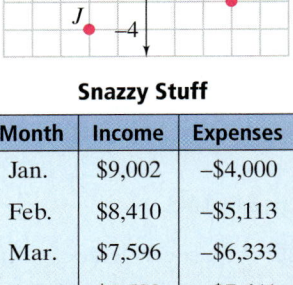

Snazzy Stuff

Month	Income	Expenses
Jan.	$9,002	−$4,000
Feb.	$8,410	−$5,113
Mar.	$7,596	−$6,333
Apr.	$7,523	−$7,641
May	$7,941	−$8,027
June	$8,569	−$6,299

33. km $= \frac{m}{1,000}$;

m	1,000	1,500	2,000	2,500
km	1	1.5	2	2.5

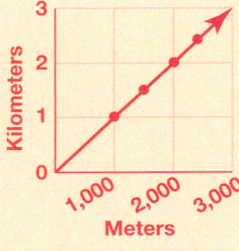

Word Problems

Lessons 11-1 and 11-2

35. A river has a depth of 6 feet. The water then rises 5 feet. Find the new water level.

36. On a thermometer, the air temperature reads 10°F. It rises 2°F and then falls 13°F. What is the final air temperature?

Lessons 11-3 and 11-4

37. Football A football team gains 6 yards on one play and loses 11 yards on the next play. What is the result of the two plays?

38. Use the table. Find the range of surface temperatures on Mars.

Surface Temperatures on Mars

Low	−125°F
High	23°F

SOURCE: National Aeronautics and Space Administration

Lessons 11-5 and 11-6

39. A fishing line sinks at 4 inches per second. Find the change in depth of the fishing line after 30 seconds.

40. Animals Over five months, a horse loses 15 pounds. Find the rate of change in pounds per month.

Lessons 11-7 and 11-8

41. A diver 100 feet below sea level rises 25 feet per minute. Use an equation to find the time it takes her to reach the surface.

42. Your cousin is at $(-5, -2)$. He walks 3 blocks west and 1 block south to the park. Find the coordinates of the park.

Lesson 11-9

43. The table shows the population growth in the United States. Make a graph of the data and predict the population in 2010.

Year	Population (in millions)
1900	76
1920	106
1940	132
1960	179
1980	227
2000	281

Lesson 11-10

44. Sales A uniform company sells name patches for uniforms. The company charges $2 per patch plus a handling fee of $5 for each order. The function $p = 2n + 5$ shows how price p relates to the number of patches n. Make a table and graph the function.

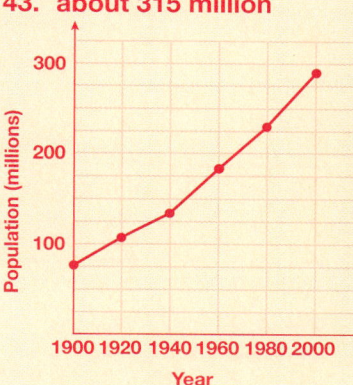
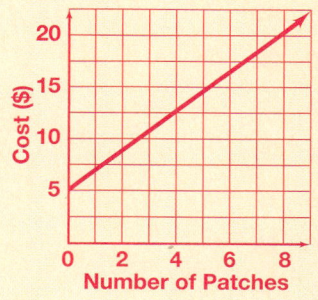
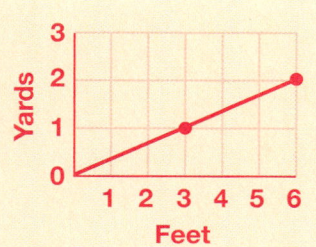

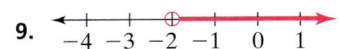
Skills

● **Lesson 12-1** **Solve each equation.**

1. $2a + 8 = 26$ **2.** $3c + 2.5 = 29.5$ **3.** $5b - 13 = 17$ **4.** $7.5d - 7 = 53$

5. $4e - 1 = -93$ **6.** $\dfrac{f}{8} + 6 = 8$ **7.** $2 + 8g = 34$ **8.** $-4 + \dfrac{h}{4} = 4$

● **Lesson 12-2** **Write an inequality for each graph.**

9.   **10.**    **11.**

Write an inequality to represent each situation. Then graph the inequality.

12. The temperature stayed below 0°.

13. You must bring at least $5 to cover the cost of lunch.

14. The paintings for display can be a maximum of 12 inches wide.

● **Lesson 12-3** **Solve each inequality.**

15. $m + 8 < 14$ **16.** $n - 16 \ge 3$ **17.** $p + 9 \le -5$ **18.** $q - 8 > 7$

● **Lesson 12-4** **Find each square root.**

19. $\sqrt{49}$ **20.** $\sqrt{81}$ **21.** $\sqrt{169}$ **22.** $\sqrt{484}$

● **Lesson 12-5** **Find the missing side length of each right triangle.**

23. $a = 16, b = 30, c = \blacksquare$ **24.** $a = 21, b = \blacksquare, c = 35$ **25.** $a = \blacksquare, b = 9, c = 15$

Word Problems

● **Lesson 12-1**

26. Your brother buys 4 games. Each game costs the same amount. He uses a coupon for $5 off the total purchase price and owes the cashier $31. How much does each game cost? Use c for the cost of one game. Use the equation $4c - 5 = 31$.

27. You deliver boxes weighing 20 pounds each to a business on the sixth floor of a building. The elevator has a weight limit of 1,500 pounds. Your weight is 180 pounds. How many boxes can you load on the elevator? Use b for the number of boxes. Use the equation $20b + 180 = 1500$.

Lesson 12-2

Use the table on the right.

28. Careers Officers in local law enforcement must meet certain requirements at the time of hire. Write and graph an inequality showing the usual age requirement for local law enforcement officers.

29. The requirements for federal law enforcement officers are different from those for local law enforcement officers. Write and graph an inequality showing the maximum age for federal law enforcement officers.

Law Enforcement Hiring Requirements

Level	Federal	Local
U.S. Citizen	Yes	Yes
Age (years) Minimum Maximum	21 36	20 None

Source: *Occupational Outlook Handbook*

Lesson 12-3

30. Angelica sells magazines. She earns $30 a day plus $2 for each magazine subscription sold. Angelica would like to earn a minimum of $65 each day. How many magazine subscriptions must she sell per day to earn the minimum?

Lesson 12-4

31. A square floor has an area of 225 square feet. How long is each side of the floor?

Lesson 12-5

32. Quilting To ensure that a quilting frame is exactly rectangular, a quilter measures the diagonals of the frame to be sure they are equal. What should the lengths of the diagonals be for the quilting frame shown in the diagram below? Round your answer to the nearest tenth.

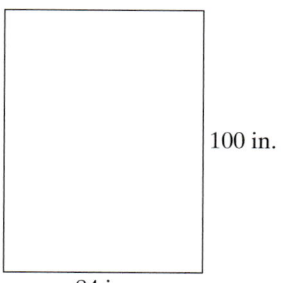

100 in.

84 in.

28. $x \geq 20$

10 15 20 25 30

29. $x \leq 36$

20 25 30 35 40

30. at least 18 magazine subscriptions

31. 15 ft

32. 130.6 in.

Skills Handbook

Place Value of Whole Numbers

The digits in a whole number are grouped into periods. A period has three digits, and each period has a name. Each digit in a whole number has both a place and a value.

Billions Period			Millions Period			Thousands Period			Ones Period		
Hundred billions	Ten billions	Billions	Hundred millions	Ten millions	Millions	Hundred thousands	Ten thousands	Thousands	Hundreds	Tens	Ones
9	5	1	6	3	7	0	4	1	1	8	2

The digit 5 is in the ten billions place. So its value is 5 ten billions, or 50 billion.

EXAMPLE

a. In what place is the digit 7?

   millions

b. What is the value of the digit 7?

   7 million

Exercises

Use the chart above. Write the place of each digit.

1. the digit 3   2. the digit 4   3. the digit 6
4. the digit 8   5. the digit 9   6. the digit 0

Use the chart above. Write the value of each digit.

7. the digit 3   8. the digit 4   9. the digit 6
10. the digit 8   11. the digit 9   12. the digit 0

Write the value of the digit 6 in each number.

13. 633   14. 761,523   15. 163,500,000   16. 165,417
17. 265   18. 4,396   19. 618,920   20. 204,602
21. 162,450,000,000   22. 7,682   23. 358,026,113   24. 76,030,100
25. 642,379   26. 16,403   27. 45,060   28. 401,601,001

Rounding Whole Numbers

Number lines can help you round numbers. On a number line, 5 is halfway between 0 and 10, 50 is halfway between 0 and 100, and 500 is halfway between 1 and 1,000. The accepted method of rounding is to round 5 up to 10, 50 up to 100, and 500 up to 1,000.

EXAMPLE

1 Round 2,462 to the nearest ten.

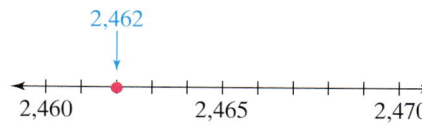

2,462 is closer to 2,460 than to 2,470.

2,462 rounded to the nearest ten is 2,460.

EXAMPLE

2 Round 247,451 to the nearest hundred.

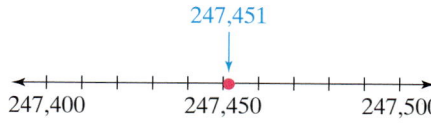

247,451 is closer to 247,500 than to 247,400.

247,451 rounded to the nearest hundred is 247,500.

Exercises

Round each number to the nearest ten.

1. 65	**2.** 832	**3.** 4,437	**4.** 21,024	**5.** 3,545

Round each number to the nearest hundred.

6. 889	**7.** 344	**8.** 2,861	**9.** 1,138	**10.** 50,549
11. 6,411	**12.** 88,894	**13.** 13,735	**14.** 17,459	**15.** 6,059

Round each number to the nearest thousand.

16. 2,400	**17.** 16,218	**18.** 7,430	**19.** 89,375	**20.** 9,821
21. 15,631	**22.** 76,900	**23.** 163,875	**24.** 38,295	**25.** 102,359

26. Describe a situation in which it is helpful to round data.

27. Explain how to round number 17 in the exercises above to the nearest ten thousand.

28. Suppose you round 31 to the nearest hundred. Is 0 the correct response? Explain your answer.

1. 70
2. 830
3. 4,440
4. 21,020
5. 3,550
6. 900
7. 300
8. 2,900
9. 1,100
10. 50,500
11. 6,400
12. 88,900
13. 13,700
14. 17,500
15. 6,100
16. 2,000
17. 16,000
18. 7,000
19. 89,000
20. 10,000
21. 16,000
22. 77,000
23. 164,000
24. 38,000
25. 102,000
26. Check students' work.
27. Check students' work.
28. Answers may vary. Sample: Yes; 31 is closer to 0 than it is to 100.

Adding Whole Numbers

When you add, line up the digits in the correct columns. Begin by adding the ones. You may need to regroup from one column to the next.

EXAMPLE

1 Add 463 + 58.

Step 1	Step 2	Step 3
1	11	11
463	463	463
+ 58	+ 58	+ 58
1	21	521

EXAMPLE

2 Find each sum.

a. 962 + 120

$$
\begin{array}{r}
962 \\
+ 120 \\
\hline
1,082
\end{array}
$$

b. 25 + 9 + 143

$$
\begin{array}{r}
1 \\
25 \\
9 \\
+ 143 \\
\hline
177
\end{array}
$$

c. 3,887 + 1,201

$$
\begin{array}{r}
1 \\
3,887 \\
+ 1,201 \\
\hline
5,088
\end{array}
$$

Exercises

Find each sum.

1. 45 + 31	2. 56 + 80	3. 25 + 16	4. 43 + 29	5. 66 + 78	6. 87 + 35
7. 81 + 312	8. 406 + 123	9. 207 + 72	10. 480 + 365	11. 217 + 347	12. 675 + 329
13. 2,051 + 843	14. 786 + 4,109	15. 5,227 + 1,527	16. 3,104 + 2,698	17. 5,337 + 1,812	18. 4,282 + 7,518

19. 78 + 56   20. 35 + 96   21. 105 + 71   22. 29 + 342   23. 654 + 103

24. 286 + 42   25. 55 + 77   26. 242 + 83   27. 32 + 68   28. 108 + 13

29. 589 + 318   30. 642 + 975   31. 2,308 + 451   32. 976 + 4,035

33. 8,228 + 1,024   34. 5,417 + 2,391   35. 6,470 + 9,828   36. 7,121 + 5,359

Subtracting Whole Numbers

When you subtract, line up the digits in the correct columns. Begin by subtracting the ones. Rename if the bottom digit is greater than the top digit. You may need to rename more than once.

EXAMPLE

1 Subtract 725 − 86.

Step 1
```
  115
  725
−  86
    9
```

Step 2
```
   11
  6115
  725
−  86
   39
```

Step 3
```
   11
  6115
  725
−  86
  639
```

EXAMPLE

2 Find each difference.

a. 602 − 174
```
    9
  51012
  602
− 174
  428
```

b. 625 − 273
```
  512
  625
− 273
  352
```

c. 5,002 − 1,247
```
   9 9
  4101012
  5,002
− 1,247
  3,755
```

Exercises

Find each difference.

1. 81 − 37	**2.** 59 − 23	**3.** 41 − 19	**4.** 83 − 25	**5.** 99 − 78	**6.** 87 − 31
7. 707 − 361	**8.** 680 − 47	**9.** 240 − 63	**10.** 881 − 391	**11.** 517 − 287	**12.** 973 − 529
13. 7,411 − 583	**14.** 3,789 − 809	**15.** 6,508 − 2,147	**16.** 8,000 − 5,274	**17.** 3,003 − 1,998	**18.** 8,282 − 4,118

19. 78 − 19 **20.** 231 − 99 **21.** 901 − 65 **22.** 629 − 382 **23.** 918 − 133

24. 800 − 435 **25.** 403 − 122 **26.** 973 − 228 **27.** 721 − 119 **28.** 522 − 146

29. 642 − 223 **30.** 427 − 193 **31.** 444 − 345 **32.** 988 − 489 **33.** 601 − 425

Skills Handbook **639**

1. 44
2. 36
3. 22
4. 58
5. 21
6. 56
7. 346
8. 633
9. 177
10. 490
11. 230
12. 444
13. 6,828
14. 2,980
15. 4,361
16. 2,726
17. 1,005
18. 4,164
19. 59
20. 132
21. 836
22. 247
23. 785
24. 365
25. 281
26. 745
27. 602
28. 376
29. 419
30. 234
31. 99
32. 499
33. 176

Multiplying Whole Numbers

When you multiply by a one-digit number, multiply the one-digit number by each digit in the other number.

EXAMPLE

1 **Multiply 294 × 7.**

Step 1 Multiply 7 by the ones digit.

$$
\begin{array}{r}
2 \\
294 \\
\times\ 7 \\
\hline
8
\end{array}
$$

Step 2 Multiply 7 by the tens digit.

$$
\begin{array}{r}
6\,2 \\
294 \\
\times\ 7 \\
\hline
58
\end{array}
$$

Step 3 Multiply 7 by the hundreds digit.

$$
\begin{array}{r}
6\,2 \\
294 \\
\times\quad 7 \\
\hline
2{,}058
\end{array}
$$

When you multiply by a two-digit number, first multiply by the ones. Then multiply by the tens. Add the products. Remember, 0 times any number is equal to 0.

EXAMPLE

2 **Multiply 48 × 327.**

Step 1 Multiply the ones.

$$
\begin{array}{r}
25 \\
327 \\
\times\ 48 \\
\hline
2{,}616
\end{array}
$$

Step 2 Multiply the tens.

$$
\begin{array}{r}
12 \\
327 \\
\times\ 48 \\
\hline
2616 \\
+\ 1308
\end{array}
$$

Step 3 Add the products.

$$
\begin{array}{r}
327 \\
\times\ 48 \\
\hline
2616 \\
+\ 1308 \\
\hline
15696
\end{array}
$$

Exercises

Find each product.

1. $\begin{array}{r} 81 \\ \times\ 3 \end{array}$
2. $\begin{array}{r} 47 \\ \times\ 2 \end{array}$
3. $\begin{array}{r} 58 \\ \times\ 6 \end{array}$
4. $\begin{array}{r} 678 \\ \times\ 5 \end{array}$
5. $\begin{array}{r} 412 \\ \times\ 7 \end{array}$
6. $\begin{array}{r} 326 \\ \times\ 4 \end{array}$

7. 7×45
8. 62×3
9. 213×4
10. 8×177
11. 673×9

12. $\begin{array}{r} 25 \\ \times\ 46 \end{array}$
13. $\begin{array}{r} 62 \\ \times\ 88 \end{array}$
14. $\begin{array}{r} 808 \\ \times\ 60 \end{array}$
15. $\begin{array}{r} 409 \\ \times\ 70 \end{array}$
16. $\begin{array}{r} 915 \\ \times\ 27 \end{array}$
17. $\begin{array}{r} 312 \\ \times\ 53 \end{array}$

18. 415×76
19. 500×80
20. 320×47
21. 562×18
22. 946×37

23. 76×103
24. 32×558
25. 371×84
26. 505×40
27. 620×19

Multiplying and Dividing Whole Numbers by 10, 100, and 1,000

Basic facts and patterns can help you when multiplying and dividing whole numbers by 10, 100, and 1,000.

$8 \times 1 = 8$
$8 \times 10 = 80$
$8 \times 100 = 800$
$8 \times 1,000 = 8,000$

Count the number of ending zeros.

The product will have this many zeros.

$5,000 \div 1 = 5,000$
$5,000 \div 10 = 500$
$5,000 \div 100 = 50$
$5,000 \div 1,000 = 5$

Count the zeros in the divisor.

If possible, remove this many zeros from the dividend. This number will be the quotient.

EXAMPLE

Multiply or divide.

a. $77 \times 1,000$

$77,000$ ← Insert three zeros.

b. $430 \div 10$

43 ← Remove one zero.

Exercises

Multiply.

1. 85×10	**2.** 85×100	**3.** $85 \times 1,000$	**4.** $420 \times 1,000$	**5.** 420×100
6. 420×10	**7.** 603×100	**8.** 97×10	**9.** 31×100	**10.** 10×17
11. 100×56	**12.** $1,000 \times 4$	**13.** 13×10	**14.** 68×100	**15.** $19 \times 1,000$

Divide.

16. $3,200 \div 10$	**17.** $3,200 \div 100$	**18.** $32,000 \div 1,000$	**19.** $8,000 \div 100$	**20.** $8,000 \div 10$
21. $170 \div 10$	**22.** $45,000 \div 1,000$	**23.** $9,300 \div 10$	**24.** $90 \div 10$	**25.** $6,100 \div 100$
26. $7,900 \div 100$	**27.** $2,400 \div 10$	**28.** $240 \div 10$	**29.** $78,000 \div 1,000$	**30.** $9,900 \div 10$

Multiply or divide.

31. 76×100	**32.** $52 \times 1,000$	**33.** $370 \div 10$	**34.** 505×10	**35.** $6,200 \div 100$
36. $340 \div 10$	**37.** $14,000 \div 1,000$	**38.** 253×100	**39.** $3,700 \div 10$	**40.** 418×10

Skills Handbook **641**

Skills Handbook

1. 850
2. 8,500
3. 85,000
4. 420,000
5. 42,000
6. 4,200
7. 60,300
8. 970
9. 3,100
10. 170
11. 5,600
12. 4,000
13. 130
14. 6,800
15. 19,000
16. 320
17. 32
18. 32
19. 80
20. 800
21. 17
22. 45
23. 930
24. 9
25. 61
26. 79
27. 240
28. 24
29. 78
30. 990
31. 7,600
32. 52,000
33. 37
34. 5,050
35. 62
36. 34
37. 14
38. 25,300
39. 370
40. 4,180

Dividing Whole Numbers

Division is the opposite of multiplication. So you multiply the divisor by your estimate for each digit in the quotient. Then subtract. You repeat this step until you have a remainder that is less than the divisor.

EXAMPLE

Divide 23$\overline{)1,178}$.

Step 1 Estimate the quotient.

$1,178 \div 23$ ← The dividend is 1,178. The divisor is 23.

$1,200 \div 20 = 60$ ← Round 1,178 to the nearest hundred.
Round 23 to the nearest ten.

Step 2

$$\begin{array}{r} 6 \\ 23\overline{)1178} \\ -138 \end{array}$$

← Try 6 tens.

← 6 × 23 = 138
You cannot subtract, so 6 tens is too much.

Step 3

$$\begin{array}{r} 5 \\ 23\overline{)1178} \\ -115 \\ \hline 2 \end{array}$$

← Try 5 tens.

← 5 × 23 = 115

← Subtract.

Step 4

$$\begin{array}{r} 51 \text{ R5} \\ 23\overline{)1178} \\ -115\downarrow \\ \hline 28 \\ -23 \\ \hline 5 \end{array}$$

← Bring down 8.

← 1 × 23 = 23

← Subtract. The remainder is 5.

Step 5 Check your answer.

First compare your answer to the estimate. Since 51 R5 is close to 60, the answer is reasonable.

● Then find $51 \times 23 + 5$.

Exercises

Find each quotient. Check your answer.

1. $9\overline{)659}$
2. $9\overline{)376}$
3. $3\overline{)280}$
4. $8\overline{)541}$
5. $8\overline{)232}$

6. $1,058 \div 5$
7. $3,591 \div 3$
8. $5,072 \div 7$
9. $1,718 \div 4$
10. $3,767 \div 6$

11. $3,872 \div 17$
12. $19\overline{)1,373}$
13. $27\overline{)1,853}$
14. $4,195 \div 59$
15. $41\overline{)4,038}$

16. $2,612 \div 31$
17. $34\overline{)1,609}$
18. $1,937 \div 40$
19. $54\overline{)1,350}$
20. $1,824 \div 32$

21. **Writing in Math** Describe how to estimate a quotient. Use the words *dividend* and *divisor* in your description.

Zeros in Quotients

When you divide, after you bring down a digit you must write a digit in the quotient. In this example, the second digit in the quotient is 0.

EXAMPLE

Find $19\overline{)5{,}823}$.

Step 1

Estimate the quotient.

$5{,}823 \div 19$
$\downarrow \quad \downarrow$
$5{,}800 \div 20 = 290$

Step 2

$$\begin{array}{r} 3 \\ 19\overline{)5{,}823} \\ -57 \\ \hline 1 \end{array}$$

Step 3

$$\begin{array}{r} 30 \\ 19\overline{)5{,}823} \\ -57 \\ \hline 12 \\ -0 \\ \hline 12 \end{array}$$

Step 4

$$\begin{array}{r} 306 \text{ R9} \\ 19\overline{)5{,}823} \\ -57 \\ \hline 12 \\ -0 \\ \hline 123 \\ -114 \\ \hline 9 \end{array}$$

Step 5

Check your answer.
Since 306 is close to 290,
the answer is reasonable.
Find $306 \times 19 + 9$.

Exercises

Find each quotient.

1. $7\overline{)212}$

2. $9\overline{)367}$

3. $3\overline{)271}$

4. $8\overline{)485}$

5. $6\overline{)483}$

6. $34\overline{)1{,}371}$

7. $19\overline{)1{,}335}$

8. $62\overline{)1{,}881}$

9. $54\overline{)1{,}094}$

10. $41\overline{)3{,}710}$

11. $282 \div 4$

12. $143 \div 7$

13. $181 \div 3$

14. $400 \div 8$

15. $365 \div 9$

16. $1{,}008 \div 5$

17. $3{,}018 \div 6$

18. $4{,}939 \div 7$

19. $1{,}682 \div 4$

20. $3{,}647 \div 6$

21. $2{,}488 \div 31$

22. $3{,}372 \div 67$

23. $1{,}937 \div 48$

24. $4{,}165 \div 59$

25. $1{,}686 \div 82$

1. 30 R2
2. 40 R7
3. 90 R1
4. 60 R5
5. 80 R3
6. 40 R11
7. 70 R5
8. 30 R21
9. 20 R14
10. 90 R20
11. 70 R2
12. 20 R3
13. 60 R1
14. 50
15. 40 R5
16. 201 R3
17. 503
18. 705 R4
19. 420 R2
20. 607 R5
21. 80 R8
22. 50 R22
23. 40 R17
24. 70 R35
25. 20 R46

1. 36.8°C

2. 37.5°C

3. 38.4°C

4. 94.6°F

5. 96.6°F

6. 106.2°F

7. G

8. I

9. F

10. Y

11. W

12. X

Reading Thermometer Scales

The thermometer at the right shows temperature in degrees Celsius (°C) and degrees Fahrenheit (°F).

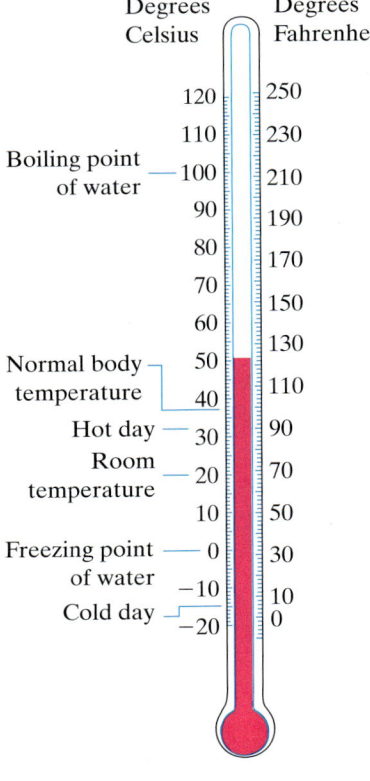

EXAMPLE

1 How do you read point *A* on the Celsius thermometer below?

Each 1-degree interval is divided into 10 smaller intervals of 0.1 degree each. The reading at point *A* is 36.2°C.

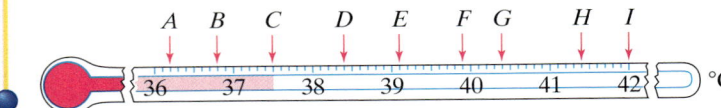

EXAMPLE

2 How do you read point *V* on the Fahrenheit thermometer below?

Each 1-degree interval is divided into 5 smaller intervals. Since $10 \div 5 = 2$, each smaller interval represents 0.2 degree. Count by 0.2, beginning with 98.0. The reading at point *V* is 98.6°F.

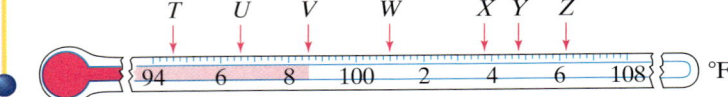

Exercises

Use the thermometers above to write the temperature reading for each point. Tell whether the reading is in degrees Celsius (°C) or degrees Fahrenheit (°F).

1. *B*　　　2. *C*　　　3. *D*　　　4. *T*　　　5. *U*　　　6. *Z*

Use the thermometers above to name the point that relates to each temperature reading.

7. 40.4°C　　8. 42.0°C　　9. 39.9°C　　10. 104.8°F　　11. 101°F　　12. 103.8°F

Roman Numerals

The ancient Romans used letters to represent numerals. The table below shows the value of each Roman numeral.

I	V	X	L	C	D	M
1	5	10	50	100	500	1,000

Here are the Roman numerals from 1 to 10.

1	2	3	4	5	6	7	8	9	10
I	II	III	IV	V	VI	VII	VIII	IX	X

Roman numerals are read in groups from left to right.

If the value of the second numeral is the same as or less than the first numeral, add the values. The Roman numerals II, III, VI, VII, and VIII are examples in which you use addition.

If the value of the second numeral is greater than the first numeral, subtract the values. The Roman numerals IV and IX are examples in which you use subtraction.

EXAMPLE

Find the value of each Roman numeral.

a. CD

$500 - 100$

400

b. MXXVI

$1,000 + 10 + 10 + 5 + 1$

1,026

c. XCIV

$(100 - 10) + (5 - 1)$

$90 + 4 = 94$

Exercises

Find the value of each Roman numeral.

1. XI
2. DIII
3. XCV
4. CMX
5. XXIX
6. DLIX
7. MLVI
8. LX
9. CDIV
10. DCV

Write each number as a Roman numeral.

11. 15
12. 35
13. 1,632
14. 222
15. 159
16. 67
17. 92
18. 403
19. 1,990
20. 64

1. 11
2. 503
3. 95
4. 910
5. 29
6. 559
7. 1,056
8. 60
9. 404
10. 605
11. XV
12. XXXV
13. MDCXXXII
14. CCXXII
15. CLIX
16. LXVII
17. XCII
18. CDIII
19. MCMXC
20. LXIV

Estimating Lengths Using Nonstandard Units

Jan wanted to find a way to estimate lengths when she did not have any measuring tools. She measured her hand in several ways, the length of her foot, and the length of her walking stride. Then she used these "natural units" as measuring tools.

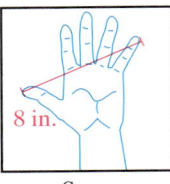
Span

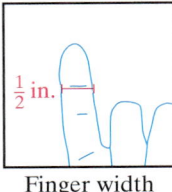
Finger width

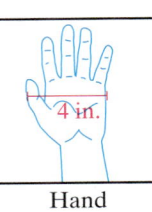
Hand

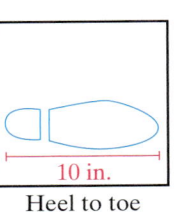
Heel to toe

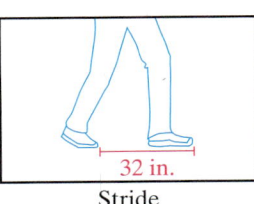
Stride

EXAMPLE

Jan used strides to measure the length of her room. She counted about 5 strides. What is the approximate length of the room?

1 stride ≈ 32 in.	← Write the relationship between strides and inches.
5 × 1 stride ≈ 5 × 32 in.	← Multiply both sides by 5.
5 strides ≈ 160 in.	← Change strides to inches.
160 in. = (160 ÷ 12) ft	← Change inches to feet.
160 in. ≈ 13 ft	

● The approximate length of the room is 13 feet.

Exercises

Measure your "finger width," "hand," "span," and "heel to toe." Use these natural units to find the indicated measure for each object. Then give the approximate measure in inches, feet, or yards.

1. thickness of a math book   **2.** height of a chair   **3.** height of a door

4. length of an eraser   **5.** height of your desk   **6.** length of a new pencil

7. distance across a room   **8.** thickness of a door   **9.** length of a chalkboard

10. Open-Ended Measure your stride. Then measure something such as a hallway in strides, and approximate the length in feet or yards. Tell what distance you measured.

Writing Equivalent Times

The standard unit of time is the second (s). You use equivalent units to change from one unit of time to another.

Units of Time
1 minute (min) = 60 s
1 hour (h) = 60 min = 3,600 s
1 day (d) = 24 h = 1,440 min
1 week (wk) = 7 d = 168 h

EXAMPLE

How many seconds are equivalent to 1 minute 20 seconds?

$$1 \text{ minute } 20 \text{ seconds} = 60 \text{ s} + 20 \text{ s} \quad \leftarrow \text{One minute is equivalent to 60 seconds.}$$
$$= 80 \text{ s} \quad \leftarrow \text{Simplify.}$$

So 1 minute 20 seconds is equivalent to 80 seconds.

Exercises

For each time, write an equivalent time using only the smaller unit.

1. 4 wk 3 days
2. 1 h 30 min
3. 2 min 59 s
4. 8 h 2 min
5. 5 min 36 s
6. 3 wk 5 days
7. 2 days 17 h
8. 2 h 15 min
9. 1 yr 2 wk
10. 12 min 4 s
11. 2 wk 1 day
12. 4 days 14 h
13. 3 yr 14 wk
14. 23 min 32 s
15. 3 h 47 min
16. 7 min 46 s
17. 5 wk 3 days
18. 1 yr 8 wk
19. 12 h 12 min
20. 3 days 4 h
21. 9 min 9 s
22. 5 yr 40 wk
23. 4 h 52 min
24. 7 wk 1 day

Skills Handbook

Skills Handbook

1. 31 days
2. 90 min
3. 179 s
4. 482 min
5. 336 s
6. 26 days
7. 65 hours
8. 135 min
9. 54 wk
10. 724 s
11. 15 days
12. 110 h
13. 170 wk
14. 1,412 s
15. 227 min
16. 466 s
17. 38 days
18. 60 wk
19. 732 min
20. 76 h
21. 549 s
22. 300 wk
23. 292 min
24. 50 days

Table 1 Measures

Metric	Customary
Length	**Length**
10 millimeters (mm) = 1 centimeter (cm) 100 cm = 1 meter (m) 1,000 mm = 1 meter 1,000 m = 1 kilometer (km)	12 inches (in.) = 1 foot (ft) 36 in. = 1 yard (yd) 3 ft = 1 yard 5,280 ft = 1 mile (mi) 1,760 yd = 1 mile
Area	**Area**

100 square millimeters (mm^2) =
    1 square centimeter (cm^2)
10,000 cm^2 = 1 square meter (m^2)
	144 square inches (in.^{2}) =
	    1 square foot (ft^2)
	9 ft^2 = 1 square yard (yd^2)
	4,840 yd^2 = 1 acre

Volume	**Volume**

1,000 cubic millimeters (mm^3) =
    1 cubic centimeter (cm^3)
1,000,000 cm^3 = 1 cubic meter (m^3)
	1,728 cubic inches (in.^{3}) =
	    1 cubic foot (ft^3)
	27 ft^3 = 1 cubic yard (yd^3)

Mass	**Mass**
1,000 milligrams (mg) = 1 gram (g) 1,000 g = 1 kilogram (kg)	16 ounces (oz) = 1 pound (lb) 2,000 lb = 1 ton (t)
Liquid Capacity	**Liquid Capacity**
1,000 milliliters (mL) = 1 liter (L) 1,000 L = 1 kiloliter (kL)	8 fluid ounces (fl oz) = 1 cup (c) 2 c = 1 pint (pt) 2 pt = 1 quart (qt) 4 qt = 1 gallon (gal)
	Time
	60 seconds (s) = 1 minute (min) 60 min = 1 hour (h) 24 h = 1 day 7 days = 1 week (wk) 365 days ≈ 52 wk = 1 year (yr)

Table 2 Reading Math Symbols

Symbol	Meaning	Page	Symbol	Meaning	Page
+	plus (addition)	p. 2	P	perimeter	p. 426
−	minus (subtraction)	p. 2	ℓ	length	p. 426
×, ·	times (multiplication)	p. 2	w	width	p. 426
÷, $\sqrt{\ }$	divide (division)	p. 2	A	area	p. 426
=	is equal to	p. 5	s	side	p. 427
>	is greater than	p. 5	b	base	p. 432
<	is less than	p. 5	h	height	p. 432
≈	is approximately equal to	p. 8	C	circumference	p. 439
( )	parentheses for grouping	p. 16	d	diameter	p. 439
*	multiply (in a spreadsheet formula)	p. 81	π	pi; ≈ 3.14	p. 439
…	and so on	p. 108	r	radius	p. 439
≠	is not equal to	p. 124	S.A.	surface area	p. 454
$\stackrel{?}{=}$	Is the statement true?	p. 124	V	volume	p. 458
3^4	3 to the power 4	p. 162	B	area of base	p. 458
$\frac{1}{4}$	reciprocal of 4	p. 272	$P(event)$	probability of event	p. 482
3 : 5	ratio of 3 to 5	p. 306	-6	opposite of 6	p. 516
%	percent	p. 331	$|5|$	absolute value of 5	p. 517
$\overline{AB}$	segment AB	p. 362	$(2, 3)$	ordered pair with x-coordinate 2 and	
$\overrightarrow{AB}$	ray AB	p. 362		y-coordinate 3	p. 548
$\overleftrightarrow{AB}$	line AB	p. 362	≥	is greater than or equal to	p. 578
∠ABC	angle with sides BA and BC	p. 367	≤	is less than or equal to	p. 578
∠A	angle with vertex A	p. 367	$\sqrt{9}$	square root of 9	p. 578
°	degree(s)	p. 367			
∟	right angle (90°)	p. 368			

Table 3 For Use With Problem Solving Applications

Chapter 2
Highest Peak on Each Continent

Land Mass	Highest Peak	Height (feet)	Height (meters)
Africa	Kilimanjaro	19,340	5,895
Asia	Everest	29,035	8,850
Australia	Kosciusko	7,310	2,228
Antarctica	Vinson Massif	16,066	4,897
Europe	Elbrus	18,510	5,642
North America	McKinley	20,320	6,194
South America	Aconcagua	22,834	6,960

SOURCE: *Time Almanac 2003*

Chapter 5
Top Speeds in Miles per Minute

Animal	Top Speed	Animal	Top Speed
Black mamba snake	$\frac{1}{3}$	Peregrine falcon	$\frac{10}{3}$
Cheetah	$\frac{7}{6}$	Rabbit	$\frac{3}{5}$
Chicken	$\frac{3}{20}$	Spider	$\frac{1}{25}$
Giant tortoise	$\frac{1}{300}$	Whippet	$\frac{71}{120}$

SOURCE: *Natural History Magazine*

Chapter 7
Animal Tracks

Animal	Track	Track Size (inches)	Animal Height (feet)
Beaver		7	2 to $3\frac{3}{5}$
Grizzly bear		12	$5\frac{3}{5}$ to $9\frac{1}{5}$
Moose		$6\frac{1}{4}$	$7\frac{9}{10}$ to $10\frac{1}{5}$
Norway rat		$\frac{5}{8}$	$\frac{3}{10}$ to 1
Striped skunk		$1\frac{1}{2}$	$\frac{9}{10}$ to $1\frac{1}{5}$

SOURCE: *Mammals of the World*

Chapter 11
Selected Earth Temperatures

Location	Temperature (°F)	Elevation (feet)
Vostok Station, Antarctica	−129 (record low)	11,220
Colossal Cave, Arizona	70 (constant)	3,660
El Azizia, Libya	136 (record high)	367
Land surface (average)	47.3	2,559
Sea surface (average)	60.9	0
Upper mantle	932	Above −2,196,480
Lower mantle	3,632	−2,900,000 to −2,196,480
Outer core	9,032	−5,100,000 to −2,900,000
Inner core	12,632	Below −5,100,000

SOURCE: National Oceanic and Atmospheric Administration, *Glossary of Geology*

$P = 2\ell + 2w$, or $P = 2(\ell + w)$
$A = \ell \times w$
Rectangle

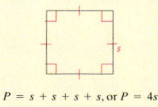

$P = s + s + s + s$, or $P = 4s$
$A = s \times s$, or $A = s^2$
Square

$A = \frac{1}{2}b \times h$
Triangle

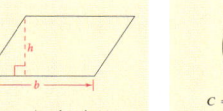

$A = b \times h$
Parallelogram

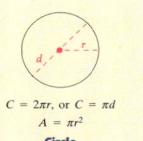

$C = 2\pi r$, or $C = \pi d$
$A = \pi r^2$
Circle

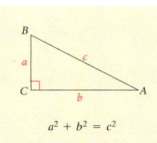

$a^2 + b^2 = c^2$
Pythagorean Theorem

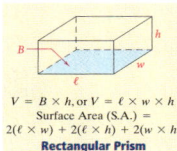

$V = B \times h$, or $V = \ell \times w \times h$
Surface Area (S.A.) =
$2(\ell \times w) + 2(\ell \times h) + 2(w \times h)$
Rectangular Prism

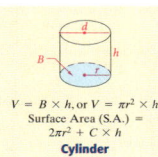

$V = B \times h$, or $V = \pi r^2 \times h$
Surface Area (S.A.) =
$2\pi r^2 + C \times h$
Cylinder

Properties of Numbers

Unless otherwise stated, the variables $a, b, c,$ and d used in these properties can be replaced with any number represented on a number line.

Associative Properties
Addition $(a + b) + c = a + (b + c)$
Multiplication $(a \cdot b) \cdot c = a \cdot (b \cdot c)$

Commutative Properties
Addition $a + b = b + a$
Multiplication $a \cdot b = b \cdot a$

Identity Properties
Addition $a + 0 = a$ and $0 + a = a$
Multiplication $a \cdot 1 = a$ and $1 \cdot a = a$

Inverse Properties
Addition
$a + (-a) = 0$ and $-a + a = 0$
Multiplication
$a \cdot \frac{1}{a} = 1$ and $\frac{1}{a} \cdot a = 1 (a \neq 0)$

Distributive Properties
$a(b + c) = ab + ac$
$a(b - c) = ab - ac$

Cross Products Property
If $\frac{a}{c} = \frac{b}{d}$, then $ad = bc$ ($c \neq 0, d \neq 0$).

Zero-Product Property
If $ab = 0$, then $a = 0$ or $b = 0$.

Properties of Equality
Addition   If $a = b$, then $a + c = b + c$.
Subtraction   If $a = b$, then $a - c = b - c$.
Multiplication   If $a = b$, then $a \cdot c = b \cdot c$.
Division   If $a = b$, and $c \neq 0$, then $\frac{a}{c} = \frac{b}{c}$.
Substitution   If $a = b$, then b can replace a in any expression.

Reflexive $a = a$
Symmetric   If $a = b$, then $b = a$.
Transitive   If $a = b$ and $b = c$, then $a = c$.

Properties of Inequality
Addition   If $a > b$, then $a + c > b + c$.
   If $a < b$, then $a + c < b + c$.
Subtraction   If $a > b$, then $a - c > b - c$.
   If $a < b$, then $a - c < b - c$.
Multiplication
If $a > b$ and c is positive, then $ac > bc$.
If $a < b$ and c is positive, then $ac < bc$.
Division
If $a > b$ and c is positive, then $\frac{a}{c} > \frac{b}{c}$.
If $a < b$ and c is positive, then $\frac{a}{c} < \frac{b}{c}$.

Note: The Properties of Inequality apply also to $\leq$ and $\geq$.

English/Spanish Illustrated Glossary

A

EXAMPLES

Absolute value (p. 517)   The absolute value of a number is its distance from 0 on a number line.

Valor absoluto (p. 517)   El valor absoluto de un número es su distancia del 0 en una recta numérica.

-7 is 7 units from 0, so $|-7| = 7$.

Acute angle (p. 368)   An acute angle is an angle with a measure between 0° and 90°.

Ángulo agudo (p. 368)   Un ángulo agudo es un ángulo que mide entre 0° y 90°.

$0° <$ measure of $\angle 1 < 90°$

Acute triangle (p. 380)   An acute triangle has three acute angles.

Triángulo acutángulo (p. 380)   Un triángulo acutángulo tiene tres ángulos agudos.

$\angle 1, \angle 2,$ and $\angle 3$ are acute.

Addition Property of Equality (p. 134)   The Addition Property of Equality states that if the same value is added to each side of an equation, the results are equal.

Propiedad aditiva de la igualdad (p. 134)   La propiedad aditiva de la igualdad establece que si se suma el mismo valor a cada lado de una ecuación, los resultados son iguales.

Since $\frac{20}{2} = 10, \frac{20}{2} + 3 = 10 + 3$.
If $a = b$, then $a + c = b + c$.

Algebraic expression (p. 113)   An algebraic expression is a mathematical phrase that uses variables, numbers, and operation symbols.

Expresión algebraica (p. 113)   Una expresión algebraica es un enunciado matemático que usa variables, números y símbolos de operaciones.

$2x - 5$ is an algebraic expression.

Angle (p. 367)   An angle is formed by two rays with a common endpoint called a vertex.

Ángulo (p. 367)   Un ángulo está formado por dos rayos que tienen un punto final común llamado vértice.

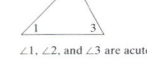

$\angle 1$ is made up of $\overrightarrow{GP}$ and $\overrightarrow{GS}$ with common endpoint G.

EXAMPLES

Angle bisector (p. 373)   An angle bisector is a ray that divides an angle into angles of equal measure.

Bisectriz de un ángulo (p. 373)   La bisectriz de un ángulo es un rayo que divide un ángulo en ángulos de igual medida.

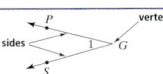

$\overrightarrow{DB}$ bisects $\angle ADC$, so $\angle 1 \cong \angle 2$.

Area (p. 426)   The area of a figure is the number of square units it encloses.

Área (p. 426)   El área de una figura es el número de unidades cuadradas que contiene.

Each square equals 1 ft². With $\ell = 6$ ft and $w = 4$ ft, the area is 24 ft².

Arithmetic sequence (p. 123)   In an arithmetic sequence, each term is the result of adding a fixed number (called the common difference) to the previous term.

Progresión aritmética (p. 123)   En una progresión aritmética, cada término es el resultado de sumar un número fijo al término anterior.

The sequence 4, 10, 16, 22, 28, ... is an arithmetic sequence. You add 6 to each term to find the next term.

Associative Property of Addition (pp. 12, 126)   The Associative Property of Addition states that changing the grouping of the addends does not change the sum.

Propiedad asociativa de la suma (pp. 12, 126)   La propiedad asociativa de la suma establece que cambiar la agrupación de los sumandos no cambia la suma.

$(2 + 3) + 7 = 2 + (3 + 7)$
$(a + b) + c = a + (b + c)$

Associative Property of Multiplication (pp. 13, 126)   The Associative Property of Multiplication states that changing the grouping of factors does not change the product.

Propiedad asociativa de la multiplicación (pp. 13, 126)   La propiedad asociativa de la multiplicación establece que cambiar la agrupación de los factores no altera el producto.

$(3 \cdot 4) \cdot 5 = 3 \cdot (4 \cdot 5)$
$(a \cdot b) \cdot c = a \cdot (b \cdot c)$

B

Bar graph (p. 74) A bar graph uses vertical or horizontal bars to display numerical information.

Gráfica de barras (p. 74) Una gráfica de barras usa barras horizontales o verticales para mostrar información numérica.

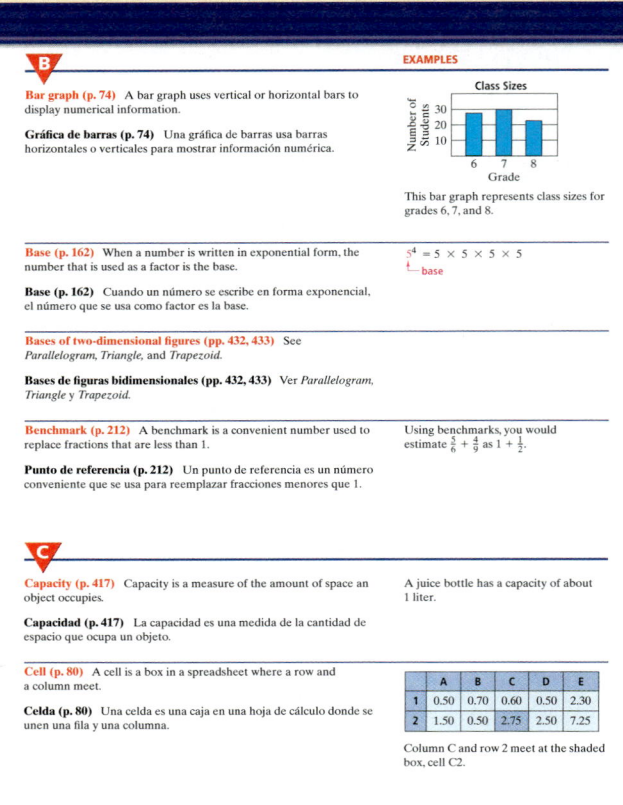

This bar graph represents class sizes for grades 6, 7, and 8.

Base (p. 162) When a number is written in exponential form, the number that is used as a factor is the base.

Base (p. 162) Cuando un número se escribe en forma exponencial, el número que se usa como factor es la base.

$$5^4 = 5 \times 5 \times 5 \times 5$$
base

Bases of two-dimensional figures (pp. 432, 433) See *Parallelogram*, *Triangle*, and *Trapezoid*.

Bases de figuras bidimensionales (pp. 432, 433) Ver *Parallelogram*, *Triangle* y *Trapezoid*.

Benchmark (p. 212) A benchmark is a convenient number used to replace fractions that are less than 1.

Punto de referencia (p. 212) Un punto de referencia es un número conveniente que se usa para reemplazar fracciones menores que 1.

Using benchmarks, you would estimate $\frac{5}{6} + \frac{4}{9}$ as $1 + \frac{1}{2}$.

C

Capacity (p. 417) Capacity is a measure of the amount of space an object occupies.

Capacidad (p. 417) La capacidad es una medida de la cantidad de espacio que ocupa un objeto.

A juice bottle has a capacity of about 1 liter.

Cell (p. 80) A cell is a box in a spreadsheet where a row and a column meet.

Celda (p. 80) Una celda es una caja en una hoja de cálculo donde se unen una fila y una columna.

	A	B	C	D	E
1	0.50	0.70	0.60	0.50	2.30
2	1.50	0.50	2.75	2.50	7.25

Column C and row 2 meet at the shaded box, cell C2.

Center of a circle (p. 438) A circle is named by its center.

Centro de un círculo (p. 438) Un círculo es denominado por su centro.

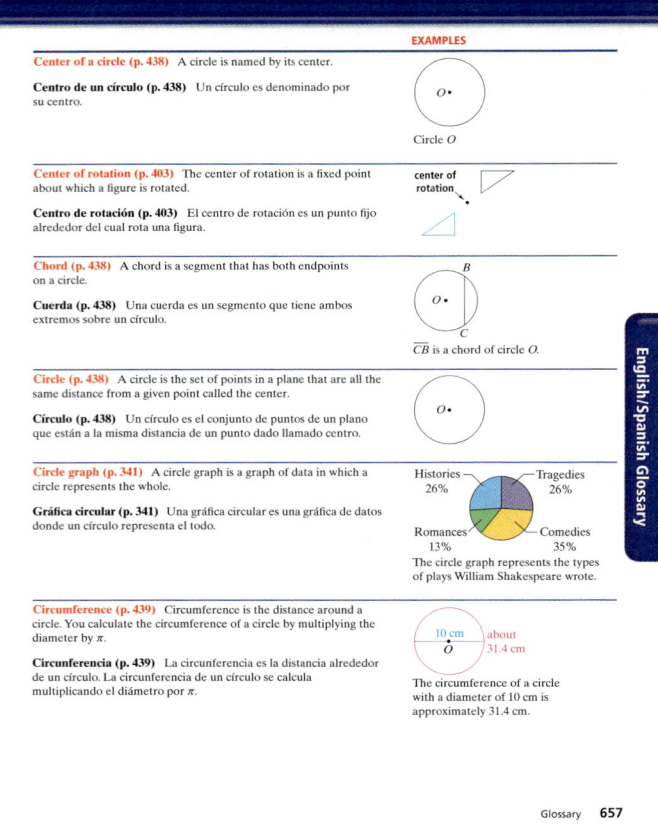

Circle *O*

Center of rotation (p. 403) The center of rotation is a fixed point about which a figure is rotated.

Centro de rotación (p. 403) El centro de rotación es un punto fijo alrededor del cual rota una figura.

center of rotation

Chord (p. 438) A chord is a segment that has both endpoints on a circle.

Cuerda (p. 438) Una cuerda es un segmento que tiene ambos extremos sobre un círculo.

$\overline{CB}$ is a chord of circle *O*.

Circle (p. 438) A circle is the set of points in a plane that are all the same distance from a given point called the center.

Círculo (p. 438) Un círculo es el conjunto de puntos de un plano que están a la misma distancia de un punto dado llamado centro.

Circle graph (p. 341) A circle graph is a graph of data in which a circle represents the whole.

Gráfica circular (p. 341) Una gráfica circular es una gráfica de datos donde un círculo representa el todo.

Histories 26% Tragedies 26% Romances 13% Comedies 35%

The circle graph represents the types of plays William Shakespeare wrote.

Circumference (p. 439) Circumference is the distance around a circle. You calculate the circumference of a circle by multiplying the diameter by π.

Circunferencia (p. 439) La circunferencia es la distancia alrededor de un círculo. La circunferencia de un círculo se calcula multiplicando el diámetro por π.

10 cm   about 31.4 cm

The circumference of a circle with a diameter of 10 cm is approximately 31.4 cm.

English/Spanish Glossary

Common factor (p. 171) A factor that two or more numbers share is a common factor.

Factor común (p. 171) Un número que es factor de dos o más números, es un factor común.

4 is a common factor of 8 and 20.

Common multiple (p. 188) A multiple shared by two or more numbers is a common multiple.

Múltiplo común (p. 188) Un número que es múltiplo de dos o más números, es un múltiplo común.

12 is a common multiple of 4 and 6.

Commutative Property of Addition (pp. 12, 126) The Commutative Property of Addition states that changing the order of the addends does not change the sum.

Propiedad conmutativa de la suma (pp. 12, 126) La propiedad conmutativa de la suma establece que al cambiar el orden de los sumandos no se altera la suma.

$3 + 1 = 1 + 3$
$a + b = b + a$

Commutative Property of Multiplication (pp. 12, 126) The Commutative Property of Multiplication states that changing the order of the factors does not change the product.

Propiedad conmutativa de la multiplicación (pp. 12, 126) La propiedad conmutativa de la multiplicación establece que al cambiar el orden de los factores no se altera el producto.

$6 \cdot 3 = 3 \cdot 6$
$a \cdot b = b \cdot a$

Compass (p. 372) A compass is a geometric tool used to draw circles or arcs.

Compás (p. 372) Un compás es una herramienta que se usa en geometría para dibujar círculos o arcos.

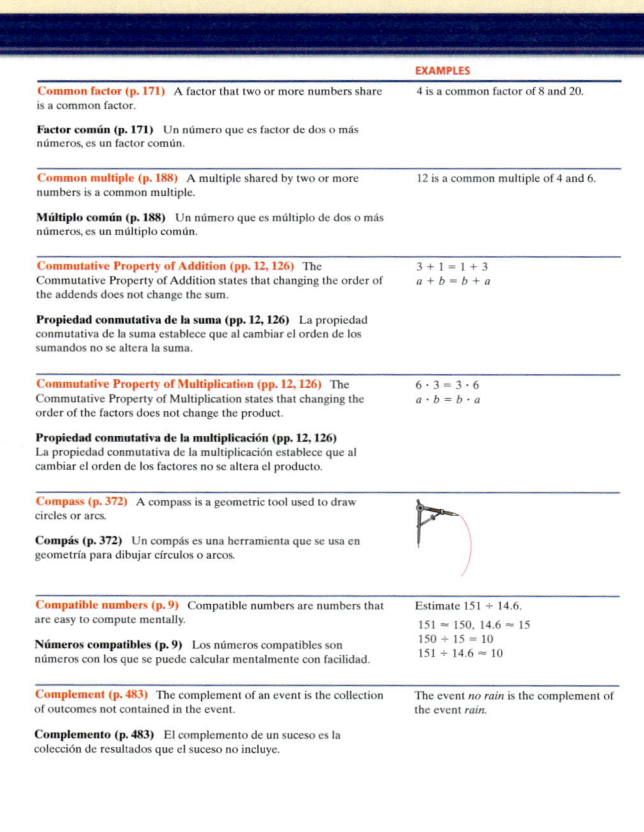

Compatible numbers (p. 9) Compatible numbers are numbers that are easy to compute mentally.

Números compatibles (p. 9) Los números compatibles son números con los que se puede calcular mentalmente con facilidad.

Estimate $151 \div 14.6$.
$151 \approx 150, 14.6 \approx 15$
$150 \div 15 = 10$
$151 \div 14.6 \approx 10$

Complement (p. 483) The complement of an event is the collection of outcomes not contained in the event.

Complemento (p. 483) El complemento de un suceso es la colección de resultados que el suceso no incluye.

The event *no rain* is the complement of the event *rain*.

Complementary (p. 374) Two angles are complementary if the sum of their measures is 90°.

Complementario (p. 374) Dos ángulos son complementarios si la suma de sus medidas es 90°.

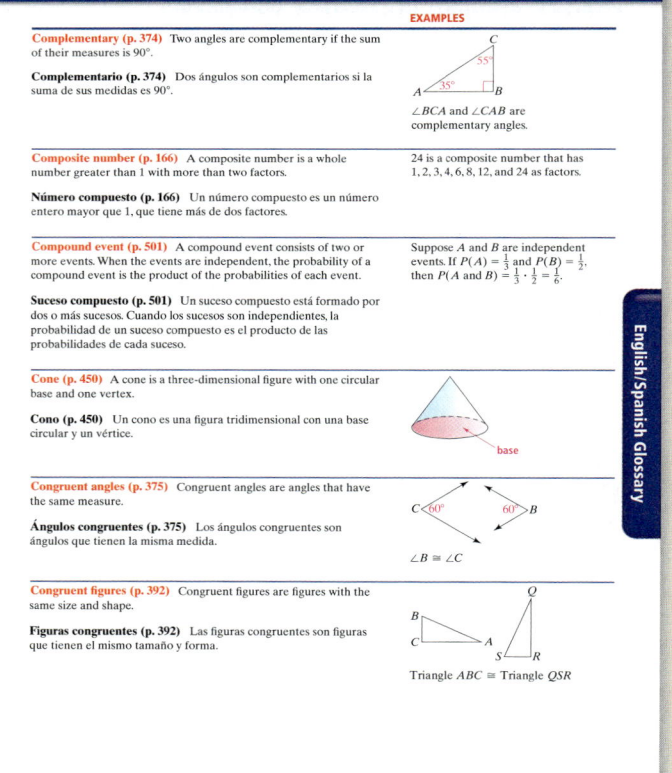

∠BCA and ∠CAB are complementary angles.

Composite number (p. 166) A composite number is a whole number greater than 1 with more than two factors.

Número compuesto (p. 166) Un número compuesto es un número entero mayor que 1, que tiene más de dos factores.

24 is a composite number that has 1, 2, 3, 4, 6, 8, 12, and 24 as factors.

Compound event (p. 501) A compound event consists of two or more events. When the events are independent, the probability of a compound event is the product of the probabilities of each event.

Suceso compuesto (p. 501) Un suceso compuesto está formado por dos o más sucesos. Cuando los sucesos son independientes, la probabilidad de un suceso compuesto es el producto de las probabilidades de cada suceso.

Suppose A and B are independent events. If $P(A) = \frac{1}{3}$ and $P(B) = \frac{1}{2}$, then $P(A \text{ and } B) = \frac{1}{3} \cdot \frac{1}{2} = \frac{1}{6}$.

Cone (p. 450) A cone is a three-dimensional figure with one circular base and one vertex.

Cono (p. 450) Un cono es una figura tridimensional con una base circular y un vértice.

base

Congruent angles (p. 375) Congruent angles are angles that have the same measure.

Ángulos congruentes (p. 375) Los ángulos congruentes son ángulos que tienen la misma medida.

$\angle B \cong \angle C$

Congruent figures (p. 392) Congruent figures are figures with the same size and shape.

Figuras congruentes (p. 392) Las figuras congruentes son figuras que tienen el mismo tamaño y forma.

Triangle $ABC \cong$ Triangle QSR

English/Spanish Glossary

Congruent segments (p. 381) Segments that have the same length are congruent segments.

Segmentos congruentes (p. 381) Los segmentos que tienen la misma longitud son segmentos congruentes.

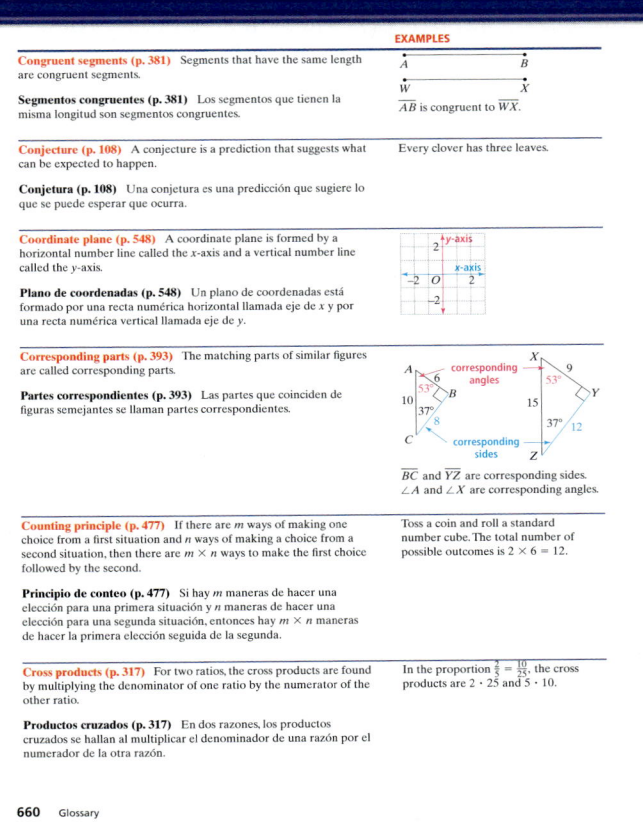

$\overline{AB}$ is congruent to $\overline{WX}$.

Conjecture (p. 108) A conjecture is a prediction that suggests what can be expected to happen.

Conjetura (p. 108) Una conjetura es una predicción que sugiere lo que se puede esperar que ocurra.

Every clover has three leaves.

Coordinate plane (p. 548) A coordinate plane is formed by a horizontal number line called the x-axis and a vertical number line called the y-axis.

Plano de coordenadas (p. 548) Un plano de coordenadas está formado por una recta numérica horizontal llamada eje de x y por una recta numérica vertical llamada eje de y.

Corresponding parts (p. 393) The matching parts of similar figures are called corresponding parts.

Partes correspondientes (p. 393) Las partes que coinciden de figuras semejantes se llaman partes correspondientes.

$\overline{BC}$ and $\overline{YZ}$ are corresponding sides.
$\angle A$ and $\angle X$ are corresponding angles.

Counting principle (p. 477) If there are m ways of making one choice from a first situation and n ways of making a choice from a second situation, then there are $m \times n$ ways to make the first choice followed by the second.

Principio de conteo (p. 477) Si hay m maneras de hacer una elección para una primera situación y n maneras de hacer una elección para una segunda situación, entonces hay $m \times n$ maneras de hacer la primera elección seguida de la segunda.

Toss a coin and roll a standard number cube. The total number of possible outcomes is $2 \times 6 = 12$.

Cross products (p. 317) For two ratios, the cross products are found by multiplying the denominator of one ratio by the numerator of the other ratio.

Productos cruzados (p. 317) En dos razones, los productos cruzados se hallan al multiplicar el denominador de una razón por el numerador de la otra razón.

In the proportion $\frac{4}{5} = \frac{10}{25}$, the cross products are $2 \cdot 25$ and $5 \cdot 10$.

Cube (p. 449) A cube is a rectangular prism whose faces are all squares.

Cubo (p. 449) Un cubo es un prisma rectangular cuyas caras son todas cuadrados.

Cubic unit (p. 458) A cubic unit is a cube whose edges are one unit long.

Unidad cúbica (p. 458) Una unidad cúbica es un cubo cuyos lados tienen una unidad de longitud.

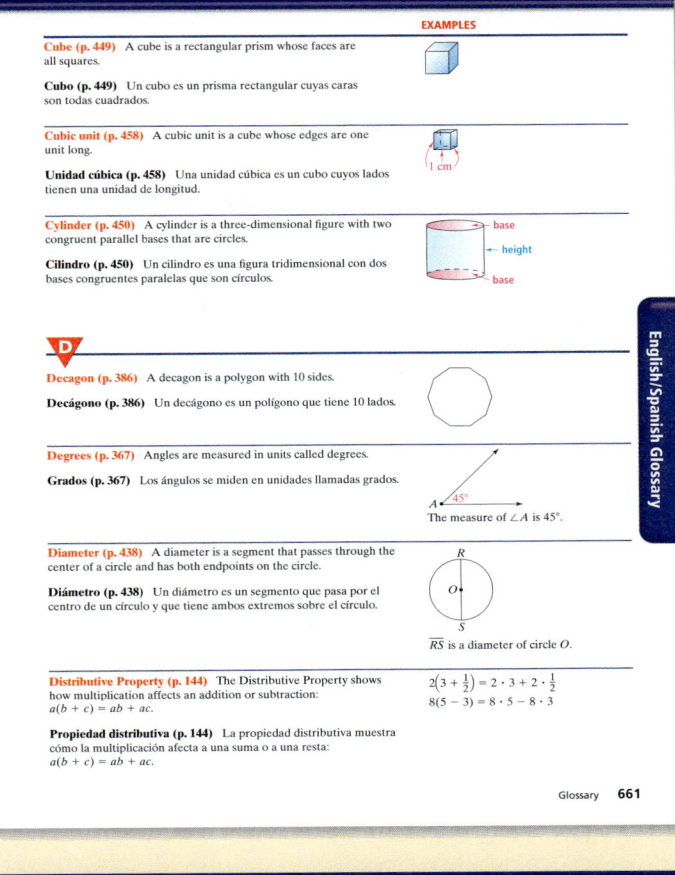

1 cm

Cylinder (p. 450) A cylinder is a three-dimensional figure with two congruent parallel bases that are circles.

Cilindro (p. 450) Un cilindro es una figura tridimensional con dos bases congruentes paralelas que son círculos.

base
height
base

D

Decagon (p. 386) A decagon is a polygon with 10 sides.

Decágono (p. 386) Un decágono es un polígono que tiene 10 lados.

Degrees (p. 367) Angles are measured in units called degrees.

Grados (p. 367) Los ángulos se miden en unidades llamadas grados.

A 45°
The measure of $\angle A$ is 45°.

Diameter (p. 438) A diameter is a segment that passes through the center of a circle and has both endpoints on the circle.

Diámetro (p. 438) Un diámetro es un segmento que pasa por el centro de un círculo y que tiene ambos extremos sobre el círculo.

R
O
S

$\overline{RS}$ is a diameter of circle O.

Distributive Property (p. 144) The Distributive Property shows how multiplication affects an addition or subtraction:
$a(b + c) = ab + ac$.

Propiedad distributiva (p. 144) La propiedad distributiva muestra cómo la multiplicación afecta a una suma o a una resta:
$a(b + c) = ab + ac$.

$2\left(3 + \frac{1}{2}\right) = 2 \cdot 3 + 2 \cdot \frac{1}{2}$
$8(5 - 3) = 8 \cdot 5 - 8 \cdot 3$

Divisible (p. 158) A whole number is divisible by a second whole number if the first number can be divided by the second number with a remainder of 0.

Divisible (p. 158) Un número entero es divisible por un segundo número entero si el primer número se puede dividir por el segundo número y el residuo es 0.

16 is divisible by 1, 2, 4, 8, and 16.

Division Property of Equality (p. 138) The Division Property of Equality states that if both sides of an equation are divided by the same nonzero number, the sides remain equal.

Propiedad de división de la igualdad (p. 138) La propiedad de división de la igualdad establece que si ambos lados de una ecuación se dividen por el mismo número distinto de cero, los dos lados se mantienen iguales.

Since $3(2) = 6$, $3(2) \div 2 = 6 \div 2$. If $a = b$ and $c \neq 0$, then $\frac{a}{c} = \frac{b}{c}$.

Double bar graph (p. 79) A double bar graph is a graph that uses bars to compare two sets of data.

Gráfica de doble barra (p. 79) Una gráfica de doble barra es una gráfica que usa barras para comparar dos conjuntos de datos.

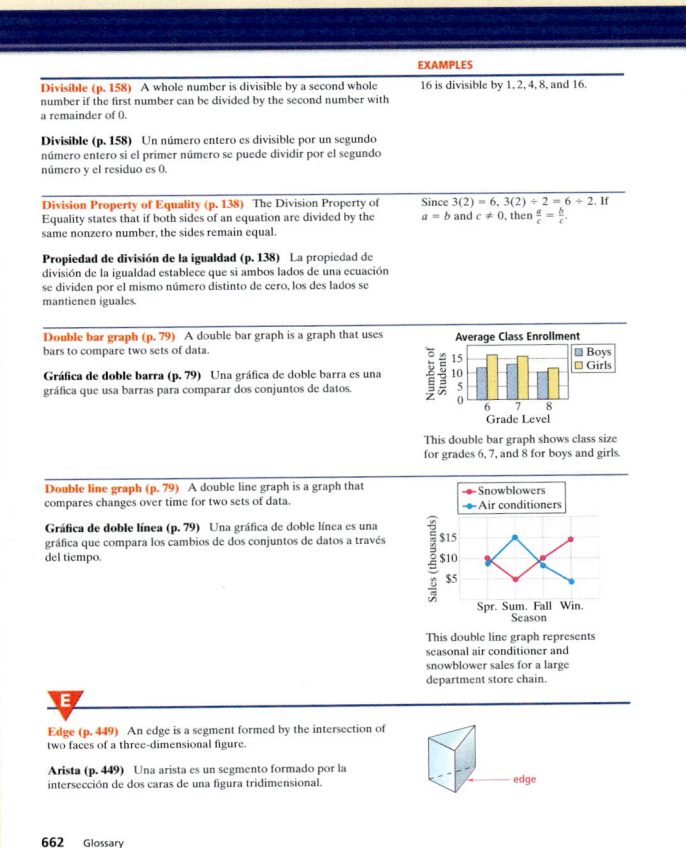

Average Class Enrollment

This double bar graph shows class size for grades 6, 7, and 8 for boys and girls.

Double line graph (p. 79) A double line graph is a graph that compares changes over time for two sets of data.

Gráfica de doble línea (p. 79) Una gráfica de doble línea es una gráfica que compara los cambios de dos conjuntos de datos a través del tiempo.

Snowblowers
Air conditioners

This double line graph represents seasonal air conditioner and snowblower sales for a large department store chain.

E

Edge (p. 449) An edge is a segment formed by the intersection of two faces of a three-dimensional figure.

Arista (p. 449) Una arista es un segmento formado por la intersección de dos caras de una figura tridimensional.

edge

Elapsed time (p. 246) The time between two events is elapsed time.

Tiempo transcurrido (p. 246) El tiempo que hay entre dos sucesos es el tiempo transcurrido.

The elapsed time between 8:10 A.M. and 8:45 A.M. is 35 minutes.

Equally likely outcomes (p. 482) Equally likely outcomes are outcomes that have the same chance of occurring.

Resultados igualmente probables (p. 482) Los resultados igualmente probables son resultados que tienen la misma posibilidad de ocurrir.

When a number cube is rolled once, the outcomes 1, 2, 3, 4, 5, and 6 are all equally likely outcomes.

Equation (p. 124) An equation is a mathematical sentence with an equal sign.

Ecuación (p. 124) Una ecuación es una oración matemática con un signo igual.

$27 \div 9 = 3$ and $x + 10 = 8$ are examples of equations.

Equilateral triangle (p. 381) An equilateral triangle is a triangle with three congruent sides.

Triángulo equilátero (p. 381) Un triángulo equilátero es un triángulo que tiene tres lados congruentes.

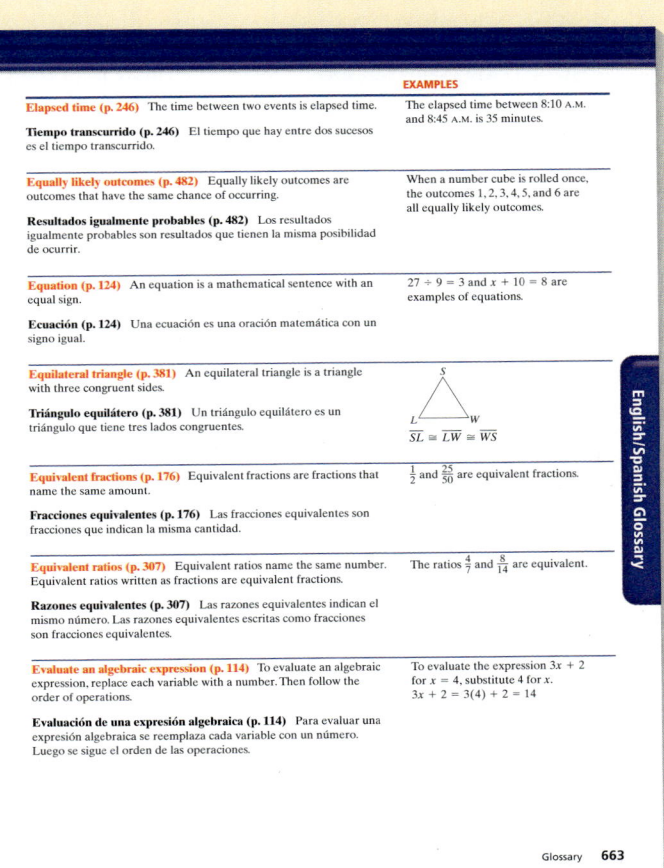

$\overline{SL} \cong \overline{LW} \cong \overline{WS}$

Equivalent fractions (p. 176) Equivalent fractions are fractions that name the same amount.

Fracciones equivalentes (p. 176) Las fracciones equivalentes son fracciones que indican la misma cantidad.

$\frac{1}{2}$ and $\frac{25}{50}$ are equivalent fractions.

Equivalent ratios (p. 307) Equivalent ratios name the same number. Equivalent ratios written as fractions are equivalent fractions.

Razones equivalentes (p. 307) Las razones equivalentes indican el mismo número. Las razones equivalentes escritas como fracciones son fracciones equivalentes.

The ratios $\frac{4}{7}$ and $\frac{8}{14}$ are equivalent.

Evaluate an algebraic expression (p. 114) To evaluate an algebraic expression, replace each variable with a number. Then follow the order of operations.

Evaluación de una expresión algebraica (p. 114) Para evaluar una expresión algebraica se reemplaza cada variable con un número. Luego se sigue el orden de las operaciones.

To evaluate the expression $3x + 2$ for $x = 4$, substitute 4 for x.
$3x + 2 = 3(4) + 2 = 14$

Even number (p. 159) An even number is any whole number that ends with a 0, 2, 4, 6, or 8.

Número par (p. 159) Un número par es cualquier número entero que termina en 0, 2, 4, 6 u 8.

20 and 534 are even numbers.

Event (p. 476) A collection of possible outcomes is an event.

Suceso (p. 476) Un suceso es un grupo de resultados posibles.

In a game that includes tossing a coin and rolling a standard number cube, "heads and a 2" is an event.

Expanded form (p. 23) The expanded form of a number is the sum that shows the place and value of each digit. See also *Standard form.*

Forma desarrollada (p. 23) La forma desarrollada de un número es la suma que muestra el lugar y valor de cada dígito. Ver también *Standard form.*

4.85 can be written in expanded form as $4 + 0.8 + 0.05$.

Experimental probability (p. 488) For a series of trials, the experimental probability of an event is the ratio of the number of times an event occurs to the total number of trials.

$$P(\text{event}) = \frac{\text{number of times an event occurs}}{\text{total number of trials}}$$

Probabilidad experimental (p. 488) En una serie de pruebas, la probabilidad experimental de un suceso es la razón del número de veces que ocurre un suceso al número total de pruebas.

$$P(\text{suceso}) = \frac{\text{número de veces que ocurre un suceso}}{\text{número de pruebas}}$$

A basketball player makes 15 baskets in 28 attempts. The experimental probability that the player makes a basket is $\frac{15}{28} \approx 54\%$.

Exponent (p. 162) An exponent tells how many times a number, or base, is used as a factor.

Exponente (p. 162) Un exponente dice cuántas veces se usa como factor un número o base.

exponent
$$3^4 = 3 \times 3 \times 3 \times 3$$
Read 3^4 as *three to the fourth power.*

Expression (p. 16) An expression is a mathematical phrase containing numbers and operation symbols.

Expresión (p. 16) Una expresión es un enunciado matemático que contiene números y símbolos de operaciones.

The expression $24 - 6 \div 3$ contains two operations.

Exterior angles (p. 378) The angles outside two lines that are crossed by a transversal are called exterior angles.

Ángulos exteriores (p. 378) Los ángulos que están fuera de las dos rectas cruzadas por una secante se llaman ángulos exteriores.

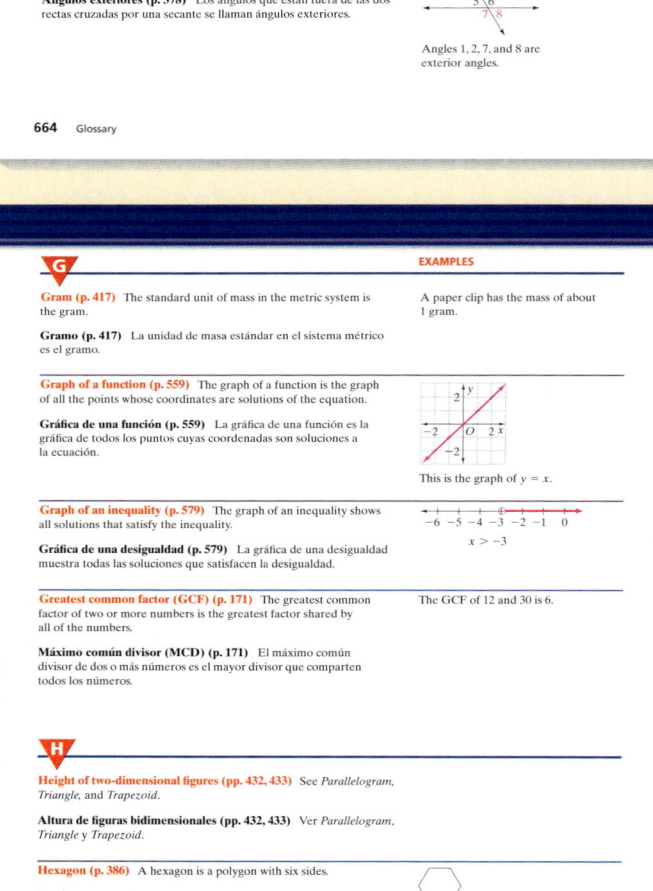

Angles 1, 2, 7, and 8 are exterior angles.

664   Glossary

F

Face (p. 449) A face is a flat, polygon-shaped surface of a three-dimensional figure.

Cara (p. 449) Una cara es una superficie plana de una figura tridimensional que tiene la forma de un polígono.

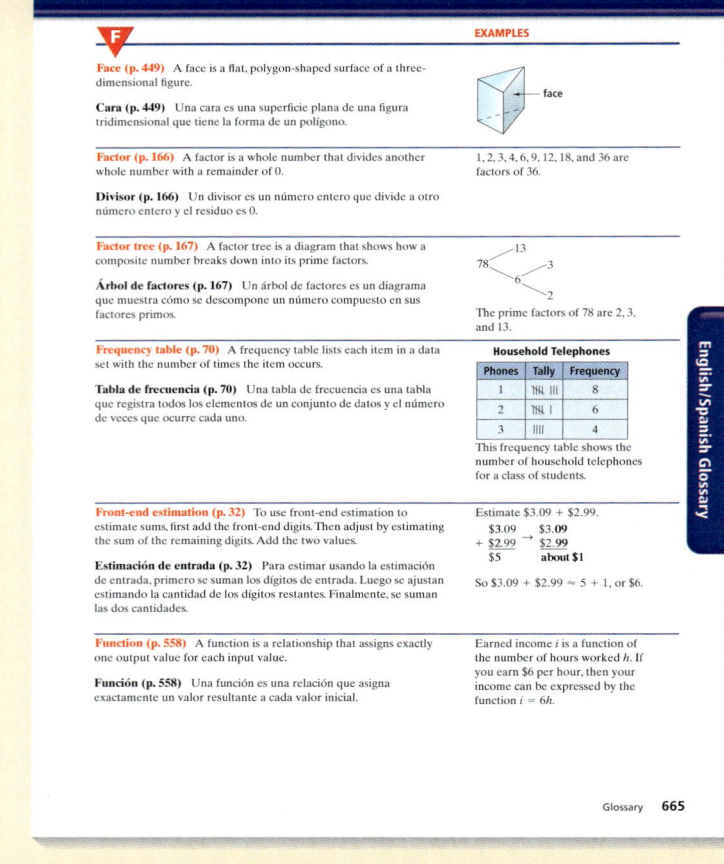

face

Factor (p. 166) A factor is a whole number that divides another whole number with a remainder of 0.

Divisor (p. 166) Un divisor es un número entero que divide a otro número entero y el residuo es 0.

1, 2, 3, 4, 6, 9, 12, 18, and 36 are factors of 36.

Factor tree (p. 167) A factor tree is a diagram that shows how a composite number breaks down into its prime factors.

Árbol de factores (p. 167) Un árbol de factores es un diagrama que muestra cómo se descompone un número compuesto en sus factores primos.

The prime factors of 78 are 2, 3, and 13.

Frequency table (p. 70) A frequency table lists each item in a data set with the number of times the item occurs.

Tabla de frecuencia (p. 70) Una tabla de frecuencia es una tabla que registra todos los elementos de un conjunto de datos y el número de veces que ocurre cada uno.

Household Telephones

Phones	Tally	Frequency
1										8
2								6
3						4

This frequency table shows the number of household telephones for a class of students.

Front-end estimation (p. 32) To use front-end estimation to estimate sums, first add the front-end digits. Then adjust by estimating the sum of the remaining digits. Add the two values.

Estimación de entrada (p. 32) Para estimar usando la estimación de entrada, primero se suman los dígitos de entrada. Luego se ajustan estimando la cantidad de los dígitos restantes. Finalmente, se suman las dos cantidades.

Estimate $\$3.09 + \$2.99$.
$$\begin{aligned}\$3.09 &\quad \$3.09\\ + \$2.99 &\quad \underline{\$2.99}\\ \hline \$5 &\quad \text{about } \$1\end{aligned}$$
So $\$3.09 + \$2.99 \approx 5 + 1$, or $\$6$.

Function (p. 558) A function is a relationship that assigns exactly one output value for each input value.

Función (p. 558) Una función es una relación que asigna exactamente un valor resultante a cada valor inicial.

Earned income i is a function of the number of hours worked h. If you earn $\$6$ per hour, then your income can be expressed by the function $i = 6h$.

Glossary   665

G

Gram (p. 417) The standard unit of mass in the metric system is the gram.

Gramo (p. 417) La unidad de masa estándar en el sistema métrico es el gramo.

A paper clip has the mass of about 1 gram.

Graph of a function (p. 559) The graph of a function is the graph of all the points whose coordinates are solutions of the equation.

Gráfica de una función (p. 559) La gráfica de una función es la gráfica de todos los puntos cuyas coordenadas son soluciones a la ecuación.

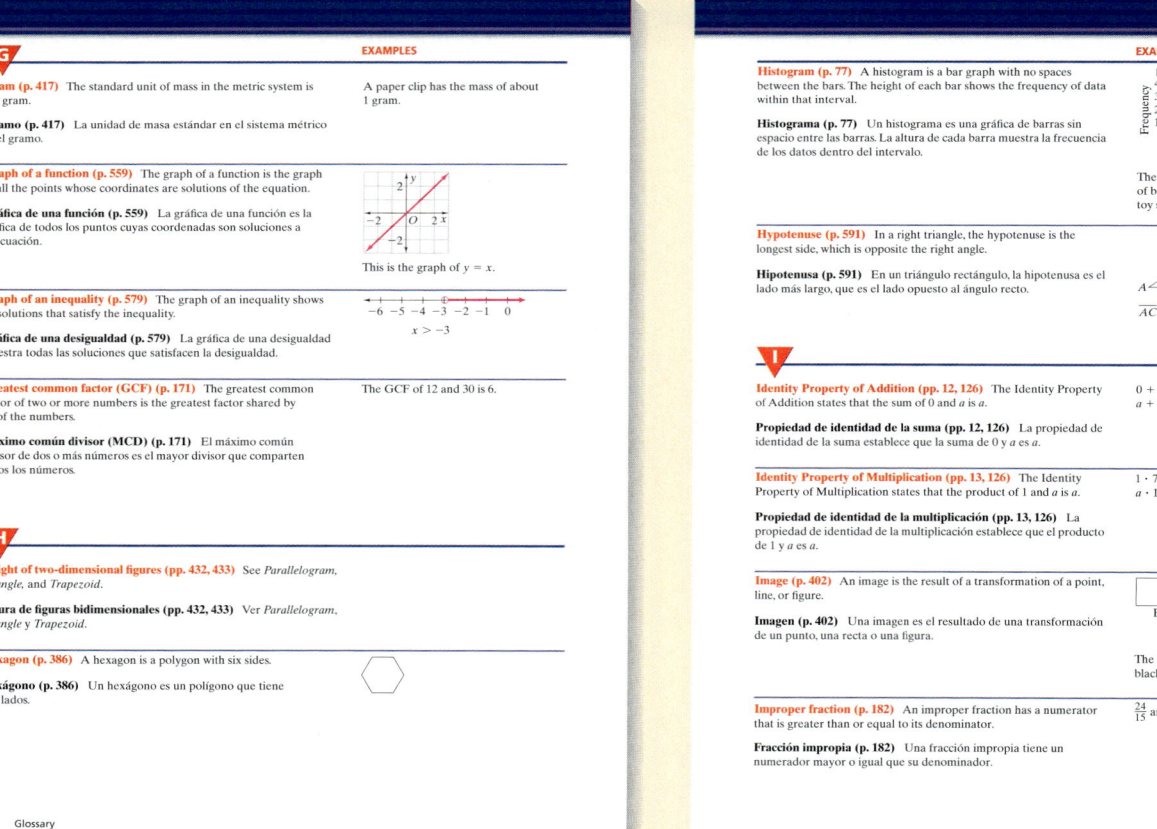

This is the graph of $y = x$.

Graph of an inequality (p. 579) The graph of an inequality shows all solutions that satisfy the inequality.

Gráfica de una desigualdad (p. 579) La gráfica de una desigualdad muestra todas las soluciones que satisfacen la desigualdad.

$x > -3$

Greatest common factor (GCF) (p. 171) The greatest common factor of two or more numbers is the greatest factor shared by all of the numbers.

Máximo común divisor (MCD) (p. 171) El máximo común divisor de dos o más números es el mayor divisor que comparten todos los números.

The GCF of 12 and 30 is 6.

H

Height of two-dimensional figures (pp. 432, 433) See *Parallelogram, Triangle,* and *Trapezoid.*

Altura de figuras bidimensionales (pp. 432, 433) Ver *Parallelogram, Triangle* y *Trapezoid.*

Hexagon (p. 386) A hexagon is a polygon with six sides.

Hexágono (p. 386) Un hexágono es un polígono que tiene seis lados.

666   Glossary

Histogram (p. 77) A histogram is a bar graph with no spaces between the bars. The height of each bar shows the frequency of data within that interval.

Histograma (p. 77) Un histograma es una gráfica de barras sin espacio entre las barras. La altura de cada barra muestra la frecuencia de los datos dentro del intervalo.

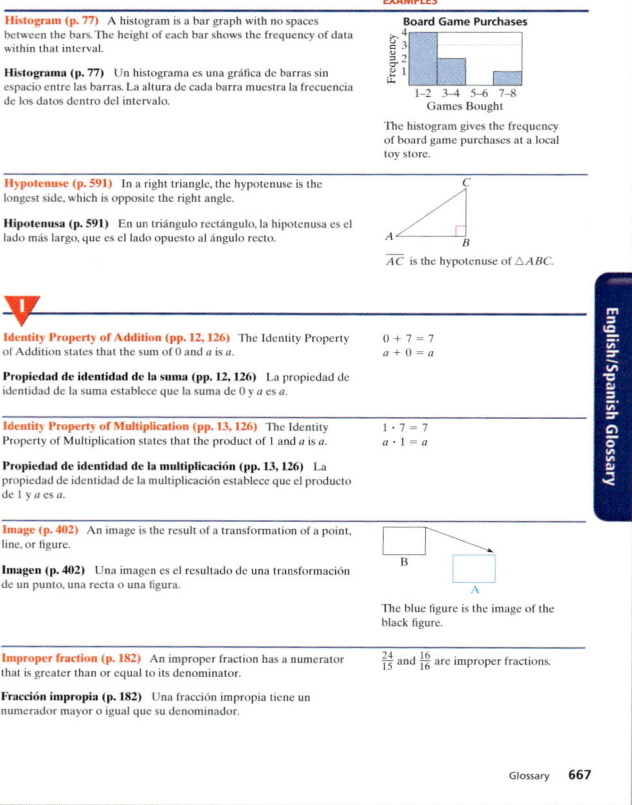

The histogram gives the frequency of board game purchases at a local toy store.

Hypotenuse (p. 591) In a right triangle, the hypotenuse is the longest side, which is opposite the right angle.

Hipotenusa (p. 591) En un triángulo rectángulo, la hipotenusa es el lado más largo, que es el lado opuesto al ángulo recto.

$\overline{AC}$ is the hypotenuse of $\triangle ABC$.

I

Identity Property of Addition (pp. 12, 126) The Identity Property of Addition states that the sum of 0 and a is a.

Propiedad de identidad de la suma (pp. 12, 126) La propiedad de identidad de la suma establece que la suma de 0 y a es a.

$0 + 7 = 7$
$a + 0 = a$

Identity Property of Multiplication (pp. 13, 126) The Identity Property of Multiplication states that the product of 1 and a is a.

Propiedad de identidad de la multiplicación (pp. 13, 126) La propiedad de identidad de la multiplicación establece que el producto de 1 y a es a.

$1 \cdot 7 = 7$
$a \cdot 1 = a$

Image (p. 402) An image is the result of a transformation of a point, line, or figure.

Imagen (p. 402) Una imagen es el resultado de una transformación de un punto, una recta o una figura.

The blue figure is the image of the black figure.

Improper fraction (p. 182) An improper fraction has a numerator that is greater than or equal to its denominator.

Fracción impropia (p. 182) Una fracción impropia tiene un numerador mayor o igual que su denominador.

$\frac{24}{15}$ and $\frac{16}{16}$ are improper fractions.

Glossary   667

Independent events (p. 500) Two events are independent events if the occurrence of one event does not affect the probability of the occurrence of the other.

Sucesos independientes (p. 500) Dos sucesos son independientes si el acontecimiento de uno no afecta la probabilidad de que el otro suceso ocurra.

Suppose you draw two marbles one after the other from a bag. If you replace the first marble before drawing the second marble, the events are independent.

Inequality (p. 572) An inequality is a mathematical sentence that contains $<$, $>$, $\leq$, $\geq$, or $\neq$.

Desigualdad (p. 572) Una desigualdad es una oración matemática que contiene los signos $<$, $>$, $\leq$, $\geq$ o $\neq$.

$x < -5$
$x > 8$
$x \leq 1$
$x \geq -11$
$x \neq 3$

Integers (p. 516) Integers are the set of positive whole numbers, their opposites, and 0.

Enteros (p. 516) Los enteros son el conjunto de números enteros positivos, sus opuestos y el 0.

$\ldots -3, -2, -1, 0, 1, 2, 3, \ldots$

Interior angles (p. 378) The angles between two lines that are crossed by a transversal are called interior angles.

Ángulos interiores (p. 378) Los ángulos que están entre dos rectas, cruzadas por una secante se llaman ángulos interiores.

Angles 3, 4, 5, and 6 are interior angles.

Intersecting lines (p. 363) Intersecting lines lie in the same plane and have exactly one point in common.

Rectas que se intersectan (p. 363) Las rectas que se intersectan están en el mismo plano y tienen exactamente un punto en común.

Inverse operations (p. 130) Inverse operations are operations that undo each other.

Operaciones inversas (p. 130) Las operaciones inversas son las operaciones que se anulan entre ellas.

Addition and subtraction are inverse operations.

Irregular polygon (p. 387) An irregular polygon is a polygon with sides that are not all congruent and/or angles that are not all congruent.

Polígono irregular (p. 387) Un polígono irregular es un polígono que tiene lados que no son todos congruentes y/o ángulos que no son todos congruentes.

$KLMN$ is an irregular polygon.

Isosceles triangle (p. 381) An isosceles triangle is a triangle with at least two congruent sides.

Triángulo isósceles (p. 381) Un triángulo isósceles es un triángulo que tiene al menos dos lados congruentes.

$\overline{LM} \cong \overline{LB}$

L

Least common denominator (LCD) (p. 192) The least common denominator of two or more fractions is the least common multiple (LCM) of their denominators.

Mínimo común denominador (mcd) (p. 192) El mínimo común denominador de dos o más fracciones es el mínimo común múltiplo (mcm) de sus denominadores.

The LCD of the fractions $\frac{3}{8}$ and $\frac{7}{10}$ is 40.

Least common multiple (LCM) (p. 188) The least common multiple of two numbers is the smallest number that is a multiple of both numbers.

Mínimo común múltiplo (mcm) (p. 188) El mínimo común múltiplo de dos números es el menor número que es múltiplo de ambos números.

The LCM of 15 and 6 is 30.

Legs of a right triangle (p. 591) The legs of a right triangle are the two shorter sides of the triangle.

Catetos de un triángulo rectángulo (p. 591) Los catetos de un triángulo rectángulo son los dos lados más cortos del triángulo.

$\overline{AB}$ and $\overline{BC}$ are the legs of triangle ABC.

Line (p. 362) A line is a series of points that extends in two opposite directions without end.

Recta (p. 362) Una recta es una serie de puntos que se extiende indefinidamente en dos direcciones opuestas.

$\overleftrightarrow{CG}$ is shown.

Line graph (p. 75) A line graph is a graph that uses a series of line segments to show changes in data. Typically, a line graph shows changes over time.

Gráfica lineal (p. 75) Una gráfica lineal es una gráfica que usa una serie de segmentos de recta para mostrar cambios en los datos. Típicamente, una gráfica lineal muestra cambios a través del tiempo.

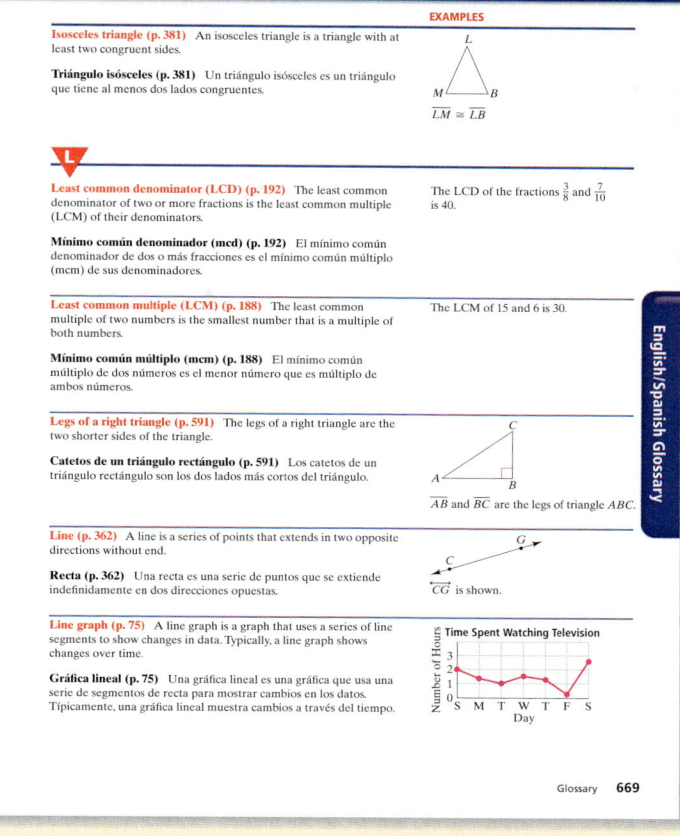

Time Spent Watching Television

Line of reflection (p. 403) A line of reflection is a line over which a figure is reflected.

Eje de reflexión (p. 403) Un eje de reflexión es una recta sobre la cual se refleja una figura.

line of reflection

Figure B is a reflection of Figure A.

Line of symmetry (p. 398) A line of symmetry divides a figure into mirror images.

Eje de simetría (p. 398) Un eje de simetría divide una figura en imágenes reflejas.

line of symmetry

Line plot (p. 71) A line plot is a graph that shows the shape of a data set by stacking ✗'s above each data value on a number line.

Diagrama de puntos (p. 71) Un diagrama de puntos es una gráfica que muestra la forma de un conjunto de datos agrupando ✗ sobre cada valor de una recta numérica.

Pets Owned by Students

The line plot shows the number of pets owned by each of 12 students.

Liter (p. 417) The liter (L) is the standard unit of capacity in the metric system.

Litro (p. 417) El litro (L) es la unidad de capacidad estándar en el sistema métrico.

A pitcher holds about 2 liters of juice.

M

Mass (p. 417) Mass is a measure of the amount of matter in an object.

Masa (p. 417) La masa es la medida de la cantidad de materia en un objeto.

A brick has a greater mass than a feather.

Mean (p. 61) The mean of a set of data values is the sum of the data divided by the number of data items.

Media (p. 61) La media de un conjunto de valores de datos es la suma de los datos dividida por el número de datos.

The mean temperature (°F) for the set of temperatures 44, 52, 48, 55, 61, and 67 is

$$\frac{44 + 52 + 48 + 55 + 61 + 67}{6} = 54.5.$$

Median (p. 66) The median of a data set is the middle value when the data are arranged in numerical order. When there is an even number of data values, the median is the mean of the two middle values.

Mediana (p. 66) La mediana de un conjunto de datos es el valor del medio cuando los datos están organizados en orden numérico. Cuando hay un número par de valores de datos, la mediana es la media de los dos valores del medio.

Five temperatures (°F) arranged in order are 44, 48, 52, 55, and 58. The median temperature is 52°F, because it is the middle number in the set of data.

Meter (p. 416) The meter (m) is the standard unit of length in the metric system.

Metro (p. 416) El metro (m) es la unidad de longitud estándar en el sistema métrico.

A doorknob is about 1 meter from the floor.

Metric system (p. 416) The metric system of measurement is a decimal system. Prefixes indicate the relative size of units.

Sistema métrico (p. 416) El sistema métrico de medidas es un sistema decimal. Los prefijos indican el tamaño relativo de las unidades.

1 kilogram = 1,000 grams
1 centimeter = $\frac{1}{100}$ meter
1 milliliter = $\frac{1}{1,000}$ liter

Midpoint (p. 372) The midpoint of a segment is the point that divides the segment into two segments of equal length.

Punto medio (p. 372) El punto medio de un segmento es el punto que divide el segmento en dos segmentos de igual longitud.

$\overline{XM} = \overline{YM}$. M is the midpoint of $\overline{XY}$.

Mixed number (p. 182) A mixed number is the sum of a whole number and a fraction.

Número mixto (p. 182) Un número mixto es la suma de un número entero y una fracción.

$3\frac{11}{16}$ is a mixed number. $3\frac{11}{16} = 3 + \frac{11}{16}$.

Mode (p. 67) The mode of a data set is the item that occurs with the greatest frequency.

Moda (p. 67) La moda de un conjunto de datos es el dato que sucede con mayor frecuencia.

The mode of the set of prices $2.50, $2.75, $3.60, $2.75, and $3.70 is $2.75.

Multiple (p. 188) A multiple of a number is the product of the number and any nonzero whole number.

Múltiplo (p. 188) Un múltiplo de un número es el producto de ese número y cualquier número entero diferente de cero.

The number 39 is a multiple of 13.

Multiplication Property of Equality (p. 139) The Multiplication Property of Equality states that if each side of an equation is multiplied by the same number, the results are equal.

Since $\frac{12}{2} = 6$, $\frac{12}{2} \cdot 2 = 6 \cdot 2$. If $a = b$, then $a \cdot c = b \cdot c$.

Propiedad multiplicativa de la igualdad (p. 139) La propiedad multiplicativa de la igualdad establece que si cada lado de una ecuación se multiplica por el mismo número, los resultados son iguales.

N

Net (p. 453) A net is a two-dimensional pattern that can be folded to form a three-dimensional figure.

Plantilla (p. 453) Una plantilla es un patrón bidimensional que se puede doblar para formar una figura tridimensional.

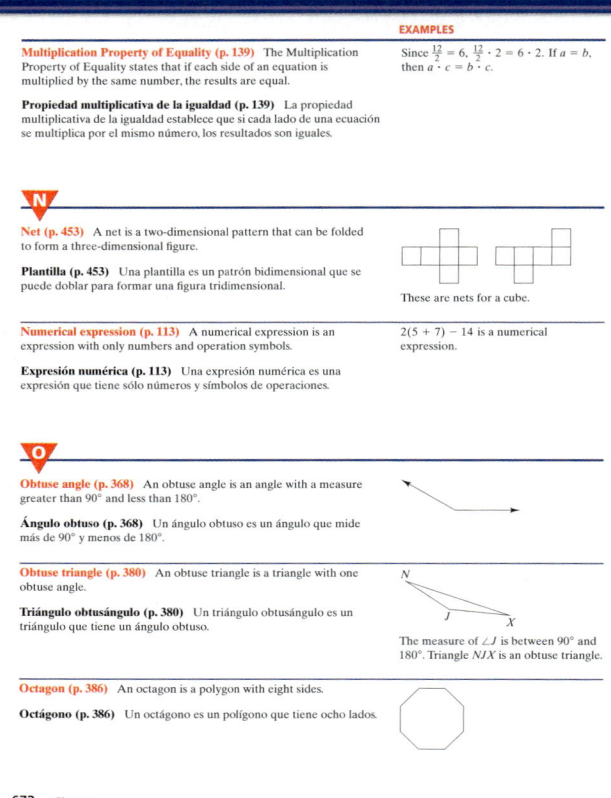

These are nets for a cube.

Numerical expression (p. 113) A numerical expression is an expression with only numbers and operation symbols.

$2(5 + 7) - 14$ is a numerical expression.

Expresión numérica (p. 113) Una expresión numérica es una expresión que tiene sólo números y símbolos de operaciones.

O

Obtuse angle (p. 368) An obtuse angle is an angle with a measure greater than 90° and less than 180°.

Ángulo obtuso (p. 368) Un ángulo obtuso es un ángulo que mide más de 90° y menos de 180°.

Obtuse triangle (p. 380) An obtuse triangle is a triangle with one obtuse angle.

Triángulo obtusángulo (p. 380) Un triángulo obtusángulo es un triángulo que tiene un ángulo obtuso.

The measure of $\angle J$ is between 90° and 180°. Triangle NJX is an obtuse triangle.

Octagon (p. 386) An octagon is a polygon with eight sides.

Octágono (p. 386) Un octágono es un polígono que tiene ocho lados.

Odd number (p. 159) An odd number is a whole number that ends with a 1, 3, 5, 7, or 9.

43 and 687 are odd numbers.

Número impar (p. 159) Un número impar es un número entero que termina en 1, 3, 5, 7 o 9.

Open sentence (p. 125) An open sentence is an equation with one or more variables.

$b - 7 = 12$

Proposición abierta (p. 125) Una proposición abierta es una ecuación con una o más variables.

Opposites (p. 516) Opposites are two numbers that are the same distance from 0 on a number line, but in opposite directions.

17 and −17 are opposites.

Opuestos (p. 516) Opuestos son dos números que están a la misma distancia del 0 en una recta numérica, pero en direcciones opuestas.

Ordered pair (p. 548) An ordered pair identifies the location of a point. The x-coordinate shows a point's position left or right of the y-axis. The y-coordinate shows a point's position up or down from the x-axis.

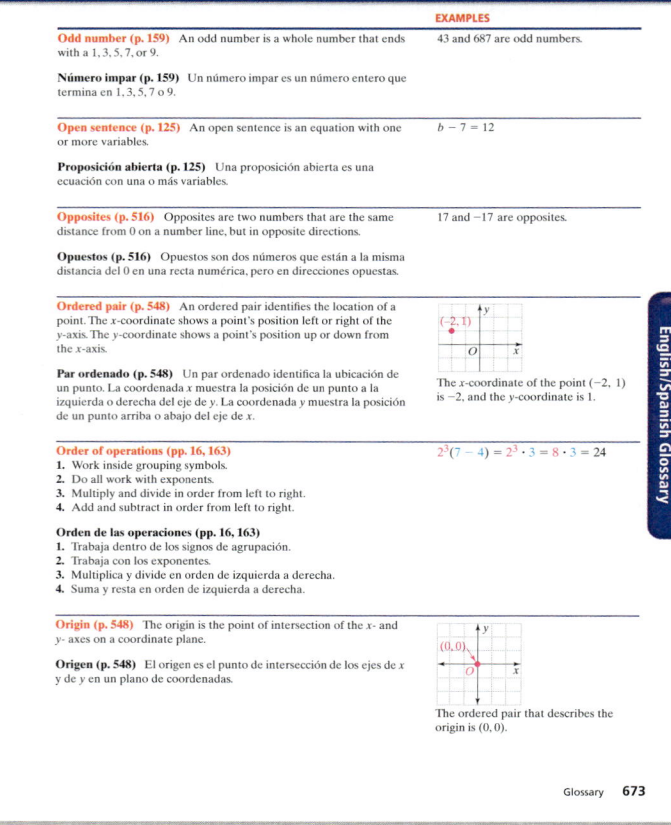

Par ordenado (p. 548) Un par ordenado identifica la ubicación de un punto. La coordenada x muestra la posición de un punto a la izquierda o derecha del eje de y. La coordenada y muestra la posición de un punto arriba o abajo del eje de x.

The x-coordinate of the point $(-2, 1)$ is −2, and the y-coordinate is 1.

Order of operations (pp. 16, 163)
1. Work inside grouping symbols.
2. Do all work with exponents.
3. Multiply and divide in order from left to right.
4. Add and subtract in order from left to right.

$2^3(7 - 4) = 2^3 \cdot 3 = 8 \cdot 3 = 24$

Orden de las operaciones (pp. 16, 163)
1. Trabaja dentro de los signos de agrupación.
2. Trabaja con los exponentes.
3. Multiplica y divide en orden de izquierda a derecha.
4. Suma y resta en orden de izquierda a derecha.

Origin (p. 548) The origin is the point of intersection of the x- and y- axes on a coordinate plane.

Origen (p. 548) El origen es el punto de intersección de los ejes de x y de y en un plano de coordenadas.

The ordered pair that describes the origin is (0, 0).

English/Spanish Glossary

Outcome (p. 476) An outcome is any of the possible results that can occur in an experiment.

The outcomes of rolling a standard number cube are 1, 2, 3, 4, 5, and 6.

Resultado (p. 476) Un resultado es cualquiera de los posibles desenlaces que pueden ocurrir en un experimento.

Outlier (p. 62) An outlier is a data item that is much greater or less than the other items in a data set.

The outlier in the data set 6, 7, 9, 10, 11, 12, 14, and 52 is 52.

Valor extremo (p. 62) Un valor extremo es un dato que es mucho más alto o más bajo que los demás datos de un conjunto de datos.

P

Parallel lines (p. 363) Parallel lines are lines in the same plane that never intersect.

Rectas paralelas (p. 363) Las rectas paralelas son rectas en el mismo plano que nunca se intersectan.

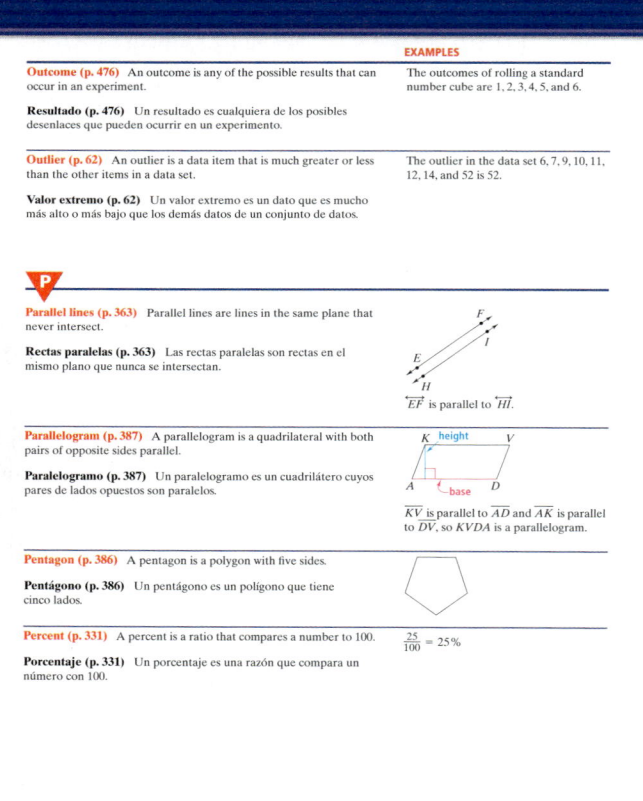

$\overleftrightarrow{EF}$ is parallel to $\overleftrightarrow{HI}$.

Parallelogram (p. 387) A parallelogram is a quadrilateral with both pairs of opposite sides parallel.

Paralelogramo (p. 387) Un paralelogramo es un cuadrilátero cuyos pares de lados opuestos son paralelos.

$\overline{KV}$ is parallel to $\overline{AD}$ and $\overline{AK}$ is parallel to $\overline{DV}$, so $KVDA$ is a parallelogram.

Pentagon (p. 386) A pentagon is a polygon with five sides.

Pentágono (p. 386) Un pentágono es un polígono que tiene cinco lados.

Percent (p. 331) A percent is a ratio that compares a number to 100.

$\frac{25}{100} = 25\%$

Porcentaje (p. 331) Un porcentaje es una razón que compara un número con 100.

Perfect square (p. 588) A perfect square is a number that is the square of an integer.

Since $25 = 5^2$, 25 is a perfect square.

Cuadrado perfecto (p. 588) Un cuadrado perfecto es un número que es el cuadrado de un entero.

Perimeter (p. 426) The perimeter of a figure is the distance around the figure.

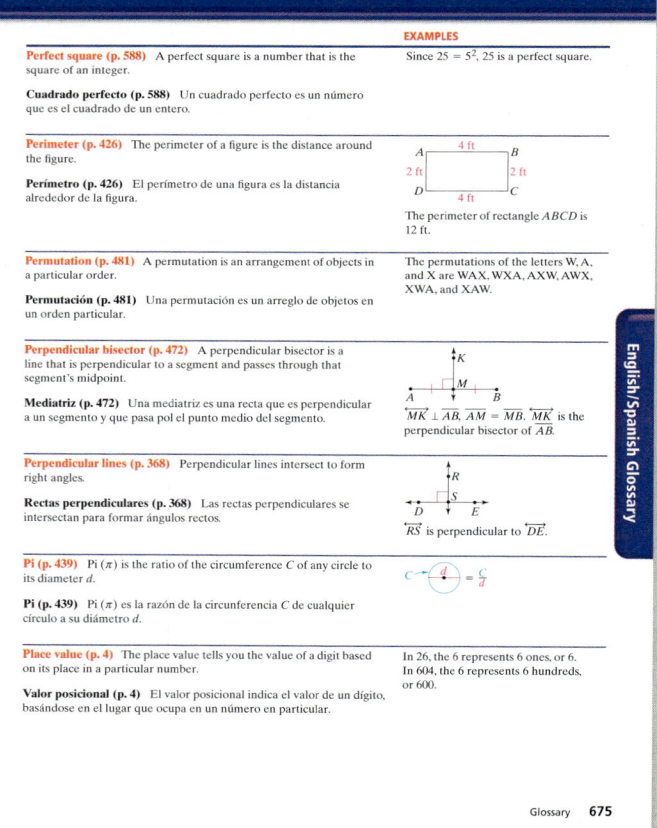

Perímetro (p. 426) El perímetro de una figura es la distancia alrededor de la figura.

The perimeter of rectangle $ABCD$ is 12 ft.

Permutation (p. 481) A permutation is an arrangement of objects in a particular order.

The permutations of the letters W, A, and X are WAX, WXA, AXW, AWX, XWA, and XAW.

Permutación (p. 481) Una permutación es un arreglo de objetos en un orden particular.

Perpendicular bisector (p. 472) A perpendicular bisector is a line that is perpendicular to a segment and passes through that segment's midpoint.

Mediatriz (p. 472) Una mediatriz es una recta que es perpendicular a un segmento y que pasa por el punto medio del segmento.

$\overleftrightarrow{MK} \perp \overline{AB}$, $\overline{AM} = \overline{MB}$. $\overleftrightarrow{MK}$ is the perpendicular bisector of $\overline{AB}$.

Perpendicular lines (p. 368) Perpendicular lines intersect to form right angles.

Rectas perpendiculares (p. 368) Las rectas perpendiculares se intersectan para formar ángulos rectos.

$\overleftrightarrow{RS}$ is perpendicular to $\overleftrightarrow{DE}$.

Pi (p. 439) Pi (π) is the ratio of the circumference C of any circle to its diameter d.

$C = \frac{C}{d}$

Pi (p. 439) Pi (π) es la razón de la circunferencia C de cualquier círculo a su diámetro d.

Place value (p. 4) The place value tells you the value of a digit based on its place in a particular number.

In 26, the 6 represents 6 ones, or 6. In 604, the 6 represents 6 hundreds, or 600.

Valor posicional (p. 4) El valor posicional indica el valor de un dígito, basándose en el lugar que ocupa en un número en particular.

English/Spanish Glossary

Plane (p. 363) A plane is a flat surface with no thickness that extends without end in all directions on the surface.

Plano (p. 363) Un plano es una superficie plana que no tiene grosor, que se extiende indefinidamente en todas las direcciones sobre la superficie.

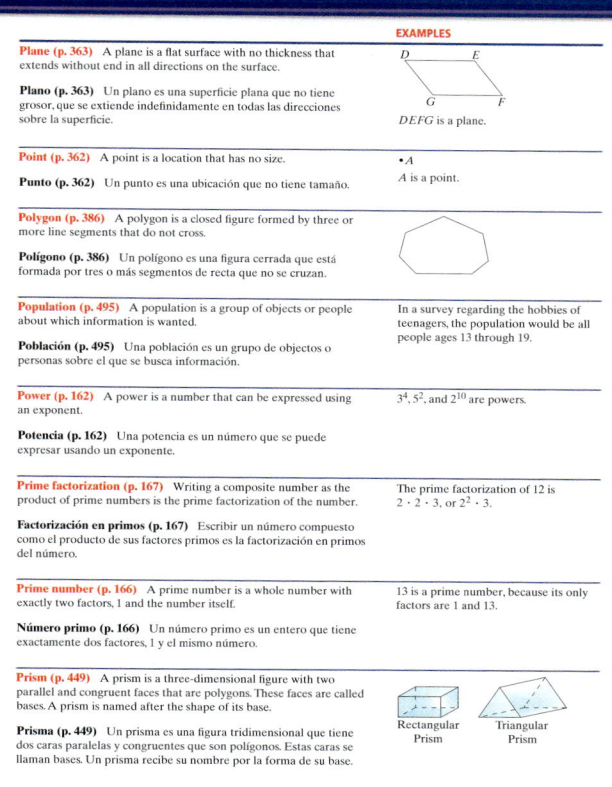

DEFG is a plane.

Point (p. 362) A point is a location that has no size.

Punto (p. 362) Un punto es una ubicación que no tiene tamaño.

•*A*

A is a point.

Polygon (p. 386) A polygon is a closed figure formed by three or more line segments that do not cross.

Polígono (p. 386) Un polígono es una figura cerrada que está formada por tres o más segmentos de recta que no se cruzan.

Population (p. 495) A population is a group of objects or people about which information is wanted.

Población (p. 495) Una población es un grupo de objetos o personas sobre el que se busca información.

In a survey regarding the hobbies of teenagers, the population would be all people ages 13 through 19.

Power (p. 162) A power is a number that can be expressed using an exponent.

Potencia (p. 162) Una potencia es un número que se puede expresar usando un exponente.

3^4, 5^2, and 2^{10} are powers.

Prime factorization (p. 167) Writing a composite number as the product of prime numbers is the prime factorization of the number.

Factorización en primos (p. 167) Escribir un número compuesto como el producto de sus factores primos es la factorización en primos del número.

The prime factorization of 12 is $2 \cdot 2 \cdot 3$, or $2^2 \cdot 3$.

Prime number (p. 166) A prime number is a whole number with exactly two factors, 1 and the number itself.

Número primo (p. 166) Un número primo es un entero que tiene exactamente dos factores, 1 y el mismo número.

13 is a prime number, because its only factors are 1 and 13.

Prism (p. 449) A prism is a three-dimensional figure with two parallel and congruent faces that are polygons. These faces are called bases. A prism is named after the shape of its base.

Prisma (p. 449) Un prisma es una figura tridimensional que tiene dos caras paralelas y congruentes que son polígonos. Estas caras se llaman bases. Un prisma recibe su nombre por la forma de su base.

Rectangular Prism   Triangular Prism

Probability of an event (p. 482) When outcomes are equally likely, the probability of an event is given by this formula:

$$P(\text{event}) = \frac{\text{number of favorable outcomes}}{\text{total number of possible outcomes}}$$

See *Experimental probability*.

Probabilidad de un suceso (p. 482) Cuando los resultados son igualmente posibles, la probabilidad de un suceso se da por esta fórmula:

$$P(\text{suceso}) = \frac{\text{número favorable de resultados}}{\text{número total de resultados posibles}}$$

Ver *Probabilidad experimental*.

Proper fraction (p. 182) A proper fraction has a numerator that is less than its denominator.

Fracción propia (p. 182) Una fracción propia tiene un numerador que es menos que su denominador.

$\frac{3}{8}$ and $\frac{11}{12}$ are proper fractions.

Proportion (p. 316) A proportion is an equation stating that two ratios are equal.

Proporción (p. 316) Una proporción es una ecuación que establece que dos razones son iguales.

$\frac{3}{12} = \frac{9}{36}$ is a proportion.

Pyramid (p. 450) A pyramid is a three-dimensional figure with triangular faces that meet at a vertex. A pyramid's base is a polygon. A pyramid is named after the shape of its base.

Pirámide (p. 450) Una pirámide es una figura tridimensional que tiene caras triangulares que coinciden en un vértice. Su base es un polígono. Una pirámide recibe su nombre por la forma de su base.

Triangular Pyramid   Rectangular Pyramid

Pythagorean Theorem (p. 591) In any right triangle, the sum of the squares of the lengths of the legs (*a* and *b*) is equal to the square of the length of the hypotenuse (*c*): $a^2 + b^2 = c^2$.

Teorema de Pitágoras (p. 591) En cualquier triángulo rectángulo, la suma del cuadrado de la longitud de los catetos (*a* y *b*) es igual al cuadrado de la longitud de la hipotenusa (*c*): $a^2 + b^2 = c^2$.

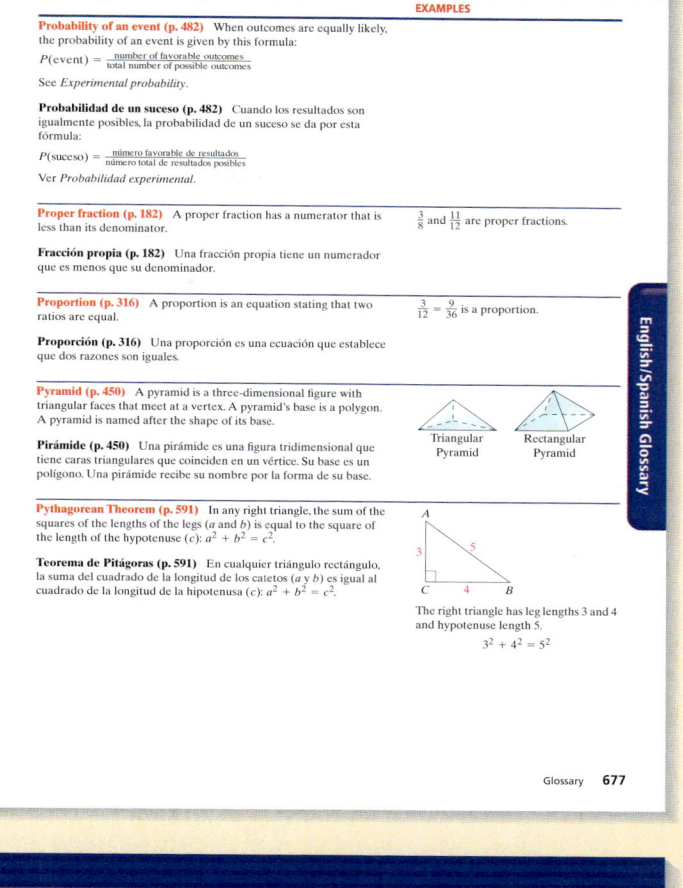

The right triangle has leg lengths 3 and 4 and hypotenuse length 5.

$$3^2 + 4^2 = 5^2$$

Q

Quadrants (p. 548) The *x*- and *y*-axes divide the coordinate plane into four regions called quadrants.

Cuadrantes (p. 548) Los ejes de *x* y de *y* dividen el plano de coordenadas en cuatro regiones llamadas cuadrantes.

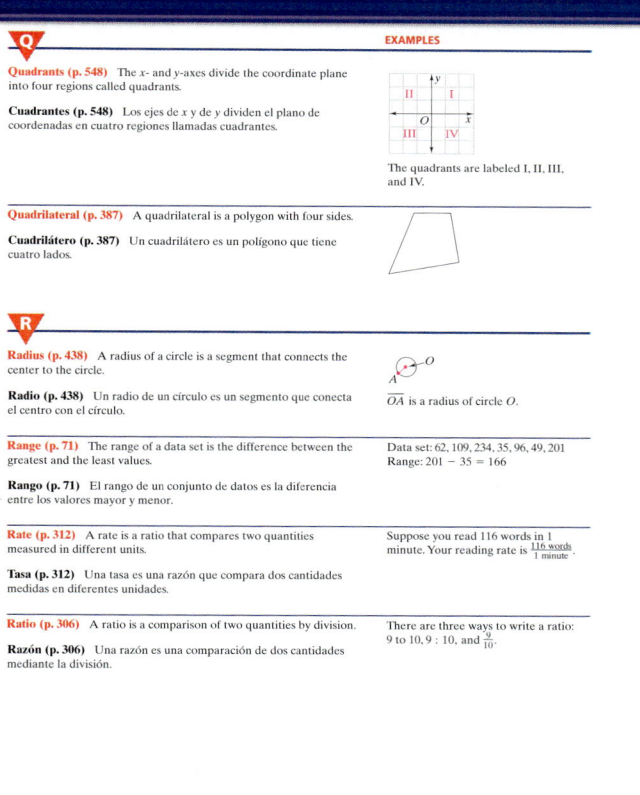

The quadrants are labeled I, II, III, and IV.

Quadrilateral (p. 387) A quadrilateral is a polygon with four sides.

Cuadrilátero (p. 387) Un cuadrilátero es un polígono que tiene cuatro lados.

R

Radius (p. 438) A radius of a circle is a segment that connects the center to the circle.

Radio (p. 438) Un radio de un círculo es un segmento que conecta el centro con el círculo.

$\overline{OA}$ is a radius of circle *O*.

Range (p. 71) The range of a data set is the difference between the greatest and the least values.

Rango (p. 71) El rango de un conjunto de datos es la diferencia entre los valores mayor y menor.

Data set: 62, 109, 234, 35, 96, 49, 201
Range: $201 - 35 = 166$

Rate (p. 312) A rate is a ratio that compares two quantities measured in different units.

Tasa (p. 312) Una tasa es una razón que compara dos cantidades medidas en diferentes unidades.

Suppose you read 116 words in 1 minute. Your reading rate is $\frac{116 \text{ words}}{1 \text{ minute}}$.

Ratio (p. 306) A ratio is a comparison of two quantities by division.

Razón (p. 306) Una razón es una comparación de dos cantidades mediante la división.

There are three ways to write a ratio: 9 to 10, 9 : 10, and $\frac{9}{10}$.

Rational number (p. 588) A rational number is any number that can be written as a quotient of two integers where the denominator is not 0.

Número racional (p. 588) Un número racional es cualquier número que puede ser escrito como cociente de dos enteros, donde el denominador es diferente de 0.

$\frac{1}{3}$, -5, 6.4, $0.666\ldots$, $-2\frac{4}{5}$, 0, and $\frac{7}{3}$ are rational numbers.

Ray (p. 362) A ray is part of a line. It has one endpoint and all the points of the line on one side of the endpoint.

Rayo (p. 362) Un rayo es parte de una recta. Tiene un extremo y todos los puntos de la recta a un lado del extremo.

endpoint of $\overrightarrow{CG}$

$\overrightarrow{CG}$ represents a ray.

Reciprocal (p. 272) Two numbers are reciprocals if their product is 1.

Recíproco (p. 272) Dos números son recíprocos si su producto es 1.

The numbers $\frac{4}{9}$ and $\frac{9}{4}$ are reciprocals.

Rectangle (p. 387) A rectangle is a parallelogram with four right angles.

Rectángulo (p. 387) Un rectángulo es un paralelogramo que tiene cuatro ángulos rectos.

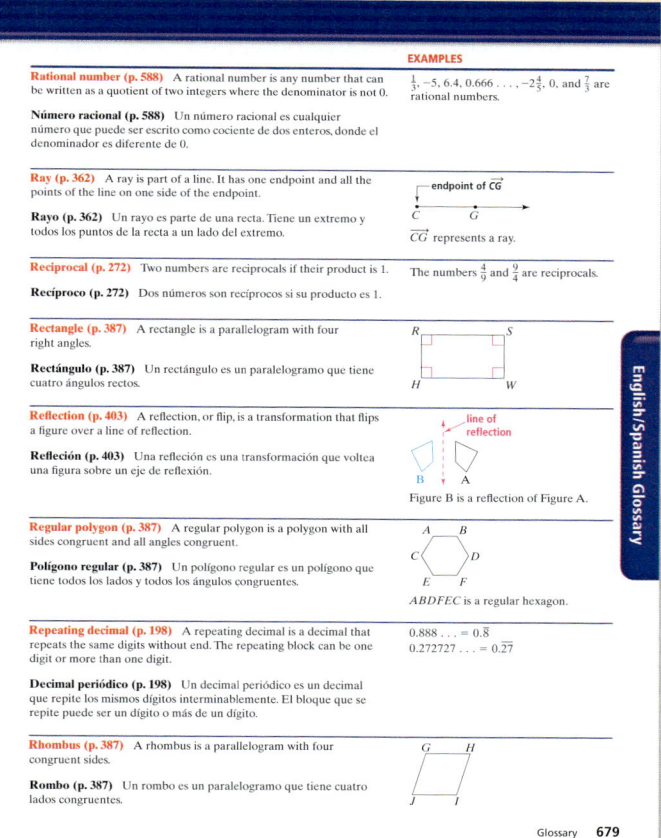

Reflection (p. 403) A reflection, or flip, is a transformation that flips a figure over a line of reflection.

Reflexión (p. 403) Una reflexión es una transformación que voltea una figura sobre un eje de reflexión.

line of reflection

Figure B is a reflection of Figure A.

Regular polygon (p. 387) A regular polygon is a polygon with all sides congruent and all angles congruent.

Polígono regular (p. 387) Un polígono regular es un polígono que tiene todos los lados y todos los ángulos congruentes.

ABDFEC is a regular hexagon.

Repeating decimal (p. 198) A repeating decimal is a decimal that repeats the same digits without end. The repeating block can be one digit or more than one digit.

Decimal periódico (p. 198) Un decimal periódico es un decimal que repite los mismos dígitos interminablemente. El bloque que se repite puede ser un dígito o más de un dígito.

$0.888\ldots = 0.\overline{8}$
$0.272727\ldots = 0.\overline{27}$

Rhombus (p. 387) A rhombus is a parallelogram with four congruent sides.

Rombo (p. 387) Un rombo es un paralelogramo que tiene cuatro lados congruentes.

English/Spanish Glossary

T655

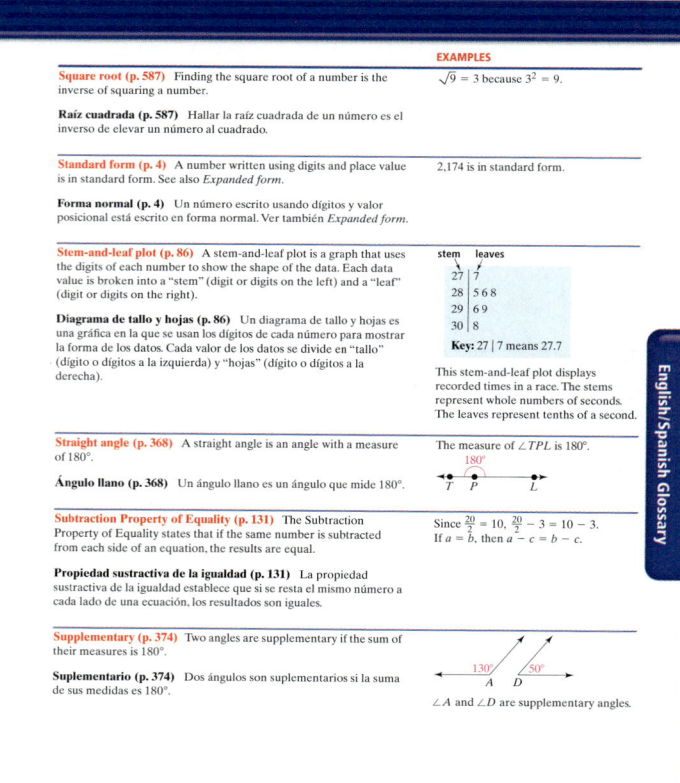

Page 680

Right angle (p. 368) A right angle is an angle with a measure of 90°.

Ángulo recto (p. 368) Un ángulo recto es un ángulo que mide 90°.

$m\angle D = 90°$

Right triangle (p. 380) A right triangle is a triangle with one right angle.

Triángulo rectángulo (p. 380) Un triángulo rectángulo es un triángulo que tiene un ángulo recto.

$\triangle ABC$ is a right triangle since $\angle B$ is a right angle.

Rotation (p. 403) A rotation is a transformation that turns a figure about a fixed point called the center of rotation.

Rotación (p. 403) Una rotación es una transformación que gira una figura sobre un punto fijo llamado centro de rotación.

center of rotation

The blue triangle is a rotation of the black triangle.

S

Sample (p. 495) A sample is a part of a population. You use a sample to make predictions about a population.

Muestra (p. 495) Una muestra es una parte de una población. Se usa una muestra para hacer predicciones acerca de una población.

Suppose 50 students out of the 700 students at a school are surveyed. The 50 students represent a sample population.

Sample space (p. 476) A sample space is the collection of all possible outcomes in a probability experiment.

Espacio muestral (p. 476) El espacio muestral es el total de todos los resultados posibles en un experimento de probabilidad.

The sample space for tossing two coins is HH, HT, TH, and TT.

Scale (p. 326) A scale is the ratio that compares a length in a scale drawing to the corresponding length in the actual object.

Escala (p. 326) Una escala es la razón que compara la longitud en un dibujo con la longitud correspondiente en el objeto real.

A 25-mile road is 1 inch long on a map. The scale can be written three ways:

1 inch : 25 miles, $\frac{1\ inch}{25\ miles}$,

1 inch = 25 miles.

Page 681

Scale drawing (p. 326) A scale drawing is an enlarged or reduced drawing of an object that is similar to the actual object.

Dibujo a escala (p. 326) Un dibujo a escala es un dibujo aumentado o reducido de un objeto que es semejante al objeto real.

Maps and floor plans are scale drawings.

Scalene triangle (p. 381) A scalene triangle is a triangle with no congruent sides.

Triángulo escaleno (p. 381) Un triángulo escaleno es un triángulo cuyos lados no son congruentes.

Scatter plot (p. 84) A scatter plot is a graph that relates two sets of data.

Diagrama de dispersión (p. 84) Un diagrama de dispersión es una gráfica que relaciona dos conjuntos de datos.

Sales and Advertising

The scatter plot shows amounts spent by several companies on advertising (in dollars) versus product sales (in thousands of dollars).

Segment (p. 362) A segment is part of a line. It has two endpoints and all the points of the line between the endpoints.

Segmento (p. 362) Un segmento es parte de una línea. Tiene dos extremos y todos los puntos de la recta entre los puntos extremos.

endpoints of $\overline{EF}$

$\overline{EF}$ is a segment.

Sequence (p. 105) A sequence is a set of numbers that follow a pattern.

Secuencia (p. 105) Una secuencia es un conjunto de números que sigue un patrón.

3, 6, 9, 12, 15, . . . is a sequence.

Similar figures (p. 393) Two figures are similar if their corresponding angles have the same measure and the lengths of their corresponding sides are proportional. The symbol ~ means "is similar to."

Figuras semejantes (p. 393) Dos figuras son semejantes si sus ángulos correspondientes tienen la misma medida y las longitudes de sus lados correspondientes son proporcionales. El símbolo ~ significa "es semejante a."

$\triangle ABC \sim \triangle RTS$

English/Spanish Glossary

Page 682

Simplest form (p. 177) A fraction is in simplest form when the numerator and denominator have no common factors other than 1.

Mínima expresión (p. 177) Una fracción está en su mínima expresión cuando el numerador y el denominador no tienen otro factor común más que el uno.

The simplest form of $\frac{3}{9}$ is $\frac{1}{3}$.

Simulation (p. 498) A simulation of a real-world situation is a model used to find experimental probabilities.

Simulación (p. 498) Una simulación de una situación real es un modelo que se usa para hallar probabilidades experimentales.

A baseball team has equal chances of winning or losing the next game. You can use a coin to simulate the outcome.

Skew lines (p. 363) Skew lines are neither parallel nor intersecting. They lie in different planes.

Rectas cruzadas (p. 363) Las rectas cruzadas no son paralelas ni se intersecan. Están en planos diferentes.

$\overleftrightarrow{MT}$ and $\overleftrightarrow{QR}$ are skew lines.

Solution (pp. 125, 579) A solution is any value or values that makes an equation or inequality true.

Solución (pp. 125, 579) Una solución es cualquier valor o valores que hacen que una ecuación o una desigualdad sea verdadera.

4 is the solution of $x + 5 = 9$.

7 is a solution of $x < 15$.

Sphere (p. 450) A sphere is the set of all points in space that are the same distance from a center point.

Esfera (p. 450) Una esfera es el conjunto de todos los puntos en el espacio que están a la misma distancia de un punto central.

Spreadsheet (p. 80) A spreadsheet is a tool used for organizing and analyzing data. Spreadsheets are arranged in numbered rows and lettered columns.

Hoja de cálculo (p. 80) Una hoja de cálculo es una herramienta que se usa para organizar o analizar datos. Las hojas de cálculo se organizan en filas numeradas y columnas en orden alfabético.

	A	B	C	D	E
1	0.50	0.70	0.60	0.50	2.30
2	1.50	0.50	2.75	2.50	7.25

Column C and row 2 meet at cell C2.

Square (p. 387) A square is a parallelogram with four right angles and four congruent sides.

Cuadrado (p. 387) Una cuadrado es un paralelógramo que tiene cuatro ángulos rectos y cuatro lados congruentes.

$QRST$ is a square. $\angle Q$, $\angle R$, $\angle S$, and $\angle T$ are right angles, and $\overline{QR} \cong \overline{RS} \cong \overline{ST} \cong \overline{QT}$.

Page 683

Square root (p. 587) Finding the square root of a number is the inverse of squaring a number.

Raíz cuadrada (p. 587) Hallar la raíz cuadrada de un número es el inverso de elevar un número al cuadrado.

$\sqrt{9} = 3$ because $3^2 = 9$.

Standard form (p. 4) A number written using digits and place value is in standard form. See also *Expanded form*.

Forma normal (p. 4) Un número escrito usando dígitos y valor posicional está escrito en forma normal. Ver también *Expanded form*.

2,174 is in standard form.

Stem-and-leaf plot (p. 86) A stem-and-leaf plot is a graph that uses the digits of each number to show the shape of the data. Each data value is broken into a "stem" (digit or digits on the left) and a "leaf" (digit or digits on the right).

Diagrama de tallo y hojas (p. 86) Un diagrama de tallo y hojas es una gráfica en la que se usan los dígitos de cada número para mostrar la forma de los datos. Cada valor de los datos se divide en "tallo" (dígito o dígitos a la izquierda) y "hojas" (dígito o dígitos a la derecha).

stem	leaves
27	7
28	5 6 8
29	6 9
30	8

Key: 27 | 7 means 27.7

This stem-and-leaf plot displays recorded times in a race. The stems represent whole numbers of seconds. The leaves represent tenths of a second.

Straight angle (p. 368) A straight angle is an angle with a measure of 180°.

Ángulo llano (p. 368) Un ángulo llano es un ángulo que mide 180°.

The measure of $\angle TPL$ is 180°.

Subtraction Property of Equality (p. 131) The Subtraction Property of Equality states that if the same number is subtracted from each side of an equation, the results are equal.

Propiedad sustractiva de la igualdad (p. 131) La propiedad sustractiva de la igualdad establece que si se resta el mismo número a cada lado de una ecuación, los resultados son iguales.

Since $\frac{20}{2} = 10$, $\frac{20}{2} - 3 = 10 - 3$. If $a = b$, then $a - c = b - c$.

Supplementary (p. 374) Two angles are supplementary if the sum of their measures is 180°.

Suplementario (p. 374) Dos ángulos son suplementarios si la suma de sus medidas es 180°.

$\angle A$ and $\angle D$ are supplementary angles.

English/Spanish Glossary

Page 684

EXAMPLES

Surface area of a three-dimensional figure (p. 454) The surface area of a three-dimensional figure is the sum of the areas of all the surfaces.

Área total de una figura tridimensional (p. 454) El área total de una figura tridimensional es la suma de las áreas de todas sus superficies.

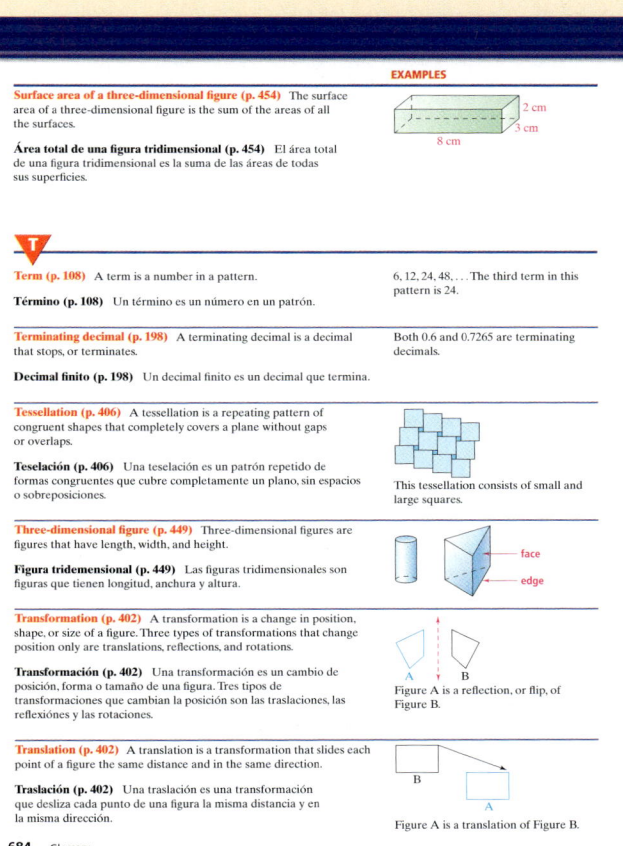

2 cm
3 cm
8 cm

T

Term (p. 108) A term is a number in a pattern.

Término (p. 108) Un término es un número en un patrón.

6, 12, 24, 48, . . . The third term in this pattern is 24.

Terminating decimal (p. 198) A terminating decimal is a decimal that stops, or terminates.

Decimal finito (p. 198) Un decimal finito es un decimal que termina.

Both 0.6 and 0.7265 are terminating decimals.

Tessellation (p. 406) A tessellation is a repeating pattern of congruent shapes that completely covers a plane without gaps or overlaps.

Teselación (p. 406) Una teselación es un patrón repetido de formas congruentes que cubre completamente un plano, sin espacios o sobreposiciones.

This tessellation consists of small and large squares.

Three-dimensional figure (p. 449) Three-dimensional figures are figures that have length, width, and height.

Figura tridimensional (p. 449) Las figuras tridimensionales son figuras que tienen longitud, anchura y altura.

face
edge

Transformation (p. 402) A transformation is a change in position, shape, or size of a figure. Three types of transformations that change position only are translations, reflections, and rotations.

Transformación (p. 402) Una transformación es un cambio de posición, forma o tamaño de una figura. Tres tipos de transformaciones que cambian la posición son las traslaciones, las reflexiónes y las rotaciones.

A   B

Figure A is a reflection, or flip, of Figure B.

Translation (p. 402) A translation is a transformation that slides each point of a figure the same distance and in the same direction.

Traslación (p. 402) Una traslación es una transformación que desliza cada punto de una figura la misma distancia y en la misma dirección.

B

A

Figure A is a translation of Figure B.

684   Glossary

Page 685

EXAMPLES

Transversal (p. 378) A line that intersects two or more lines is called a transversal.

Secante (p. 378) Una recta que interseca a dos o más rectas se llama secante.

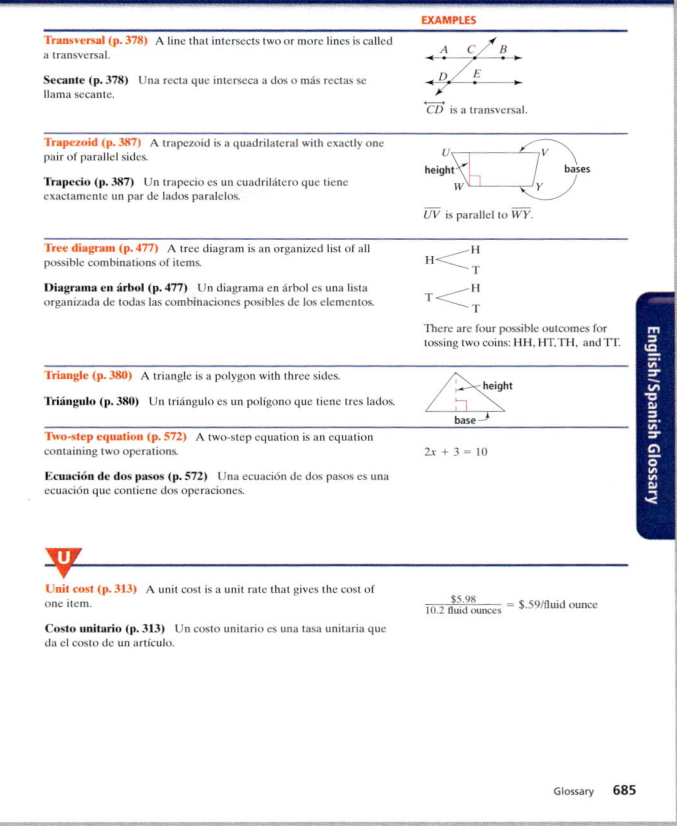

$\overleftrightarrow{CD}$ is a transversal.

Trapezoid (p. 387) A trapezoid is a quadrilateral with exactly one pair of parallel sides.

Trapecio (p. 387) Un trapecio es un cuadrilátero que tiene exactamente un par de lados paralelos.

U   V
height   bases
W   Y

$\overline{UV}$ is parallel to $\overline{WY}$.

Tree diagram (p. 477) A tree diagram is an organized list of all possible combinations of items.

Diagrama en árbol (p. 477) Un diagrama en árbol es una lista organizada de todas las combinaciones posibles de los elementos.

H — H
H — T
T — H
T — T

There are four possible outcomes for tossing two coins: HH, HT, TH, and TT.

Triangle (p. 380) A triangle is a polygon with three sides.

Triángulo (p. 380) Un triángulo es un polígono que tiene tres lados.

height
base

Two-step equation (p. 572) A two-step equation is an equation containing two operations.

Ecuación de dos pasos (p. 572) Una ecuación de dos pasos es una ecuación que contiene dos operaciones.

$2x + 3 = 10$

U

Unit cost (p. 313) A unit cost is a unit rate that gives the cost of one item.

Costo unitario (p. 313) Un costo unitario es una tasa unitaria que da el costo de un artículo.

$\frac{\$5.98}{10.2 \text{ fluid ounces}} = \$.59/\text{fluid ounce}$

Glossary   685

Page 686

EXAMPLES

Unit rate (p. 312) The rate for one unit of a given quantity is called the unit rate.

Tasa unitaria (p. 312) La tasa para una unidad de una cantidad dada se llama tasa unitaria.

If you drive 130 miles in 2 hours, your unit rate is $\frac{65 \text{ miles}}{1 \text{ hour}}$ or 65 mi/h.

V

Variable (p. 113) A variable is a letter that stands for a number. The value of an algebraic expression varies, or changes, depending upon the value given to the variable.

Variable (p. 113) Una variable es una letra que representa un número. El valor de una expresión algebraica varía, o cambia, dependiendo del valor que se le dé a la variable.

x is a variable in the equation $9 + x = 7$.

Vertex of an angle (p. 367) The vertex of an angle is the point of intersection of two sides of an angle or figure.

Vértice de un ángulo (p. 367) El vértice de un ángulo es el punto de intersección de dos lados de un ángulo o figura.

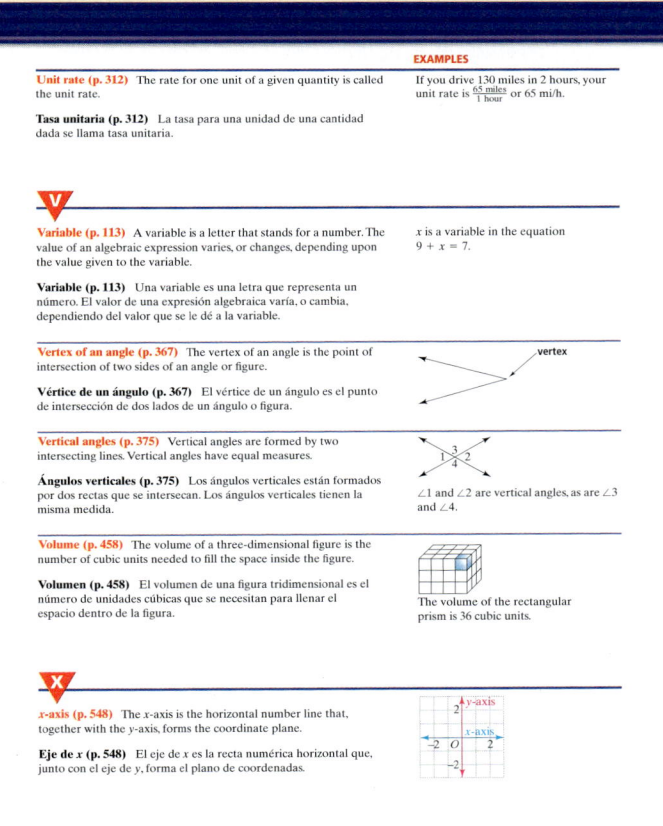

vertex

Vertical angles (p. 375) Vertical angles are formed by two intersecting lines. Vertical angles have equal measures.

Ángulos verticales (p. 375) Los ángulos verticales están formados por dos rectas que se intersecan. Los ángulos verticales tienen la misma medida.

1 3
4 2

$\angle 1$ and $\angle 2$ are vertical angles, as are $\angle 3$ and $\angle 4$.

Volume (p. 458) The volume of a three-dimensional figure is the number of cubic units needed to fill the space inside the figure.

Volumen (p. 458) El volumen de una figura tridimensional es el número de unidades cúbicas que se necesitan para llenar el espacio dentro de la figura.

The volume of the rectangular prism is 36 cubic units.

X

x-axis (p. 548) The x-axis is the horizontal number line that, together with the y-axis, forms the coordinate plane.

Eje de x (p. 548) El eje de x es la recta numérica horizontal que, junto con el eje de y, forma el plano de coordenadas.

y-axis
x-axis
-2   O   2

686   Glossary

Page 687

EXAMPLES

x-coordinate (p. 548) The x-coordinate is the first number in an ordered pair. It tells the number of horizontal units a point is from 0.

Coordenada x (p. 548) La coordenada x es el primer número en un par ordenado. Indica el número de unidades horizontales a las que un punto está del cero.

The x-coordinate is −2 for the ordered pair (−2, 1). The x-coordinate is 2 units to the left of the y-axis.

Y

y-axis (p. 548) The y-axis is the vertical number line that, together with the x-axis, forms the coordinate plane.

Eje de y (p. 548) El eje de y es la recta numérica vertical que, junto con el eje de x, forma el plano de coordenadas.

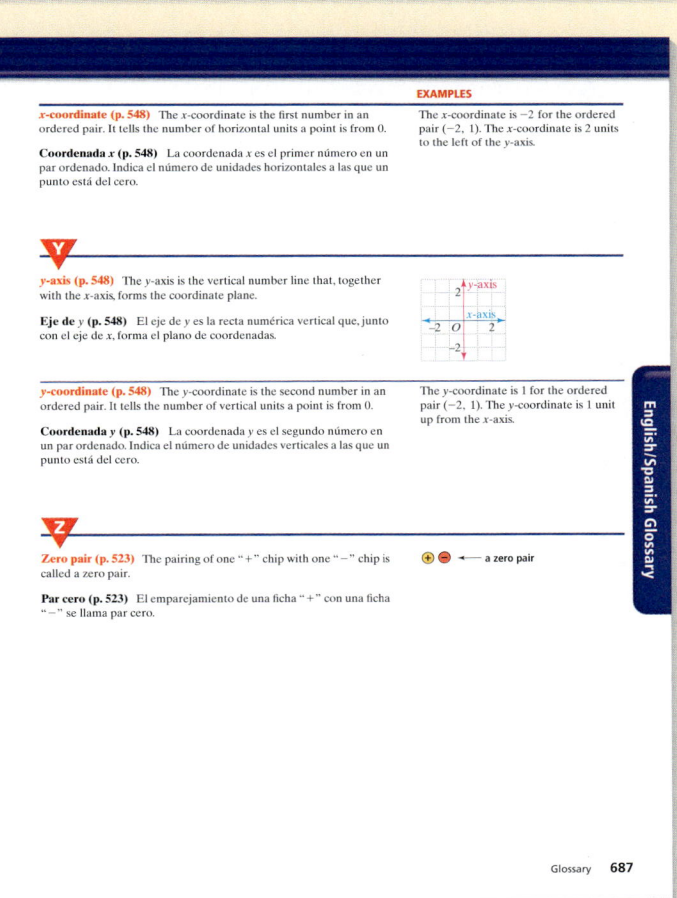

y-axis
x-axis
-2   O   2

y-coordinate (p. 548) The y-coordinate is the second number in an ordered pair. It tells the number of vertical units a point is from 0.

Coordenada y (p. 548) La coordenada y es el segundo número en un par ordenado. Indica el número de unidades verticales a las que un punto está del cero.

The y-coordinate is 1 for the ordered pair (−2, 1). The y-coordinate is 1 unit up from the x-axis.

Z

Zero pair (p. 523) The pairing of one "+" chip with one "−" chip is called a zero pair.

Par cero (p. 523) El emparejamiento de una ficha "+" con una ficha "−" se llama par cero.

a zero pair

Glossary   687

T657

Answers to Instant Check System™

Chapter 1

Check Your Readiness p. 2

1. 310 **2.** 7,530 **3.** 40 **4.** 60 **5.** 700 **6.** 1,990 **7.** 175 **8.** 145 **9.** 14,192 **10.** 3,027 **11.** 10,000 **12.** 1,392 **13.** 747 **14.** 4,544 **15.** 43,700 **16.** 462 **17.** 5 **18.** 17 **19.** 32 **20.** 72

Lesson 1-1 pp. 4–5

Check Skills You'll Need **1.** Answers may vary. Sample: 8, 3.5 **2.** 2 tens or 20 **3.** 2 ones or 2 **4.** 2 thousands or 2,000 **5.** 2 hundreds or 200

Quick Check **1.** twenty-six billion, two hundred thirty-six million, eight hundred forty-eight thousand, eighty dollars. **2.** < **3.** 978; 9,897; 9,987

Lesson 1-2 pp. 8–9

Check Skills You'll Need **1.** hundreds **2.** 50 **3.** 60 **4.** 140 **5.** 490

Quick Check **1a.** about 170 **b.** about 20 **2a.** about 320 **b.** about 14 **3.** about 30

Lesson 1-3 pp. 12–13

Check Skills You'll Need **1.** addition **2.** 150 **3.** 90 **4.** 350

Quick Check **1.** 95 **2.** 600

Lesson 1-4 pp. 16–20

Check Skills You'll Need **1.** Comm. Prop. of Add. **2.** 57 **3.** 30 **4.** 175

Quick Check **1a.** 27 **b.** 16 **2.** $43

Checkpoint Quiz 1 **1.** > **2.** < **3.** > **4.** about 200 **5.** about 9,000 **6.** about 2 **7.** 57 **8.** 38 **9.** 1,000 **10.** 0 **11.** 70 **12.** $70 **13.** about 1,200 feet **14.** 6,893,000; 7,134,000; 7,283,000; 7,293,000

Lesson 1-5 pp. 22–23

Check Skills You'll Need **1.** 1,321 **2.** twenty-eight **3.** eight thousand, six hundred seventy-two **4.** six hundred twelve thousand, nine hundred eighty **5.** fifty-eight thousand, twenty-six

Quick Check **1a.** sixty-seven and three tenths **b.** six and seven hundred thirty-four thousandths **c.** sixty-seven hundredths **2.** 0.15; 0.1 + 0.05 **3a.** 2.34 **b.** 0.1735 **c.** 9.1

Lesson 1-6 pp. 26–27

Check Skills You'll Need **1.** Answers may vary. Sample: Compare the digits, starting with the greatest place value. **2.** > **3.** <

Quick Check **1.** Model may vary. Sample:

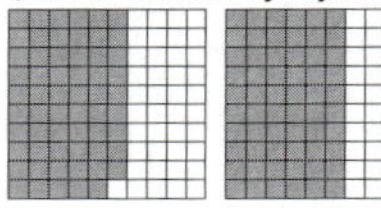

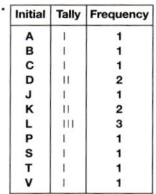

0.59 0.6

0.6 is greater. **2.** > **3.** 3.059, 3.46, 3.64

Lesson 1-7 pp. 32–33

Check Skills You'll Need **1.** Rounding **2.** 70 **3.** 110 **4.** 100 **5.** 3,200

Quick Check **1.** about 6; 6.16 **2.** about $22 **3.** 2.72 m

Lesson 1-8 pp. 38–43

Check Skills You'll Need **1.** Yes; 130 is easy to divide by 5 mentally. **2.** about 600 **3.** about 180 **4.** about 100 **5.** about 10

Quick Check **1a.** 0.78 **b.** 21.85 **2a.** 0.06 **b.** 10.108 **c.** 0.126 **3.** $3.55

Checkpoint Quiz 2 **1.** twelve and thirty-five thousandths **2.** 8.0; 8.05; 8.7; 9; 9.31 **3.** 7.8 **4.** 8.0 **5.** 17.1 **6.** 7.32 **7.** 8.26 **8.** 32.76 **9.** 1.42 **10.** 1.65 lb

Lesson 1-9 pp. 44–45

Check Skills You'll Need **1.** A dividend is the number being divided. A divisor is the number that divides. **2.** 187 **3.** 37 **4.** 53

Quick Check **1a.** 48.2 **b.** 1.52 **2.** 11 trading cards

Chapter 2

Check Your Readiness p. 58

1. 0.12, 0.13, 0.21, 0.35, 0.45 **2.** 44.0, 45.01, 45.1, 46.01 **3.** 63.1 **4.** 423.9 **5.** 105.82 **6.** 25.87 **7.** 20.21 **8.** 1.06 **9.** 1.8 **10.** 14.203 **11.** 22.6 **12.** 4.03

Lesson 2-1 pp. 61–62

Check Skills You'll Need **1.** quotient **2.** 27.5 **3.** 42.75 **4.** 59.35

Quick Check **1.** 4 **2.** 20 **3.** The outlier increases the value of the mean.

Lesson 2-2 pp. 66–67

Check Skills You'll Need **1.** 5 **2.** 20 **3.** 22.4 **4.** 57

Quick Check **1.** 28 **2.** 2 **3.** Answers may vary. Sample: The median is the best measure, as 288.75 is an outlier that affects the mean, and there is no mode.

Lesson 2-3 pp. 70–71

Check Skills You'll Need **1.** The mode is the data item(s) that appear(s) most often. **2.** 5.25; 5; 4 **3.** about 2.29; 1.5; 0

Quick Check **1.**

Initial	Tally	Frequency
A	I	1
B	I	1
C	I	1
D	II	2
J	I	1
K	II	2
L	III	3
P	I	1
S	I	1
T	I	1
V	I	1

2.

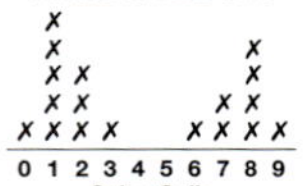

Number of Sales Calls
0 1 2 3 4 5 6 7 8 9
Sales Calls

Answers may vary. Sample: Either a low number of sales calls were made each hour (0–3), or a high number (6–9).
3. 32

Lesson 2-4 pp. 74–75

Check Skills You'll Need **1.** The range is the difference between the least and greatest values.
2.

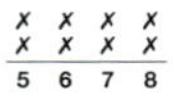

5 6 7 8

3.

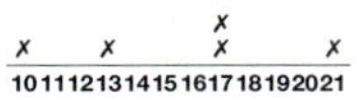

10 11 12 13 14 15 16 17 18 19 20 21

Quick Check **1.** 380 mg **2.** Less than; it is decreasing. **3.** Line graph; it shows change over time.

Lesson 2-5 pp. 80–85

Check Skills You'll Need **1.** usually **2.** 159 **3.** 814

Quick Check **1.** 30; the minutes of country music on disc 3 **2.** = D2 + D3 + D4

Checkpoint Quiz 1 **1.** 21.07; 21; 21 **2.** 9 **3.** Yes; 26 is much higher than the majority of the data.
4. Answers may vary. Sample: The mode represents which high temperature occurred the most.
5.

Grams of Fat	Tally	Frequency
0	~~IIII~~ III	8
1	~~IIII~~ III	8
2	~~IIII~~	5
3	III	3

6. L = B2 + B3 + B4 + B5
7. $800
8.

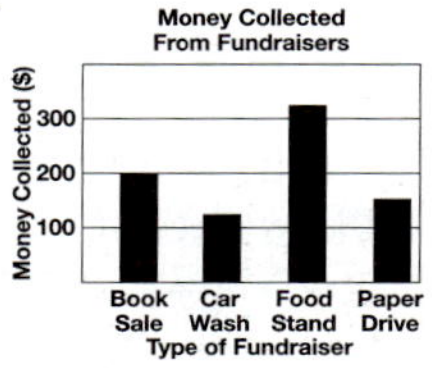

Money Collected From Fundraisers
Money Collected ($)
300
200
100
Book Sale
Car Wash
Food Stand
Paper Drive
Type of Fundraiser

9.

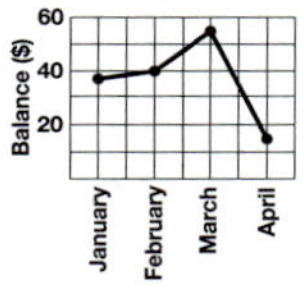

Account Balance
Balance ($)
60
40
20
January
February
March
April

Lesson 2-6 pp. 86–87

Check Skills You'll Need **1.** The median of a data set is the middle value when the data are arranged in numerical order. **2.** 32 **3.** 15 **4.** 5.2

Quick Check **1.** 35 **2.**

12	1 3 4 5 5 6 7
13	0 2 3 6 7 8 8
14	0 1 4 5
15	0 5
16	
17	
18	1

Key: 12|3 means 123

Lesson 2-7 pp. 93–98

Check Skills You'll Need **1.** The mean of a set of data values is the sum of the data divided by the number of data values. **2.** 55.5 **3.** 13.5 **4.** 131

Quick Check **1.**

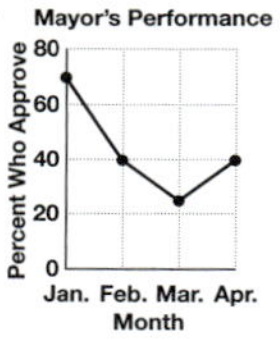

Mayor's Performance
Percent Who Approve
80
60
40
20
0
Jan. Feb. Mar. Apr.
Month

2a. It's twice as tall. **b.** 3 cars **3.** Median; the mode is the least data value. It occurs only twice, so its value is really too low to give a good idea of what a typical data value is.

Checkpoint Quiz 2 **1.** Test Scores

6	4 8
7	6
8	1 4 4 5 5 6 9
9	1 2 5 7

Key: 6 | 4 means 64%

2. 15 years **3.** 8 **4.** 36 **5.** Answers may vary. Sample: Median; an outlier affects the mean.
6. Answers may vary. Sample: Starting a graph at 60 ft^3 on the vertical axis will make the differences in cars seem very large.

Chapter 3

Check Your Readiness p. 106

1. 29 **2.** 39 **3.** 18 **4.** 30 **5.** about 42; 42.15 **6.** about 9; 9.5 **7.** about 5; 5.1 **8.** about 2; 2.16 **9.** about 2; 2.27 **10.** about 15; 14.36 **11.** 18.95 **12.** 19.456 **13.** 310.27 **14.** 3.3 **15.** 170 **16.** 0.71

Lesson 3-1 pp. 108–109

Check Skills You'll Need **1.** value **2.** 3.1, 3.31, 3.331 **3.** 0.0105, 0.105, 10.5

Quick Check **1.** 22 tiles **2a.** 90, 75, 60, 45, 30, 15 **b.** 1, 3, 9, 27, 81, 243 **3a.** Start with 1.5 and multiply by 3 repeatedly; 121.5, 364.5, 1,093.5. **b.** Start with 256 and divide by 2 repeatedly; 32, 16, 8.

Lesson 3-2 pp. 113–114

Check Skills You'll Need **1.** A mathematical expression is a phrase containing numbers, variables, and operation symbols. **2.** 32 **3.** 19 **4.** 441

Quick Check **1.**

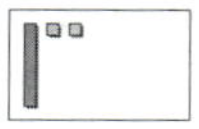

2a. 36 **b.** 5 **c.** 28 **3.** $255

Lesson 3-3 pp. 118–119

Check Skills You'll Need **1.** To evaluate an expression means to replace a variable with a number and simplify it. **2.** 10 **3.** 30 **4.** 48 **5.** 11

Quick Check **1.** $x + 2$ **2.** Let b = Brandon's age; $b + 28$ **3.** $n + 4$

Lesson 3-4 pp. 124–129

Check Skills You'll Need **1.** Add the whole dollars first and then estimate when adding the cents. **2.** about 6; 6.37 **3.** about 4; 3.7 **4.** about 2; 1.7

Quick Check **1a.** true **b.** false **c.** false **2a.** 9 **b.** 80 **c.** 1.2 **3.** 43

Checkpoint Quiz 1 **1.** Start with 1 and multiply by 6 repeatedly; 1,296; 7,776; 46,656. **2.** Start with 285 and subtract 15 repeatedly; 225, 210, 195. **3.** Start with 50 and divide by 10 repeatedly; 0.005, 0.0005, 0.00005. **4.** 56 **5.** 9 **6.** 70 **7.** $17 - d$ **8.** ae **9.** $14 \div q$

Lesson 3-5 pp. 130–131

Check Skills You'll Need **1.** It has one or more variables. **2.** 1 **3.** 70 **4.** 14

Quick Check **1.** 4.8 **2.** w = the cat's weight last year; $1.8 + w = 11.6$; 9.8 lb

Lesson 3-6 pp. 134–137

Check Skills You'll Need **1.** It makes the equation true. **2.** 14 **3.** 11 **4.** 10

Quick Check **1a.** 81 **b.** 55 **2.** Let t = temperature at 7 P.M.; $t - 9 = 54$; $t = 63$.

Checkpoint Quiz 2 **1.** 60 **2.** 18.2 **3.** 2.2 **4.** 7.6 **5.** 10.8 **6.** 26.6 **7.** 7 **8.** 38.4
9. x = change received;
$x + 5.73 = 10.00$; $x = \$4.27$

Lesson 3-7 pp. 138–139

Check Skills You'll Need **1.** Answers may vary. Sample: Equations contain equal signs, and expressions do not. **2.** 9 **3.** 2 **4.** 9 **5.** 3

Quick Check **1.** 40 **2.** 865 cards **3.** 15

Lesson 3-8 pp. 144–145

Check Skills You'll Need **1.** Answers may vary. Sample: The Associative Property changes the grouping of numbers and the Commutative Property changes the order of the numbers. **2.** 58 **3.** 173 **4.** 183

Quick Check **1.** $5 \times (70 - 2) = (5 \times 70) - (5 \times 2) = 350 - 10 = 340$ **2.** $14.00

Chapter 4

Check Your Readiness p. 156

1. four tenths **2.** thirty-seven hundredths **3.** one and eight tenths **4.** two hundred five thousandths **5.** twenty and eighty-eight hundredths **6.** one hundred fifty thousandths **7.** 4.02, 4.2, 4.21 **8.** 0.033, 0.3, 0.33 **9.** 6.032, 6.203, 6.302 **10.** 9.013, 9.031, 9.103 **11.** 0.8 **12.** 0.55 **13.** 19 **14.** 36.3 **15.** 132 **16.** 53

Lesson 4-1 pp. 158–159

Check Skills You'll Need **1.** division **2.** 49 **3.** 41 **4.** 50

Quick Check **1a.** no **b.** yes **2a.** divisible by 2, 3, 5, and 10 **b.** divisible by none of these **c.** divisible by 2 and 3 **3.** yes

Lesson 4-2 pp. 162–163

Check Skills You'll Need **1.** expression **2.** 25 **3.** 0 **4.** 2

Quick Check **1a.** 3.94^2; 3.94; 2 **b.** 7^4; 7; 4 **c.** x^3; x; 3 **2.** 27 **3a.** 6 **b.** 14

Lesson 4-3 pp. 166–170

Check Skills You'll Need **1.** No; 25 is divisible by 5 but not divisible by 10. **2.** 2, 3, 5, 9, 10 **3.** divisible by none of these **4.** 2, 5, and 10 **5.** 2, 5, and 10

Quick Check **1.** 1×24, 2×12, 3×8, 4×6 **2a.** composite; $39 = 3 \times 13$ **b.** Prime; it has only two factors, 1 and 47. **c.** composite; $63 = 3 \times 21$ or $63 = 7 \times 9$ **3.** 3^3

Checkpoint Quiz 1 **1.** 3, 5 **2.** 2 **3.** 2, 3, 5, 10 **4.** 64 **5.** 10 **6.** 3,125 **7.** 64 **8.** $2 \times 3 \times 7$ **9.** $2^4 \times 5$ **10.** $2^3 \times 5^3$ **11.** 1×105, 3×35, 5×21, 7×15

Lesson 4-4 pp. 171–172

Check Skills You'll Need **1.** Answers may vary. Sample: Multiply two factors together to find the product. **2.** $3^2 \times 5$ **3.** 3×7 **4.** $3^2 \times 11$

Quick Check **1 a.** factors of 6: 1, 2, 3, 6; factors of 21: 1, 3, 7, 21; GCF of 6 and 21: 3 **b.** factors of 18: 1, 2, 3, 6, 9, 18; factors of 49: 1, 7, 49; GCF of 18 and 49: 1 **c.** factors of 14: 1, 2, 7, 14; factors of 28: 1, 2, 4, 7, 14, 28; GCF of 14 and 28: 14 **2.** 6 in. **3 a.** GCF = 16 **b.** GCF = 12

Lesson 4-5 pp. 176–177

Check Skills You'll Need **1.** The GCF is the largest number in the set of common factors. **2.** 5 **3.** 6 **4.** 1

Quick Check **1a–b.** Answers may vary. Samples are given.
1a. $\frac{2}{5}$, $\frac{8}{20}$ **b.** $\frac{10}{16}$, $\frac{15}{24}$ **2.** $\frac{3}{4}$ **3.** $\frac{7}{20}$

Lesson 4-6 pp. 182–187

Check Skills You'll Need **1.** when the only common factor of the numerator and denominator is 1 **2.** $\frac{1}{3}$ **3.** $\frac{2}{3}$ **4.** $\frac{5}{16}$

Quick Check **1.** $\frac{25}{7}$ **2.** 9 qt **3a.** $4\frac{4}{9}$ **b.** $5\frac{1}{3}$ **c.** $5\frac{3}{4}$

Checkpoint Quiz 2 **1.** 5 **2.** 24 **3.** 3 **4.** 6 **5.** $\frac{16}{5}$ **6.** $1\frac{5}{8}$ **7.** $\frac{8}{3}$ **8.** 2 toys, 6 balloons, 12 bags of peanuts

Lesson 4-7 — pp. 188–189

Check Skills You'll Need **1.** A factor tree helps you write a number as a product of prime factors. **2.** $2^4 \times 5$ **3.** 2^5 **4.** $2^4 \times 13$ **5.** $2^2 \times 5^3$

Quick Check **1 a.** 60 **b.** 70 **2.** 24

Lesson 4-8 — pp. 192–193

Check Skills You'll Need **1.** When you write a fraction in simplest form, you are writing an equivalent fraction using division. **2–5.** Answers may vary. Samples are given.
2. $\frac{1}{3}, \frac{21}{63}$ **3.** $\frac{1}{5}, \frac{2}{10}$ **4.** $\frac{4}{6}, \frac{20}{30}$ **5.** $\frac{1}{6}, \frac{5}{30}$

Quick Check **1.** < **2.** Yes; $\frac{7}{8} = \frac{28}{32}$, and $\frac{28}{32} > \frac{27}{32}$. So $6\frac{7}{8} > 6\frac{27}{32}$. **3.** $\frac{1}{3}, \frac{3}{8}, 1\frac{2}{3}, 2\frac{4}{5}, 2\frac{5}{6}$

Lesson 4-9 — pp. 198–199

Check Skills You'll Need **1.** 3; 12 **2.** 1.5 **3.** $0.\overline{6}$ **4.** 1.6 **5.** 0.3

Quick Check **1.** $5\frac{2}{25}$ **2.** you **3.** 1.8, $2\frac{2}{3}$, 2.7, $3\frac{1}{5}$

Chapter 5

Check Your Readiness — p. 210

1. 2.59 **2.** 1.99 **3.** 6.22 **4.** 7.65 **5.** $\frac{1}{2}$ **6.** $\frac{2}{5}$ **7.** $\frac{3}{4}$ **8.** $9\frac{2}{3}$ **9.** $5\frac{1}{4}$ **10.** $7\frac{1}{2}$ **11.** 72 **12.** 80 **13.** 210

Lesson 5-1 — pp. 212–213

Check Skills You'll Need **1.** Compatible numbers are numbers that are easy to compute mentally. **2.** 60 **3.** 150 **4.** 900 **5.** 1,230

Quick Check **1.** 1 **2 a.** $1\frac{1}{2}$ **b.** 1 **3.** about 5 h

Lesson 5-2 — pp. 217–218

Check Skills You'll Need **1.** A fraction is in simplest form when the GCF of the numerator and denominator is 1. **2.** $\frac{1}{4}$ **3.** $\frac{1}{3}$ **4.** $\frac{5}{6}$ **5.** $\frac{3}{7}$

Quick Check **1 a.** $\frac{1}{3}$ **b.** $\frac{2}{3}$ **2 a.** $1\frac{1}{8}$ **b.** $1\frac{2}{5}$ **3.** $\frac{1}{3}$ foot

Lesson 5-3 — pp. 222–226

Check Skills You'll Need **1.** Answers may vary. Sample: Write the prime factorization for each number. **2.** 18 **3.** 120 **4.** 150 **5.** 60

Quick Check **1.** $\frac{7}{10}$ **2.** $\frac{5}{6}$ h **3.** $\frac{1}{6}$ yd

Checkpoint Quiz 1 **1.** $1\frac{1}{2}$ **2.** 1 **3.** $1\frac{1}{2}$ **4.** 0 **5.** $1\frac{1}{5}$ **6.** $\frac{1}{2}$ **7.** $1\frac{1}{4}$ **8.** $\frac{17}{30}$ **9.** $\frac{1}{2}$ **10.** $\frac{7}{10}$ **11.** $\frac{11}{18}$ of the class **12.** $1\frac{1}{6}$ c **13.** $\frac{3}{8}$ gal

Lesson 5-4 — pp. 228–229

Check Skills You'll Need **1.** The numerator is greater than the denominator. **2.** $1\frac{1}{3}$ **3.** $2\frac{1}{2}$ **4.** $1\frac{3}{4}$ **5.** $2\frac{1}{2}$

Quick Check **1.** $5\frac{5}{6}$ yd **2 a.** $9\frac{3}{4}$ **b.** $21\frac{4}{15}$ **3.** $4\frac{1}{8}$ in.

Lesson 5-5 — pp. 232–238

Check Skills You'll Need **1.** Answers may vary. Sample: Write multiples of 6 until a multiple is divisible by 4. 12 is divisible by both 6 and 4. **2.** $\frac{3}{5}, \frac{13}{20}, \frac{7}{10}$ **3.** $2\frac{7}{32}, 2\frac{1}{4}, 2\frac{5}{16}, 2\frac{3}{8}$

Quick Check **1.** $7\frac{3}{16}$ in. **2 a.** $1\frac{1}{3}$ **b.** $5\frac{3}{4}$ **3.** $2\frac{1}{12}$ ft

Checkpoint Quiz 2 **1.** $5\frac{5}{8}$ **2.** $4\frac{3}{4}$ **3.** $14\frac{5}{6}$ **4.** $5\frac{8}{9}$ **5.** $5\frac{5}{6}$ **6.** $\frac{4}{9}$ **7.** $9\frac{7}{8}$ **8.** $4\frac{1}{6}$ **9.** $4\frac{1}{4}$ hours **10.** $\frac{11}{20}$ mile

Lesson 5-6 — pp. 240–241

Check Skills You'll Need **1.** subtraction **2.** 26 **3.** 3.8 **4.** 18.9

Quick Check **1 a.** $2\frac{3}{4}$ **b.** $11\frac{1}{4}$ **c.** $3\frac{2}{3}$ **2 a.** $\frac{7}{12}$ **b.** $\frac{1}{4}$ **3.** $1\frac{3}{4}$ in.

Lesson 5-7 — pp. 246–248

Check Skills You'll Need **1.** Answers may vary. Sample: seconds, hours, days, weeks **2.** 482 min **3.** 123 hours **4.** 26 days

Quick Check **1.** 1 h 26 min **2.** 4 h **3.** 9 h 15 min **4.** 6:20 P.M.

Chapter 6

Check Your Readiness — p. 258

1. 4 **2.** 5 **3.** 12 **4.** 112 **5.** 100 **6.** 0.6 **7.** 12 **8.** 7 **9.** 3 **10.** 20 **11.** 6 **12.** 21 **13.** $\frac{3}{7}$ **14.** $\frac{2}{3}$ **15.** $\frac{1}{3}$ **16.** $\frac{3}{8}$ **17.** $\frac{1}{4}$ **18.** $\frac{3}{7}$

Lesson 6-1 — pp. 261–262

Check Skills You'll Need **1.** Answers may vary. Sample: $\frac{2}{5}$ and $\frac{4}{10}$ **2.** $\frac{1}{2}$ **3.** $\frac{3}{5}$ **4.** $\frac{2}{3}$ **5.** $\frac{9}{10}$

Quick Check **1a.** $\frac{3}{20}$ **b.** $\frac{10}{63}$ **2.** 10 ft

Lesson 6-2 — pp. 266–267

Check Skills You'll Need **1.** A proper fraction has a numerator that is less than the denominator. An improper fraction has a denominator that is less than or equal to the numerator.
2. $\frac{27}{7}$ **3.** $\frac{17}{3}$ **4.** $\frac{47}{4}$ **5.** $\frac{79}{9}$

Quick Check **1a.** 36 **b.** 56 **2a.** $28\frac{3}{16}$ **b.** $27\frac{1}{2}$ **3.** $2\frac{5}{8}$ mi

Lesson 6-3 — pp. 272–273

Check Skills You'll Need **1.** List the factors of 4 and 15. Choose the largest number that is a factor of both 4 and 15. **2.** 6 **3.** $\frac{1}{5}$ **4.** $\frac{1}{7}$ **5.** $\frac{4}{11}$

Quick Check **1a.** $\frac{4}{3}$ or $1\frac{1}{3}$ **b.** $\frac{1}{7}$ **2a.** $\frac{3}{4}$ **b.** $2\frac{2}{5}$ **3.** $\frac{1}{6}$ yard

Lesson 6-4 — pp. 276–281

Check Skills You'll Need **1.** The product of the fractions is not 1. **2.** 28 **3.** $\frac{7}{24}$ **4.** $\frac{1}{6}$ **5.** $2\frac{8}{11}$

Quick Check **1a.** about 7 **b.** about 5 **2.** $1\frac{1}{4}$ cups **3a.** 6 **b.** $2\frac{1}{20}$

Checkpoint Quiz 1 **1.** 15 **2.** $23\frac{5}{8}$ **3.** 64 **4.** $\frac{1}{6}$ **5.** $1\frac{11}{21}$ **6.** $\frac{3}{5}$ **7.** $16\frac{1}{3}$ **8.** $2\frac{7}{30}$ **9.** 34 **10.** $4\frac{1}{2}$ **11.** $2\frac{1}{5}$ **12.** $15\frac{1}{2}$ **13.** 39 ft **14.** 24 cookies **15.** about 13

Lesson 6-5 — pp. 282–283

Check Skills You'll Need **1.** Divide each side by 4. **2.** $\frac{7}{30}$ **3.** $\frac{3}{11}$ **4.** $\frac{2}{5}$ **5.** $\frac{9}{25}$

Quick Check **1 a.** 30 **b.** 72 **2.** 48 **3.** 20 flags

Lesson 6-6 — pp. 288–289

Check Skills You'll Need **1.** Answers may vary. Sample: Find the least common denominator of 4 and 12 and write equivalent fractions using the LCD to compare. **2.** > **3.** > **4.** >

Quick Check **1–3.** Answers may vary. Samples are given.
1a. Inches; pencils are shorter than a foot. **b.** Feet or yards; small whales are twice as long as a man. **2.** Pounds; a refrigerator weighs less than a piano. **3a.** Gallons; a tanker truck holds more gasoline than can fit in a small bucket. **b.** Fluid ounces or cups; a container of yogurt is usually less than a pint.

Lesson 6-7 — pp. 292–296

Check Skills You'll Need **1.** An improper fraction has a numerator greater than the denominator. A mixed number is the sum of an integer and a proper fraction. **2.** $25\frac{1}{2}$ **3.** $\frac{55}{78}$ **4.** $\frac{3}{8}$ **5.** $\frac{20}{27}$

Quick Check **1.** 4,000 lb **2.** $1\frac{1}{4}$ qt **3.** 8 lb 1 oz

Checkpoint Quiz 2 **1.** $10\frac{1}{2}$ **2.** $\frac{2}{5}$ **3.** 46 **4.** $\frac{8}{5}$ or $1\frac{3}{5}$ **5.** mile **6.** pound **7.** 51 markers

Chapter 7

Check Your Readiness — p. 304

1. 48 **2.** 42 **3.** 24 **4.** 9 **5.** $\frac{2}{5}$ **6.** $\frac{5}{11}$ **7.** $\frac{2}{3}$ **8.** $\frac{1}{3}$ **9.** > **10.** > **11.** < **12.** = **13.** $\frac{8}{21}$ **14.** $\frac{1}{2}$ **15.** $3\frac{8}{9}$ **16.** $4\frac{1}{8}$

Lesson 7-1 — pp. 306–307

Check Skills You'll Need **1.** A fraction is in simplest form when the numerator and denominator have only a common factor of 1. **2.** $\frac{1}{3}$ **3.** $\frac{2}{3}$ **4.** $\frac{2}{9}$ **5.** $\frac{1}{16}$

Quick Check **1a.** 2 to 4, 2 : 4, $\frac{2}{4}$ **b.** 2 to 6, 2 : 6, $\frac{2}{6}$ **2a–c.** Answers may vary. Samples are given. **2a.** 2 to 7, 4 to 14 **b.** 4 to 1, 8 to 2 **c.** 4 to 11, 12 to 33 **3.** 1 : 8

Lesson 7-2 — pp. 312–313

Check Skills You'll Need **1.** division **2.** 4 **3.** 4 **4.** 5 **5.** 6

Quick Check **1.** 79 cents per pound **2.** \$.11 per ounce; \$.09 per ounce; the 32 ounce container **3a.** $\frac{\$5.25}{1 \text{ hour}} = \frac{\$26.25}{5 \text{ hours}}$ **b.** $\frac{25 \text{ words}}{1 \text{ minute}} = \frac{250 \text{ words}}{10 \text{ minutes}}$

Lesson 7-3 — pp. 316–317

Check Skills You'll Need **1.** You see whether the two fractions are equal or whether one is greater. **2.** < **3.** = **4.** < **5.** <

Quick Check **1.** No; $\frac{36}{20}$ cannot reduce to $\frac{8}{5}$. **2.** No; $\frac{1}{12}$ and $\frac{3}{26}$ are not equal.

Lesson 7-4 — pp. 320–325

Check Skills You'll Need **1.** Answers may vary. Sample: The ratios do not form a proportion, because their cross products are not equal. **2.** yes **3.** no

Quick Check **1.** 15 **2a.** 15 **b.** 4 **3.** \$4.71

Checkpoint Quiz 1 **1.** 18 to 40, $\frac{18}{40}$ **2.** \$2.85 **3.** \$37.50 **4.** no **5.** no **6.** yes **7.** 12 **8.** 78 **9.** \$16.20 **10.** \$7.92

Lesson 7-5 — pp. 326–327

Check Skills You'll Need **1.** Answers may vary. Sample: You could rewrite the ratios so the numerators or the denominators are equal. **2.** 25 **3.** 2

Quick Check **1.** 1 in. : 14 in. **2.** about 100 mi **3.** 17 in.

Lesson 7-6 — pp. 331–335

Check Skills You'll Need **1.** No; $\frac{10}{12}$ in simplest form equals $\frac{5}{6}$, which is larger than $\frac{3}{4}$. **2.** $\frac{6}{25}$ **3.** $\frac{2}{5}$ **4.** $\frac{3}{4}$ **5.** $\frac{1}{3}$

Quick Check **1a.** $\frac{11}{20}$ **b.** $\frac{1}{25}$ **2a.** 0.25 **b.** 0.02 **3 a.** 52% **b.** 5% **c.** 50% **4.** 5%

Checkpoint Quiz 2 **1.** 0.74, $\frac{37}{50}$ **2.** 0.06, $\frac{3}{50}$ **3.** 0.6, $\frac{3}{5}$ **4.** 84% **5.** 70% **6.** 5% **7.** about 268 mi **8.** about 587 mi **9.** about 570 mi **10.** 1 in. : 3 ft

Lesson 7-7 — pp. 336–337

Check Skills You'll Need **1.** Answers may vary. Sample: You can set the cross products equal to each other to write and solve an equation. **2.** 8 **3.** 15 **4.** 78 **5.** 230

Quick Check **1.** \$8 **2a.** 10.92 **b.** 21.78 **3.** 9

Lesson 7-8 — pp. 341–342

Check Skills You'll Need **1.** Answers may vary. Sample: You can write a proportion by setting the ratio equal to $\frac{x}{100}$. Solve the proportion and write the solution with a percent sign. **2.** 98 **3.** 104 **4.** 96

Quick Check **1.** They are processed.
2. processed; 39% > 13%
3. Lunches for 50 Students

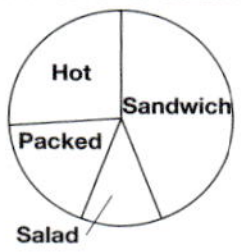

Lesson 7-9 — pp. 348–349

Check Skills You'll Need **1.** Write 98 as 100 − 2 and multiply by 3; 3(100 − 2). **2.** 5,015 **3.** 40.8

Quick Check **1.** about \$10.60 **2.** about \$6 **3.** about \$24

Chapter 8

Check Your Readiness — p. 360

1. 9 **2.** 9 **3.** 4 **4.** 10 **5.** 1.27 **6.** 59.5 **7.** 27.1 **8.** 17.5 **9.** 33.3 **10.** 12.07 **11.** yes **12.** no **13.** no **14.** yes **15.** no **16.** yes

Lesson 8-1 — pp. 362–363

Check Skills You'll Need **1.** Answers may vary. Sample: Numbers are ordered from smallest to largest as you move from left to right on a number line. **2.** 1.03, 1.06, 1.3, 1.6 **3.** 0.2, 0.4, 0.6, 0.9 **4.** 1.04, 1.3, 1.4, 1.5

Quick Check **1 a.** Answers may vary. Samples are given. $\overleftrightarrow{VP}$, $\overleftrightarrow{MV}$ **b.** $\overline{VM}$, $\overline{VP}$, $\overline{MP}$ **2.** Answers may vary. Samples are given. **a.** NE 4th St. and NE 2nd St. **b.** N. Miami Ave. and NE 2nd St.

Lesson 8-2 — pp. 367–368

Check Skills You'll Need **1.** A line continues in opposite directions without end. A ray has one endpoint and continues in one direction without end.
2. Answers may vary. Samples are given. $\overleftrightarrow{AC}$, $\overline{BE}$, $\overline{DB}$
3. Answers may vary. Sample: $\overleftrightarrow{EB}$, $\overleftrightarrow{BD}$

Quick Check **1.** 125° **2.** about 60°; acute **3a.** acute **b.** right **c.** right

Lesson 8-3 — pp. 374–379

Check Skills You'll Need **1.** Check students' work.

2.

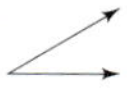

3.

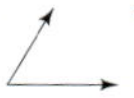

4.

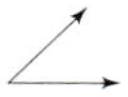

5.

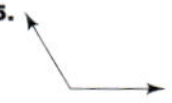

Quick Check **1.** 37° **2.** 35° **3.** 38°; 142°

Checkpoint Quiz 1 **1–10.** Answers may vary. Samples are given.
1. $\overleftrightarrow{LM}$ and $\overleftrightarrow{KN}$ **2.** $\overrightarrow{JP}$ and $\overleftrightarrow{NK}$ **3.** ∠PJM
4. ∠PJK **5.** ∠PJN **6.** ∠LJM
7. ∠KJL and ∠MJN **8.** ∠KJL
9. ∠PJK and ∠KJL
10. ∠LJN and ∠NJM

Lesson 8-4 — pp. 380–381

Check Skills You'll Need **1.** No; an obtuse angle itself is already larger than 90°. **2.** acute **3.** obtuse **4.** right **5.** straight

Quick Check **1.** right triangle **2.** 50°. **3.** isosceles triangle; two sides are congruent

Lesson 8-5 — pp. 386–391

Check Skills You'll Need **1.** No; skew lines are not in the same plane. **2.** Answers may vary. Sample: $\overline{CB}$ and $\overline{GH}$

Quick Check **1a.** quadrilateral **b.** hexagon **c.** octagon **2a.** irregular **b.** irregular **3.** Parallelogram, rectangle; rectangle; answers may vary. Sample: a rectangle has four right angles and two pairs of parallel lines. **4.** 56°

Checkpoint Quiz 2 **1.** obtuse **2.** right **3.** acute **4.** isosceles **5.** scalene **6.** equilateral **7.** 4 m **8.** pentagon **9.** octagon **10.** quadrilateral **11.** trapezoid; trapezoid **12.** parallelogram, rhombus; rhombus **13.** parallelogram, rectangle; rectangle

Lesson 8-6 — pp. 392–393

Check Skills You'll Need **1.** They have the same measure. **2.** isosceles **3.** scalene

Quick Check **1a.** no **b.** yes **2.** yes; $\frac{17}{20} = \frac{34}{40}$ **3.** 15

Lesson 8-7 — pp. 398–399

Check Skills You'll Need **1.** Answers may vary. Sample:

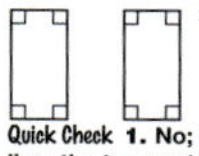

2. yes **3.** yes

Quick Check **1.** No; if you fold the figure along the line, the two parts do not match.
2 a. 1

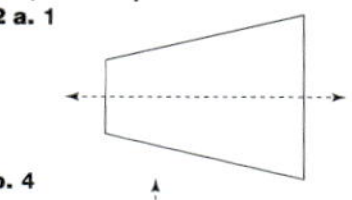

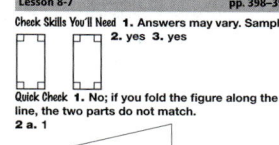

b. 4

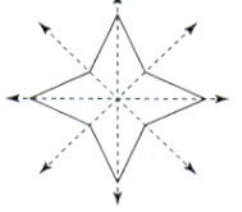

Lesson 8-8 — pp. 402–403

Check Skills You'll Need **1.** See if the two sides match when the paper is folded.

2.

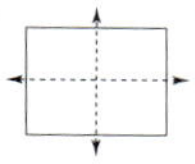

3.

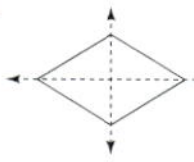

Quick Check **1.** no **2.**

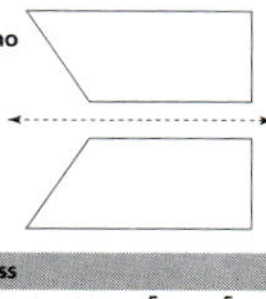

3 a. no **b.** yes **c.** no

Chapter 9

Check Your Readiness — p. 414

1. pounds **2.** miles **3.** 144 **4.** $3\frac{5}{6}$ **5.** $3\frac{5}{8}$ **6.** > **7.** < **8.** > **9.** rhombus **10.** isosceles triangle **11.** trapezoid

Lesson 9-1 — pp. 416–417

Check Skills You'll Need **1.** Answers may vary. Sample: ft, lb, fl oz **2.** Feet (yards would also be appropriate). **3.** Pints (cups or fluid ounces would also be appropriate).

Quick Check **1.** meters **2a.** kilograms **b.** kilograms **c.** milligrams **3a.** liters **b.** kiloliters **c.** milliliters

Lesson 9-2 — pp. 421–422

Check Skills You'll Need **1.** multiplication **2.** 144 **3.** 16 **4.** 2

Quick Check **1a.** 150 mm **b.** 837,000 m **2.** 60 km **3a.** 0.015 **b.** 0.386 **c.** 0.082

Lesson 9-3 — pp. 426–427

Check Skills You'll Need **1.** base: 3; exponent: 2 **2.** 16 **3.** 36 **4.** 29.16 **5.** 2.56

Quick Check **1.** $P = 26$ ft, $A = 40$ ft^2 **2.** 49 in.^{2}

Lesson 9-4 — pp. 432–436

Check Skills You'll Need **1.** square
2. $P = 20$ in.; $A = 24$ in.^{2}
3. $P = 34$ m; $A = 60$ m^2

Quick Check **1.** 70 m^2 **2.** 259.5 m^2 **3.** 16 m^2

Page 696

Checkpoint Quiz 1 **1.** cm **2.** kg **3.** 0.062 L
4. 4,300 g **5.** 1.78 m **6.** 0.0031 g **7.** 500 L
8. 0.083 g **9.** $P = 34$ cm, $A = 72.25$ cm² **10.** $P = 26$ mi, $A = 36$ mi² **11.** 193.6 ft²
12. 70.65 cm² **13.** 30.5 in.²

Lesson 9-5   pp. 438–440
Check Skills You'll Need **1.** product **2.** 6.28 **3.** 25.12
4. 219.8 **5.** 62.8

Quick Check **1.** $\overline{AC}, \overline{BD}$ **2.** 4 cm **3.** 22π **4.** 18 cm

Lesson 9-6   pp. 444–445
Check Skills You'll Need **1.** $2^3 \cdot 3^2$ **2.** 144 **3.** 16
4. 100 **5.** 18

Quick Check **1a.** about 452.16 km² **b.** about 28.26 in.² **c.** about 50.24 yd.² **2.** 154 in.²

Lesson 9-7   pp. 449–450
Check Skills You'll Need **1.** A rectangle that is not a square is a 4-sided polygon with 4 right angles and with the length different from the width. **2.** hexagon **3.** triangle

Quick Check **1a.** pentagonal prism **b.** rectangular prism **c.** triangular prism **2.** rectangular prism

Lesson 9-8   pp. 453–454
Check Skills You'll Need **1.** The area of a piece of paper is the two-dimensional space a rectangle of the same dimensions as the paper encloses. **2.** 21 m² **3.** 60 m²

Quick Check **1.** Answers may vary. Sample:
2. 1,728 m²

Lesson 9-9   pp. 458–461
Check Skills You'll Need **1.** base **2.** 110.5 **3.** 2.7

Quick Check **1.** 36 units³ **2.** 560 m³

Checkpoint Quiz 1 **1.** 346.8 ft² **2.** triangular pyramid **3.** cone **4.** pentagonal pyramid **5.** hexagonal prism **6.** 62 cm² **7.** 30 cm³

Lesson 9-10   pp. 462–464
Check Skills You'll Need **1.** The radius of a circle is the distance from the center to the edge of the circle. **2.** 200.96 m² **3.** 12.56 yd²

Quick Check **1.** 96.6 in.² **2.** 452 in.³

Chapter 10

Check Your Readiness   p. 474
1. 0.68 **2.** 0.92 **3.** 0.4 **4.** 0.766 **5.** $\frac{4}{5}$ **6.** $\frac{2}{3}$ **7.** $\frac{7}{8}$ **8.** $\frac{3}{5}$
9. $\frac{5}{12}$ **10.** $\frac{2}{3}$ **11.** $\frac{1}{4}$ **12.** $\frac{16}{27}$ **13.** 0.25; 25%
14. 0.$\overline{3}$; $\approx$ 33% **15.** 0.8; 80% **16.** 0.7; 70%

Lesson 10-1   pp. 476–477
Check Skills You'll Need **1.** Associative **2.** 5.2
3. 1,800 **4.** 1,200

Quick Check **1.** 9 outcomes
2. Pants   Shirts   **3.** 48 desserts

```
        R
B <     Y
        G

        R
K <     Y
        G
```

6 outcomes

Lesson 10-2   pp. 482–487
Check Skills You'll Need **1.** A percent is a ratio that compares a number to 100. **2.** 32% **3.** 36%
4. 40% **5.** 2%

Quick Check **1.** $\frac{1}{3}$ **2.** $\frac{5}{6}$ **3.** 0.6

Checkpoint Quiz 1 **1.** shirt 1, jeans 1; shirt 1, jeans 2; shirt 2, jeans 1; shirt 2, jeans 2; shirt 3, jeans 1; shirt 3, jeans 2
2. Roll   Toss   **3.** 48 desserts **4.** $\frac{2}{6}$ or $\frac{1}{3}$ **5.** 0

```
1 <  H
     T
2 <  H
     T
3 <  H
     T
4 <  H
     T
5 <  H
     T
6 <  H
     T
```

12 outcomes

6. $\frac{2}{6}$ or $\frac{1}{3}$ **7.** $\frac{3}{8}$ **8.** $\frac{3}{8}$ **9.** $\frac{1}{8}$
10. $\frac{2}{8}$ or $\frac{1}{4}$ **11.** $\frac{7}{8}$ **12.** $\frac{1}{8}$
13. 60 hairdos

Lesson 10-3   pp. 488–489
Check Skills You'll Need **1.** You can write a ratio as a fraction, as a phrase using "to," or as an expression using a colon. **2.** $\frac{3}{5}$ **3.** $\frac{4}{15}$ **4.** $\frac{4}{15}$ **5.** $\frac{13}{20}$

Page 697

Quick Check **1.** $\frac{11}{20}$ **2.** Yes; the probabilities are about the same.

Lesson 10-4   pp. 494–499
Check Skills You'll Need **1.** A proportion must be an equality. **2.** 6 **3.** 2 **4.** 3

Quick Check **1.** 6 times **2.** 1,080 toy robots

Checkpoint Quiz 2 **1.** $\frac{4}{20}$ or $\frac{1}{5}$ **2.** $\frac{3}{20}$ **3.** $\frac{12}{20}$ or $\frac{3}{5}$
4. $\frac{8}{20}$ or $\frac{2}{5}$ **5.** $\frac{8}{20}$ or $\frac{2}{5}$ **6.** 28,000 men
7. 315 customers **8.** 750 hats

Lesson 10-5   pp. 500–501
Check Skills You'll Need **1.** no **2.** $\frac{9}{16}$ **3.** $\frac{4}{21}$ **4.** $\frac{2}{9}$ **5.** $\frac{1}{4}$

Quick Check **1.** Not independent; after selecting the first card, there is one card fewer from which to choose. The first selection affects the second selection. **2.** $\frac{4}{25}$ **3.** $\frac{1}{16}$

Chapter 11

Check Your Readiness   p. 514
1. 79 **2.** 31 **3.** 39 **4.** 31 **5.** 0.6 **6.** 66 **7.** 41
8. 72 **9.** 15 **10.** 252 **11.** < **12.** > **13.** =
14. $\frac{1}{12}, \frac{1}{8}, \frac{1}{3}$ **15.** $\frac{7}{12}, \frac{5}{6}, \frac{11}{12}$ **16.** $\frac{4}{2}, \frac{6}{7}, \frac{2}{7}$

Lesson 11-1   pp. 516–517
Check Skills You'll Need **1.** The Identity Property of Addition states that the sum of any number and 0 is that number. The Identity Property of Multiplication states that the product of any number and 1 is that number. **2.** 9 **3.** 10 **4.** 0

Quick Check **1.** −8 **2.** 5 **3a.** 1 **b.** 7

Lesson 11-2   pp. 520–521
Check Skills You'll Need **1.** less than; greater than
2. < **3.** = **4.** >

Quick Check **1a.** > **b.** < **2.** −50, −25, 75, 100

Lesson 11-3   pp. 524–528
Check Skills You'll Need **1.** −6, 6 **2.** 15 **3.** 12 **4.** 8
5. 8

Quick Check **1.** −4 **2.** −3 **3.** −21 **4.** −7

Checkpoint Quiz 1 **1.** 13 **2.** 64 **3.** −3 **4.** −12
5. −32 **6.** −17, −15, −14, 16, 18 **7.** 12°F

Lesson 11-4   pp. 530–531
Check Skills You'll Need **1.** −6 **2.** 10 **3.** −5 **4.** −11
5. 14

Lesson 11-5   pp. 534–535
Check Skills You'll Need **1.** negative **2.** −8 **3.** 64
4. −28 **5.** −90

Quick Check **1a.** −12 **b.** 12 **2a.** 27 **b.** −15 **3.** −20

Lesson 11-6   pp. 540–541
Check Skills You'll Need **1.** positive **2.** 16 **3.** 1,024
4. 196 **5.** 2,025

Quick Check **1a.** −4 **b.** 18 **c.** −4 **2.** −$4/day

Lesson 11-7   pp. 543–544
Check Skills You'll Need **1.** addition and subtraction, multiplication and division **2.** 17 **3.** 25 **4.** 14
5. 64

Quick Check **1a.** 10 **b.** 28 **c.** −6 **2.** $20

Lesson 11-8   pp. 548–552
Check Skills You'll Need **1.** 0 **2.**
3.

4.   **5.**

Quick Check **1a.** B(−3, 2) **b.** D(−2, −3) **c.** E(2, −2)
2a.–c.   **3a.** City Hall
b. (3, −1)

Checkpoint Quiz 2 **1.** −2 **2.** −12 **3.** −36 **4.** −16
5. −7 **6.** 7 **7.** −13 **8.** 9 **9.** −4
10. $t − 15 = −2$; 13°F **11.** (2, −4) **12.** (1.5, 1.5)
13. (−2, −1.5) **14.** (−3.5, 2) **15.** (0.5, 0)

Lesson 11-9   pp. 554–555
Check Skills You'll Need **1.** Answers may vary. Sample: If the signs of both integers are the same, add their absolute values and use the same sign. If the integers' signs are different, subtract their absolute values and use the sign of the integer with the greatest absolute value. **2.** 38 **3.** 9
4. −13 **5.** −29

Page 698

Quick Check **1.** −$2,886; $821 **2.** Mar., Apr., June, July, Aug., Nov., Dec.

Lesson 11-10   pp. 558–559
Check Skills You'll Need **1.** An expression does not have an equal sign. **2.** 11 **3.** 6 **4.** 12 **5.** 18

Quick Check **1a.** 4, −6, 9 **b.** −14, −9, −4
2.

x	−2	0	2	6
y	−5	−3	−1	3

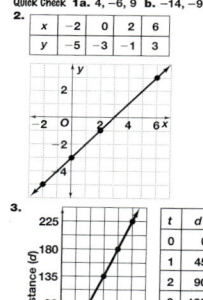

3.

t	d
0	0
1	45
2	90
3	135
4	180
5	225

Chapter 12

Check Your Readiness   p. 570
1. 25 **2.** −13 **3.** 43 **4.** 10 **5.** 13 **6.** 7 **7.** 19
8. 64 **9.** 63 **10.** 125 **11.** 4^3; 4; 3 **12.** 2^2; 2; 2
13. 1^4; 1; 4 **14.** < **15.** < **16.** >

Lesson 12-1   pp. 570–571
Check Skills You'll Need **1.** = **2.** 20 **3.** 48 **4.** 21
5. 192

Quick Check **1a.** 3 **b.** 9 **2.** $42

Lesson 12-2   pp. 578–579
Check Skills You'll Need **1.** A number line shows integers from least to greatest. A number to the left of another number on a number line is less than the other number. **2.** > **3.** > **4.** < **5.** <

Quick Check **1.** Let a represent the altitude from which most skydivers jump. $a \leq 14,500$ **2.** Let t represent the number of hours you spend studying. $t \geq 2$.   **3.** no

Lesson 12-3   pp. 582–585
Check Skills You'll Need **1.** If you subtract the same value from each side of an equation, the two sides remain equal. **2.** −9 **3.** 15

Quick Check **1.** $u \leq 9$ **2.** $z > 9$ **3.** Let $p =$ the number of additional people the restaurant can serve; $p + 97 \leq 115$, $p \leq 18$; the restaurant can serve at most 18 more people.

Checkpoint Quiz 1 **1.** 8 **2.** 8 **3.** 13
4. $p < −5$
5. $n \geq −12$
6. $d \leq 4$

Lesson 12-4   pp. 587–588
Check Skills You'll Need **1.** multiplication **2.** 4^5
3. 999^3 **4.** 3.6^2

Quick Check **1.** 10 **2.** 3.2 **3.** No; the decimal does not terminate or repeat.

Lesson 12-5   pp. 591–592
Check Skills You'll Need **1.** Answers may vary. Sample: 36; 25; 16 **2.** 3 **3.** 8 **4.** 5 **5.** 6 **6.** 11 **7.** 25

Quick Check **1.** 20 in. **2.** 4.6 ft

Chapter 1

Lesson 1-1 pp. 6–7

EXERCISES 1. 1,273 3. hundred; two 5. <
9. one hundred forty-five thousand, six hundred
seventy-five 11. seven million, three hundred
forty-seven thousand, two hundred 15. > 17. >
21. 901; 910; 990 23. 17,414; 17,444; 17,671
33. 2,129

Lesson 1-2 pp. 10–11

EXERCISES 1. Yes; 60 can be divided by 6
mentally. 3. 40 5. 70 7. 10; 10 9. 600; 20
11. about 300 13. about 190 19. about 8,000
21. about 10 31a. about $9 b. Compatible
numbers make division easy to compute mentally.
33. about 1,300 41. 4,541; 4,567; 4,678; 4,687

Lesson 1-3 pp. 14–15

EXERCISES 1. Comm. Prop. of Add. 5. 50 7. 61
9. 66 17. 470 19. 1,300 27. = 33. $360

Lesson 1-4 pp. 18–19

EXERCISES 1. expression 3. multiplication
7. > 9. 15 11. 19 19. $60 21. $91
29. $(1 + 2) \times (15 - 4) = 33$ 31. 76 g

Lesson 1-5 pp. 24–25

EXERCISES 1. 5; it is in the hundredths place. 7 is
in the thousandths place. 3. 3 tenths 5. 3
thousandths 7. 1 + 0.2 9. 7 + 0.5 + 0.02
11. two and three tenths 13. six thousandths
21. 40.009; 40 + 0.009 23. 0.700; 0.7 27. 2.7
29. 10.96 35. B: $0.9 million; $900,000 C: $1.6
million; $1,600,000 37. 4 tenths, or 0.4 39. 4
ten-thousandths, or 0.0004 49. 70

Lesson 1-6 pp. 29–30

EXERCISES 1. Answers may vary. Sample: I
would compare the values of numbers in similar
places. In the hundredths place, 1.697 has
9 hundredths. 1.697 > 1.679 3. 0.57 5. 0.575

7.

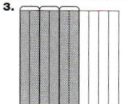

0.4   0.5

0.5 is greater.

11. = 13. < 17. 13.7, 17.1, 17.7 19. 9.02,
9.024, 9.2, 9.209 23. The Top . . .: 031.02; Going
to . . .: 370.973; How Music . . .: 398.2; The
Night . . .: 398.9; Art of . . .: 709.52; France: 944;
Japan: 952 25. 0.6595, 0.6095, 0.62 33. 26

Lesson 1-7 pp. 34–35

EXERCISES 1. The decimal points were not lined
up before subtracting. 5.8 − 2 = 3.8. 3. 1.38
5. $9 9. about 6; 6.644 11. about 21; 21.516
15. about $15 17. about $48 19. about 3; 2.83
21. about 3; 3.05 27. $47.99 29. < 31. >
33. 1.26 million 41. 800 43. 1,400

Lesson 1-8 pp. 40–41

EXERCISES 1. 7; there are 3 decimal places in the
first number and 4 decimal places in the second
number. So 3 + 4 = 7. 7. 262.0 9. 56.414
11. 17.1 13. 2.34 19. 0.32 21. 0.63 37. 40;
Methods may vary. Sample: paper and pencil
41. 483.48 million mi 47. 11.61

Lesson 1-9 pp. 46–47

EXERCISES 1. quotient
3.

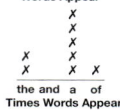

3

5. 3; 7 7. 25.25 9. 7.2 15. 73.75 17. 3.31
23a. 90 pieces b. yes 25. $7.65 27. 4.40
29. 33.16 37. 8.03, 8.035, 8.3, 8.308

Chapter Review pp. 52–53

1. Ident. Prop. of Add. 2. compatible numbers
3. standard form 4. expression 5. Assoc. Prop.
of Add. 6. five million, twenty-five 7. five
thousand, twenty-five 8. 1,001; 1,010; 1,100;
1,101 9. 2,232; 2,322; 2,323; 2,332 10. about
8,000 11. about 180 12. about 400 13. about
3,000 14. about 1,000 15. about 60 16. 350
17. 130 18. 30 19. 37 20. 0 21. 42 22. five
hundred twenty-five and five tenths 23. five
thousand, two hundred fifty-five ten-thousandths
24. five and twenty-five thousandths 25. fifty
and twenty-five ten-thousandths 26. 45.2
27. 98.6 28. 5.13 29. 1.25 30. 0.06; 0.14; 0.4;
0.52 31. 23; 23.03; 23.2; 23.25

32–37. Answers may vary. Samples are given.

32. about 357; 357.48 33. about 1; 0.931
34. about 3; 3.4 35. about 2; 1.7 36. about 4;
3.867 37. about 7; 7.4 38. 35.4 39. 2.02
40. 480 41. 9.18 42. 6.94 43. 31.458 44. 10.4
45. 170

Chapter 2

Lesson 2-1 pp. 63–64

EXERCISES 1. Answers may vary. Sample: Add
the data and divide the sum by 5. 3. 6 5. 5
7. 10 15. 50; increases 18. Check students'
work. 19. 10.2 23. 91 29. 19.341

Lesson 2-2 pp. 68–69

EXERCISES 1. median 3. 8; 8 5. Answers may
vary. Sample: 60, 100. 7. 0.5 9. 475 13. 8
19. 13.2; 13.5; 13.5 21. 45 25a. mean:
6,172.75 m; median: 6,044.5 m b. They both
increase. The mean becomes 6,708.2 m. The
median becomes 6,194 m. 31. 15

Lesson 2-3 pp. 72–73

EXERCISES 1. Answers may vary. Sample: Both
the line plot and frequency table show the data
grouped in an easy-to-read way.
3.
```
        x
        x
   x    x    x
   x    x    x    x
   ─────────────────
   5    6    7    8
```
5. Answers may vary. Sample: A line plot
immediately shows the mode.

7.

Type of Car	Tally	Frequency
Compact	IIII	4
Mid-size	III	3
SUV	II	2
Wagon	I	1
Pick-up	II	2

compact
9. Word Lengths in a Sentence
```
     x  x       x   x
  x  x  x  x    x x x x x
  1 2 3 4 5 6 7 8 9 10
  Word Lengths (letters)
```
There are very few words with fewer than 3
letters. 11. 1.7 m 13. 25 mph 15. the number of
organisms in a sample 17. Answers may vary.
Sample: Data items 3 and 4 did not occur often
but will affect the mean. 23. 60

Lesson 2-4 pp. 76–77

EXERCISES 1. line 3. Number of days
5.

11.

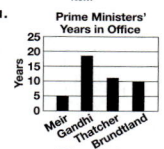

13. Hours of Battery Life 17. <

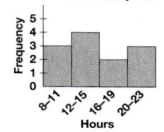

Lesson 2-5 pp. 81–83

EXERCISES 1. A cell is a box in a spreadsheet
where a specific row and column meet. 3. 9
7. F2, F3, F4, F5 11. 80
15. = (B4 + C4 + D4)/3 or = E4/3 19. 5
25. = C8 ÷ 6 29. 7

Lesson 2-6 pp. 89–90

EXERCISES 1. stem-and-leaf 3. 4 7. 3 entries
9. Heights of Tomato Plants (inches)
```
2 | 6 7 9
3 | 0 1 3 3 5 6 6
4 | 0 1
Key: 2|6 means 26 in.
```
13a.   Ages of People
```
0 | 9
1 | 1 2 2 2 2 3 3 5 5 0
2 | 0 1 3 4
3 | 5
4 | 0
Key: 2 | 6 means 26 years old
```
Ages of Eighteen People
```
                    x
     x
     x  x
x  x x x  x x    x x x x         x      x
─────────────────────────────────────────
10    15    20    25    30    35    40
               Years
```
b. Stem-and-leaf plot; explanations may vary.
Sample: The data with a stem of 1 and a leaf of 3
or more represent the teenagers. 21. 13

Lesson 2-7 pp. 95–96

EXERCISES 1. It looks like there was a dramatic
decrease in sales. 3. 3 more sales 5. The graph
is misleading because the intervals on the vertical
axis are unequal; it appears there was a greater
increase in January than there actually was.

Dogs in Animal Shelter

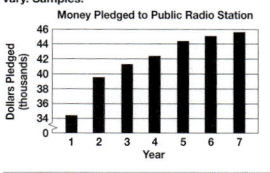

9. Candidate A: graph I, Candidate B: graph II; the
candidate would present a graph to make the
results look more favorable. 11. Graphs may
vary. Samples:

Money Pledged to Public Radio Station
(graph: Dollars Pledged (thousands) vs Year)

Chapter Review pp. 100–101

1. C 2. A 3. G 4. F 5. E 6. 45, 49, 50 7. 6, 7, 9
8.

Number of Times Vowels Occur		
Vowels	Tally	Frequency
A	THL THL THL IIII	18
E	THL THL THL III	18
I	THL THL	10
O	THL	5
U	THL	5
Y	III	3

9. Number of Times Listed
Words Appear
```
              x
              x
              x
       x      x
   x   x      x
  ─────────────────
  the and  a  of
  Times Words Appear
```

---

10.   Ticket Prices

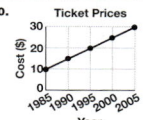

11.   Ticket Prices

12. Line graph; it shows changes over time.
13. B2, B3 14. 5 15. = B2 + C2 + D2
16.
```
3 | 01 41 67 79 88 99
4 | 65 79 79 83
5 | 07 12 43 48
  Key: 4|65 means 465
```
17. mean or median, since they are the same
18. median or mode 19. mode 20. median
21. Answers may vary. Sample: Start the vertical
axis at zero and use intervals of 10.

Chapter 3

Lesson 3-1 pp. 110–111

EXERCISES 1. conjecture 3. Start with 53 and
subtract 4 repeatedly. 5. 18, 22 11. 512, 256,
128, 64, 32, 16 13. Start with 0.12 and multiply by
10 repeatedly; 1,200; 12,000. 17. 48; 60
21.

25. about 12; 12.7

Lesson 3-2 pp. 115–116

EXERCISES 1. Answers may vary. Sample: A
numerical expression is a mathematical phrase
with only numbers and operation symbols. An

algebraic expression is a mathematical
expression with one or more variables. 3. 20
5. 16
7.
9.

15. 8 17. 193
21.

x	x + 6
1	7
4	10
7	13

25. 75 27. 4,620 bricks 29. 10 hits; 15 misses
33. 29.16

Lesson 3-3 pp. 120–122

EXERCISES 1. Answers may vary. Sample: Your
grandfather is 50 years older than you. The
expression y + 50 relates his age to yours.
3. m + 4 5. 6 × z 7. k − 34 9. 50 + d
17. n − 3 19. n + 2 25. m ÷ n − 5 27. h + 2
29. (20 + 0.75n)t 33. 14.505

Lesson 3-4 pp. 126–127

EXERCISES 1. The value(s) of the variable(s) that
make(s) the equation true is (are) unknown.
3. 15 5. 3 7. false 9. true 11. false 13. true
15. 2 17. 4.3 29. 3.3 lb

Lesson 3-5 pp. 132–133

EXERCISES 1. subtracting 6 3. 18 5. 2.7
7. 48 9. 39
19. y = the year Mozart
was born;
y + 6 = 1762; y = 1756
21. m = number of minutes
of music before adding
song;
m + 4 = 120; m = 116
23. 10 minutes 25. 8.2 27. 0.29 29. 5.5 33. 37,
40, 43, 46, 49

Lesson 3-6 pp. 135–136

EXERCISES 1. She subtracted 4 from each side
instead of adding 4 to each side. 3. C 5. B
7. 4.2 9. 108 21. 12 25. 0

Lesson 3-7 pp. 140–141

EXERCISES **1.** The Multiplication Property of Equality states that you can multiply each side of an equation by the same nonzero number and the equation will be the same. The Division Property states the same is true for division. **3.** B **5.** A **7.** 14 **9.** 9.5 **11.** 18 **19.** 441 **21.** 51,772 **29.** about 8.25 feet **31.** 0.2 **33.** 3.42 **41.** =

Lesson 3-8 pp. 146–147

EXERCISES **1.** C **3.** J **5.** 72 **7.** $5 \times (60 + 3) = 5 \times 60 + 5 \times 3 = 300 + 15 = 315$ **9.** $6 \times (100 - 1) = 6 \times 100 - 6 \times 1 = 600 - 6 = 594$ **19.** y **21.** $23.20 **23.** C **27.** false

Chapter Review pp. 150–151

1. term **2.** algebraic expression **3.** solution **4.** variable **5.** equation **6.** Start with 2 and multiply by 3 repeatedly; 162; 486; 1,458. **7.** Start with 7 and add 12 repeatedly; 55, 67, 79. **8.** Start with 7 and multiply by 2 repeatedly; 112, 224, 448. **9.** 8 **10.** 49 **11.** 42 **12.** $x \div 12$ **13.** $2b$ **14.** $h + k$ **15.** false **16.** true **17.** false **18.** 5 **19.** 8 **20.** 8 **21.** 5,640 **22.** 7 **23.** 1.4 **24.** 6.06 **25.** 129.7 lb **26.** 56 **27.** 128 **28.** 2.5 **29.** 10.8 **30.** 60.8 **31.** 0.9 **32.** $16.68 **33.** $7(20 + 8) = 140 + 56 = 196$ **34.** $5(3 + 0.4) = 15 + 2.0 = 17$ **35.** $(10 + 1)57 = 570 + 57 = 627$

Chapter 4

Lesson 4-1 pp. 160–161

EXERCISES **1.** If the number is divisible by 2, then the number is even; otherwise, the number is odd. **3.** C **5.** A **7.** no **11.** 3 and 5 **13.** 2 and 3 **23.** no **27.** 4 **29.** 4 **31.** Yes; 5 + 6 + 6 + 1 = 18 and 18 is divisible by 9, so 5661 or $56.61, is divisible by 9. **33.** $1.00 **39.** 36

Lesson 4-2 pp. 164–165

EXERCISES **1.** The exponent tells how many times the base is used as a factor. **3.** 3^2 **5.** 9^3 **7.** 2, 2, 2 **9.** 29^1; 29; 1 **11.** 25^3; 25; 3 **19.** 64 **21.** 25 **29.** 64 **31.** 40 **33.** 2^8 cells **35.** 5 and 6

39. Length of Lake Trout

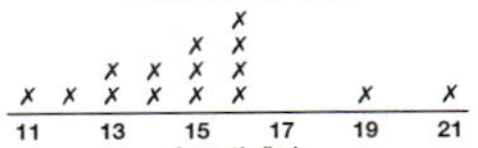
11
13
15
17
19
21
Length (in.)

Lesson 4-3 pp. 168–169

EXERCISES **1.** A prime number has exactly two factors and a composite number has more than two factors. **3.** 7; 7 has just two factors, 1 and 7. **5.** 1, 2, 4, 7, 14, 28 **7.** 1, 17 **15.** Prime; the only factors are 1 and 67. **19.** $2 \times 3 \times 7$ **21.** $2^4 \times 5^2$ **27.** 1,001 **29.** 9 rows **31.** If $p > 2$ and prime, then p is always odd. So $p + 1$ is even and always composite. **33.** 3, 5; 5, 7; 11, 13; 17, 19; 29, 31; 41, 43; 59, 61; 71, 73 **37.** >

Lesson 4-4 pp. 173–174

EXERCISES **1.** When two numbers have 1 as their only common factor, then the GCF = 1. **3.** B **5.** A **7.** factors of 24: 1, 2, 3, 4, 6, 8, 12, 24; factors of 45: 1, 3, 5, 9, 15, 45; GCF of 24 and 45: 3 **9.** factors of 30: 1, 2, 3, 5, 6, 10, 15, 30; factors of 35: 1, 5, 7, 35; GCF of 30 and 35: 5

13.
```
2)24  60    GCF = 12
2)12  30
3) 6  15
    2   5
```

15.
```
3)27  30    GCF = 3
    9  10
```

19.

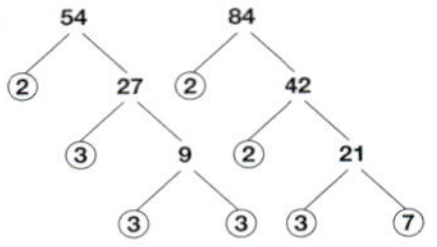
54
2
27
3
9
3
3
84
2
42
2
21
3
7

GCF = 6

21.

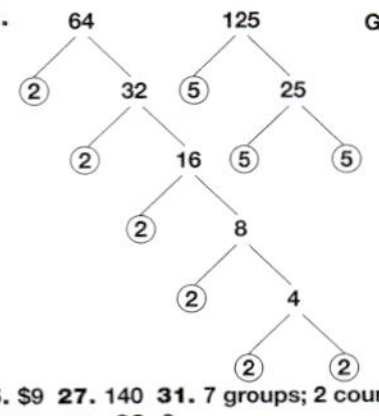
64
2
32
2
16
2
8
2
4
2
2
125
5
25
5
5

GCF = 1

25. $9 **27.** 140 **31.** 7 groups; 2 counselors; 11 campers **33.** 2

Lesson 4-5 pp. 178–179

EXERCISES **1.** simplest form **3.** A **5.** B **7.** $\frac{12}{14}, \frac{24}{28}$ **9.** $\frac{6}{32}, \frac{9}{48}$ **15.** $\frac{2}{7}$ **17.** $\frac{4}{5}$ **25.** yes **27.** no; $\frac{1}{3}$ **29.** $\frac{1}{2}$ **31a.** $\frac{2}{3}, \frac{4}{6}, \frac{10}{15}, \frac{20}{30}$ **b.** $\frac{2}{3}$; when you divide the numerator and the denominator by the common factor a, the result is in simplest form. **35.** 8

Lesson 4-6 pp. 184–185

EXERCISES **1.** C **3.** B **5.** $3\frac{1}{4}$; $\frac{13}{4}$ **7.** $\frac{22}{7}$ **9.** $\frac{11}{2}$ **15.** $3\frac{2}{5}$ **17.** $2\frac{1}{4}$ **25.** $\frac{7}{5}$; $1\frac{2}{5}$ **27.** $\frac{13}{5}$; $2\frac{3}{5}$ **31.** 9 boxes; $1,350 **33.** $1\frac{5}{8}$ in.; $1\frac{13}{16}$ in. **35.** 374 squares **39.** true

Lesson 4-7 pp. 190–191

EXERCISES **1.** Answers may vary. Sample: One number has many multiples. **3.** 16, 24, 32, 40 **5.** 48 **7.** 30 **9.** 80 **19.** 72 **21.** 56 **29.** 120th customer **31.** 48 **33 a.** 2, 4, 5 **b.** 40 **35.** $2x$ **37.** $200xy$

41.

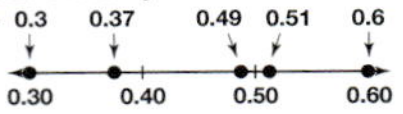
0.3
0.37
0.49
0.51
0.6
0.30
0.40
0.50
0.60

Lesson 4-8 pp. 194–195

EXERCISES **1.** It is the LCM of the denominators. **3.** 8 **5.** > **7.** > **9.** > **11.** = **25.** $3\frac{2}{5}, 3\frac{7}{15}, 3\frac{2}{3}$ **27.** $\frac{3}{12}, \frac{1}{2}, 2\frac{2}{3}, 3\frac{1}{4}$ **31.** >; the numerators are equal, so the fraction with the lesser denominator is larger. **33.** >; the numerators are equal, so the fraction with the lesser denominator is larger.

35a. $\frac{1}{2}, \frac{1}{4}, \frac{1}{8}, \frac{1}{16}$ **b.**

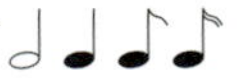

The note symbol that is "open" has the greatest value, and for the other symbols, the more flags there are, the less the value of the note. **43.** $\frac{4}{9}$

Lesson 4-9 pp. 200–201

EXERCISES **1.** $\frac{3}{10}$ **3.** $\frac{3}{4}$ **5.** $2\frac{3}{4} = 2 + \frac{3}{4} = 2 + 0.75 = 2.75$ **7.** A **9.** 1.6, $1\frac{3}{4}$, 2.3 **11.** 3.1, $3\frac{3}{8}$, $4\frac{3}{5}$ **13.** $\frac{17}{100}$ **15.** $5\frac{1}{2}$ **21.** $0.4\overline{6}$ **23.** $1.\overline{1}$ **31.** A **33.** B **37.** $6.625, $8.50 **39.** $5\frac{7}{8}$ in., 5.875 in. **45.** 612

Chapter Review pp. 204–205

1. equivalent fractions **2.** mixed number **3.** prime factorization **4.** 3 and 9 **5.** 3, 5, and 9 **6.** 2, 3, and 9 **7.** 2, 3, 5, 9, and 10 **8.** 17 **9.** 5 **10.** $2^2 \times 7$ **11.** 3×17 **12.** $2^2 \times 5^2$ **13.** 2×5^3 **14.** 2 **15.** 2 **16.** 5 **17.** 8 **18.** No; $\frac{1}{4}$; answers may vary. Sample: $\frac{2}{8}, \frac{3}{12}, \frac{10}{40}$ **19.** No; $\frac{2}{3}$; answers may vary. Sample: $\frac{10}{15}, \frac{8}{12}, \frac{20}{30}$ **20.** Yes; answers may vary. Sample: $\frac{2}{6}, \frac{3}{9}, \frac{4}{12}$ **21.** Yes; answers may vary. Sample: $\frac{4}{18}, \frac{6}{27}, \frac{8}{36}$ **22.** $\frac{14}{3}$ **23.** $\frac{41}{5}$ **24.** $4\frac{1}{3}$ **25.** $9\frac{2}{3}$ **26.** 132 **27.** 140 **28.** $\frac{1}{6}, \frac{1}{4}, \frac{1}{2}$ **29.** $2\frac{4}{15}, 2\frac{1}{3}, 2\frac{2}{5}$ **30.** $\frac{5}{16}, \frac{7}{20}, \frac{17}{40}$ **31.** 0.1875 **32.** $6.208\overline{3}$ **33.** $\frac{3}{50}$ **34.** $4\frac{13}{25}$

Chapter 5

Lesson 5-1 pp. 214–215

EXERCISES **1.** Benchmarks are whole numbers or fractions that are easy to use, such as 0, $\frac{1}{2}$, or 1. Rounding uses place value to find approximate values for numbers. **3.** 0 **5.** 1 **7.** 0 **9.** 1 **13.** $\frac{1}{2}$ **15.** $1\frac{1}{2}$ **27.** about $3\frac{1}{2}$ in. **31.** < **35.** 0.047 **37.** 0.006

Lesson 5-2 pp. 219–220

EXERCISES **1.** $\frac{3}{5}$; you do not add the denominators when adding two or more fractions. **3.** $\frac{2}{6} + \frac{3}{6} = \frac{5}{6}$ **5.** $\frac{1}{2}$ **7.** $\frac{2}{3}$ **13.** $\frac{2}{3}$ **15.** $\frac{1}{5}$ **25.** $\frac{71}{100}$ **27.** $\frac{1}{2}$ in. **31.** 5 **35.** Answer may vary. Sample: $\frac{6}{16}, \frac{9}{24}$

Lesson 5-3 pp. 224–225

EXERCISES **1.** $\frac{9}{10}$ **3.** $\frac{1}{2}$ **5.** $\frac{1}{2}$ **7.** $1\frac{13}{18}$ **15.** $\frac{9}{20}$ **17.** $\frac{2}{3}$ **23.** $1\frac{7}{8}$ **27a.** $1\frac{1}{2}$ in. **b.** $1\frac{7}{40}$ in. **29.** greater than 1 mi **35.** 11

Lesson 5-4 pp. 230–231

EXERCISES **1.** Answers may vary. Sample: $1\frac{1}{4} + 3\frac{3}{4}$ **3.** $6\frac{2}{3}$ **5.** $11\frac{3}{5}$ **7.** $11\frac{1}{2}$ **9.** $6\frac{7}{10}$ **21.** > **23a.** $7\frac{2}{3}$ ft **b.** $8\frac{1}{4}$ ft **25.** 13 yd **27.** $8\frac{1}{18}$ **31.** 77

Lesson 5-5 pp. 234–236

EXERCISES **1.** C **3.** $1\frac{1}{4}$ **5.** $1\frac{7}{20}$ **7.** $5\frac{8}{15}$ **15.** $3\frac{3}{8}$ **17.** $6\frac{7}{10}$ **25.** $\frac{11}{12}$ ft **27.** 6 in. **29.** 1 ft $4\frac{1}{4}$ in. **33.** $\frac{3}{5}$

Lesson 5-6 pp. 242–243

EXERCISES **1.** C **3.** D **5.** $11\frac{1}{6}$ ft **7.** $14\frac{1}{3}$ **9.** $5\frac{1}{5}$ **13.** $\frac{13}{45}$ **15.** $\frac{1}{8}$ **31.** n has the greater value. **35.** $\frac{3}{10}, \frac{1}{2}, \frac{4}{7}, \frac{2}{3}$

Lesson 5-7 pp. 248–250

EXERCISES **1.** elapsed time

3.

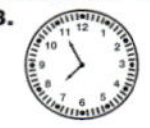

5. 1 h 25 min **7.** 1 h 17 min **11.** 7 h **15.** 1 h 39 min **19.** 29 min **23.** 2:00 P.M. **25.** $x + 3$

27.

Activity	Start Time	End Time
1st show	10:00 A.M.	10:45 A.M.
Break	10:45 A.M.	11:45 A.M.
2nd show	11:45 A.M.	12:30 P.M.
Break	12:30 P.M.	1:30 P.M.
3rd show	1:30 P.M.	2:15 P.M.

31. 39

Chapter Review pp. 252–253

1. benchmark **2.** elapsed time

3–10. Answers may vary. Samples are given.

3. $1\frac{1}{2}$ **4.** 0 **5.** 1 **6.** 0 **7.** 14 **8.** 10 **9.** 15 **10.** 6 **11.** about 6 c **12.** $1\frac{2}{5}$ **13.** $\frac{1}{2}$ **14.** $\frac{3}{5}$ **15.** $\frac{5}{9}$ **16.** $\frac{7}{8}$ **17.** $\frac{1}{2}$ **18.** $\frac{1}{8}$ **19.** $1\frac{7}{30}$ **20.** $\frac{13}{15}$ mi **21.** $7\frac{1}{8}$ **22.** $17\frac{1}{3}$ **23.** $63\frac{9}{10}$ **24.** about $59\frac{7}{12}$ in. **25.** $3\frac{3}{5}$ **26.** $6\frac{3}{8}$ **27.** $16\frac{7}{9}$ **28.** $\frac{3}{7}$ **29.** $\frac{1}{8}$ **30.** $1\frac{1}{9}$ **31.** $3\frac{1}{3}$ **32.** $11\frac{1}{18}$ **33.** $6\frac{2}{5}$ **34.** 3 h 41 min **35.** 8 h 48 min **36.** 8:10 P.M.

Chapter 6

Lesson 6-1 pp. 263–264

EXERCISES **1.** Greater; you are multiplying by a greater number. **3.** B **5.** C **7.** $\frac{10}{77}$ **9.** $\frac{1}{9}$ **25.** 1 **31.** 65 **35.** $\frac{7}{6}$ or $1\frac{1}{6}$

Lesson 6-2 pp. 269–270

EXERCISES **1.** $3 \times 3\frac{1}{2}$; $3\frac{1}{2}$ is greater than 3. **3.** $\frac{10}{3}$ **5.** $\frac{1}{2}$ **7.** $3\frac{1}{8}$ **9.** 75 **11.** 80 **15.** 65 **17.** $10\frac{1}{2}$ **25.** 14 **29.** $2\frac{1}{3}$ ft by $2\frac{1}{6}$ ft **37.** 4

Lesson 6-3 pp. 274–275

EXERCISES **1.** 1 **3.** Answers may vary. Sample: $\frac{2}{3}, \frac{3}{2}$ **5.** 2 **7.** 7 **11.** $11\frac{2}{3}$ **13.** 15 **27.** 2 **31.** about $1\frac{3}{10}$ times more **33.** 4 **37.** 2, 3

Lesson 6-4 pp. 278–279

EXERCISES **1.** about 3 **3.** Annie; Jocelyn incorrectly renamed $4\frac{1}{2}$ as $\frac{8}{2}$. **5.** about 7 **9.** $1\frac{7}{12}$ **13.** 4 **15.** $2\frac{2}{9}$ **19.** $1\frac{1}{25}$ **23.** $4.55 **25.** 30 books **31.** 2×7^2

Lesson 6-5 pp. 284–285

EXERCISES **1.** Answers may vary. Sample: Let $b = 8$. Since $\frac{8}{4} = 2$, b must be greater than 8. **3.** $\frac{5}{2}$ **5.** 44 **7.** 10 **9.** 56 **11.** 45 **23.** $4\frac{1}{6}$ **27.** $\frac{d}{12} = 14\frac{1}{2}$; 174 mi **29.** 4 **33.** $2\frac{1}{4}$

Lesson 6-6 pp. 290–291

EXERCISES **3.** cups

5–13. Answers may vary. Samples are given.

5. Feet; lots are usually measured in feet. **9.** Pounds; one orange weighs less than a pound, so a bag of oranges would weigh more than a pound. **13.** Fluid ounces; a sample size bottle of shampoo holds less than a cup. **19.** < **23.** 960 grains **27.** 1 h 59 min

Lesson 6-7 pp. 294–295

EXERCISES

1.

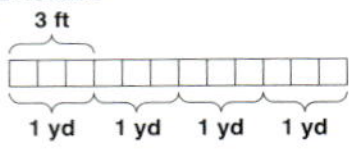
3 ft
1 yd
1 yd
1 yd
1 yd

3. divide **5.** false; 6 ft = 2 yd **7.** false; $2\frac{1}{2}$ t = 5,000 lb **9.** 15,840 **11.** 9 **21.** 11 gal **27.** > **31.** Yes. You have 192 cups of punch and you need 180. **35.** A: $5\frac{1}{2}$ lb; B: 9 lb; C: 15 lb **39.** $5\frac{3}{14}$

Chapter Review pp. 298–299

1. 12 **2.** 12 **3.** 80 **4.** 84 **5.** $\frac{3}{10}$ **6.** $\frac{2}{39}$ **7.** $\frac{2}{5}$ **8.** 15 **9.** $17\frac{1}{2}$ **10.** $3\frac{7}{8}$ **11.** $6\frac{14}{15}$ **12.** $20\frac{15}{22}$ **13.** $\frac{1}{3}$ c **14.** 16 **15.** $5\frac{2}{3}$ **16.** $\frac{5}{11}$ **17.** $\frac{8}{9}$ **18.** $1\frac{3}{7}$ **19.** $\frac{2}{25}$ **20.** $4\frac{17}{52}$ **21.** $12\frac{3}{7}$ **22.** 20 buckets **23.** 1; $\frac{33}{35}$ **24.** 3; $2\frac{76}{105}$ **25.** 3; $3\frac{51}{112}$ **26.** 2; $1\frac{11}{13}$ **27.** about 19 appointments **28.** 96 **29.** 25 **30.** 2 **31.** $\frac{3}{4}$ **32.** 4 **33.** 2 **34.** $7\frac{1}{5}$ **35.** $\frac{13}{50}$ **36.** tons **37.** fluid ounces **38.** $73\frac{1}{3}$ **39.** 40 **40.** 6 **41.** 150 ft

Chapter 7

Lesson 7-1 pp. 308–309

EXERCISES **1.** $\frac{9}{5}$ is a comparison of two numbers by division; $1\frac{4}{5}$ is not. **3.** D **5.** C **7.** 35 to 24, 35 : 24, $\frac{35}{24}$ **11.** $\frac{2}{7}, \frac{16}{56}, \frac{28}{98}$ **15.** 4 : 3 **17.** $\frac{1}{3}$ **23.** 2 **25.** 64 **29.** 5 : 7 **31.** Yes; 14 to 20 is equivalent to $\frac{7}{10}$. **33.** 1 : 2 **37.** $\frac{6}{35}$

Lesson 7-2 pp. 314–315

EXERCISES **1.** $\frac{12 \text{ inches}}{1 \text{ foot}}$ is a unit rate because it has 1 in the denominator. **3.** C **5.** D **7.** 23 desks per classroom **11.** $.15 per oz; $.16 per oz; 16 oz for $2.39 **19.** 208 words in 8 min **21.** 132 points in 12 games **23.** About 28.6 miles per gallon; answers may vary. Sample: I divided 279.9 by 9.8. **25.** 0.15 mi/s

Lesson 7-3 pp. 318–319

EXERCISES **1.** The cross products are equal. **3.** Answers may vary. Sample: $\frac{2}{5}, \frac{4}{10}, \frac{24}{60}$ **5.** yes **7.** no **25.** yes **29.** no **31.** No; answers may vary. Sample: If two ratios are equivalent, a third ratio must be equivalent to both of them or neither of them. **37.** $1\frac{8}{9}$

Lesson 7-4 pp. 322–324

EXERCISES **1.** Answers may vary. Sample: You could determine whether their cross products are equal or put each ratio in simplest form and see if they are equivalent. **7.** 84 **9.** 5 **25.** 33 in. **27.** $6.40 **31.** 16 teachers **33.** $x = 2$; $y = 21$ **37.** 5

Lesson 7-5 pp. 328–329

EXERCISES **1.** One inch on the map represents an actual distance of 50 miles. **3.** approximate; Explanations may vary. Sample: It's very difficult to get exact measurements using a ruler. **5.** 1 ft : 20 ft **7.** 47 mi **11.** 4 in. **17.** 1.25 cm **19.** 1.7 cm **21 a.** Reduce. The map is 4 cm wide and 3 cm high. For each centimeter on the map, I would draw 0.5 centimeter on my drawing. My drawing would measure 2 cm wide and 1.5 cm high.

b.

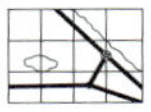

27. $7\frac{1}{2}$

Lesson 7-6 pp. 332–334

EXERCISES **1.** The ratio does not compare a number to 100. **3.** Answers may vary. Samples: $\frac{5}{6}$ and 0.85. **5.** $\frac{7}{10}$ **7.** $\frac{1}{20}$ **15.** 0.15 **17.** 0.82 **27.** 8% **31.** 95% **33.** 25% **39.** C **43.** $\frac{1}{5}$, 22%, 0.24, $\frac{1}{4}$ **45.** $\frac{17}{20}, \frac{22}{25}$, 0.9, 95% **49.** 75% **51.** 25%

Lesson 7-7	pp. 338–339

EXERCISES **1.** 5 **3.** 3 **5.** 30 **7.** 16.8 **9.** 66 **19.** 36 **25.** 6 **27.** 152 **29.** No; 50% off is half the price. The 10%-off coupon is applied to a price that is less than \$60. **31.** \$120 **35.** Store B has a better rate; $\frac{2}{3}$ is equal to $66\frac{2}{3}$%, which is greater than 60%. **39.** $\frac{2}{5}$

Lesson 7-8	pp. 342–344

EXERCISES **1.** whole **3.** The sum of the fractions is not 1. **5.** basketball

9.

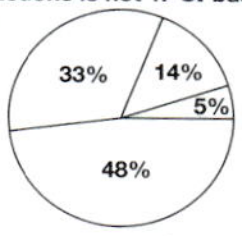

33%
14%
5%
48%

13.

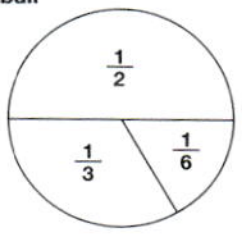

1/2
1/3
1/6

19. \$57.05 **23.** $1\frac{1}{2}$

Lesson 7-9	pp. 350–351

EXERCISES **1.** about \$55 **3.** \$20 × 0.09 **5.** \$40 × 0.05 **7.** \$1.96, \$29.96 **11.** \$6.30 **15.** \$24 **23.** 36, underestimate **25.** \$31.85 **27.** Florida: \$3.90, \$68.90 Georgia: \$2.60, \$67.60 Massachusetts: \$3.25, \$68.25 Tennessee: \$4.55, \$69.55 **29.** 5 ft 6 in. **33.** 75

Chapter Review	pp. 354–355

1. B **2.** D **3.** C **4.** A **5.** 15 to 23, 15 : 23, $\frac{15}{23}$ **6.** 15 to 8, 15 : 8, $\frac{15}{8}$ **7.** 23 to 8, 23 : 8, $\frac{23}{8}$ **8.** 15 to 46, 15 : 46, $\frac{15}{46}$ **9.** 1 to 4 **10.** $\frac{3}{5}$ **11.** 3 ft : 1 yd **12.** $\frac{5 \text{ boys}}{6 \text{ girls}}$ **13.** 40 min **14.** \$12.50 **15.** \$.10 per oz, \$.06 per oz, A 24-oz loaf is the better buy. **16.** no **17.** yes **18.** yes **19.** no **20.** 354 marbles **21.** 99 ft **22.** 148.5 in. **23.** 132 in. **24.** $\frac{3}{10}$, 0.3 **25.** $\frac{1}{4}$, 0.25 **26.** $\frac{14}{25}$, 0.56 **27.** $\frac{3}{25}$, 0.12 **28.** 60 students **29.** 60%

30.

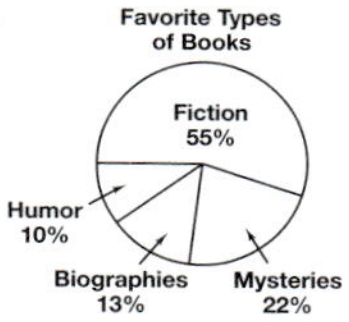

Favorite Types of Books
Fiction 55%
Humor 10%
Biographies 13%
Mysteries 22%

31. 10 **32.** \$1.20 **33.** \$6.00

Chapter 8

Lesson 8-1	pp. 364–365

EXERCISES **1.** C **3.** A **5.** C **7.** $\overrightarrow{KJ}$ **9.** $\overrightarrow{QP}$ **17.** always **23.** Answers may vary. Sample: $\overline{DH}$ **29.** 7

Lesson 8-2	pp. 370–371

EXERCISES **1.** A right angle measures 90°; an obtuse angle measures between 90° and 180°.

3. **4.** **5.**

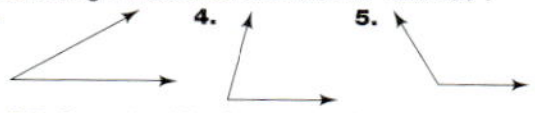

7. 60° **9.** acute **13.** obtuse **21.** 20° **25.** acute **29.** 165°

Lesson 8-3	pp. 376–377

EXERCISES **1.** Complementary angles have a sum of 90°; supplementary angles add to 180°. **3.** C **5.** B **7.** 45° **11.** 90° **15.** 62° **21.** never **23.** 20° **25.** An obtuse angle does not have a complement. **29.** 5

Lesson 8-4	pp. 382–383

EXERCISES **1.** right, scalene **3.** acute, scalene **5.** right **9.** 65° **11.** scalene **15.** scalene **19.** right **21.** right; right **25.** $3x = 180$ or $x + x + x = 180$ **27.** $180° - 2x$ **31.** 50 people

Lesson 8-5	pp. 389–390

EXERCISES **1.** All four sides will be congruent. **5.** decagon **7.** irregular **11.** rectangle, parallelogram **13.** 14°

17.

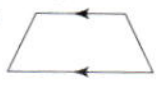

19.

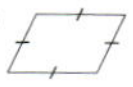

23.

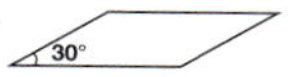

30°

25. All **27.** All **31.** 36%

Lesson 8-6	pp. 394–395

EXERCISES **1.** congruent **3.** A **5.** B **7.** no **9.** no **13.** 63° **17a.** ∠*MNO* and ∠*PQR*, ∠*MON* and ∠*PRQ*, ∠*OMN* and ∠*RPQ*

b. 3 : 4 : 5 = 12 : 16 : 20 **19.** 149 **21.** 4, 5

Lesson 8-7	pp. 399–401

EXERCISES **1.** yes **5.** No; the two sides do not match. **7.** 2

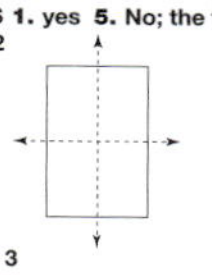

11. no **15.** 3 **23.** Answers may vary. Sample: $\overrightarrow{AC}$, $\overrightarrow{BC}$, $\overrightarrow{AD}$

Lesson 8-8	pp. 404–405

EXERCISES **1.** C **3.** B **5.** no

10.

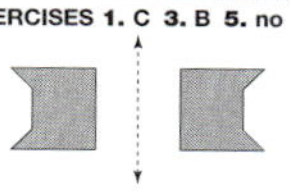

11. no **17.** Answers may vary. Sample:

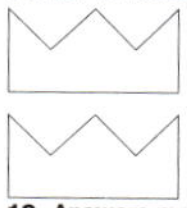

19. Answers may vary. Sample: directly left, directly right, up and slightly to the right **21.** reflection or 180° rotation **27.** $9\frac{1}{9}$

Chapter Review	pp. 408–409

1. obtuse **2.** equilateral **3.** perpendicular **4.** rectangle **5.** line **6.** Answers may vary. Sample: $\overleftrightarrow{EF}$ and $\overleftrightarrow{AB}$ **7.** Answers may vary. Sample: $\overrightarrow{BC}$, $\overrightarrow{BA}$ **8.** ∠*DEG* and ∠*BEF* **9.** ∠*FEG* **10.** ∠*ABE* and ∠*EBC* **11.** ∠*DEG* **12.** rectangle **13.** hexagon **14.** pentagon **15.** similar **16.** congruent **17.** Answers may vary. Sample:

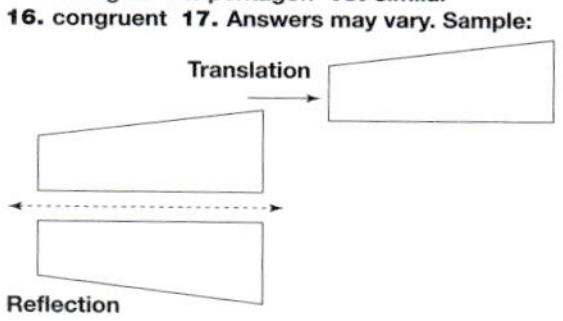

Translation
Reflection

Chapter 9

Lesson 9-1	pp. 418–419

EXERCISES **1a.** mass **3.** Answers may vary. Sample: pencil, finger **5.** true **7.** false; 1 L = 1,000 mL **9.** meters **11.** centimeters **15.** grams **17.** kilograms **21.** liters **23.** kiloliters **29.** 0.001 **33.** No; a ladybug would be measured in grams or milligrams. **35.** Less; 8 × 12 = 96, so 96 cm < 1 m. **41.** 46°; 136°

Lesson 9-2	pp. 423–424

EXERCISES **1.** 5 m; 5 m = 5,000 mm **3.** divide **5.** divide **7.** 600,000 cm **9.** 20,000,000 cm **15.** 3.07 **17.** 610 **25.** about 299,792.458 km (or about 300,000 km) **27.** 7 g **29.** 340 m **35.** 519 m **41.** right isosceles triangle

Lesson 9-3	pp. 429–430

EXERCISES **1.** Perimeter is the distance around a figure. Area is the two-dimensional space the figure takes up. **3.** P = 26 ft, A = 36 ft^2 **5.** P = 38 in., A = 84 in.^{2} **7.** P = 45 in., A = 123.5 in.^{2} **15.** 25 m^2

19. There are 3 ft × 3 ft, or 9 ft^2, in 1 yd^2.

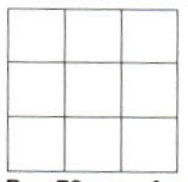

21. P = 70 mm; A = 294 mm^2 **23.** 84 ft^2

Lesson 9-4	pp. 434–435

EXERCISES **1.** The height of a triangle is the length of the perpendicular segment from a vertex to the base opposite that vertex. **3.** The triangle's area is half of the rectangle's area. **5.** 16 m^2 **7.** 31.5 m^2 **11.** 10 ft^2 **15.** 157.5 in.^{2} **17.** 220.5 ft^2 **19.** 13.2 in. **21.** 6 ft **25.** 246

Lesson 9-5	pp. 440–441

EXERCISES **1.** Yes; a chord that does not pass through the center is not a diameter. **3.** $\overline{QR}$, $\overline{QS}$, $\overline{QT}$ **7.** 70 mi **13.** 15.7 in. **15.** 87.92 mi **19.** 30.6 ft **25.** about 6.3 ft **29.** 7.5

Lesson 9-6	pp. 446–447

EXERCISES **1.** 616 cm^2 **3.** 12 in.^{2} **5.** 1,200 cm^2 **7.** 200.96 mm^2 **11.** 379.94 yd^2 **13.** $17\frac{1}{9}$ mm^2 **19.** 4.5 cm^2 **23.** 38.28 ft^2 **25.** 30.96 cm^2 **29.** When the diameter is tripled, the area becomes 9 times greater. **33.** four

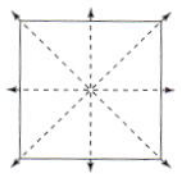

Lesson 9-7	pp. 451–452

EXERCISES **1.** Answers may vary. Sample: They are both three-dimensional shapes. A prism has two parallel and congruent bases, but a pyramid has only one base. **3.** cone **5.** cylinder **7.** hexagonal prism **9.** pentagonal prism **13.** pyramid **17.** trapezoidal prism; 6 faces, 8 vertices, 12 edges **19.** Answers may vary. Sample:

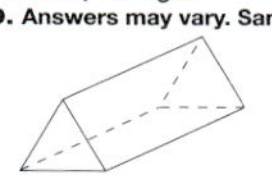

Lesson 9-8	pp. 454–456

EXERCISES **1.** A net lets you see a 3-dimensional object in 2 dimensions. **3.** 24 cm^2

5.

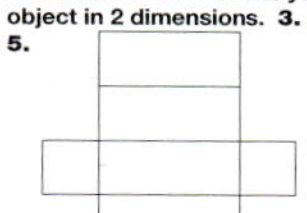

7. 78 cm^2 **9.** 216 ft^2 **17.** 3 in. **19.** 243.8 in.^{2} **21.** 4 times larger; 9 times larger; 16 times larger **27.** milliliters

Lesson 9-9	pp. 459–460

EXERCISES **1.** Volume is the measure of an object's capacity. Area is the measure of the number of square units on the surface of the figure. **3.** 264 m^3 **5.** 192 cubic units **9.** 5,940 m^3 **13.** Answers may vary. Sample: 5 feet by 4 feet by 4 feet **15.** 480,000 bottles **19.** 36 ft^2

Lesson 9-10	pp. 464–466

EXERCISES **1.** $2\pi r^2$ represents the area of the two circular bases and $C \times h$ represents the area of the rectangle; their sum represents the total surface area. **3.** 200.48 in.^{2} **5.** 351.68 cm^2 **9.** 706.5 m^3 **15.** 71.3 cm^2; 44.2 cm^3 **17.** 824.06 cm^3 **21.** 2,574,466.7 m^3

Chapter Review	pp. 468–469

1. faces **2.** pyramid or cone **3.** radius **4.** 300 **5.** 1.5 **6.** 5.7 **7.** 30 ft; 48 ft^2 **8.** 68.9 m; 187.72 m^2 **9.** 64 in.; 240 in.^{2} **10.** $\overline{XV}$, $\overline{YW}$, $\overline{VW}$ **11.** $\overline{XV}$ **12.** $\overline{OV}$, $\overline{OX}$, $\overline{OY}$ **13.** 31.4 in. **14.** 79 in.^{2} **15.** triangular prism **16.** rectangular pyramid **17.** cylinder **18.** 40 in.^{2}; 16 in.^{3} **19.** 122 m^2; 84 m^3 **20.** 715.92 ft^2; 1,469.52 ft^3

Chapter 10

Lesson 10-1	pp. 479–480

EXERCISES **1.** sample space **3.** Answers may vary. Sample: You can use the counting principle to multiply 5 × 6 and find 30 different ways.

5. 9 outcomes

7. Flip 1 Flip 2 4 outcomes

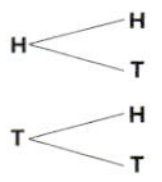

H
H
T
T
H
T

9. 8 outcomes **13.** 6 colors **15.** 500 four-digit numbers **17.** tons

Lesson 10-2	pp. 484–486

EXERCISES **1.** The sum of the probability of an event and the probability of its complement always equals 1. **5.** B **7.** $\frac{4}{10}$ or $\frac{2}{5}$ **13.** 0.2 **19.** $\frac{2}{6}$ or $\frac{1}{3}$ **21.** $\frac{3}{6}$ or $\frac{1}{2}$ **23.** Answers may vary. Sample: 0.55 **25.** Answers may vary. Sample: 0.65 **27.** $\frac{3}{4}$ **33.** $5\frac{2}{3}$

Lesson 10-3	pp. 490–491

EXERCISES **1.** Experimental probability is found by conducting an experiment. **3.** $\frac{20}{50}$ or $\frac{2}{5}$ **5.** $\frac{8}{50}$ or $\frac{4}{25}$ **7.** $\frac{7}{15}$ **9.** 0 **11.** No; the experimental probability of rolling an even number is $\frac{27}{80}$. **15.** $\frac{2}{3}$ **23.** $\frac{13}{20}$; $\frac{7}{20}$ **25.** 24 in.^{2} **29.** congruent

Lesson 10-4	pp. 495–497

EXERCISES **1.** A sample is a part of a population. **3.** B **5.** 2 **7.** 6 **13.** 450 pairs of socks **19.** 4,650 gadgets **21.** $\frac{16}{20}$ or $\frac{4}{5}$ **23.** 48 red marbles **27.** 10.5

Lesson 10-5	pp. 502–503

EXERCISES **1.** are **5.** Independent; none of the rolls has an effect on another. **7.** $\frac{9}{100}$ **9.** $\frac{25}{100}$ or $\frac{1}{4}$ **13.** $\frac{1}{8}$ **19.** $\frac{1}{48}$ **21.** $\frac{1}{4}$ **23.** Yes; the first spin has no effect on the second spin. **25.** $\frac{1}{2}$ **29.** 48 cm^3

Chapter Review	pp. 508–509

1. C **2.** B **3.** A **4.** D **5.** 24 ways **6.** $\frac{1}{6}$ **7.** $\frac{3}{6}$ or $\frac{1}{2}$ **8.** $\frac{2}{6}$ or $\frac{1}{3}$ **9.** Kayla: $\frac{1}{3}$; Noel: $\frac{2}{3}$ **10.** $\frac{1}{4}$ **11.** $\frac{1}{3}$ **12.** $\frac{7}{12}$ **13.** 2,200 defective computers

14. Check students' work. **15.** Independent; the first roll does not affect the fourth roll. **16.** Not independent; after drawing the first cube, there is one cube fewer in the bag. **17.** $\frac{9}{81}$ or $\frac{1}{9}$ **18.** $\frac{6}{81}$ or $\frac{2}{27}$ **19.** $\frac{8}{81}$

Chapter 11

Lesson 11-1	pp. 517–519

EXERCISES **1.** Answers may vary. Sample: Some integers are –1, 0, 1, 2, and 3; –5.7, 0.3, 2.92, and 10.5 are not integers. **3.** *M* **5.** *P* **7.** 100 **9.** –12 **13.** 10 **15.** –14 **21.** 38 **23.** 9 **31.** Janet **33.** –6 **35.** 5 **37.** –3; 3 **39.** –101; 101 **41.** negative **47.** Dudhsagar Falls

Lesson 11-2	pp. 521–522

EXERCISES **1.** C **5.** < **7.** < **17.** –5, –2, 0, 2, 5 **21.** –62°F, –54°F, –34°F, –22°F, 85°F, 86°F, 90°F, 96°F

23. 9 **25 a.** < **b.** > **29.** 15 yd^2

Lesson 11-3	pp. 526–527

EXERCISES **1.** always **3.** sometimes **5.** –8 **7.** –4 **13.** –3 **15.** –47 **25.** 45°F **27.** –3 **32.** Placement of numbers may vary. Sample:

3	–4	1
–2	0	2
–1	4	–3

37. $\overline{CF}$, $\overline{DG}$, $\overline{EH}$

Lesson 11-4	pp. 532–533

EXERCISES **1.** –3 – (–2) **3.** –10 + (–3) **5.** –1 + 3 **7.** 9 **9.** –7 **13.** –5 **15.** –16 **23.** –1,250 ft **25.** –43 **27.** 26 **29.** Answers may vary. Sample: 3 – 7 = –4, 7 – 3 = 4, –4 ≠ 4. **33.** Answers may vary. Sample: $\overrightarrow{AB}$, $\overrightarrow{DC}$, $\overrightarrow{DE}$

Lesson 11-5 pp. 536–537
EXERCISES 1. Start at 0. Make 5 groups of −2 on the number line. 3. negative 5. negative 7. 8
9. −8 13. −22 15. 54 25. 144 27. −126
29. −940 31. −3; $1 − 2 + 3 − 4 \times 5 − 6$
35. 318 m²

Lesson 11-6 pp. 541–542
EXERCISES 1. Zarita; the quotient of 2 negative numbers is always positive. 3. −2°/hour
5. negative 7. 8 9. 6 15. 18 stairs/min
19. −$6/day 21. Yes; fresh water evaporates at 125 mL/day. Salt water evaporates at 120 mL/day. 25. 40°; 130°

Lesson 11-7 pp. 544–545
EXERCISES 3. 4 min 5. B 7. C 9. −3 11. −5
23. $80 25. 5 hours 29. 64

Lesson 11-8 pp. 550–551
EXERCISES 1. Answers may vary. Sample: The first coordinate tells how far to move left or right. The second coordinate tells how far to move up or down. 3. B 5. (−1, 1) 9. P 19. (2, −1) 23. III
25. y-axis 27. x-axis 29. x-axis 31. (−3, 0)
33a. Africa b. Europe 35. (−1, 2), (7, 2), (5, 8)

Lesson 11-9 pp. 555–557
EXERCISES 1a. negative b. positive c. negative d. positive 3. −$2,256 7. Monday: $9; Tuesday: $18; Wednesday: −$9; Thursday: $17; Friday: −$12; Saturday: −$1 11. 120 bottles 15. 30
17. Weeks 1 and 3
19.
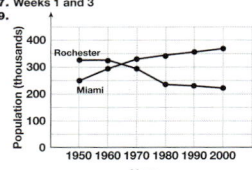

21. Rochester 25. obtuse 27. right

Lesson 11-10 pp. 561–562
EXERCISES 1. x 3. multiply 5. −1; 12; 35
7.

x	y
−2	0
−1	1
0	2
1	3
2	4

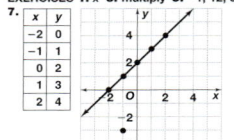

9.

x	y
−2	−4
−1	−2
0	0
1	2
2	4

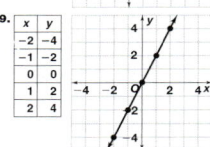

17. 5; 6; divide by 5. 19. Linear; the graph is a line. 21. Not linear; the graph is not a line. 25. 9:00 A.M.

Chapter Review pp. 564–565
1. function 2. integers 3. quadrants
4. opposites 5. −14 6. > 7. < 8. < 9. >
10. −2, −1, 1, 2 11. −6, −4, 0, 5
12. −7, −3, 5, 9 13. 11 14. −4 15. −2
16. −13 17. 8 18. 8 19. −11 20. −8
21. 36 22. −21 23. −10 24. 48 25. 4 26. −5
27. 7 28. −4 29. −15 30. −9 31. −4 32. −36
33–36.

37. $26,286 38. profit

39.
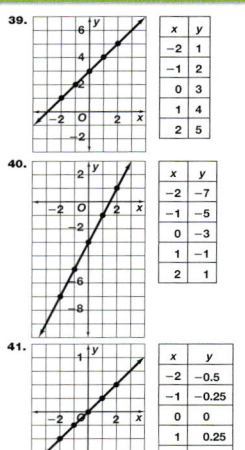

x	y
−2	1
−1	2
0	3
1	4
2	5

40.

x	y
−2	−7
−1	−5
0	−3
1	−1
2	1

41.

x	y
−2	−0.5
−1	−0.25
0	0
1	0.25
2	0.5

Chapter 12

Lesson 12-1 pp. 574–576
EXERCISES 1. two-step 3. two-step
5. $2b + 4 = 12$;
$2b + 4 − 4 = 12 − 4$;
$2b \div 2 = 8 \div 2$;
$b = 4$
7. −5 9. 8 19. 5
21. 5 25. The error is dividing by 5 instead of multiplying by 5. 27. A; $2,000 29. Rule: Multiply by 2 and then add 3. 19; 33 31. $9\frac{1}{3}$ 35. $\frac{1}{4}$ in.

Lesson 12-2 pp. 580–581
EXERCISES 1. solutions 3. $x < −1$ 5. $\ell > 15$
7. $p \le 4$
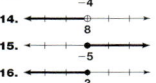
13. true 15. true
19.

Lesson 12-3 pp. 583–584
EXERCISES 1. addition 3. subtraction
5. $c \le 10$ 7. $z < 5$ 9. $j > −7$
21. $a + 2,500 < 32,000$;
$a < 29,500$ ft
27. rectangular prism

Lesson 12-4 pp. 589–590
EXERCISES 1. Yes. $\sqrt{4} = 2$; 2 is an integer, and integers are rational numbers. 3. 2.6 5. 1 7. 9
13. 4.6 15. 7.1 19. rational 21. rational 31. 2
33. 3 35. Yes; no; explanations may vary.
Sample: Since $\sqrt{1} = 1$, $\sqrt{2}$ must be greater than 1. Since $\sqrt{4} = 2$, $\sqrt{2}$ must be less than 2.
37. 230 m 45. 12.6 ft²

Lesson 12-5 pp. 593–594
EXERCISES 1. It is the longest side and opposite the right angle. 3. yes; $5^2 + 12^2 = 13^2$ 5. 30
7. 5 17. 26 in. 19. $r^2 + s^2 = t^2$ 23. 0

Chapter Review pp. 598–599
1. E 2. D 3. B 4. F 5. A 6. 3 7. 1 8. 125
9. no 10. yes 11. no 12. yes
13.
14.
15.
16.

17. $q < 3$ 18. $t < 5$ 19. $v > 16$ 20. $y \ge −20$
21. 9 22. 4.9 23. 5.5 24. 12 25. between 2 and 3 26. between 3 and 4 27. between 4 and 5
28. between 5 and 6 29. rational 30. not rational 31. rational 32. rational 33. 10 34. 8
35. 2.2 36. 5.3 37. 132 in.

T664

Additional Answers

CHAPTER 1

Lesson 1-1

page 4   Check Skills You'll Need

1. Answers may vary. Sample: 8, 3.5
2. 2 tens or 20
3. 2 ones or 2
4. 2 thousands or 2,000
5. 2 hundreds or 200

Lesson 1-5

page 21   Activity Lab

7a.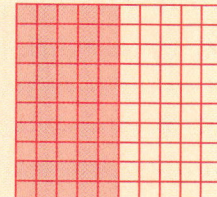

b. Both include the same amount of shaded area.

Lesson 1-6

page 26   Quick Check

1. Model may vary. Sample:

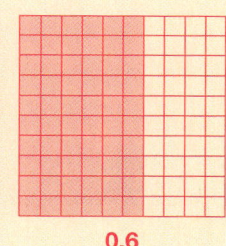

0.59   0.6

0.6 is greater.

page 29   Homework Exercises

7.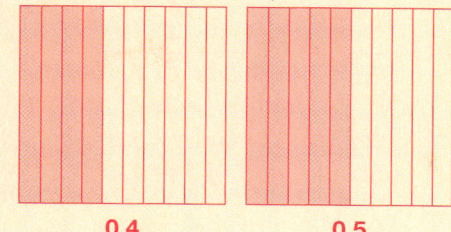

0.4   0.5

0.5 is greater.

8.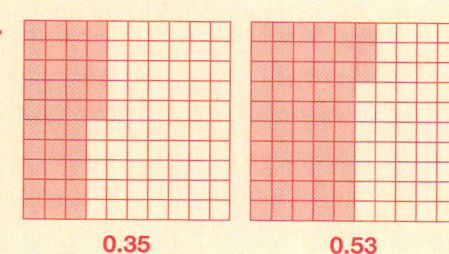

0.35   0.53

0.53 is greater.

9.

0.2   0.02

0.2 is greater.

page 31   Activity Lab

1–4. Models may vary. Samples are given.

1.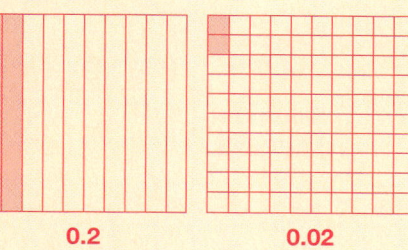

0.9

2.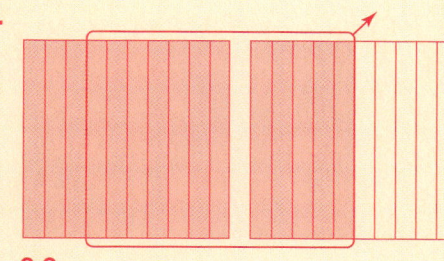

0.3

3.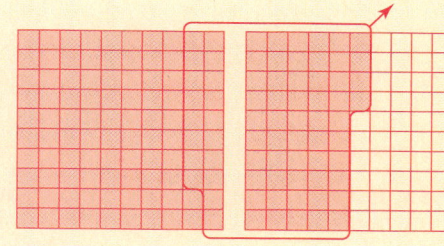

0.61

4.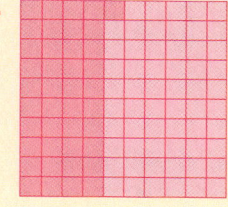

0.82

5a.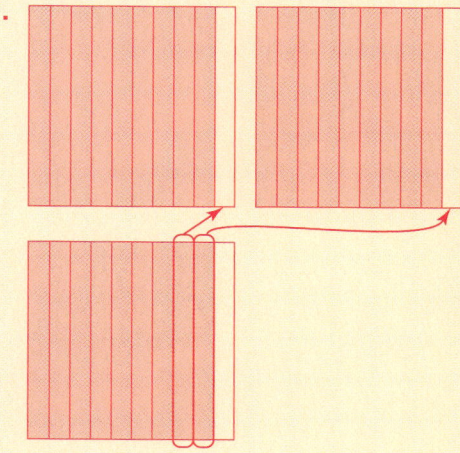

1.0

b. Answers may vary. Sample: The sum completely fills all hundredths.

Lesson 1-8

page 37   Activity Lab

1.

2.7

2.

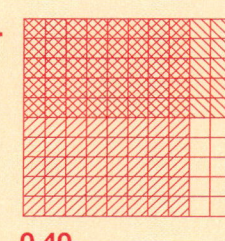

1.22

Move 39 squares.

3.

0.40

page 39   TE Closure

Sample: Multiply decimals like whole numbers. Then count the number of decimal places in the factors, count off that many places in the product, and place the decimal point.

CHAPTER 2

Lesson 2-3

page 70   Quick Check

1.

Initial	Tally	Frequency
A	I	1
B	I	1
C	I	1
D	II	2
J	I	1
K	II	2
L	III	3
P	I	1
S	I	1
T	I	1
V	I	1

L

page 71   Quick Check

2.   Number of Sales Calls

```
 X
 X                    X
 X X                  X
 X X            X X
 X X X X      X X X X
 0 1 2 3 4 5 6 7 8 9
     Sales Calls
```

Answers may vary. Sample: Either a low number of sales calls were made each hour (0–3) or a high number (6–9).

page 72   Homework Exercises

6.

Number of Days	Tally	Frequency
28	I	1
30	IIII	4
31	NHII	7

31

7.

Type of Car	Tally	Frequency
Compact	IIII	4
Mid-size	III	3
SUV	II	2
Wagon	I	1
Pick-up	II	2

compact

9.   Word Lengths in a Sentence

```
 X X          X X
 X X X X    X X X X X
 1 2 3 4 5 6 7 8 9 10
 Word Lengths (letters)
```

page 73   Homework Exercises

14a.

Letter	Tally	Frequency
a	III	3
b	I	1
c	II	2
d	I	1
e	I	1
f	I	1
g	NHII	7
h	II	2
i	III	3
l	NH NH I	11
n	IIII	4
o	NHI	6
p	I	1
r	IIII	4
s	I	1
t	I	1
w	IIII	4
y	NH	5

b.   The mode is l. The letter l alone makes up about 19% of the letters in the name.

18a.

Scores	Tally	Frequency
2	I	1
6	I	1
7	II	2
8	IIII	4
9	I	1
10	III	3

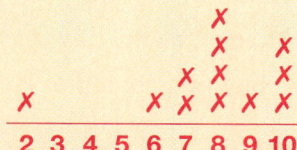

```
                    X
                    X    X
                  X X X
 X            X X X X X
 2 3 4 5 6 7 8 9 10
```

Lesson 2-4

page 74   Check Skills You'll Need

3.

```
       X        X        X        X
 10 11 12 13 14 15 16 17 18 19 20 21
```

1.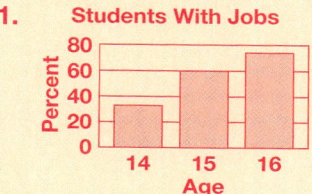

Students With Jobs

2.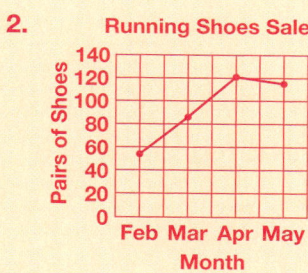

Running Shoes Sales

4.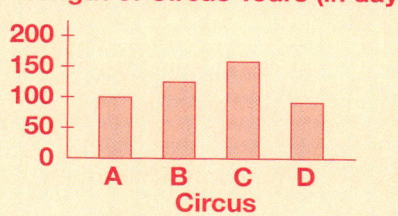

Length of Circus Tours (in days)

Circus D toured about $\frac{1}{2}$ as many days as Circus C.

6.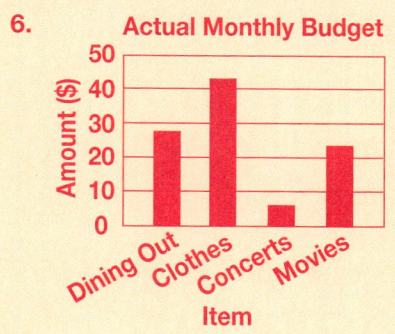

Actual Monthly Budget

7.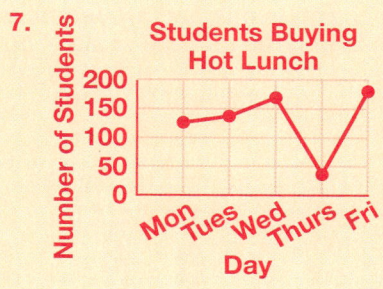

Students Buying Hot Lunch

9.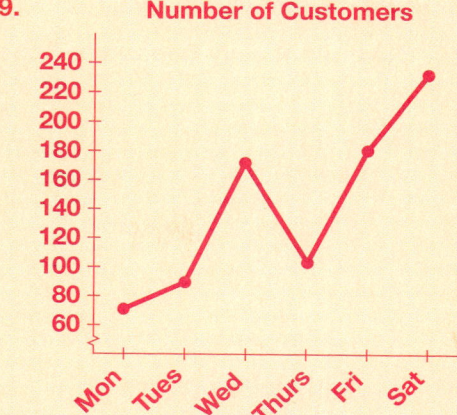

Number of Customers

It generally increases during the week.

1.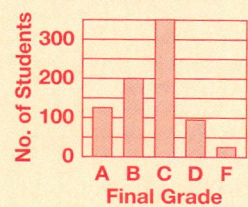

Final Math Grades

2.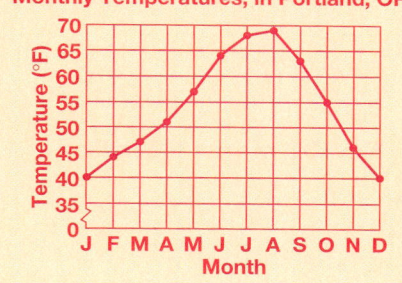

Monthly Temperatures, in Portland, OR

11.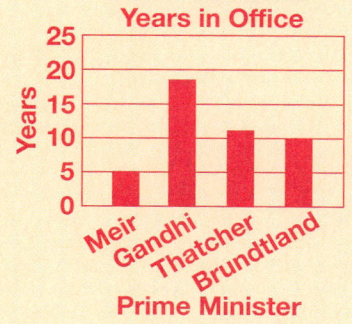

Prime Ministers' Years in Office

13.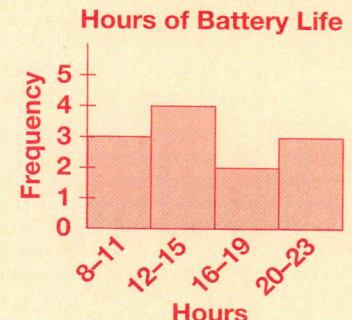

Hours of Battery Life

3.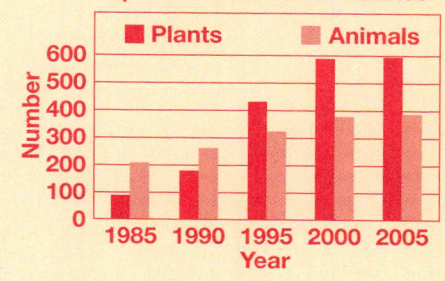

Number of Endangered Species in the United States

4.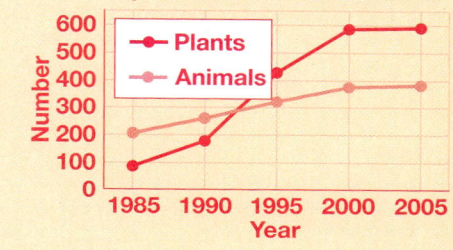

Number of Endangered Species in the United States

Lesson 2-5

1. Graphs may vary. Sample:

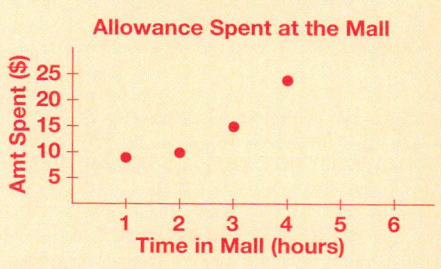

Allowance Spent at the Mall

Check students' work.

Additional Answers

T667

2. Graphs may vary. Sample:

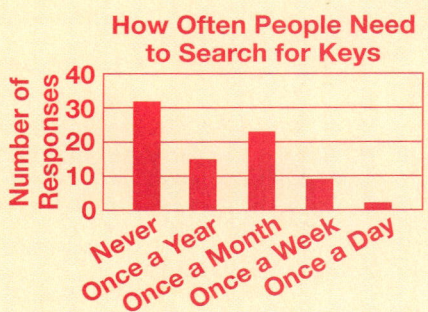

How Often People Need to Search for Keys

Check students' work.

page 85 Checkpoint Quiz 1

8.

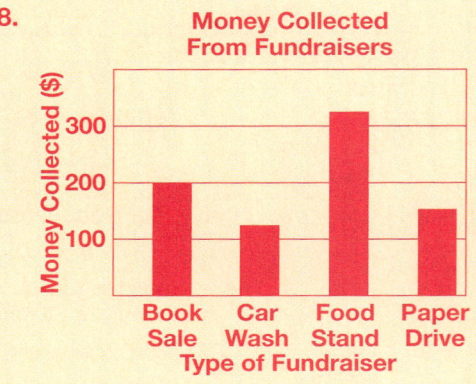

Money Collected From Fundraisers

9.

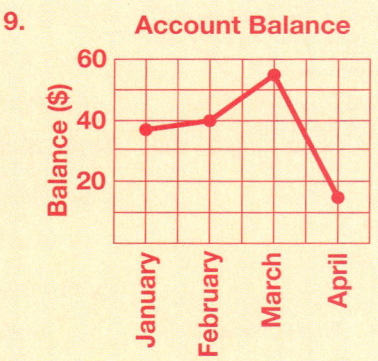

Account Balance

Lesson 2-6

page 88 More Than One Way

Answers may vary. Sample given.

Minutes Needed for Tutoring		
Minutes	Tally	Frequency
30	卌	5
45						4
60	卌 |||	8

---

page 89 Homework Exercises

10. Number of Jelly Beans in a Scoop

```
2 | 7 8
3 | 2 4 5 5 8
4 | 3 5 7 7
5 | 3 8
6 |
7 | 6
```

Key: 2|7 means 27 jelly beans

11. Lengths of Eruptions of Mauna Loa

```
1 | 2 5 5 6 6
2 | 0 1 3 4 5
3 | 9
4 | 6 8
5 |
6 | 1
```

Key: 1 | 2 means 12 days

page 90 Homework Exercises

12. State Populations in Millions

```
3 | 6
4 | 1 6
5 | 0 5 6 7 9
6 | 2
```

Key: 3|6 means 3.6 million

13a.   Ages of People

```
0 | 9
1 | 1 2 2 2 2 3 3 5 5 6 9
2 | 0 1 3 4
3 | 5
4 | 0
```

Key: 2 | 6 means 26 years old

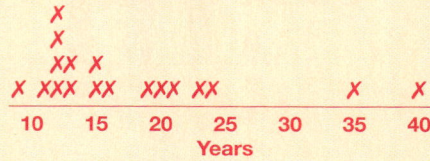

Ages of Eighteen People

b. Stem-and-leaf plot; explanations may vary. Sample: The data with a stem of 1 and a leaf of 3 or more represent the teenagers.

16.

```
Group D | Group F
    6 4 | 2 | 5 9
  9 5 3 | 3 | 4 6 7
```

Key:
means ← 4 | 2 | 5 → means
  24   25

Lesson 2-7

page 93 Quick Check

1.   Mayor's Performance

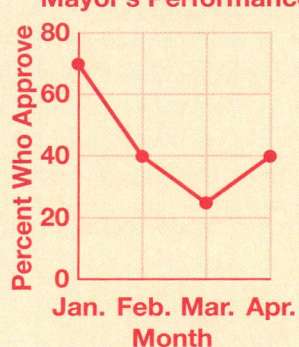

page 95 Homework Exercises

5. The graph is misleading because the intervals on the vertical axis are unequal; it appears there was a greater increase in January than there actually was.

Dogs in Animal Shelter

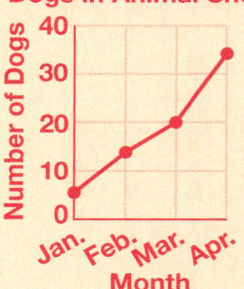

6. The graph is misleading because by starting the vertical scale at 100, it gives the impression that each year is very different from the others.

Number of Complaints to City Hall

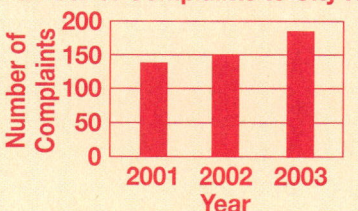

page 96   Homework Exercises

11–12. Graphs may vary. Samples are given.

11.
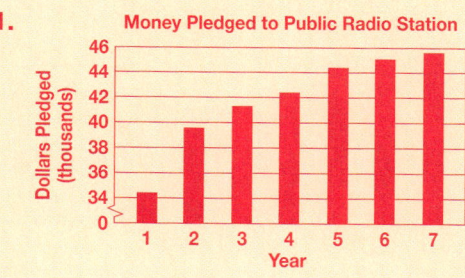

12.

13. Answers may vary. Sample: Mean; the mean of $41,637.14 is a little less than the median of $42,209.

page 96   Tune-Up and Mixed Review

17.

```
1 | 4 4 6 6 6
2 | 3 5 8
3 | 3 3 7
4 | 2 5
```

Key: 1|4 means 14

page 100   Chapter Review

8.

Number of Times Vowels Occur		
Vowels	**Tally**	**Frequency**
A	⦀⦀⦀⦀⦀⦀⦀III	18
E	⦀⦀⦀⦀⦀⦀⦀III	18
I	⦀⦀⦀⦀⦀	10
O	⦀⦀	5
U	⦀⦀	5
Y	III	3

9. **Number of Times Listed Words Appear**

```
          X
          X
          X
   X      X
   X   X  X
  _____
  the and a  of
```
Times Words Appear

page 101   Skills and Concepts

11.
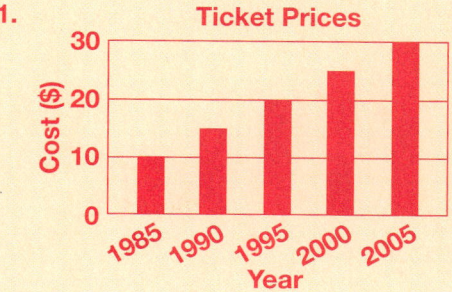

16.

```
3 | 01 41 67 79 88 99
4 | 65 79 79 83
5 | 07 12 43 48
```

Key: 4|65 means 465

page 102   Chapter Test

3.

Children in Families		
Number of Children	**Tally**	**Frequency**
1	III	3
2	III	3
3	⦀I	5
4	II	2
5	I	1
6	I	1

4.
```
           X
           X
    X  X   X
    X  X   X  X
    X  X   X  X  X
   _____
   1  2  3  4  5  6
   Number of Children
```

7. **State Fair Pumpkin Weights (lb)**

```
20 | 3 7
21 | 0 2 2 8
22 | 6
23 | 3
24 | 7
25 |
26 | 2 9
27 | 1
28 | 8
```

Key: 27|1 means 271

CHAPTER 3

Lesson 3-1

page 111   Homework Exercises

21.
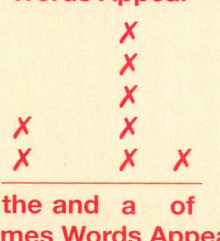

22. Start with 156. Divide by 2 to get the next term. Subtract 2 to get the next term. Repeat this pattern of dividing and subtracting; 8, 6, 3

Lesson 3-2

page 115   Homework Exercises

11.
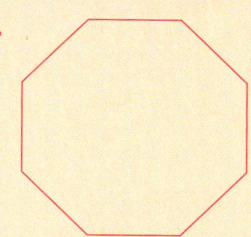

12.
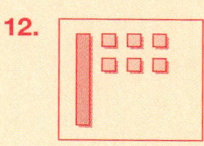

13.
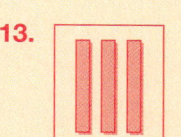

14.
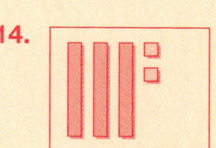

Lesson 3-3

page 117   Exercises

Word Phrase	Diagram 1	Diagram 2
1. Height *h* divided by 6	h / ? ? ? ? ? ?	h / ? ? ? ? ? ?
2. Answers may vary. Sample: 8 more than *q*	q 8	q	8
3. Answers may vary. Sample: 7 times *r*	r r r r r r r	r r r r r r r
4. 6.3 smaller than *t*	t / ? 6.3	t / ?	6.3

Lesson 3-5

page 133   Homework Exercises

22a. 15; the sum of the diagonal
  numbers $8 + 5 + 2 = 15$

  b. $a + 1 + 8 = 15; a = 6$
   $2 + b + 4 = 15; b = 9$
   $7 + 5 + c = 15; c = 3$

Lesson 3-8

page 146   Homework Exercises

12. $9 \times (50 - 2) = 9 \times 50 -$
   $9 \times 2 = 450 - 18 = 432$

13. $3 \times (9 - 0.3) = 3 \times 9 -$
   $3 \times 0.3 = 27 - 0.9 = 26.1$

14. $6 \times (50 + 2) =$
   $6 \times 50 + 6 \times 2 =$
   $300 + 12 = 312$

page 152   Chapter Test

12–13. **Answers may vary. Samples are
  given.**

12.

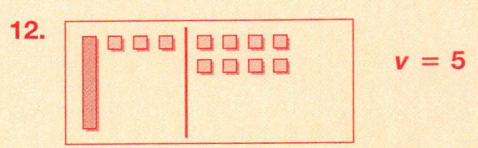

$v = 5$

13.

$g = 5$

28. $8 \times (40 - 1) = 8 \times 40 -$
   $8 \times 1 = 320 - 8 = 312$

29. $4 \times (70 + 1) = 4 \times 70 +$
   $4 \times 1 = 280 + 4 = 284$

30. $6 \times (80 + 2) = 6 \times 80 +$
   $6 \times 2 = 480 + 12 = 492$

31. $3 \times (100 - 2) = 3 \times 100 -$
   $3 \times 2 = 300 - 6 = 294$

CHAPTER 4

Lesson 4-2

page 165   Homework Exercises

34. **The expressions do not have the
  same value. In order of operations,
  $2^2 \cdot 3^2 - 2^3 - 1$ simplifies to 27,
  but $2^2 \cdot (3^2 - 2^3) - 1$ simplifies
  to 3.**

---

page 165   Tune-Up and Mixed Review

39.

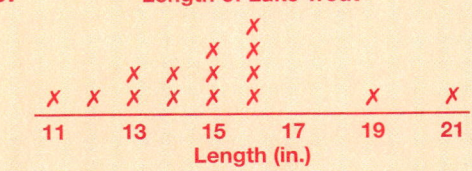

Lesson 4-4

page 171   Quick Check

1a. factors of 6: 1, 2, 3, 6
   factors of 21: 1, 3, 7, 21
   GCF of 6 and 21: 3

  b. factors of 18: 1, 2, 3, 6, 9, 18
   factors of 49: 1, 7, 49
   GCF of 18 and 49: 1

  c. factors of 14: 1, 2, 7, 14
   factors of 28: 1, 2, 4, 7, 14, 28
   GCF of 14 and 28: 14

page 172   Quick Check

3a.

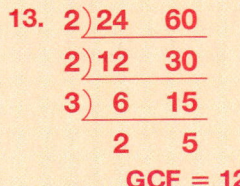

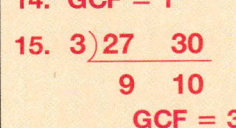

GCF = 16

  b.

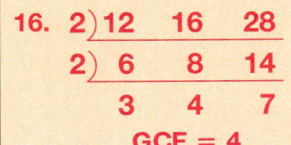

GCF = 12

page 173   Homework Exercises

6. factors of 14: 1, 2, 7, 14
   factors of 35: 1, 5, 7, 35
   GCF of 14 and 35: 7

7. factors of 24: 1, 2, 3, 4, 6, 8, 12, 24
   factors of 45: 1, 3, 5, 9, 15, 45
   GCF of 24 and 45: 3

8. factors of 26: 1, 2, 13, 26
   factors of 34: 1, 2, 17, 34
   GCF of 26 and 34: 2

---

9. factors of 30: 1, 2, 3, 5, 6, 10, 15, 30
   factors of 35: 1, 5, 7, 35
   GCF of 30 and 35: 5

10. factors of 48: 1, 2, 3, 4, 6, 8, 12, 16,
   24, 48
   factors of 88: 1, 2, 4, 8, 11, 22,
   44, 88
   GCF of 48 and 88: 8

11. factors of 36: 1, 2, 3, 4, 6, 9, 12,
   18, 36
   factors of 63: 1, 3, 7, 9, 21, 63
   GCF of 36 and 63: 9

12. $2\overline{)10 \quad 18}$
   $\quad 5 \quad\quad 9$
   GCF = 2

13. $2\overline{)24 \quad 60}$
   $2\overline{)12 \quad 30}$
   $3\overline{)\ 6 \quad 15}$
   $\quad 2 \quad\quad 5$
   GCF = 12

14. GCF = 1

15. $3\overline{)27 \quad 30}$
   $\quad 9 \quad\quad 10$
   GCF = 3

16. $2\overline{)12 \quad 16 \quad 28}$
   $2\overline{)\ 6 \quad\ 8 \quad 14}$
   $\quad 3 \quad\quad 4 \quad\quad 7$
   GCF = 4

17. $11\overline{)33 \quad 55 \quad 132}$
   $\quad\ 3 \quad\quad 5 \quad\quad 12$
   GCF = 11

18.

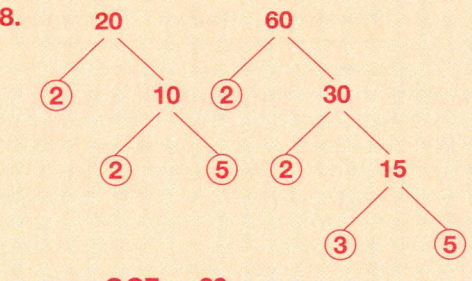

GCF = 20

19.

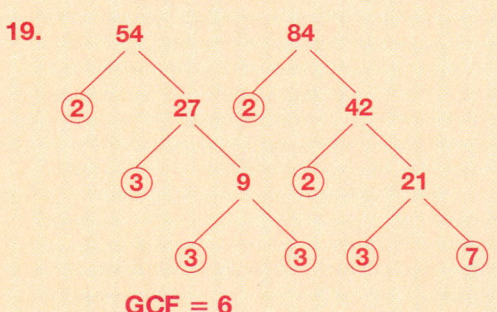

GCF = 6

20.

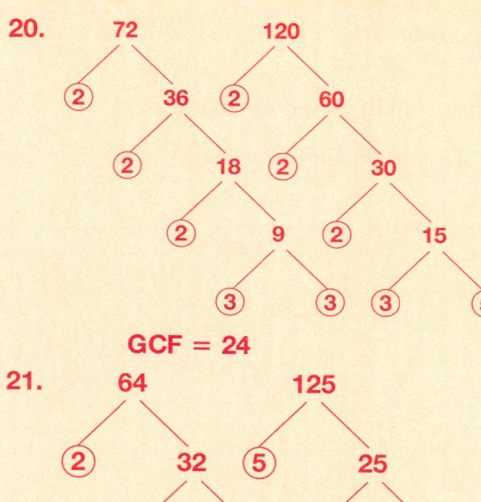

GCF = 24

21.

64 / 125 tree

2 · 32 · 5 · 25
2 · 16 · 5 · 5
2 · 8
2 · 4
2 · 2

GCF = 1

22.

117 / 130 tree
3 · 39 · 2 · 65
3 · 13 · 5 · 13

GCF = 13

23.

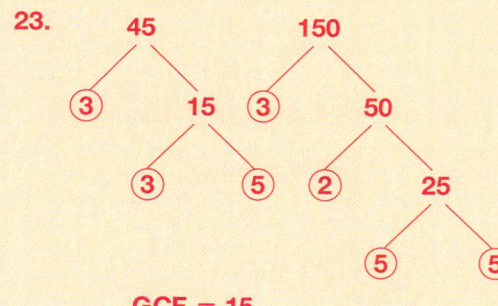

GCF = 15

page 174   Homework Exercises

30. Brand B with 12 cards and Brand C with 15 cards because 3 is a common factor of 12 and 15

32. 48; 1, 2, 3, 4, 6, 8, 12, 16, 24, 48; any other number that is less than 50 has fewer than 10 factors.

Lesson 4-7

page 191   Tune-Up and Mixed Review

41.

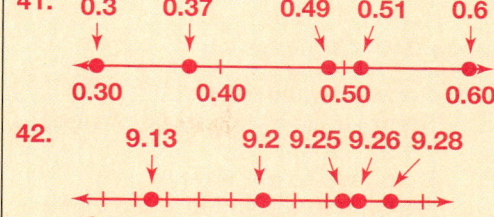

42.

9.13   9.2 9.25 9.26 9.28

9.1   9.2   9.3

Lesson 4-8

page 195   Homework Exercises

35a. $\frac{1}{2}, \frac{1}{4}, \frac{1}{8}, \frac{1}{16}$

b.

The note symbol that is "open" has the greatest value, and for the other symbols, the more flags there are, the less the value of the note.

36. 19 ft $4\frac{1}{4}$ in.;

19 ft $2\frac{1}{4}$ in.; 19 ft 2 in.;

19 ft $1\frac{1}{2}$ in.; 18 ft $8\frac{1}{4}$ in.

37. In fractions with the same numerator, the fraction with the larger denominator is the smaller fraction.

CHAPTER 5

Lesson 5-2

page 220   Homework Exercises

29. Answers may vary. Sample: Add the numerators and keep the denominator. Change the improper fraction $\frac{12}{9}$ to the mixed number $1\frac{3}{9}$. Reduce to $1\frac{1}{3}$.

Lesson 5-3

page 221   Activity Lab

7.

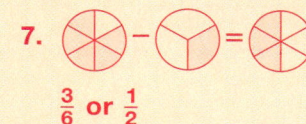

$\frac{3}{6}$ or $\frac{1}{2}$

8.

$\frac{5}{6}$

Lesson 5-7

page 249   Homework Exercises

21. Answers may vary. Sample:

List Item	Start Time	End Time
Mix cake	1:00 P.M.	1:40 P.M.
Bake cake	1:40 P.M.	2:15 P.M.
Shower and dress	1:40 P.M.	2:05 P.M.
Decorate room	2:05 P.M.	3:05 P.M.
Cool cake	2:15 P.M.	3:00 P.M.
Frost cake	3:05 P.M.	3:25 P.M.

mix cake, bake cake, cool cake, frost cake; shower and dress while baking cake, decorate room while cooling cake

CHAPTER 6

Lesson 6-1

page 260   Activity Lab

4.

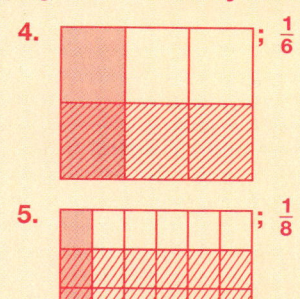

; $\frac{1}{6}$

5.

; $\frac{1}{8}$

Lesson 6-2

page 266   Check Skills You'll Need

1. A proper fraction has a numerator that is less than the denominator. An improper fraction has a denominator that is less than or equal to the numerator.

Lesson 6-3

page 271   Activity Lab

2.

Number of Circles	Fraction	Number of Pieces	Division Problem
3	$\frac{1}{2}$	6	$3 \div \frac{1}{2} = 6$
4	$\frac{1}{2}$	8	$4 \div \frac{1}{2} = 8$
5	$\frac{1}{2}$	10	$5 \div \frac{1}{2} = 10$
6	$\frac{1}{2}$	12	$6 \div \frac{1}{2} = 12$

page 274   Homework Exercises

26. Answers may vary. Sample: When you divide a number by 2, the quotient is less than the dividend. When you divide a number by $\frac{1}{2}$, the quotient is greater than the dividend. For example:

$$3 \div 2 = 1\frac{1}{2}$$

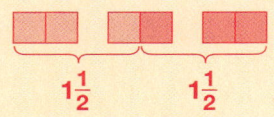

$$1\frac{1}{2} \qquad 1\frac{1}{2}$$

$$3 \div \frac{1}{2} = 6$$

$$\frac{1}{2} \ \frac{1}{2} \qquad \frac{1}{2} \ \frac{1}{2} \qquad \frac{1}{2} \ \frac{1}{2}$$

Lesson 6-6

page 290   Homework Exercises

10–16. Answers may vary. Samples are given.

10. Ounces; a package of chewing gum weighs about as much as a slice of bread.

11. Pounds; a bowling ball weighs more than a loaf of bread.

12. Tons or pounds; a pickup truck is very heavy. Ounces are much too small.

13. Fluid ounces; a sample size bottle of shampoo holds less than a cup.

14. Cup; a bowl can usually hold a cup of soup or a bit more.

15. Gallon; lawnmower tanks usually hold about 1 gallon of gas.

16. Fluid ounces; a tube of toothpaste usually is measured in fluid ounces.

CHAPTER 7

Lesson 7-1

page 310   Activity Lab

4. Answers may vary.
   Sample: Blue jays to goldfinches, 7 : 9
   Blue jays to all birds, 7 : 16
   Goldfinches to all birds, 9 : 16

Lesson 7-4

page 324   Homework Exercises

30b. No; the ratios only need to have the same units in corresponding places. Example: $\frac{\text{feet}}{\text{in.}} = \frac{\text{feet}}{\text{in.}}$

Lesson 7-5

page 329   Homework Exercises

22.

Part	Toy Size	Actual Size
Car	3 in.	120 in.
Door Handle	0.125 in.	5 in.
Headlight	0.2 in.	8 in.
Front Bumper	0.18 ft	7.2 ft
Rear Window	1.35 in.	4.5 ft

Lesson 7-6

page 330   Activity Lab

2.

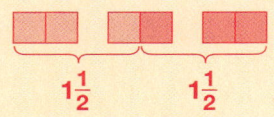

3. Two models with one grid completely shaded and the second grid with only 50 squares shaded.

page 334   Homework Exercises

47.

Fraction	$\frac{11}{50}$	$\frac{39}{50}$	$\frac{22}{25}$	$\frac{9}{20}$	$\frac{21}{50}$	$\frac{4}{5}$
Decimal	0.22	0.78	0.88	0.45	0.42	0.8
Percent	22%	78%	88%	45%	42%	80%

Lesson 7-8

page 340   Activity Lab

1. Favorite Colors

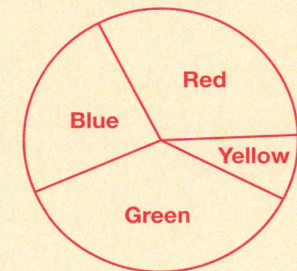

2. Hours of Sleep Each Night

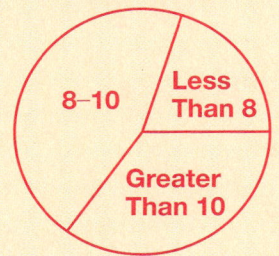

3. Homework on Saturdays

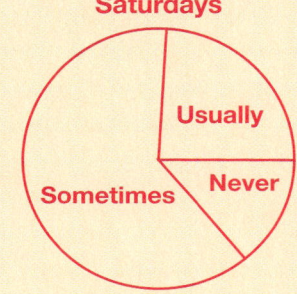

page 342   TE Additional Examples

2. Weekly Budget

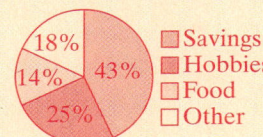

page 342   Quick Check

3. Lunches for 50 Students

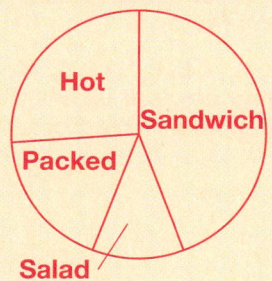

page 343   Homework Exercises

8.

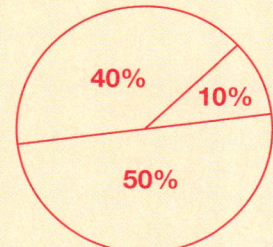

40%   10%
50%

9.

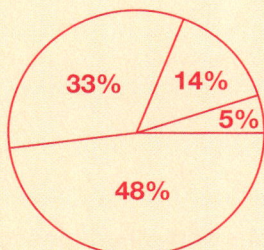

33%   14%
5%
48%

10.

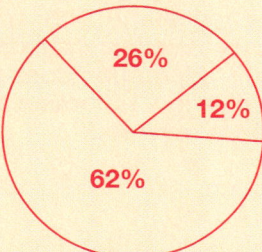

26%
12%
62%

11.

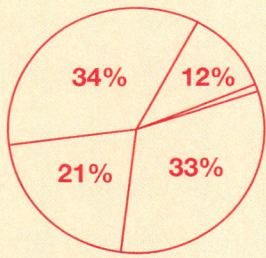

34%   12%
21%   33%

12. What Part of the U.S. Price of Gasoline Is Tax?

Tax   Price Minus Tax

What Part of the U.K. Price of Gasoline Is Tax?

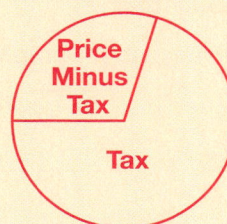

Price Minus Tax

Tax

13.

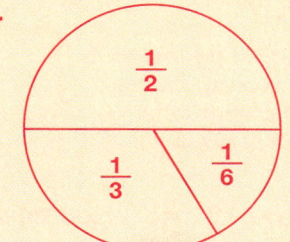

$\frac{1}{2}$
$\frac{1}{3}$ $\frac{1}{6}$

14.

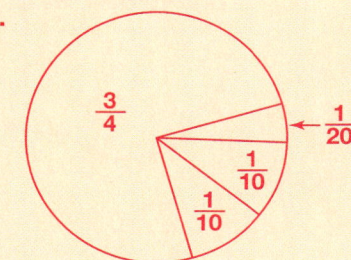

$\frac{3}{4}$ $\leftarrow \frac{1}{20}$
$\frac{1}{10}$
$\frac{1}{10}$

15.

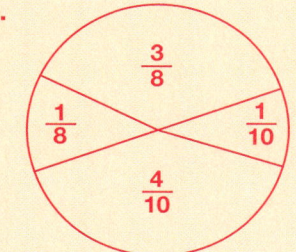

$\frac{3}{8}$
$\frac{1}{8}$ $\frac{1}{10}$
$\frac{4}{10}$

16.   Human Body Composition

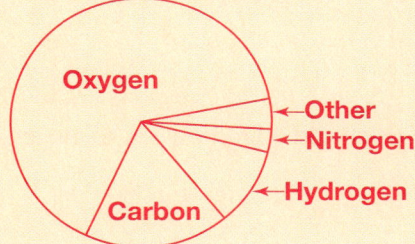

Oxygen
←Other
←Nitrogen
←Hydrogen
Carbon

page 355   Chapter Review

30.

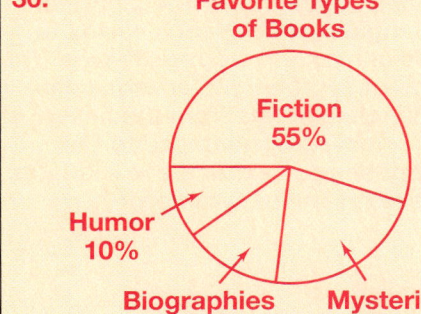

Favorite Types of Books

Fiction 55%
Humor 10%
Biographies 13%   Mysteries 22%

CHAPTER 8

Lesson 8-1

page 363   TE Additional Examples

2a. $\overleftrightarrow{XY}$ and $\overleftrightarrow{WU}$ or $\overleftrightarrow{XW}$ and $\overleftrightarrow{YU}$

b. 9 possibilities exist; Sample: $\overleftrightarrow{WU}$ and $\overleftrightarrow{UY}$, or $\overleftrightarrow{WX}$ and $\overleftrightarrow{XY}$, or $\overleftrightarrow{XY}$ and $\overleftrightarrow{YZ}$

c. $\overleftrightarrow{WX}$ and $\overleftrightarrow{ZU}$, $\overleftrightarrow{WX}$ and $\overleftrightarrow{ZY}$, $\overleftrightarrow{YZ}$ and $\overleftrightarrow{WU}$, or $\overleftrightarrow{ZU}$ and $\overleftrightarrow{XY}$

Lesson 8-2

page 371   Homework Exercises

17–20. Check students' work.

17.

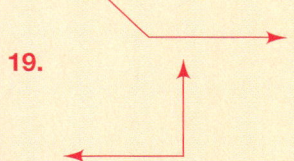

18.

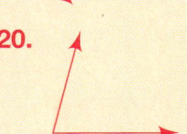

19.

20.

27. Fold the piece of paper lengthwise. Without unfolding, fold it crosswise.

28.

Lesson 8-3

page 374   Check Skills You'll Need

2–5. Check students' work.

2.

3.

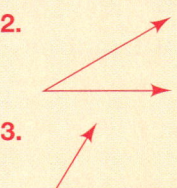

4.

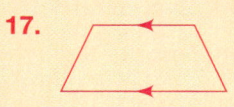

5.

Lesson 8-5

page 386   Check Skills You'll Need

1. No; skew lines are not in the same plane.

2. Answers may vary. Sample: $\overline{CB}$ and $\overline{GH}$

page 390   Homework Exercises

17.

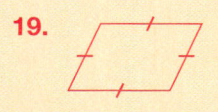

18.

19.

20.

21.

22. Hexagon; drawings may vary. Sample:

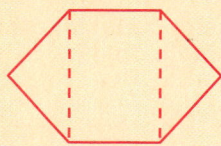

Lesson 8-6

page 392   Check Skills You'll Need

1. They have the same measure.

2. isosceles

3. scalene

page 393   TE Additional Examples

2a. $\frac{4}{2} = \frac{6}{3}$ similar

b. $\frac{4}{20} \neq \frac{6}{25}$ not similar

3. Similar; corresponding sides are proportional.

TE Closure

Sample: Similar figures have congruent corresponding angles and proportional corresponding sides.

page 395   Tune-Up and Mixed Review

24.

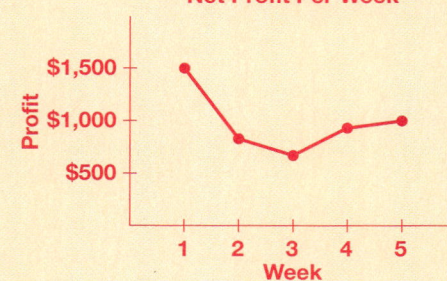

Lesson 8-7

page 399   Quick Check

2a. 1

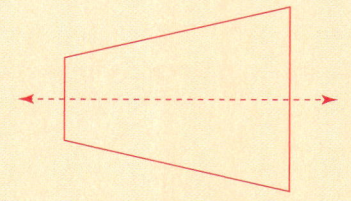

page 401   Homework Exercises

17.

Lines of symmetry in equilateral triangles go from each vertex to the center of the opposite side. The line of symmetry in an isosceles triangle extends from the center of the non-congruent side to the opposite vertex. Scalene triangles have no line of symmetry.

Lesson 8-8

page 405   Homework Exercises

16.

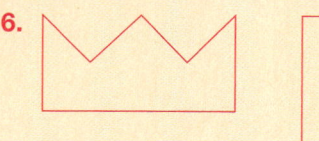

---

17. Answers may vary. Sample:

18.

22. Translations and reflections are alike because the figures stay the same size and shape. They are different because in a translation the object's orientation does not change, while in a reflection its orientation is reversed.

Translation

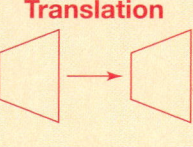

Reflection

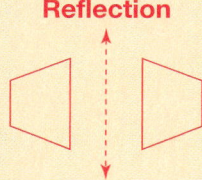

page 409   Chapter Review

17. Answers may vary. Sample:

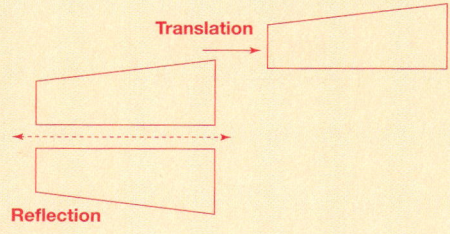

Translation

Reflection

page 410   Chapter Test

20–22. Answers may vary. Sample:

20.

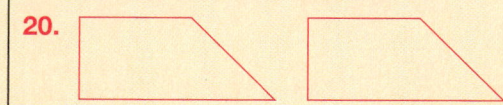

21.

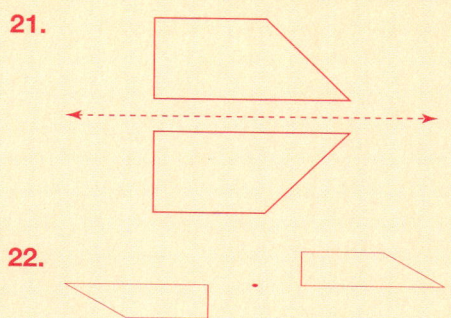

22.

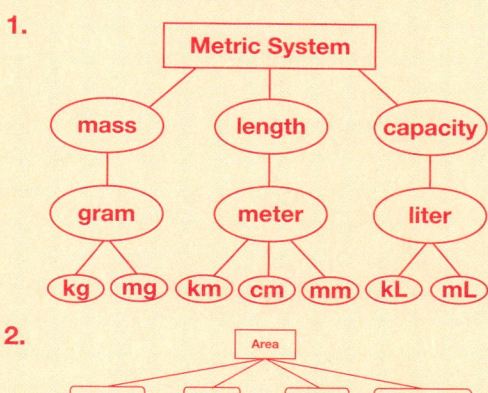

CHAPTER 9

Lesson 9-1

page 416   Check Skills You'll Need

1. Answers may vary. Sample: ft, lb, fl oz

2. Feet (yards would also be appropriate).

3. Pints (cups or fluid ounces would also be appropriate).

Lesson 9-2

page 425   Vocabulary Builder

1.

```
              Metric System
         /         |          \
      mass      length      capacity
        |          |            |
      gram       meter        liter
      /  \       / | \         / \
    kg   mg    km cm mm      kL  mL
```

2.

```
                        Area
        /          |            |              \
   Rectangle    Square      Triangle      Parallelogram
   A = lw       A = s²      A = ½ bh       A = bh
    /   \         |         /    \           /    \
length width    side     base   base      base   height
                                  |
                                height
```

Lesson 9-3

page 430   Homework Exercises

25b. Answers may vary. Sample:

L	W	P	A
11	1	24	11
10	2	24	20
9	3	24	27
8	4	24	32
7	5	24	35
6	6	24	36

26. Answers may vary. Sample: Knowing the area alone is not enough information to find the perimeter. For example, if the area is 24 square units, you cannot tell whether the dimensions are 4 by 6 or 3 by 8.

27. There are 12 in. × 12 in., or 144 in.^{2}, in 1 ft^2.

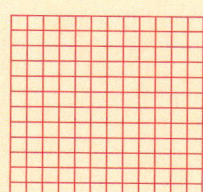

So 1 yd^2, or 9 ft^2, equals 9 × 144 in.^{2}, or 1,296 in.^{2}.

Lesson 9-6

page 447   Tune-Up and Mixed Review

32.

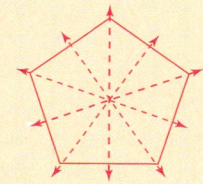

five

33.

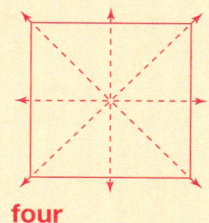

four

34.

ten

Lesson 9-7

page 448   Exercises

3.

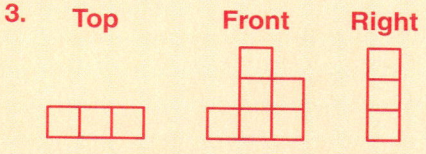

Top   Front   Right

4–5. Answers may vary. Samples are given.

4.

5.

Lesson 9-9

page 457   Activity

6–7. Answers may vary. Sample:

Width	Length	Height	S.A.
1	1	24	98
2	6	2	56
2	3	4	52
3	8	1	70
3	4	2	52
4	1	6	68
4	2	3	52
6	1	4	68
6	2	2	56
8	3	1	70
12	1	2	76

The dimensions can differ, which results in different surface areas.

CHAPTER 10

Lesson 10-1

page 479   Check Your Understanding

2. Spin   Flip

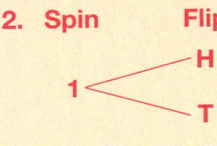
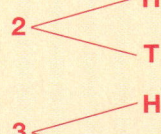
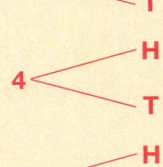

12 outcomes

page 479   Homework Exercises

6. Spin 1   Spin 2

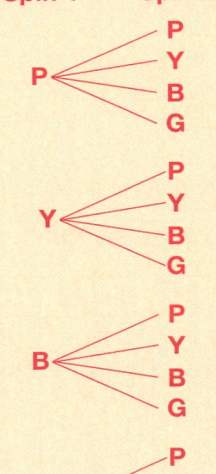

16 outcomes

7. Flip 1   Flip 2

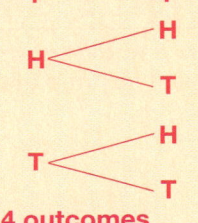

4 outcomes

8. Flip   Roll

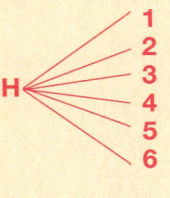
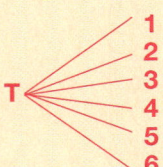

12 outcomes

page 480   Homework Exercises

12a. 1 space, Free Turn
      1 space, Lose a Turn
      1 space, No Change
      2 spaces, Free Turn
      2 spaces, Lose a Turn
      2 spaces, No Change
      3 spaces, Free Turn
      3 spaces, Lose a Turn
      3 spaces, No Change
      4 spaces, Free Turn
      4 spaces, Lose a Turn
      4 spaces, No Change

  b. **10 outcomes**

page 481   Extension

2.

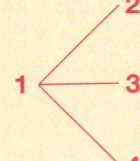
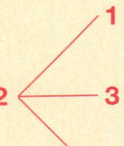
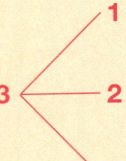

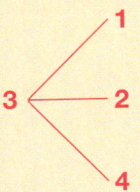

12 permutations

3.

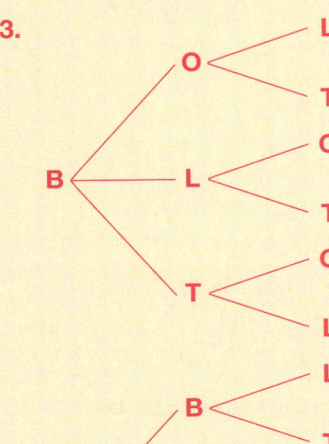
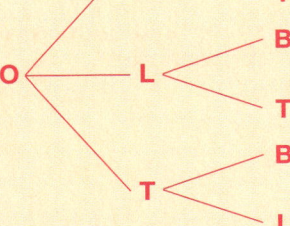
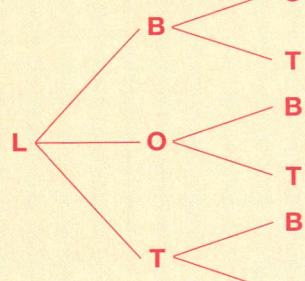
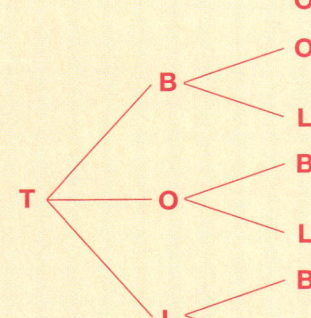

24 permutations

T676

4. carrots, peppers, tomatoes, peas;
carrots, peppers, peas, tomatoes;
carrots, tomatoes, peppers, peas;
carrots, tomatoes, peas, peppers;
carrots, peas, peppers, tomatoes;
carrots, peas, tomatoes, peppers;
peppers, carrots, tomatoes, peas;
peppers, carrots, peas, tomatoes;
peppers, tomatoes, carrots, peas;
peppers, tomatoes, peas, carrots;
peppers, peas, carrots, tomatoes;
peppers, peas, tomatoes, carrots;
tomatoes, carrots, peppers, peas;
tomatoes, carrots, peas, peppers;
tomatoes, peppers, carrots, peas;
tomatoes, peppers, peas, carrots;
tomatoes, peas, carrots, peppers;
tomatoes, peas, peppers, carrots;
peas, carrots, peppers, tomatoes;
peas, carrots, tomatoes, peppers;
peas, tomatoes, carrots, peppers;
peas, tomatoes, peppers, carrots;
peas, peppers, carrots, tomatoes;
peas, peppers, tomatoes, carrots

Lesson 10-2

page 487   Checkpoint Quiz

2. Roll   Toss

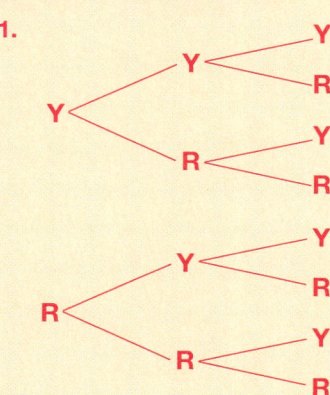

12 outcomes

page 510   Chapter Test

1.

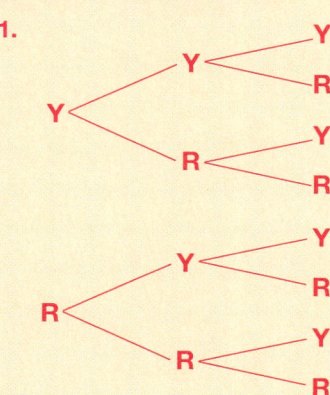

CHAPTER 11

Lesson 11-1

page 516   Check Skills You'll Need

1. The Identity Property of Addition states that the sum of any number and 0 is that number. The Identity Property of Multiplication states that the product of any number and 1 is that number.

page 519   Homework Exercises

42.

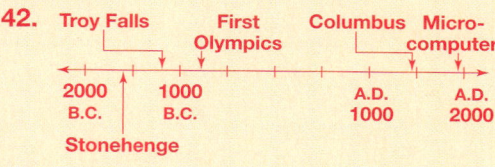

43. Answers may vary. Sample: Place 3 marks between 200 and 300 to divide the segment into 4 equal-size segments. The mark closest to 200 is the mark for 225.

Lesson 11-6

page 542   Homework Exercises

18.

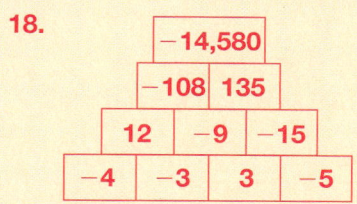

Lesson 11-7

page 546   Exercises

3a. True; the given positive number must be multiplied by a negative number to result in a negative number.

b. False; the left side would be much smaller than −16.

c. False; the left side would be positive.

4a. False; the left side would be greater than 8.

b. True; adding an integer to an integer results in another integer.

c. True; the integer on the right is smaller than the integer being added on the left.

5a. False; the left side would be closer to 10 than to $49\frac{1}{2}$.

b. True; subtracting a number from 100 could result in $49\frac{1}{2}$.

c. True; the left side would result in a number close to 50, and $49\frac{1}{2}$ is close to 50.

6. True: $x < 0$ and $x \approx -40$; false: $x > 0$ and x is an integer.

Lesson 11-8

page 549   Quick Check

2a–c.

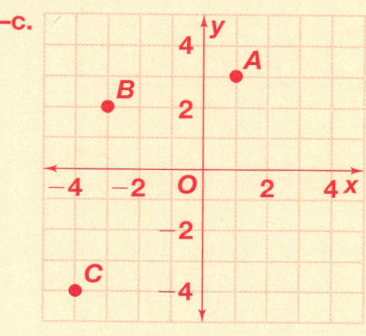

page 550   Homework Exercises

12–17.

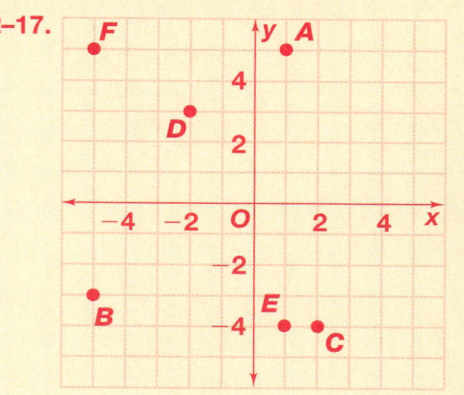

page 553   Extension

1.

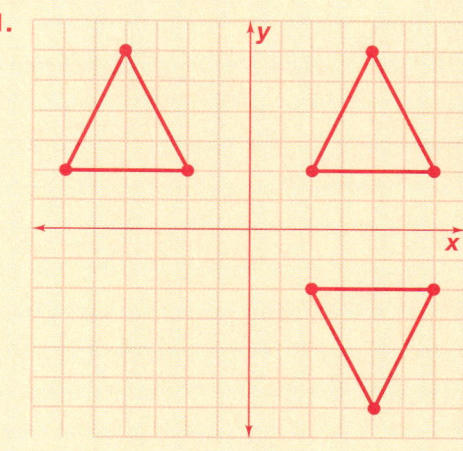

2.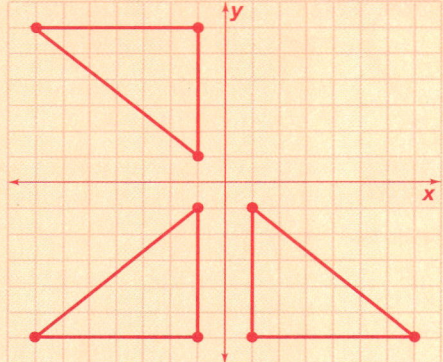

3.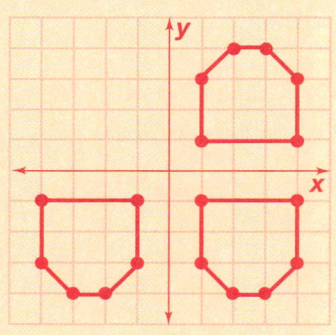

Lesson 11-9

page 556   Homework Exercises

8.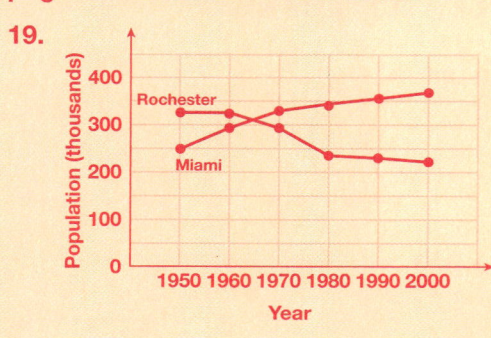

page 557   Homework Exercises

19.

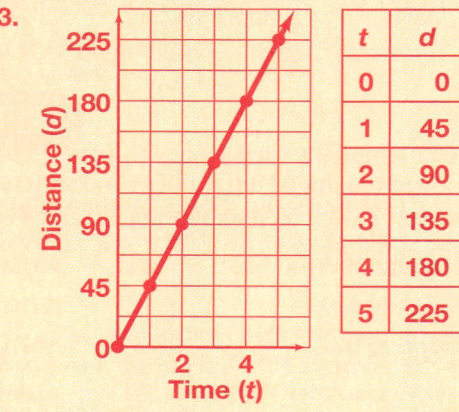

2.

x	−2	0	2	6
y	−5	−3	−1	3

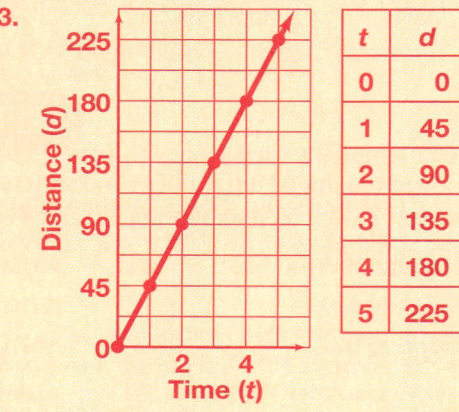

3.

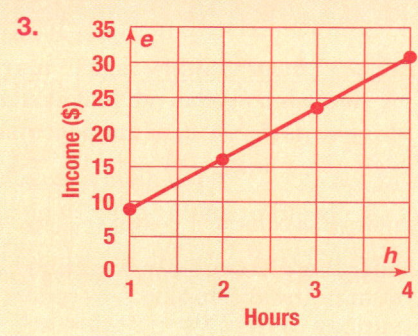

t	d
0	0
1	45
2	90
3	135
4	180
5	225

Lesson 11-10

page 560   TE Additional Examples

3.

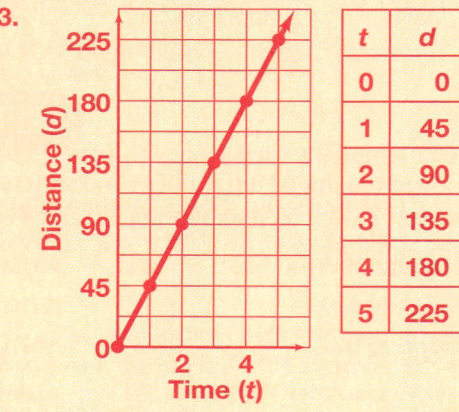

page 561   Check Your Understanding

4.

x	y
−2	−6
−1	−3
0	0
1	3
2	6

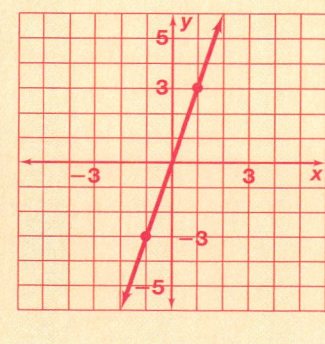

7.

x	y
−2	0
−1	1
0	2
1	3
2	4

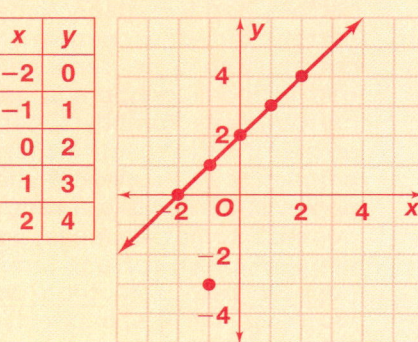

8.

x	y
−2	−4
−1	−3
0	−2
1	−1
2	0

9.

x	y
−2	−4
−1	−2
0	0
1	2
2	4

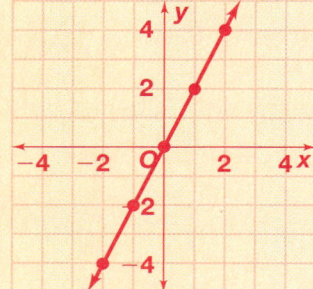

10.

x	y
−2	−1
−1	−0.5
0	0
1	0.5
2	1

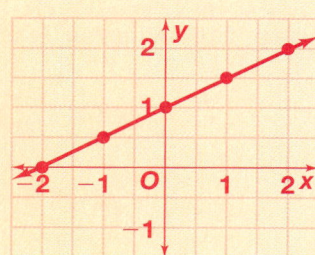

11.

x	y
−2	0
−1	0.5
0	1
1	1.5
2	2

12.

x	y
−2	1
−1	0.5
0	0
1	−0.5
2	1

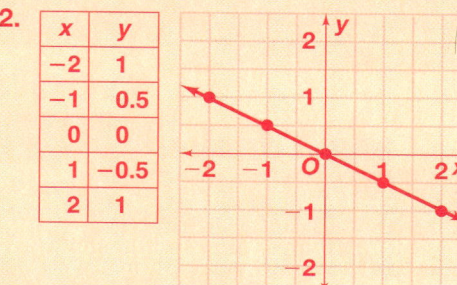

13.

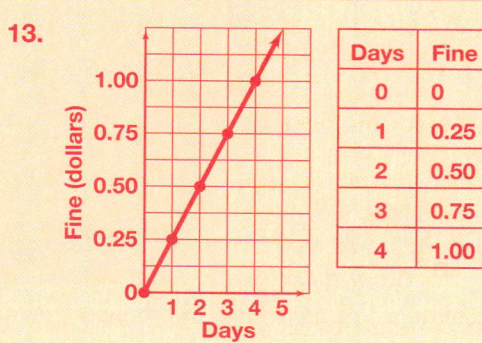

Days	Fine
0	0
1	0.25
2	0.50
3	0.75
4	1.00

page 562   Homework Exercises

22.

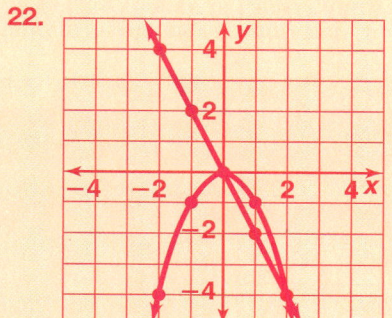

(0, 0), (2, −4); answers may vary.
Sample: The graph of $y = -2x$ is a straight line. The graph of $y = -x^2$ is a curve. The graph of $y = -x^2$ is symmetric with respect to the y-axis, but $y = -2x$ is not.

page 565   Chapter Review

33–36.

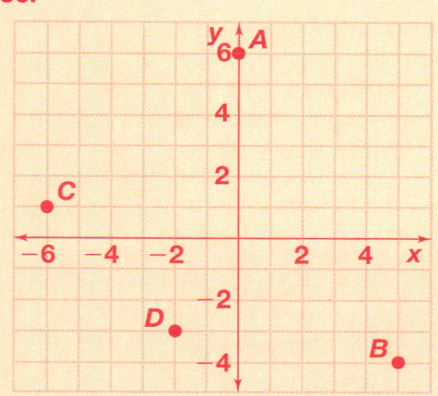

39.

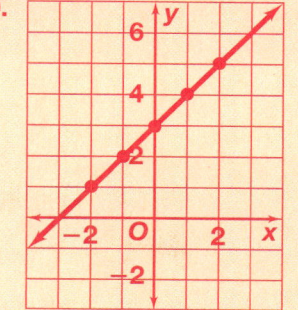 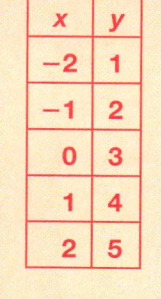

x	y
−2	1
−1	2
0	3
1	4
2	5

40.

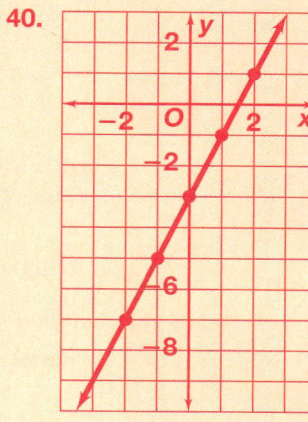

x	y
−2	−7
−1	−5
0	−3
1	−1
2	1

41.

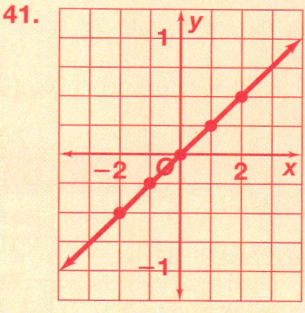

x	y
−2	−0.5
−1	−0.25
0	0
1	0.25
2	0.5

page 566   Chapter Test

7. Answers may vary. Sample: The absolute value of a number is its distance from 0 on a number line. −5 is 5 units from 0 on a number line, so its absolute value is 5. 5 is 5 units from 0 on a number line, so its absolute value is also 5.

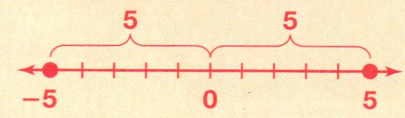

25a–c.

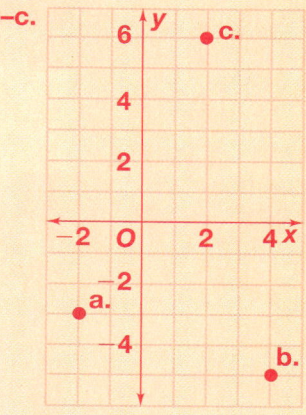

26a.   Jan.: $486
Feb.: $2,000
Mar.: −$266
Apr.: $673

b.

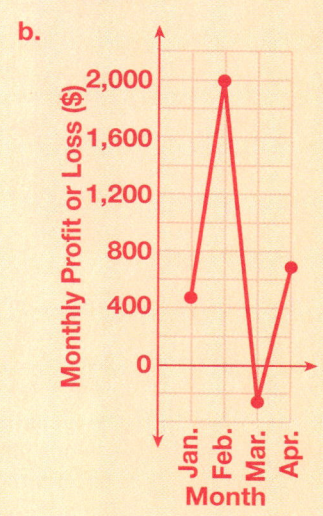

27.

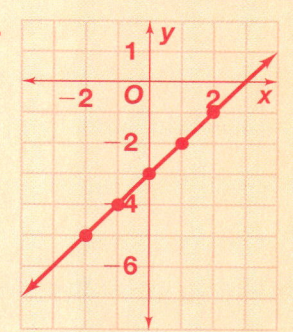

CHAPTER 12

Lesson 12-2

page 579   TE Closure

Sample: when you are showing less than or greater than and you don't want to include the number at that point

Sample: Replace the variable with the number and simplify. If the inequality statement is true, the number is a solution to the inequality.

page 586   Activity Lab

1b.

Area of Square (units^2)	Length of Side (units)
1	1
4	2
9	3
16	4

2b.

Area of Square (units^2)	Length of Side (units)
25	5
36	6
49	7

Index

Teacher's Edition entries appear in blue type.

Index

solving one-step equations, 124–127, 130, 134, 138, 151, 240–241, 242, 253, 284, 360, 546, 574, 575, 583
solving one-step inequalities, 582–584, 598, 599
solving proportions, 320–324, 325, 326, 336, 494
solving subtraction equations, 134–136
solving two-step equations, 572–576, 598
subtracting integers, 529–533
variables and expressions, 113–116, 150
writing algebraic expressions, 250, 424
See also Equation(s); Solving equations

Algebra tiles, 113, 115, 129, 137, 152, 572

Algebraic expressions
defined, 113, 150
evaluating, 114, 118, 165, 264, 270, 274, 275, 344, 497, 558
modeling, 113
using, 123
writing, 118–123, 250, 424

Altitude. *See* **Height**

Analysis
data analysis. *See* Data Analysis
error analysis, 10, 15, 18, 34, 40, 135, 146, 219, 274, 278, 541, 575

Angle(s)
acute, 368, 370, 374, 377, 380, 409, 410, 467, 557
classifying, 368, 370, 380–383
complementary, 374–377, 380, 409, 410, 419, 542
congruent, 375, 392, 409
constructing, 368, 372
defined, 367, 409
exterior, 378
interior, 378
measuring, 367–368, 370, 371, 374–375, 381, 388, 393, 401, 557, 576
obtuse, 368, 370, 377, 380, 409, 410, 557
in quadrilateral, 385, 557
right, 368, 370, 380, 409, 410, 557, 591
special pairs of, 374–377
straight, 368, 370, 380, 409, 410, 557
supplementary, 374–377, 409, 410, 419, 542
in triangles, 379, 380–383, 576
vertex of, 367
vertical, 375, 376, 409

Angle benchmarks, 366

Angle bisector, 373

Angle measures, 367–368, 370, 371, 374–375, 381, 388, 393, 401, 557, 576

Applications. *See* Real-World Applications

Area
of circle, 444–447, 462, 470, 551, 590
comparing, 431
of complex figures, 433, 434, 435
defined, 426, 468
estimating, 445, 446
formulas for. *See* Formulas
of parallelogram, 431, 432, 434, 435, 444, 468, 522
of rectangle, 203, 426–427, 429, 430, 432, 436, 453
of square, 163, 427, 428, 429, 436, 586, 589
surface. *See* Surface area
of trapezoid, 434
of triangle, 431, 433, 434, 435, 458, 468

Assessment
Chapter Reviews, 52–53, 100–101, 150–151, 204–205, 252–253, 298–299, 354–355, 408–409, 468–469, 508–509, 564–565, 598–599
Chapter Tests, 54, 102, 152, 206, 254, 300, 356, 410, 470, 510, 566, 600
Checkpoint Quizzes, 20, 43, 85, 98, 129, 137, 170, 187, 226, 238, 281, 296, 325, 335, 379, 391, 436, 461, 487, 499, 528, 552, 585
Open-Ended, 24, 30, 63, 68, 111, 120, 132, 173, 185, 202, 230, 239, 274, 278, 290, 309, 332, 371, 399, 405, 418, 517, 527, 544, 550, 646
Test Prep, 7, 11, 15, 19, 25, 30, 35, 41, 47, 64, 69, 73, 77, 83, 90, 96, 111, 116, 122, 127, 133, 136, 141, 147, 161, 165, 169, 174, 179, 185, 191, 195, 201, 215, 220, 225, 231, 236, 243, 250, 264, 270, 275, 279, 285, 291, 295, 309, 315, 319, 324, 329, 334, 339, 344, 351, 365, 371, 377, 383, 390, 395, 401, 405, 419, 424, 430, 435, 441, 447, 452, 456, 460, 466, 480, 486, 491, 497, 503, 519, 522, 527, 533, 537, 542, 545, 551, 557, 562, 576, 581, 584, 590, 594
Test Prep Cumulative Review, 153, 255, 357, 411, 567, 601–603

Test Prep Reading Comprehension, 55, 103, 207, 301, 471, 511
See also Chapter Projects; Instant Check System; Mixed Reviews; Test-Taking Strategies

Associative Property
of Addition, 12, 13, 52, 126, 138, 144
of Multiplication, 13, 52, 126

Attribute, 290

Average. *See* **Mean**

Axis, 548, 553, 565

B

Balance (profit and loss), 554, 556, 565

Balance scales, 265

Bar graphs, 74, 76, 79, 94–96, 98, 101, 507, 539, 585

Base
defined, 162, 204
identifying, 426
of parallelogram, 432, 435, 444, 458
of prism, 459
of triangle, 433, 434

Benchmark
angle, 366
with fractions, 212, 214, 215, 252

Bias, 202

Bisector
    angle, 373
    perpendicular, 372

Block Scheduling, Teacher's Edition pages T58–T61

C

Calculator
    changing mixed numbers to decimals, 232
    dividing by zero, 138
    exercises that use, 42, 169, 200, 237, 437, 588, 589, 590
    exponent key of, 163
    expressing an opposite, 517
    finding length of side of square, 586
    fraction, 180, 237
    graphing, 490, 547
    for multiplication and division of decimals, 42
    pi (π) key on, 440
    ratio, 437
    square root, 588, 589, 590
    using for fractions, 280

Calculator Tips, 138, 145, 163, 232, 490, 517

Capacity
    customary units of, 288, 289, 290, 414, 416, 421
    defined, 417
    metric units of, 417, 418, 419, 422, 430, 466
    See also Volume

Careers
    accountant, 20
    architect, 318
    board game designer, 487
    cartoonist, 391
    chef, 226
    event planner, 436
    graphic designer, 552
    help-desk technician, 335
    librarian, 480
    meteorologist, 541
    nutritionist, 19
    oceanographer, 231
    park ranger, 85
    photographer, 371
    physician, 332
    sales representative, 576
    shoe designer, 69
    tailor, 193

Careers, Teacher's Edition pages 606, 608

Carry Out the Plan, xxxii–xli, 18, 194, 329, 364, 370, 389, 594

Cartesian plane. *See* Coordinate plane

CAT6 Terra Nova (California Achievement Test, 6th Ed.), *2B, 58B, 106B, 156B, 210B, 258B, 304B, 360B, 414B, 474B, 514B, 570B*

Cell, 80, 81, 101

Celsius temperature scale, 644

Center
    of circle, 438, 527
    of rotation, 403

Centimeter, 161, 416, 420

Central tendency. *See* Measures of central tendency

Challenge, 7, 11, 15, 19, 25, 30, 35, 41, 47, 64, 69, 73, 77, 83, 90, 96, 111, 116, 122, 127, 133, 136, 141, 147, 161, 165, 169, 174, 179, 185, 191, 195, 201, 215, 220, 225, 231, 236, 243, 250, 264, 270, 275, 279, 285, 291, 295, 309, 315, 319, 324, 329, 334, 339, 344, 351, 365, 371, 377, 383, 390, 395, 401, 405, 419, 424, 430, 435, 441, 447, 452, 456, 460, 466, 480, 486, 491, 497, 503, 519, 522, 527, 533, 537, 542, 545, 551, 557, 562, 576, 581, 584, 590, 594

Chance. *See* Probability

Chapter Overviews, Teacher's Edition pages 3, 59, 107, 157, 211, 259, 305, 361, 415, 475, 515, 571

Chapter Projects, 606–611

Chapter Reviews. *See* Assessment

Chapter Tests. *See* Assessment

Check Skills You'll Need. *See* Instant Check System

Check Skills You'll Need, 2E, 58E, 106E, 156E, 210E, 258E, 304E, 360E, 414E, 474E, 514E, 570E, Teacher's Edition pages 4, 8, 12, 16, 22, 26, 32, 38, 44, 61, 66, 70, 74, 80, 86, 93, 108, 113, 118, 124, 130, 134, 138, 144, 158, 162, 166, 171, 176, 182, 188, 192, 198, 212, 217, 222, 228, 232, 240, 246, 261, 266, 272, 276, 282, 288, 292, 306, 312, 316, 320, 326, 331, 336, 341, 348, 362, 367, 374, 380, 386, 392, 398, 402, 416, 421, 426, 432, 438, 444, 449, 453, 458, 462, 476, 482, 488, 494, 500, 516, 520, 524, 530, 534, 540, 543, 548, 554, 558, 572, 578, 582, 587, 591

Check the Answer, xxxii–xli, 168, 184, 235, 396, 397, 400, 404, 496, 532, 584, 589

Check Understanding. *See* Instant Check System, Quick Check

Check Your Readiness. *See* Instant Check System

Check Your Readiness, Teacher's Edition pages 2, 58, 106, 156, 210, 258, 304, 360, 414, 474, 514, 570

Checkpoint Quizzes. *See* Assessment; Instant Check System

Choose a Method, 11, 15, 28, 30, 35, 41, 88, 120, 189, 234, 236, 268, 319, 322, 324, 369, 428, 478, 480, 503, 560, 561, 574

Chord, 438, 469

Circle(s)
    area of, 444–447, 462, 470, 551, 590
    center of, 438, 527
    circumference of, 437, 439–441, 469, 470, 551
    defined, 438, 469
    diameter of, 437, 438, 439, 469, 527, 576
    dividing, 342
    exploring, 437
    identifying parts of, 438
    radius of, 438, 439, 441, 462, 469, 527, 576
    segments of, 112
    semicircle, 447

Circle graphs, 340–345, 355, 383, 401, 456

Circumference, 437, 439–441, 469, 470, 551

Classification
    of angles, 368, 370, 380–383
    of polygons, 386–390, 414
    of quadrilaterals, 388, 409
    of triangles, 380–383, 391, 392, 409, 414, 424

Clockwise rotation, 403, 404

Closure, Teacher's Edition pages 5, 9, 13, 17, 23, 28, 33, 39, 45, 62, 67, 71, 75, 81, 88, 94, 109, 114, 119, 125, 131, 135, 139, 145, 159, 163, 167, 172, 177, 183, 189, 193, 199, 213, 218, 223, 229, 234, 241, 248, 262, 268, 273, 277, 283, 289, 293, 307, 313, 317, 322, 327, 332, 337, 342, 349, 363, 369, 375, 381, 388, 393, 399, 403, 417, 422, 428, 433, 439, 445, 450, 454, 459, 464, 478, 484, 489, 495, 501, 517, 521, 525, 531, 535, 541, 544, 549, 555, 560, 574, 579, 583, 588, 592

Common denominator. *See* Least common denominator (LCD)

Common factor. *See* Factor(s)

Common multiple, 188, 205

Communication. *See* Error Analysis; Reasoning; Vocabulary; Writing in Math

Commutative Property
    of Addition, 12, 13, 52, 126, 144, 148
    of Multiplication, 13, 52, 126

Comparing
    area, 431
    decimals, 26–30, 156
    equations and expressions, 138, 558
    fractions, 192–195, 266, 288, 292, 304, 316, 514, 520
    integers, 520–522, 564, 570, 578
    mixed numbers, 193
    standard form and expanded form, 22
    symbols for, 5
    unit price, 313, 314
    whole numbers, 5

Compass, 370, 372, 373

Compatible numbers, 9, 10, 38, 52, 212

Complement of an event, 483–484, 485

Complementary angles, 374–377, 380, 409, 410, 419, 542

Complex figures, area of, 433, 434, 435

Composite numbers, 166–167, 169, 204

Compound event, 501, 509

Computer(s)
    exercises, 7, 509
    geometry software, 379
    spreadsheets, 80–83, 85, 101, 498
    See also Technology

Concept maps, 425

Cone, 450, 451

Congruent angles, 375, 392, 409

Congruent figures, 392–395
    corresponding parts in, 392
    defined, 392, 409
    identifying, 392, 394–395

Congruent rectangles, 398

Congruent triangles, 392, 395, 409

Conjecture, 108, 150, 379, 385

Index

T687

M

Make a Plan, xxxii–xli, 18, 63, 110, 168, 184, 194, 235, 263, 323, 329, 370, 400, 455, 496, 532, 584, 589, 594

***Make a Table* Problem Solving Strategy,** xxxviii

Manipulative materials, Teacher's Edition pages 21, 31, 117, 129, 137, 216, 221, 227, 239, 260, 310, 325, 330, 340, 345, 431, 448, 523, 529, 586

Manipulatives
algebra tiles. *See* Algebra tiles
centimeter cubes, 457
chips, 43, 523, 529
coins, 487, 489, 492, 499, 500, 502
compass, 370, 372, 373
geoboard, 586
graph paper, 330, 390, 431
metric ruler, 328, 420
metric tape measure, 437
note cards, 43
number cubes, 98, 483, 484, 485, 486, 487, 489, 490, 491, 499, 502, 508, 510, 528
pattern blocks, 181
place markers, 528
protractor, 367, 369, 370, 371, 374, 378, 395, 467, 542
ruler, 186, 327, 430, 467
spinner, 325, 479, 480, 484, 485, 486, 489, 491, 498, 503, 510, 512
straightedge, 372, 373
See also Calculator

Map(s)
concept, 425
coordinates on, 549, 550, 551
exercises that use, 328, 329, 335, 550, 551
finding distances on, 326–327, 328, 329, 335
Real-World Applications of, 326–327, 329, 356, 363, 364, 549, 550, 551

Map scales, 326–329, 356, 430

Mass
customary units of, 414, 416, 421
defined, 417
metric units of, 417, 418, 419, 422, 424

Math at Work
accountant, 20
board game designer, 487
cartoonist, 391
chef, 226
event planner, 436
graphic designer, 552
help-desk technician, 335
park ranger, 85
See also Careers

Math Background, 2C–D, 58C–D, 106C–D, 156C–D, 210C–D, 258C–D, 304C–D, 360C–D, 414C–D, 474C–D, 514C–D, 570C–D, Teacher's Edition pages 4, 8, 12, 16, 22, 26, 32, 38, 44, 61, 66, 70, 74, 80, 86, 93, 108, 113, 118, 124, 130, 134, 138, 158, 166, 171, 176, 182, 188, 192, 198, 212, 217, 222, 228, 232, 240, 246, 261, 266, 272, 276, 282, 288, 292, 306, 312, 316, 320, 326, 331, 336, 341, 348, 362, 367, 380, 386, 392, 398, 402, 416, 421,

426, 432, 438, 444, 449, 453, 458, 462, 476, 482, 494, 500, 516, 520, 530, 534, 543, 548, 554, 558, 572, 587

Math Games. *See* Games

Math Understandings, 2C–D, 58C–D, 106C–D, 156C–D, 210C–D, 258C–D, 304C–D, 360C–D, 414C–D, 474C–D, 514C–D, 570C–D

Mathematical techniques. *See* Estimation; Mental Math; Number Sense; Problem Solving Strategies

Mean, 60–64, 66, 69, 70, 93, 95, 98–100
Golden, 25

Measurement
of angles, 367–368, 370, 371, 374–375, 381, 388, 393, 401, 557, 576
of capacity, 288, 289, 290, 414, 416, 421
choosing appropriate units for, 289, 296, 299, 300, 414, 416, 456, 470
customary system of. *See* Customary system of measurement
of elapsed time, 246–250, 253, 291
exercises that use, 213, 227, 274, 290–291, 370, 414, 418–419, 486
fractions and, 186
in metric units. *See* Metric units
of objects, 296, 299
to solve problems, 467
units of. *See* Units of measurement

Measures of central tendency
mean, 60, 61–64, 66, 69, 70, 93, 95, 98, 99, 100
median, 66, 68, 69, 70, 86, 93, 95, 98, 99, 100, 365, 441
mode, 66, 67, 68, 69, 70, 95, 98, 99, 100

Median
defined, 66, 100
finding, 66, 68, 69, 70, 86, 93, 95, 98, 99, 100, 365, 441

Mental Math
addition using, 13, 16, 54, 144, 230, 240, 523
area of a circle, 446
computing compatible numbers, 9
with decimals, 42
determining whether equations are true or false, 148
divisibility, 158, 160
division using, 42
equations, 240
estimating area, 446
estimating percents, 355
example that uses, 125
exercises that use, 13, 14, 20, 25, 42, 52, 54, 73, 125, 127, 151, 158, 160, 230, 242, 332, 337, 338, 350, 446, 523, 529, 544, 574, 575, 583
with fractions, 230, 240, 332
with mixed numbers, 230
multiplication using, 42, 54
ordering decimals, 28
with percents, 337, 338, 355
probability, 502
solving equations using, 125, 127, 130, 134, 138, 151, 240–241, 242, 253, 284, 360, 544, 574, 575, 583

Meter, 416, 468

Metric system, 416–425, 468

Metric units, 416–420, 468
of capacity, 417, 418, 419, 422, 430, 466
choosing appropriate, 456, 470
converting, 421–424, 436
of length, 416–419, 420, 421, 422
of mass, 417, 418, 419, 422, 424

Midpoint, 372

Milligram, 417

Millimeter, 416, 420

Misleading graphs, 93–96

Misleading statistics, 94–96

Mixed numbers
adding, 228–231, 253
changing to decimals, 232
comparing, 193, 292
dividing, 276–279, 298
estimating with, 213, 227, 228, 266, 276
Mental Math with, 230
multiplying, 266–270, 298
ordering, 193, 194
renaming, 233
renaming improper fractions as, 218
solving equations with, 242, 253, 284, 285
subtracting, 232–236, 253
using, 227
writing as improper fractions, 184, 187, 205, 233, 266, 267, 269
writing improper fractions as, 183, 187, 205, 210, 218, 228
See also Fraction(s)

Mixed Reviews, 7, 11, 15, 19, 25, 30, 35, 41, 47, 64, 69, 73, 77, 83, 90, 96, 111, 122, 127, 133, 136, 141, 147, 161, 165, 169, 174, 179, 185, 191, 195, 201, 215, 220, 225, 231, 236, 243, 250, 264, 270, 275, 279, 285, 291, 295, 309, 315, 319, 324, 329, 334, 339, 344, 351, 365, 371, 377, 383, 390, 395, 401, 405, 419, 424, 430, 435, 441, 447, 452, 456, 460, 466, 480, 486, 491, 497, 503, 519, 522, 527, 533, 537, 542, 545, 551, 557, 562, 576, 581, 584, 590, 594

Mode
defined, 67, 100
finding, 66, 67, 68, 69, 70, 95, 98, 99, 100

Models and modeling
addition, 31, 221, 227, 291, 523
algebra tiles for. *See* Algebra tiles
algebraic expressions, 113, 117
in architecture, 327
of area, 431
circle graphs, 340
concrete, 21, 26, 31, 37, 38, 45, 60, 113, 129, 137, 181, 186, 216, 221, 222, 224, 227, 260, 271, 310, 330, 340, 366, 385, 406, 431, 448, 457, 461, 523, 529, 572, 586
cylinders, 461
decimals, 21, 26, 29, 31, 37, 38, 45, 46
with diagram, 131, 367
division, 45, 46, 271, 272
drawing pictures, 229, 230, 262, 263, 294, 333, 429
exercises that use, 15, 31, 37, 46, 175, 178, 219, 221, 224, 264, 330

Acknowledgments

Staff Credits

The people who make up the **Prentice Hall Math** team—representing design services, editorial, editorial services, educational technology, marketing, market research, photo research and art development, production services, publishing processes, and rights & permissions—are listed below. Bold type denotes core team members.

Dan Anderson, Carolyn Artin, Nick Blake, **Stephanie Bradley**, Kyla Brown, Patrick Culleton, Kathleen J. Dempsey, **Frederick Fellows**, **Suzanne Finn**, Paul Frisoli, Ellen Granter, **Richard Heater**, Betsy Krieble, Lisa LaVallee, Christine Lee, Kendra Lee, Cheryl Mahan, **Carolyn McGuire**, Eve Melnechuk, Terri Mitchell, Jeffrey Paulhus, Mark Roop-Kharasch, Marcy Rose, Rashid Ross, Irene Rubin, Siri Schwartzman, Vicky Shen, **Dennis Slattery**, Elaine Soares, Dan Tanguay, Tiffany Taylor, Mark Tricca, Paula Vergith, Kristin Winters, Helen Young

Additional Credits

Paul Astwood, Sarah J. Aubry, Jonathan Ashford, Peter Chipman, Patty Fagan, Tom Greene, Kevin Keane, Mary Landry, Jon Kier, Dan Pritchard, Sara Shelton, Jewel Simmons, Ted Smykal, Steve Thomas, Michael Torocsik, Maria Torti

TE Design

Susan Gerould/Perspectives

Illustration

Additional artwork: Rich McMahon; Ted Smykal

Kenneth Batelman: **186**, **267**, **257**
Joel Dubin: **263**, **306**
John Edwards, Inc.: **307**, **477**
Trevor Johnston: **264**, **341**, **342**
Precision Graphics: **77**
XNR Productions, Inc.: **249**, **250**, **285**, **327**, **328**
Wilkinson Studios: **289**

Photography

Front cover: Wolfgang Kaehler/CORBIS
Back cover: Ian Cartwright/Getty Images.

Title page: tl, Bob Daemmrich Photography; tr, Williamson Edwards/The Image Bank; bl, David Muench; br, Bob Daemmrich Photography.

Front matter: Page x, David Young-Wolff/PhotoEdit, Inc.; **xi,** STUDIO CARLO DANI/Animals Animals; **xii,** ThinkStock/SuperStock; **xiii,** Tony Freeman/Photo Edit; **xiv,** Faidley/Agliolo/International Stock/Grant Heilman Photography, Inc., **xv,** David Young-Wolff/Photo Edit, Inc.; **xvi,** AP Photo/The Grand Rapids Press, Lance Wynn; **xvii,** Raphael Gaillarde/Liaison/Getty Images, Inc.; **xviii,** Theo Allofs/Corbis; **xix,** Pearson Education; **xx,** 2004 Jay Wade, www.JayWade.com; **xxi,** AFP Photo/Don Emmert/Corbis; **xlviii & xlix,** Richard Haynes; **l,** PhotoEdit; **lii,** Bob Daemmrich/Stock Boston; **liii,** Getty Images; **liv,** Ryan McVay/Getty Images, Inc., **lv,** Owaki-Kulla/Corbis; **lvi,** Russell Illig/Getty Images, Inc., **lvii,** Michael Spingler/AP Wide World Photos

Chapter 1: Page 3, Andrew Leyerle/Dorling Kindersley; **4,** Prentice Hall School; **7,** www.SellPhotos.CA; **8,** Mary Kate Denny/PhotoEdit Inc.; **9,** Nancy Richmond/The Image Works; **11,** Stockdisc Classic/Getty Images; **12,** Mitch Kezar/Getty Images, Inc.; **13 bl,** Richard Haynes; **15,** Jonathan Nourok/PhotoEdit Inc.; **16,** Lori Adamski Peek/Getty Images, Inc.; **18,** John Moore; **19,** Nathan Benn/Corbis; **21 tr,** Richard Haynes; **22,** ©Syracuse Newspapers/Dick Blume/The Image Works; **23,** AP Photo/Tom Gannam; **24,** Royalty-Free/Getty Images, Inc. 26, David Young-Wolff/PhotoEdit Inc.; **28 mr & bl,** Richard Haynes; **30 bl,** L. Clarke/Corbis; **31,** Richard Haynes; **32,** David Young-Wolff/PhotoEdit Inc.; **32 bl,** PictureQuest; **33** Bob Daemmrich/The Image Works; **34,** Royalty-Free/Getty Images, Inc.; **36 tr,** Richard Haynes; **37,** Tony Freeman/PhotoEdit; **38,** Marc Romanelli/Alamy; **39 tl,** Richard Haynes; **42,** David Young-Wolff/PhotoEdit; **44,** Chad Slattery/Getty Images, Inc.; **45,** John Moore; **47,** Toyofumi Mori/Getty Images; **56 t,** The British Museum/Dorling Kindersley; **56 bl,** The Science Museum/Dorling Kindersley; **56 br,** Russ Lappa; **57 tl,** The Science Museum/Dorling Kindersley; **57 tr,** Steve Gorton/Dorling Kindersley; **57 br,** Alistair Duncan/Dorling Kindersley; **57 br,** Gianni Dagli Orti/Corbis

Chapter 2: Page 59, Mark Newman/Alamy; **60,** Richard Haynes; **61,** Bob Daemmrich/Stock Boston; **62,** STUDIO CARLO DANI/Animals Animals; **64,** Gary Braasch/Getty Images, Inc.; **65,** Richard Haynes; **66,** Dick Blume/Syracuse Newspaper/The Image Works; **67,** Richard Haynes; **68,** RO-MA Stock/Omni-Photo Communications; **69,** Photo Courtesy of Adidas America, Public Relations Office; **71,** Craig Lovell/Corbis; **73,** Nancy Sheehan/PhotoEdit **77 tl,** AP/Wide World Photos; **77 t4,** Pascal Volery/Reuters/Corbis; **77 t2,** Eddie Adams/Getty Images, Inc.; **77 t3,** Homer Sykes/Woodfin Camp & Associates; **80,** ROB & SAS/Corbis; **82,** Bob Daemmrich/Stock Boston; **83,** Myrleen Ferguson Cate/Photo Edit; **85,** Jeff Greenberg/The Image Works; **86,** Mary Kate Denny/Photo Edit; **87,** Syracuse Newspapers/The Image Works; **88 tl & mr,** Richard Haynes; **89,** Jim Sugar/Getty Images; **93,** Jon Riley/Stone/Getty Images, Inc.; **94,** NBAE/Getty Images; **105 br,** David Robbins/Getty Images, Inc.

Chapter 3: Page 107, Vanessa Vick/Photo Researchers, Inc.; **108,** Michael Rosenfeld/Getty Images, Inc.; **110,** Gunter Marx Photography/Corbis; **110,** Russ Lappa; **111,** Jerry Lodriguss/Photo Researchers, Inc.; **112 tr,** Richard Haynes; **113,** Tom Prettyman/PhotoEdit; **114,** Index Stock Imagery, Inc.; **116,** ThinkStock/SuperStock; **118,** Getty Images; **120 tl,** Richard Haynes; **120 mr,** Richard Haynes; **122,** NASA; **124** Peter Beck/Corbis; **124,** Park Street/Photo Edit; **125,** Russ Lappa; **128 tr,** Richard Haynes; **129,** Richard Haynes; **131,** Image Source/SuperStock, Inc.; **131 bl,** Richard Haynes; **133,** National Geographic Society; **134,** David Young-Wolff/Photo Edit; **137,** Richard Haynes; **138,** Digital Vision/Getty Images; **140,** RubberBall Productions/IndexStock; **141,** Dianna Blell/Peter Arnold, Inc.; **144,** Spencer Grant/Photo Edit; **147 br,** Richard Megna/Fundamental Photographs; **154 b,** Carlyn Iverson/Absolute Science; **154 tr,** Julian Baum/Dorling Kindersley; **154 ml,** R.P. Meleski; **155 t,** Grace Davies/Omni-Photo Communications, Inc.

Chapter 4: Page 157, Blair Seitz/Photo Researchers, Inc.; **158,** Scott Payne/FoodPix; **159 bl,** Wally McNamee/Corbis; **159 tl,** Richard Haynes; **160,** Prentice Hall; **161,** Bob Daemmrich/Photo Edit; **162,** Frank Zullo/Photo Researchers; **163 bl,** Richard Haynes; **164,** Terry W. Eggers; **165,** Prof. G. Schatten/ Science Photo Library/Photo Researchers; **166,** Tom Carter/PhotoEdit; **169,** Jeremy Horner/Corbis; **170,** Richard Haynes; **171,** Osterreichische Post AG; **172,** Rhoda Sidney/PhotoEdit; **173,** Steve Cole/Getty Images; **174,** Jeff Greenberg/PhotoEdit; **175 tr,** Richard Haynes; **177,** TSI Pictures/Getty Images, Inc.; **179,** David Young-Wolff/PhotoEdit; **181,** Richard Haynes; **182,** Mark Burnett/Stock Boston; **183,** Chris Salvo/Getty Images, Inc.; **183 mr,** Russ Lappa; **184,** Jeff Greenberg/Photo Edit; **186 bl,** Russ Lappa; **186 bc,** Russ Lappa; **186 br,** Russ Lappa; **186 tr,** Richard Haynes; **187 tr,** Richard Haynes; **188,** Tom Stewart/Corbis; **189 mr,** Richard Haynes; **189 ml,** Russ Lappa; **191,** Tony Freeman/Photo Edit; **192,** David Young-Wolff/Photo Edit; **193,** Bloom Productions/Getty Images; **195,** Tim Ridley/DK Picture Library; **198,** Bill Miles/Corbis; **200,** Joseph D. Poellot/Index Stock; **201 t,** Alan Schein Photography/Corbis; **201 b,** Alan Schein Photography/Corbis; **208 tr,** Geoff Brightling/Dorling Kindersley; **208 br,** S. Wanke/Getty Images, Inc.; **209 t,** Dorling Kindersley; **209 br,** Richard Megna/Fundamental Photographs

Chapter 5: Page 211, Mark C. Burnett/Photo Researchers, Inc.; **212,** David Young-Wolff/PhotoEdit, Inc.; **214,** Adrian Sherratt/Alamy; **214 m,** Russ Lappa; **215,** Russ Lappa; **216 tr,** Richard Haynes; **217,** Todd Powell/Index

Stock; **218,** SuperStock; **220,** NIBSC/Science Photo Library-Photo Researchers, Inc.; **222 tr,** Spencer Grant/PhotoEdit; **222 ml,** Richard Haynes; **223,** Bob Daemmrich/Stock Boston; **225,** Faidley/Agliolo/International Stock/Grant Heilman Photography, Inc.; **226,** Dave Bartruff/Corbis; **227 tr,** Richard Haynes; **228 mr,** Michael S. Yamashita/Corbis; **228 bl,** Ronn Maratea/Image State; **229 tl,** Richard Haynes; **231,** Tony Freeman/PhotoEdit; **232,** Michael Rosenfeld/Getty Images; **233,** Renee Lynn/Corbis; **234 tl & mr,** Richard Haynes; **236,** Tony Freeman/PhotoEdit; **238 mr,** John Moore; **238 br,** Richard Haynes; **240,** Adam Smith/Getty Images, Inc.; **243,** Frozen Images/The Image Works; **246,** Dave Bartruff/Corbis; **248,** Royalty-Free/Corbis; **250,** Vicki Silbert/PhotoEdit; **256 ml,** AFP/Corbis; **256 tr,** Al Grillo/AP/Wide World Photos; **257 m,** Robert Laberge/Getty Images, Inc.; **257 br,** Jerome Delay/AP/Wide World Photos

Chapter 6: Page 259, Frank Siteman/IndexStock; **260,** Richard Haynes; **261,** age fotostock/SuperStock; **262,** Silver Burdett & Ginn/Pearson Education; **264,** Brian Parker/Tom Stack & Associates, Inc.; **266,** Guinness World Records, Ltd.; **268 tl,** Richard Haynes; **268 br,** Richard Haynes; **270,** John Moore; **271,** Richard Haynes; **272,** Dan McCoy/Rainbow; **272 bl,** Richard Haynes; **273,** Alan Linda Detrick/Grant Heilman Photography, Inc.; **275,** Prentice Hall; **277 tl,** Russ Lappa; **277 bl,** Richard Haynes; **279,** Ariel Skelley/Corbis; **281,** Richard Haynes; **282,** Richard Cummings/SuperStock; **284,** Joseph Nettis/Photo Researchers, Inc.; **289,** David Young-Wolff/Photo Edit, Inc.; **290,** Past /Project Exploration; **292,** Russ Lappa; **293,** Bettmann/Corbis; **295,** AP/Wide World Photos; **296,** Richard Haynes; **302 tr,** James Muldowney/Getty Images, Inc.; **302 bl,** Annabelle Halls/Dorling Kindersley; **303 b,** Mike Powell/Getty Images, Inc.; **303 tm tl & tr,** James Jackson/Dorling Kindersley

Chapter 7: Page 317 tl, Jeffrey Sylvester/Getty Images, Inc.; **305** Mack Henley/Visuals Unlimited; **306 bl,** Richard Haynes; **308,** Russ Lappa; **309,** LWA-Dann Tardif/CORBIS; **310 tr,** Richard Haynes; **311 tr,** Richard Haynes; **312,** Michael Newman/PhotoEdit; **315,** AP Photo/The Grand Rapids Press, Lance Wynn; **316,** SW Production/Index Stock Imagery, Inc.; **317,** Andersen/Ross/Brand X Pictures/Getty Images, Inc.; **319,** Fotopic/Omni-Photo Communications, Inc.; **320,** American Honda Motor Co., Inc.; **321,** Ken O'Donoghue; **322, ml & mr,** Richard Haynes; **324,** AP/Wide World Photos; **325 tr,** Richard Haynes; **326,** David Young-Wolff/PhotoEdit, Inc.; **330 tr,** Richard Haynes/PhotoEdit; **332,** David Hanover/Getty Images, Inc; **334,** The Academy of Natural Science/Corbis; **335,** SuperStock, Inc.; **336,** Dennis MacDonald/PhotoEdit; **340 tl,** Richard Haynes; **342 tl,** Richard Haynes; **351 & 352,** Russ Lappa; **358 tr,** Royal Tyrrell Museum/Alberta Community Development/Dorling Kindersley; **359 tl,** Jeffrey Sylvester/Getty Images, Inc.; **359 mr,** Andy Crawford/Dorling Kindersley; **359 br,** Prentice Hall; **359 m,** John Paul Endress/Silver Burdett Ginn/Pearson Education

Chapter 8: Page 361, Joseph Nettis/Photo Researchers, Inc.; **362,** Dennis Di Cicco/Peter Arnold, Inc.; **366** Richard Haynes; **367,** David Brooks/Corbis; **368 bl,** Richard Haynes; **369 tl,** Richard Haynes; **369 br,** Richard Haynes; **371,** Howie Garber/Animals Animals/Earth Scenes; **374,** Alvis Upitis/SuperStock; **375,** Peter Menzel/Stock Boston; **376,** ©Charles C. Benton; **377,** Corbis; **378 br,** Shadows & Light/The Image Works; **378 tr,** Richard Haynes; **380,** W. Cody/Corbis; **381 bl,** Richard Haynes; **382,** Russ Lappa **383,** Rob Crandall/Stock Boston; **384 & 385 tr,** Richard Haynes; **386 bl,** S. Wanke/PhotoDisc/Getty Images, Inc.; **386 bm,** Ryan McVay/Getty Images, Inc.; **386 br,** Russel Illig/Getty Images, Inc.; **390,** Raphael Gaillarde/Liaison/Getty Images, Inc.; **391,** AP/Wide World Photos; **392,** age fotostock/Superstock; **393,** AP/Wide World Photos; **398,** Corel Corporation; **400 ml,** Siede Preis/Getty Images, Inc.; **400 bl,** Andrew J. Martinez/Photo Researchers, Inc.; **400 br,** Rod Planck/Photo Researchers, Inc.; **402,** Corbis; **405 tl,** Dallas & John Heaton/Stock Boston; **405,** Russ Lappa; **406,** Richard Haynes; **412 tr,** Tony Freeman/PhotoEdit; **412 bl,** Paul Barton/Corbis; **413 Bkgd,** David Jeffrey/Getty Images, Inc.; **413 mr,** PhotoEdit; **413 tr,** Jim Hiss/Hispanic Business Inc.

Chapter 9: Page 415, Jeff Greenberg/Peter Arnold, Inc.; **416,** Ken O'Donoghue; **417 tl,** Russ Lappa; **417 ml,** Russ Lappa; **419,** Topham/The Image Works; **421,** Theo Allofs/Corbis; **422,** NASA/Goddard Flight Center;

423, Audrey Gibson/Gibson Stock Photography; **424,** Warren Bolster/Getty Images, Inc.; **425,** Richard Haynes; **426,** Evan Sklar/Botanica/PictureQuest; **428 mr & tl,** Richard Haynes; **429,** George McLean/CardinalSpellman Philatelic Museum; **430,** Digital Vision/Getty Images; **431,** Richard Haynes; **432,** Tim Thompson/Getty Images, Inc.; **435,** Tony Hopewell/Getty Images, Inc.; **436,** Stephen Simpson/Getty Images, Inc.; **438,** L. Clarke/Corbis; **439,** Tony Freeman/Getty Images, Inc.; **441,** Digital Vision/Getty Images, Inc.; **444,** Craig Aurness/Corbis; **445,** Russ Lappa; **446,** Photo Researchers, Inc.; **448 ml, mr, & tr,** Russ Lappa; **449,** Royalty Free/Corbis; **450,** Sara Karulwich/NYT Pictures; **451 ml,** Tony Freeman/PhotoEdit; **451 mr,** R. M. Arakaki/International Stock; **451 bl,** Tony Freeman/PhotoEdit; **451 br,** John Elk III/Stock Boston; **453,** Alan Klehr/Getty Images, Inc.; **457,** Richard Haynes; **458,** Zigmund Leszcynski/Animals Animals; **461,** Richard Haynes; **462,** David Young-Wolff/PhotoEdit, Inc.; **472–473 b,** Elfi Kluck/Index Stock Imagery, Inc.; **472 tr,** Kim Sayer/Dorling Kindersley; **472 ml,** Photo Courtesy of Northland College, Ashland, Wisconsin; **473 mr,** Neil Setchfield/Dorling Kindersley

Chapter 10: Page 475, Robert Llewellyn/ImageState/Alamy; **476,** Bob Daemmrich/The Image Works; **478 tl & br,** Richard Haynes; **480,** EyeWire/Getty Images, Inc.; **482,** Cleo Photography; **483,** Richard Haynes; **484,** David Young-Wolff/PhotoEdit, Inc.; **487,** Courtesy of Milton Bradley Co.; **488,** Tony Di Zinno/See Jane Run; **489,** Richard Haynes; **491,** Corbis; **492 ml,** Pearson Education; **492 mr,** Pearson Education; **493,** Richard Haynes; **494,** Anthea Sieveking/Petit Format/Photo Researchers, Inc.; **495,** HARUYOSHI YAMAGUCHI/CORBIS SYGMA; **497,** Pearson Education; **499,** Richard Haynes; **501,** Randi Anglin/Syracuse Newspaper/The Image Works; **503,** Ken Ross/Taxi/Getty Images, Inc.; **503,** Russ Lappa; **509 tr,** C Squared Studios/Getty Images, Inc; **509 ml,** Al Francekevich/Corbis; **510 b,** MMI Flash! Light/Stock Boston; **512 tr,** C Squared Studios/Getty Images, Inc.; **512 ml,** Al Francekevich/Corbis; **513,** MMI Flash! Light/Stock Boston

Chapter 11: Page 515, Science VU/Visuals Unlimited; **516,** Neal Preston/Corbis; **518,** Rene Frederick/Getty Images; **519,** Corbis; **520,** Tom Carter/PhotoEdit; **523,** Richard Haynes; **525,** Michael Yelman/SuperStock; **526,** Norbert Wu/Minden Pictures; **527,** Walter Bibikow/Index Stock Imagery/PictureQuest; **528 & 529,** Richard Haynes; **530,** 2005 Jay Wade, www.JayWade.com; **531,** Richard Haynes; **533,** Judith Canty/Stock Boston; **534,** Tom Sanders/Corbis; **535,** Richard Haynes; **537,** Bob Daemmrich Photo, Inc.; **540,** Newsmakers/Getty Images, Inc.; **541,** Michael Schwartz/The Image Works; **543,** David Young-Wolff/PhotoEdit, Inc.; **549,** Myrleen Ferguson Cate/PhotoEdit; **552,** Jack Kurtz/The Image Works; **554,** Ariel Skelley/Masterfile; **555,** Tom Stewart/Corbis; **560 tl & br,** Richard Haynes; **562,** Sally & Derk Kuper; **568 t,** Art Wolfe, Inc.; **568 b,** Harald Sund/Getty Images, Inc.; **568–569 bkgrd,** Planetary Visions, Ltd.; **568 tl,** Gery Randall/Getty Images, Inc.; **569 tr,** Peter Gridley/Getty Images, Inc.; **569 ml,** Jeff Greenberg/Omni-Photo Communications, Inc.; **569 mr,** Getty Images/Eyewire, Inc.; **569 bl,** David Muench/Getty Images, Inc.; **569 br,** Harvey Lloyd/Getty Images, Inc.

Chapter 12: Page 571, Andrea Wells/Getty Images; **572,** Pete Saloutos/Corbis; **573,** Gary Conner/PhotoEdit; **574 tl,** Richard Haynes; **574 mr,** Richard Haynes; **576,** T. Krüsselmann/Zefa/Masterfile; **578,** 1986 James Mayo/Chicago Tribune; **579,** Tony Freeman/PhotoEdit; **581,** Mike Dobel/Masterfile; **582,** AFP Photo/Don Emmert/Corbis; **586 tm,** Russ Lappa; **586 mr,** Russ Lappa; **586,** Richard Haynes; **587,** Photodisc/Getty Images; **590,** Roger Wood/Corbis; **592 bl,** Zigy Kaluzny/Getty Images, Inc.; **592 tl,** Richard Haynes; **594,** Ron Fehling/Masterfile; **604 tr,** Tim Flach/Getty Images, Inc.; **604 tl,** Chris Bjornberg/Photo Researchers, Inc.; **604–605 b,** Amanda Friedman/Getty Images, Inc.; **605 tm,** Davies & Starr/Getty Images, Inc.; **605 mr,** General Electric Lighting

Teacher's Edition

Editorial Services: Pearson Education Development Group
PubSmarts, LLC
Production Services: GGS Book Services